Finite Math and Applied Calculus

Select Chapters

6th EDITION

Stefan Waner | Steven R. Costenoble

CENGAGE Learning

Australia • Brazil • Japan • Korea • Mexico • Singapore • Spain • United Kingdom • United States

CENGAGE Learning

Finite Math and Applied Calculus: Select Chapters, 6th Edition

Senior Manager, Student Engagement:

Linda deStefano

Janey Moeller

Manager, Student Engagement:

Julie Dierig

Marketing Manager:

Rachael Kloos

Manager, Production Editorial:

Kim Fry

Manager, Intellectual Property Project Manager:

Brian Methe

Senior Manager, Production and Manufacturing:

Donna M. Brown

Manager, Production:

Terri Daley

Printed in the United States of America

FINITE MATHEMATICS AND APPLIED CALCULUS, SIXTH EDITION
Waner | Costenoble

For product information and technology assistance, contact us at
Cengage Learning Customer & Sales Support, 1-800-354-9706
For permission to use material from this text or product,
submit all requests online at **cengage.com/permissions**
Further permissions questions can be emailed to
permissionrequest@cengage.com

This book contains select works from existing Cengage Learning resources and was produced by Cengage Learning Custom Solutions for collegiate use. As such, those adopting and/or contributing to this work are responsible for editorial content accuracy, continuity and completeness.

ISBN-13: 978-1-305-31675-1

ISBN-10: 1-305-31675-4

WCN: 01-100-101

Cengage Learning

5191 Natorp Boulevard
Mason, Ohio 45040
USA

Cengage Learning is a leading provider of customized learning solutions with office locations around the globe, including Singapore, the United Kingdom, Australia, Mexico, Brazil, and Japan. Locate your local office at: **international.cengage.com/region.**

Cengage Learning products are represented in Canada by Nelson Education, Ltd.
For your lifelong learning solutions, visit **www.cengage.com/custom.**
Visit our corporate website at **www.cengage.com.**

Brief Contents

2

The Mathematics of Finance

Case Study Adjustable Rate and Subprime Mortgages

Mr. and Mrs. Wong have an appointment tomorrow with you, their investment counselor, to discuss their plan to purchase a $400,000 house in Orlando, Florida. Their combined annual income is $80,000 per year, which they estimate will increase by 4% annually over the foreseeable future, and they are considering three different specialty 30-year mortgages:

Hybrid: The interest is fixed at a low introductory rate of 4% for 5 years.

Interest-Only: During the first 5 years, the rate is set at 4.2% and no principal is paid.

Negative Amortization: During the first 5 years, the rate is set at 4.7% based on a principal of 60% of the purchase price of the home.

How would you advise them?

Andy Dean Photography/Shutterstock

Website
www.WanerMath.com
At the Website you will find:

- A detailed chapter summary
- A true/false quiz
- A time value of money utility
- Excel tutorials for every section

Introduction

A knowledge of the mathematics of investments and loans is important not only for business majors but also for everyone who deals with money, which is all of us. This chapter is largely about *interest*: interest paid by an investment, interest paid on a loan, and variations on these.

We focus on three forms of investment: investments that pay simple interest, investments in which interest is compounded, and annuities. An investment that pays *simple interest* periodically gives interest directly to the investor, perhaps in the form of a monthly check. If instead, the interest is reinvested, the interest is *compounded*, and the value of the account grows as the interest is added. An *annuity* is an investment earning compound interest into which periodic payments are made or from which periodic withdrawals are made; in the case of periodic payments, such an investment is more commonly called a *sinking fund*. From the point of view of the lender, a loan is a kind of annuity.

We also look at bonds, the primary financial instrument used by companies and governments to raise money. Although bonds nominally pay simple interest, determining their worth, particularly in the secondary market, requires an annuity calculation.

2.1 Simple Interest

You deposit $1,000, called the **principal** or **present value**, into a savings account. The bank pays you 5% interest, in the form of a check, each year. How much interest will you earn each year? Because the bank pays you 5% interest each year, your annual (or yearly) interest will be 5% of $1,000, or $1{,}000 \times 0.05 = \$50$.

Generalizing this calculation, call the present value PV and the interest rate (expressed as a decimal) r. Then INT, the annual interest paid to you, is given by*

$$INT = PVr.$$

If the investment is made for a period of t years, then the total interest accumulated is t times this amount, which gives us the following:

* Multiletter variables like *PV* and *INT* used here may be unusual in a math textbook but are almost universally used in finance textbooks, calculators (such as the TI-83/84 Plus), and such places as study guides for the finance portion of the Society of Actuaries exams. Just watch out for expressions like *PVr*, which is the product of two things, *PV* and *r*, not three.

Simple Interest

The **simple interest** on an investment (or loan) of PV dollars at an annual interest rate of r for a period of t years is

$$INT = PVrt.$$

Quick Example

The simple interest over a period of 4 years on a $5,000 investment earning 8% per year is

$$\begin{aligned} INT &= PVrt \\ &= (5{,}000)(0.08)(4) = \$1{,}600. \end{aligned}$$

Given your \$1,000 investment at 5% simple interest, how much money will you have after 2 years? To find the answer, we need to add the accumulated interest to the principal to get the **future value** (FV) of your deposit.

$$FV = PV + INT = \$1{,}000 + (1{,}000)(0.05)(2) = \$1{,}100$$

In general, we can compute the future value as follows:

$$FV = PV + INT = PV + PVrt = PV(1 + rt).$$

Future Value for Simple Interest

The **future value** of an investment of PV dollars at an annual simple interest rate of r for a period of t years is

$$FV = PV(1 + rt).$$

Quick Examples

1. The value, at the end of 4 years, of a \$5,000 investment earning 8% simple interest per year is

$$FV = PV(1 + rt)$$
$$= 5{,}000[1 + (0.08)(4)] = \$6{,}600.$$

2. Writing the future value in Quick Example 1 as a function of time, we get

$$FV = 5{,}000(1 + 0.08t)$$
$$= 5{,}000 + 400t,$$

which is a linear function of time t. The intercept is $PV = \$5{,}000$, and the slope is the annual interest, \$400 per year.

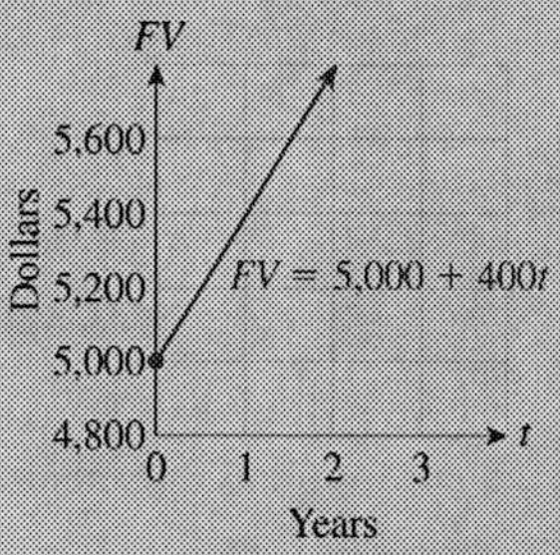

In general: *Simple interest growth is a linear function of time, with intercept given by the present value and slope given by annual interest.*

EXAMPLE 1 Savings Accounts

In November 2011, the Bank of Montreal was paying 1.30% interest on savings accounts.[1] If the interest is paid as simple interest, find the future value of a \$2,000 deposit in 6 years. What is the total interest paid over the period?

[1]Source: Canoe Money (http://money.canoe.ca/rates/savings.html)

Solution We use the future value formula:

$$\begin{aligned} FV &= PV(1 + rt) \\ &= 2{,}000[1 + (0.013)(6)] = 2{,}000[1.078] = \$2{,}156. \end{aligned}$$

The total interest paid is given by the simple interest formula:

$$\begin{aligned} INT &= PVrt \\ &= (2{,}000)(0.013)(6) = \$156. \end{aligned}$$

Note To find the interest paid, we could also have computed

$$INT = FV - PV = 2{,}156 - 2{,}000 = \$156. \blacksquare$$

➡ **Before we go on...** In the preceding example, we could look at the future value as a function of time:

$$FV = 2{,}000(1 + 0.013t) = 2{,}000 + 26t.$$

Thus, the future value is growing linearly at a rate of \$26 per year. ■

EXAMPLE 2 Bridge Loans

When "trading up," homeowners sometimes have to buy a new house before they sell their old house. One way to cover the costs of the new house until they get the proceeds from selling the old house is to take out a short-term *bridge loan*. Suppose a bank charges 12% simple annual interest on such a loan. How much will be owed at the maturation (the end) of a 90-day bridge loan of \$90,000?

Solution We use the future value formula

$$FV = PV(1 + rt)$$

with $t = 90/365$, the fraction of a year represented by 90 days:

$$\begin{aligned} FV &= 90{,}000[1 + (0.12)(90/365)] \\ &= \$92{,}663.01. \end{aligned}$$

(We will always round our answers to the nearest cent after calculation. Be careful not to round intermediate results.)

➡ **Before we go on...** Many banks use 360 days for this calculation rather than 365, which makes a "year" for the purposes of the loan slightly shorter than a calendar year. The effect is to increase the amount owed:

$$FV = 90{,}000[1 + (0.12)(90/360)] = \$92{,}700$$ ■

One of the primary ways companies and governments raise money is by selling **bonds**. At its most straightforward, a corporate bond promises to pay simple interest, usually twice a year, for a length of time until it **matures**, at which point it returns the original investment to the investor (U.S. Treasury notes and bonds are similar). Things get more complicated when the selling price is negotiable, as we will see later in this chapter.

EXAMPLE 3 Corporate Bonds

The Megabucks Corporation is issuing 10-year bonds paying an annual rate of 6.5%. If you buy \$10,000 worth of bonds, how much interest will you earn every 6 months, and how much interest will you earn over the life of the bonds?

Solution Using the simple interest formula, every 6 months you will receive

$$\begin{aligned} INT &= PVrt \\ &= (10{,}000)(0.065)\left(\frac{1}{2}\right) = \$325. \end{aligned}$$

Over the 10-year life of the bonds, you will earn

$$\begin{aligned} INT &= PVrt \\ &= (10{,}000)(0.065)(10) = \$6{,}500 \end{aligned}$$

in interest. So, at the end of 10 years, when your original investment is returned to you, your \$10,000 will have turned into \$16,500.

We often want to turn an interest calculation around: Rather than starting with the present value and finding the future value, there are times when we know the future value and need to determine the present value. Solving the future value formula for PV gives us the following.

Present Value for Simple Interest

The present value of an investment at an annual simple interest rate of r for a period of t years, with future value FV, is

$$PV = \frac{FV}{1+rt}.$$

Quick Example

If an investment earns 5% simple interest and will be worth \$1,000 in 4 years, then its present value (its initial value) is

$$\begin{aligned} PV &= \frac{FV}{1+rt} \\ &= \frac{1{,}000}{1+(0.05)(4)} = \$833.33. \end{aligned}$$

Here is a typical example. U.S. Treasury bills (T-bills) are short-term investments (up to 1 year) that pay you a set amount after a period of time; what you pay to buy a T-bill depends on the interest rate.

EXAMPLE 4 Treasury Bills

A U.S. Treasury bill paying \$10,000 after 6 months earns 3.67% simple annual interest. How much did it cost to buy?

Solution The future value of the T-bill is $10,000; the price we paid is its present value. We know that

$$FV = \$10{,}000$$
$$r = 0.0367$$

and

$$t = 0.5.$$

Substituting into the present value formula, we have

$$PV = \frac{10{,}000}{1 + (0.0367)(0.5)} = 9{,}819.81$$

so we paid $9,819.81 for the T-bill.

➡ **Before we go on...** The simplest way to find the interest earned on the T-bill is by subtraction:

$$INT = FV - PV = 10{,}000 - 9{,}819.81 = \$180.19.$$

So, after 6 months we received back $10,000, which is our original investment plus $180.19 in interest. ■

Here is some additional terminology on Treasury bills:

Treasury Bills (T-Bills): Maturity Value, Discount Rate, and Yield

The **maturity value** of a T-bill is the amount of money it will pay at the end of its life, that is, upon **maturity**.

Quick Example

A 1-year $10,000 T-bill has a maturity value of $10,000, and so will pay you $10,000 after one year.

The cost of a T-bill is generally less than its maturity value.* In other words, a T-bill will generally sell at a *discount*, and the **discount rate** is the *annualized* percentage of this discount; that is, the percentage is adjusted to give an annual percentage. (See Quick Examples 2 and 3.)

* An exception occurred during the financial meltdown of 2008, when T-bills were heavily in demand as "safe haven" investments and were sometimes selling at—or even above—their maturity values.

Quick Examples

1. A 1-year $10,000 T-bill with a discount rate of 5% will sell for 5% less than its maturity value of $10,000, that is, for $9,500.
2. A 6-month $10,000 T-bill with a discount rate of 5% will sell at an actual discount of half of that—2.5% less than its maturity value, or $9,750—because 6 months is half of a year.
3. A 3-month $10,000 T-bill with a discount rate of 5% will sell at an actual discount of a fourth of that: 1.25% less than its maturity value, or $9,875.

The annual **yield** of a T-bill is the simple annual interest rate an investor earns when the T-bill matures, as calculated in the next example.

EXAMPLE 5 Treasury Bills

A T-bill paying \$10,000 after 6 months sells at a discount rate of 3.6%. What does it sell for? What is the annual yield?

Solution The (annualized) discount rate is 3.6%; so, for a 6-month bill, the actual discount will be half of that: $3.6\%/2 = 1.8\%$ below its maturity value. This makes the selling price

$$10{,}000 - (0.018)(10{,}000) = \$9{,}820. \qquad \text{Maturity value} - \text{Discount}$$

To find the annual yield, note that the present value of the investment is the price the investor pays, \$9,820, and the future value is its maturity value, \$10,000 six months later. So,

$$PV = \$9{,}820 \qquad FV = \$10{,}000 \qquad t = 0.5$$

and we wish to find the annual interest rate r. Substituting in the future value formula, we get

$$FV = PV(1 + rt)$$
$$10{,}000 = 9{,}820(1 + 0.5r)$$

so

$$1 + 0.5r = 10{,}000/9{,}820$$

and

$$r = (10{,}000/9{,}820 - 1)/0.5 \approx 0.0367.$$

Thus, the T-bill is paying 3.67% simple annual interest, so we say that its annual yield is 3.67%.

➡ **Before we go on...** The T-bill in Example 5 is the same one as in Example 4 (with a bit of rounding). The yield and the discount rate are two different ways of telling what the investment pays. One of the Communication and Reasoning Exercises asks you to find a formula for the yield in terms of the discount rate. ■

Fees on loans can also be thought of as a form of interest.

EXAMPLE 6 Tax Refunds

You are expecting a tax refund of \$800. Because it may take up to 6 weeks to get the refund, your tax preparation firm offers, for a fee of \$40, to give you an "interest-free" loan of \$800 to be paid back with the refund check. If we think of the fee as interest, what simple annual interest rate is the firm actually charging?

Solution If we view the \$40 as interest, then the future value of the loan (the value of the loan to the firm, or the total you will pay the firm) is \$840. Thus, we have

$$FV = 840$$
$$PV = 800$$
$$t = 6/52 \qquad \text{Using 52 weeks in a year}$$

and we wish to find r. Substituting, we get

$$FV = PV(1 + rt)$$

$$840 = 800(1 + 6r/52) = 800 + \frac{4{,}800r}{52}$$

so

$$\frac{4{,}800r}{52} = 840 - 800 = 40$$

$$r = \frac{40 \times 52}{4{,}800} \approx 0.43.$$

In other words, the firm is charging you 43% annual interest! Save your money and wait 6 weeks for your refund.

2.1 EXERCISES

▼ more advanced ◆ challenging

T indicates exercises that should be solved using technology

In Exercises 1–6, compute the simple interest for the specified period and the future value at the end of the period. Round all answers to the nearest cent. HINT [See Example 1.]

1. \$2,000 is invested for 1 year at 6% per year.
2. \$1,000 is invested for 10 years at 4% per year.
3. \$20,200 is invested for 6 months at 5% per year.
4. \$10,100 is invested for 3 months at 11% per year.
5. You borrow \$10,000 for 10 months at 3% per year.
6. You borrow \$6,000 for 5 months at 9% per year.

In Exercises 7–12, find the present value of the given investment. HINT [See the Quick Example on page 129.]

7. An investment earns 2% per year and is worth \$10,000 after 5 years.
8. An investment earns 5% per year and is worth \$20,000 after 2 years.
9. An investment earns 7% per year and is worth \$1,000 after 6 months.
10. An investment earns 10% per year and is worth \$5,000 after 3 months.
11. An investment earns 3% per year and is worth \$15,000 after 15 months.
12. An investment earns 6% per year and is worth \$30,000 after 20 months.

APPLICATIONS

In Exercises 13–30, compute the specified quantity. Round all answers to the nearest month, the nearest cent, or the nearest 0.001%, as appropriate.

13. ***Simple Loans*** You take out a 6-month, \$5,000 loan at 8% simple interest. How much would you owe at the end of the 6 months? HINT [See Example 2.]
14. ***Simple Loans*** You take out a 15-month, \$10,000 loan at 11% simple interest. How much would you owe at the end of the 15 months? HINT [See Example 2.]
15. ***Savings*** How much would you have to deposit in an account earning 4.5% simple interest if you wanted to have \$1,000 after 6 years? HINT [See Example 4.]
16. ***Simple Loans*** Your total payment on a 4-year loan, which charged 9.5% simple interest, amounted to \$30,360. How much did you originally borrow? HINT [See Example 4.]
17. ***Bonds*** A 5-year bond costs \$1,000 and will pay a total of \$250 interest over its lifetime. What is its annual interest rate? HINT [See Example 3.]
18. ***Bonds*** A 4-year bond costs \$10,000 and will pay a total of \$2,800 in interest over its lifetime. What is its annual interest rate? HINT [See Example 3.]
19. ***Treasury Bills*** In December 2008 (in the midst of the financial crisis) a \$5,000 6-month T-bill was selling at a discount rate of only 0.25%.[2] What was its simple annual yield? HINT [See Example 5.]
20. ***Treasury Bills*** In December 2008 (in the midst of the financial crisis) a \$15,000 3-month T-bill was selling at a discount rate of only 0.06%.[3] What was its simple annual yield? HINT [See Example 5.]
21. ▼ ***Simple Loans*** A \$4,000 loan, taken now, with a simple interest rate of 8% per year, will require a total repayment of \$4,640. When will the loan mature?
22. ▼ ***Simple Loans*** The simple interest on a \$1,000 loan at 8% per year amounted to \$640. When did the loan mature?

[2]Discount rate on December 29, 2008. Source: U.S. Treasury (www.ustreas.gov/offices/domestic-finance/debt-management/interest-rate/daily_treas_bill_rates.shtml).

[3]*Ibid.*

23. ▼ ***Treasury Bills*** At auction on August 18, 2005, 6-month T-bills were sold at a discount of 3.705%.[4] What was the simple annual yield? HINT [See Example 5.]

24. ▼ ***Treasury Bills*** At auction on August 18, 2005, 3-month T-bills were sold at a discount of 3.470%.[5] What was the simple annual yield? HINT [See Example 5.]

25. ▼ ***Fees*** You are expecting a tax refund of $1,000 in 4 weeks. A tax preparer offers you a $1,000 loan for a fee of $50 to be repaid by your refund check when it arrives in 4 weeks. Thinking of the fee as interest, what annual simple interest rate would you be paying on this loan? HINT [See Example 6.]

26. ▼ ***Fees*** You are expecting a tax refund of $1,500 in 3 weeks. A tax preparer offers you a $1,500 loan for a fee of $60 to be repaid by your refund check when it arrives in 3 weeks. Thinking of the fee as interest, what annual simple interest rate would you be paying on this loan?

27. ▼ ***Fees*** You take out a 2-year, $5,000 loan at 9% simple annual interest. The lender charges you a $100 fee. Thinking of the fee as additional interest, what is the actual annual interest rate you will pay?

28. ▼ ***Fees*** You take out a 3-year, $7,000 loan at 8% simple annual interest. The lender charges you a $100 fee. Thinking of the fee as additional interest, what is the actual annual interest rate you will pay?

29. ▼ ***Layaway Fees*** Layaway plans allow you, for a fee, to pay for an item over a period of time and then receive the item when you finish paying for it. In November 2011, Senator Charles E. Schumer of New York warned that the holiday layaway programs recently reinstated by several popular retailers were, when you took the fees into account, charging interest at a rate significantly higher than the highest credit card rates.[6] Suppose that you bought a $69 item on November 15 on layaway, with the final payment due December 15, and that the retailer charged you a $5 service fee. Thinking of the fee as interest, what simple interest rate would you be paying for this layaway plan?

30. ▼ ***Layaway Fees*** Referring to Exercise 29, suppose that you bought a $99 item on October 15 on layaway, with the final payment due December 15, and that the retailer charged you a $10 service fee. Thinking of the fee as interest, what simple interest rate would you be paying for this layaway plan?

Stock Investments *Exercises 31–36 are based on the following chart, which shows monthly figures for* Apple Computer, Inc. *stock in 2010.*[7]

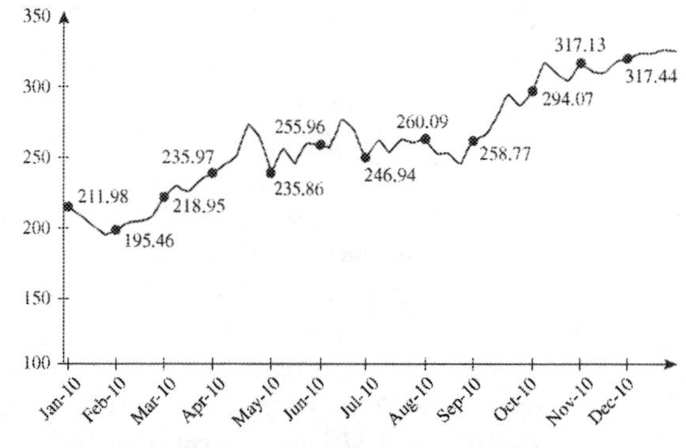

Marked are the following points on the chart:

Jan. 10	Feb. 10	Mar. 10	Apr. 10	May 10	June 10
211.98	195.46	218.95	235.97	235.86	255.96
July 10	Aug. 10	Sep. 10	Oct. 10	Nov. 10	Dec. 10
246.94	260.09	258.77	294.07	317.13	317.44

31. Calculate to the nearest 0.01% your annual percentage return (on a simple interest basis) if you had bought Apple stock in June and sold in December.

32. Calculate to the nearest 0.01% your annual percentage return (on a simple interest basis) if you had bought Apple stock in February and sold in June.

33. ▼ Suppose you bought Apple stock in April. If you later sold at one of the marked dates on the chart, which of those dates would have given you the largest annual return (on a simple interest basis), and what would that return have been?

34. ▼ Suppose you bought Apple stock in May. If you later sold at one of the marked dates on the chart, which of those dates would have given you the largest annual return (on a simple interest basis), and what would that return have been?

35. ▼ Did Apple's stock undergo simple interest change in the period January through May? (Give a reason for your answer.)

36. ▼ If Apple's stock had undergone simple interest change from April to June at the same simple rate as from March to April, what would the price have been in June?

Population *Exercises 37–42 are based on the following graph, which shows the population of San Diego County from 1950 to 2000.*[8]

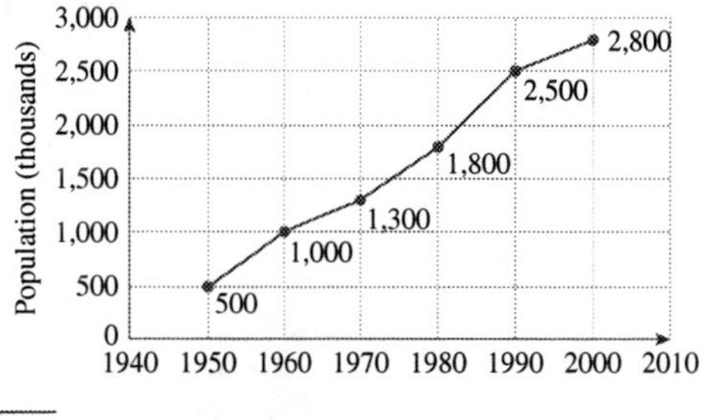

[4]Source: The Bureau of the Public Debt's Web site: www.publicdebt.treas.gov.

[5]*Ibid.*

[6]Source: November 14, 2011 press release from the office of Senator Charles E. Schumer (http://schumer.senate.gov/Newsroom/releases.cfm)

[7]Source: Yahoo! Finance (http://finance.yahoo.com).

[8]Source: Census Bureau/*New York Times*, April 2, 2002, p. F3.

37. At what annual (simple interest) rate did the population of San Diego County increase from 1950 to 2000?

38. At what annual (simple interest) rate did the population of San Diego County increase from 1950 to 1990?

39. ▼ If you used your answer to Exercise 37 as the annual (simple interest) rate at which the population was growing since 1950, what would you predict the San Diego County population to be in 2010?

40. ▼ If you used your answer to Exercise 38 as the annual (simple interest) rate at which the population was growing since 1950, what would you predict the San Diego County population to be in 2010?

41. ▼ Use your answer to Exercise 37 to give a linear model for the population of San Diego County from 1950 to 2000. Draw the graph of your model over that period of time.

42. ▼ Use your answer to Exercise 38 to give a linear model for the population of San Diego County from 1950 to 2000. Draw the graph of your model over that period of time.

COMMUNICATION AND REASONING EXERCISES

43. One or more of the following three graphs represents the future value of an investment earning simple interest. Which one(s)? Give the reason for your choice(s).

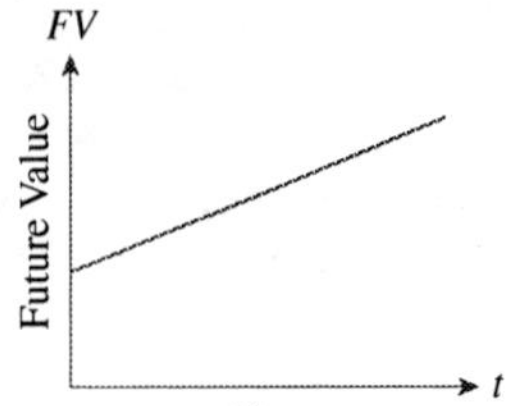
(A)

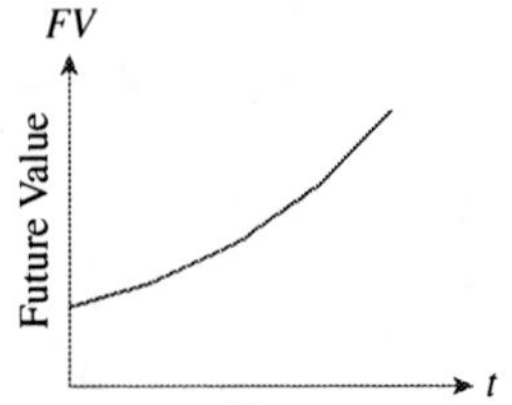
(B)

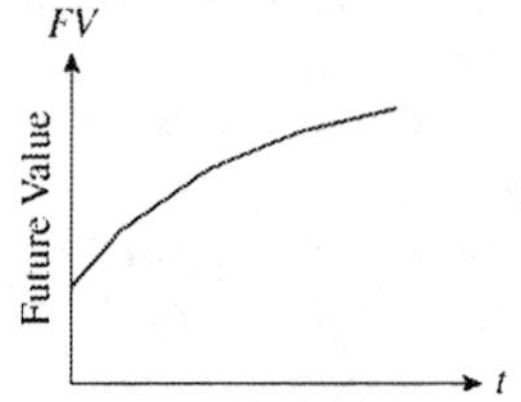
(C)

44. Given that $FV = 5t + 400$, for what interest rate is this the equation of future value (in dollars) as a function of time t (in years)?

45. ▼ *Interpreting the News* You hear the following on your local radio station's business news: "The economy last year grew by 1%. This was the second year in a row in which the economy showed a 1% growth." Because the rate of growth was the same two years in a row, this represents simple interest growth, right? Explain your answer.

46. ▼ *Interpreting the News* You hear the following on your local radio station's business news: "The economy last year grew by 1%. This was the second year in a row in which the economy showed a 1% growth." This means that, in dollar terms, the economy grew more last year than the year before. Why?

47. ▼ Explain why simple interest is not the appropriate way to measure interest on a savings account that pays interest directly into your account.

48. ▼ Suppose that a one-year T-bill sells at a discount rate d. Find a formula, in terms of d, for the simple annual interest rate r the bill will pay.

2.2 Compound Interest

You deposit $1,000 into a savings account. The bank pays you 5% interest, which it deposits into your account, or **reinvests**, at the end of each year. At the end of 5 years, how much money will you have accumulated? Let us compute the amount you have at the end of each year. At the end of the first year, the bank will pay you simple interest of 5% on your $1,000, which gives you

$$PV(1 + rt) = 1,000(1 + 0.05)$$
$$= \$1,050.$$

At the end of the second year, the bank will pay you another 5% interest, but this time computed on the total in your account, which is $1,050. Thus, you will have a total of

$$1,050(1 + 0.05) = \$1,102.50.$$

If you were being paid simple interest on your original $1,000, you would have only $1,100 at the end of the second year. The extra $2.50 is the interest earned on the $50 interest added to your account at the end of the first year. Having interest earn interest is called **compounding** the interest. We could continue like this until the end of the fifth year, but notice what we are doing: Each year we are multiplying by $1 + 0.05$. So, at the end of 5 years, you will have

$$1{,}000(1 + 0.05)^5 \approx \$1{,}276.28.$$

It is interesting to compare this to the amount you would have if the bank paid you simple interest:

$$1{,}000(1 + 0.05 \times 5) = \$1{,}250.00.$$

The extra \$26.28 is again the effect of compounding the interest.

Banks often pay interest more often than once a year. Paying interest quarterly (four times per year) or monthly is common. If your bank pays interest monthly, how much will your \$1,000 deposit be worth after 5 years? The bank will not pay you 5% interest every month, but will give you 1/12 of that,* or 5/12% interest each month. Thus, instead of multiplying by $1 + 0.05$ every year, we should multiply by $1 + 0.05/12$ each month. Because there are $5 \times 12 = 60$ months in 5 years, the total amount you will have at the end of 5 years is

* This is approximate. They will actually give you 31/365 of the 5% at the end of January and so on, but it's simpler and reasonably accurate to call it 1/12.

$$1{,}000\left(1 + \frac{0.05}{12}\right)^{60} \approx \$1{,}283.36.$$

Compare this to the \$1,276.28 you would get if the bank paid the interest every year. You earn an extra \$7.08 if the interest is paid monthly because interest gets into your account and starts earning interest earlier. The amount of time between interest payments is called the **compounding period**.

The following table summarizes the results above.

Time in Years	*Amount with Simple Interest*	*Amount with Annual Compounding*	*Amount with Monthly Compounding*
0	\$1,000	\$1,000	\$1,000
1	$1{,}000(1 + 0.05)$ $= \$1{,}050$	$1{,}000(1 + 0.05)$ $= \$1{,}050$	$1{,}000(1 + 0.05/12)^{12}$ $= \$1{,}051.16$
2	$1{,}000(1 + 0.05 \times 2)$ $= \$1{,}100$	$1{,}000(1 + 0.05)^2$ $= \$1{,}102.50$	$1{,}000(1 + 0.05/12)^{24}$ $= \$1{,}104.94$
5	$1{,}000(1 + 0.05 \times 5)$ $= \$1{,}250$	$1{,}000(1 + 0.05)^5$ $= \$1{,}276.28$	$1{,}000(1 + 0.05/12)^{60}$ $= \$1{,}283.36$

The preceding calculations generalize easily to give the general formula for future value when interest is compounded.

Future Value for Compound Interest

The future value of an investment of PV dollars earning interest at an annual rate of r compounded (reinvested) m times per year for a period of t years is

$$FV = PV\left(1 + \frac{r}{m}\right)^{mt}$$

or

$$FV = PV(1 + i)^n,$$

where $i = r/m$ is the interest paid each compounding period and $n = mt$ is the total number of compounding periods.

Quick Examples

1. To find the future value after 5 years of a \$10,000 investment earning 6% interest, with interest reinvested every month, we set $PV = 10{,}000$, $r = 0.06$, $m = 12$, and $t = 5$. Thus,

$$FV = PV\left(1 + \frac{r}{m}\right)^{mt} = 10{,}000\left(1 + \frac{0.06}{12}\right)^{60} \approx \$13{,}488.50.$$

2. Writing the future value in Quick Example 1 as a function of time, we get

$$FV = 10{,}000\left(1 + \frac{0.06}{12}\right)^{12t}$$
$$= 10{,}000(1.005)^{12t},$$

which is an **exponential** function of time t.

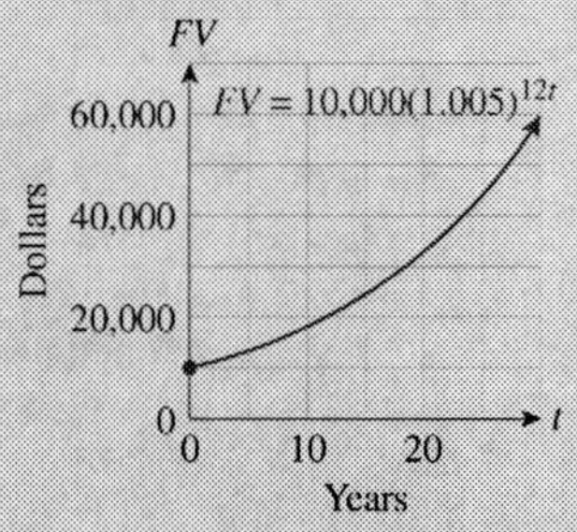

In general: *Compound interest growth is an exponential function of time.*

using Technology

All three technologies discussed in this book have built-in mathematics of finance capabilities. See the Technology Guides at the end of the chapter for details on using a TI-83/84 Plus or a spreadsheet to do the calculations in Example 1. [Details: TI-83/84 Plus: page 166, Spreadsheet: page 170]

Website

www.WanerMath.com
→ On Line Utilities
→ Time Value of Money Utility

This utility is similar to the TVM Solver on the TI-83/84 Plus. To compute the future value, enter the values shown, and press "Compute" next to FV.

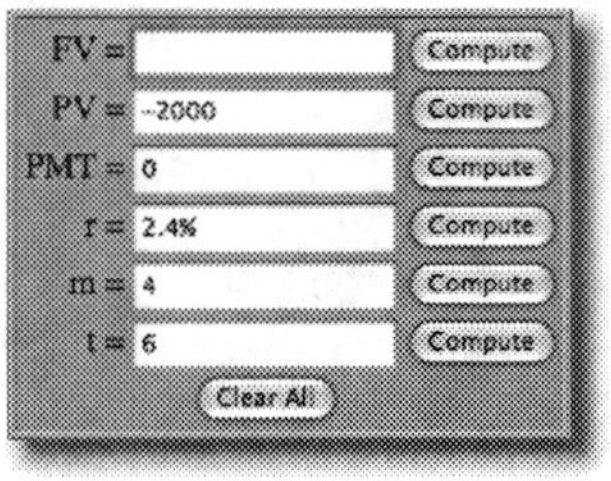

(For an explanation of the terms, see the Technology Guide for the TI-83/84 Plus.)

EXAMPLE 1 Savings Accounts

In November 2011, the Bank of Montreal was paying 1.30% interest on savings accounts.[9] If the interest is compounded quarterly, find the future value of a \$2,000 deposit in 6 years. What is the total interest paid over the period?

Solution We use the future value formula with $m = 4$:

$$FV = PV\left(1 + \frac{r}{m}\right)^{mt}$$
$$= 2{,}000\left(1 + \frac{0.0130}{4}\right)^{4\times 6} \approx \$2{,}161.97.$$

The total interest paid is

$$INT = FV - PV = 2{,}161.97 - 2{,}000 = \$161.97.$$

[9]Source: Canoe Money (http://money.canoe.ca/rates/savings.html)

Example 1 illustrates the concept of the **time value of money**: A given amount of money received now will usually be worth a different amount to us than the same amount received some time in the future. In the example above, we can say that \$2,000 received now is worth the same as \$2,161.97 received 6 years from now, because if we receive \$2,000 now, we can turn it into \$2,161.97 by the end of 6 years.

We often want to know, for some amount of money in the future, what is the equivalent value at present. As we did for simple interest, we can solve the future value formula for the present value and obtain the following formula.

Present Value for Compound Interest

The present value of an investment earning interest at an annual rate of r compounded m times per year for a period of t years, with future value FV, is

$$PV = \frac{FV}{\left(1 + \frac{r}{m}\right)^{mt}}$$

or

$$PV = \frac{FV}{(1+i)^n} = FV(1+i)^{-n},$$

where $i = r/m$ is the interest paid each compounding period and $n = mt$ is the total number of compounding periods.

Quick Example

To find the amount we need to invest in an investment earning 12% per year, compounded annually, so that we will have \$1 million in 20 years, use $FV = \$1{,}000{,}000$, $r = 0.12$, $m = 1$, and $t = 20$:

$$PV = \frac{FV}{\left(1 + \frac{r}{m}\right)^{mt}} = \frac{1{,}000{,}000}{(1 + 0.12)^{20}} \approx \$103{,}666.77.$$

Put another way, \$1,000,000 20 years from now is worth only \$103,666.77 to us now, if we have a 12% investment available.

In the preceding section, we mentioned that a bond pays interest until it reaches maturity, at which point it pays you back an amount called its **maturity value** or **par value**. The two parts, the interest and the maturity value, can be separated and sold and traded by themselves. A **zero coupon bond** is a form of corporate bond that pays no interest during its life but, like U.S. Treasury bills, promises to pay you the maturity value when it reaches maturity. Zero coupon bonds are often created by removing or *stripping* the interest coupons from an ordinary bond, so are also known as **strips**. Zero coupon bonds sell for less than their maturity value, and the return on the investment is the difference between what the investor pays and the maturity value. Although no interest is actually paid, we measure the return on investment by thinking of the interest rate that would make the selling price (the present value) grow to become the maturity value (the future value).*

* The IRS refers to this kind of interest as **original issue discount (OID)** and taxes it as if it were interest actually paid to you each year.

EXAMPLE 2 Zero Coupon Bonds

Megabucks Corporation is issuing 10-year zero coupon bonds. How much would you pay for bonds with a maturity value of \$10,000 if you wish to get a return of 6.5% compounded annually?*

Solution As we said earlier, we think of a zero coupon bond as if it were an account earning (compound) interest. We are asked to calculate the amount you will pay for the bond—the present value PV. We have

$$FV = \$10{,}000$$
$$r = 0.065$$
$$t = 10$$
$$m = 1.$$

We can now use the present value formula:

$$PV = \frac{FV}{\left(1+\frac{r}{m}\right)^{mt}}$$

$$PV = \frac{10{,}000}{\left(1+\frac{0.065}{1}\right)^{10\times 1}} \approx \$5{,}327.26.$$

Thus, you should pay \$5,327.26 to get a return of 6.5% annually.

* The return investors look for depends on a number of factors, including risk (the chance that the company will go bankrupt and you will lose your investment); the higher the risk, the higher the return. U.S. Treasuries are considered risk free because the federal government has never defaulted on its debts. On the other hand, so-called junk bonds are high-risk investments (below investment grade) and have correspondingly high yields.

using Technology

See the Technology Guides at the end of the chapter for details on using TVM Solver on the TI-83/84 Plus or the built-in finance functions in spreadsheets to do the calculations in Example 2. [Details: TI-83/84 Plus: page 166, Spreadsheet: page 171]

Website

www.WanerMath.com

→ On Line Utilities

→ Time Value of Money Utility

This utility is similar to the TVM Solver on the TI-83/84 Plus. To compute the present value, enter the values shown, and press "Compute" next to PV.

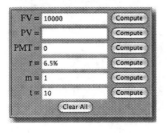

Before we go on... Particularly in financial applications, you will hear the word **"discounted"** in place of "compounded" when discussing present value. Thus, the result of Example 2 might be phrased, "The present value of \$10,000 to be received 10 years from now, with an interest rate of 6.5% discounted annually, is \$5,327.26." ■

Time value of money calculations are often done to take into account inflation, which behaves like compound interest. Suppose, for example, that inflation is running at 5% per year. Then prices will increase by 5% each year, so if PV represents the price now, the price one year from now will be 5% higher, or $PV(1+0.05)$. The price a year from then will be 5% higher still, or $PV(1+0.05)^2$. Thus, the effects of inflation are compounded just as reinvested interest is.

EXAMPLE 3 Inflation

Inflation in East Avalon is 5% per year. TruVision television sets cost \$200 today. How much will a comparable set cost 2 years from now?

Solution To find the price of a television set 2 years from now, we compute the future value of \$200 at an inflation rate of 5% compounded yearly:

$$FV = 200(1+0.05)^2 = \$220.50.$$

EXAMPLE 4 Constant Dollars

Inflation in North Avalon is 6% per year. Which is really more expensive, a car costing \$20,000 today or one costing \$22,000 in 3 years?

Solution We cannot compare the two costs directly because inflation makes \$1 today worth more (it buys more) than a dollar 3 years from now. We need the two prices expressed in comparable terms, so we convert to **constant dollars**. We take the car costing \$22,000 three years from now and ask what it would cost in today's dollars. In other words, we convert the future value of \$22,000 to its present value:

$$\begin{aligned} PV &= FV(1+i)^{-n} \\ &= 22{,}000(1+0.06)^{-3} \\ &\approx \$18{,}471.62. \end{aligned}$$

Thus, the car costing \$22,000 in 3 years actually costs less, after adjusting for inflation, than the one costing \$20,000 now.

➡ **Before we go on...** In the presence of inflation, the only way to compare prices at different times is to convert all prices to constant dollars. We pick some fixed time and compute future or present values as appropriate to determine what things would have cost at that time. ■

There are some other interesting calculations related to compound interest, besides present and future values.

EXAMPLE 5 Effective Interest Rate

You have just won \$1 million in the lottery and are deciding what to do with it during the next year before you move to the South Pacific. Bank Ten offers 10% interest, compounded annually, while Bank Nine offers 9.8% compounded monthly. In which should you deposit your money?

Solution Let's calculate the future value of your \$1 million after one year in each of the banks:

$$\text{Bank Ten:} \quad FV = 1(1+0.10)^1 = \$1.1 \text{ million}$$

$$\text{Bank Nine:} \quad FV = 1\left(1+\frac{0.098}{12}\right)^{12} = \$1.1025 \text{ million.}$$

Bank Nine turns out to be better: It will pay you a total of \$102,500 in interest over the year, whereas Bank Ten will pay only \$100,000 in interest.

Another way of looking at the calculation in Example 5 is that Bank Nine gave you a total of 10.25% interest on your investment over the year. We call 10.25% the **effective interest rate** of the investment (also referred to as the **annual percentage**

yield, or **APY** in the banking industry); the stated 9.8% is called the **nominal** interest rate. In general, to best compare two different investments, it is wisest to compare their *effective*—rather than nominal—interest rates.

Notice that we got 10.25% by computing

$$\left(1+\frac{0.098}{12}\right)^{12} = 1.1025$$

and then subtracting 1 to get 0.1025, or 10.25%. Generalizing, we get the following formula.

Effective Interest Rate

The effective interest rate r_{eff} of an investment paying a nominal interest rate of r_{nom} compounded m times per year is

$$r_{\text{eff}} = \left(1+\frac{r_{\text{nom}}}{m}\right)^{m} - 1.$$

To compare rates of investments with different compounding periods, always compare the effective interest rates rather than the nominal rates.

Quick Example

To calculate the effective interest rate of an investment that pays 8% per year, with interest reinvested monthly, set $r_{\text{nom}} = 0.08$ and $m = 12$, to obtain

$$r_{\text{eff}} = \left(1+\frac{0.08}{12}\right)^{12} - 1 \approx 0.0830, \text{ or } 8.30\%.$$

EXAMPLE 6 How Long to Invest

You have \$5,000 to invest at 6% interest compounded monthly. How long will it take for your investment to grow to \$6,000?

Solution If we use the future value formula, we already have the values

$$FV = 6{,}000$$
$$PV = 5{,}000$$
$$r = 0.06$$
$$m = 12.$$

Substituting, we get

$$6{,}000 = 5{,}000\left(1+\frac{0.06}{12}\right)^{12t}.$$

using Technology

See the Technology Guides at the end of the chapter for details on using TVM Solver on the TI-83/84 Plus or the built-in finance functions in spreadsheets to do the calculations in Example 6. [Details: TI-83/84 Plus: page 167, Spreadsheet: page 171]

Website

www.WanerMath.com

→ On Line Utilities

→ Time Value of Money Utility

This utility is similar to the TVM Solver on the TI-83/84 Plus. To compute the time needed, enter the values shown, and press "Compute" next to *t*.

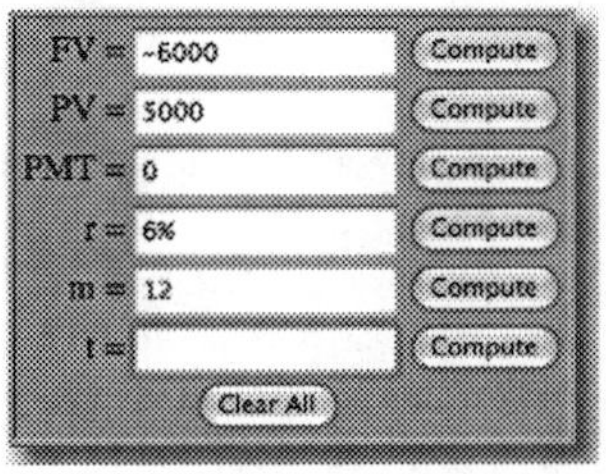

If you are familiar with logarithms, you can solve explicitly for *t* as follows:

$$\left(1+\frac{0.06}{12}\right)^{12t} = \frac{6{,}000}{5{,}000} = 1.2$$

$$\log\left(1+\frac{0.06}{12}\right)^{12t} = \log 1.2$$

$$12t\log\left(1+\frac{0.06}{12}\right) = \log 1.2$$

$$t = \frac{\log 1.2}{12\log\left(1+\frac{0.06}{12}\right)} \approx 3.046 \approx 3 \text{ years.}$$

Another approach is to use a bit of trial and error to find the answer. Let's see what the future value is after 2, 3, and 4 years:

$$5{,}000\left(1+\frac{0.06}{12}\right)^{12\times 2} = 5{,}635.80 \quad \text{Future value after 2 years}$$

$$5{,}000\left(1+\frac{0.06}{12}\right)^{12\times 3} = 5{,}983.40 \quad \text{Future value after 3 years}$$

$$5{,}000\left(1+\frac{0.06}{12}\right)^{12\times 4} = 6{,}352.45. \quad \text{Future value after 4 years}$$

From these calculations, it looks as if the answer should be a bit more than 3 years, but is certainly between 3 and 4 years. We could try 3.5 years next and then narrow it down systematically until we have a pretty good approximation of the correct answer.

Graphing calculators and spreadsheets give us alternative methods of solution.

FAQs

Recognizing When to Use Compound Interest and the Meaning of Present Value

Q: *How do I distinguish a problem that calls for compound interest from one that calls for simple interest?*

A: Study the scenario to ascertain whether the interest is being withdrawn as it is earned or reinvested (deposited back into the account). If the interest is being withdrawn, the problem is calling for simple interest because the interest is not itself earning interest. If it is being reinvested, the problem is calling for compound interest.

Q: *How do I distinguish present value from future value in a problem?*

A: The present value always refers to the value of an investment before any interest is included (or, in the case of a depreciating investment, before any depreciation takes place). As an example, the future value of a bond is its maturity value. The value of $1 today in constant 2010 dollars is its present value (even though 2010 is in the past).

2.2 EXERCISES

▼ more advanced ◆ challenging

indicates exercises that should be solved using technology

In Exercises 1–8, calculate, to the nearest cent, the future value of an investment of $10,000 at the stated interest rate after the stated amount of time. HINT [See Example 1.]

1. 3% per year, compounded annually, after 10 years

2. 4% per year, compounded annually, after 8 years

3. 2.5% per year, compounded quarterly (4 times/year), after 5 years

4. 1.5% per year, compounded weekly (52 times/year), after 5 years

5. 6.5% per year, compounded daily (assume 365 days/year), after 10 years

6. 11.2% per year, compounded monthly, after 12 years

7. 0.2% per month, compounded monthly, after 10 years

8. 0.45% per month, compounded monthly, after 20 years

In Exercises 9–14, calculate, to the nearest cent, the present value of an investment that will be worth $1,000 at the stated interest rate after the stated amount of time. HINT [See Example 2]

9. 10 years, at 5% per year, compounded annually

10. 5 years, at 6% per year, compounded annually

11. 5 years, at 4.2% per year, compounded weekly (assume 52 weeks per year)

12. 10 years, at 5.3% per year, compounded quarterly

13. 4 years, depreciating 5% each year

14. 5 years, depreciating 4% each year

In Exercises 15–20, find the effective annual interest rates of the given annual interest rates. Round your answers to the nearest 0.01%. HINT [See Quick Example on page 140.]

15. 5% compounded quarterly

16. 5% compounded monthly

17. 10% compounded monthly

18. 10% compounded daily (assume 365 days per year)

19. 10% compounded hourly (assume 365 days per year)

20. 10% compounded every minute (assume 365 days per year)

APPLICATIONS

21. ***Savings*** You deposit $1,000 in an account at the *Lifelong Trust Savings and Loan* that pays 6% interest compounded quarterly. By how much will your deposit have grown after 4 years?

22. ***Investments*** You invest $10,000 in *Rapid Growth Funds*, which appreciate by 2% per year, with yields reinvested quarterly. By how much will your investment have grown after 5 years?

23. ***Depreciation*** During 2008, the S&P 500 index depreciated by 37.6%.[10] Assuming that this trend had continued, how much would a $3,000 investment in an S&P index fund have been worth after 3 years?

24. ***Depreciation*** During 2008, the NASDAQ Composite Index depreciated by 42%.[11] Assuming that this trend had continued, how much would a $5,000 investment in a NASDAQ Composite Index fund have been worth after 4 years?

25. ***Bonds*** You want to buy a 10-year zero coupon bond with a maturity value of $5,000 and a yield of 5.5% annually. How much will you pay?

26. ***Bonds*** You want to buy a 15-year zero coupon bond with a maturity value of $10,000 and a yield of 6.25% annually. How much will you pay?

27. ▼ ***Investments*** When I was considering what to do with my $10,000 Lottery winnings, my broker suggested I invest half of it in gold, the value of which was growing by 10% per year, and the other half in certificates of deposit (CDs), which were yielding 5% per year, compounded every 6 months. Assuming that these rates are sustained, how much will my investment be worth in 10 years?

28. ▼ ***Investments*** When I was considering what to do with the $10,000 proceeds from my sale of technology stock, my broker suggested I invest half of it in municipal bonds, whose value was growing by 6% per year, and the other half in CDs, which were yielding 3% per year, compounded every 2 months. Assuming that these interest rates are sustained, how much will my investment be worth in 10 years?

29. ▼ ***Depreciation*** During a prolonged recession, property values on Long Island depreciated by 2% every 6 months. If my house cost $200,000 originally, how much was it worth 5 years later?

30. ▼ ***Depreciation*** Stocks in the health industry depreciated by 5.1% in the first 9 months of 1993.[12] Assuming that this trend continued, how much would a $40,000 investment be worth in 9 years? HINT [Nine years corresponds to 12 nine-month periods.]

31. ▼ ***Retirement Planning*** I want to be earning an annual salary of $100,000 when I retire in 15 years. I have been offered a job that guarantees an annual salary increase of 4% per year, and the starting salary is negotiable. What salary should I request in order to meet my goal?

[10] Source: http://finance.google.com.

[11] *Ibid.*

[12] Source: *New York Times*, October 9, 1993, p. 37.

32. ▼ ***Retirement Planning*** I want to be earning an annual salary of $80,000 when I retire in 10 years. I have been offered a job that guarantees an annual salary increase of 5% per year, and the starting salary is negotiable. What salary should I request in order to meet my goal?

33. ▼ ***Present Value*** Determine the amount of money, to the nearest dollar, you must invest at 6% per year, compounded annually, so that you will be a millionaire in 30 years.

34. ▼ ***Present Value*** Determine the amount of money, to the nearest dollar, you must invest now at 7% per year, compounded annually, so that you will be a millionaire in 40 years.

35. ▼ ***Stocks*** Six years ago, I invested some money in *Dracubunny Toy Co.* stock, acting on the advice of a "friend." As things turned out, the value of the stock decreased by 5% every 4 months, and I discovered yesterday (to my horror) that my investment was worth only $297.91. How much did I originally invest?

36. ▼ ***Sales*** My recent marketing idea, the *Miracle Algae Growing Kit*, has been remarkably successful, with monthly sales growing by 6% every 6 months over the past 5 years. Assuming that I sold 100 kits the first month, how many kits did I sell in the first month of this year?

37. ▼ ***Inflation*** Inflation has been running 2% per year. A car now costs $30,000. How much would it have cost 5 years ago? HINT [See Example 3.]

38. ▼ ***Inflation*** (Compare Exercise 37.) Inflation has been running 1% every 6 months. A car now costs $30,000. How much would it have cost 5 years ago?

39. ▼ ***Inflation*** Housing prices have been rising 6% per year. A house now costs $200,000. What would it have cost 10 years ago?

40. ▼ ***Inflation*** (Compare Exercise 39.) Housing prices have been rising 0.5% each month. A house now costs $200,000. What would it have cost 10 years ago? HINT [See Example 4.]

41. ▼ ***Constant Dollars*** Inflation is running 3% per year when you deposit $1,000 in an account earning interest of 5% per year compounded annually. In *constant dollars*, how much money will you have 2 years from now? HINT [First calculate the value of your account in 2 years' time, and then find its present value based on the inflation rate.]

42. ▼ ***Constant Dollars*** Inflation is running 1% per month when you deposit $10,000 in an account earning 8% compounded monthly. In *constant dollars*, how much money will you have 2 years from now? HINT [See Exercise 41.]

43. ▼ ***Investments*** You are offered two investments. One promises to earn 12% compounded annually. The other will earn 11.9% compounded monthly. Which is the better investment? HINT [See Example 5.]

44. ▼ ***Investments*** You are offered three investments. The first promises to earn 15% compounded annually, the second will earn 14.5% compounded quarterly, and the third will earn 14% compounded monthly. Which is the best investment? HINT [See Example 5.]

45. ▼ ***History*** Legend has it that a band of Lenape Indians known as the "Manhatta" sold Manhattan Island to the Dutch in 1626 for $24. In 2011, the total value of Manhattan real estate was estimated to be $314,119 million.[13] Suppose that the Lenape had instead taken that $24 and invested it at 6.3% compounded annually (a relatively conservative investment goal). Could they then have bought back the island in 2011?

46. ▼ ***History*** Repeat Exercise 45, assuming that the Lenape had invested the $24 at 6.2% compounded annually.

Inflation *Exercises 47–54 are based on the following table, which shows the 2008 annual inflation rates in several Latin American countries.*[14] *Assume that the rates shown continue indefinitely.*

Country	Argentina	Brazil	Bolivia	Nicaragua	Venezuela	Mexico	Uruguay
Currency	Peso	Real	Boliviano	Gold cordoba	Bolivar	Peso	Peso
Inflation Rate (%)	9.2	6.3	15.1	13.8	25.7	5.0	8.5

47. If an item in Brazil now costs 100 reals, what do you expect it to cost 5 years from now? (Answer to the nearest real.)

48. If an item in Argentina now costs 1,000 pesos, what do you expect it to cost 5 years from now? (Answer to the nearest peso.)

49. If an item in Bolivia will cost 1,000 bolivianos in 10 years, what does it cost now? (Answer to the nearest boliviano.)

50. If an item in Mexico will cost 20,000 pesos in 10 years, what does it cost now? (Answer to the nearest peso.)

51. ▼ You wish to invest 1,000 bolivars in Venezuela at 8% annually, compounded twice a year. Find the value of your investment in 10 years, expressing the answer in constant bolivars. (Answer to the nearest bolivar.)

52. ▼ You wish to invest 1,000 pesos in Uruguay at 8% annually, compounded twice a year. Find the value of your investment in 10 years, expressing the answer in constant pesos. (Answer to the nearest peso.)

53. ▼ Which is the better investment: an investment in Mexico yielding 5.3% per year, compounded annually, or an investment in Nicaragua yielding 14% per year, compounded every 6 months? Support your answer with figures that show the future value of an investment of 1 unit of currency in constant units.

[13]Source: FY12 Tentative Assessment Roll summary, New York City Department of Finance, January 14, 2011 (www.nyc.gov/finance)

[14]Sources: www.bloomberg.com, www.csmonitor.com, www.indexmundi.com.

1322.5
1329.59

54. ▼ Which is the better investment: an investment in Argentina yielding 10% per year, compounded annually, or an investment in Uruguay, yielding 9% per year, compounded every 6 months? Support your answer with figures that show the future value of an investment of 1 unit of currency in constant units.

Stock Investments *Exercises 55–60 are based on the following chart, which shows monthly figures for Apple Computer, Inc. stock in 2010.*[15]

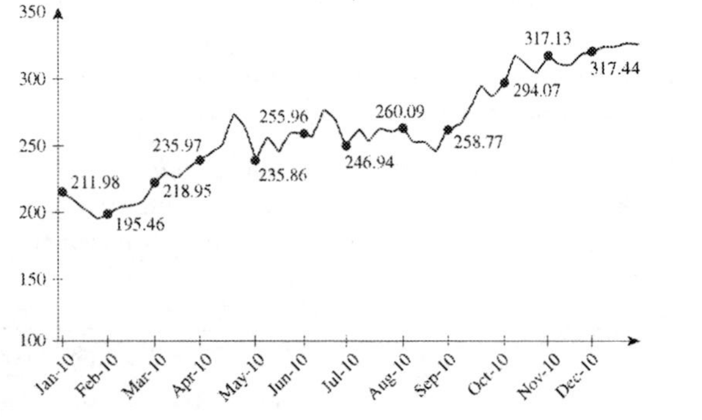

Marked are the following points on the chart:

Jan. 10	Feb. 10	Mar. 10	Apr. 10	May 10	June 10
211.98	195.46	218.95	235.97	235.86	255.96

July 10	Aug. 10	Sep. 10	Oct. 10	Nov. 10	Dec. 10
246.94	260.09	258.77	294.07	317.13	317.44

55. ▼ Calculate to the nearest 0.01% your annual percentage return (assuming annual compounding) if you had bought Apple stock in June and sold in December.

56. ▼ Calculate to the nearest 0.01% your annual percentage return (assuming annual compounding) if you had bought Apple stock in February and sold in June.

57. ▼ Suppose you bought Apple stock in April. If you later sold at one of the marked dates on the chart, which of those dates would have given you the largest annual return (assuming annual compounding), and what would that return have been?

58. ▼ Suppose you bought Apple stock in May. If you later sold at one of the marked dates on the chart, which of those dates would have given you the largest annual return (assuming annual compounding), and what would that return have been?

59. ▼ Did Apple's stock undergo compound interest change in the period January through May? (Give a reason for your answer.)

60. ▼ If Apple's stock had undergone compound interest change from April to June at the same monthly rate as from March to April, what would the price have been in June?

61. 📊 ▼ ***Competing Investments*** I just purchased $5,000 worth of municipal funds that are expected to yield 5.4% per year, compounded every 6 months. My friend has just purchased $6,000 worth of CDs that will earn 4.8% per year,

compounded every 6 months. Determine when, to the nearest year, the value of my investment will be the same as hers, and what this value will be. **HINT** [You can either graph the values of both investments or make tables of the values of both investments.]

62. 📊 ▼ ***Investments*** Determine when, to the nearest year, $3,000 invested at 5% per year, compounded daily, will be worth $10,000.

63. 📊 ▼ ***Epidemics*** At the start of 1985, the incidence of AIDS was doubling every 6 months and 40,000 cases had been reported in the United States. Assuming this trend would have continued, determine when, to the nearest tenth of a year, the number of cases would have reached 1 million.

64. 📊 ▼ ***Depreciation*** My investment in *Genetic Splicing, Inc.*, is now worth $4,354 and is depreciating by 5% every 6 months. For some reason, I am reluctant to sell the stock and swallow my losses. Determine when, to the nearest year, my investment will drop below $50.

65. ◆ ***Bonds*** Once purchased, bonds can be sold in the secondary market. The value of a bond depends on the prevailing interest rates, which vary over time. Suppose that in January 2020, you buy a 30-year zero-coupon U.S. Treasury bond with a maturity value of $100,000 and a yield of 15% annually.
  a. How much do you pay for the bond?
  b. In January 2037, your bond has 13 years remaining until maturity. Rates on U.S. Treasury bonds of comparable length are now about 4.75%. If you sell your bond to an investor looking for a return of 4.75% annually, how much money do you receive?
  c. Using your answers to parts (a) and (b), what was the annual yield (assuming annual compounding) on your 17-year investment?

66. ◆ ***Bonds*** Suppose that in January 2040, you buy a 30-year zero-coupon U.S. Treasury bond with a maturity value of $100,000 and a yield of 5% annually.
  a. How much do you pay for the bond?
  b. Suppose that, 15 years later, interest rates have risen again, to 12%. If you sell your bond to an investor looking for a return of 12%, how much money will you receive?
  c. Using your answers to parts (a) and (b), what will be the annual yield (assuming annual compounding) on your 15-year investment?

COMMUNICATION AND REASONING EXERCISES

67. Why is the graph of the future value of a compound interest investment as a function of time not a straight line (assuming a nonzero rate of interest)?

68. An investment that earns 10% (compound interest) every year is the same as an investment that earns 5% (compound interest) every 6 months, right?

69. ▼ If a bacteria culture is currently 0.01 g and increases in size by 10% each day, then its growth is linear, right?

70. ▼ At what point is the future value of a compound interest investment the same as the future value of a simple interest investment at the same annual rate of interest?

---

[15]Source: Yahoo! Finance (http://finance.yahoo.com).

71. ▼ If two equal investments have the same effective interest rate and you graph the future value as a function of time for each of them, are the graphs necessarily the same? Explain your answer.

72. ▼ For what kind of compound interest investments is the effective rate the same as the nominal rate? Explain your answer.

73. ▼ For what kind of compound interest investments is the effective rate greater than the nominal rate? When is it smaller? Explain your answer.

74. ▼ If an investment appreciates by 10% per year for 5 years (compounded annually) and then depreciates by 10% per year (compounded annually) for 5 more years, will it have the same value as it had originally? Explain your answer.

75. ▼ You can choose between two investments that mature at different times in the future. If you knew the rate of inflation, how would you decide which is the better investment?

76. ▼ If you knew the various inflation rates for the years 2000 through 2011, how would you convert $100 in 2012 dollars to 2000 dollars?

77. ▼ On the same set of axes, graph the future value of a $100 investment earning 10% per year as a function of time over a 20-year period, compounded once a year, 10 times a year, 100 times a year, 1,000 times a year, and 10,000 times a year. What do you notice?

78. ▼ By graphing the future value of a $100 investment that is depreciating by 1% each year, convince yourself that, eventually, the future value will be less than $1.

Practice Problems 2.2

1. Which will double in value faster: \$6000 invested at an annual rate of 5.9% compounded semiannually, or \$6000 invested at an annual rate of 5.8% compounded monthly?

2. How long will it take a single deposit of \$8000 grow in value to at least \$12,000 if it earns an annual interest rate of 3% with interest compounded daily?

3. What annual interest rate, compounded quarterly, would result in the same effective rate as an annual rate of 6% compounded monthly? Give your result as a percentage, correct to two decimal places.

2.3 Annuities, Loans, and Bonds

A typical defined-contribution pension fund works as follows*: Every month while you work, you and your employer deposit a certain amount of money in an account. This money earns (compound) interest from the time it is deposited. When you retire, the account continues to earn interest, but you may then start withdrawing money at a rate calculated to reduce the account to zero after some number of years. This account is an example of an **annuity**, an account earning interest into which you make periodic deposits or from which you make periodic withdrawals. In common usage, the term "annuity" is used for an account from which you make withdrawals. There are various terms used for accounts into which you make payments, based on their purpose. Examples include **savings account**, **pension fund**, and **sinking fund**. A sinking fund is generally used by businesses or governments to accumulate money to pay off an anticipated debt, but we'll use the term to refer to any account into which you make periodic payments.

* Defined-contribution pension plans have largely replaced the defined-benefit pensions that were once the norm in private industry. In a defined-benefit plan, the size of your pension is guaranteed; it is typically a percentage of your final working salary. In a defined-contribution plan, the size of your pension depends on how well your investments do.

Sinking Funds

Suppose you make a payment of \$100 at the end of every month into an account earning 3.6% interest per year, compounded monthly. This means that your investment is earning $3.6\%/12 = 0.3\%$ per month. We write $i = 0.036/12 = 0.003$. What will be the value of the investment at the end of 2 years (24 months)?

Think of the deposits separately. Each earns interest from the time it is deposited, and the total accumulated after 2 years is the sum of these deposits and the interest they earn. In other words, the accumulated value is the sum of the future values of the deposits, taking into account how long each deposit sits in the account. Figure 1 shows a timeline with the deposits and the contribution of each to the final value. For example, the very last deposit (at the end of month 24) has no time to earn interest, so it contributes only \$100. The very first deposit, which earns interest for 23 months, by the future value formula for compound interest contributes $\$100(1 + 0.003)^{23}$ to the total. Adding together all of the future values gives us the total future value:

$$\begin{aligned} FV &= 100 + 100(1 + 0.003) + 100(1 + 0.003)^2 + \cdots + 100(1 + 0.003)^{23} \\ &= 100[1 + (1 + 0.003) + (1 + 0.003)^2 + \cdots + (1 + 0.003)^{23}] \end{aligned}$$

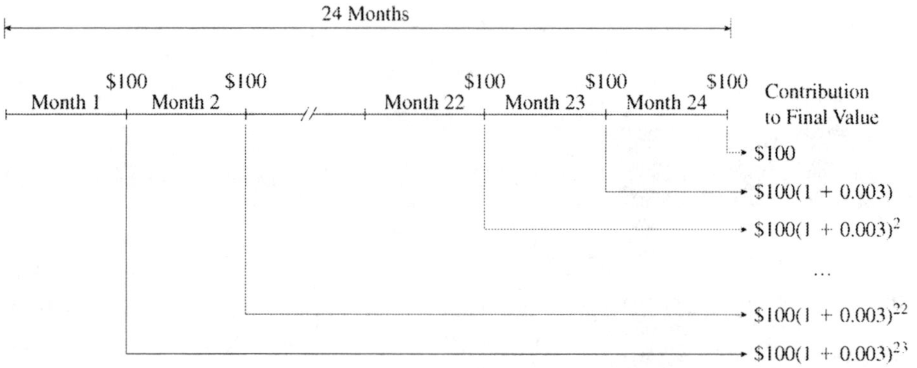

Figure 1

Fortunately, this sort of sum is well-known (to mathematicians, anyway*) and there is a convenient formula for its value†:

$$1 + x + x^2 + \cdots + x^{n-1} = \frac{x^n - 1}{x - 1}.$$

In our case, with $x = 1 + 0.003$, this formula allows us to calculate the future value:

$$FV = 100\frac{(1 + 0.003)^{24} - 1}{(1 + 0.003) - 1} = 100\frac{(1.003)^{24} - 1}{0.003} \approx \$2{,}484.65.$$

It is now easy to generalize this calculation.

* It is called a **geometric series**.

† The quickest way to convince yourself that this formula is correct is to multiply out $(x - 1)(1 + x + x^2 + \cdots + x^{n-1})$ and see that you get $x^n - 1$. You should also try substituting some numbers. For example, $1 + 3 + 3^2 = 13 = (3^3 - 1)/(3 - 1)$.

Future Value of a Sinking Fund

A **sinking fund** is an account earning compound interest into which you make periodic deposits. Suppose that the account has an annual rate of r compounded m times per year, so that $i = r/m$ is the interest rate per compounding period. If you make a payment of PMT at the end of each period, then the future value after t years, or $n = mt$ periods, will be

$$FV = PMT\frac{(1 + i)^n - 1}{i}.$$

Quick Example

At the end of each month you deposit $50 into an account earning 2% annual interest compounded monthly. To find the future value after 5 years, we use $i = 0.02/12$ and $n = 12 \times 5 = 60$ compounding periods, so

$$FV = 50\frac{(1 + 0.02/12)^{60} - 1}{0.02/12} = \$3{,}152.37.$$

using Technology

To automate the computations in Example 1 using a graphing calculator or a spreadsheet, see the Technology Guides at the end of the chapter. Outline:

EXAMPLE 1 Retirement Account

Your retirement account has $5,000 in it and earns 5% interest per year compounded monthly. Every month for the next 10 years you will deposit $100 into the account. How much money will there be in the account at the end of those 10 years?

TI-83/84 Plus
[APPS] `1:Finance`, then `1:TVM Solver`
N = 120, I% = 5, PV = −5000, PMT = −100, P/Y = 12, C/Y = 12
With cursor on FV line, [ALPHA] [SOLVE] [More details on page 167.]

Spreadsheet
`=FV(5/12,10*12,-100,-5000)`
[More details on page 171.]

Website
www.WanerMath.com
→ On Line Utilities
→ Time Value of Money Utility
Enter the values shown, and press "Compute" next to FV.

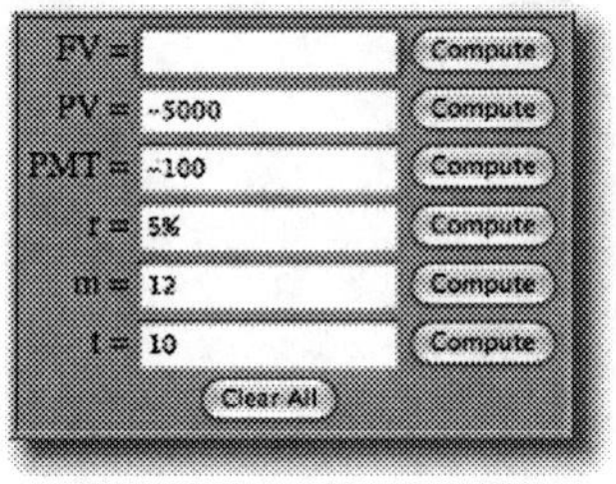

Solution This is a sinking fund with $PMT = \$100$, $r = 0.05$, $m = 12$, so $i = 0.05/12$, and $n = 12 \times 10 = 120$. Ignoring for the moment the \$5,000 already in the account, your payments have the following future value:

$$\begin{aligned} FV &= PMT\frac{(1+i)^n - 1}{i} \\ &= 100\frac{(1+0.05/12)^{120} - 1}{0.05/12} \\ &\approx \$15{,}528.23. \end{aligned}$$

What about the \$5,000 that was already in the account? That sits there and earns interest, so we need to find its future value as well, using the compound interest formula:

$$\begin{aligned} FV &= PV(1+i)^n \\ &= 5{,}000(1+0.05/12)^{120} \\ &= \$8{,}235.05. \end{aligned}$$

Hence, the total amount in the account at the end of 10 years will be

$$\$15{,}528.23 + 8{,}235.05 = \$23{,}763.28.$$

Sometimes we know what we want the future value to be and need to determine the payments necessary to achieve that goal. We can simply solve the future value formula for the payment.

Payment Formula for a Sinking Fund

Suppose that an account has an annual rate of r compounded m times per year, so that $i = r/m$ is the interest rate per compounding period. If you want to accumulate a total of FV in the account after t years, or $n = mt$ periods, by making payments of PMT at the end of each period, then each payment must be

$$PMT = FV\frac{i}{(1+i)^n - 1}.$$

EXAMPLE 2 Education Fund

Tony and Maria have just had a son, José Phillipe. They establish an account to accumulate money for his college education, in which they would like to have \$100,000 after 17 years. If the account pays 4% interest per year compounded quarterly, and they make deposits at the end of every quarter, how large must each deposit be for them to reach their goal?

using Technology

To automate the computations in Example 2 using a graphing calculator or a spreadsheet, see the Technology Guides at the end of the chapter. Outline:

TI-83/84 Plus
[APPS] `1:Finance`, then `1:TVM Solver`
N = 68, I% = 4, PV = 0, FV = 100000, P/Y = 4, C/Y = 4
With cursor on PMT line, [ALPHA] [SOLVE]
[More details on page 167.]

Solution This is a sinking fund with $FV = \$100{,}000$, $m = 4$, $n = 4 \times 17 = 68$, and $r = 0.04$, so $i = 0.04/4 = 0.01$. From the payment formula, we get

$$PMT = 100{,}000\frac{0.01}{(1+0.01)^{68} - 1} \approx \$1{,}033.89.$$

So, Tony and Maria must deposit \$1,033.89 every quarter in order to meet their goal.

Spreadsheet
=PMT(4/4,17*4,0,100000)
[More details on page 172.]

Website
www.WanerMath.com
→ On Line Utilities
→ Time Value of Money Utility
Enter the values shown, and press "Compute" next to PMT.

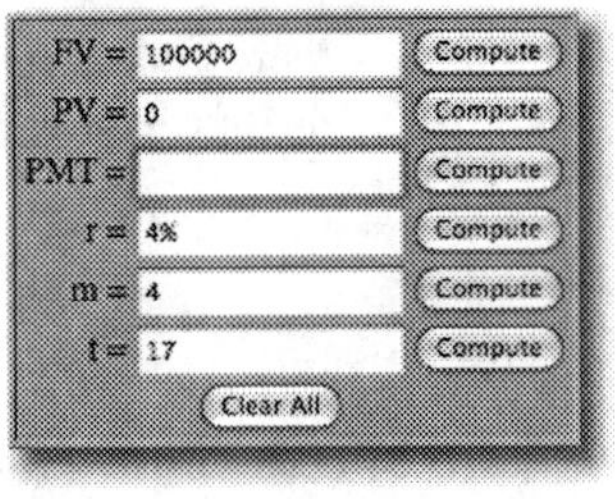

Annuities

Suppose we deposit an amount *PV* now in an account earning 3.6% interest per year, compounded monthly. Starting 1 month from now, the bank will send us monthly payments of \$100. What must *PV* be so that the account will be drawn down to \$0 in exactly 2 years?

As before, we write $i = r/m = 0.036/12 = 0.003$, and we have $PMT = 100$. The first payment of \$100 will be made 1 month from now, so its present value is

$$\frac{PMT}{(1+i)^n} = \frac{100}{1+0.003} = 100(1+0.003)^{-1} \approx \$99.70.$$

In other words, that much of the original *PV* goes toward funding the first payment. The second payment, 2 months from now, has a present value of

$$\frac{PMT}{(1+i)^n} = \frac{100}{(1+0.003)^2} = 100(1+0.003)^{-2} \approx \$99.40.$$

That much of the original *PV* funds the second payment. This continues for 2 years, at which point we receive the last payment, which has a present value of

$$\frac{PMT}{(1+i)^n} = \frac{100}{(1+0.003)^{24}} = 100(1+0.003)^{-24} \approx \$93.06$$

and that exhausts the account. Figure 2 shows a timeline with the payments and the present value of each.

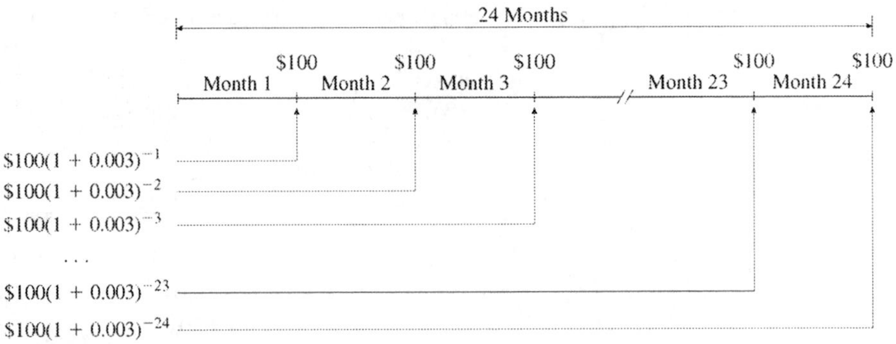

Figure 2

Because *PV* must be the sum of these present values, we get

$$\begin{aligned} PV &= 100(1+0.003)^{-1} + 100(1+0.003)^{-2} + \cdots + 100(1+0.003)^{-24} \\ &= 100[(1+0.003)^{-1} + (1+0.003)^{-2} + \cdots + (1+0.003)^{-24}]. \end{aligned}$$

We can again find a simpler formula for this sum:

$$\begin{aligned} x^{-1} + x^{-2} + \cdots + x^{-n} &= \frac{1}{x^n}(x^{n-1} + x^{n-2} + \cdots + 1) \\ &= \frac{1}{x^n} \cdot \frac{x^n - 1}{x - 1} = \frac{1 - x^{-n}}{x - 1}. \end{aligned}$$

So, in our case,

$$PV = 100\frac{1-(1+0.003)^{-24}}{(1+0.003)-1}$$

or

$$PV = 100\frac{1-(1.003)^{-24}}{0.003} \approx \$2{,}312.29.$$

If we deposit $2,312.29 initially and the bank sends us $100 per month for 2 years, our account will be exhausted at the end of that time.

Generalizing, we get the following formula:

Present Value of an Annuity

An **annuity** is an account earning compound interest from which periodic withdrawals are made. Suppose that the account has an annual rate of r compounded m times per year, so that $i = r/m$ is the interest rate per compounding period. Suppose also that the account starts with a balance of PV. If you receive a payment of PMT at the end of each compounding period, and the account is down to \$0 after t years, or $n = mt$ periods, then

$$PV = PMT\frac{1-(1+i)^{-n}}{i}.$$

Quick Example

At the end of each month you want to withdraw \$50 from an account earning 2% annual interest compounded monthly. If you want the account to last for 5 years (60 compounding periods), it must have the following amount to begin with:

$$PV = 50\frac{1-(1+0.02/12)^{-60}}{0.02/12} = \$2{,}852.62.$$

Note If you make your withdrawals at the end of each compounding period, as we've discussed so far, you have an **ordinary annuity**. If, instead, you make withdrawals at the beginning of each compounding period, you have an **annuity due**. Because each payment occurs one period earlier, there is one less period in which to earn interest, hence the present value must be larger by a factor of $(1+i)$ to fund each payment. So, the present value formula for an annuity due is

$$PV = PMT(1+i)\frac{1-(1+i)^{-n}}{i}.$$

In this book, we will concentrate on ordinary annuities. ■

EXAMPLE 3 Trust Fund

You wish to establish a trust fund from which your niece can withdraw \$2,000 every 6 months for 15 years, at the end of which time she will receive the remaining money in the trust, which you would like to be \$10,000. The trust will be invested at 7% per year compounded every 6 months. How large should the trust be?

using Technology

To automate the computations in Example 3 using a graphing calculator or a spreadsheet, see the Technology Guides at the end of the chapter. Outline:

TI-83/84 Plus

[APPS] `1:Finance`, then `1:TVM Solver`

N = 30, I% = 7, PMT = 2000, FV = 10000, P/Y = 2, C/Y = 2

With cursor on PV line.

[ALPHA] [SOLVE]

[More details on page 168.]

Spreadsheet

`=PV(7/2,15*2,2000,10000)`

[More details on page 172.]

Website

www.WanerMath.com

→ On Line Utilities

→ Time Value of Money Utility

Enter the values shown, and press "Compute" next to PV.

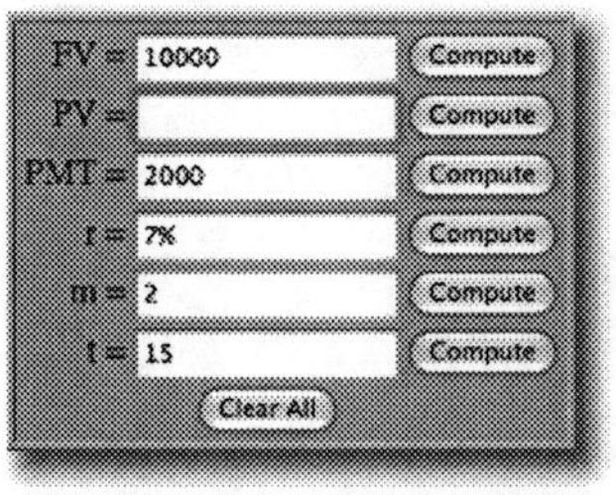

Solution We view this account as having two parts, one funding the semiannual payments and the other funding the $10,000 lump sum at the end. The amount of money necessary to fund the semiannual payments is the present value of an annuity, with $PMT = 2{,}000$, $r = 0.07$, and $m = 2$, so $i = 0.07/2 = 0.035$, and $n = 2 \times 15 = 30$. Substituting gives

$$PV = 2{,}000\frac{1-(1+0.035)^{-30}}{0.035}$$
$$= \$36{,}784.09.$$

To fund the lump sum of $10,000 after 15 years, we need the present value of $10,000 under compound interest:

$$PV = 10{,}000(1+0.035)^{-30}$$
$$= \$3{,}562.78.$$

Thus the trust should start with $36,784.09 + 3,562.78 = $40,346.87.

Sometimes we know how much money we begin with and for how long we want to make withdrawals. We then want to determine the amount of money we can withdraw each period. For this, we simply solve the present value formula for the payment.

using Technology

To automate the computations in Example 4 using a graphing calculator or a spreadsheet, see the Technology Guides at the end of the chapter. Outline:

TI-83/84 Plus

[APPS] `1:Finance`, then `1:TVM Solver`
N = 16, I% = 4, PV = −100000, FV = 0, P/Y = 4, C/Y = 4
With cursor on PMT line, [ALPHA] [SOLVE]
[More details on page 168.]

Spreadsheet

`=PMT(4/4,4*4,-100000,0)`
[More details on page 172.]

Website

www.WanerMath.com
→ On Line Utilities
→ Time Value of Money Utility

Enter the values shown, and press "Compute" next to PMT.

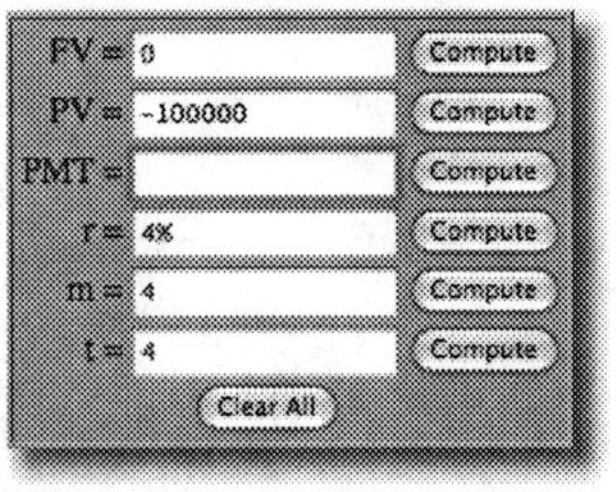

Payment Formula for an Ordinary Annuity

Suppose that an account has an annual rate of r compounded m times per year, so that $i = r/m$ is the interest rate per compounding period. Suppose also that the account starts with a balance of PV. If you want to receive a payment of PMT at the end of each compounding period, and the account is down to $0 after t years, or $n = mt$ periods, then

$$PMT = PV\frac{i}{1-(1+i)^{-n}}.$$

EXAMPLE 4 Education Fund

Tony and Maria (see Example 2), having accumulated $100,000 for José Phillipe's college education, would now like to make quarterly withdrawals over the next 4 years. How much money can they withdraw each quarter in order to draw down the account to zero at the end of the 4 years? (Recall that the account pays 4% interest compounded quarterly.)

Solution Now Tony and Maria's account is acting as an annuity with a present value of $100,000. So, $PV = \$100{,}000$, $r = 0.04$, and $m = 4$, giving $i = 0.04/4 = 0.01$, and $n = 4 \times 4 = 16$. We use the payment formula to get

$$PMT = 100{,}000\frac{0.01}{1-(1+0.01)^{-16}} \approx \$6{,}794.46.$$

So, they can withdraw $6,794.46 each quarter for 4 years, at the end of which time their account balance will be 0.

EXAMPLE 5 Saving for Retirement

Jane Q. Employee has just started her new job with *Big Conglomerate, Inc.*, and is already looking forward to retirement. BCI offers her as a pension plan an annuity that is guaranteed to earn 6% annual interest compounded monthly. She plans to work for 40 years before retiring and would then like to be able to draw an income of \$7,000 per month for 20 years. How much do she and BCI together have to deposit per month into the fund to accomplish this?

Solution Here we have the situation we described at the beginning of the section: a sinking fund accumulating money to be used later as an annuity. We know the desired payment out of the annuity, so we work backward. The first thing we need to do is calculate the present value of the annuity required to make the pension payments. We use the annuity present value formula with $PMT = 7{,}000$, $i = r/m = 0.06/12 = 0.005$ and $n = 12 \times 20 = 240$.

$$\begin{aligned} PV &= PMT\frac{1-(1+i)^{-n}}{i} \\ &= 7{,}000\frac{1-(1+0.005)^{-240}}{0.005} \approx \$977{,}065.40 \end{aligned}$$

This is the total that must be accumulated in the sinking fund during the 40 years she plans to work. In other words, this is the *future* value, *FV*, of the sinking fund. (Thus, the present value in the first step of our calculation is the future value in the second step.) To determine the payments necessary to accumulate this amount, we use the sinking fund payment formula with $FV = 977{,}065.40$, $i = 0.005$, and $n = 12 \times 40 = 480$.

$$\begin{aligned} PMT &= FV\frac{i}{(1+i)^n - 1} \\ &= 977{,}065.40\frac{0.005}{1.005^{480}-1} \\ &\approx \$490.62 \end{aligned}$$

So, if she and BCI collectively deposit \$490.62 per month into her retirement fund, she can retire with the income she desires.

Installment Loans

In a typical installment loan, such as a car loan or a home mortgage, we borrow an amount of money and then pay it back with interest by making fixed payments (usually every month) over some number of years. From the point of view of the lender, this is an annuity. Thus, loan calculations are identical to annuity calculations.

EXAMPLE 6 Home Mortgages

Marc and Mira are buying a house, and have taken out a 30-year, \$90,000 mortgage at 8% interest per year. What will their monthly payments be?

Solution From the bank's point of view, a mortgage is an annuity. In this case, the present value is $PV = \$90{,}000$, $r = 0.08$, $m = 12$, and $n = 12 \times 30 = 360$. To find the payments, we use the payment formula:

$$PMT = 90{,}000\frac{0.08/12}{1-(1+0.08/12)^{-360}} \approx \$660.39.$$

The word "mortgage" comes from the French for "dead pledge." The process of paying off a loan is called **amortizing** the loan, meaning to kill the debt owed.

EXAMPLE 7 Amortization Schedule

Continuing Example 6: Mortgage interest is tax deductible, so it is important to know how much of a year's mortgage payments represents interest. How much interest will Marc and Mira pay in the first year of their mortgage?

Solution Let us calculate how much of each month's payment is interest and how much goes to reducing the outstanding principal. At the end of the first month Marc and Mira must pay 1 month's interest on $90,000, which is

$$\$90{,}000 \times \frac{0.08}{12} = \$600.$$

The remainder of their first monthly payment, $\$660.39 - 600 = \$60.39$, goes to reducing the principal. Thus, in the second month the outstanding principal is $\$90{,}000 - 60.39 = \$89{,}939.61$, and part of their second monthly payment will be for the interest on this amount, which is

$$\$89{,}939.61 \times \frac{0.08}{12} \approx \$599.60.$$

The remaining $\$660.39 - \$599.60 = \$60.79$ goes to further reduce the principal. If we continue this calculation for the 12 months of the first year, we get the beginning of the mortgage's **amortization schedule**.

using Technology

To automate the construction of the amortization schedule in Example 7 using a graphing calculator or a spreadsheet, see the Technology Guides at the end of the chapter. [Details: TI-83/84 Plus: page 169, Spreadsheet: page 173]

Month	*Interest Payment*	*Payment on Principal*	*Outstanding Principal*
0			$90,000.00
1	$600.00	$60.39	89,939.61
2	599.60	60.79	89,878.82
3	599.19	61.20	89,817.62
4	598.78	61.61	89,756.01
5	598.37	62.02	89,693.99
6	597.96	62.43	89,631.56
7	597.54	62.85	89,568.71
8	597.12	63.27	89,505.44
9	596.70	63.69	89,441.75
10	596.28	64.11	89,377.64
11	595.85	64.54	89,313.10
12	595.42	64.97	89,248.13
Total	$7,172.81	$751.87	

As we can see from the totals at the bottom of the columns, Marc and Mira will pay a total of $7,172.81 in interest in the first year.

Bonds

Suppose that a corporation offers a 10-year bond paying 6.5% with payments every 6 months. As we saw in Example 3 of Section 2.1, this means that if we pay \$10,000 for bonds with a maturity value of \$10,000, we will receive $6.5/2 = 3.25\%$ of \$10,000, or \$325, every 6 months for 10 years, at the end of which time the corporation will give us the original \$10,000 back. But bonds are rarely sold at their maturity value. Rather, they are auctioned off and sold at a price the bond market determines they are worth.

For example, suppose that bond traders are looking for an investment that has a **rate of return** or **yield** of 7% rather than the stated 6.5% (sometimes called the **coupon interest rate** to distinguish it from the rate of return). How much would they be willing to pay for the bonds above with a maturity value of \$10,000? Think of the bonds as an investment that will pay the owner \$325 every 6 months for 10 years, and will pay an additional \$10,000 on maturity at the end of the 10 years. We can treat the \$325 payments as if they come from an annuity and determine how much an investor would pay for such an annuity if it earned 7% compounded semiannually. Separately, we determine the present value of an investment worth \$10,000 ten years from now, if it earned 7% compounded semiannually. For the first calculation, we use the annuity present value formula, with $i = 0.07/2$ and $n = 2 \times 10 = 20$.

$$\begin{aligned} PV &= PMT\frac{1-(1+i)^{-n}}{i} \\ &= 325\frac{1-(1+0.07/2)^{-20}}{0.07/2} \\ &= \$4{,}619.03 \end{aligned}$$

For the second calculation, we use the present value formula for compound interest:

$$\begin{aligned} PV &= 10{,}000(1+0.07/2)^{-20} \\ &= \$5{,}025.66. \end{aligned}$$

Thus, an investor looking for a 7% return will be willing to pay \$4,619.03 for the semiannual payments of \$325 and \$5,025.66 for the \$10,000 payment at the end of 10 years, for a total of $\$4{,}619.03 + 5{,}025.66 = \$9{,}644.69$ for the \$10,000 bond.

EXAMPLE 8 Bonds

Suppose that bond traders are looking for only a 6% yield on their investment. How much would they pay per \$10,000 for the 10-year bonds above, which have a coupon interest rate of 6.5% and pay interest every 6 months?

Solution We redo the calculation with $r = 0.06$. For the annuity calculation we now get

$$PV = 325\frac{1-(1+0.06/2)^{-20}}{0.06/2} = \$4{,}835.18.$$

For the compound interest calculation we get

$$PV = 10{,}000(1+0.06/2)^{-20} = \$5{,}536.76.$$

Thus, traders would be willing to pay a total of $\$4{,}835.18 + 5{,}536.76 = \$10{,}371.94$ for bonds with a maturity value of \$10,000.

Before we go on... Notice how the selling price of the bonds behaves as the desired yield changes. As desired yield goes up, the price of the bonds goes down, and as desired yield goes down, the price of the bonds goes up. When the desired yield equals the coupon interest rate, the selling price will equal the maturity value. Therefore, when the yield is higher than the coupon interest rate, the price of the bond will be below its maturity value, and when the yield is lower than the coupon interest rate, the price will be above the maturity value.

As we've mentioned before, the desired yield depends on many factors, but it generally moves up and down with prevailing interest rates. And interest rates have historically gone up and down cyclically. The effect on the value of bonds can be quite dramatic (see Exercises 65 and 66 in the preceding section). Because bonds can be sold again once bought, someone who buys bonds while interest rates are high and then resells them when interest rates decline can make a healthy profit. ■

using Technology

To automate the computations in Example 9 using a graphing calculator or a spreadsheet, see the Technology Guides at the end of the chapter. Outline:

TI-83/84 Plus

[APPS] `1:Finance`, then `1:TVM Solver`

N = 40, PV = −9800, PMT = 250, FV = 10000, P/Y = 2, C/Y = 2

With cursor on I% line, [ALPHA] [SOLVE]

[More details on page 170.]

Spreadsheet

`=RATE(20*2,250,-9800,10000)*2`

[More details on page 174.]

Website

www.WanerMath.com

→ On Line Utilities

→ Time Value of Money Utility

Enter the values shown, and press "Compute" next to r.

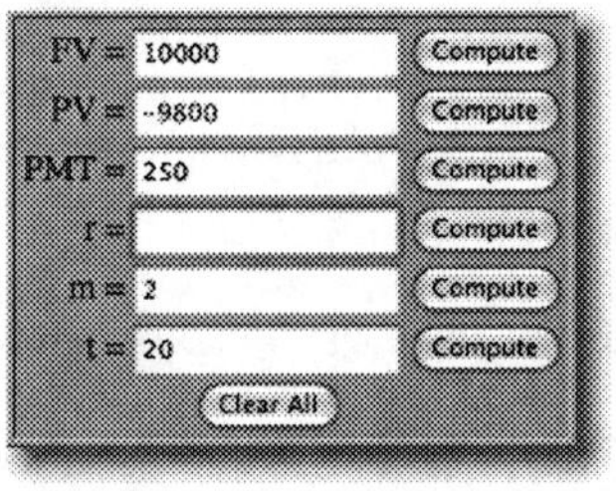

EXAMPLE 9 Rate of Return on a Bond

Suppose that a 5%, 20-year bond sells for \$9,800 per \$10,000 maturity value. What rate of return will investors get?

Solution Assuming the usual semiannual payments, we know the following about the annuity calculation:

$$PMT = 0.05 \times 10{,}000/2 = 250$$
$$n = 20 \times 2 = 40.$$

What we do not know is r or i, the annual or semiannual rate of return, respectively. So, we write

$$PV = 250\frac{1-(1+i)^{-40}}{i}.$$

For the compound interest calculation, we know $FV = 10{,}000$ and $n = 40$ again, so we write

$$PV = 10{,}000(1+i)^{-40}.$$

Adding these together should give the selling price of \$9,800:

$$250\frac{1-(1+i)^{-40}}{i} + 10{,}000(1+i)^{-40} = 9{,}800.$$

This equation cannot be solved for i directly. The best we can do by hand is a sort of trial-and-error approach, substituting a few values for i in the left-hand side of the above equation to get an estimate; we use the fact that, because the selling price is below the maturity value, r must be larger than 0.05, so i must be more than 0.025:

i	0.025	0.03	0.035
$250\frac{1-(1+i)^{-40}}{i} + 10{,}000(1+i)^{-40}$	10,000	8,844	7,864

Since we want the value to be 9,800, we see that the correct answer is somewhere between $i = 0.025$ and $i = 0.03$. Let us try the value midway between 0.025 and 0.03; namely $i = 0.0275$.

i	0.025	0.0275	0.03
$250\frac{1-(1+i)^{-40}}{i} + 10{,}000(1+i)^{-40}$	10,000	9,398	8,844

Now we know that the correct value of i is somewhere between 0.025 and 0.0275, so we can choose for our next estimate of i the number midway between them: 0.02625. We could continue in this fashion to obtain i as accurately as we like. In fact, $i \approx 0.02581$, corresponding to an annual rate of return of approximately 5.162%.

FAQs

Which Formula to Use

Q: *We have retirement accounts, trust funds, loans, bonds, and so on. Some are sinking funds, others are annuities. How do we distinguish among them, so we can tell which formula to use?*

A: In general, remember that a sinking fund is an interest-bearing fund into which payments are made, while an annuity is an interest-bearing fund from which money is withdrawn. Here is a list of some of the accounts we have discussed in this section:

- *Retirement Accounts* A retirement account is a sinking fund while payments are being made into the account (prior to retirement) and an annuity while a pension is being withdrawn (after retirement).
- *Education Funds* These are similar to retirement accounts.
- *Trust Funds* A trust fund is an annuity if periodic withdrawals are made.
- *Installment Loans* We think of an installment loan as an investment a bank makes in the lender. In this way, the lender's payments can be viewed as the bank's withdrawals, and so a loan is an annuity.
- *Bonds* A bond pays regular fixed amounts until it matures, at which time it pays its maturity value. We think of the bond as an annuity coupled with a compound interest investment funding the payment of the maturity value. We can then determine its present value based on the current market interest rate.

From a mathematical point of view, sinking funds and annuities are really the same thing. See the Communication and Reasoning Exercises for more about this.

2.3 EXERCISES

▼ more advanced ◆ challenging

T indicates exercises that should be solved using technology

Find the amount accumulated in the sinking funds in Exercises 1–6. (Assume end-of-period deposits and compounding at the same intervals as deposits.) HINT [See Example 1.]

1. $100 deposited monthly for 10 years at 5% per year
2. $150 deposited monthly for 20 years at 3% per year
3. $1,000 deposited quarterly for 20 years at 7% per year
4. $2,000 deposited quarterly for 10 years at 7% per year
5. ▼ $100 deposited monthly for 10 years at 5% per year in an account containing $5,000 at the start
6. ▼ $150 deposited monthly for 20 years at 3% per year in an account containing $10,000 at the start

Find the periodic payments necessary to accumulate the amounts given in Exercises 7–12 in a sinking fund. (Assume end-of-period deposits and compounding at the same intervals as deposits.) HINT [See Example 2.]

7. $10,000 in a fund paying 5% per year, with monthly payments for 5 years
8. $20,000 in a fund paying 3% per year, with monthly payments for 10 years
9. $75,000 in a fund paying 6% per year, with quarterly payments for 20 years
10. $100,000 in a fund paying 7% per year, with quarterly payments for 20 years
11. ▼ $20,000 in a fund paying 5% per year, with monthly payments for 5 years, if the fund contains $10,000 at the start

12. ▼ $30,000 in a fund paying 3% per year, with monthly payments for 10 years, if the fund contains $10,000 at the start

Find the present value of the annuity necessary to fund the withdrawals given in Exercises 13–18. (Assume end-of-period withdrawals and compounding at the same intervals as withdrawals.) HINT [See Example 3.]

13. $500 per month for 20 years, if the annuity earns 3% per year
14. $1,000 per month for 15 years, if the annuity earns 5% per year
15. $1,500 per quarter for 20 years, if the annuity earns 6% per year
16. $2,000 per quarter for 20 years, if the annuity earns 4% per year
17. ▼ $500 per month for 20 years, if the annuity earns 3% per year and if there is to be $10,000 left in the annuity at the end of the 20 years
18. ▼ $1,000 per month for 15 years, if the annuity earns 5% per year and if there is to be $20,000 left in the annuity at the end of the 15 years

Find the periodic withdrawals for the annuities given in Exercises 19–24. (Assume end-of-period withdrawals and compounding at the same intervals as withdrawals.) HINT [See Example 4.]

19. $100,000 at 3%, paid out monthly for 20 years
20. $150,000 at 5%, paid out monthly for 15 years
21. $75,000 at 4%, paid out quarterly for 20 years
22. $200,000 at 6%, paid out quarterly for 15 years
23. ▼ $100,000 at 3%, paid out monthly for 20 years, leaving $10,000 in the account at the end of the 20 years
24. ▼ $150,000 at 5%, paid out monthly for 15 years, leaving $20,000 in the account at the end of the 15 years

Determine the periodic payments on the loans given in Exercises 25–28. HINT [See Example 6.]

25. $10,000 borrowed at 9% for 4 years, with monthly payments
26. $20,000 borrowed at 8% for 5 years, with monthly payments
27. $100,000 borrowed at 5% for 20 years, with quarterly payments
28. $1,000,000 borrowed at 4% for 10 years, with quarterly payments

Determine the selling price, per $1,000 maturity value, of the bonds[16] in Exercises 29–34. (Assume twice-yearly interest payments.) HINT [See Example 8.]

29. ▼ 10 year, 4.875% bond, with a yield of 4.880%
30. ▼ 30 year, 5.375% bond, with a yield of 5.460%
31. ▼ 2 year, 3.625% bond, with a yield of 3.705%
32. ▼ 5 year, 4.375% bond, with a yield of 4.475%
33. ▼ 10 year, 5.5% bond, with a yield of 6.643%
34. ▼ 10 year, 6.25% bond, with a yield of 33.409%

Determine the yield on the bonds[17] in Exercises 35–40. (Assume twice-yearly interest payments.) HINT [See Example 9.]

35. ▼ 5 year, 3.5% bond, selling for $994.69 per $1,000 maturity value
36. ▼ 10 year, 3.375% bond, selling for $991.20 per $1,000 maturity value
37. ▼ 2 year, 3% bond, selling for $998.86 per $1,000 maturity value
38. ▼ 5 year, 4.625% bond, selling for $998.45 per $1,000 maturity value
39. ▼ 5 year, 4.25% bond, selling for $923.81 per $1,000 maturity value
40. ▼ 5 year 3.6% bond, selling for $216.96 per $1,000 maturity value

APPLICATIONS

41. ***Car Loans*** While shopping for a car loan, you get the following offers: Solid Savings & Loan is willing to loan you $10,000 at 9% interest for 4 years. Fifth Federal Bank & Trust will loan you the $10,000 at 7% interest for 3 years. Both require monthly payments. You can afford to pay $250 per month. Which loan, if either, can you take?
42. ***Business Loans*** You need to take out a loan of $20,000 to start up your T-shirt business. You have two possibilities: One bank is offering a 10% loan for 5 years, and another is offering a 9% loan for 4 years. Which will have the lower monthly payments? On which will you end up paying more interest total?
43. ▼ ***Pensions*** Your pension plan is an annuity with a guaranteed return of 3% per year (compounded monthly). You would like to retire with a pension of $5,000 per month for 20 years. If you work 40 years before retiring, how much must you and your employer deposit each month into the fund? HINT [See Example 5.]
44. ▼ ***Pensions*** Meg's pension plan is an annuity with a guaranteed return of 5% per year (compounded quarterly). She would like to retire with a pension of $12,000 per quarter for 25 years. If she works 45 years before retiring, how much money must she and her employer deposit each quarter? HINT [See Example 5.]
45. ▼ ***Pensions*** Your pension plan is an annuity with a guaranteed return of 4% per year (compounded quarterly). You can afford to put $1,200 per quarter into the fund, and you will work for 40 years before retiring. After you retire, you will

[16]The first four are actual U.S. Treasury notes and bonds auctioned in 2001 and 2002. The last two are, respectively, a Spanish and a Greek government bond auctioned November 17, 2011, during the Eurozone crisis. Sources: The Bureau of the Public Debt's Web site (www.publicdebt.treas.gov) and The Wall Street Journal's Web site (www.wsj.com).

[17]*Ibid.*

be paid a quarterly pension based on a 25-year payout. How much will you receive each quarter?

46. ▼ ***Pensions*** Jennifer's pension plan is an annuity with a guaranteed return of 5% per year (compounded monthly). She can afford to put $300 per month into the fund, and she will work for 45 years before retiring. If her pension is then paid out monthly based on a 20-year payout, how much will she receive per month?

Note: *In Exercises 47–52 we suggest the use of the finance functions in the TI-83/84 Plus or amortization tables in a spreadsheet.*

47. ▼ ***Mortgages*** You take out a 15-year mortgage for $50,000, at 8%, to be paid off monthly. Construct an amortization table showing how much you will pay in interest each year, and how much goes toward paying off the principal. HINT [See Example 7.]

48. ▼ ***Mortgages*** You take out a 30-year mortgage for $95,000 at 9.75%, to be paid off monthly. If you sell your house after 15 years, how much will you still owe on the mortgage? HINT [See Example 7.]

49. ▼ ***Mortgages*** This exercise describes a popular kind of mortgage. You take out a $75,000, 30-year mortgage. For the first 5 years the interest rate is held at 5%, but for the remaining 25 years it rises to 9.5%. The payments for the first 5 years are calculated as if the 5% rate were going to remain in effect for all 30 years, and then the payments for the last 25 years are calculated to amortize the debt remaining at the end of the fifth year. What are your monthly payments for the first 5 years, and what are they for the last 25 years?

50. ▼ ***Adjustable Rate Mortgages*** You take out an adjustable rate mortgage for $100,000 for 20 years. For the first 5 years, the rate is 4%. It then rises to 7% for the next 10 years, and then 9% for the last 5 years. What are your monthly payments in the first 5 years, the next 10 years, and the last 5 years? (Assume that each time the rate changes, the payments are recalculated to amortize the remaining debt if the interest rate were to remain constant for the remaining life of the mortgage.)

51. ▼ ***Refinancing*** Your original mortgage was a $96,000, 30-year 9.75% mortgage. After 4 years you refinance the remaining principal for 30 years at 6.875%. What was your original monthly payment? What is your new monthly payment? How much will you save in interest over the course of the loan by refinancing?

52. ▼ ***Refinancing*** Kara and Michael take out a $120,000, 30-year, 10% mortgage. After 3 years they refinance the remaining principal with a 15-year, 6.5% loan. What were their original monthly payments? What is their new monthly payment? How much did they save in interest over the course of the loan by refinancing?

53. ▼ ***Fees*** You take out a 2-year, $5,000 loan at 9% interest with monthly payments. The lender charges you a $100 fee that can be paid off, interest free, in equal monthly installments over the life of the loan. Thinking of the fee as additional interest, what is the actual annual interest rate you will pay?

54. ▼ ***Fees*** You take out a 3-year, $7,000 loan at 8% interest with monthly payments. The lender charges you a $100 fee that can be paid off, interest free, in equal monthly installments over the life of the loan. Thinking of the fee as additional interest, what is the actual annual interest rate you will pay?

55. ▼ ***Savings*** You wish to accumulate $100,000 through monthly payments of $500. If you can earn interest at an annual rate of 4% compounded monthly, how long (to the nearest year) will it take to accomplish your goal?

56. ▼ ***Retirement*** Alonzo plans to retire as soon as he has accumulated $250,000 through quarterly payments of $2,500. If Alonzo invests this money at 5.4% interest, compounded quarterly, when (to the nearest year) can he retire?

57. ▼ ***Loans*** You have a $2,000 credit card debt, and you plan to pay it off through monthly payments of $50. If you are being charged 15% interest per year, how long (to the nearest 0.5 years) will it take you to repay your debt?

58. ▼ ***Loans*** You owe $2,000 on your credit card, which charges you 15% interest. Determine, to the nearest 1¢, the minimum monthly payment that will allow you to eventually repay your debt.

59. ▼ ***Savings*** You are depositing $100 per month in an account that pays 4.5% interest per year (compounded monthly) while your friend Lucinda is depositing $75 per month in an account that earns 6.5% interest per year (compounded monthly). When, to the nearest year, will her balance exceed yours?

60. ▼ ***Car Leasing*** You can lease a $15,000 car for $300 per month. For how long (to the nearest year) should you lease the car so that your monthly payments are lower than if you were purchasing it with an 8%-per-year loan?

COMMUNICATION AND REASONING EXERCISES

61. Your cousin Simon claims that you have wasted your time studying annuities: If you wish to retire on an income of $1,000 per month for 20 years, you need to save $1,000 per month for 20 years, period. Explain why he is wrong.

62. ▼ Your other cousin Cecilia claims that you will earn more interest by depositing $10,000 through smaller more frequent payments than through larger less frequent payments. Is she correct? Give a reason for your answer.

63. ▼ A real estate broker tells you that doubling the period of a mortgage halves the monthly payments. Is he correct? Support your answer by means of an example.

64. ▼ Another real estate broker tells you that doubling the size of a mortgage doubles the monthly payments. Is he correct? Support your answer by means of an example.

65. ◆ Consider the formula for the future value of a sinking fund with given payments. Show algebraically that the present value of that future value is the same as the present value of the annuity required to fund the same payments.

66. ◆ Give a non-algebraic justification for the result from the preceding exercise.

Practice Problems 2.3, Part 1

1. Consider an ordinary annuity with quarterly payments of $500 and an annual interest rate of 3.25% compounded quarterly.

a. Find the future value of the annuity after 8 years.

b. Determine the amount of interest that has been earned after 8years.

2. Damien can afford to make monthly deposits of $100 into an investment account to save up for a road trip across Canada. He wants to have $4000 in the account after making 24 deposits. What annual interest rate, compounded monthly, does the account need to earn in order for Damien to meet his goal? Give your result as a percentage, accurate to two decimal places.

3. Every week, I have extra money taken out of my paycheck and deposited in a retirement fund that earns an annual interest rate of 2.75% with interest compounded weekly. I'm planning on using that money to do repairs on my house when I retire in 10 years. I expect I'll need $60,000 to do the repairs. How much needs to be taken out of my paycheck weekly to accomplish my savings goal?

Practice Problems 2.3, Part 2

1. A couple wishes to plan for their child's college education. The child is six years old now and will leave for college in exactly 12 years. The parents estimate that the total cost of the college education will be $120,000.

   a. If the couple can make monthly deposits into an account that earns 4% interest compounded monthly, then how much should their deposits be in order to ensure that the account balance will be at least $120,000 in 12 years?

   b. Suppose that the couple will make monthly deposits for the next 10 years, and then cease making deposits. What should be deposited in the account each month so that the account balance will be at least $120,000 in 12 years?

   c. In each of the scenarios above, how much interest is earned on the account during the 12 years?

   d. If the couple can only afford to make monthly deposits of $500 for the next 12 years, then what annual interest rate, compounded monthly, would the account need to offer so that the account balance would be at least $120,000 in 12 years? Give your result as a percentage, accurate to two decimal places.

Practice Problems 2.3, Part 3

1. A trust fund is set up with a deposit of $50,000 into an account that pays an annual interest rate of 3%, with interest compounded quarterly. Starting in one quarter, a sequence of quarterly payments will be distributed to the beneficiary of the fund, and after 18 years the account will have no money left. Given this, calculate the quarterly payment amount and the amount of interest that this trust fund earns over the course of its life.

2. Margot recently received a lump payment of $200,000 from winning a lottery. She wishes to deposit all of her winning in an investment account, leaving it to earn interest for 15 years, at which time she hopes to begin making monthly withdrawals of $8000 for the ensuing 10 years, at which time the account will be empty. Given this, what annual interest rate, compounded monthly, does the investment account need to pay? Give your result as a percentage, accurate to two decimal places.

Practice Problems 2.3, Part 4

1. Fred just took out an installment loan to purchase a used car. He will repay the loan over the course of the next 40 months. If his monthly payments are \$125 and the interest rate on the loan is 6.9%, then how much was this loan?

2. Clyde borrowed \$31,000 five years ago to purchase a new truck. He repaid the installment loan with monthly payments over the course of those five years, and the interest rate was 5.4%.
   a. What were his monthly payments?

   b. How much interest was due on his first payment?

   c. How much total interest did he pay?

   d. How much of the loan had he repaid after three years of payments?

Return to the loan of $12,000. The interest rate and proposed term remain the same as before, but suppose the borrower wishes to make semiannual payments of $2200. Fill out a new amortization schedule for the loan. Keep in mind that the final payment must pay all interest due and the remaining loan balance.

Payment #	Payment Amount	Interest Due	Loan Reduction	Loan Balance
0	X	X	X	$12,000
1	$2000	0.08		

1. How much interest was paid on this loan?

2. Calculate the savings in interest the borrower realizes by making $2200 payments instead of the payments indicated by the terms of the loan.

Practice Problems 2.3, Part 6

1. An *adjustable rate mortgage* (ARM) is a type of installment loan that allows for changing interest rates over the repayment term. Suppose that you take out an ARM for $100,000 and a repayment term of 20 years with monthly payments. For the first five years, the interest rate is 5%. That rate goes up to 6.5% for the next 10 years, and then to 8% for the final five years. Assume that each time the interest rate changes, a new monthly payment is calculated based on the current interest rate and the remaining term of the loan.
   a. Calculate the monthly payments for the first five years.

   b. Calculate the monthly payments for the second 10 years.

   c. Calculate the monthly payments for the final five years.

   d. How much interest is paid over the entire 20 year repayment period?

Practice Problems 2.3, Part 6

1. Suppose that you take out a home improvement loan for \$12,000 and the lender charges you a processing fee of \$600. The loan is an installment loan with an interest rate of 9% and a repayment term of five years, with monthly payments. The processing fee can be repaid, interest-free, with monthly payments over the term of the loan. If you consider the processing fee as additional interest, what actual interest rate are you being charged on the loan? Give your percentage accurate to two decimal places.

2. Some types of student loans allow the option of making interest payments while you are still in school (without actually repaying the principal borrowed). Suppose you have one such loan for \$6000 that carries an interest rate of 6%. You elect to make quarterly interest-only payments to the lender for the four years you take to complete college, and then the loan becomes a standard installment loan requiring monthly payments over the course of 10 years.

a. How much interest will you pay while in school?

b. By the time you have repaid the loan, how much total interest will you have paid?

Practice Problems 2.3, Part 7

1. Suppose that you take out a home improvement loan for $12,000 and the lender charges you a processing fee of $600. The loan is an installment loan with an interest rate of 9% and a repayment term of five years, with monthly payments. The processing fee can be repaid, interest-free, with monthly payments over the term of the loan. If you consider the processing fee as additional interest, what actual interest rate are you being charged on the loan? Give your percentage accurate to two decimal places.

2. Some types of student loans allow the option of making interest payments while you are still in school (without actually repaying the principal borrowed). Suppose you have one such loan for $6000 that carries an interest rate of 6%. You elect to make quarterly interest-only payments to the lender for the four years you take to complete college, and then the loan becomes a standard installment loan requiring monthly payments over the course of 10 years.

a. How much interest will you pay while in school?

b. By the time you have repaid the loan, how much total interest will you have paid?

CHAPTER 2 REVIEW

KEY CONCEPTS

Website www.WanerMath.com

Go to the Website at www.WanerMath.com to find a comprehensive and interactive Web-based summary of Chapter 2.

2.1 Simple Interest

Simple interest *p. 126*
Future value *p. 127*
Bond, maturity *p. 128*
Present value *p. 129*
Treasury bills (T-bills); maturity value, discount rate, yield *p. 130*

2.2 Compound Interest

Compound interest *p. 134*
Future value for compound interest *p. 135*
Present value for compound interest *p. 137*
Zero coupon bond or strip *p. 137*
Inflation, constant dollars *pp. 138–139*
Effective interest rate, annual percentage yield (APY) *p. 139*

2.3 Annuities, Loans, and Bonds

Annuity, sinking fund *p. 145*
Future value of a sinking fund *p. 146*
Payment formula for a sinking fund *p. 147*
Present value of an annuity *p. 149*
Ordinary annuity, annuity due *p. 149*
Payment formula for an annuity *p. 150*
Installment loan *p. 151*
Amortization schedule *p. 152*
Bond *p. 153*

REVIEW EXERCISES

In each of Exercises 1–6, find the future value of the investment.

1. $6,000 for 5 years at 4.75% simple annual interest
2. $10,000 for 2.5 years at 5.25% simple annual interest
3. $6,000 for 5 years at 4.75% compounded monthly
4. $10,000 for 2.5 years at 5.25% compounded semiannually
5. $100 deposited at the end of each month for 5 years, at 4.75% interest compounded monthly
6. $2,000 deposited at the end of each half-year for 2.5 years, at 5.25% interest compounded semiannually

In each of Exercises 7–12, find the present value of the investment.

7. Worth $6,000 after 5 years at 4.75% simple annual interest
8. Worth $10,000 after 2.5 years at 5.25% simple annual interest
9. Worth $6,000 after 5 years at 4.75% compounded monthly
10. Worth $10,000 after 2.5 years at 5.25% compounded semiannually
11. Funding $100 withdrawals at the end of each month for 5 years, at 4.75% interest compounded monthly
12. Funding $2,000 withdrawals at the end of each half-year for 2.5 years, at 5.25% interest compounded semiannually

In each of Exercises 13–18, find the amounts indicated.

13. The monthly deposits necessary to accumulate $12,000 after 5 years in an account earning 4.75% compounded monthly
14. The semiannual deposits necessary to accumulate $20,000 after 2.5 years in an account earning 5.25% compounded semiannually
15. The monthly withdrawals possible over 5 years from an account earning 4.75% compounded monthly and starting with $6,000
16. The semiannual withdrawals possible over 2.5 years from an account earning 5.25% compounded semiannually and starting with $10,000
17. The monthly payments necessary on a 5-year loan of $10,000 at 4.75%
18. The semiannual payments necessary on a 2.5-year loan of $15,000 at 5.25%
19. How much would you pay for a $10,000, 5-year, 6% bond if you want a return of 7%? (Assume that the bond pays interest every 6 months.)
20. How much would you pay for a $10,000, 5-year, 6% bond if you want a return of 5%? (Assume that the bond pays interest every 6 months.)
21. T A $10,000, 7-year, 5% bond sells for $9,800. What return does it give you? (Assume that the bond pays interest every 6 months.)
22. T A $10,000, 7-year, 5% bond sells for $10,200. What return does it give you? (Assume that the bond pays interest every 6 months.)

In each of Exercises 23–28, find the time requested, to the nearest 0.1 year.

23. The time it would take $6,000 to grow to $10,000 at 4.75% simple annual interest
24. The time it would take $10,000 to grow to $15,000 at 5.25% simple annual interest
25. T The time it would take $6,000 to grow to $10,000 at 4.75% interest compounded monthly
26. T The time it would take $10,000 to grow to $15,000 at 5.25% interest compounded semiannually
27. T The time it would take to accumulate $10,000 by depositing $100 at the end of each month in an account earning 4.75% interest compounded monthly
28. T The time it would take to accumulate $15,000 by depositing $2,000 at the end of each half-year in an account earning 5.25% compounded semiannually

APPLICATIONS

Stock Investments *Exercises 29–34 are based on the following table, which shows some values of ABCromD (ABCD) stock:*

Dec. 2002	Aug. 2004	Mar. 2005	May 2005	Aug. 2005	Dec. 2005
3.28	16.31	33.95	21.00	30.47	7.44
Jan. 2007	Mar. 2008	Oct. 2008	Nov. 2009	Feb. 2010	Aug. 2010
12.36	7.07	11.44	33.53	44.86	45.74

29. Marjory Duffin purchased ABCD stock in December 2002 and sold it in August 2010. Calculate her annual return on a simple interest basis to the nearest 0.01%.

30. John O'Hagan purchased ABCD stock in March 2005 and sold it in January 2007. Calculate his annual return on a simple interest basis to the nearest 0.01%.

31. Suppose Marjory Duffin had bought ABCD stock in January 2007. If she had later sold at one of the dates in the table, which of those dates would have given her the largest annual return on a simple interest basis, and what would that return have been?

32. Suppose John O'Hagan had purchased ABCD stock in August 2004. If he had later sold at one of the dates in the table, which of those dates would have given him the largest annual loss on a simple interest basis, and what would that loss have been?

33. Did ABCD stock undergo simple interest increase in the period December 2002 through March 2005? (Give a reason for your answer.)

34. If ABCD stock underwent simple interest increase from February 2010 through August 2010 and into 2011, what would the price have been in December 2011?

35. ***Revenue*** Total Online revenues at OHaganBooks.com during 1999, its first year of operation, amounted to $150,000. After December, 1999, revenues increased by a steady 20% each year. Track OHaganBooks.com's revenues for the subsequent 5 years, assuming that this rate of growth continued. During which year did the revenue surpass $300,000?

36. ***Net Income*** Unfortunately, the picture for net income was not so bright: The company lost $20,000 in the fourth quarter of 1999. However, the quarterly loss decreased at an annual rate of 15%. How much did the company lose during the third quarter of 2001?

37. ***Stocks*** In order to finance anticipated expansion, CEO John O'Hagan is considering making a public offering of OHaganBooks.com shares at $3.00 a share. O'Hagan is not sure how many shares to offer, but would like the shares to reach a total market value of at least $500,000 6 months after the initial offering. He estimates that the value of the stock will double in the first day of trading, and then appreciate at around 8% per month for the first 6 months. How many shares of stock should the company offer?

38. ***Stocks*** Unfortunately, renewed panic about the Monaco debt crisis cause the U.S. stock market to plunge on the very first day of OHaganBooks.com's initial public offering (IPO) of 600,000 shares at $3.00 per share, and the shares ended the trading day 60% lower. Subsequently, as the Monaco debt crisis worsened, the stock depreciated by 10% per week during the subsequent 5 weeks. What was the total market value of the stocks at the end of 5 weeks?

39. ***Loans*** OHaganBooks.com is seeking a $250,000 loan to finance its continuing losses. One of the best deals available is offered by Industrial Bank, which offers a 10-year 9.5% loan. What would the monthly payments be for this loan?

40. ***Loans*** (See Exercise 39.) Expansion Loans offers an 8-year 6.5% loan. What would the monthly payments be for the $250,000 loan from Expansion?

41. ***Loans*** (See Exercise 39.) OHaganBooks.com can afford to pay only $3,000 per month to service its debt. What, to the nearest dollar, is the largest amount the company can borrow from Industrial Bank?

42. ***Loans*** (See Exercise 40.) OHaganBooks.com can afford to pay only $3,000 per month to service its debt. What, to the nearest dollar, is the largest amount the company can borrow from Expansion Loans?

43. T ***Loans*** (See Exercise 39.) What interest rate would Industrial Bank have to offer in order to meet the company's loan requirements at a price (no more than $3,000 per month) it can afford?

44. T ***Loans*** (See Exercise 40.) What interest rate would Expansion Loans have to offer in order to meet the company's loan requirements at a price (no more than $3,000 per month) it can afford?

Retirement Planning *OHaganBooks.com has just introduced a retirement package for the employees. Under the annuity plan operated by Sleepy Hollow, the monthly contribution by the company on behalf of each employee is $800. Each employee can then supplement that amount through payroll deductions. The current rate of return of Sleepy Hollow's retirement fund is 7.3%. Use this information in Exercises 45–52.*

45. Jane Callahan, the Web site developer at OHaganBooks.com, plans to retire in 10 years. She contributes $1,000 per month to the plan (in addition to the company contribution of $800). Currently, there is $50,000 in her retirement annuity. How much (to the nearest dollar) will it be worth when she retires?

46. Percy Egan, the assistant Web site developer at OHaganBooks.com, plans to retire in 8 years. He contributes $950 per month to the plan (in addition to the company contribution of $800). Currently, there is $60,000 in his retirement annuity. How much (to the nearest dollar) will it be worth when he retires?

47. When she retires, how much of Jane Callahan's retirement fund will have resulted from the company contribution? (See Exercise 45. The company did not contribute toward the $50,000 Callahan now has.)

48. When he retires, how much of Percy Egan's retirement fund will have resulted from the company contribution? (See Exercise 46. The company began contributing $800 per month to his retirement fund when he was hired 5 years ago. Assume the rate of return from Sleepy Hollow has been unchanged.)

49. (See Exercise 45.) Jane Callahan actually wants to retire with $500,000. How much should she contribute each month to the annuity?

50. (See Exercise 46.) Percy Egan actually wants to retire with $600,000. How much should he contribute each month to the annuity?

51. (See Exercise 45.) On second thought, Callahan wants to be in a position to draw at least $5,000 per month for 30 years after her retirement. She feels she can invest the proceeds of her retirement annuity at 8.7% per year in perpetuity. Given the information in Exercise 45, how much will she need to contribute to the plan starting now?

52. (See Exercise 46.) On second thought, Egan wants to be in a position to draw at least $6,000 per month for 25 years after his retirement. He feels he can invest the proceeds of his retirement annuity at 7.8% per year in perpetuity. Given the information in Exercise 46, how much will he need to contribute to the plan starting now?

Actually, Jane Callahan is quite pleased with herself; 1 year ago she purchased a $50,000 government bond paying 7.2% per year (with interest paid every 6 months) and maturing in 10 years, and interest rates have come down since then.

53. The current interest rate on 10-year government bonds is 6.3%. If she were to auction the bond at the current interest rate, how much would she get?

54. If she holds on to the bond for 6 more months and the interest rate drops to 6%, how much will the bond be worth then?

55. Jane suspects that interest rates will come down further during the next 6 months. If she hopes to auction the bond for $54,000 in 6 months' time, what will the interest rate need to be at that time?

56. If, in 6 months' time, the bond is auctioned for only $52,000, what will the interest rate be at that time?

Case Study

Adjustable Rate and Subprime Mortgages

Andy Dean Photography/Shutterstock

The term **subprime mortgage** refers to mortgages given to home buyers with a heightened perceived risk of default, as when, for instance, the price of the home being purchased is higher than the borrower can reasonably afford. Such loans are typically **adjustable rate** loans, meaning that the lending rate varies through the duration of the loan.* Subprime adjustable rate loans typically start at artificially low "teaser rates" that the borrower can afford, but then increase significantly over the life of the mortgage. The U.S. real estate bubble of 2000–2005 led to a frenzy of subprime lending, the rationale being that a borrower having trouble meeting mortgage payments could either sell the property at a profit or re-finance the loan, or the lending institution could earn a hefty profit by repossessing the property in the event of foreclosure.

Mr. and Mrs. Wong have an appointment tomorrow with you, their investment counselor, to discuss their plan to purchase a $400,000 house in Orlando, Florida. They have saved $20,000 for a down payment, so want to take out a $380,000 mortgage. Their combined annual income is $80,000 per year, which they estimate will increase by 4% annually over the foreseeable future, and they are considering three different specialty 30-year mortgages:

Hybrid: The interest is fixed at a low introductory rate of 4% for 5 years, and then adjusts annually to 5% over the U.S. federal funds rate.†

Interest-Only: During the first 5 years, the rate is set at 4.2% and no principal is paid. After that time, the mortgage adjusts annually to 5% over the U.S. federal funds rate.

Negative Amortization: During the first 5 years, the rate is set at 4.7% based on a principal of 60% of the purchase price of the home, with the result that the balance on the principal actually grows during this period. After that time, the mortgage adjusts annually to 5% over the U.S. federal funds rate.

* In an adjustable rate mortgage, the payments are recalculated each time the interest rate changes, based on the assumption that the new interest rate will be unchanged for the remaining life of the loan. We say that the loan is **re-amortized** at the new rate.

† The U.S. federal funds rate is the rate banks charge each other for loans and is often used to set rates for other loans. Manipulating this rate is one way the U.S. Federal Reserve regulates the money supply.

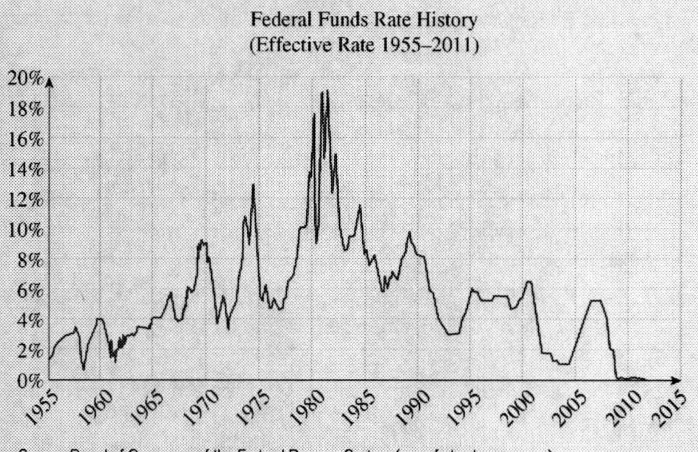

Source: Board of Governors of the Federal Reserve System (www.federalreserve.gov)

Figure 3

You decide that you should create an Excel worksheet that will compute the monthly payments for the three types of loan. Of course, you have no way of predicting what the U.S. federal funds rate will be in over the next 30 years (see Figure 3 for historical values), so you decide to include three scenarios for the federal funds rate in each case:

Scenario 1: Federal funds rate is 4.25% in year 6 and then increases by 0.25% per year.

Scenario 2: Federal funds rate is steady at 4% during the term of the loan.

Scenario 3: Federal funds rate is 15% in year 6 and then decreases by 0.25% per year.

Each worksheet will show month-by-month payments for the specific type of loan. Typically, to be affordable, payments should not exceed 28% of gross monthly income, so you will tabulate that quantity as well.

Hybrid Loan: You begin to create your worksheet by estimating 28% of the Wongs' monthly income, assuming a 4% increase each year (the income is computed using the compound interest formula for annual compounding):

	A	B	C	D	E	F	G	H
1	Year	28% of Monthly Income		Interest Rate			Monthly Payment	
2			Scenario 1	Scenario 2	Scenario 3	Scenario 1	Scenario 2	Scenario 3
3	1	=0.28*80000*(1.04)^(A3-1)/12						
4	2							
5	3							
30	28							
31	29							
32	30							

The next sheet shows the result, as well as the formulas for computing the interest rate in each scenario.

	A	B	C	D	E	F	G	H
1	Year	28% of Monthly Income		Interest Rate			Monthly Payment	
2			Scenario 1	Scenario 2	Scenario 3	Scenario 1	Scenario 2	Scenario 3
3	1	$1,866.67	4	4	4			
4	2	$1,941.33	4	4	4			
5	3	$2,018.99	4	4	4			
6	4	$2,099.75	4	4	4			
7	5	$2,183.74	4	4	4			
8	6	$2,271.09	9.25	9	15			
9	7	$2,361.93	=C8+0.25	=D8	=E8-0.25			
10	8	$2,456.41						
30	28	$5,382.29						
31	29	$5,597.58						
32	30	$5,821.48						

To compute the monthly payment, you decide to use the built-in function PMT, which has the format

$$PMT(i, n, PV, [FV], [type]),$$

where $i =$ interest per period, $n =$ total number of periods of the loan, $PV =$ present value, $FV =$ future value (optional); the *type*, also optional, is 0 or omitted if payments are at the end of each period, and 1 if at the start of each period. The present value will be the outstanding principal owed on the home each time the rate is changed and so that too will need to be known. During the first 5 years we can use as the present value the original cost of the home, but each year thereafter, the loan is re-amortized at the new interest rate, and so the outstanding principal will need to be computed. Although Excel has a built-in function that calculates payment on the principal, it returns only the payment for a single period (month), so without creating a month-by-month amortization table it would be difficult to use this function to track the outstanding principal. On the other hand, the total outstanding principal at any point in time can be computed using the future value formula FV. You decide to add three more columns to your Excel worksheet to show the principal outstanding at the start of each year. Here is the spreadsheet with the formulas for the payments and outstanding principal for the first 5 years.

	A	B	C	D	E	F	G	H	I	J	K
1	Year	28% of Monthly Income		Interest Rate			Monthly Payment			Balance on Principal	
2			Scenario 1	Scenario 2	Scenario 3	Scenario 1	Scenario 2	Scenario 3	Scenario 1	Scenario 2	Scenario 3
3	1	$1,866.67	4	4	4	=-PMT(C3/1200,360,I$3)			$380,000.00	$380,000.00	$380,000.00
4	2	$1,941.33	4	4	4				=FV(C3/1200,12*$A3,F3,-I$3)		
5	3	$2,018.99	4	4	4						
6	4	$2,099.75	4	4	4						
7	5	$2,183.74	4	4	4						
8	6	$2,271.09	9.25	9	15						
9	7	$2,361.93	9.5	9	14.75						
10	8	$2,456.41	9.75	9	14.5						

The two formulas will each be copied across to the adjacent two cells for the other scenarios. A few things to notice: The negative sign before *PMT* converts the negative quantity returned by *PMT* to a positive amount. The dollar sign in I$3 in the *PMT* formula fixes the present value for each year at the original cost of the home for the first 5 years, during which payments are computed as for a fixed rate loan. In the formula for the balance on principal at the start of each year, the number of periods is the total number of months up through the preceding year, and the present value is the same initial price of the home each year during the 5-year fixed rate period.

The next sheet shows the calculated results for the fixed-rate period, and the new formulas to be added for the adjustable rate period starting with the sixth year.

	C	D	E	F	G	H	I	J	K
1		Interest Rate			Monthly Payment			Balance on Principal	
2	Scenario 1	Scenario 2	Scenario 3	Scenario 1	Scenario 2	Scenario 3	Scenario 1	Scenario 2	Scenario 3
3	4	4	4	$1,814.18	$1,814.18	$1,814.18	$380,000.00	$380,000.00	$380,000.00
4	4	4	4	$1,814.18	$1,814.18	$1,814.18	$373,308.06	$373,308.06	$373,308.06
5	4	4	4	$1,814.18	$1,814.18	$1,814.18	$366,343.48	$366,343.48	$366,343.48
6	4	4	4	$1,814.18	$1,814.18	$1,814.18	$359,095.16	$359,095.16	$359,095.16
7	4	4	4	$1,814.18	$1,814.18	$1,814.18	$351,551.52	$351,551.52	$351,551.52
8	9.25	9	15	=-PMT(C8/1200,360-12*$A7,I8)			=FV(C7/1200,12,F7,-I7)		
9	9.5	9	14.75						
10	9.75	9	14.5						

Notice the changes: The loan is re-amortized each year starting with year 6, and the payment calculation needs to take into account the reduced, remaining lifetime of the loan each time. You now copy these formulas across for the remaining two scenarios, and then copy all six formulas down the remaining rows to complete the calculation. Following is a portion of the complete worksheet showing, in red, those years during which the monthly payment will exceed 28% of the gross monthly income.

	A	B	C	D	E	F	G	H	I	J	K
1	Year	28% of Monthly Income		Interest Rate			Monthly Payment			Balance on Principal	
2			Scenario 1	Scenario 2	Scenario 3	Scenario 1	Scenario 2	Scenario 3	Scenario 1	Scenario 2	Scenario 3
3	1	$1,866.67	4	4	4	$1,814.18	$1,814.18	$1,814.18	$380,000.00	$380,000.00	$380,000.00
4	2	$1,941.33	4	4	4	$1,814.18	$1,814.18	$1,814.18	$373,308.06	$373,308.06	$373,308.06
5	3	$2,018.99	4	4	4	$1,814.18	$1,814.18	$1,814.18	$366,343.48	$366,343.48	$366,343.48
6	4	$2,099.75	4	4	4	$1,814.18	$1,814.18	$1,814.18	$359,095.16	$359,095.16	$359,095.16
7	5	$2,183.74	4	4	4	$1,814.18	$1,814.18	$1,814.18	$351,551.52	$351,551.52	$351,551.52
8	6	$2,271.09	9.25	9	15	$2,943.39	$2,884.32	$4,402.22	$343,700.55	$343,700.55	$343,700.55
9	7	$2,361.93	9.5	9	14.75	$3,001.60	$2,884.32	$4,336.46	$340,018.68	$339,866.12	$342,337.80
10	8	$2,456.41	9.75	9	14.5	$3,058.89	$2,884.32	$4,271.84	$336,135.05	$335,671.99	$340,686.40
11	9	$2,554.66	10	9	14.25	$3,115.17	$2,884.32	$4,208.48	$332,020.97	$331,084.43	$338,694.96
12	10	$2,656.85	10.25	9	14	$3,170.39	$2,884.32	$4,146.53	$327,643.98	$326,066.52	$336,305.10
13	11	$2,763.12	10.5	9	13.75	$3,224.44	$2,884.32	$4,086.13	$322,967.19	$320,577.89	$333,450.89
14	12	$2,873.65	10.75	9	13.5	$3,277.24	$2,884.32	$4,027.41	$317,948.51	$314,574.40	$330,058.36
15	13	$2,988.59	11	9	13.25	$3,328.70	$2,884.32	$3,970.53	$312,539.70	$308,007.73	$326,045.01
16	14	$3,108.14	11.25	9	13	$3,378.71	$2,884.32	$3,915.64	$306,685.30	$300,825.07	$321,319.42
17	15	$3,232.46	11.5	9	12.75	$3,427.16	$2,884.32	$3,862.89	$300,321.34	$292,968.62	$315,780.91
18	16	$3,361.76	11.75	9	12.5	$3,473.93	$2,884.32	$3,812.43	$293,373.72	$284,375.19	$309,319.29
19	17	$3,496.23	12	9	12.25	$3,518.89	$2,884.32	$3,764.40	$285,756.40	$274,975.63	$301,814.76
20	18	$3,636.08	12.25	9	12	$3,561.90	$2,884.32	$3,718.94	$277,369.15	$264,694.33	$293,137.86
21	19	$3,781.52	12.5	9	11.75	$3,602.81	$2,884.32	$3,676.20	$268,094.83	$253,448.57	$283,149.60
22	20	$3,932.79	12.75	9	11.5	$3,641.47	$2,884.32	$3,636.32	$257,796.15	$241,147.88	$271,701.73

In the third scenario, the Wongs' payments would more than double at the start of the sixth year, and remain above what they can reasonably afford for 13 more years. Even if the Fed rate were to remain at the low rate of 4%, the monthly payments would still jump to above what the Wongs can afford at the start of the sixth year.

Interest-Only Loan: Here, the only change in the worksheet constructed previously is the computation of the payments for the first 5 years; because the loan is interest-only during this period, the monthly payment is computed as simple interest at 4.2% on the $380,000 loan for a 30-year period:

$$INT = PVr = 380{,}000 \times .042/12 = \$1{,}330.00$$

The formula you could use in the spreadsheet in cell F3 is `=C3/1200*I$3`, and then copy this across and down the entire block of payments for the first 5 years. The rest of the spreadsheet (including the balance on principal) will adjust itself accordingly with the formulas you had for the hybrid loan. Below is a portion of the result, with a lot more red than in the hybrid loan case!

	A	B	C	D	E	F	G	H	I	J	K
1	Year	28% of Monthly Income		Interest Rate			Monthly Payment			Balance on Principal	
2			Scenario 1	Scenario 2	Scenario 3	Scenario 1	Scenario 2	Scenario 3	Scenario 1	Scenario 2	Scenario 3
3	1	$1,866.67	4.2	4.2	4.2	$1,330.00	$1,330.00	$1,330.00	$380,000.00	$380,000.00	$380,000.00
4	2	$1,941.33	4.2	4.2	4.2	$1,330.00	$1,330.00	$1,330.00	$380,000.00	$380,000.00	$380,000.00
5	3	$2,018.99	4.2	4.2	4.2	$1,330.00	$1,330.00	$1,330.00	$380,000.00	$380,000.00	$380,000.00
6	4	$2,099.75	4.2	4.2	4.2	$1,330.00	$1,330.00	$1,330.00	$380,000.00	$380,000.00	$380,000.00
7	5	$2,183.74	4.2	4.2	4.2	$1,330.00	$1,330.00	$1,330.00	$380,000.00	$380,000.00	$380,000.00
8	6	$2,271.09	9.25	9	15	$3,254.25	$3,188.95	$4,867.16	$380,000.00	$380,000.00	$380,000.00
9	7	$2,361.93	9.5	9	14.75	$3,318.61	$3,188.95	$4,794.45	$375,929.28	$375,760.60	$378,493.33
10	8	$2,456.41	9.75	9	14.5	$3,381.95	$3,188.95	$4,723.00	$371,635.48	$371,123.52	$376,667.51
11	9	$2,554.66	10	9	14.25	$3,444.18	$3,188.95	$4,652.96	$367,086.90	$366,051.44	$374,465.75
12	10	$2,656.85	10.25	9	14	$3,505.22	$3,188.95	$4,584.46	$362,247.64	$360,503.57	$371,823.49
13	11	$2,763.12	10.5	9	13.75	$3,564.98	$3,188.95	$4,517.68	$357,076.92	$354,435.28	$368,667.84
14	12	$2,873.65	10.75	9	13.5	$3,623.37	$3,188.95	$4,452.76	$351,528.19	$347,797.73	$364,917.01
15	13	$2,988.59	11	9	13.25	$3,680.26	$3,188.95	$4,389.88	$345,548.14	$340,537.54	$360,479.80
16	14	$3,108.14	11.25	9	13	$3,735.55	$3,188.95	$4,329.19	$339,075.44	$332,596.29	$355,255.12
17	15	$3,232.46	11.5	9	12.75	$3,789.12	$3,188.95	$4,270.87	$332,039.35	$323,910.09	$349,131.66
18	16	$3,361.76	11.75	9	12.5	$3,840.82	$3,188.95	$4,215.07	$324,357.97	$314,409.07	$341,987.61
19	17	$3,496.23	12	9	12.25	$3,890.53	$3,188.95	$4,161.97	$315,936.16	$304,016.79	$333,690.51
20	18	$3,636.08	12.25	9	12	$3,938.08	$3,188.95	$4,111.71	$306,663.10	$292,649.65	$324,097.21
21	19	$3,781.52	12.5	9	11.75	$3,983.32	$3,188.95	$4,064.46	$296,409.28	$280,216.18	$313,054.05
22	20	$3,932.79	12.75	9	11.5	$4,026.06	$3,188.95	$4,020.37	$285,022.93	$266,616.37	$300,397.13
23	21	$4,090.10	13	9	11.25	$4,066.11	$3,188.95	$3,979.57	$272,325.66	$251,740.81	$285,952.80
24	22	$4,253.70	13.25	9	11	$4,103.29	$3,188.95	$3,942.23	$258,107.21	$235,469.81	$269,538.33

In all three scenarios, this type of mortgage is worse for the Wongs than the hybrid loan; in particular, their payments in Scenario 3 would jump to more than double what they can afford at the start of the sixth year.

Negative Amortization Loan: Again, the only change in the worksheet is the computation of the payments for the first 5 years. This time, the loan amortizes negatively during the initial 5-year period, so the payment formula in this period is adjusted to reflect this

```
=-PMT(C3/1200,360,I$3*0.6).
```

	A	B	C	D	E	F	G	H	I	J	K
1	Year	28% of Monthly Income		Interest Rate			Monthly Payment			Balance on Principal	
2			Scenario 1	Scenario 2	Scenario 3	Scenario 1	Scenario 2	Scenario 3	Scenario 1	Scenario 2	Scenario 3
3	1	$1,866.67	4.7	4.7	4.7	$1,182.49	$1,182.49	$1,182.49	$380,000.00	$380,000.00	$380,000.00
4	2	$1,941.33	4.7	4.7	4.7	$1,182.49	$1,182.49	$1,182.49	$383,750.17	$383,750.17	$383,750.17
5	3	$2,018.99	4.7	4.7	4.7	$1,182.49	$1,182.49	$1,182.49	$387,680.45	$387,680.45	$387,680.45
6	4	$2,099.75	4.7	4.7	4.7	$1,182.49	$1,182.49	$1,182.49	$391,799.48	$391,799.48	$391,799.48
7	5	$2,183.74	4.7	4.7	4.7	$1,182.49	$1,182.49	$1,182.49	$396,116.32	$396,116.32	$396,116.32
8	6	$2,271.09	9.25	9	15	$3,431.01	$3,362.16	$5,131.53	$400,640.49	$400,640.49	$400,640.49
9	7	$2,361.93	9.5	9	14.75	$3,498.87	$3,362.16	$5,054.87	$396,348.66	$396,170.82	$399,051.98
10	8	$2,456.41	9.75	9	14.5	$3,565.64	$3,362.16	$4,979.54	$391,821.64	$391,281.87	$397,127.00
11	9	$2,554.66	10	9	14.25	$3,631.26	$3,362.16	$4,905.69	$387,025.99	$385,934.29	$394,805.64
12	10	$2,656.85	10.25	9	14	$3,695.62	$3,362.16	$4,833.48	$381,923.88	$380,085.08	$392,019.86
13	11	$2,763.12	10.5	9	13.75	$3,758.62	$3,362.16	$4,763.06	$376,472.30	$373,687.17	$388,692.80
14	12	$2,873.65	10.75	9	13.5	$3,820.18	$3,362.16	$4,694.62	$370,622.18	$366,689.09	$384,738.24
15	13	$2,988.59	11	9	13.25	$3,880.16	$3,362.16	$4,628.32	$364,317.31	$359,034.55	$380,060.01
16	14	$3,108.14	11.25	9	13	$3,938.46	$3,362.16	$4,564.34	$357,493.03	$350,661.95	$374,551.54
17	15	$3,232.46	11.5	9	12.75	$3,994.93	$3,362.16	$4,502.85	$350,074.77	$341,503.95	$368,095.48
18	16	$3,361.76	11.75	9	12.5	$4,049.45	$3,362.16	$4,444.02	$341,976.15	$331,486.86	$360,563.39
19	17	$3,496.23	12	9	12.25	$4,101.85	$3,362.16	$4,388.03	$333,096.90	$320,530.10	$351,815.60
20	18	$3,636.08	12.25	9	12	$4,151.99	$3,362.16	$4,335.05	$323,320.15	$308,545.52	$341,701.22
21	19	$3,781.52	12.5	9	11.75	$4,199.68	$3,362.16	$4,285.23	$312,509.37	$295,436.71	$330,058.23
22	20	$3,932.79	12.75	9	11.5	$4,244.74	$3,362.16	$4,238.74	$300,504.55	$281,098.20	$316,713.83
23	21	$4,090.10	13	9	11.25	$4,286.97	$3,362.16	$4,195.73	$287,117.60	$265,414.64	$301,484.92
24	22	$4,253.70	13.25	9	11	$4,326.17	$3,362.16	$4,156.36	$272,126.84	$248,259.85	$284,178.86
25	23	$4,423.85	13.5	9	10.75	$4,362.10	$3,362.16	$4,120.77	$255,270.30	$229,495.82	$264,594.34
26	24	$4,600.80	13.75	9	10.5	$4,394.53	$3,362.16	$4,089.09	$236,237.47	$208,971.60	$242,522.55

Clearly the Wongs should steer clear of this type of loan in order to be able to continue to afford making payments!

In short, it seems unlikely that the Wongs will be able to afford payments on any of the three mortgages in question, and you decide to advise them to either seek a less expensive home or wait until their income has appreciated to enable them to afford a home of this price.

EXERCISES

1. T In the case of a hybrid loan, what would the federal funds rate have to be in Scenario 2 to ensure that the Wongs can afford to make all payments?
2. T Repeat the preceding exercise in the case of an interest-only loan.
3. T Repeat the preceding exercise in the case of a negative-amortization loan.
4. T What home price, to the nearest $5,000, could the Wongs afford if they took out a hybrid loan, regardless of scenario? HINT [Adjust the original value of the loan on your spreadsheet to obtain the desired result.]
5. T What home price, to the nearest $5,000, could the Wongs afford if they took out a negative-amortization loan, regardless of scenario? HINT [Adjust the original value of the loan on your spreadsheet to obtain the desired result.]
6. T How long would the Wongs need to wait before they could afford to purchase a $400,000 home, assuming that their income continues to increase as above, they still have $20,000 for a down payment, and the mortgage offers remain the same?

TI-83/84 Plus Technology Guide

Section 2.2

Example 1 (page 136) In November 2011, the Bank of Montreal was paying 1.30% interest on savings accounts. If the interest is compounded quarterly, find the future value of a $2,000 deposit in 6 years. What is the total interest paid over the period?

Solution with Technology

We could calculate the future value using the TI-83/84 Plus by entering

`2000(1+0.0130/4)^(4*6)`

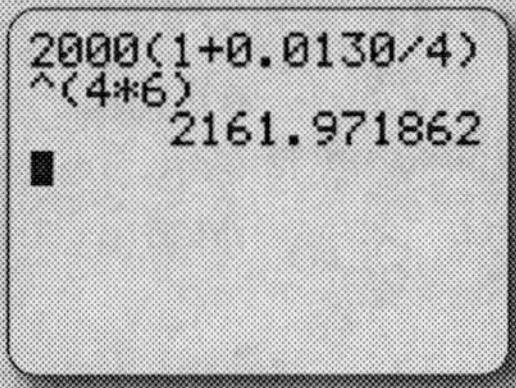

However, the TI-83/84 Plus has this and other useful calculations built into its TVM (Time Value of Money) Solver.

1. Press APPS then choose item `1:Finance...` and then choose item `1:TVM Solver...`. This brings up the TVM Solver window.

The second screen shows the values you should enter for this example. The various variables are:

`N`	Number of compounding periods
`I%`	Annual interest rate, as percent, not decimal
`PV`	Negative of present value
`PMT`	Payment per period (0 in this section)
`FV`	Future value
`P/Y`	Payments per year
`C/Y`	Compounding periods per year
`PMT:`	Not used in this section

Several things to notice:

- *I%* is the *annual* interest rate, corresponding to *r*, not *i*, in the compound interest formula.
- The present value, *PV*, is entered as a negative number. In general, when using the TVM Solver, any amount of money you give to someone else (such as the $2,000 you deposit in the bank) will be a negative number, whereas any amount of money someone gives to you (such as the future value of your deposit, which the bank will give back to you) will be a positive number.
- *PMT* is not used in this example (it will be used in the next section) and should be 0.
- *FV* is the future value, which we shall compute in a moment; it doesn't matter what you enter now.
- *P/Y* and *C/Y* stand for payments per year and compounding periods per year, respectively: They should both be set to the number of compounding periods per year for compound interest problems (setting *P/Y* automatically sets *C/Y* to the same value).
- *PMT*: *END* or *BEGIN* is not used in this example and it doesn't matter which you select.

2. To compute the future value, use the up or down arrow to put the cursor on the *FV* line, then press ALPHA SOLVE.

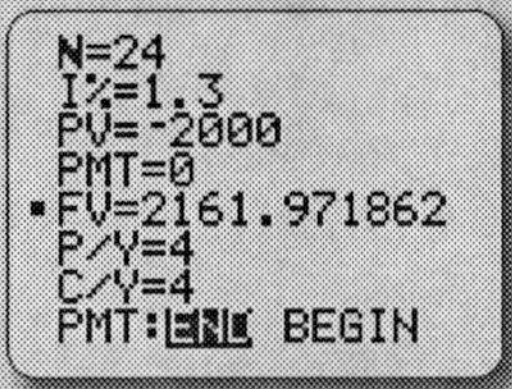

Example 2 (page 138) Megabucks Corporation is issuing 10-year zero coupon bonds. How much would you pay for bonds with a maturity value of $10,000 if you wish to get a return of 6.5% compounded annually?

Solution with Technology

To compute the present value using a TI-83/84 Plus:

1. Enter the numbers shown below (top) in the TVM Solver window.
2. Put the cursor on the PV line, and press ALPHA SOLVE.

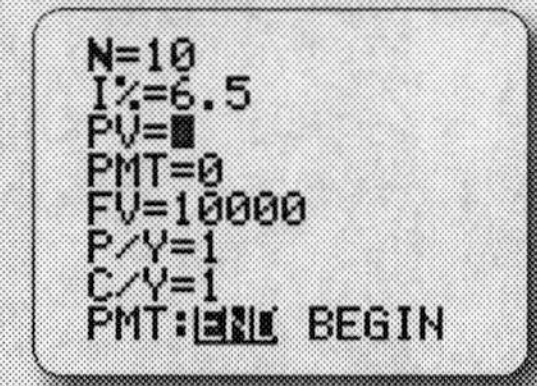

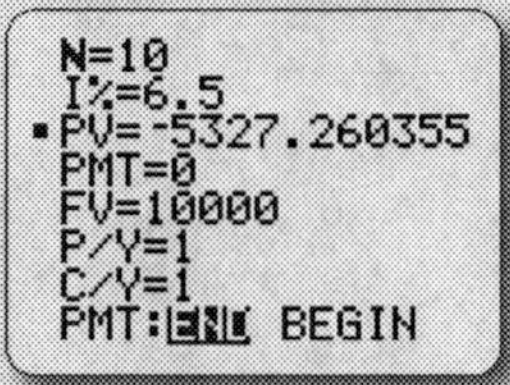

Why is the present value given as negative?

Example 6 (page 141) You have $5,000 to invest at 6% interest compounded monthly. How long will it take for your investment to grow to $6,000?

Solution with Technology

1. Enter the numbers shown below (top) in the TVM Solver window.
2. Put the cursor on the N line, and press ALPHA SOLVE.

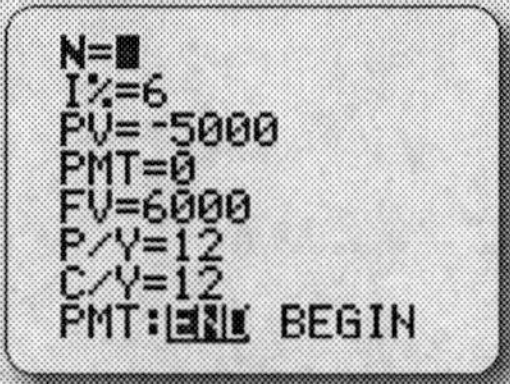

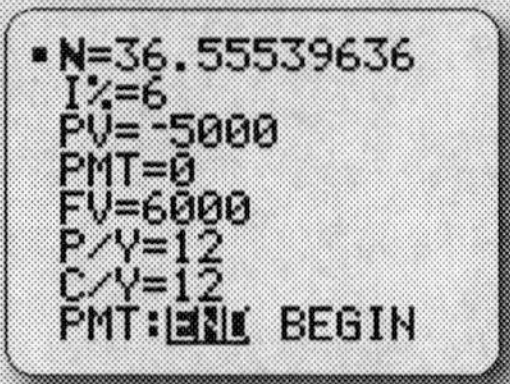

Recall that I% is the annual interest rate, corresponding to r in the formula, but N is the number of compounding periods, so number of months in this example. Thus, you will need to invest your money for about 36.5 months, or just over 3 years, before it grows to $6,000.

Section 2.3

Example 1 (page 146) Your retirement account has $5,000 in it and earns 5% interest per year compounded monthly. Every month for the next 10 years, you will deposit $100 into the account. How much money will there be in the account at the end of those 10 years?

Solution with Technology

We can use the TVM Solver in the TI-83/84 Plus to calculate future values like these:

1. The TVM Solver allows you to put the $5,000 already in the account as the present value of the account. Following the TI-83/84 Plus's usual convention, set PV to the *negative* of the present value because this is money you paid into the account.
2. Likewise, set PMT to −100 since you are paying $100 each month.
3. Set the number of payment and compounding periods to 12 per year.
4. Set the payments to be made at the end of each period.
5. With the cursor on the FV line, press ALPHA SOLVE to find the future value.

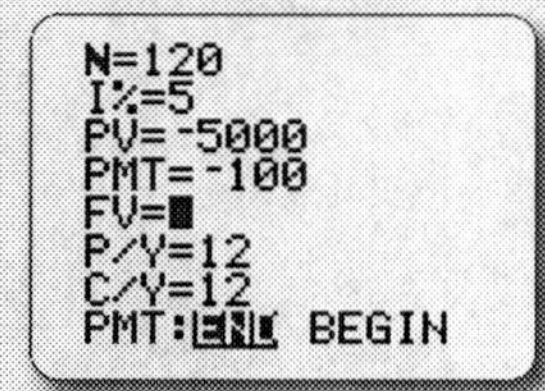

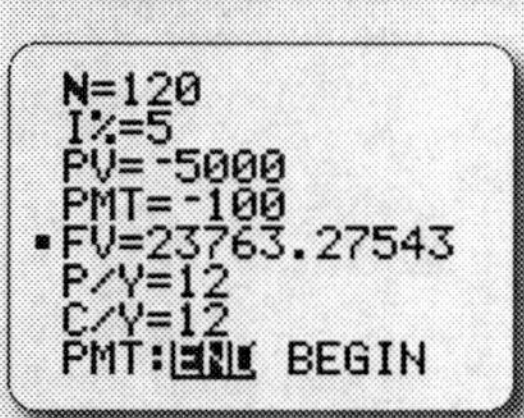

Example 2 (page 147) Tony and Maria have just had a son, José Phillipe. They establish an account to accumulate money for his college education. They would like to have $100,000 in this account after 17 years. If the account pays 4% interest per year compounded quarterly, and they make deposits at the end of every quarter, how large must each deposit be for them to reach their goal?

Solution with Technology

1. In the TVM Solver in the TI-83/84 Plus, enter the values shown below.
2. Solve for *PMT*.

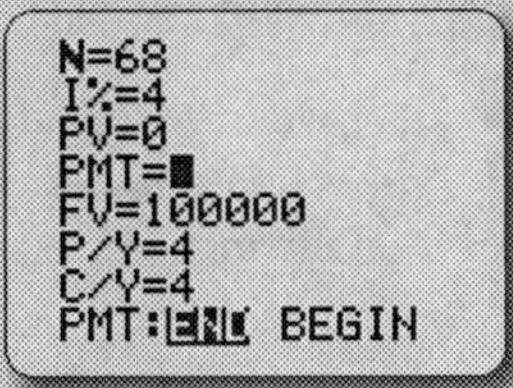

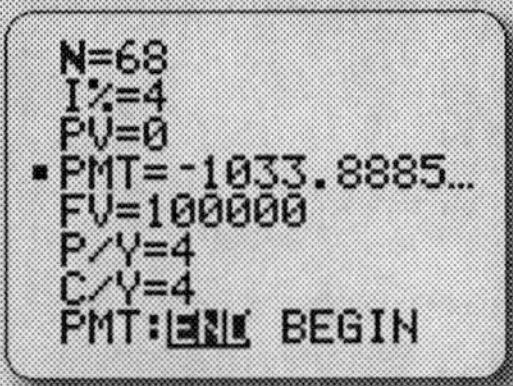

Why is *PMT* negative?

Example 3 (page 149) You wish to establish a trust fund from which your niece can withdraw $2,000 every 6 months for 15 years, at which time she will receive the remaining money in the trust, which you would like to be $10,000. The trust will be invested at 7% per year compounded every 6 months. How large should the trust be?

Solution with Technology

1. In the TVM Solver in the TI-83/84 Plus, enter the values shown below.
2. Solve for *PV*.

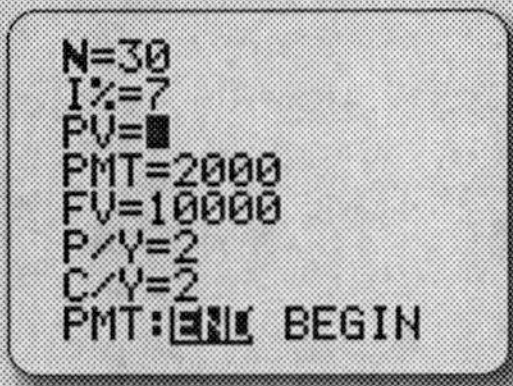

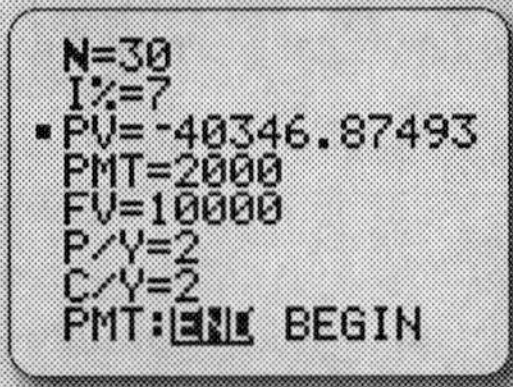

The payment and future value are positive because you (or your niece) will be receiving these amounts from the investment.

Note We have assumed that your niece receives the withdrawals at the end of each compounding period, so that the trust fund is an ordinary annuity. If, instead, she receives the payments at the beginning of each compounding period, it is an annuity due. You switch between the two types of annuity by changing PMT: END at the bottom to PMT: BEGIN. ■

As mentioned in the text, the present value must be higher to fund payments at the beginning of each period, because the money in the account has less time to earn interest.

Example 4 (page 150) Tony and Maria (see Example 2), having accumulated $100,000 for José Phillipe's college education, would now like to make quarterly withdrawals over the next 4 years. How much money can they withdraw each quarter in order to draw down the account to zero at the end of the 4 years? (Recall that the account pays 4% interest compounded quarterly.)

Solution with Technology

1. Enter the values shown below in the TI-83/84 Plus TVM Solver.
2. Solve for *PMT*.

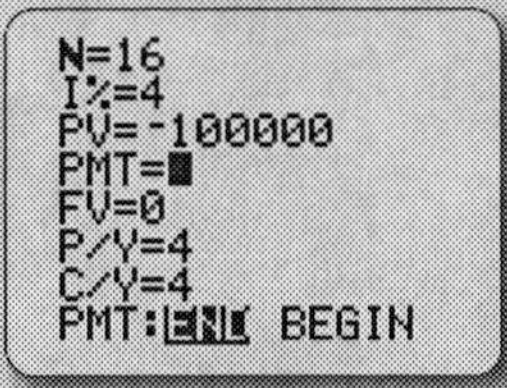

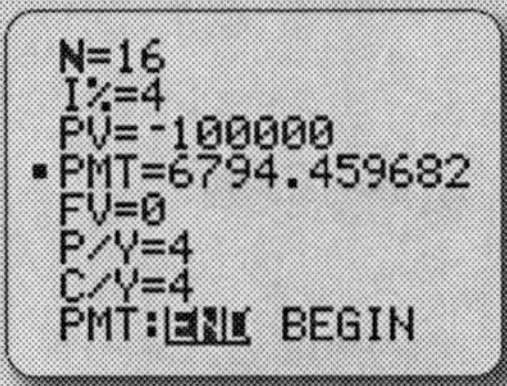

The present value is negative because Tony and Maria do not possess it; the bank does.

Example 7 (page 152) Marc and Mira are buying a house and have taken out a 30-year, $90,000 mortgage at 8% interest per year. Mortgage interest is tax deductible, so it is important to know how much of a year's mortgage payments represents interest. How much interest will Marc and Mira pay in the first year of their mortgage?

Solution with Technology

The TI-83/84 Plus has built-in functions to compute the values in an amortization schedule.

1. First, use the TVM Solver to find the monthly payment.

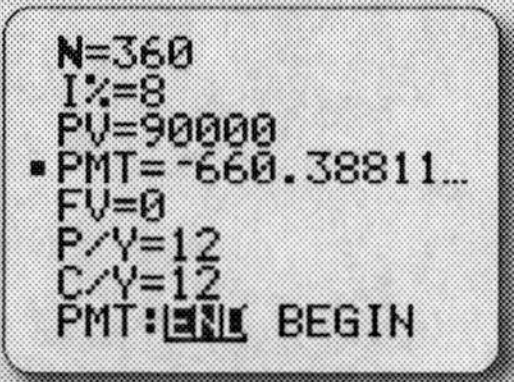

   Three functions correspond to the last three columns of the amortization schedule given in the text: `ΣInt`, `ΣPrn`, and `bal`, (found in the `Finance` menu accessed through APPS). They all require that the values of I%, PV, and PMT be entered or calculated ahead of time; calculating the payment in the TVM Solver in Step 1 accomplishes this.

2. Use `ΣInt(`*m*`,`*n*`,2)` to compute the sum of the interest payments from payment *m* through payment *n*. For example,

   `ΣInt(1,12,2)`

   will return −7,172.81, the total paid in interest in the first year, which answers the question asked in this example. (The last argument, 2, tells the calculator to round all intermediate calculations to two decimal places—that is, the nearest cent—as would the mortgage lender.)

3. Use `ΣPrn(`*m*`,`*n*`,2)` to compute the sum of the payments on principal from payment *m* through payment *n*. For example,

   `ΣPrn(1,12,2)`

   will return −751.87, the total paid on the principal in the first year.

4. Finally, `bal(`*n*`,2)` finds the balance of the principal outstanding after *n* payments. For example,

   `bal(12,2)`

   will return the value 89,248.13, the balance remaining at the end of one year.

5. To construct an amortization schedule as in the text, make sure that `FUNC` is selected in the MODE window; then enter the functions in the Y= window as shown below.

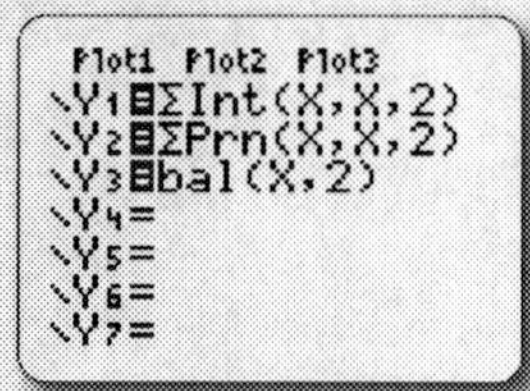

6. Press 2ND TBLSET and enter the values shown here.

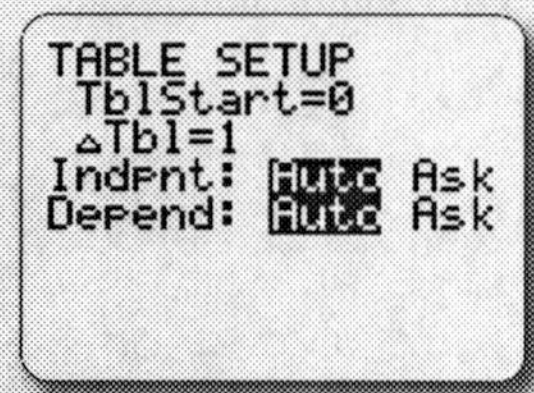

7. Press 2ND TABLE, to get the table shown here.

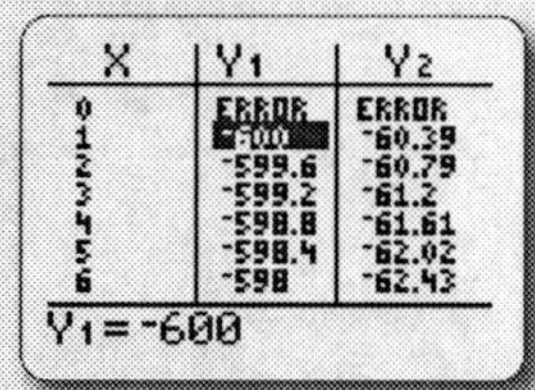

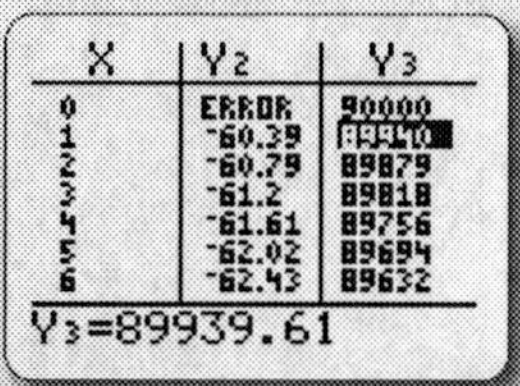

   The column labeled `X` gives the month, the column labeled Y_1 gives the interest payment for each month, the column labeled Y_2 gives the payment on principal for each month, and the column labeled Y_3 (use the right arrow button to make it visible) gives the outstanding principal.

8. To see later months, use the down arrow. As you can see, some of the values will be rounded in the table, but by selecting a value (as the outstanding principal at the end of the first month is selected in the second screen) you can see its exact value at the bottom of the screen.

Example 9 (page 154) Suppose that a 5%, 20-year bond sells for \$9,800 per \$10,000 maturity value. What rate of return will investors get?

Solution with Technology

We can use the TVM Solver in the TI-83/84 Plus to find the interest rate just as we use it to find any other one of the variables.

1. Enter the values shown in the TVM Solver window.

2. Solve for *I%*. (Recall that *I%* is the annual interest rate, corresponding to *r* in the formula.)

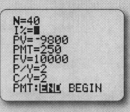

```
N=40
I%=■
PV=-9800
PMT=250
FV=10000
P/Y=2
C/Y=2
PMT:END BEGIN
```

```
N=40
▪I%=5.161519731
PV=-9800
PMT=250
FV=10000
P/Y=2
C/Y=2
PMT:END BEGIN
```

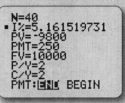

Thus, at \$9,800 per \$10,000 maturity value, these bonds yield 5.162% compounded semiannually.

SPREADSHEET Technology Guide

Section 2.2

Example 1 (page 136) In November 2011, the Bank of Montreal was paying 1.30% interest on savings accounts. If the interest is compounded quarterly, find the future value of a \$2,000 deposit in 6 years. What is the total interest paid over the period?

Solution with Technology

You can either compute compound interest directly or use financial functions built into your spreadsheet. The following worksheet has more than we need for this example, but will be useful for other examples in this and the next section.

	A	B	C	D
1		Entered	Calculated	
2	Rate	1.30%		
3	Years	6		
4	Payment	\$0.00		
5	Present Value	-\$2,000.00		
6	Future Value		=FV(B2/B7,B3*B7,B4,B5)	
7	Periods per year	4		

For this example the payment amount in B4 should be 0 (we shall use it in the next section).

1. Enter the other numbers as shown. As with other technologies, like the TVM Solver in the TI-83/84 Plus calculator, money that you pay to others (such as the \$2,000 you deposit in the bank) should be entered as negative, whereas money that is paid to you is positive.

2. The formula entered in C6 uses the built-in FV function to calculate the future value based on the entries in column B. This formula has the following format:

=FV(*i*,*n*,*PMT*,*PV*)

$i =$ interest per period   We use B2/B7 for the interest.

$n =$ number of periods   We use B3*B7 for the number of periods.

$PMT =$ payment per period   The payment is 0 (cell B4).

$PV =$ present value   The present value is in cell B5.

Instead of using the built-in FV function, we could use

```
=-B5*(1+B2/B7)^(B3*B7)
```

based on the future value formula for compound interest. After calculation the result will appear in cell C6.

	A	B	C	D
1		Entered	Calculated	
2	Rate	1.30%		
3	Years	6		
4	Payment	$0.00		
5	Present Value	-$2,000.00		
6	Future Value		$2,161.97	
7	Periods per year	4		

Note that we have formatted the cells B4:C6 as currency with two decimal places. If you change the values in column B, the future value in column C will be automatically recalculated.

Example 2 (page 138) Megabucks Corporation is issuing 10-year zero coupon bonds. How much would you pay for bonds with a maturity value of $10,000 if you wish to get a return of 6.5% compounded annually?

Solution with Technology

You can compute present value in your spreadsheet using the PV worksheet function. The following worksheet is similar to the one in the preceding example, except that we have entered a formula for computing the present value from the entered values.

	A	B	C	D
1		Entered	Calculated	
2	Rate	6.50%		
3	Years	10		
4	Payment	$0.00		
5	Present Value		=PV(B2/B7,B3*B7,B4,B6)	
6	Future Value	$10,000.00		
7	Periods per year	1		

The next worksheet shows the calculated value.

	A	B	C	D
1		Entered	Calculated	
2	Rate	6.50%		
3	Years	10		
4	Payment	$0.00		
5	Present Value		-$5,327.26	
6	Future Value	$10,000.00		
7	Periods per year	1		

Why is the present value negative?

Example 6 (page 141) You have $5,000 to invest at 6% interest compounded monthly. How long will it take for your investment to grow to $6,000?

Solution with Technology

You can compute the requisite length of an investment in your spreadsheet using the NPER worksheet function. The following worksheets show the calculation.

	A	B	C	D
1		Entered	Calculated	
2	Rate	6.00%		
3	Years		=NPER(B2/B7,B4,B5,B6)/B7	
4	Payment	$0.00		
5	Present Value	-$5,000.00		
6	Future Value	$6,000.00		
7	Periods per year	12		

	A	B	C	D
1		Entered	Calculated	
2	Rate	6.00%		
3	Years		3.04628303	
4	Payment	$0.00		
5	Present Value	-$5,000.00		
6	Future Value	$6,000.00		
7	Periods per year	12		

The NPER function computes the number of compounding periods, months in this case, so we divide by B7, the number of periods per year, to calculate the number of years, which appears as 3.046. So, you need to invest your money for just over 3 years for it to grow to $6,000.

Section 2.3

Example 1 (page 146) Your retirement account has $5,000 in it and earns 5% interest per year compounded monthly. Every month for the next 10 years you will deposit $100 into the account. How much money will there be in the account at the end of those 10 years?

Solution with Technology

We can use exactly the same worksheet that we used in Example 1 in the preceding section. In fact, we included the "Payment" row in that worksheet just for this purpose.

	A	B	C	D
1		Entered	Calculated	
2	Rate	5.00%		
3	Years	10		
4	Payment	-$100.00		
5	Present Value	-$5,000.00		
6	Future Value		=FV(B2/B7,B3*B7,B4,B5)	
7	Periods per year	12		

	A	B	C	D
1		Entered	Calculated	
2	Rate	5.00%		
3	Years	10		
4	Payment	-$100.00		
5	Present Value	-$5,000.00		
6	Future Value		$23,763.28	
7	Periods per year	12		

Note that the FV function allows us to enter, as the last argument, the amount of money already in the account. Following the usual convention, we enter the present value and the payment as *negative*, because these are amounts you pay into the account.

Example 2 (page 147) Tony and Maria have just had a son, José Phillipe. They establish an account to accumulate money for his college education, in which they would like to have $100,000 after 17 years. If the account pays 4% interest per year compounded quarterly, and they make deposits at the end of every quarter, how large must each deposit be for them to reach their goal?

Solution with Technology

Use the following worksheet, in which the PMT worksheet function is used to calculate the required payments.

	A	B	C	D
1		Entered	Calculated	
2	Rate	4.00%		
3	Years	17		
4	Payment		=PMT(B2/B7,B3*B7,B5,B6)	
5	Present Value	$0.00		
6	Future Value	$100,000.00		
7	Periods per year	4		

	A	B	C	D
1		Entered	Calculated	
2	Rate	4.00%		
3	Years	17		
4	Payment		-$1,033.89	
5	Present Value	$0.00		
6	Future Value	$100,000.00		
7	Periods per year	4		

Why is the payment negative?

Example 3 (page 149) You wish to establish a trust fund from which your niece can withdraw $2,000 every 6 months for 15 years, at which time she will receive the remaining money in the trust, which you would like to be $10,000. The trust will be invested at 7% per year compounded every 6 months. How large should the trust be?

Solution with Technology

You can use the same worksheet as in Example 2 in Section 2.2.

	A	B	C	D
1		Entered	Calculated	
2	Rate	7.00%		
3	Years	15		
4	Payment	$2,000.00		
5	Present Value		=PV(B2/B7,B3*B7,B4,B6)	
6	Future Value	$10,000.00		
7	Periods per year	2		

	A	B	C	D
1		Entered	Calculated	
2	Rate	7.00%		
3	Years	15		
4	Payment	$2,000.00		
5	Present Value		-$40,346.87	
6	Future Value	$10,000.00		
7	Periods per year	2		

The payment and future value are positive because you (or your niece) will be receiving these amounts from the investment.

Note We have assumed that your niece receives the withdrawals at the end of each compounding period, so that the trust fund is an ordinary annuity. If, instead, she receives the payments at the beginning of each compounding period, it is an annuity due. You switch to an annuity due by adding an optional last argument of 1 to the PV function (and similarly for the other finance functions in spreadsheets).

	A	B	C	D
1		Entered	Calculated	
2	Rate	7.00%		
3	Years	15		
4	Payment	$2,000.00		
5	Present Value		=PV(B2/B7,B3*B7,B4,B6,1)	
6	Future Value	$10,000.00		
7	Periods per year	2		

	A	B	C	D
1		Entered	Calculated	
2	Rate	7.00%		
3	Years	15		
4	Payment	$2,000.00		
5	Present Value		-$41,634.32	
6	Future Value	$10,000.00		
7	Periods per year	2		

As mentioned in the text, the present value must be higher to fund payments at the beginning of each period, because the money in the account has less time to earn interest. ■

Example 4 (page 150) Tony and Maria (see Example 2), having accumulated $100,000 for José Phillipe's college education, would now like to make quarterly withdrawals over the next 4 years. How much money can they withdraw each quarter in order to draw down the account to zero at the end of the four years? (Recall that the account pays 4% interest compounded quarterly.)

Solution with Technology

You can use the same worksheet as in Example 2.

	A	B	C	D
1		Entered	Calculated	
2	Rate	4.00%		
3	Years	4		
4	Payment		=PMT(B2/B7,B3*B7,B5,B6)	
5	Present Value	-$100,000.00		
6	Future Value	$0.00		
7	Periods per year	4		

	A	B	C	D
1		Entered	Calculated	
2	Rate	4.00%		
3	Years	4		
4	Payment		$6,794.46	
5	Present Value	-$100,000.00		
6	Future Value	$0.00		
7	Periods per year	4		

The present value is negative since Tony and Maria do not possess it; the bank does.

Example 7 (page 152) Marc and Mira are buying a house and have taken out a 30-year, $90,000 mortgage at 8% interest per year. Mortgage interest is tax deductible, so it is important to know how much of a year's mortgage payments represents interest. How much interest will Marc and Mira pay in the first year of their mortgage?

Solution with Technology

We construct an amortization schedule with which we can answer the question.

1. Begin with the worksheet below.

	A	B	C	D	E	F	G	H
1	Month	Interest Payment	Payment on Principal	Outstanding Principal				
2	0			$90,000.00	Rate	8%		
3					Years	30		
4					Payment	=DOLLAR(-PMT(F2/12,F3*12,D2))		

	A	B	C	D	E	F
1	Month	Interest Payment	Payment on Principal	Outstanding Principal		
2	0			$90,000.00	Rate	8%
3					Years	30
4					Payment	$660.39

Note the formula for the monthly payment:

```
=DOLLAR(-PMT(F2/12,F3*12,D2))
```

The function DOLLAR rounds the payment to the nearest cent, as the bank would.

2. Calculate the interest owed at the end of the first month using the formula

```
=DOLLAR(D2*F$2/12)
```

in cell B3.

3. The payment on the principal is the remaining part of the payment, so enter

```
=F$4-B3
```

in cell C3.

4. Calculate the outstanding principal by subtracting the payment on the principal from the previous outstanding principal, by entering

```
=D2-C3
```

in cell D3.

5. Copy the formulas in cells B3, C3, and D3 into the cells below them to continue the table.

	A	B	C	D	E	F
1	Month	Interest Payment	Payment on Principal	Outstanding Principal		
2	0			$90,000.00	Rate	8%
3	1	$600.00	$60.39	$89,939.61	Years	30
4	2				Payment	$660.39
5	3					
6	4					
7	5					
8	6					
9	7					
10	8					
11	9					
12	10					
13	11					
14	12					

The result should be something like the following:

	A	B	C	D	E	F
1	Month	Interest Payment	Payment on Principal	Outstanding Principal		
2	0			$90,000.00	Rate	8%
3	1	$600.00	$60.39	$89,939.61	Years	30
4	2	$599.60	$60.79	$89,878.82	Payment	$660.39
5	3	$599.19	$61.20	$89,817.62		
6	4	$598.78	$61.61	$89,756.01		
7	5	$598.37	$62.02	$89,693.99		
8	6	$597.96	$62.43	$89,631.56		
9	7	$597.54	$62.85	$89,568.71		
10	8	$597.12	$63.27	$89,505.44		
11	9	$596.70	$63.69	$89,441.75		
12	10	$596.28	$64.11	$89,377.64		
13	11	$595.85	$64.54	$89,313.10		
14	12	$595.42	$64.97	$89,248.13		

6. Adding the calculated interest payments gives us the total interest paid in the first year: $7,172.81.

Note Spreadsheets have built-in functions that compute the interest payment (IPMT) or the payment on the principle (PPMT) in a given period. We could also have used the built-in future value function (FV) to calculate the outstanding principal each month. The main problem with using these functions is that, in a sense, they are too accurate. They do not take into account the fact that payments and interest are rounded to the nearest cent. Over time, this rounding causes the actual value of the outstanding principal to differ from what the FV

TECHNOLOGY GUIDE

function would tell us. In fact, because the actual payment is rounded slightly upward (to \$660.39 from 660.38811...), the principal is reduced slightly faster than necessary and a last payment of \$660.39 would be \$2.95 larger than needed to clear out the debt. The lender would reduce the last payment by \$2.95 for this reason; Marc and Mira will pay only \$657.44 for their final payment. This is common: The last payment on an installment loan is usually slightly larger or smaller than the others, to compensate for the rounding of the monthly payment amount. ■

Example 9 (page 154) Suppose that a 5%, 20-year bond sells for \$9,800 per \$10,000 maturity value. What rate of return will investors get?

Solution with Technology

Use the following worksheet, in which the RATE worksheet function is used to calculate the interest rate.

	A	B	C	D
1		Entered	Calculated	
2	Rate		=RATE(B3*B7,B4,B5,B6)*B7	
3	Years	20		
4	Payment	\$250.00		
5	Present Value	-\$9,800.00		
6	Future Value	\$10,000.00		
7	Periods per year	2		

	A	B	C	D
1		Entered	Calculated	
2	Rate		5.162%	
3	Years	20		
4	Payment	\$250.00		
5	Present Value	-\$9,800.00		
6	Future Value	\$10,000.00		
7	Periods per year	2		

CHAPTER 2 QUIZ

1. Paul and Janet are arguing the merits of two different schemes for putting money into a retirement account. The retirement account earns 6.9% interest compounded monthly, and it is assumed that in 30 years the money in the account will be available.

   - *Paul's Plan:* Make monthly deposits of $200 for the first five years, make monthly deposits of $150 for the following five years, and then make monthly deposits of $100 for the remaining 20 years.
   - *Janet's Plan:* Make monthly deposits of $125 for 30 years.

   Which plan do you recommend, and why?

2. How long does it take for an investment of $5500 to grow to a value of $8000 if it can be invested in an account earning 4.6% interest compounded monthly?

3. If quarterly deposits of \$600 are being made into an ordinary annuity, what annual rate of interest must be offered in order for the annuity to be worth \$35,000 after 12 years? Give the percentage accurate to two decimal places.

4. A couple can make quarterly deposits of \$300 into an account that earns an annual interest rate of 5% compounded quarterly. In six years years, when one of their children leaves for college, they will cease making payments into the account. Starting one quarter after that last deposit, equal quarterly payments will be issued from the account for four years to help pay college expenses. After the final payment, the account should be empty.

a. Calculate the quarterly payments that will be issued.

b. How much interest does the money in the account ultimately earn?

5. A corporate bond with a face value of $30,000 matured over a period of 10 years. Including all interest payments made over that period of time, the purchaser of the bond was paid a sum of money amounting to $42,500. What annual interest rate was the bond carrying?

6. Suppose that a credit card carries an annual interest rate of 18%, but compounds interest daily on any unpaid balance carried over a statement term. Suppose that a statement term is 30 days and right now you are carrying a card balance of $2000. You can afford to make $500 payments each statement term, starting in 30 days. Assume that you will not be using the credit card to make any purchases while you carry a balance.

a. What will your statement balance be when you prepare to make your first payment?

b. What will your statement balance be when you prepare to make your second payment?

c. How much is you unpaid statement balance **after** you have made your third payment?

7. Suppose that you borrow \$220,000 to purchase a home. The loan is a standard mortgage that will be repaid over the course of 30 years with equal monthly payments. The annual interest rate on the loan is 3.8%, giving monthly payments of \$1025.11.

   a. How much interest is due on the first payment? How much interest is due on the second payment?

   b. What will the unpaid loan balance be after 18 years of payments?

   c. If you can afford monthly payments of \$1300, then how much could you have borrowed under the same loan terms?

   d. Suppose that you can only afford monthly payments of \$1000 on the mortgage. What annual interest rate would the loan have to carry (with the same repayment term) so that you could afford the payments? Give the percentage accurate to two decimal places.

8. Crystal recently purchased a condominium for \$199,000. She obtained an installment loan with a term of 22 years carrying an annual interest rate of 5% to make the purchase.

a. Determine the monthly payments on her loan.

b. Suppose that Crystal wants to add \$50 to each of her loan payments. If she does this, starting with her first payment, then how long will it take her to repay the loan?

c. Suppose that after making monthly payments for 10 years, Crystal refinances the unpaid loan balance at an annual interest rate of 3.75%, to be repaid with equal monthly payments over the course of another 10 years. Will this result in a savings on interest paid compared to just sticking with the original 22-year loan? If so, how much? If not, explain why.

5

Linear Programming

Website
www.WanerMath.com
At the Website you will find:

- Section-by-section tutorials, including game tutorials with randomized quizzes
- A detailed chapter summary
- A true/false quiz
- Additional review exercises
- A linear programming grapher
- A pivot and Gauss-Jordan tool
- A simplex method tool

Case Study The Diet Problem

The Galaxy Nutrition health-food mega-store chain provides free online nutritional advice and support to its customers. As Web site technical consultant, you are planning to construct an interactive Web page to assist customers prepare a diet tailored to their nutritional and budgetary requirements. Ideally, the customer would select foods to consider and specify nutritional and/or budgetary constraints, and the tool should return the optimal diet meeting those requirements. You would also like the Web page to allow the customer to decide whether, for instance, to find the cheapest possible diet meeting the requirements, the diet with the lowest number of calories, or the diet with the least total carbohydrates. **How do you go about constructing such a Web page?**

Image Studios/UpperCut Images/Getty Images

Introduction

In this chapter we begin to look at one of the most important types of problems for business and the sciences: finding the largest or smallest possible value of some quantity (such as profit or cost) under certain constraints (such as limited resources). We call such problems **optimization** problems because we are trying to find the best, or optimum, value. The optimization problems we look at in this chapter involve linear functions only and are known as **linear programming** (LP) problems. One of the main purposes of calculus, which you may study later, is to solve nonlinear optimization problems.

Linear programming problems involving only two unknowns can usually be solved by a graphical method that we discuss in Sections 5.1 and 5.2. When there are three or more unknowns, we must use an algebraic method, as we had to do for systems of linear equations. The method we use is called the **simplex method**. Invented in 1947 by George B. Dantzig* (1914–2005), the simplex method is still the most commonly used technique to solve LP problems in real applications, from finance to the computation of trajectories for guided missiles.

* Dantzig is the real-life source of the story of the student who, walking in late to a math class, copies down two problems on the board, thinking they're homework. After much hard work he hands in the solutions, only to discover that he's just solved two famous unsolved problems. This actually happened to Dantzig in graduate school in 1939.[1]

The simplex method can be used for hand calculations when the numbers are fairly small and the unknowns are few. Practical problems often involve large numbers and many unknowns, however. Problems such as routing telephone calls or airplane flights, or allocating resources in a manufacturing process can involve tens of thousands of unknowns. Solving such problems by hand is obviously impractical, and so computers are regularly used. Although computer programs most often use the simplex method, mathematicians are always seeking faster methods. The first radically different method of solving LP problems was the **ellipsoid algorithm** published in 1979 by the Soviet mathematician Leonid G. Khachiyan[2] (1952–2005). In 1984, Narendra Karmarkar (1957–), a researcher at Bell Labs, created a more efficient method now known as **Karmarkar's algorithm**. Although these methods (and others since developed) can be shown to be faster than the simplex method in the worst cases, it seems to be true that the simplex method is still the fastest in the applications that arise in practice.

Calculators and spreadsheets are very useful aids in the simplex method. In practice, software packages do most of the work, so you can think of what we teach you here as a peek inside a "black box." What the software cannot do for you is convert a real situation into a mathematical problem, so the most important lessons to get out of this chapter are (1) how to recognize and set up a linear programming problem, and (2) how to interpret the results.

5.1 Graphing Linear Inequalities

By the end of the next section, we will be solving linear programming (LP) problems with two unknowns. We use inequalities to describe the constraints in a problem, such as limitations on resources. Recall the basic notation for inequalities.

[1]Sources: D. J. Albers, and C. Reid, "An Interview of George B. Dantzig: The Father of Linear Programming," *College Math. Journal,* v. 17 (1986), pp. 293–314. Quoted and discussed in the context of the urban legends it inspired at www.snopes.com/college/homework/unsolvable.asp.

[2]Dantzig and Khachiyan died approximately two weeks apart in 2005. The *New York Times* ran their obituaries together on May 23, 2005.

Non-Strict Inequalities

$a \le b$ means that a **is less than or equal to** b.

$a \ge b$ means that a **is greater than or equal to** b.

Quick Examples

$3 \le 99$, $-2 \le -2$, $0 \le 3$

$3 \ge 3$, $1.78 \ge 1.76$, $\frac{1}{3} \ge \frac{1}{4}$

There are also the inequalities < and >, called **strict** inequalities because they do not permit equality. We do not use them in this chapter.

Following are some of the basic rules for manipulating inequalities. Although we illustrate all of them with the inequality $\le$, they apply equally well to inequalities with $\ge$ and to the strict inequalities < and >.

Rules for Manipulating Inequalities

Rules for Manipulating Inequalities	Quick Examples
1. The same quantity can be added to or subtracted from both sides of an inequality: If $x \le y$, then $x + a \le y + a$ for any real number a.	$x \le y$ implies $x - 4 \le y - 4$
2. Both sides of an inequality can be multiplied or divided by a positive constant: If $x \le y$ and a is positive, then $ax \le ay$.	$x \le y$ implies $3x \le 3y$
3. Both sides of an inequality can be multiplied or divided by a negative constant if the inequality is *reversed*: If $x \le y$ and a is negative, then $ax \ge ay$.	$x \le y$ implies $-3x \ge -3y$
4. The left and right sides of an inequality can be switched if the inequality is *reversed*: If $x \le y$, then $y \ge x$; if $y \ge x$, then $x \le y$.	$3x \ge 5y$ implies $5y \le 3x$

Here are the particular kinds of inequalities in which we're interested:

Linear Inequalities and Solving Inequalities

An **inequality in the unknown** x is the statement that one expression involving x is less than or equal to (or greater than or equal to) another. Similarly, we can have an **inequality in** x **and** y, which involves expressions that contain x and y; an **inequality in** x, y, **and** z; and so on. A **linear inequality** in one or more unknowns is an inequality of the form

$ax \le b$ (or $ax \ge b$), *a and b real constants*

$ax + by \le c$ (or $ax + by \ge c$), *a, b, and c real constants*

$ax + by + cz \le d$, *a, b, c, and d real constants*

$ax + by + cz + dw \le e$, *a, b, c, d, and e real constants*

and so on.

Quick Examples

$2x + 8 \geq 89$	Linear inequality in x
$2x^3 \leq x^3 + y$	Nonlinear inequality in x and y
$3x - 2y \geq 8$	Linear inequality in x and y
$x^2 + y^2 \leq 19z$	Nonlinear inequality in x, y, and z
$3x - 2y + 4z \leq 0$	Linear inequality in x, y, and z

A **solution** of an inequality in the unknown x is a value for x that makes the inequality true. For example, $2x + 8 \geq 89$ has a solution $x = 50$ because $2(50) + 8 \geq 89$. Of course, it has many other solutions as well. Similarly, a solution of an inequality in x and y is a pair of values (x, y) making the inequality true. For example, $(5, 1)$ is a solution of $3x - 2y \geq 8$ because $3(5) - 2(1) \geq 8$. To **solve** an inequality is to find the set of *all* solutions.

Solving Linear Inequalities in Two Variables

Our first goal is to solve linear inequalities in two variables—that is, inequalities of the form $ax + by \leq c$. As an example, let's solve

$$2x + 3y \leq 6.$$

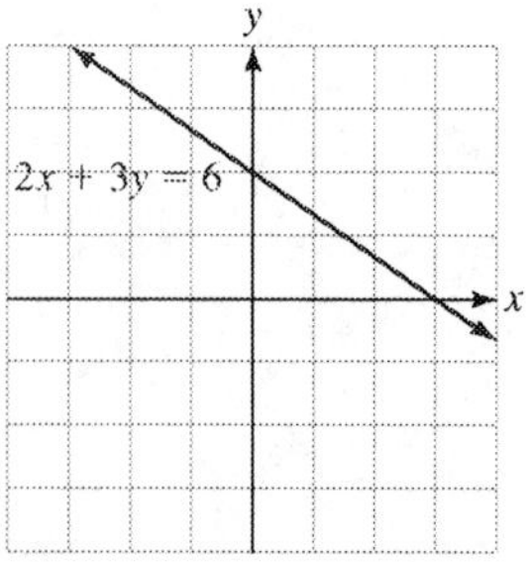

Figure 1

We already know how to solve the *equation* $2x + 3y = 6$. As we saw in Chapter 1, the solution of this equation may be pictured as the set of all points (x, y) on the straight-line graph of the equation. This straight line has x-intercept 3 (obtained by putting $y = 0$ in the equation) and y-intercept 2 (obtained by putting $x = 0$ in the equation) and is shown in Figure 1.

Notice that, if (x, y) is any point on the line, then x and y not only satisfy the *equation* $2x + 3y = 6$, but they also satisfy the *inequality* $2x + 3y \leq 6$, because being equal to 6 qualifies as being less than or equal to 6.

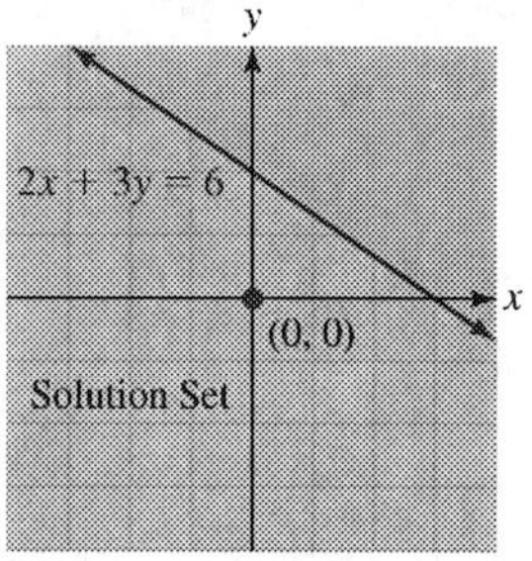

Figure 2

Q: *Do the points on the line give all possible solutions to the inequality?*

A: No. For example, try the origin, (0, 0). Because $2(0) + 3(0) = 0 \leq 6$, the point (0, 0) is a solution that does not lie on the line. In fact, here is a possibly surprising fact: The solution to any linear inequality in two unknowns is represented by an entire **half plane:** the set of all points on one side of the line (including the line itself). Thus, because (0, 0) is a solution of $2x + 3y \leq 6$ and is not on the line, every point on the same side of the line as (0, 0) is a solution as well (the colored region below the line in Figure 2 shows which half plane constitutes the solution set).

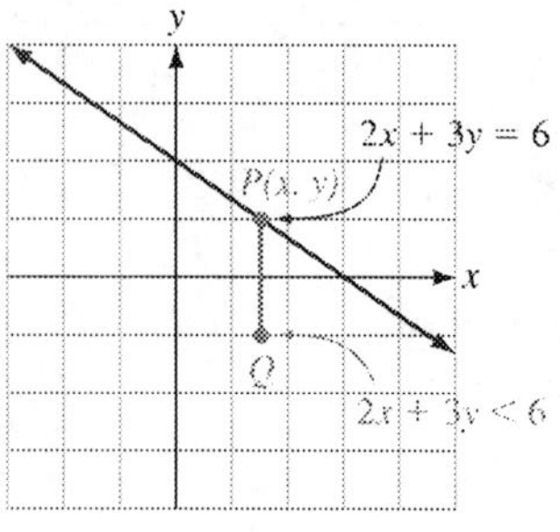

Figure 3

To see why the solution set of $2x + 3y \leq 6$ is the entire half plane shown in Figure 2, start with any point P on the line $2x + 3y = 6$. We already know that P is a solution of $2x + 3y \leq 6$. If we choose any point Q directly below P, the x-coordinate of Q will be the same as that of P, and the y-coordinate will be smaller. So the value of $2x + 3y$ at Q will be smaller than the value at P, which is 6. Thus, $2x + 3y < 6$ at Q, and so Q is another solution of the inequality. (See Figure 3.) In other words, *every point beneath the line is a solution of* $2x + 3y \leq 6$.

On the other hand, any point above the line is directly above a point on the line, and so $2x + 3y > 6$ for such a point. Thus, *no point above the line is a solution of* $2x + 3y \leq 6$.

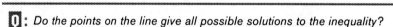

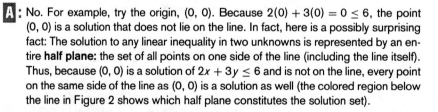

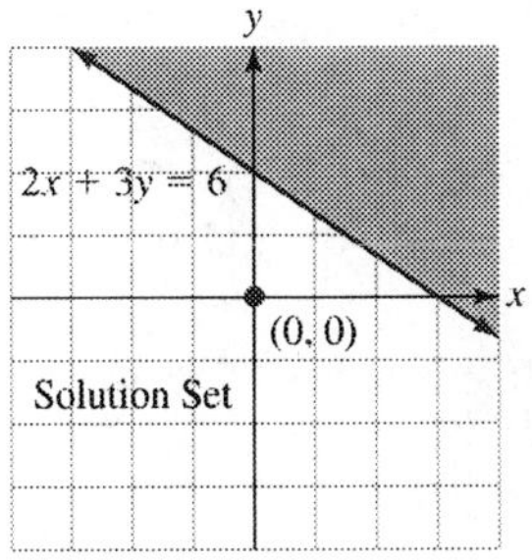

Figure 4

The same kind of argument can be used to show that the solution set of every inequality of the form $ax + by \le c$ or $ax + by \ge c$ consists of the half plane above or below the line $ax + by = c$. The "test-point" procedure we describe below gives us an easy method for deciding whether the solution set includes the region above or below the corresponding line.

Now we are going to do something that will appear backward at first (but makes it simpler to sketch sets of solutions of *systems* of linear inequalities). For our standard drawing of the region of solutions of $2x + 3y \le 6$, we are going to *shade only the part that we do not want and leave the solution region blank.* Think of covering over or "blocking out" the unwanted points, leaving those that we do want in full view (but remember that the points on the boundary line are also points that we want). The result is Figure 4. The reason we do this should become clear in Example 2.

Sketching the Region Represented by a Linear Inequality in Two Variables

1. Sketch the straight line obtained by replacing the given inequality with an equality.
2. Choose a test point not on the line; (0, 0) is a good choice if the line does not pass through the origin.
3. If the test point satisfies the inequality, then the set of solutions is the entire region on the same side of the line as the test point. Otherwise, it is the region on the other side of the line. In either case, shade (block out) the side that does *not* contain the solutions, leaving the solution set unshaded.

Quick Example

Here are the three steps used to graph the inequality $x + 2y \ge 5$:

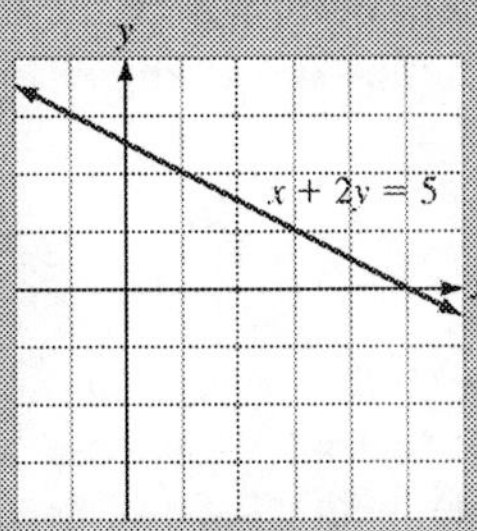

1. Sketch the line $x + 2y = 5$.

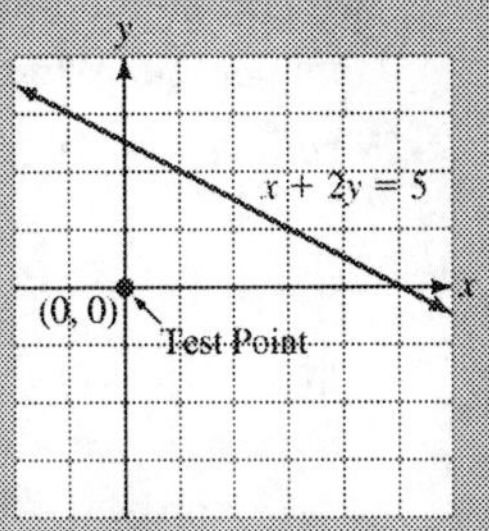

2. Test the point (0, 0) $0 + 2(0) \not\ge 5$. Inequality is not satisfied.

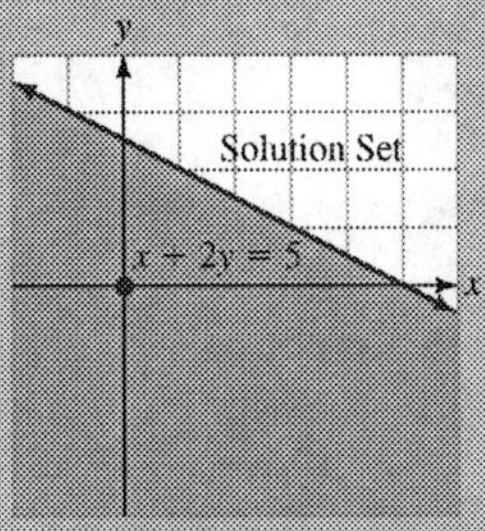

3. Because the inequality is not satisfied, shade the region containing the test point.

EXAMPLE 1 Graphing Single Inequalities

Sketch the regions determined by each of the following inequalities:

a. $3x - 2y \le 6$ **b.** $6x \le 12 + 4y$ **c.** $x \le -1$ **d.** $y \ge 0$ **e.** $x \ge 3y$

using Technology

Technology can be used to graph inequalities. Here is an outline (see the Technology Guides at the end of the chapter for additional details on using a TI-83/84 Plus or a spreadsheet):

TI-83/84 Plus

Solve the inequality for y and enter the resulting function of x; for example,

`Y1=-(2/3)*X+2.`

Position the cursor on the icon to the left of Y_1 and press ENTER until you see the kind of shading desired (above or below the line). [More details on page 391.]

Spreadsheet

Solve the inequality for y and create a scattergraph using two points on the line. Then use the drawing palette to create a polygon to provide the shading. [More details on page 393.]

Website

www.WanerMath.com

→ On Line Utilities

→ Linear Programming Grapher

Type "graph" and enter one or more inequalities (each one on a new line) as shown:

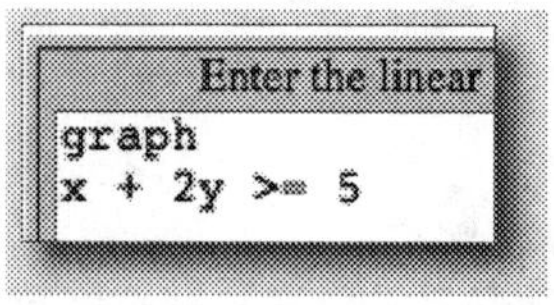

Adjust the graph window settings, and press "Graph".

Solution

a. The boundary line $3x - 2y = 6$ has x-intercept 2 and y-intercept -3 (Figure 5). We use (0, 0) as a test point (because it is not on the line). Because $3(0) - 2(0) \leq 6$, the inequality is satisfied by the test point (0, 0), and so it lies inside the solution set. The solution set is shown in Figure 5.

b. The given inequality, $6x \leq 12 + 4y$, can be rewritten in the form $ax + by \leq c$ by subtracting $4y$ from both sides:

$$6x - 4y \leq 12.$$

Dividing both sides by 2 gives the inequality $3x - 2y \leq 6$, which we considered in part (a). Now, *applying the rules for manipulating inequalities does not affect the set of solutions.* Thus, the inequality $6x \leq 12 + 4y$ has the same set of solutions as $3x - 2y \leq 6$. (See Figure 5.)

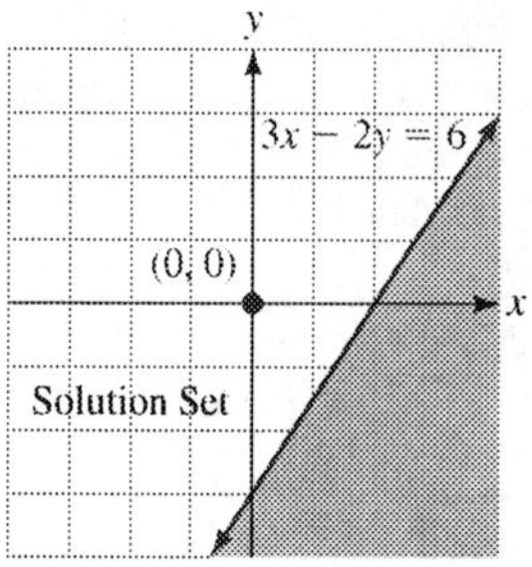

Figure 5

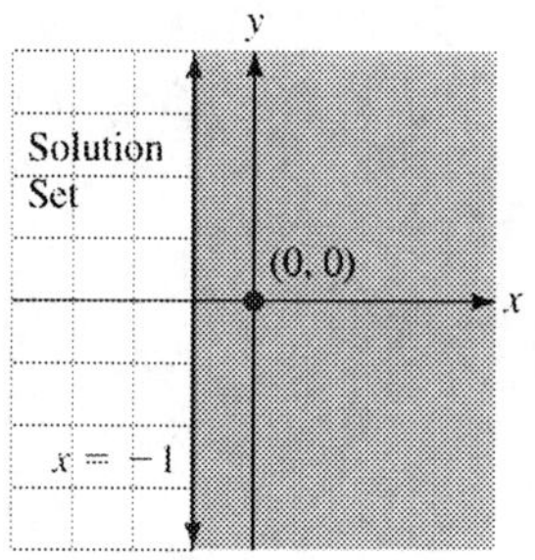

Figure 6

c. The region $x \leq -1$ has as boundary the vertical line $x = -1$. The test point (0, 0) is not in the solution set, as shown in Figure 6.

d. The region $y \geq 0$ has as boundary the horizontal line $y = 0$ (that is, the x-axis). We cannot use (0, 0) for the test point because it lies on the boundary line. Instead, we choose a convenient point not on the line $y = 0$—say, (0, 1). Because $1 \geq 0$, this point is in the solution set, giving us the region shown in Figure 7.

e. The line $x \geq 3y$ has as boundary the line $x = 3y$ or, solving for y,

$$y = \frac{1}{3}x.$$

This line passes through the origin with slope $1/3$, so again we cannot choose the origin as a test point. Instead, we choose (0, 1). Substituting these coordinates in $x \geq 3y$ gives $0 \geq 3(1)$, which is false, so (0, 1) is not in the solution set, as shown in Figure 8.

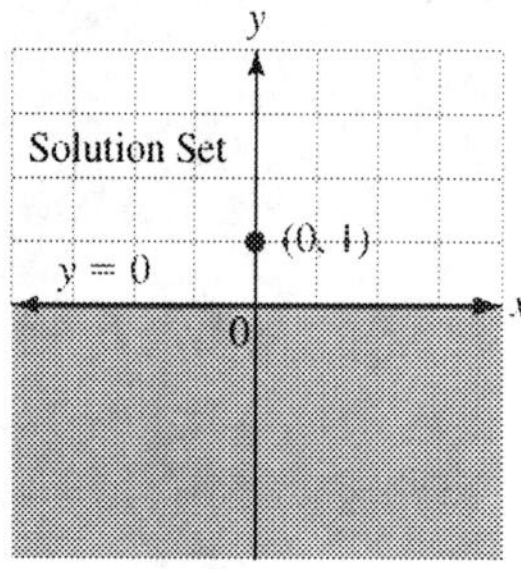

Figure 7

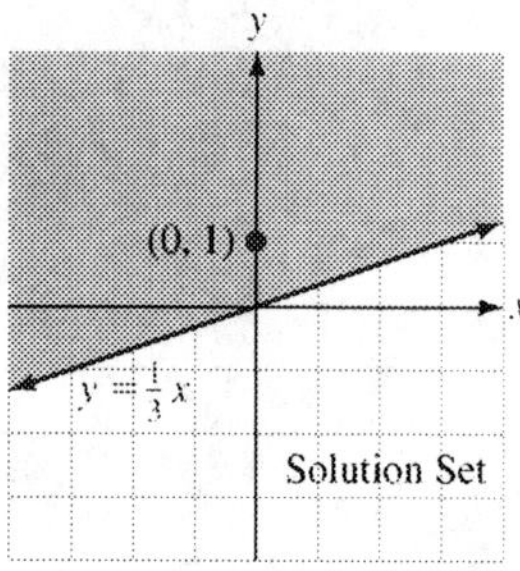

Figure 8

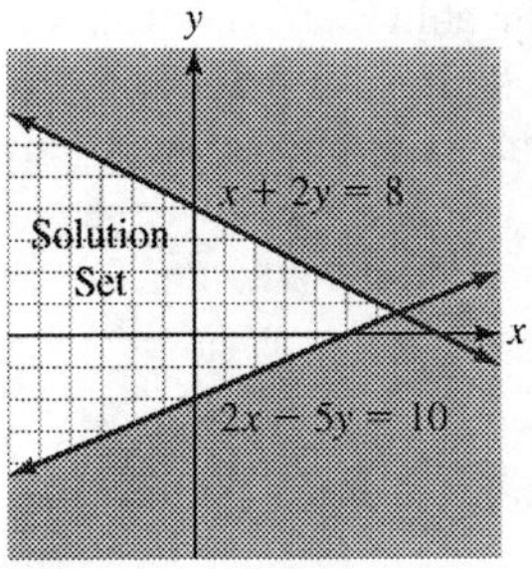

Figure 9

EXAMPLE 2 Graphing Simultaneous Inequalities

Sketch the region of points that satisfy both inequalities:

$$2x - 5y \le 10$$
$$x + 2y \le 8.$$

Solution Each inequality has a solution set that is a half plane. If a point is to satisfy *both* inequalities, it must lie in both sets of solutions. Put another way, if we cover the points that are not solutions to $2x - 5y \le 10$ and then also cover the points that are not solutions to $x + 2y \le 8$, the points that remain uncovered must be the points we want, those that are solutions to both inequalities. The result is shown in Figure 9, where the unshaded region is the set of solutions.*

As a check, we can look at points in various regions in Figure 9. For example, our graph shows that (0, 0) should satisfy both inequalities, and it does:

$$2(0) - 5(0) = 0 \le 10 \quad ✓$$
$$0 + 2(0) = 0 \le 8. \quad ✓$$

On the other hand, (0, 5) should fail to satisfy one of the inequalities:

$$2(0) - 5(5) = -25 \le 10 \quad ✓$$
$$0 + 2(5) = 10 > 8 \quad ✗$$

One more: (5, −1) should fail one of the inequalities:

$$2(5) - 5(-1) = 15 > 10 \quad ✗$$
$$5 + 2(-1) = 3 \le 8. \quad ✓$$

* Although these graphs are quite easy to do by hand, the more lines we have to graph the more difficult it becomes to get everything in the right place, and this is where graphing technology can become important. This is especially true when, for instance, three or more lines intersect in points that are very close together and hard to distinguish in hand-drawn graphs.

EXAMPLE 3 Corner Points

Sketch the region of solutions of the following system of inequalities and list the coordinates of all the corner points.

$$3x - 2y \le 6$$
$$x + y \ge -5$$
$$y \le 4$$

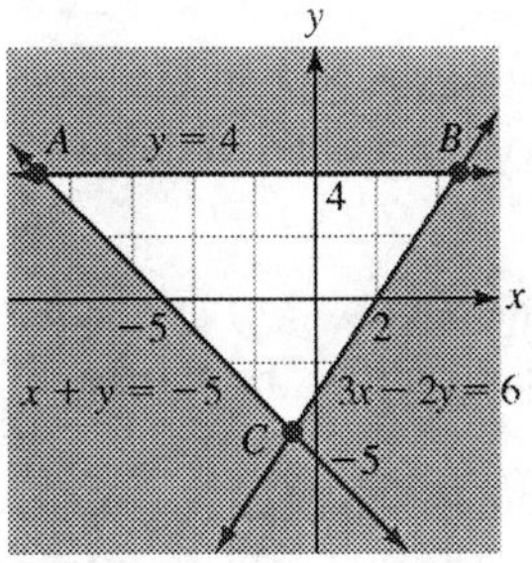

Figure 10

Solution Shading the regions that we do not want leaves us with the triangle shown in Figure 10. We label the corner points *A*, *B*, and *C* as shown.

Each of these corner points lies at the intersection of two of the bounding lines. So, to find the coordinates of each corner point, we need to solve the system of equations given by the two lines. To do this systematically, we make the following table:

Point	*Lines through Point*	*Coordinates*
A	$y = 4$ $x + y = -5$	$(-9, 4)$
B	$y = 4$ $3x - 2y = 6$	$\left(\frac{14}{3}, 4\right)$
C	$x + y = -5$ $3x - 2y = 6$	$\left(-\frac{4}{5}, -\frac{21}{5}\right)$

* **Technology Note** Using the trace feature makes it easy to locate corner points graphically. Remember to zoom in for additional accuracy when appropriate. Of course, you can also use technology to help solve the systems of equations, as we discussed in Chapter 3.

Here, we have solved each system of equations in the middle column to get the point on the right, using the techniques of Chapter 2. You should do this for practice.*

As a partial check that we have drawn the correct region, let us choose any point in its interior—say, (0, 0). We can easily check that (0, 0) satisfies all three given inequalities. It follows that all of the points in the triangular region containing (0, 0) are also solutions.

Take another look at the regions of solutions in Examples 2 and 3 (Figure 11).

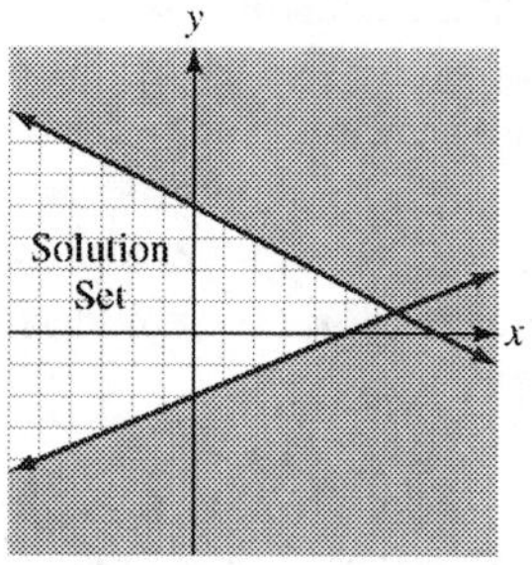

(a) Example 2 Solution Set

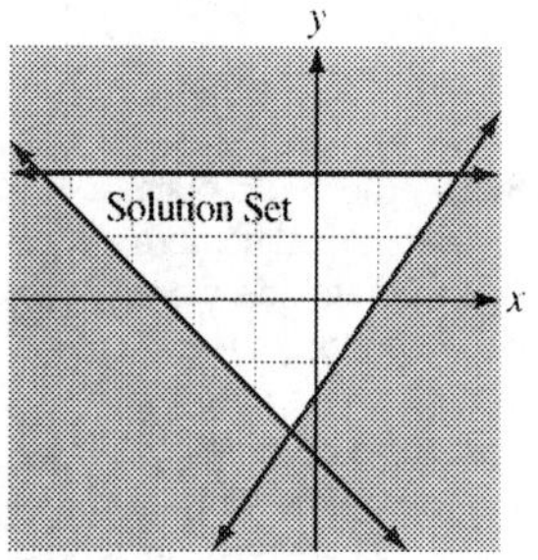

(b) Example 3 Solution Set

Figure 11

Notice that the solution set in Figure 11(a) extends infinitely far to the left, whereas the one in Figure 11(b) is completely enclosed by a boundary. Sets that are completely enclosed are called **bounded**, and sets that extend infinitely in one or more directions are **unbounded**. For example, all the solution sets in Example 1 are unbounded.

EXAMPLE 4 Resource Allocation

Socaccio Pistachio Inc. makes two types of pistachio nuts: Dazzling Red and Organic. Pistachio nuts require food color and salt, and the following table shows the amount of food color and salt required for a 1-kilogram batch of pistachios, as well as the total amount of these ingredients available each day.

	Dazzling Red	*Organic*	*Total Available*
Food Color (g)	2	1	20
Salt (g)	10	20	220

Use a graph to show the possible numbers of batches of each type of pistachio Socaccio can produce each day. This region (the solution set of a system of inequalities) is called the **feasible region**.

Solution As we did in Chapter 3, we start by identifying the unknowns: Let x be the number of batches of Dazzling Red manufactured per day and let y be the number of batches of Organic manufactured each day.

Now, because of our experience with systems of linear equations, we are tempted to say: For food color $2x + y = 20$ and for salt, $10x + 20y = 220$. However, no one is saying that Socaccio has to use all available ingredients; the company might choose to use fewer than the total available amounts if this proves more profitable. Thus, $2x + y$ can be anything *up to a total of* 20. In other words,

$$2x + y \le 20.$$

Similarly,

$$10x + 20y \le 220.$$

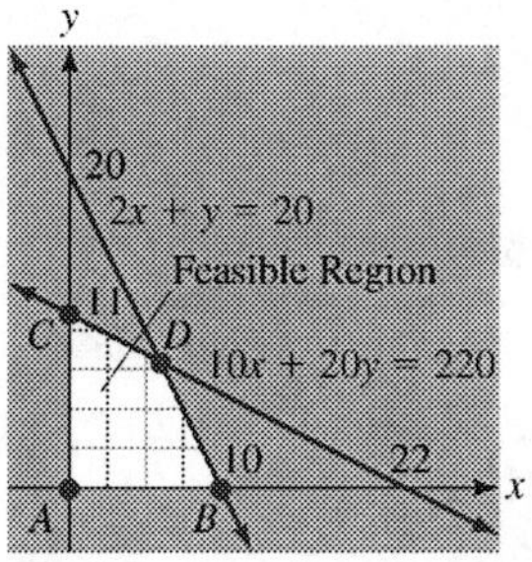

Figure 12

There are two more restrictions not explicitly mentioned: Neither x nor y can be negative. (The company cannot produce a negative number of batches of nuts.) Therefore, we have the additional restrictions

$$x \geq 0 \quad y \geq 0.$$

These two inequalities tell us that the feasible region (solution set) is restricted to the first quadrant, because in the other quadrants, either x or y or both x and y are negative. So instead of shading out all other quadrants, we can simply restrict our drawing to the first quadrant.

The (bounded) feasible region shown in Figure 12 is a graphical representation of the limitations the company faces.

Before we go on... Every point in the feasible region in Example 4 represents a value for x and a value for y that do not violate any of the company's restrictions. For example, the point (5, 6) lies well inside the region, so the company can produce five batches of Dazzling Red nuts and six batches of Organic without exceeding the limitations on ingredients [that is, $2(5) + 6 = 16 \leq 20$ and $10(5) + 20(6) = 170 \leq 220$]. The corner points A, B, C, and D are significant if the company wishes to realize the greatest profit, as we will see in Section 5.2. We can find the corners as in the following table:

Point	*Lines through Point*	*Coordinates*
A		(0, 0)
B		(10, 0)
C		(0, 11)
D	$2x + y = 20$ $10x + 20y = 220$	(6, 8)

(We have not listed the lines through the first three corners because their coordinates can be read easily from the graph.) Points on the line segment DB represent use of all the food color (because the segment lies on the line $2x + y = 20$), and points on the line segment CD represent use of all the salt (because the segment lies on the line $10x + 20y = 220$). Note that the point D is the only solution that uses all of both ingredients. ■

FAQs

Recognizing Whether to Use a Linear Inequality or a Linear Equation

Q: *How do I know whether to model a situation by a linear inequality like* $3x + 2y \leq 10$ *or by a linear equation like* $3x + 2y = 10$*?*

A: Here are some key phrases to look for: *at most, up to, no more than, at least, or more, exactly.* Suppose, for instance, that nuts cost 3¢, bolts cost 2¢, x is the number of nuts you can buy, and y is the number of bolts you can buy.

- If you have *up to* 10¢ to spend, then $3x + 2y \leq 10$.
- If you must spend *exactly* 10¢, then $3x + 2y = 10$.
- If you plan to spend *at least* 10¢, then $3x + 2y \geq 10$.

The use of inequalities to model a situation is often more realistic than the use of equations; for instance, one cannot always expect to exactly fill all orders, spend the exact amount of one's budget, or keep a plant operating at exactly 100% capacity.

5.1 EXERCISES

▼ more advanced ◆ challenging

[T] indicates exercises that should be solved using technology

In Exercises 1–26, sketch the region that corresponds to the given inequalities, say whether the region is bounded or unbounded, and find the coordinates of all corner points (if any). HINT [See Example 1.]

1. $2x + y \leq 10$

2. $4x - y \leq 12$

3. $-x - 2y \leq 8$

4. $-x + 2y \geq 4$

5. $3x + 2y \geq 5$

6. $2x - 3y \leq 7$

7. $x \leq 3y$

8. $y \geq 3x$

9. $\frac{3x}{4} - \frac{y}{4} \leq 1$

10. $\frac{x}{3} + \frac{2y}{3} \geq 2$

11. $x \geq -5$

12. $y \leq -4$

13. $4x - y \leq 8$
$x + 2y \leq 2$
HINT [See Examples 2 and 3.]

14. $2x + y \leq 4$
$x - 2y \geq 2$
HINT [See Examples 2 and 3.]

15. $3x + 2y \geq 6$
$3x - 2y \leq 6$
$x \geq 0$

16. $3x + 2y \leq 6$
$3x - 2y \geq 6$
$-y \geq 2$

17. $x + y \geq 5$
$x \leq 10$
$y \leq 8$
$x \geq 0, y \geq 0$

18. $2x + 4y \geq 12$
$x \leq 5$
$y \leq 3$
$x \geq 0, y \geq 0$

19. $20x + 10y \leq 100$
$10x + 20y \leq 100$
$10x + 10y \leq 60$
$x \geq 0, y \geq 0$

20. $30x + 20y \leq 600$
$10x + 40y \leq 400$
$20x + 30y \leq 450$
$x \geq 0, y \geq 0$

21. $20x + 10y \geq 100$
$10x + 20y \geq 100$
$10x + 10y \geq 80$
$x \geq 0, y \geq 0$

22. $30x + 20y \geq 600$
$10x + 40y \geq 400$
$20x + 30y \geq 600$
$x \geq 0, y \geq 0$

23. $-3x + 2y \leq 5$
$3x - 2y \leq 6$
$x \leq 2y$
$x \geq 0, y \geq 0$

24. $-3x + 2y \leq 5$
$3x - 2y \geq 6$
$y \leq x/2$
$x \geq 0, y \geq 0$

25. $2x - y \geq 0$
$x - 3y \leq 0$
$x \geq 0, y \geq 0$

26. $-x + y \geq 0$
$4x - 3y \geq 0$
$x \geq 0, y \geq 0$

[T] *In Exercises 27–32, we suggest you use technology. Graph the regions corresponding to the inequalities, and find the coordinates of all corner points (if any) to two decimal places.*

27. $2.1x - 4.3y \geq 9.7$

28. $-4.3x + 4.6y \geq 7.1$

29. $-0.2x + 0.7y \geq 3.3$
$1.1x + 3.4y \geq 0$

30. $0.2x + 0.3y \geq 7.2$
$2.5x - 6.7y \leq 0$

31. $4.1x - 4.3y \leq 4.4$
$7.5x - 4.4y \leq 5.7$
$4.3x + 8.5y \leq 10$

32. $2.3x - 2.4y \leq 2.5$
$4.0x - 5.1y \leq 4.4$
$6.1x + 6.7y \leq 9.6$

APPLICATIONS

33. ***Resource Allocation*** You manage an ice cream factory that makes two flavors: Creamy Vanilla and Continental Mocha. Into each quart of Creamy Vanilla go 2 eggs and 3 cups of cream. Into each quart of Continental Mocha go 1 egg and 3 cups of cream. You have in stock 500 eggs and 900 cups of cream. Draw the feasible region showing the number of quarts of vanilla and number of quarts of mocha that can be produced. Find the corner points of the region. HINT [See Example 4.]

34. ***Resource Allocation*** Podunk Institute of Technology's Math Department offers two courses: Finite Math and Applied Calculus. Each section of Finite Math has 60 students, and each section of Applied Calculus has 50. The department is allowed to offer a total of up to 110 sections. Furthermore, no more than 6,000 students want to take a math course. (No student will take more than one math course.) Draw the feasible region that shows the number of sections of each class that can be offered. Find the corner points of the region. HINT [See Example 4.]

35. ***Nutrition*** *Ruff Inc.* makes dog food out of chicken and grain. Chicken has 10 grams of protein and 5 grams of fat per ounce, and grain has 2 grams of protein and 2 grams of fat per ounce. A bag of dog food must contain at least 200 grams of protein and at least 150 grams of fat. Draw the feasible region that shows the number of ounces of chicken and number of ounces of grain Ruff can mix into each bag of dog food. Find the corner points of the region.

36. ***Purchasing*** Enormous State University's Business School is buying computers. The school has two models to choose from: the Pomegranate and the iZac. Each Pomegranate comes with 400 GB of memory and 80 TB of disk space, and each iZac has 300 GB of memory and 100 TB of disk space. For reasons related to its accreditation, the school would like to be able to say that it has a total of at least 48,000 GB of memory and at least 12,800 TB of disk space. Draw the feasible region that shows the number of each kind of computer it can buy. Find the corner points of the region.

37. ***Nutrition*** Gerber Products' Gerber Mixed Cereal for Baby contains, in each serving, 60 calories and 11 grams of carbohydrates. Gerber Mango Tropical Fruit Dessert contains, in each serving, 80 calories and 21 grams of carbohydrates.[3] You want to provide your child with at least 140 calories and at least 32 grams of carbohydrates. Draw the feasible region that shows the number of servings of cereal and number of servings of dessert that you can give your child. Find the corner points of the region.

38. ***Nutrition*** Gerber Products' Gerber Mixed Cereal for Baby contains, in each serving, 60 calories, 11 grams of carbohydrates, and no vitamin C. Gerber Apple Banana Juice contains, in each serving, 60 calories, 15 grams of carbohydrates, and 120 percent of the U.S. Recommended Daily Allowance (RDA) of Vitamin C for infants.[4] You want to provide your child with at least 120 calories, at least 26 grams of carbohydrates, and at least 50 percent of the U.S. RDA of vitamin C for infants. Draw the feasible region that shows the number of servings of cereal and number of servings of juice that you can give your child. Find the corner points of the region.

39. ***Municipal Bond Funds*** The Pimco New York Municipal Bond Fund (PNF) and the Fidelity Spartan Mass Fund (FDMMX) are tax-exempt municipal bond funds. In 2003, the Pimco fund yielded 6% while the Fidelity fund yielded 5%.[5] You would like to invest a total of up to $80,000 and earn at least $4,200 in interest in the coming year (based on the given yields). Draw the feasible region that shows how much money you can invest in each fund. Find the corner points of the region.

40. ***Municipal Bond Funds*** In 2003, the Fidelity Spartan Mass Fund (FDMMX) yielded 5%, and the Fidelity Spartan Florida Fund (FFLIX) yielded 7%.[6] You would like to invest a total of up to $60,000 and earn at least $3,500 in interest. Draw the feasible region that shows how much money you can invest in each fund (based on the given yields). Find the corner points of the region.

41. ▼ ***Investments: Financial Stocks*** (Compare Exercise 37 in Section 3.1.) In August 2011, Bank of Hawaii (BOH) stock cost $45 per share and yielded 4% per year in dividends, while JPMorgan Chase (JPM) stock cost $40 per share and yielded 2.5% per year in dividends.[7] You have up to $25,000 to invest in these stocks and would like to earn at least $760 in dividends over the course of a year. (Assume the dividend to be unchanged for the year.) Draw the feasible region that shows how many shares in each company you can buy. Find the corner points of the region. (Round each coordinate to the nearest whole number.)

42. ▼ ***Investments: Utility Stocks*** (Compare Exercise 38 in Section 3.1.) In April 2011, Consolidated Edison (ED) stock cost $50 per share and yielded 5% per year in dividends, while National Grid (NGG) stock cost $50 per share and yielded 6% per year in dividends.[8] You have up to $45,000 to invest in these stocks and would like to earn at least $2,400 in dividends over the course of a year. (Assume the dividend to be unchanged for the year.) Draw the feasible region that shows how many shares in each company you can buy. Find the corner points of the region. (Round each coordinate to the nearest whole number.)

43. ▼ ***Advertising*** You are the marketing director for a company that manufactures bodybuilding supplements and you are planning to run ads in *Sports Illustrated* and *GQ Magazine*. Based on readership data, you estimate that each one-page ad in *Sports Illustrated* will be read by 650,000 people in your target group, while each one-page ad in *GQ* will be read by 150,000.[9] You would like your ads to be read by at least three million people in the target group and, to ensure the broadest possible audience, you would like to place at least three full-page ads in each magazine. Draw the feasible region that shows how many pages you can purchase in each magazine. Find the corner points of the region. (Round each coordinate to the nearest whole number.)

44. ▼ ***Advertising*** You are the marketing director for a company that manufactures bodybuilding supplements and you are planning to run ads in *Sports Illustrated* and *Muscle and Fitness*. Based on readership data, you estimate that each one-page ad in *Sports Illustrated* will be read by 650,000 people in your target group, while each one-page ad in *Muscle and Fitness* will be read by 250,000 people in your target group.[10] You would like your ads to be read by at least four million people in the target group and, to ensure the broadest possible audience, you would like to place at least three full-page ads in each magazine during the year. Draw the feasible region showing how many pages you can purchase in each magazine. Find the corner points of the region. (Round each coordinate to the nearest whole number.)

COMMUNICATION AND REASONING EXERCISES

45. Find a system of inequalities whose solution set is unbounded.

46. Find a system of inequalities whose solution set is empty.

47. How would you use linear inequalities to describe the triangle with corner points (0, 0), (2, 0), and (0, 1)?

---

[3]Source: Nutrition information supplied with the products.

[4]*Ibid.*

[5]Yields are rounded. Sources: www.pimcofunds.com, www.fidelity.com

[6]Yields are rounded. Source: www.fidelity.com

[7]Stock prices and yields are approximate. Source: http://finance.google.com

[8]*Ibid.*

[9]The readership data for *Sports Illustrated* is based, in part, on the results of a readership survey taken in March 2000. The readership data for *GQ* is fictitious. Source: Mediamark Research Inc./*New York Times*, May 29, 2000, p. C1.

[10]The readership data for both magazines are based on the results of a readership survey taken in March 2000. Source: Mediamark Research Inc./*New York Times*, May 29, 2000, p. C1.

48. Explain the advantage of shading the region of points that do not satisfy the given inequalities. Illustrate with an example.

49. Describe at least one drawback to the method of finding the corner points of a feasible region by drawing its graph, when the feasible region arises from real-life constraints.

50. Draw several bounded regions described by linear inequalities. For each region you draw, find the point that gives the greatest possible value of $x + y$. What do you notice?

In Exercises 51–54, you are mixing x grams of ingredient A and y grams of ingredient B. Choose the equation or inequality that models the given requirement.

51. There should be at least 3 more grams of ingredient A than ingredient B.

(A) $3x - y \leq 0$ **(B)** $x - 3y \geq 0$
(C) $x - y \geq 3$ **(D)** $3x - y \geq 0$

52. The mixture should contain at least 25% of ingredient A by weight.

(A) $4x - y \leq 0$ **(B)** $x - 4y \geq 0$
(C) $x - y \geq 4$ **(D)** $3x - y \geq 0$

53. ▼ There should be at least 3 parts (by weight) of ingredient A to 2 parts of ingredient B.

(A) $3x - 2y \geq 0$ **(B)** $2x - 3y \geq 0$
(C) $3x + 2y \geq 0$ **(D)** $2x + 3y \geq 0$

54. ▼ There should be no more of ingredient A (by weight) than ingredient B.

(A) $x - y = 0$ **(B)** $x - y \leq 0$
(C) $x - y \geq 0$ **(D)** $x + y \geq y$

55. ▼ You are setting up a system of inequalities in the unknowns x and y. The inequalities represent constraints faced by Fly-by-Night Airlines, where x represents the number of first-class tickets it should issue for a specific flight and y represents the number of business-class tickets it should issue for that flight. You find that the feasible region is empty. How do you interpret this?

56. ▼ In the situation described in the preceding exercise, is it possible instead for the feasible region to be unbounded? Explain your answer.

57. ▼ Create an interesting scenario that leads to the following system of inequalities:

$$20x + 40y \leq 1{,}000$$
$$30x + 20y \leq 1{,}200$$
$$x \geq 0, y \geq 0.$$

58. ▼ Create an interesting scenario that leads to the following system of inequalities:

$$20x + 40y \geq 1{,}000$$
$$30x + 20y \geq 1{,}200$$
$$x \geq 0, y \geq 0.$$

Practice Problems 5.1, Part 1

Sketch graphs of the following systems of inequalities. Label all corner points with exact coordinates.

1.
$$\begin{aligned} 2y - 6x &> 2 \\ x - y &\geq 8 \\ x &\geq 0 \\ y &\leq 4 \end{aligned}$$

2.
$$\begin{aligned} x + y &\leq 6 \\ -3x + y &\geq 6 \\ y &\geq -2 \end{aligned}$$

Practice Problems 5.1, Part 2

1. A furniture manufacturer makes two types of sofas, one with standard upholstery and one with covers that can be taken off and washed. The first model takes 5 labor hours for assembling the sofa and 3 labor hours to cover the sofa. The second model takes 4 labor hours for assembling the sofa and 5 labor hours to cover the sofa. The maximum number of labor hours available for assembly is 260 and the maximum number of labor hours available for covering is 195. Set up a system of inequalities that models the situation and sketch the feasible region. Declare what variables represent and label all corner points with exact coordinates.

2. Consider the feasible region shown to the right. Find a system of linear inequalities that generates this feasible region. Assume that gridlines each mark one unit.

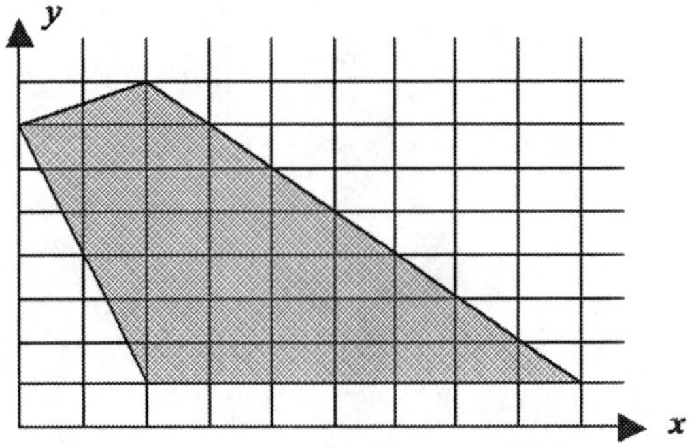

5.2 Solving Linear Programming Problems Graphically

As we saw in Example 4 in Section 5.1, in some scenarios the possibilities are restricted by a system of linear inequalities. In that example, it would be natural to ask which of the various possibilities gives the company the largest profit. This is a kind of problem known as a *linear programming problem* (commonly referred to as an LP problem).

Linear Programming (LP) Problems

A **linear programming problem** in two unknowns x and y is one in which we are to find the maximum or minimum value of a linear expression

$$ax + by$$

called the **objective function,** subject to a number of linear **constraints** of the form

$$cx + dy \leq e \quad \text{or} \quad cx + dy \geq e.$$

The largest or smallest value of the objective function is called the **optimal value,** and a pair of values of x and y that gives the optimal value constitutes an **optimal solution.**

Quick Example

$$\begin{aligned}&\text{Maximize} && p = x + y && \text{Objective function}\\ &\text{subject to} && \left.\begin{aligned} x + 2y &\le 12\\ 2x + y &\le 12\\ x \ge 0, y &\ge 0.\end{aligned}\right\} && \text{Constraints}\end{aligned}$$

See Example 1 for a method of solving this LP problem (that is, finding an optimal solution and value).

The set of points (x, y) satisfying all the constraints is the **feasible region** for the problem. Our methods of solving LP problems rely on the following facts:

Fundamental Theorem of Linear Programming

- If an LP problem has optimal solutions, then at least one of these solutions occurs at a corner point of the feasible region.
- Linear programming problems with bounded, nonempty feasible regions always have optimal solutions.

Let's see how we can use this to solve an LP problem, and then we'll discuss why it's true.

EXAMPLE 1 Solving an LP Problem

$$\begin{aligned}&\text{Maximize} && p = x + y\\ &\text{subject to} && x + 2y \le 12\\ & && 2x + y \le 12\\ & && x \ge 0, y \ge 0.\end{aligned}$$

Solution We begin by drawing the feasible region for the problem. We do this using the techniques of Section 5.1, and we get Figure 13.

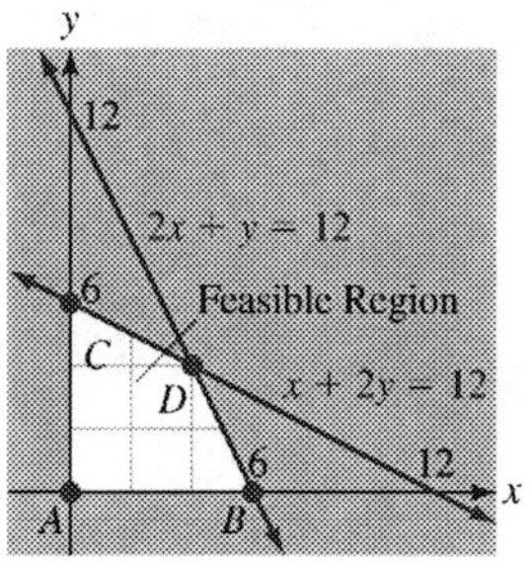

Figure 13

Each **feasible point** (point in the feasible region) gives an x and a y satisfying the constraints. The question now is, which of these points gives the largest value of the objective function $p = x + y$? The Fundamental Theorem of Linear Programming tells us that the largest value must occur at one (or more) of the corners of the feasible region. In the following table, we list the coordinates of each corner point and we compute the value of the objective function at each corner.

Corner Point	*Lines through Point*	*Coordinates*	$p = x + y$
A		(0, 0)	0
B		(6, 0)	6
C		(0, 6)	6
D	$x + 2y = 12$ $2x + y = 12$	(4, 4)	8

Now we simply pick the one that gives the largest value for p, which is D. Therefore, the optimal value of p is 8, and an optimal solution is (4, 4).

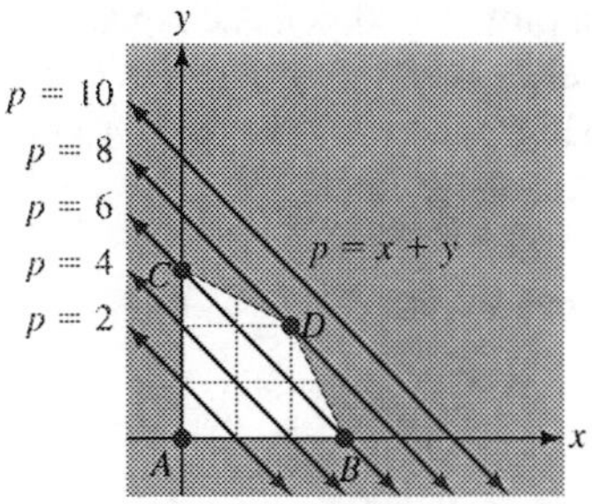

Figure 14

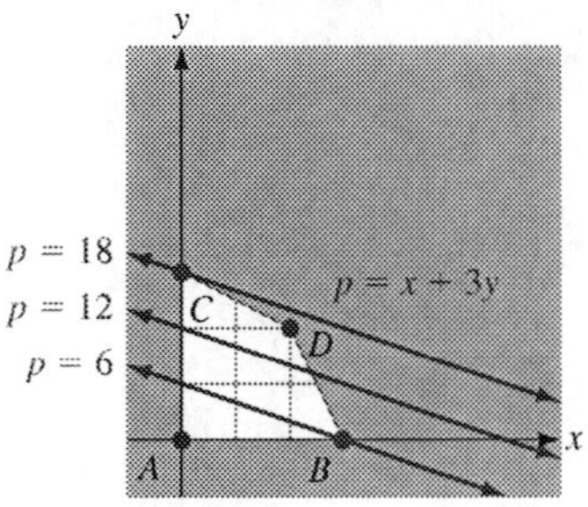

Figure 15

Now we owe you an explanation of why one of the corner points should be an optimal solution. The question is, which point in the feasible region gives the largest possible value of $p = x + y$?

Consider first an easier question: Which points result in a *particular value* of p? For example, which points result in $p = 2$? These would be the points on the line $x + y = 2$, which is the line labeled $p = 2$ in Figure 14.

Now suppose we want to know which points make $p = 4$: These would be the points on the line $x + y = 4$, which is the line labeled $p = 4$ in Figure 14. Notice that this line is parallel to but higher than the line $p = 2$. (If p represented profit in an application, we would call these **isoprofit lines**, or **constant-profit lines**.) Imagine moving this line up or down in the picture. As we move the line down, we see smaller values of p, and as we move it up, we see larger values. Several more of these lines are drawn in Figure 14. Look, in particular, at the line labeled $p = 10$. This line does not meet the feasible region, meaning that no feasible point makes p as large as 10. Starting with the line $p = 2$, as we move the line up, increasing p, there will be a last line that meets the feasible region. In the figure it is clear that this is the line $p = 8$, and this meets the feasible region in only one point, which is the corner point D. Therefore, D gives the greatest value of p of all feasible points.

If we had been asked to maximize some other objective function, such as $p = x + 3y$, then the optimal solution might be different. Figure 15 shows some of the isoprofit lines for this objective function. This time, the last point that is hit as p increases is C, not D. This tells us that the optimal solution is (0, 6), giving the optimal value $p = 18$.

This discussion should convince you that the optimal value in an LP problem will always occur at one of the corner points. By the way, it is possible for the optimal value to occur at *two* corner points and at all points along an edge connecting them. (Do you see why?) We will see this in Example 3(b).

Here is a summary of the method we have just been using.

Graphical Method for Solving Linear Programming Problems in Two Unknowns (Bounded Feasible Regions)

1. Graph the feasible region and check that it is bounded.

2. Compute the coordinates of the corner points.

3. Substitute the coordinates of the corner points into the objective function to see which gives the maximum (or minimum) value of the objective function.

4. Any such corner point is an optimal solution.

Note If the feasible region is unbounded, this method will work only if there are optimal solutions; otherwise, it will not work. We will show you a method for deciding this on page 328. ■

APPLICATIONS

EXAMPLE 2 Resource Allocation

Acme Baby Foods mixes two strengths of apple juice. One quart of Beginner's juice is made from 30 fluid ounces of water and 2 fluid ounces of apple juice concentrate. One quart of Advanced juice is made from 20 fluid ounces of water and 12 fluid ounces of concentrate. Every day Acme has available 30,000 fluid ounces of water and 3,600 fluid ounces of concentrate. Acme makes a profit of 20¢ on each quart of Beginner's juice and 30¢ on each quart of Advanced juice. How many quarts of each should Acme make each day to get the largest profit? How would this change if Acme made a profit of 40¢ on Beginner's juice and 20¢ on Advanced juice?

Solution Looking at the question that we are asked, we see that our unknown quantities are

$$x = \text{number of quarts of Beginner's juice made each day}$$
$$y = \text{number of quarts of Advanced juice made each day.}$$

(In this context, x and y are often called the **decision variables**, because we must decide what their values should be in order to get the largest profit.) We can write down the data given in the form of a table (the numbers in the first two columns are amounts per quart of juice):

	Beginner's, x	*Advanced, y*	*Available*
Water (ounces)	30	20	30,000
Concentrate (ounces)	2	12	3,600
Profit (¢)	20	30	

Because nothing in the problem says that Acme must use up all the water or concentrate, just that it can use no more than what is available, the first two rows of the table give us two inequalities:

$$30x + 20y \le 30{,}000$$
$$2x + 12y \le 3{,}600.$$

Dividing the first inequality by 10 and the second by 2 gives

$$3x + 2y \le 3{,}000$$
$$x + 6y \le 1{,}800.$$

We also have that $x \ge 0$ and $y \ge 0$ because Acme can't make a negative amount of juice. To finish setting up the problem, we are asked to maximize the profit, which is

$$p = 20x + 30y. \qquad \text{Expressed in ¢}$$

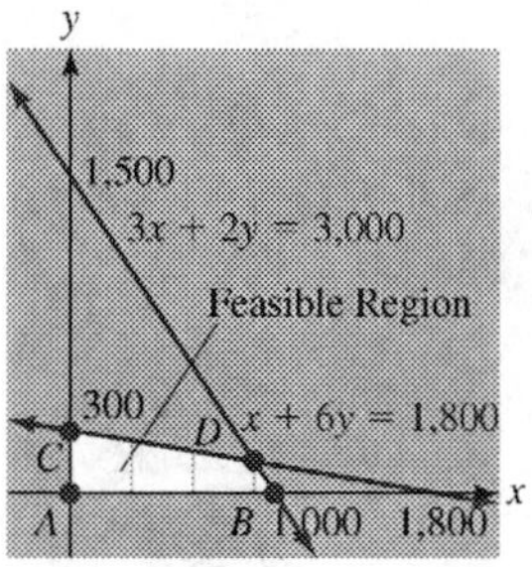

Figure 16

This gives us our LP problem:

$$\begin{aligned} \text{Maximize} \quad & p = 20x + 30y \\ \text{subject to} \quad & 3x + 2y \le 3{,}000 \\ & x + 6y \le 1{,}800 \\ & x \ge 0,\ y \ge 0. \end{aligned}$$

The (bounded) feasible region is shown in Figure 16.

The corners and the values of the objective function are listed in the following table:

Point	*Lines through Point*	*Coordinates*	***p = 20x + 30y***
A		(0, 0)	0
B		(1,000, 0)	20,000
C		(0, 300)	9,000
D	$3x + 2y = 3{,}000$ $x + 6y = 1{,}800$	(900, 150)	22,500

We are seeking to maximize the objective function p, so we look for corner points that give the maximum value for p. Because the maximum occurs at the point D, we conclude that the (only) optimal solution occurs at D. Thus, the company should make 900 quarts of Beginner's juice and 150 quarts of Advanced juice, for a largest possible profit of 22,500¢, or \$225.

If, instead, the company made a profit of 40¢ on each quart of Beginner's juice and 20¢ on each quart of Advanced juice, then we would have $p = 40x + 20y$. This gives the following table:

Point	Lines through Point	Coordinates	$p = 40x + 20y$
A		(0, 0)	0
B		(1,000, 0)	40,000
C		(0, 300)	6,000
D	$3x + 2y = 3{,}000$ $x + 6y = 1{,}800$	(900, 150)	39,000

We can see that, in this case, Acme should make 1,000 quarts of Beginner's juice and no Advanced juice, for a largest possible profit of 40,000¢, or \$400.

Before we go on... Notice that, in the first version of the problem in Example 2, the company used all the water and juice concentrate:

Water: $30(900) + 20(150) = 30{,}000$

Concentrate: $2(900) + 12(150) = 3{,}600.$

In the second version, it used all the water but not all the concentrate:

Water: $30(100) + 20(0) = 30{,}000$

Concentrate: $2(100) + 12(0) = 200 < 3{,}600.$ ■

EXAMPLE 3 Investments

The Solid Trust Savings & Loan Company has set aside \$25 million for loans to home buyers. Its policy is to allocate at least \$10 million annually for luxury condominiums. A government housing development grant it receives requires, however, that at least one third of its total loans be allocated to low-income housing.

a. Solid Trust's return on condominiums is 12% and its return on low-income housing is 10%. How much should the company allocate for each type of housing to maximize its total return?

b. Redo part (a), assuming that the return is 12% on both condominiums and low-income housing.

Solution

a. We first identify the unknowns: Let x be the annual amount (in millions of dollars) allocated to luxury condominiums and let y be the annual amount allocated to low-income housing.

We now look at the constraints. The first constraint is mentioned in the first sentence: The total the company can invest is \$25 million. Thus,

$$x + y \le 25.$$

(The company is not required to invest all of the \$25 million; rather, it can invest *up to* \$25 million.) Next, the company has allocated at least \$10 million to condos. Rephrasing this in terms of the unknowns, we get

The amount allocated to condos is at least \$10 *million.*

The phrase "is at least" means $\geq$. Thus, we obtain a second constraint:

$$x \geq 10.$$

The third constraint is that at least one third of the total financing must be for low-income housing. Rephrasing this, we say:

The amount allocated to low-income housing is at least one third of the total.

Because the total investment will be $x + y$, we get

$$y \geq \frac{1}{3}(x + y).$$

We put this in the standard form of a linear inequality as follows:

$$3y \geq x + y \qquad \text{Multiply both sides by 3.}$$
$$-x + 2y \geq 0. \qquad \text{Subtract } x + y \text{ from both sides.}$$

There are no further constraints.

Now, what about the return on these investments? According to the data, the annual return is given by

$$p = 0.12x + 0.10y.$$

We want to make this quantity p as large as possible. In other words, we want to

$$\begin{aligned} \text{Maximize} \quad & p = 0.12x + 0.10y \\ \text{subject to} \quad & x + y \leq 25 \\ & x \geq 10 \\ & -x + 2y \geq 0 \\ & x \geq 0, y \geq 0. \end{aligned}$$

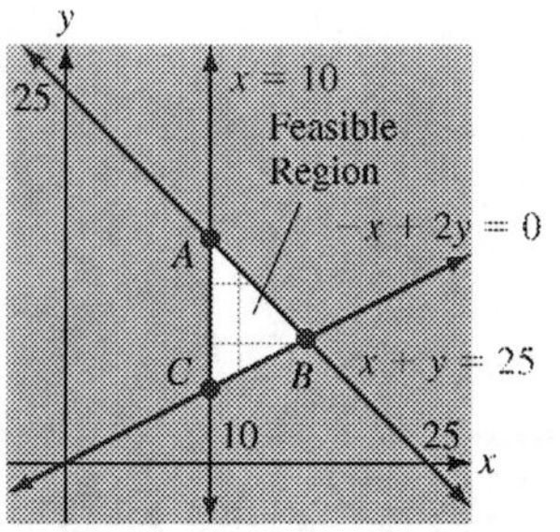

Figure 17

(Do you see why the inequalities $x \geq 0$ and $y \geq 0$ are slipped in here?) The feasible region is shown in Figure 17.

We now make a table that gives the return on investment at each corner point:

Point	*Lines through Point*	*Coordinates*	$p = 0.12x + 0.10y$
A	$x = 10$ $x + y = 25$	(10, 15)	2.7
B	$x + y = 25$ $-x + 2y = 0$	(50/3, 25/3)	2.833
C	$x = 10$ $-x + 2y = 0$	(10, 5)	1.7

From the table, we see that the values of x and y that maximize the return are $x = 50/3$ and $y = 25/3$, which give a total return of \$2.833 million. In other words, the most profitable course of action is to invest \$16.667 million in loans for condominiums and \$8.333 million in loans for low-income housing, giving a maximum annual return of \$2.833 million.

b. The LP problem is the same as for part (a) except for the objective function:

$$\begin{aligned}\text{Maximize}\quad & p = 0.12x + 0.12y\\ \text{subject to}\quad & x + y \le 25\\ & x \ge 10\\ & -x + 2y \ge 0\\ & x \ge 0,\ y \ge 0.\end{aligned}$$

Here are the values of p at the three corners:

Point	*Coordinates*	$p = 0.12x + 0.12y$
A	(10, 15)	3
B	(50/3, 25/3)	3
C	(10, 5)	1.8

Looking at the table, we see that a curious thing has happened: We get the same maximum annual return at both A and B. Thus, we could choose either option to maximize the annual return. In fact, any point along the line segment AB will yield an annual return of \$3 million. For example, the point (12, 13) lies on the line segment AB and also yields an annual revenue of \$3 million. This happens because the "isoreturn" lines are parallel to that edge.

Before we go on... What breakdowns of investments would lead to the *lowest* return for parts (a) and (b)? ■

The preceding examples all had bounded feasible regions. If the feasible region is unbounded, then, *provided there are optimal solutions,* the fundamental theorem of linear programming guarantees that the above method will work. The following procedure determines whether or not optimal solutions exist and finds them when they do.

Solving Linear Programming Problems in Two Unknowns (Unbounded Feasible Regions)

If the feasible region of an LP problem is unbounded, proceed as follows:

1. Draw a rectangle large enough so that all the corner points are inside the rectangle (and not on its boundary):

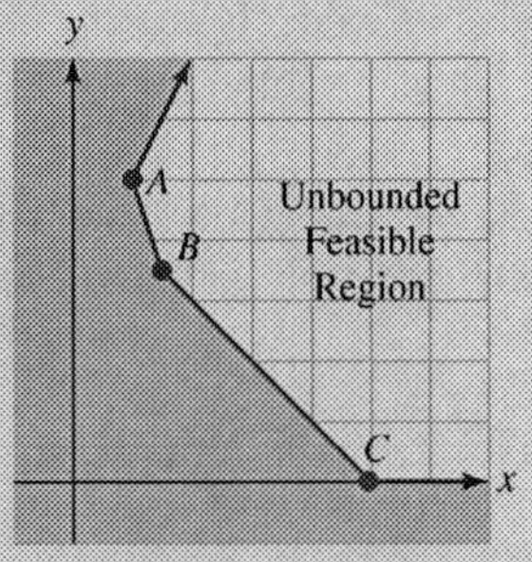

Corner points: A, B, C

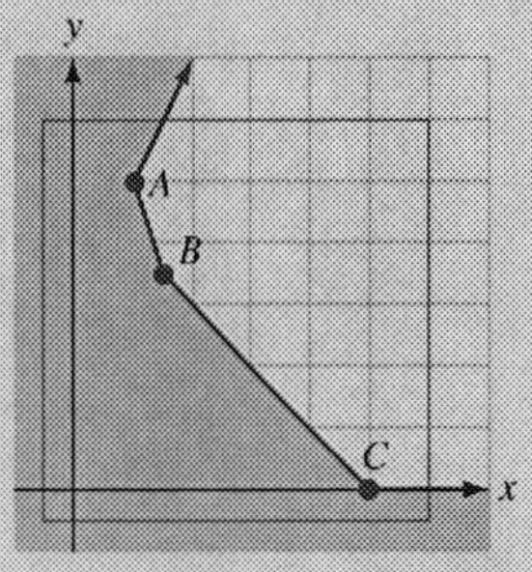

Corner points inside the rectangle

2. Shade the outside of the rectangle so as to define a new bounded feasible region, and locate the new corner points:

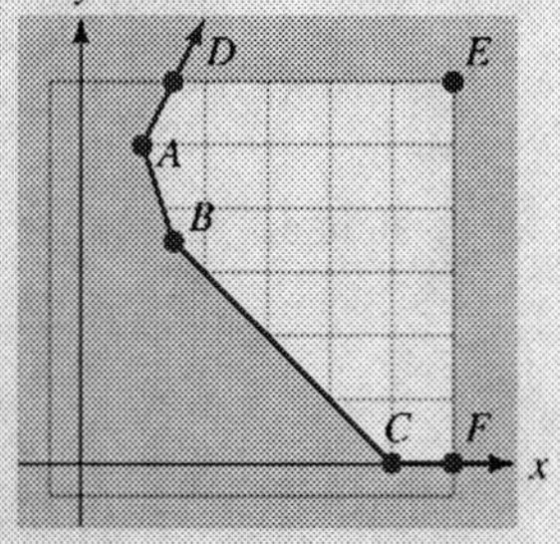

New corner points: D, E, and F

3. Obtain the optimal solutions using this bounded feasible region.
4. If any optimal solutions occur at one of the original corner points (A, B, and C in the figure), then the LP problem has that corner point as an optimal solution. Otherwise, the LP problem has no optimal solutions. When the latter occurs, we say that the **objective function is unbounded,** because it can assume arbitrarily large (positive or negative) values.

In the next two examples, we work with unbounded feasible regions.

EXAMPLE 4 Cost

You are the manager of a small store that specializes in hats, sunglasses, and other accessories. You are considering a sales promotion of a new line of hats and sunglasses. You will offer the sunglasses only to those who purchase two or more hats, so you will sell at least twice as many hats as pairs of sunglasses. Moreover, your supplier tells you that, due to seasonal demand, your order of sunglasses cannot exceed 100 pairs. To ensure that the sale items fill out the large display you have set aside, you estimate that you should order at least 210 items in all.

a. Assume that you will lose \$3 on every hat and \$2 on every pair of sunglasses sold. Given the constraints above, how many hats and pairs of sunglasses should you order to lose the least amount of money in the sales promotion?

b. Suppose instead that you lose \$1 on every hat sold but make a profit of \$5 on every pair of sunglasses sold. How many hats and pairs of sunglasses should you order to make the largest profit in the sales promotion?

c. Now suppose that you make a profit of \$1 on every hat sold but lose \$5 on every pair of sunglasses sold. How many hats and pairs of sunglasses should you order to make the largest profit in the sales promotion?

Solution

a. The unknowns are:

x = number of hats you order
y = number of pairs of sunglasses you order.

The objective is to minimize the total loss:

$$c = 3x + 2y.$$

Now for the constraints. The requirement that you will sell at least twice as many hats as sunglasses can be rephrased as:

The number of hats is at least twice the number of pairs of sunglasses,

or

$$x \geq 2y$$

which, in standard form, is

$$x - 2y \geq 0.$$

Next, your order of sunglasses cannot exceed 100 pairs, so

$$y \leq 100.$$

Finally, you would like to sell at least 210 items in all, giving

$$x + y \geq 210.$$

Thus, the LP problem is the following:

$$\begin{aligned} \text{Minimize} \quad & c = 3x + 2y \\ \text{subject to} \quad & x - 2y \geq 0 \\ & \quad\;\; y \leq 100 \\ & x + \;\, y \geq 210 \\ & x \geq 0, y \geq 0. \end{aligned}$$

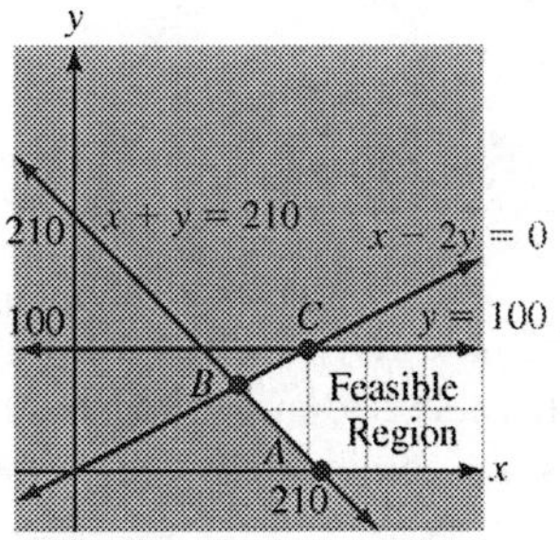

Figure 18

The feasible region is shown in Figure 18. This region is unbounded, so there is no guarantee that there are any optimal solutions. Following the procedure described above, we enclose the corner points in a rectangle as shown in Figure 19. (There are many infinitely many possible rectangles we could have used. We chose one that gives convenient coordinates for the new corners.)

We now list all the corners of this bounded region along with the corresponding values of the objective function c:

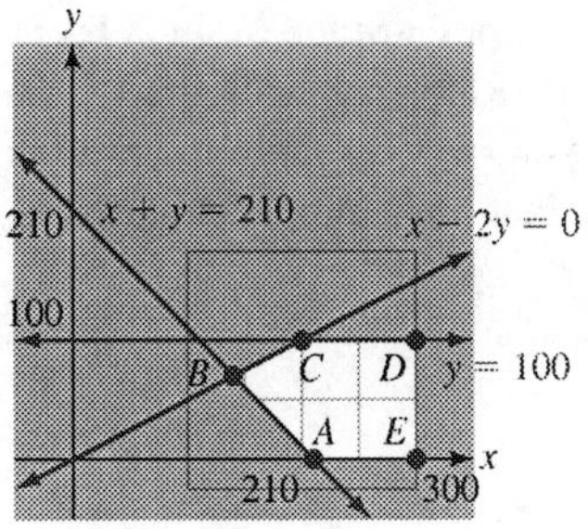

Figure 19

Point	*Lines through Point*	*Coordinates*	$c = 3x + 2y$ (\$)
A		(210, 0)	630
B	$x + y = 210$ $x - 2y = 0$	(140, 70)	560
C	$x - 2y = 0$ $y = 100$	(200, 100)	800
D		(300, 100)	1,100
E		(300, 0)	900

The corner point that gives the minimum value of the objective function c is B. Because B is one of the corner points of the original feasible region, we conclude that our linear programming problem has an optimal solution at B. Thus, the combination that gives the smallest loss is 140 hats and 70 pairs of sunglasses.

b. The LP problem is the following:

$$\begin{aligned} \text{Maximize} \quad & p = -x + 5y \\ \text{subject to} \quad & x - 2y \geq 0 \\ & y \leq 100 \\ & x + y \geq 210 \\ & x \geq 0, y \geq 0. \end{aligned}$$

Because most of the work is already done for us in part (a), all we need to do is change the objective function in the table that lists the corner points:

Point	*Lines through Point*	*Coordinates*	$p = -x + 5y$ (\$)
A		(210, 0)	−210
B	$x + y = 210$ $x - 2y = 0$	(140, 70)	210
C	$x - 2y = 0$ $y = 100$	(200, 100)	300
D		(300, 100)	200
E		(300, 0)	−300

The corner point that gives the maximum value of the objective function p is C. Because C is one of the corner points of the original feasible region, we conclude that our LP problem has an optimal solution at C. Thus, the combination that gives the largest profit (\$300) is 200 hats and 100 pairs of sunglasses.

c. The objective function is now $p = x - 5y$, which is the negative of the objective function used in part (b). Thus, the table of values of p is the same as in part (b), except that it has opposite signs in the p column. This time we find that the maximum value of p occurs at E. However, E is not a corner point of the original feasible region, so the LP problem has no optimal solution. Referring to Figure 18, we can make the objective p as large as we like by choosing a point far to the right in the unbounded feasible region. Thus, the objective function is unbounded; that is, it is possible to make an arbitrarily large profit.

EXAMPLE 5 Resource Allocation

You are composing a very avant-garde ballade for violins and bassoons. In your ballade, each violinist plays a total of two notes and each bassoonist only one note. To make your ballade long enough, you decide that it should contain at least 200 instrumental notes. Furthermore, after playing the requisite two notes, each violinist will sing one soprano note, while each bassoonist will sing three soprano notes.* To make the ballade sufficiently interesting, you have decided on a minimum of 300 soprano notes. To give your composition a sense of balance, you wish to have no more than three times as many bassoonists as violinists. Violinists charge \$200 per performance and bassoonists \$400 per performance. How many of each should your ballade call for in order to minimize personnel costs?

* Whether or not these musicians are capable of singing decent soprano notes will be left to chance. You reason that a few bad notes will add character to the ballade.

Solution First, the unknowns are x = number of violinists and y = number of bassoonists. The constraint on the number of instrumental notes implies that

$$2x + y \geq 200$$

because the total number is to be *at least* 200. Similarly, the constraint on the number of soprano notes is

$$x + 3y \geq 300.$$

The next one is a little tricky. As usual, we reword it in terms of the quantities x and y.

The number of bassoonists should be no more than three times the number of violinists.

Thus, $y \leq 3x$

or $3x - y \geq 0.$

Finally, the total cost per performance will be

$$c = 200x + 400y.$$

We wish to minimize total cost. So, our linear programming problem is as follows:

$$\begin{aligned} \text{Minimize} \quad & c = 200x + 400y \\ \text{subject to} \quad & 2x + y \geq 200 \\ & x + 3y \geq 300 \\ & 3x - y \geq 0 \\ & x \geq 0, y \geq 0. \end{aligned}$$

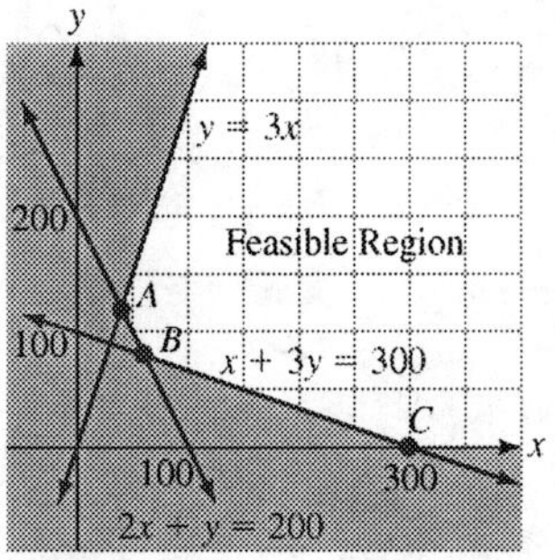

Figure 20

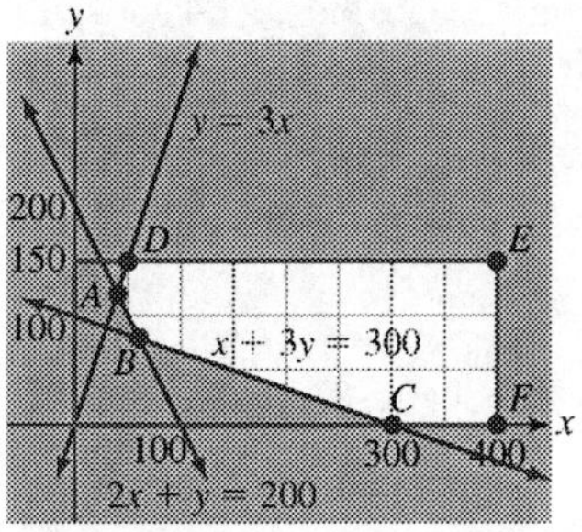

Figure 21

We get the feasible region shown in Figure 20.* The feasible region is unbounded, and so we add a convenient rectangle as before (Figure 21).

* In Figure 20 you can see how graphing technology would help in determining the corner points: Unless you are very confident in the accuracy of your sketch, how do you know that the line $y = 3x$ falls to the left of the point B? If it were to fall to the right, then B would not be a corner point and the solution would be different. You could (and should) check that B satisfies the inequality $3x - y \geq 0$, so that the line falls to the left of B as shown. However, if you use a graphing calculator or computer, you can be fairly confident of the picture produced without doing further calculations.

Point	*Lines through Point*	*Coordinates*	$c = 200x + 400y$
A	$2x + y = 200$ $3x - y = 0$	(40, 120)	56,000
B	$2x + y = 200$ $x + 3y = 300$	(60, 80)	44,000
C		(300, 0)	60,000
D	$3x - y = 0$ $y = 150$	(50, 150)	70,000
E		(400, 150)	140,000
F		(400, 0)	80,000

From the table we see that the minimum cost occurs at B, a corner point of the original feasible region. The linear programming problem thus has an optimal solution, and the minimum cost is $44,000 per performance, employing 60 violinists and 80 bassoonists. (Quite a wasteful ballade, one might say.)

using Technology

Website
www.WanerMath.com
For an online utility that does everything (solves linear programming problems with two unknowns and even draws the feasible region), go to the Website and follow
→ On Line Utilities
→ Linear Programming Grapher.

FAQs

Recognizing a Linear Programming Problem, Setting Up Inequalities, and Dealing with Unbounded Regions

Q: *How do I recognize when an application leads to an LP problem as opposed to a system of linear equations?*

A: Here are some cues that suggest an LP problem:

- Key phrases suggesting inequalities rather than equalities, like *at most, up to, no more than, at least,* and *or more.*
- A quantity that is being maximized or minimized (this will be the objective). Key phrases are *maximum, minimum, most, least, largest, greatest, smallest, as large as possible,* and *as small as possible.*

Q: *How do I deal with tricky phrases like "there should be no more than twice as many nuts as bolts" or "at least 50% of the total should be bolts"?*

A: The easiest way to deal with phrases like this is to use the technique we discussed in Chapter 3: reword the phrases using "the number of . . . ", as in

The number of nuts (x) is no more than twice the number of bolts (y)	$x \le 2y$
The number of bolts is at least 50% of the total	$y \ge 0.50(x + y)$

Q: *Do I always have to add a rectangle to deal with unbounded regions?*

A: Under some circumstances, you can tell right away whether optimal solutions exist, even when the feasible region is unbounded.

Note that the following apply only when we have the constraints $x \ge 0$ and $y \ge 0$.

1. If you are minimizing $c = ax + by$ with a and b nonnegative, then optimal solutions always exist. (Examples 4(a) and 5 are of this type.)
2. If you are maximizing $p = ax + by$ with a and b nonnegative (and not both zero), then there is no optimal solution unless the feasible region is bounded.

Do you see why statements (1) and (2) are true?

5.2 EXERCISES

▼ more advanced ◆ challenging
T indicates exercises that should be solved using technology

In Exercises 1–20, solve the LP problems. If no optimal solution exists, indicate whether the feasible region is empty or the objective function is unbounded. HINT [See Example 1.]

1. Maximize $p = x + y$
subject to $x + 2y \le 9$
$2x + y \le 9$
$x \ge 0, y \ge 0.$

2. Maximize $p = x + 2y$
subject to $x + 3y \le 24$
$2x + y \le 18$
$x \ge 0, y \ge 0.$

3. Minimize $c = x + y$
subject to $x + 2y \ge 6$
$2x + y \ge 6$
$x \ge 0, y \ge 0.$

4. Minimize $c = x + 2y$
subject to $x + 3y \ge 30$
$2x + y \ge 30$
$x \ge 0, y \ge 0.$

5. Maximize $p = 3x + y$
subject to $3x - 7y \le 0$
$7x - 3y \ge 0$
$x + y \le 10$
$x \ge 0, y \ge 0.$

6. Maximize $p = x - 2y$
subject to $x + 2y \le 8$
$x - 6y \le 0$
$3x - 2y \ge 0$
$x \ge 0, y \ge 0.$

7. Maximize $p = 3x + 2y$
subject to
$0.2x + 0.1y \le 1$
$0.15x + 0.3y \le 1.5$
$10x + 10y \le 60$
$x \ge 0, y \ge 0.$

8. Maximize $p = x + 2y$
subject to
$30x + 20y \le 600$
$0.1x + 0.4y \le 4$
$0.2x + 0.3y \le 4.5$
$x \ge 0, y \ge 0.$

9. Minimize $c = 0.2x + 0.3y$
subject to
$0.2x + 0.1y \ge 1$
$0.15x + 0.3y \ge 1.5$
$10x + 10y \ge 80$
$x \ge 0, y \ge 0.$

10. Minimize $c = 0.4x + 0.1y$
subject to
$30x + 20y \ge 600$
$0.1x + 0.4y \ge 4$
$0.2x + 0.3y \ge 4.5$
$x \ge 0, y \ge 0.$

11. Maximize and minimize $p = x + 2y$
subject to
$x + y \ge 2$
$x + y \le 10$
$x - y \le 2$
$x - y \ge -2.$

12. Maximize and minimize $p = 2x - y$
subject to
$x + y \ge 2$
$x - y \le 2$
$x - y \ge -2$
$x \le 10, y \le 10.$

13. Maximize $p = 2x + 3y$
subject to
$0.1x + 0.2y \ge 1$
$2x + y \ge 10$
$x \ge 0, y \ge 0.$

14. Maximize $p = 3x + 2y$
subject to
$0.1x + 0.1y \ge 0.2$
$y \le 10$
$x \ge 0, y \ge 0.$

15. Minimize $c = 2x + 4y$
subject to
$0.1x + 0.1y \ge 1$
$x + 2y \ge 14$
$x \ge 0, y \ge 0.$

16. Maximize $p = 2x + 3y$
subject to
$-x + y \ge 10$
$x + 2y \le 12$
$x \ge 0, y \ge 0.$

17. Minimize $c = 3x - 3y$
subject to
$\frac{x}{4} \le y$
$y \le \frac{2x}{3}$
$x + y \ge 5$
$x + 2y \le 10$
$x \ge 0, y \ge 0.$

18. Minimize $c = -x + 2y$
subject to
$y \le \frac{2x}{3}$
$x \le 3y$
$y \ge 4$
$x \ge 6$
$x + y \le 16.$

19. Maximize $p = x + y$
subject to
$x + 2y \ge 10$
$2x + 2y \le 10$
$2x + y \ge 10$
$x \ge 0, y \ge 0.$

20. Minimize $c = 3x + y$
subject to
$10x + 20y \ge 100$
$0.3x + 0.1y \ge 1$
$x \ge 0, y \ge 0.$

APPLICATIONS

21. ***Resource Allocation*** You manage an ice cream factory that makes two flavors: Creamy Vanilla and Continental Mocha. Into each quart of Creamy Vanilla go 2 eggs and 3 cups of cream. Into each quart of Continental Mocha go 1 egg and 3 cups of cream. You have in stock 500 eggs and 900 cups of cream. You make a profit of \$3 on each quart of Creamy Vanilla and \$2 on each quart of Continental Mocha. How many quarts of each flavor should you make in order to earn the largest profit? HINT [See Example 2.]

22. ***Resource Allocation*** Podunk Institute of Technology's Math Department offers two courses: Finite Math and Applied Calculus. Each section of Finite Math has 60 students, and each section of Applied Calculus has 50. The department is allowed to offer a total of up to 110 sections. Furthermore, no more than 6,000 students want to take a math course (no student will take more than one math course). Suppose the university makes a profit of \$100,000 on each section of Finite Math and \$50,000 on each section of Applied Calculus (the profit is the difference between what the students are charged and what the professors are paid). How many sections of each course should the department offer to make the largest profit? HINT [See Example 2.]

23. ***Nutrition*** *Ruff, Inc.* makes dog food out of chicken and grain. Chicken has 10 grams of protein and 5 grams of fat per ounce, and grain has 2 grams of protein and 2 grams of fat per ounce. A bag of dog food must contain at least 200 grams of protein and at least 150 grams of fat. If chicken costs 10¢ per ounce and grain costs 1¢ per ounce, how many ounces of each should Ruff use in each bag of dog food in order to minimize cost? HINT [See Example 4.]

24. ***Purchasing*** Enormous State University's Business School is buying computers. The school has two models from which to choose, the Pomegranate and the iZac. Each Pomegranate comes with 400 GB of memory and 80 TB of disk space; each iZac has 300 GB of memory and 100 TB of disk space. For reasons related to its accreditation, the school would like to be able to say that it has a total of at least 48,000 GB of memory and at least 12,800 TB of disk space. If the Pomegranate and the iZac cost $2,000 each, how many of each should the school buy to keep the cost as low as possible? HINT [See Example 4.]

25. ***Nutrition*** Gerber Products' Gerber Mixed Cereal for Baby contains, in each serving, 60 calories and 11 grams of carbohydrates. Gerber Mango Tropical Fruit Dessert contains, in each serving, 80 calories and 21 grams of carbohydrates.[11] If the cereal costs 30¢ per serving and the dessert costs 50¢ per serving, and you want to provide your child with at least 140 calories and at least 32 grams of carbohydrates, how can you do so at the least cost? (Fractions of servings are permitted.)

26. ***Nutrition*** Gerber Products' Gerber Mixed Cereal for Baby contains, in each serving, 60 calories, 10 grams of carbohydrates, and no Vitamin C. Gerber Apple Banana Juice contains, in each serving, 60 calories, 15 grams of carbohydrates, and 120% of the U.S. Recommended Daily Allowance (RDA) of Vitamin C for infants.[12] The cereal costs 10¢ per serving and the juice costs 30¢ per serving. If you want to provide your child with at least 120 calories, at least 25 grams of carbohydrates, and at least 60% of the U.S. RDA of Vitamin C for infants, how can you do so at the least cost? (Fractions of servings are permitted.)

27. ***Energy Efficiency*** You are thinking of making your home more energy efficient by replacing some of the light bulbs with compact fluorescent bulbs, and insulating part or all of your exterior walls. Each compact fluorescent light bulb costs $4 and saves you an average of $2 per year in energy costs, and each square foot of wall insulation costs $1 and saves you an average of $0.20 per year in energy costs.[13] Your home has 60 light fittings and 1,100 sq. ft. of uninsulated exterior wall. You can spend no more than $1,200 and would like to save as much per year in energy costs as possible. How many compact fluorescent light bulbs and how many square feet of insulation should you purchase? How much will you save in energy costs per year?

28. ***Energy Efficiency*** (Compare with the preceding exercise.) You are thinking of making your mansion more energy efficient by replacing some of the light bulbs with compact fluorescent bulbs, and insulating part or all of your exterior walls. Each compact fluorescent light bulb costs $4 and saves you an average of $2 per year in energy costs, and each square foot of wall insulation costs $1 and saves you an average of $0.20 per year in energy costs.[14] Your mansion has 200 light fittings and 3,000 sq. ft. of uninsulated exterior wall. To impress your friends, you would like to spend as much as possible, but save no more than $800 per year in energy costs (you are proud of your large utility bills). How many compact fluorescent light bulbs and how many square feet of insulation should you purchase? How much will you save in energy costs per year?

Bodybuilding Supplements *Exercises 29 and 30 are based on the following data on three bodybuilding supplements. (Figures shown correspond to a single serving.)*[15]

	Creatine (g)	*Carbohydrates (g)*	*Taurine (g)*	*Alpha Lipoic Acid (mg)*	*Cost ($)*
Cell-Tech® (MuscleTech)	10	75	2	200	2.20
RiboForce HP® (EAS)	5	15	1	0	1.60
Creatine Transport® (Kaizen)	5	35	1	100	0.60

29. You are thinking of combining Cell-Tech and RiboForce HP to obtain a 10-day supply that provides at least 80 grams of creatine and at least 10 grams of taurine, but no more than 750 grams of carbohydrates and no more than 1,000 milligrams of alpha lipoic acid. How many servings of each supplement should you combine to meet your specifications at the least cost?

30. You are thinking of combining Cell-Tech and Creatine Transport to obtain a 10-day supply that provides at least 80 grams of creatine and at least 10 grams of taurine, but no more than 600 grams of carbohydrates and no more than 2,000 milligrams of alpha lipoic acid. How many servings of each supplement should you combine to meet your specifications at the least cost?

31. ***Resource Allocation*** Your salami manufacturing plant can order up to 1,000 pounds of pork and 2,400 pounds of beef per day for use in manufacturing its two specialties: "Count Dracula Salami" and "Frankenstein Sausage." Production of the Count Dracula variety requires 1 pound of pork and

[11] Source: Nutrition information supplied with the products.

[12] *Ibid.*

[13] Source: American Council for an Energy-Efficient Economy/*New York Times*, December 1, 2003, p. C6.

[14] *Ibid.*

[15] Source: Nutritional information supplied by the manufacturers (www.netrition.com). Cost per serving is approximate and varies.

3 pounds of beef for each salami, while the Frankenstein variety requires 2 pounds of pork and 2 pounds of beef for every sausage. In view of your heavy investment in advertising Count Dracula Salami, you have decided that at least one-third of the total production should be Count Dracula. On the other hand, due to the health-conscious consumer climate, your Frankenstein Sausage (sold as having less beef) is earning your company a profit of $3 per sausage, while sales of the Count Dracula variety are down and it is earning your company only $1 per salami. Given these restrictions, how many of each kind of sausage should you produce to maximize profits, and what is the maximum possible profit? HINT [See Example 3.]

32. *Project Design* The *Megabuck Hospital Corp.* is to build a state-subsidized nursing home catering to homeless patients as well as high-income patients. State regulations require that every subsidized nursing home must house a minimum of 1,000 homeless patients and no more than 750 high-income patients in order to qualify for state subsidies. The overall capacity of the hospital is to be 2,100 patients. The board of directors, under pressure from a neighborhood group, insists that the number of homeless patients should not exceed twice the number of high-income patients. Due to the state subsidy, the hospital will make an average profit of $10,000 per month for every homeless patient it houses, whereas the profit per high-income patient is estimated at $8,000 per month. How many of each type of patient should it house in order to maximize profit? HINT [See Example 3.]

33. *Television Advertising* Each Monday evening in August 2011, each episode of *WWE Raw* was typically watched by 1.8 million viewers, while each episode of *Family Guy* was typically watched by 1.5 million viewers.[16] Your marketing services firm has been hired to promote *Bald No More's* hair replacement process by buying at least 30 commercial spots during episodes of *WWE Raw* and *Family Guy*. You have been quoted a price of $3,000 per spot for *WWE Raw* and $1,000 per spot for *Family Guy*. Bald No More's advertising budget for TV commercials is $120,000, and, because of the company president's fondness for wrestling, it would like no more than 50% of the total number of spots to appear on *Family Guy*. How many spots should you purchase on each show to maximize exposure? HINT [Calculate exposure as Number of ads × Number of viewers.]

34. *Television Advertising* Each Friday evening in August 2011, each episode of *Family Guy* was typically watched by 1.3 million viewers, while each episode of *American Dad* was typically watched by 0.9 million viewers.[17] Your marketing services firm has been hired to promote *Gauss Jordan* Sneakers by buying at least 30 commercial spots during episodes of *Family Guy* and *American Dad*. You have been quoted a price of $2,000 per spot for *Family Guy* and $3,000 per spot for *American Dad*. Gauss Jordan Inc.'s advertising budget for TV commercials is $70,000, and it would like at

least 75% of the total number of spots to appear on *Family Guy*. How many spots should you purchase on each show to maximize exposure? HINT [Calculate exposure as Number of ads × Number of viewers.]

Investing Exercises 35 and 36 are based on the following data on four stocks.[18]

	Price	Dividend Yield	52-Week Price Change ($)
FDX (FedEx)	$90	1%	−1.9
WU (Western Union)	20	2%	0.61
DO (Diamond Offshore Drilling)	70	0%	5.5
WERN (Werner Enterprises)	25	1%	3.6

35. ▼ You are planning to invest up to $10,000 in FDX and WU shares. You want your investment to yield at least $120 in dividends, and, for tax reasons, you want to minimize the 52-week gain (or maximize the loss) in the total value of the shares. How many shares of each company should you purchase? (Fractions of shares permitted.)

36. ▼ You are planning to invest up to $43,000 in DO and WERN shares. For tax reasons, you want your investment to yield no more than $10 in dividends. You want to maximize the 52-week gain in the total value of the shares. How many shares of each company should you purchase? (Fractions of shares permitted.)

37. ▼ *Investments: Financial Stocks* (Compare Exercise 41 in Section 5.1.) In August 2011, Bank of Hawaii (BOH) stock cost $45 per share, yielded 4% per year in dividends, and had a risk index of 3.0 per share, while JPMorgan Chase (JPM) stock cost $40 per share, yielded 2.5% per year in dividends, and had a risk index of 2.0 per share.[19] You have up to $25,000 to invest in these stocks, and would like to earn at least $760 in dividends over the course of a year. (Assume the dividend to be unchanged for the year.) How many shares (to the nearest tenth of a unit) of each stock should you purchase to meet your requirements and minimize the total risk index for your portfolio? What is the minimum total risk index?

38. ▼ *Investments: Utility Stocks* (Compare Exercise 42 in Section 5.1.) In April 2011, Consolidated Edison (ED) stock cost $50 per share, yielded 5% per year in dividends, and had a risk index of 2.0, while National Grid (NGG) stock cost $50 per share, yielded 6% per year in dividends, and had a risk index of 3.0.[20] You have up to $45,000 to invest in

---

[16]Ratings are for August 29, 2011. Source: Nielsen Media Research/ www.tvbythenumbers.com

[17]*Ibid.*

[18]Approximate 150-day average price as of August 31, 2011. 52-week price changes are approximate. Source: http://finance.google.com

[19]Stock prices and yields are approximate, and risk indices are fictitious. Source: http://finance.google.com

[20]*Ibid.*

these stocks, and would like to earn at least $2,400 in dividends over the course of a year. (Assume the dividend to be unchanged for the year.) How many shares of each stock should you purchase to meet your requirements and minimize the total risk index for your portfolio? What is the minimum total risk index?

39. ▼ ***Planning*** My friends: I, the mighty Brutus, have decided to prepare for retirement by instructing young warriors in the arts of battle and diplomacy. For each hour spent in battle instruction, I have decided to charge 50 ducats. For each hour in diplomacy instruction I shall charge 40 ducats. Due to my advancing years, I can spend no more than 50 hours per week instructing the youths, although the great Jove knows that they are sorely in need of instruction! Due to my fondness for physical pursuits, I have decided to spend no more than one third of the total time in diplomatic instruction. However, the present border crisis with the Gauls is a sore indication of our poor abilities as diplomats. As a result, I have decided to spend at least 10 hours per week instructing in diplomacy. Finally, to complicate things further, there is the matter of Scarlet Brew: I have estimated that each hour of battle instruction will require 10 gallons of Scarlet Brew to quench my students' thirst, and that each hour of diplomacy instruction, being less physically demanding, requires half that amount. Because my harvest of red berries has far exceeded my expectations, I estimate that I'll have to use at least 400 gallons per week in order to avoid storing the fine brew at great expense. Given all these restrictions, how many hours per week should I spend in each type of instruction to maximize my income?

40. ▼ ***Planning*** Repeat the preceding exercise with the following changes: I would like to spend no more than half the total time in diplomatic instruction, and I must use at least 600 gallons of Scarlet Brew.

41. ▼ ***Resource Allocation*** One day, Gillian the magician summoned the wisest of her women. "Devoted followers," she began, "I have a quandary: As you well know, I possess great expertise in sleep spells and shock spells, but unfortunately, these are proving to be a drain on my aural energy resources; each sleep spell costs me 500 pico-shirleys of aural energy, while each shock spell requires 750 pico-shirleys. Clearly, I would like to hold my overall expenditure of aural energy to a minimum, and still meet my commitments in protecting the Sisterhood from the ever-present threat of trolls. Specifically, I have estimated that each sleep spell keeps us safe for an average of two minutes, while every shock spell protects us for about three minutes. We certainly require enough protection to last 24 hours of each day, and possibly more, just to be safe. At the same time, I have noticed that each of my sleep spells can immobilize three trolls at once, while one of my typical shock spells (having a narrower range) can immobilize only two trolls at once. We are faced, my sisters, with an onslaught of 1,200 trolls per day! Finally, as you are no doubt aware, the bylaws dictate that for a Magician of the Order to remain in good standing, the number of shock spells must be between one quarter and one third the number of shock and sleep spells combined. What do I do, oh Wise Ones?"

42. ▼ ***Risk Management*** The Grand Vizier of the Kingdom of Um is being blackmailed by numerous individuals and is having a very difficult time keeping his blackmailers from going public. He has been keeping them at bay with two kinds of payoff: gold bars from the Royal Treasury and political favors. Through bitter experience, he has learned that each payoff in gold gives him peace for an average of about 1 month, while each political favor seems to earn him about a month and a half of reprieve. To maintain his flawless reputation in the Court, he feels he cannot afford any revelations about his tainted past to come to light within the next year. Thus it is imperative that his blackmailers be kept at bay for 12 months. Furthermore, he would like to keep the number of gold payoffs at no more than one quarter of the combined number of payoffs because the outward flow of gold bars might arouse suspicion on the part of the Royal Treasurer. The Grand Vizier feels that he can do no more than seven political favors per year without arousing undue suspicion in the Court. The gold payoffs tend to deplete his travel budget. (The treasury has been subsidizing his numerous trips to the Himalayas.) He estimates that each gold bar removed from the treasury will cost him four trips. On the other hand, because the administering of political favors tends to cost him valuable travel time, he suspects that each political favor will cost him about two trips. Now, he would obviously like to keep his blackmailers silenced and lose as few trips as possible. What is he to do? How many trips will he lose in the next year?

43. ◆ ***Management***[21] You are the service manager for a supplier of closed-circuit television systems. Your company can provide up to 160 hours per week of technical service for your customers, although the demand for technical service far exceeds this amount. As a result, you have been asked to develop a model to allocate service technicians' time between new customers (those still covered by service contracts) and old customers (whose service contracts have expired). To ensure that new customers are satisfied with your company's service, the sales department has instituted a policy that at least 100 hours per week be allocated to servicing new customers. At the same time, your superiors have informed you that the company expects your department to generate at least $1,200 per week in revenues. Technical service time for new customers generates an average of $10 per hour (because much of the service is still under warranty) and for old customers generates $30 per hour. How many hours per week should you allocate to each type of customer to generate the most revenue?

[21] Loosely based on a similiar problem in *An Introduction to Management Science* (6th Ed.) by D. R. Anderson, D. J. Sweeney, and T. A. Williams (West, 1991).

44. ◆ ***Scheduling***[22] The *Scottsville Textile Mill* produces several different fabrics on eight dobby looms which operate 24 hours per day and are scheduled for 30 days in the coming month. The Scottsville Textile Mill will produce only Fabric 1 and Fabric 2 during the coming month. Each dobby loom can turn out 4.63 yards of either fabric per hour. Assume that there is a monthly demand of 16,000 yards of Fabric 1 and 12,000 yards of Fabric 2. Profits are calculated as 33¢ per yard for each fabric produced on the dobby looms.

   a. Will it be possible to satisfy total demand?

   b. In the event that total demand is not satisfied, the Scottsville Textile Mill will need to purchase the fabrics from another mill to make up the shortfall. Its profits on resold fabrics ordered from another mill amount to 20¢ per yard for Fabric 1 and 16¢ per yard for Fabric 2. How many yards of each fabric should it produce to maximize profits?

COMMUNICATION AND REASONING EXERCISES

45. If a linear programming problem has a bounded, nonempty feasible region, then optimal solutions

   (A) must exist **(B)** may or may not exist

   (C) cannot exist

46. If a linear programming problem has an unbounded, nonempty feasible region, then optimal solutions

   (A) must exist **(B)** may or may not exist

   (C) cannot exist

47. What can you say if the optimal value occurs at two adjacent corner points?

48. Describe at least one drawback to using the graphical method to solve a linear programming problem arising from a real-life situation.

49. Create a linear programming problem in two variables that has no optimal solution.

[22]Adapted from *The Calhoun Textile Mill Case* by J. D. Camm, P. M. Dearing, and S. K. Tadisina as presented for case study in *An Introduction to Management Science* (6th Ed.) by D. R. Anderson, D. J. Sweeney, and T. A. Williams (West, 1991). Our exercise uses a subset of the data given in the cited study.

50. Create a linear programming problem in two variables that has more than one optimal solution.

51. Create an interesting scenario leading to the following linear programming problem:

$$\begin{aligned} \text{Maximize} \quad & p = 10x + 10y \\ \text{subject to} \quad & 20x + 40y \le 1{,}000 \\ & 30x + 20y \le 1{,}200 \\ & x \ge 0,\ y \ge 0. \end{aligned}$$

52. Create an interesting scenario leading to the following linear programming problem:

$$\begin{aligned} \text{Minimize} \quad & c = 10x + 10y \\ \text{subject to} \quad & 20x + 40y \ge 1{,}000 \\ & 30x + 20y \ge 1{,}200 \\ & x \ge 0,\ y \ge 0. \end{aligned}$$

53. ▼ Use an example to show why there may be no optimal solution to a linear programming problem if the feasible region is unbounded.

54. ▼ Use an example to illustrate why, in the event that an optimal solution does occur despite an unbounded feasible region, that solution corresponds to a corner point of the feasible region.

55. ▼ You are setting up an LP problem for Fly-by-Night Airlines with the unknowns x and y, where x represents the number of first-class tickets it should issue for a specific flight and y represents the number of business-class tickets it should issue for that flight, and the problem is to maximize profit. You find that there are two different corner points that maximize the profit. How do you interpret this?

56. ▼ In the situation described in the preceding exercise, you find that there are no optimal solutions. How do you interpret this?

57. ◆ Consider the following example of a *nonlinear* programming problem: Maximize $p = xy$ subject to $x \ge 0$, $y \ge 0$, $x + y \le 2$. Show that p is zero on every corner point, but is greater than zero at many non-corner points.

58. ◆ Solve the nonlinear programming problem in Exercise 57.

Practice Problems 5.2, Part 1

Carl's Cacophonous Coffee sells two blends of coffee beans, Crunchy Blend and Calamitous Blend. Crunchy blend is one-half Colombian beans and on-half Kona beans. Calamitous Blend is one-quarter Colombian beans and three-quarters Kona beans. Profit on the Crunch Blend is $2 per pound, while profit on Calamitous Blend is $3 per pound. Each day, the shop can obtain 200 pounds of Colombian beans and 60 pounds of Kona beans. Suppose that the shop can sell all of the coffee blends it can make each day, and wishes to determine how much of each type of blend to produce daily to maximize profit.

1. Give the objective function for the linear programming problem. Declare what variables represent, and indicate if you are to maximize or minimize the objective function.

2. Write all constraints for this linear programming problem.

3. Sketch the feasible region for the system of constraints. Label all corner points with exact coordinates.

Practice Problems 5.2, Part 2

The Mathematics Association of the Dakotas (MAD) is planning a three-day conference. The committee organizing the conference will need 15 laptops for the first day, 28 for the second day, and 19 for the third day. The host of the event will rent laptops for a single day for $17, but will only charge $30 if the machine is to be used two consecutive days. The organizers of the MAD conference wish to determine how many laptops to rent for a single day and how many to rent for two days in order to minimize the total rental costs for the conference.

1. Give the objective function for the linear programming problem. Declare what variables represent, and indicate if you are to maximize or minimize the objective function.

2. Write all constraints for this linear programming problem.

3. Sketch the feasible region for the system of constraints. Label all corner points with exact coordinates.

Practice Problems 5.2, Part 3

When Robin retires in a few months, she will receive a pension payment of $200,000 from her employer. She wishes to invest as much as $120,000 of this payment in two different mutual funds. One fund is called a guaranteed income fund and the other is called a growth fund. The guaranteed income fund is expected to generate an annual return of 3%, while the growth fund is expected to generate an annual return of 9%. Because of the risk factors involved in each fund, she wishes to have at least three times as much money invested in the guaranteed income fund as in the growth fund. Robin wishes to know how much of her retirement payment of to allocate to the guaranteed income fund and how much to allocate to the growth fund in order to maximize her expected annual return. You are to set up a linear program to model the problem.

1. Give the objective function for the linear programming problem. Declare what variables represent, and indicate if you are to maximize or minimize the objective function.

2. Write all constraints for this linear programming problem.

3. Sketch the feasible region for the system of constraints. Label all corner points with exact coordinates.

Practice Problems 5.2, Part 4

Consider the objective function

$$H = 8x + 12y$$

subject to the constraints

$$2x + 10y \leq 80$$

$$6x + 2y \leq 72$$

$$3x + 2y \geq 6$$

$$x \geq 0, y \geq 0$$

1. Sketch the feasible region and label all corner points with exact coordinates.

2. Find the maximum and minimum values of H subject to the given constraints. If you believe one of those values does not exist, explain why.

Practice Problems 5.2, Part 5

1. Maximize and minimize

$$z = 2x + 9y$$

on the feasible region shown to the right. Assume that gridlines each mark one unit.

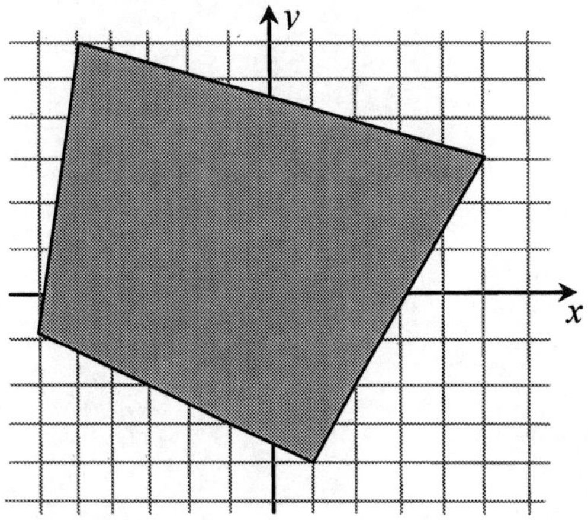

2. Give an example of a linear programming problem (with two variables) such that the objective function has a minimum value but not a maximum value. Besides showing your objective function and all constraints, sketch a graph of the feasible region.

Practice Problems 5.2, Part 6

Frank jogs, plays handball, and swims at the athletic club. Jogging burns 18 calories per minute, handball burns 12 calories per minute, and swimming burns 10 calories per minute. He always swims for at least 30 minutes and plays handball at least twice as long as he jogs. Frank is wondering about two things.

1. If he only has 90 minutes to exercise, how long should he participate in each activity in order to maximize the number of calories burned? Write an objective function and all constraints for this linear programming problem. Declare what all variables represent. Note that you don't actually have to solve the problem.

2. How long should he participate in each activity to burn at least 900 calories in the least amount of time? Write an objective function and all constraints for this linear programming problem. Declare what all variables represent. Note that you don't actually have to solve the problem.

Practice Problems 5.2, Part 7

A catering service produces two types of pasta salad. The first type is 50% carbohydrates, 30% protein, and 20% fat. The second type is 75% carbohydrates, 20% protein, and 5% fat. The first type of salad costs $2.00 per pound to produce and the second type costs $2.50 per pound to produce. Suppose that an order is put in to create a combination of the two types of pasta salad that provides at least 3 pounds of carbohydrates, 1.5 pounds of protein, and 0.5 grams of fat in the most economical way. You are to determine how many pounds of each type of salad are necessary to accomplish this goal.

1. Write an objective function and all constraints for this linear programming problem. Declare what variables represent, and indicate if you are to maximize or minimize the objective function.

2. Sketch the appropriate feasible region, label all corner points with exact coordinates, and solve the linear program. State your conclusion in a complete sentence.

5.3 The Simplex Method: Solving Standard Maximization Problems

The method discussed in Section 5.2 works quite well for LP problems in two unknowns, but what about three or more unknowns? Because we need an axis for each unknown, we would need to draw graphs in three dimensions (where we have x-, y-, and z-coordinates) to deal with problems in three unknowns, and we would have to draw in hyperspace to answer questions involving four or more unknowns. Given the state of technology as this book is being written, we can't easily do this. So we need another method for solving LP problems that will work for any number of unknowns. One such method, called the **simplex method**, has been the method of choice since it was invented by George Dantzig in 1947. (See the Introduction to this chapter for more about Dantzig.) To illustrate it best, we first use it to solve only so-called standard maximization problems.

General Linear Programming Problem

A **linear programming problem in *n* unknowns** $x_1, x_2, \ldots, x_n$ is one in which we are to find the maximum or minimum value of a linear **objective function**

$$a_1x_1 + a_2x_2 + \cdots + a_nx_n,$$

where $a_1, a_2, \ldots, a_n$ are numbers, subject to a number of linear **constraints** of the form

$$b_1x_1 + b_2x_2 + \cdots + b_nx_n \le c \quad \text{or} \quad b_1x_1 + b_2x_2 + \cdots + b_nx_n \ge c,$$

where $b_1, b_2, \ldots, b_n, c$ are numbers.

Standard Maximization Problem

A **standard maximization problem** is an LP problem in which we are required to *maximize* (not minimize) an objective function of the form

$$p = a_1x_1 + a_2x_2 + \cdots + a_nx_n$$

subject to the constraints

$$x_1 \ge 0, x_2 \ge 0, \ldots, x_n \ge 0$$

and further constraints of the form

$$b_1x_1 + b_2x_2 + \cdots + b_nx_n \le c$$

with c *nonnegative*. It is important that the inequality here be $\le$, *not* $=$ or $\ge$.

Note As in the chapter on linear equations, we will almost always use $x, y, z, \ldots$ for the unknowns. Subscripted variables $x_1, x_2, \ldots$ are very useful names when you start running out of letters of the alphabet, but we should not find ourselves in that predicament. ■

Quick Examples

1. Maximize $p = 2x - 3y + 3z$
   subject to
   $$\begin{aligned} 2x \quad\quad + z &\le 7 \\ -x + 3y - 6z &\le 6 \\ x \ge 0, y \ge 0, z &\ge 0. \end{aligned}$$
   This is a standard maximization problem.

2. Maximize $p = 2x_1 + x_2 - x_3 + x_4$
   subject to
   $$\begin{aligned} x_1 - 2x_2 \quad\quad + x_4 &\le 0 \\ 3x_1 \quad\quad\quad\quad &\le 1 \\ x_2 + x_3 \quad &\le 2 \\ x_1 \ge 0, x_2 \ge 0, x_3 \ge 0, x_4 &\ge 0. \end{aligned}$$
   This is a standard maximization problem.

3. Maximize $p = 2x - 3y + 3z$

subject to
$$\begin{aligned} 2x \quad\quad + z &\ge 7 \\ -x + 3y - 6z &\le 6 \\ x \ge 0, y \ge 0, z &\ge 0. \end{aligned}$$

This is *not* a standard maximization problem.

The inequality $2x + z \ge 7$ cannot be written in the required form. If we reverse the inequality by multiplying both sides by -1, we get $-2x - z \le -7$, but a negative value on the right side is not allowed.

The idea behind the simplex method is this: In any linear programming problem, there is a feasible region. If there are only two unknowns, we can draw the region; if there are three unknowns, it is a solid region in space; and if there are four or more unknowns, it is an abstract higher-dimensional region. But it is a faceted region with corners (think of a diamond), and it is at one of these corners that we will find the optimal solution. Geometrically, what the simplex method does is to start at the corner where all the unknowns are 0 (possible because we are talking of standard maximization problems) and then walk around the region, from corner to adjacent corner, always increasing the value of the objective function, until the best corner is found. In practice, we will visit only a small number of the corners before finding the right one. Algebraically, as we are about to see, this walking around is accomplished by matrix manipulations of the same sort as those used in the chapter on systems of linear equations.

We describe the method while working through an example.

EXAMPLE 1 Meet the Simplex Method

Maximize $p = 3x + 2y + z$

subject to
$$\begin{aligned} 2x + 2y + z &\le 10 \\ x + 2y + 3z &\le 15 \\ x \ge 0,\ y \ge 0,\ z &\ge 0. \end{aligned}$$

Solution

Step 1 ***Convert to a system of linear equations.*** The inequalities $2x + 2y + z \le 10$ and $x + 2y + 3z \le 15$ are less convenient than equations. Look at the first inequality. It says that the left-hand side, $2x + 2y + z$, must have some positive number (or zero) *added to it* if it is to equal 10. Because we don't yet know what x, y, and z are, we are not yet sure what number to add to the left-hand side. So we invent a new unknown, $s \ge 0$, called a **slack variable**, to "take up the slack," so that

$$2x + 2y + z + s = 10.$$

Turning to the next inequality, $x + 2y + 3z \le 15$, we now add a slack variable to its left-hand side, to get it up to the value of the right-hand side. We might have to add a different number than we did the last time, so we use a new slack variable, $t \ge 0$, and obtain

$$x + 2y + 3z + t = 15.$$

Use a different slack variable for each constraint.

Now we write the system of equations we have (including the one that defines the objective function) in standard form.

$$\begin{aligned} 2x + 2y + z + s &= 10 \\ x + 2y + 3z + t &= 15 \\ -3x - 2y - z + p &= 0 \end{aligned}$$

Note three things: First, all the variables are neatly aligned in columns, as they were in Chapter 3. Second, in rewriting the objective function $p = 3x + 2y + z$, we have left the coefficient of p as $+1$ and brought the other variables over to the same side of the equation as p. This will be our standard procedure from now on. *Don't* write $3x + 2y + z - p = 0$ (even though it means the same thing) because the negative coefficients will be important in later steps. Third, the above system of equations has fewer equations than unknowns, and hence cannot have a unique solution.

Step 2 ***Set up the initial tableau.*** We represent our system of equations by the following table (which is simply the augmented matrix in disguise), called **the initial tableau**:

	x	y	z	s	t	p	
	2	2	1	1	0	0	10
	1	2	3	0	1	0	15
	−3	−2	−1	0	0	1	0

The labels along the top keep track of which columns belong to which variables.

Now notice a peculiar thing. If we rewrite the matrix using the variables s, t, and p first, we get the matrix

$$\begin{array}{cccccc} s & t & p & x & y & z \end{array}$$
$$\begin{bmatrix} 1 & 0 & 0 & 2 & 2 & 1 & 10 \\ 0 & 1 & 0 & 1 & 2 & 3 & 15 \\ 0 & 0 & 1 & -3 & -2 & -1 & 0 \end{bmatrix},$$

Matrix with s, t, and p columns first

which is already in reduced form. We can therefore read off the general solution (see Section 3.2) to our system of equations as

$$\begin{aligned} s &= 10 - 2x - 2y - z \\ t &= 15 - x - 2y - 3z \\ p &= 0 + 3x + 2y + z \\ &x, y, z \text{ arbitrary.} \end{aligned}$$

Thus, we get a whole family of solutions, one for each choice of x, y, and z. One possible choice is to set x, y, and z all equal to 0. This gives the particular solution

$$s = 10, t = 15, p = 0, x = 0, y = 0, z = 0.$$

Set $x = y = z = 0$ above.

This solution is called the **basic solution** associated with the tableau. The variables s and t are called the **active** variables, and x, y, and z are the **inactive** variables. (Other terms used are **basic** and **nonbasic** variables.)

We can obtain the basic solution directly from the tableau as follows.

- The active variables correspond to the cleared columns (columns with only one nonzero entry).

- The values of the active variables are calculated as shown below.
- All other variables are inactive, and set equal to zero.

Inactive $x = 0$	Inactive $y = 0$	Inactive $z = 0$	Active $s = \frac{10}{1}$	Active $t = \frac{15}{1}$	Active $p = \frac{0}{1}$	
x	y	z	s	t	p	
2	2	1	1	0	0	**10**
1	2	3	0	1	0	**15**
–3	–2	–1	0	0	1	**0**

As an additional aid to recognizing which variables are active and which are inactive, we label each row with the name of the corresponding active variable. Thus, the complete initial tableau looks like this.

	x	y	z	s	t	p	
s	2	2	1	1	0	0	10
t	1	2	3	0	1	0	15
p	–3	–2	–1	0	0	1	0

This basic solution represents our starting position $x = y = z = 0$ in the feasible region in xyz space.

We now need to move to another corner point. To do so, we choose a pivot* in one of the first three columns of the tableau and clear its column. Then we will get a different basic solution, which corresponds to another corner point. Thus, in order to move from corner point to corner point, all we have to do is choose suitable pivots and clear columns in the usual manner.

* Also see Section 3.2 for a discussion of pivots and pivoting.

The next two steps give the procedure for choosing the pivot.

Step 3 ***Select the pivot column*** (the column that contains the pivot we are seeking).

Selecting the Pivot Column

Choose the negative number with the largest magnitude on the left-hand side of the bottom row (that is, don't consider the last number in the bottom row). Its column is the pivot column. (If there are two or more candidates, choose any one.) If all the numbers on the left-hand side of the bottom row are zero or positive, then we are done, and the basic solution is the optimal solution.

Simple enough. The most negative number in the bottom row is –3, so we choose the x column as the pivot column:

	x	y	z	s	t	p	
s	2	2	1	1	0	0	10
t	1	2	3	0	1	0	15
p	−3	−2	−1	0	0	1	0
	↑ Pivot column						

Q: *Why choose the pivot column this way?*

A: The variable labeling the pivot column is going to be increased from 0 to something positive. In the equation $p = 3x + 2y + z$, the fastest way to increase p is to increase x because p would increase by 3 units for every 1-unit increase in x.

(If we chose to increase y, then p would increase by only 2 units for every 1-unit increase in y, and if we increased z instead, p would grow even more slowly.) In short, choosing the pivot column this way makes it likely that we'll increase p as much as possible.

Step 4 ***Select the pivot in the pivot column.***

Selecting the Pivot

1. The pivot must always be a positive number. (This rules out zeros and negative numbers, such as the −3 in the bottom row.)
2. For each positive entry b in the pivot column, compute the ratio a/b, where a is the number in the rightmost column in that row. We call this a **test ratio**.
3. Of these ratios, choose the smallest one. (If there are two or more candidates, choose any one.) The corresponding number b is the pivot.

In our example, the test ratio in the first row is $10/2 = 5$, and the test ratio in the second row is $15/1 = 15$. Here, 5 is the smallest, so the 2 in the upper left is our pivot.

	x	y	z	s	t	p		Test Ratios
s	[2]	2	1	1	0	0	10	$10/2 = 5$
t	1	2	3	0	1	0	15	$15/1 = 15$
p	−3	−2	−1	0	0	1	0	

Q: *Why select the pivot this way?*

A: The rule given above guarantees that, after pivoting, all variables will be nonnegative in the basic solution. In other words, it guarantees that we will remain in the feasible region. We will explain further after finishing this example.

Step 5 ***Use the pivot to clear the column in the normal manner and then relabel the pivot row with the label from the pivot column.*** It is important to follow the exact prescription described in Section 3.2 for formulating the row operations:

$$aR_c \pm bR_p.$$

a and b both positive

↑ Row to change ↑ Pivot row

All entries in the last column should remain nonnegative after pivoting. Furthermore, because the x column (and no longer the s column) will be cleared, x will become an active variable. In other words, the s on the left of the pivot will be replaced by x. We call s the **departing**, or **exiting variable** and x the **entering variable** for this step.

Entering variable ↓ (x)

		x	y	z	s	t	p		
Departing variable →	s	[2]	2	1	1	0	0	10	
	t	1	2	3	0	1	0	15	$2R_2 - R_1$
	p	−3	−2	−1	0	0	1	0	$2R_3 + 3R_1$

This gives

	x	y	z	s	t	p	
x	2	2	1	1	0	0	10
t	0	2	5	−1	2	0	20
p	0	2	1	3	0	2	30

This is the second tableau.

Step 6 ***Go to Step 3.*** But wait! According to Step 3, we are finished because there are no negative numbers in the bottom row. Thus, we can read off the answer. Remember, though, that the solution for x, the first active variable, is not just $x = 10$, but is $x = 10/2 = 5$ because the pivot has not been reduced to a 1. Similarly, $t = 20/2 = 10$ and $p = 30/2 = 15$. All the other variables are zero because they are inactive. Thus, the solution is as follows: p has a maximum value of 15, and this occurs when $x = 5$, $y = 0$, and $z = 0$. (The slack variables then have the values $s = 0$ and $t = 10$.)

Q: *Why can we stop when there are no negative numbers in the bottom row? Why does this tableau give an optimal solution?*

A: The bottom row corresponds to the equation $2y + z + 3s + 2p = 30$, or

$$p = 15 - y - \frac{1}{2}z - \frac{3}{2}s.$$

Think of this as part of the general solution to our original system of equations, with y, z, and s as the parameters. Because these variables must be nonnegative, *the largest possible value of p in any feasible solution of the system comes when all three of the parameters are 0.* Thus, the current basic solution must be an optimal solution.*

* Calculators or spreadsheets could obviously be a big help in the calculations here, just as in Chapter 3. We'll say more about that after the next couple of examples.

We owe some further explanation for Step 4 of the simplex method. After Step 3, we knew that x would be the entering variable, and we needed to choose the departing variable. In the next basic solution, x was to have some positive value and we wanted this value to be as large as possible (to make p as large as possible) without making any other variables negative. Look again at the equations written in Step 2:

$$s = 10 - 2x - 2y - z$$
$$t = 15 - x - 2y - 3z.$$

We needed to make either s or t into an inactive variable and hence zero. Also, y and z were to remain inactive. If we had made s inactive, then we would have had $0 = 10 - 2x$, so $x = 10/2 = 5$. This would have made $t = 15 - 5 = 10$, which would be fine. On the other hand, if we had made t inactive, then we would have had $0 = 15 - x$, so $x = 15$, and this would have made $s = 10 - 2 \cdot 15 = -20$, which would *not* be fine, because slack variables must be nonnegative. In other words, we had a choice of making $x = 10/2 = 5$ or $x = 15/1 = 15$, but making x larger than 5 would have made another variable negative. We were thus compelled to choose the smaller ratio, 5, and make s the departing variable. Of course, we do not have to think it through this way every time. We just use the rule stated in Step 4. (For a graphical explanation, see Example 3.)

EXAMPLE 2 Simplex Method

Find the maximum value of $p = 12x + 15y + 5z$, subject to the constraints:

$$\begin{aligned} 2x + 2y + z &\le 8 \\ x + 4y - 3z &\le 12 \\ x \ge 0,\ y \ge 0,\ z &\ge 0. \end{aligned}$$

Solution Following Step 1, we introduce slack variables and rewrite the constraints and objective function in standard form:

$$\begin{aligned} 2x + 2y + z + s \qquad &= 8 \\ x + 4y - 3z \quad + t \quad &= 12 \\ -12x - 15y - 5z \qquad + p &= 0. \end{aligned}$$

We now follow with Step 2, setting up the initial tableau:

	x	y	z	s	t	p	
s	2	2	1	1	0	0	8
t	1	4	–3	0	1	0	12
p	–12	–15	–5	0	0	1	0

For Step 3, we select the column over the negative number with the largest magnitude in the bottom row, which is the y column. For Step 4, finding the pivot, we see that the test ratios are $8/2$ and $12/4$, the smallest being $12/4 = 3$. So we select the pivot in the t row and clear its column:

	x	y	z	s	t	p		
s	2	2	1	1	0	0	8	$2R_1 - R_2$
t	1	[4]	–3	0	1	0	12	
p	–12	–15	–5	0	0	1	0	$4R_3 + 15R_2$

The departing variable is t and the entering variable is y. This gives the second tableau.

	x	y	z	s	t	p	
s	3	0	5	2	–1	0	4
y	1	4	–3	0	1	0	12
p	–33	0	–65	0	15	4	180

We now go back to Step 3. Because we still have negative numbers in the bottom row, we choose the one with the largest magnitude (which is –65), and thus our pivot column is the z column. Because negative numbers can't be pivots, the only possible choice for the pivot is the 5. (We need not compute the test ratios because there would only be one from which to choose.) We now clear this column, remembering to take care of the departing and entering variables.

	x	y	z	s	t	p		
s	3	0	[5]	2	–1	0	4	
y	1	4	–3	0	1	0	12	$5R_2 + 3R_1$
p	–33	0	–65	0	15	4	180	$R_3 + 13R_1$

This gives

	x	y	z	s	t	p	
z	3	0	5	2	−1	0	4
y	14	20	0	6	2	0	72
p	6	0	0	26	2	4	232

Notice how the value of p keeps climbing: It started at 0 in the first tableau, went up to $180/4 = 45$ in the second, and is currently at $232/4 = 58$. Because there are no more negative numbers in the bottom row, we are done and can write down the solution: p has a maximum value of $232/4 = 58$, and this occurs when

$$x = 0$$

$$y = \frac{72}{20} = \frac{18}{5} \quad \text{and}$$

$$z = \frac{4}{5}.$$

The slack variables are both zero.

As a partial check on our answer, we can substitute these values into the objective function and the constraints:

$$58 = 12(0) + 15(18/5) + 5(4/5) \quad ✔$$

$$2(0) + 2(18/5) + (4/5) = 8 \le 8 \quad ✔$$

$$0 + 4(18/5) - 3(4/5) = 12 \le 12. \quad ✔$$

We say that this is only a partial check, because it shows only that our solution is feasible and that we have correctly calculated p. It does not show that we have the optimal solution. This check will *usually* catch any arithmetic mistakes we make, but it is not foolproof.

APPLICATIONS

In the next example (further exploits of Acme Baby Foods—compare Example 2 in Section 2) we show how the simplex method relates to the graphical method.

EXAMPLE 3 Resource Allocation

Acme Baby Foods makes two puddings, vanilla and chocolate. Each serving of vanilla pudding requires 2 teaspoons of sugar and 25 fluid ounces of water, and each serving of chocolate pudding requires 3 teaspoons of sugar and 15 fluid ounces of water. Acme has available each day 3,600 teaspoons of sugar and 22,500 fluid ounces of water. Acme makes no more than 600 servings of vanilla pudding because that is all that it can sell each day. If Acme makes a profit of 10¢ on each serving of vanilla pudding and 7¢ on each serving of chocolate, how many servings of each should it make to maximize its profit?

Solution We first identify the unknowns. Let

x = the number of servings of vanilla pudding

y = the number of servings of chocolate pudding.

The objective function is the profit $p = 10x + 7y$, which we need to maximize. For the constraints, we start with the fact that Acme will make no more than 600 servings of vanilla: $x \le 600$. We can put the remaining data in a table as follows:

	Vanilla	Chocolate	Total Available
Sugar (teaspoons)	2	3	3,600
Water (ounces)	25	15	22,500

Because Acme can use no more sugar and water than is available, we get the two constraints:

$$2x + 3y \le 3{,}600$$
$$25x + 15y \le 22{,}500. \quad \text{Note that all the terms are divisible by 5.}$$

Thus our linear programming problem is this:

$$\begin{aligned} \text{Maximize} \quad & p = 10x + 7y \\ \text{subject to} \quad & x \le 600 \\ & 2x + 3y \le 3{,}600 \\ & 5x + 3y \le 4{,}500 \qquad \text{We divided } 25x + 15y \le 22{,}500 \text{ by 5.} \\ & x \ge 0,\ y \ge 0. \end{aligned}$$

Next, we introduce the slack variables and set up the initial tableau.

$$\begin{aligned} x \quad + s \quad\quad\quad\quad &= 600 \\ 2x + 3y \quad + t \quad\quad &= 3{,}600 \\ 5x + 3y \quad\quad + u \quad &= 4{,}500 \\ -10x - 7y \quad\quad\quad + p &= 0 \end{aligned}$$

Note that we have had to introduce a third slack variable, u. There need to be as many slack variables as there are constraints (other than those of the $x \ge 0$ variety).

Q: *What do the slack variables say about Acme puddings?*

A: The first slack variable, s, represents the number you must add to the number of servings of vanilla pudding actually made to obtain the maximum of 600 servings. The second slack variable, t, represents the amount of sugar that is left over once the puddings are made, and u represents the amount of water left over.

We now use the simplex method to solve the problem:

	x	y	s	t	u	p		
s	[1]	0	1	0	0	0	600	
t	2	3	0	1	0	0	3,600	$R_2 - 2R_1$
u	5	3	0	0	1	0	4,500	$R_3 - 5R_1$
p	−10	−7	0	0	0	1	0	$R_4 + 10R_1$

	x	y	s	t	u	p		
x	1	0	1	0	0	0	600	
t	0	3	−2	1	0	0	2,400	$R_2 - R_3$
u	0	[3]	−5	0	1	0	1,500	
p	0	−7	10	0	0	1	6,000	$3R_4 + 7R_3$

using Technology

See the Technology Guides at the end of the chapter for a discussion of using a TI-83/84 Plus to help with the simplex method in Example 3. Or, go to the Website at www.WanerMath.com and follow the path

→ On Line Utilities

→ Pivot and Gauss-Jordan Tool

to find a utility that allows you to avoid doing the calculations in each pivot step: Just highlight the entry you wish to use as a pivot, and press "Pivot on Selection."

	x	y	s	t	u	p		
x	1	0	1	0	0	0	600	$3R_1 - R_2$
t	0	0	[3]	1	−1	0	900	
y	0	3	−5	0	1	0	1,500	$3R_3 + 5R_2$
p	0	0	−5	0	7	3	28,500	$3R_4 + 5R_2$

	x	y	s	t	u	p	
x	3	0	0	−1	1	0	900
s	0	0	3	1	−1	0	900
y	0	9	0	5	−2	0	9,000
p	0	0	0	5	16	9	90,000

Thus, the solution is as follows: The maximum value of p is $90{,}000/9 = 10{,}000$¢ $=$ \$100, which occurs when $x = 900/3 = 300$, and $y = 9{,}000/9 = 1{,}000$. (The slack variables are $s = 900/3 = 300$ and $t = u = 0$.)

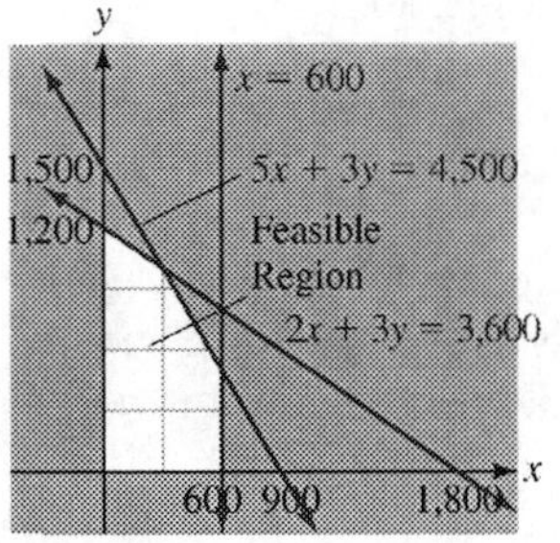

Figure 22

Before we go on... Because the problem in Example 3 had only two variables, we could have solved it graphically. It is interesting to think about the relationship between the two methods. Figure 22 shows the feasible region. Each tableau in the simplex method corresponds to a corner of the feasible region, given by the corresponding basic solution. In this example, the sequence of basic solutions is

$$(x, y) = (0, 0), (600, 0), (600, 500), (300, 1{,}000).$$

This is the sequence of corners shown in Figure 23. In general, we can think of the simplex method as walking from corner to corner of the feasible region, until it locates the optimal solution. In problems with many variables and many constraints, the simplex method usually visits only a small fraction of the total number of corners.

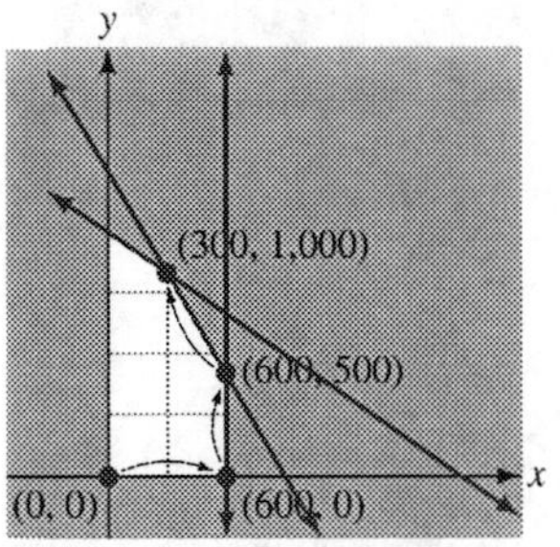

Figure 23

We can also explain again, in a different way, the reason we use the test ratios when choosing the pivot. For example, when choosing the first pivot we had to choose among the test ratios 600, 1,800, and 900 (look at the first tableau). In Figure 22, you can see that those are the three x-intercepts of the lines that bound the feasible region. If we had chosen 1,800 or 900, we would have jumped along the x-axis to a point outside of the feasible region, which we do not want to do. In general, the test ratios measure the distance from the current corner to the constraint lines, and we must choose the smallest such distance to avoid crossing any of them into the unfeasible region.

It is also interesting in an application like this to think about the values of the slack variables. We said above that s is the difference between the maximum 600 servings of vanilla that might be made and the number that is actually made. In the optimal solution, $s = 300$, which says that 300 fewer servings of vanilla were made than the maximum possible. Similarly, t was the amount of sugar left over. In the optimal solution, $t = 0$, which tells us that all of the available sugar is used. Finally, $u = 0$, so all of the available water is used as well. ■

using Technology

Website
www.WanerMath.com
On the
→ On Line Utilities
page you will find utilities that automate the simplex method to varying extents:

- Pivot and Gauss-Jordan Tool (Pivots and does row operations)
- Simplex Method Tool (Solves entire LP problems; shows all tableaux)

Summary: The Simplex Method for Standard Maximization Problems

To solve a standard maximization problem using the simplex method, we take the following steps:

1. Convert to a system of equations by introducing **slack variables** to turn the constraints into equations and by rewriting the objective function in standard form.
2. Write down the initial **tableau**.
3. Select the pivot column: Choose the negative number with the largest magnitude in the left-hand side of the bottom row. Its column is the pivot column. (If there are two or more candidates, choose any one.) If all the numbers in the left-hand side of the bottom row are zero or positive, then we are finished, and the basic solution maximizes the objective function. (See below for the basic solution.)
4. Select the pivot in the pivot column: The pivot must always be a positive number. For each positive entry b in the pivot column, compute the ratio a/b, where a is the number in the last column in that row. Of these **test ratios**, choose the smallest one. (If there are two or more candidates, choose any one.) The corresponding number b is the pivot.
5. Use the pivot to clear the column in the normal manner (taking care to follow the exact prescription for formulating the row operations described in Chapter 3) and then relabel the pivot row with the label from the pivot column. The variable originally labeling the pivot row is the **departing**, or **exiting**, **variable**, and the variable labeling the column is the **entering variable**.
6. Go to Step 3.

To get the **basic solution** corresponding to any tableau in the simplex method, set to zero all variables that do not appear as row labels. The value of a variable that does appear as a row label (an **active variable**) is the number in the rightmost column in that row divided by the number in that row in the column labeled by the same variable.

FAQs

Troubleshooting the Simplex Method

Q: *What if there is no candidate for the pivot in the pivot column? For example, what do we do with a tableau like the following?*

	x	y	z	s	t	p	
z	0	0	5	2	0	0	4
y	−8	20	0	6	5	0	72
p	−20	0	0	26	15	4	232

A: Here, the pivot column is the x column, but there is no suitable entry for a pivot (because zeros and negative numbers can't be pivots). This happens when the feasible region is unbounded and there is also no optimal solution. In other words, p can be made as large as we like without violating the constraints.

Q: *What should we do if there is a negative number in the rightmost column?*

A: A negative number will not appear above the bottom row in the rightmost column if we follow the procedure correctly. (The bottom right entry is allowed to be negative if the objective takes on negative values as in a negative profit, or loss.) Following are the most likely errors leading to this situation:

- The pivot was chosen incorrectly. (Don't forget to choose the *smallest* test ratio.) When this mistake is made, one or more of the variables will be negative in the corresponding basic solution.
- The row operation instruction was written backward or performed backward (for example, instead of $R_2 - R_1$, it was $R_1 - R_2$). This mistake can be corrected by multiplying the row by −1.
- An arithmetic error occurred. (We all make those annoying errors from time to time.)

Q: *What about zeros in the rightmost column?*

A: Zeros are permissible in the rightmost column. For example, the constraint $x - y \le 0$ will lead to a zero in the rightmost column.*

Q: *What happens if we choose a pivot column other than the one with the most negative number in the bottom row?*

A: There is no harm in doing this as long as we choose the pivot in that column using the smallest test ratio. All it might do is slow the whole calculation by adding extra steps.

* When there are zeros in the rightmost column there is a potential problem of *cycling*, where a sequence of pivots brings you back to a tableau you already considered, with no change in the objective function. You can usually break out of a cycle by choosing a different pivot. This problem should not arise in the exercises.

One last suggestion: If it is possible to do a simplification step (dividing a row by a positive number) *at any stage*, we should do so. As we saw in Chapter 3, this can help prevent the numbers from getting out of hand.

5.3 EXERCISES

▼ more advanced ◆ challenging

T indicates exercises that should be solved using technology

1. Maximize $p = 2x + y$

subject to
$$x + 2y \le 6$$
$$-x + y \le 4$$
$$x + y \le 4$$
$$x \ge 0, y \ge 0.$$

HINT [See Examples 1 and 2.]

2. Maximize $p = x$

subject to
$$x - y \le 4$$
$$-x + 3y \le 4$$
$$x \ge 0, y \ge 0.$$

HINT [See Examples 1 and 2.]

3. Maximize $p = x - y$

subject to
$$5x - 5y \le 20$$
$$2x - 10y \le 40$$
$$x \ge 0, y \ge 0.$$

4. Maximize $p = 2x + 3y$

subject to
$$3x + 8y \le 24$$
$$6x + 4y \le 30$$
$$x \ge 0, y \ge 0.$$

5. Maximize $p = 5x - 4y + 3z$

subject to
$$5x + 5z \le 100$$
$$5y - 5z \le 50$$
$$5x - 5y \le 50$$
$$x \ge 0, y \ge 0, z \ge 0.$$

6. Maximize $p = 6x + y + 3z$
subject to $3x + y \le 15$
$2x + 2y + 2z \le 20$
$x \ge 0, y \ge 0, z \ge 0.$

7. Maximize $p = 7x + 5y + 6z$
subject to $x + y - z \le 3$
$x + 2y + z \le 8$
$x + y \le 5$
$x \ge 0, y \ge 0, z \ge 0.$

8. Maximize $p = 3x + 4y + 2z$
subject to $3x + y + z \le 5$
$x + 2y + z \le 5$
$x + y + z \le 4$
$x \ge 0, y \ge 0, z \ge 0.$

9. Maximize $z = 3x_1 + 7x_2 + 8x_3$
subject to $5x_1 - x_2 + x_3 \le 1{,}500$
$2x_1 + 2x_2 + x_3 \le 2{,}500$
$4x_1 + 2x_2 + x_3 \le 2{,}000$
$x_1 \ge 0, x_2 \ge 0, x_3 \ge 0.$

10. Maximize $z = 3x_1 + 4x_2 + 6x_3$
subject to $5x_1 - x_2 + x_3 \le 1{,}500$
$2x_1 + 2x_2 + x_3 \le 2{,}500$
$4x_1 + 2x_2 + x_3 \le 2{,}000$
$x_1 \ge 0, x_2 \ge 0, x_3 \ge 0.$

11. Maximize $p = x + y + z + w$
subject to $x + y + z \le 3$
$y + z + w \le 4$
$x + z + w \le 5$
$x + y + w \le 6$
$x \ge 0, y \ge 0, z \ge 0, w \ge 0.$

12. Maximize $p = x - y + z + w$
subject to $x + y + z \le 3$
$y + z + w \le 3$
$x + z + w \le 4$
$x + y + w \le 4$
$x \ge 0, y \ge 0, z \ge 0, w \ge 0.$

13. ▼ Maximize $p = x + y + z + w + v$
subject to $x + y \le 1$
$y + z \le 2$
$z + w \le 3$
$w + v \le 4$
$x \ge 0, y \ge 0, z \ge 0, w \ge 0, v \ge 0.$

14. ▼ Maximize $p = x + 2y + z + 2w + v$
subject to $x + y \le 1$
$y + z \le 2$
$z + w \le 3$
$w + v \le 4$
$x \ge 0, y \ge 0, z \ge 0, w \ge 0, v \ge 0.$

In Exercises 15–20 we suggest the use of technology. Round all answers to two decimal places.

15. Maximize $p = 2.5x + 4.2y + 2z$
subject to $0.1x + y - 2.2z \le 4.5$
$2.1x + y + z \le 8$
$x + 2.2y \le 5$
$x \ge 0, y \ge 0, z \ge 0.$

16. Maximize $p = 2.1x + 4.1y + 2z$
subject to $3.1x + 1.2y + z \le 5.5$
$x + 2.3y + z \le 5.5$
$2.1x + y + 2.3z \le 5.2$
$x \ge 0, y \ge 0, z \ge 0.$

17. Maximize $p = x + 2y + 3z + w$
subject to $x + 2y + 3z \le 3$
$y + z + 2.2w \le 4$
$x + z + 2.2w \le 5$
$x + y + 2.2w \le 6$
$x \ge 0, y \ge 0, z \ge 0, w \ge 0.$

18. Maximize $p = 1.1x - 2.1y + z + w$
subject to $x + 1.3y + z \le 3$
$1.3y + z + w \le 3$
$x + z + w \le 4.1$
$x + 1.3y + w \le 4.1$
$x \ge 0, y \ge 0, z \ge 0, w \ge 0.$

19. Maximize $p = x - y + z - w + v$
subject to $x + y \le 1.1$
$y + z \le 2.2$
$z + w \le 3.3$
$w + v \le 4.4$
$x \ge 0, y \ge 0, z \ge 0, w \ge 0, v \ge 0.$

20. Maximize $p = x - 2y + z - 2w + v$
subject to $x + y \le 1.1$
$y + z \le 2.2$
$z + w \le 3.3$
$w + v \le 4.4$
$x \ge 0, y \ge 0, z \ge 0, w \ge 0, v \ge 0.$

APPLICATIONS

21. ***Purchasing*** You are in charge of purchases at the student-run used-book supply program at your college, and you must decide how many introductory calculus, history, and marketing texts should be purchased from students for resale. Due to budget limitations, you cannot purchase more than 650 of these textbooks each semester. There are also shelf-space limitations: Calculus texts occupy 2 units of shelf space each, history books 1 unit each, and marketing texts 3 units each, and you can spare at most 1,000 units of shelf space for the texts. If the used-book program makes a profit of \$10 on each calculus text, \$4 on each history text, and \$8 on each marketing text, how many of each type of text should you purchase to maximize profit? What is the maximum profit the program can make in a semester? HINT [See Example 3.]

22. ***Sales*** The Marketing Club at your college has decided to raise funds by selling three types of T-shirts: one with a single-color "ordinary" design, one with a two-color "fancy" design, and one with a three-color "very fancy" design. The club feels that it can sell up to 300 T-shirts. "Ordinary" T-shirts will cost the club \$6 each, "fancy" T-shirts \$8 each, and "very fancy" T-shirts \$10 each, and the club has a total purchasing budget of \$3,000. It will sell "ordinary" T-shirts at a profit of \$4 each, "fancy" T-shirts at a profit of \$5 each, and "very fancy" T-shirts at a profit of \$4 each. How many of each kind of T-shirt should the club order to maximize profit? What is the maximum profit the club can make? HINT [See Example 3.]

23. ***Resource Allocation*** *Arctic Juice Company* makes three juice blends: PineOrange, using 2 portions of pineapple juice and 2 portions of orange juice per gallon; PineKiwi, using 3 portions of pineapple juice and 1 portion of kiwi juice per gallon; and OrangeKiwi, using 3 portions of orange juice and 1 portion of kiwi juice per gallon. Each day the company has 800 portions of pineapple juice, 650 portions of orange juice, and 350 portions of kiwi juice available. Its profit on PineOrange is \$1 per gallon, its profit on PineKiwi is \$2 per gallon, and its profit on OrangeKiwi is \$1 per gallon. How many gallons of each blend should it make each day to maximize profit? What is the largest possible profit the company can make?

24. ***Purchasing*** *Trans Global Tractor Trailers* has decided to spend up to \$1,500,000 on a fleet of new trucks, and it is considering three models: the Gigahaul, which has a capacity of 6,000 cubic feet and is priced at \$60,000; the Megahaul, with a capacity of 5,000 cubic feet, priced at \$50,000; and the Picohaul, with a capacity of 2,000 cubic feet, priced at \$40,000. The anticipated annual revenues are \$500,000 for each new truck purchased (regardless of size). Trans Global would like a total capacity of up to 130,000 cubic feet, and feels that it cannot provide drivers and maintenance for more than 30 trucks. How many of each should it purchase to maximize annual revenue? What is the largest possible revenue it can make?

25. ***Resource Allocation*** The Enormous State University History Department offers three courses, Ancient, Medieval, and Modern History, and the department chairperson is trying to decide how many sections of each to offer this semester. They may offer up to 45 sections total, up to 5,000 students would like to take a course, and there are 60 professors to teach them (no student will take more than one history course, and no professor will teach more than one section). Sections of Ancient History have 100 students each, sections of Medieval History have 50 students each, and sections of Modern History have 200 students each. Modern History sections are taught by a team of two professors, while Ancient and Medieval History need only one professor per section. Ancient History nets the university \$10,000 per section, Medieval nets \$20,000, and Modern History nets \$30,000 per section. How many sections of each course should the department offer in order to generate the largest profit? What is the largest profit possible? Will there be any unused time slots, any students who did not get into classes, or any professors without anything to teach?

26. ***Resource Allocation*** You manage an ice cream factory that makes three flavors: Creamy Vanilla, Continental Mocha, and Succulent Strawberry. Into each batch of Creamy Vanilla go 2 eggs, 1 cup of milk, and 2 cups of cream. Into each batch of Continental Mocha go 1 egg, 1 cup of milk, and 2 cups of cream. Into each batch of Succulent Strawberry go 1 egg, 2 cups of milk, and 2 cups of cream. You have in stock 200 eggs, 120 cups of milk, and 200 cups of cream. You make a profit of \$3 on each batch of Creamy Vanilla, \$2 on each batch of Continental Mocha, and \$4 on each batch of Succulent Strawberry.
   a. How many batches of each flavor should you make to maximize your profit?
   b. In your answer to part (a), have you used all the ingredients?
   c. Due to the poor strawberry harvest this year, you cannot make more than 10 batches of Succulent Strawberry. Does this affect your maximum profit?

27. ***Agriculture*** Your small farm encompasses 100 acres, and you are planning to grow tomatoes, lettuce, and carrots in the coming planting season. Fertilizer costs per acre are: \$5 for tomatoes, \$4 for lettuce, and \$2 for carrots. Based on past experience, you estimate that each acre of tomatoes will require an average of 4 hours of labor per week, while tending to lettuce and carrots will each require an average of 2 hours per week. You estimate a profit of \$2,000 for each acre of tomatoes, \$1,500 for each acre of lettuce, and \$500 for each acre of carrots. You can afford to spend no more than \$400 on fertilizer, and your farm laborers can supply up to 500 hours per week. How many acres of each crop should you plant to maximize total profits? In this event, will you be using all 100 acres of your farm?

28. ***Agriculture*** Your farm encompasses 500 acres, and you are planning to grow soybeans, corn, and wheat in the coming planting season. Fertilizer costs per acre are: \$5 for soybeans, \$2 for corn, and \$1 for wheat. You estimate that each acre of soybeans will require an average of 5 hours of labor per week, while tending to corn and wheat will each require an average of 2 hours per week. Based on past yields and current market prices, you estimate a profit of \$3,000 for each acre of soybeans, \$2,000 for each acre of corn, and \$1,000 for each acre of wheat. You can afford to spend no more than \$3,000 on fertilizer, and your farm laborers can supply 3,000 hours per week. How many acres of each crop should you plant to maximize total profits? In this event, will you be using all the available labor?

29. ***Resource Allocation*** (Compare Exercise 36 in Chapter 3 Review) The Enormous State University Choral Society is planning its annual Song Festival, when it will serve three kinds of delicacies: granola treats, nutty granola treats, and nuttiest granola treats. The following table shows some of the ingredients required (in ounces) for a single serving of each delicacy, as well as the total amount of each ingredient available.

	Granola	Nutty Granola	Nuttiest Granola	Total Available
Toasted Oats	1	1	5	1,500
Almonds	4	8	8	10,000
Raisins	2	4	8	4,000

The society makes a profit of $6 on each serving of granola, $8 on each serving of nutty granola, and $3 on each serving of nuttiest granola. Assuming that the Choral Society can sell all that it makes, how many servings of each will maximize profits? How much of each ingredient will be left over?

30. ***Resource Allocation*** Repeat the preceding exercise, but this time assume that the Choral Society makes a $3 profit on each of its delicacies.

31. ***Recycling*** Safety-Kleen operates the world's largest oil refinery at Elgin, Illinois. You have been hired by the company to determine how to allocate its intake of up to 50 million gallons of used oil to its three refinery processes: A, B, and C. You are told that electricity costs for process A amount to $150,000 per million gallons treated, while for processes B and C, the costs are, respectively, $100,000 and $50,000 per million gallons treated. Process A can recover 60 percent of the used oil, process B can recover 55 percent, and process C can recover only 50 percent. Assuming a revenue of $4 million per million gallons of recovered oil and an annual electrical budget of $3 million, how much used oil would you allocate to each process in order to maximize total revenues?[23]

32. ***Recycling*** Repeat the preceding exercise, but this time assume that process C can handle only up to 20 million gallons per year.

Creatine Supplements *Exercises 33 and 34 are based on the following data on four popular bodybuilding supplements. (Figures shown correspond to a single serving.)*[24]

	Creatine (g)	Carbohydrates (g)	Taurine (g)	Alpha Lipoic Acid (mg)
Cell-Tech® (MuscleTech)	10	75	2	200
RiboForce HP® (EAS)	5	15	1	0
Creatine Transport® (Kaizen)	5	35	1	100
Pre-Load Creatine® (Optimum)	6	35	1	25

[23]These figures are realistic: Safety-Kleen's actual 1993 capacity was 50 million gallons, its recycled oil sold for approximately $4 per gallon, its recycling process could recover approximately 55 percent of the used oil, and its electrical bill was $3 million. Source: Oil Recycler Greases Rusty City's Economy, *Chicago Tribune*, May 30, 1993, Section 7, p.1.

[24]Source: Nutritional information supplied by the manufacturers (www.netrition.com).

33. You are thinking of combining the first three supplements in the previous table to obtain a 10-day supply that gives you the maximum possible amount of creatine, but no more than 1,000 milligrams of alpha lipoic acid and 225 grams of carbohydrates. How many servings of each supplement should you combine to meet your specifications, and how much creatine will you get?

34. Repeat Exercise 33, but use the last three supplements in the table instead.

Investing *Exercises 35 and 36 are based on the following data on three stocks.*[25]

	Price	Dividend Yield	52-Week Price Change ($)
FDX (FedEx)	$90	1%	−2
WU (Western Union)	$20	2%	1
DO (Diamond Offshore Drilling)	$70	0%	6

35. ▼ You are planning to invest up to $10,000 in FDX, WU, and DO shares. You desire to maximize the 52-week gain but, for tax reasons, want to earn no more than $200 in dividends. Your broker suggests that because DO stock pays no dividends, you should invest only in DO. Is she right?

36. ▼ Repeat Exercise 35 under the assumption that the 52-week change in DO stock is $3, but its price is unchanged.

37. ▼ ***Loan Planning***[26] Enormous State University's employee credit union has $5 million available for loans in the coming year. As VP in charge of finances, you must decide how much capital to allocate to each of four different kinds of loans, as shown in the following table.

Type of Loan	Annual Rate of Return
Automobile	8%
Furniture	10%
Signature	12%
Other secured	10%

State laws and credit union policies impose the following restrictions:

- Signature loans may not exceed 10 percent of the total investment of funds.

[25]Approximate 150-day average price as of August 31, 2011. 52-week price changes are approximate. Source: http://finance.google.com

[26]Adapted from an exercise in *An Introduction to Management Science* (6th. ed.) by D. R. Anderson, D. J. Sweeney, and T. A. Williams (West, 1991).

- Furniture loans plus other secured loans may not exceed automobile loans.
- Other secured loans may not exceed 200 percent of automobile loans.

How much should you allocate to each type of loan to maximize the annual return?

38. ☐ ▼ *Investments* You have $100,000 that you are considering investing in three dividend-yielding bank stocks: Banco Santander Brasil, Bank of Hawaii, and Banco Santander Chile. You have the following data:[27]

Stock	Yield
BSBR (Banco Santander Brasil)	7%
BOH (Bank of Hawaii)	5%
SAN (Banco Santander Chile)	4%

Your broker has made the following suggestions:

- At least 50 percent of your total investment should be in SAN.
- No more than 10 percent of your total investment should be in BSBR.

How much should you invest in each stock to maximize your anticipated dividends while following your broker's advice?

39. ▼ *Portfolio Management* If x dollars are invested in a company that controls, say, 30 percent of the market with five brand names, then $0.30x$ is a measure of market exposure and $5x$ is a measure of brand-name exposure. Now suppose you are a broker at a large securities firm, and one of your clients would like to invest up to $100,000 in recording industry stocks. You decide to recommend a combination of stocks in four of the world's largest recording companies: Warner Music, Universal Music, Sony, and EMI. (See the table.)[28]

	Warner Music	Universal Music	Sony	EMI
Market share	12%	20%	20%	15%
Number of labels (brands)	8	20	10	15

You would like your client's brand-name exposure to be as large as possible but his total market exposure to be $15,000 or less. (This would reflect an average of 15 percent.) Furthermore, you would like at least 20 percent of the investment to be in Universal because you feel that its control of the DGG and Phillips labels is advantageous for its classical music operations. How much should you advise your client to invest in each company?

40. ▼ *Portfolio Management* Referring to Exercise 39, suppose instead that you wanted your client to maximize his total

market exposure but limit his brand-name exposure to 1.5 million or less (representing an average of 15 labels or fewer per company), and still invest at least 20 percent of the total in Universal. How much should you advise your client to invest in each company?

41. ☐ ▼ *Transportation Scheduling* (This exercise is almost identical to Exercise 26 in Section 3.3 but is more realistic; one cannot always expect to fill all orders exactly and keep all plants operating at 100 percent capacity.) The *Tubular Ride Boogie Board Company* has manufacturing plants in Tucson, Arizona, and Toronto, Ontario. You have been given the job of coordinating distribution of the latest model, the Gladiator, to their outlets in Honolulu and Venice Beach. The Tucson plant, when operating at full capacity, can manufacture 620 Gladiator boards per week, while the Toronto plant, beset by labor disputes, can produce only 410 boards per week. The outlet in Honolulu orders 500 Gladiator boards per week, while Venice Beach orders 530 boards per week. Transportation costs are as follows: Tucson to Honolulu: $10 per board; Tucson to Venice Beach: $5 per board; Toronto to Honolulu: $20 per board; Toronto to Venice Beach: $10 per board. Your manager has informed you that the company's total transportation budget is $6,550. You realize that it may not be possible to fill all the orders, but you would like the total number of boogie boards shipped to be as large as possible. Given this, how many Gladiator boards should you order shipped from each manufacturing plant to each distribution outlet?

42. ☐ ▼ *Transportation Scheduling* Repeat the preceding exercise, but use a transportation budget of $5,050.

43. ☐ ▼ *Transportation Scheduling* Your publishing company is about to start a promotional blitz for its new book, *Advanced Quantum Mechanics for the Liberal Arts*. You have 20 salespeople stationed in Chicago and 10 in Denver. You would like to fly at most 10 into Los Angeles and at most 15 into New York. A round-trip plane flight from Chicago to LA costs $195;[29] from Chicago to New York costs $182; from Denver to LA costs $395; and from Denver to New York costs $166. You want to spend at most $4,520 on plane flights. How many salespeople should you fly from each of Chicago and Denver to each of LA and New York to have the most salespeople on the road?

44. ☐ ▼ *Transportation Scheduling* Repeat the preceding exercise, but this time, spend at most $5,770.

COMMUNICATION AND REASONING EXERCISES

45. Can the following linear programming problem be stated as a standard maximization problem? If so, do it; if not, explain why.

$$\text{Maximize} \quad p = 3x - 2y$$
$$\text{subject to} \quad x - y + z \geq 0$$
$$x - y - z \leq 6$$
$$x \geq 0, y \geq 0, z \geq 0.$$

[27]Yields are as of September 2011. Source: www.google.com/finance

[28]The number of labels includes only major labels. Market shares are approximate and represent the period 2000–2002. Sources: various, including www.emigroup.com, http://finance.vivendi.com/discover/financial, and http://business2.com, March 2002.

[29]Prices from Travelocity, at www.travelocity.com, for the week of June 3, 2002, as of May 5, 2002.

46. Can the following linear programming problem be stated as a standard maximization problem? If so, do it; if not, explain why.

$$\begin{aligned} \text{Maximize} \quad & p = -3x - 2y \\ \text{subject to} \quad & x - y + z \geq 0 \\ & x - y - z \geq -6 \\ & x \geq 0, y \geq 0, z \geq 0. \end{aligned}$$

47. Why is the simplex method useful? (After all, we do have the graphical method for solving LP problems.)

48. Are there any types of linear programming problems that cannot be solved with the methods of this section but that can be solved using the methods of the preceding section? Explain.

49. ▼ Your friend Janet is going around telling everyone that if there are only two constraints in a linear programming problem, then, in any optimal basic solution, at most two unknowns (other than the objective) will be nonzero. Is she correct? Explain.

50. ▼ Your other friend Jason is going around telling everyone that if there is only one constraint in a standard linear programming problem, then you will have to pivot at most once to obtain an optimal solution. Is he correct? Explain.

51. ▼ What is a "basic solution"? How might one find a basic solution of a given system of linear equations?

52. ▼ In a typical simplex method tableau, there are more unknowns than equations, and we know from the chapter on systems of linear equations that this typically implies the existence of infinitely many solutions. How are the following types of solutions interpreted in the simplex method?

a. Solutions in which all the variables are positive.
b. Solutions in which some variables are negative.
c. Solutions in which the inactive variables are zero.

53. ◆ Can the value of the objective function decrease in passing from one tableau to the next? Explain.

54. ◆ Can the value of the objective function remain unchanged in passing from one tableau to the next? Explain.

5.4 The Simplex Method: Solving General Linear Programming Problems

As we saw in Section 5.2, not all LP problems are standard maximization problems. We might have constraints like $2x + 3y \geq 4$ or perhaps $2x + 3y = 4$. Or, we might have to minimize, rather than maximize, the objective function. General problems like this are almost as easy to deal with as the standard kind: There is a modification of the simplex method that works very nicely. The best way to illustrate it is by means of examples. First, we discuss nonstandard maximization problems.

Nonstandard Maximization Problems

EXAMPLE 1 Maximizing with Mixed Constraints

$$\begin{aligned} \text{Maximize} \quad & p = 4x + 12y + 6z \\ \text{subject to} \quad & x + y + z \leq 100 \\ & 4x + 10y + 7z \leq 480 \\ & x + y + z \geq 60 \\ & x \geq 0, y \geq 0, z \geq 0. \end{aligned}$$

Solution We begin by turning the first two inequalities into equations as usual because they have the standard form. We get

$$\begin{aligned} x + y + z + s \phantom{{}+t} &= 100 \\ 4x + 10y + 7z \phantom{{}+s} + t &= 480. \end{aligned}$$

We are tempted to use a slack variable for the third inequality, $x + y + z \geq 60$, but *adding* something positive to the left-hand side will not make it equal to the right: It will get even bigger. To make it equal to 60, we must *subtract* some nonnegative number. We will call this number u (because we have already used s and t) and refer to u as a **surplus variable** rather than a slack variable. Thus, we write

$$x + y + z - u = 60.$$

Continuing with the setup, we have

$$\begin{aligned}
x + \quad y + \ z + s \qquad\qquad\quad &= 100 \\
4x + 10y + 7z \qquad + t \qquad\quad &= 480 \\
x + \quad y + \ z \qquad\qquad - u \quad &= 60 \\
-4x - 12y - 6z \qquad\qquad\quad + p &= 0.
\end{aligned}$$

This leads to the initial tableau:

	x	y	z	s	t	u	p	
s	1	1	1	1	0	0	0	100
t	4	10	7	0	1	0	0	480
$*u$	1	1	1	0	0	−1	0	60
p	−4	−12	−6	0	0	0	1	0

We put a star next to the third row because the basic solution corresponding to this tableau is

$$x = y = z = 0, s = 100, t = 480, u = 60/(-1) = -60.$$

Several things are wrong here. First, the values $x = y = z = 0$ do not satisfy the third inequality $x + y + z \geq 60$. Thus, this basic solution is *not feasible.* Second—and this is really the same problem—the surplus variable u is negative, whereas we said that it should be nonnegative. The star next to the row labeled u alerts us to the fact that the present basic solution is not feasible and that the problem is located in the starred row, where the active variable u is negative.

Whenever an active variable is negative, we star the corresponding row.

In setting up the initial tableau, we star those rows coming from $\geq$ inequalities.

The simplex method as described in the preceding section assumed that we began in the feasible region, but now we do not. Our first task is to get ourselves into the feasible region. In practice, we can think of this as getting rid of the stars on the rows. Once we get into the feasible region, we go back to the method of the preceding section.

There are several ways to get into the feasible region. The method we have chosen is one of the simplest to state and carry out. (We will see why this method works at the end of the example.)

The Simplex Method for General Linear Programming Problems

Star all rows that give a negative value for the associated active variable (except for the objective variable, which is allowed to be negative). If there are starred rows, you will need to begin with Phase I.

Phase I: Getting into the Feasible Region (Getting Rid of the Stars)
In the first starred row, find the largest positive number. Use test ratios as in Section 5.3 to find the pivot in that column (exclude the bottom row), and then pivot on that entry. (If the lowest ratio occurs both in a starred row and an unstarred row, pivot in a starred row rather than the unstarred one.) Check to

see which rows should now be starred. Repeat until no starred rows remain, and then go on to Phase II.

Phase II: Use the Simplex Method for Standard Maximization Problems

If there are any negative entries on the left side of the bottom row after Phase I, use the method described in the preceding section.

Because there is a starred row, we need to use Phase I. The largest positive number in the starred row is 1, which occurs three times. Arbitrarily select the first, which is in the first column. In that column, the smallest test ratio happens to be given by the 1 in the u row, so this is our first pivot.

Pivot column ↓

	x	y	z	s	t	u	p		
s	1	1	1	1	0	0	0	100	$R_1 - R_3$
t	4	10	7	0	1	0	0	480	$R_2 - 4R_3$
$*u$	[1]	1	1	0	0	-1	0	60	
p	-4	-12	-6	0	0	0	1	0	$R_4 + 4R_3$

This gives

	x	y	z	s	t	u	p	
s	0	0	0	1	0	1	0	40
t	0	6	3	0	1	4	0	240
x	1	1	1	0	0	-1	0	60
p	0	-8	-2	0	0	-4	1	240

Notice that we removed the star from row 3. To see why, look at the basic solution given by this tableau:

$$x = 60, y = 0, z = 0, s = 40, t = 240, u = 0.$$

None of the variables is negative anymore, so there are no rows to star. The basic solution is therefore feasible—it satisfies all the constraints.

Now that there are no more stars, we have completed Phase I, so we proceed to Phase II, which is just the method of the preceding section.

	x	y	z	s	t	u	p		
s	0	0	0	1	0	1	0	40	
t	0	[6]	3	0	1	4	0	240	
x	1	1	1	0	0	-1	0	60	$6R_3 - R_2$
p	0	-8	-2	0	0	-4	1	240	$3R_4 + 4R_2$

	x	y	z	s	t	u	p	
s	0	0	0	1	0	1	0	40
y	0	6	3	0	1	4	0	240
x	6	0	3	0	-1	-10	0	120
p	0	0	6	0	4	4	3	1,680

And we are finished. Thus the solution is

$$p = 1{,}680/3 = 560,\ x = 120/6 = 20,\ y = 240/6 = 40,\ z = 0.$$

The slack and surplus variables are

$$s = 40,\ t = 0,\ u = 0.$$

Before we go on... We owe you an explanation of why this method works. When we perform a pivot in Phase I, one of two things will happen. As in Example 1, we may pivot in a starred row. In that case, the negative active variable in that row will become inactive (hence zero) and some other variable will be made active with a positive value because we are pivoting on a positive entry. Thus, at least one star will be eliminated. (We will not introduce any new stars because pivoting on the entry with the smallest test ratio will keep all nonnegative variables nonnegative.)

The second possibility is that we may pivot on some row other than a starred row. Choosing the pivot via test ratios again guarantees that no new starred rows are created. A little bit of algebra shows that the value of the negative variable in the first starred row must increase toward zero. (Choosing the *largest* positive entry in the starred row will make it a little more likely that we will increase the value of that variable as much as possible; the rationale for choosing the largest entry is the same as that for choosing the most negative entry in the bottom row during Phase II.) Repeating this procedure as necessary, the value of the variable must eventually become zero or positive, assuming that there are feasible solutions to begin with.

So, one way or the other, we can eventually get rid of all of the stars. ■

Here is an example that begins with two starred rows.

EXAMPLE 2 More Mixed Constraints

$$\begin{aligned}
\text{Maximize}\quad & p = 2x + y \\
\text{subject to}\quad & x + y \geq 35 \\
& x + 2y \leq 60 \\
& 2x + y \geq 60 \\
& x \leq 25 \\
& x \geq 0,\ y \geq 0.
\end{aligned}$$

Solution We introduce slack and surplus variables, and write down the initial tableau:

$$\begin{aligned}
x + y - s &= 35 \\
x + 2y + t &= 60 \\
2x + y - u &= 60 \\
x + v &= 25 \\
-2x - y + p &= 0.
\end{aligned}$$

	x	y	s	t	u	v	p	
$^*s$	1	1	−1	0	0	0	0	35
t	1	2	0	1	0	0	0	60
$^*u$	2	1	0	0	−1	0	0	60
v	1	0	0	0	0	1	0	25
p	−2	−1	0	0	0	0	1	0

We locate the largest positive entry in the first starred row (row 1). There are two to choose from (both 1s); let's choose the one in the x column. The entry with the smallest test ratio in that column is the 1 in the v row, so that is the entry we use as the pivot:

Pivot column ↓

	x	y	s	t	u	v	p		
$*s$	1	1	−1	0	0	0	0	35	$R_1 - R_4$
t	1	2	0	1	0	0	0	60	$R_2 - R_4$
$*u$	2	1	0	0	−1	0	0	60	$R_3 - 2R_4$
v	[1]	0	0	0	0	1	0	25	
p	−2	−1	0	0	0	0	1	0	$R_5 + 2R_4$

	x	y	s	t	u	v	p	
$*s$	0	1	−1	0	0	−1	0	10
t	0	2	0	1	0	−1	0	35
$*u$	0	1	0	0	−1	−2	0	10
x	1	0	0	0	0	1	0	25
p	0	−1	0	0	0	2	1	50

Notice that both stars are still there because the basic solutions for s and u remain negative (but less so). The only positive entry in the first starred row is the 1 in the y column, and that entry also has the smallest test ratio in its column. (Actually, it is tied with the 1 in the u column, so we could choose either one.)

	x	y	s	t	u	v	p		
$*s$	0	[1]	−1	0	0	−1	0	10	
t	0	2	0	1	0	−1	0	35	$R_2 - 2R_1$
$*u$	0	1	0	0	−1	−2	0	10	$R_3 - R_1$
x	1	0	0	0	0	1	0	25	
p	0	−1	0	0	0	2	1	50	$R_5 + R_1$

	x	y	s	t	u	v	p	
y	0	1	−1	0	0	−1	0	10
t	0	0	2	1	0	1	0	15
u	0	0	1	0	−1	−1	0	0
x	1	0	0	0	0	1	0	25
p	0	0	−1	0	0	1	1	60

The basic solution is $x = 25$, $y = 10$, $s = 0$, $t = 15$, $u = 0/(-1) = 0$, and $v = 0$. Because there are no negative variables left (even u has become 0), we are in the feasible region, so we can go on to Phase II, shown next. (Filling in the instructions for the row operations is an exercise.)

	x	y	s	t	u	v	p	
y	0	1	−1	0	0	−1	0	10
t	0	0	2	1	0	1	0	15
u	0	0	[1]	0	−1	−1	0	0
x	1	0	0	0	0	1	0	25
p	0	0	−1	0	0	1	1	60

	x	y	s	t	u	v	p	
y	0	1	0	0	−1	−2	0	10
t	0	0	0	1	[2]	3	0	15
s	0	0	1	0	−1	−1	0	0
x	1	0	0	0	0	1	0	25
p	0	0	0	0	−1	0	1	60

	x	y	s	t	u	v	p	
y	0	2	0	1	0	−1	0	35
u	0	0	0	1	2	3	0	15
s	0	0	2	1	0	1	0	15
x	1	0	0	0	0	1	0	25
p	0	0	0	1	0	3	2	135

The optimal solution is

$$x = 25, y = 35/2 = 17.5, p = 135/2 = 67.5 \quad (s = 7.5, t = 0, u = 7.5).$$

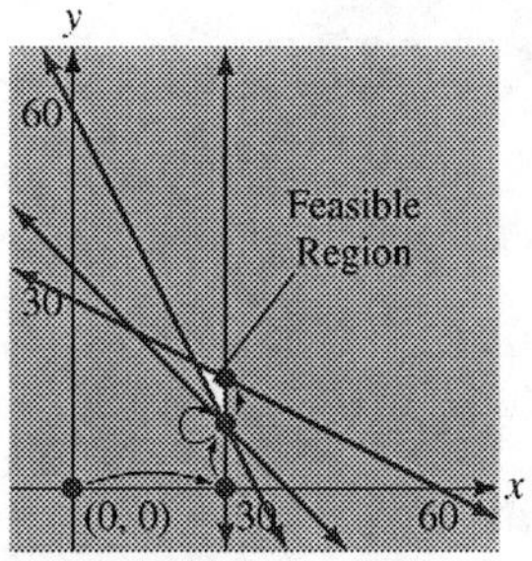

Figure 24

➡ **Before we go on...** Because Example 2 had only two unknowns, we can picture the sequence of basic solutions on the graph of the feasible region. This is shown in Figure 24.

You can see that there was no way to jump from (0, 0) in the initial tableau directly into the feasible region because the first jump must be along an axis. (Why?) Also notice that the third jump did not move at all. To which step of the simplex method does this correspond? ■

Minimization Problems

Now that we know how to deal with nonstandard constraints, we consider **minimization** problems, problems in which we have to minimize, rather than maximize, the objective function. The idea is to *convert a minimization problem into a maximization problem*, which we can then solve as usual.

Suppose, for instance, we want to minimize $c = 10x - 30y$ subject to some constraints. The technique is as follows: Define a new variable p by taking p to be the negative of c, so that $p = -c$. Then, the larger we make p, the smaller c becomes. For example, if we can make p increase from −10 to −5, then c will decrease from 10 to 5. So, if we are looking for the smallest value of c, we might as well look for the largest value of p instead. More concisely,

Minimizing c is the same as maximizing $p = -c$.

Now because $c = 10x - 30y$, we have $p = -10x + 30y$, and the requirement that we "minimize $c = 10x - 30y$" is now replaced by "maximize $p = -10x + 30y$."

Minimization Problems

We convert a minimization problem into a maximization problem by taking the negative of the objective function. All the constraints remain unchanged.

Quick Example

Minimization Problem	→	**Maximization Problem**
Minimize $c = 10x - 30y$		Maximize $p = -10x + 30y$
subject to $2x + y \le 160$		subject to $2x + y \le 160$
$x + 3y \ge 120$		$x + 3y \ge 120$
$x \ge 0, y \ge 0.$		$x \ge 0, y \ge 0.$

EXAMPLE 3 **Purchasing**

You are in charge of ordering furniture for your company's new headquarters. You need to buy at least 200 tables, 500 chairs, and 300 computer desks. Wall-to-Wall Furniture (WWF) is offering a package of 20 tables, 25 chairs, and 18 computer desks for \$2,000, whereas rival Acme Furniture (AF) is offering a package of 10 tables, 50 chairs, and 24 computer desks for \$3,000. How many packages should you order from each company to minimize your total cost?

Solution The unknowns here are

x = number of packages ordered from WWF
y = number of packages ordered from AF.

We can put the information about the various kinds of furniture in a table:

	WWF	*AF*	*Needed*
Tables	20	10	200
Chairs	25	50	500
Computer Desks	18	24	300
Cost (\$)	2,000	3,000	

From this table we get the following LP problem:

$$\begin{aligned} \text{Minimize} \quad & c = 2{,}000x + 3{,}000y \\ \text{subject to} \quad & 20x + 10y \ge 200 \\ & 25x + 50y \ge 500 \\ & 18x + 24y \ge 300 \\ & x \ge 0, y \ge 0. \end{aligned}$$

Before we start solving this problem, notice that all the inequalities may be simplified. The first is divisible by 10, the second by 25, and the third by 6. (However, this affects the meaning of the surplus variables; see Before we go on below.) Dividing gives the following simpler problem:

$$\begin{aligned} \text{Minimize} \quad & c = 2{,}000x + 3{,}000y \\ \text{subject to} \quad & 2x + y \ge 20 \\ & x + 2y \ge 20 \\ & 3x + 4y \ge 50 \\ & x \ge 0, y \ge 0. \end{aligned}$$

Following the discussion that preceded this example, we convert to a maximization problem:

$$\begin{aligned} \text{Maximize} \quad & p = -2{,}000x - 3{,}000y \\ \text{subject to} \quad & 2x + y \geq 20 \\ & x + 2y \geq 20 \\ & 3x + 4y \geq 50 \\ & x \geq 0, y \geq 0. \end{aligned}$$

We introduce surplus variables.

$$\begin{aligned} 2x + y - s \quad &= 20 \\ x + 2y - t \quad &= 20 \\ 3x + 4y - u \quad &= 50 \\ 2{,}000x + 3{,}000y + p &= 0. \end{aligned}$$

The initial tableau is then

	x	y	s	t	u	p	
$*s$	2	1	−1	0	0	0	20
$*t$	1	2	0	−1	0	0	20
$*u$	3	4	0	0	−1	0	50
p	2,000	3,000	0	0	0	1	0

The largest entry in the first starred row is the 2 in the upper left, which happens to give the smallest test ratio in its column.

	x	y	s	t	u	p		
$*s$	[2]	1	−1	0	0	0	20	
$*t$	1	2	0	−1	0	0	20	$2R_2 - R_1$
$*u$	3	4	0	0	−1	0	50	$2R_3 - 3R_1$
p	2,000	3,000	0	0	0	1	0	$R_4 - 1{,}000R_1$

	x	y	s	t	u	p		
x	2	1	−1	0	0	0	20	$3R_1 - R_2$
$*t$	0	[3]	1	−2	0	0	20	
$*u$	0	5	3	0	−2	0	40	$3R_3 - 5R_2$
p	0	2,000	1,000	0	0	1	−20,000	$3R_4 - 2{,}000R_2$

	x	y	s	t	u	p		
x	6	0	−4	2	0	0	40	$5R_1 - R_3$
y	0	3	1	−2	0	0	20	$5R_2 + R_3$
$*u$	0	0	4	[10]	−6	0	20	
p	0	0	1,000	4,000	0	3	−100,000	$R_4 - 400R_3$

	x	y	s	t	u	p		
x	30	0	−24	0	6	0	180	$R_1/6$
y	0	15	9	0	−6	0	120	$R_2/3$
t	0	0	4	10	−6	0	20	$R_3/2$
p	0	0	−600	0	2,400	3	−108,000	$R_4/3$

This completes Phase I. We are not yet at the optimal solution, so after performing the simplifications indicated we proceed with Phase II.

	x	y	s	t	u	p		
x	5	0	−4	0	1	0	30	$R_1 + 2R_3$
y	0	5	3	0	−2	0	40	$2R_2 - 3R_3$
t	0	0	[2]	5	−3	0	10	
p	0	0	−200	0	800	1	−36,000	$R_4 + 100R_3$

	x	y	s	t	u	p	
x	5	0	0	10	−5	0	50
y	0	10	0	−15	5	0	50
s	0	0	2	5	−3	0	10
p	0	0	0	500	500	1	−35,000

The optimal solution is

$x = 50/5 = 10$, $y = 50/10 = 5$, $p = -35{,}000$, so $c = 35{,}000$
$(s = 5, t = 0, u = 0)$.

You should buy 10 packages from Wall-to-Wall Furniture and 5 from Acme Furniture, for a minimum cost of $35,000.

Before we go on... The surplus variables in the preceding example represent pieces of furniture over and above the minimum requirements. The order you place will give you 50 extra tables ($s = 5$, but s was introduced after we divided the first inequality by 10, so the actual surplus is $10 \times 5 = 50$), the correct number of chairs ($t = 0$), and the correct number of computer desks ($u = 0$). ■

The preceding LP problem is an example of a **standard minimization problem**—in a sense the opposite of a standard maximization problem: We are *minimizing* an objective function, where all the constraints have the form $Ax + By + Cz + \cdots \geq N$. We will discuss standard minimization problems more fully in Section 5.5, as well as another method of solving them.

FAQs

When to Switch to Phase II, Equality Constraints, and Troubleshooting

Q: *How do I know when to switch to Phase II?*

A: After each step, check the basic solution for starred rows. You are not ready to proceed with Phase II until all the stars are gone.

Q: *How do I deal with an equality constraint, such as $2x + 7y - z = 90$?*

A: Although we haven't given examples of equality constraints, they can be treated by the following trick: Replace an equality by two inequalities. For example, replace the equality $2x + 7y - z = 90$ by the two inequalities $2x + 7y - z \leq 90$ and $2x + 7y - z \geq 90$. A little thought will convince you that these two inequalities amount to the same thing as the original equality!

Q: *What happens if it is impossible to choose a pivot using the instructions in Phase I?*

A: In that case, the LP problem has no solution. In fact, the feasible region is empty. If it is impossible to choose a pivot in Phase II, then the feasible region is unbounded and there is no optimal solution.

5.4 EXERCISES

▼ more advanced ◆ challenging

T indicates exercises that should be solved using technology

1. Maximize $p = x + y$
subject to
$$\begin{aligned} x + 2y &\geq 6 \\ -x + y &\leq 4 \\ 2x + y &\leq 8 \\ x \geq 0, y &\geq 0. \end{aligned}$$
HINT [See Examples 1 and 2.]

2. Maximize $p = 3x + 2y$
subject to
$$\begin{aligned} x + 3y &\geq 6 \\ -x + y &\leq 4 \\ 2x + y &\leq 8 \\ x \geq 0, y &\geq 0. \end{aligned}$$
HINT [See Examples 1 and 2.]

3. Maximize $p = 12x + 10y$
subject to
$$\begin{aligned} x + y &\leq 25 \\ x &\geq 10 \\ -x + 2y &\geq 0 \\ x \geq 0, y &\geq 0. \end{aligned}$$

4. Maximize $p = x + 2y$
subject to
$$\begin{aligned} x + y &\leq 25 \\ y &\geq 10 \\ 2x - y &\geq 0 \\ x \geq 0, y &\geq 0. \end{aligned}$$

5. Maximize $p = 2x + 5y + 3z$
subject to
$$\begin{aligned} x + y + z &\leq 150 \\ x + y + z &\geq 100 \\ x \geq 0, y \geq 0, z &\geq 0. \end{aligned}$$

6. Maximize $p = 3x + 2y + 2z$
subject to
$$\begin{aligned} x + y + 2z &\leq 38 \\ 2x + y + z &\geq 24 \\ x \geq 0, y \geq 0, z &\geq 0. \end{aligned}$$

7. Maximize $p = 10x + 20y + 15z$
subject to
$$\begin{aligned} x + 2y + z &\leq 40 \\ 2y - z &\geq 10 \\ 2x - y + z &\geq 20 \\ x \geq 0, y \geq 0, z &\geq 0. \end{aligned}$$

8. Maximize $p = 10x + 10y + 15z$
subject to
$$\begin{aligned} x - y + z &\leq 12 \\ 2x - 2y + z &\geq 15 \\ -y + z &\geq 3 \\ x \geq 0, y \geq 0, z &\geq 0. \end{aligned}$$

9. Maximize $p = x + y + 3z + w$
subject to
$$\begin{aligned} x + y + z + w &\leq 40 \\ 2x + y - z - w &\geq 10 \\ x + y + z + w &\geq 10 \\ x \geq 0, y \geq 0, z \geq 0, w &\geq 0. \end{aligned}$$

10. Maximize $p = x + y + 4z + 2w$
subject to
$$\begin{aligned} x + y + z + w &\leq 50 \\ 2x + y - z - w &\geq 10 \\ x + y + z + w &\geq 20 \\ x \geq 0, y \geq 0, z \geq 0, w &\geq 0. \end{aligned}$$

11. Minimize $c = 6x + 6y$
subject to
$$\begin{aligned} x + 2y &\geq 20 \\ 2x + y &\geq 20 \\ x \geq 0, y &\geq 0. \end{aligned}$$
HINT [See Example 3.]

12. Minimize $c = 3x + 2y$
subject to
$$\begin{aligned} x + 2y &\geq 20 \\ 2x + y &\geq 10 \\ x \geq 0, y &\geq 0. \end{aligned}$$
HINT [See Example 3.]

13. Minimize $c = 2x + y + 3z$
subject to
$$\begin{aligned} x + y + z &\geq 100 \\ 2x + y &\geq 50 \\ y + z &\geq 50 \\ x \geq 0, y \geq 0, z &\geq 0. \end{aligned}$$

14. Minimize $c = 2x + 2y + 3z$
subject to
$$\begin{aligned} x + z &\geq 100 \\ 2x + y &\geq 50 \\ y + z &\geq 50 \\ x \geq 0, y \geq 0, z &\geq 0. \end{aligned}$$

15. Minimize $c = 50x + 50y + 11z$
subject to
$$\begin{aligned} 2x \quad + z &\ge 3 \\ 2x + y - z &\ge 2 \\ 3x + y - z &\le 3 \\ x \ge 0, y \ge 0, z &\ge 0. \end{aligned}$$

16. Minimize $c = 50x + 11y + 50z$
subject to
$$\begin{aligned} 3x \quad + z &\ge 8 \\ 3x + y - z &\ge 6 \\ 4x + y - z &\le 8 \\ x \ge 0, y \ge 0, z &\ge 0. \end{aligned}$$

17. Minimize $c = x + y + z + w$
subject to
$$\begin{aligned} 5x - y \quad + w &\ge 1{,}000 \\ z + w &\le 2{,}000 \\ x + y \quad &\le 500 \\ x \ge 0, y \ge 0, z \ge 0, w &\ge 0. \end{aligned}$$

18. Minimize $c = 5x + y + z + w$
subject to
$$\begin{aligned} 5x - y \quad + w &\ge 1{,}000 \\ z + w &\le 2{,}000 \\ x + y \quad &\le 500 \\ x \ge 0, y \ge 0, z \ge 0, w &\ge 0. \end{aligned}$$

In Exercises 19–24, we suggest the use of technology. Round all answers to two decimal places.

19. Maximize $p = 2x + 3y + 1.1z + 4w$
subject to
$$\begin{aligned} 1.2x + y + z + w &\le 40.5 \\ 2.2x + y - z - w &\ge 10 \\ 1.2x + y + z + 1.2w &\ge 10.5 \\ x \ge 0, y \ge 0, z \ge 0, w &\ge 0. \end{aligned}$$

20. Maximize $p = 2.2x + 2y + 1.1z + 2w$
subject to
$$\begin{aligned} x + 1.5y + 1.5z + w &\le 50.5 \\ 2x + 1.5y - z - w &\ge 10 \\ x + 1.5y + z + 1.5w &\ge 21 \\ x \ge 0, y \ge 0, z \ge 0, w &\ge 0. \end{aligned}$$

21. Minimize $c = 2.2x + y + 3.3z$
subject to
$$\begin{aligned} x + 1.5y + 1.2z &\ge 100 \\ 2x + 1.5y \quad &\ge 50 \\ 1.5y + 1.1z &\ge 50 \\ x \ge 0, y \ge 0, z &\ge 0. \end{aligned}$$

22. Minimize $c = 50.3x + 10.5y + 50.3z$
subject to
$$\begin{aligned} 3.1x \quad + 1.1z &\ge 28 \\ 3.1x + y - 1.1z &\ge 23 \\ 4.2x + y - 1.1z &\ge 28 \\ x \ge 0, y \ge 0, z &\ge 0. \end{aligned}$$

23. Minimize $c = 1.1x + y + 1.5z - w$
subject to
$$\begin{aligned} 5.12x - y \quad + w &\le 1{,}000 \\ z + w &\ge 2{,}000 \\ 1.22x + y \quad &\le 500 \\ x \ge 0, y \ge 0, z \ge 0, w &\ge 0. \end{aligned}$$

24. Minimize $c = 5.45x + y + 1.5z + w$
subject to
$$\begin{aligned} 5.12x - y \quad + w &\ge 1{,}000 \\ z + w &\ge 2{,}000 \\ 1.12x + y \quad &\le 500 \\ x \ge 0, y \ge 0, z \ge 0, w &\ge 0. \end{aligned}$$

APPLICATIONS

25. ***Agriculture*** (Compare Exercise 27 in Section 5.3.) Your small farm encompasses 100 acres, and you are planning to grow tomatoes, lettuce, and carrots in the coming planting season. Fertilizer costs per acre are: \$5 for tomatoes, \$4 for lettuce, and \$2 for carrots. Based on past experience, you estimate that each acre of tomatoes will require an average of 4 hours of labor per week, while tending to lettuce and carrots will each require an average of 2 hours per week. You estimate a profit of \$2,000 for each acre of tomatoes, \$1,500 for each acre of lettuce, and \$500 for each acre of carrots. You would like to spend at least \$400 on fertilizer (your niece owns the company that manufactures it) and your farm laborers can supply up to 500 hours per week. How many acres of each crop should you plant to maximize total profits? In this event, will you be using all 100 acres of your farm? HINT [See Example 3.]

26. ***Agriculture*** (Compare Exercise 28 in Section 5.3.) Your farm encompasses 900 acres, and you are planning to grow soybeans, corn, and wheat in the coming planting season. Fertilizer costs per acre are: \$5 for soybeans, \$2 for corn, and \$1 for wheat. You estimate that each acre of soybeans will require an average of 5 hours of labor per week, while tending to corn and wheat will each require an average of 2 hours per week. Based on past yields and current market prices, you estimate a profit of \$3,000 for each acre of soybeans, \$2,000 for each acre of corn, and \$1,000 for each acre of wheat. You can afford to spend no more than \$3,000 on fertilizer, but your labor union contract stipulates at least 2,000 hours per week of labor. How many acres of each crop should you plant to maximize total profits? In this event, will you be using more than 2,000 hours of labor? HINT [See Example 3.]

27. ***Politics*** The political pollster Canter is preparing for a national election. It would like to poll at least 1,500 Democrats and 1,500 Republicans. Each mailing to the East Coast gets responses from 100 Democrats and 50 Republicans. Each mailing to the Midwest gets responses from 100 Democrats and 100 Republicans. And each mailing to the West Coast gets responses from 50 Democrats and 100 Republicans. Mailings to the East Coast cost \$40 each to produce and mail, mailings to the Midwest cost \$60 each, and mailings to the West Coast cost \$50 each. How many mailings should Canter send to each area of the country to get the responses it needs at the least possible cost? What will it cost?

28. ***Purchasing*** *Bingo's Copy Center* needs to buy white paper and yellow paper. Bingo's can buy from three suppliers. Harvard Paper sells a package of 20 reams of white and 10 reams of yellow for \$60, Yale Paper sells a package of

10 reams of white and 10 reams of yellow for \$40, and Dartmouth Paper sells a package of 10 reams of white and 20 reams of yellow for \$50. If Bingo's needs 350 reams of white and 400 reams of yellow, how many packages should it buy from each supplier to minimize the cost? What is the least possible cost?

29. ***Resource Allocation*** *Succulent Citrus* produces orange juice and orange concentrate. This year the company anticipates a demand of at least 10,000 quarts of orange juice and 1,000 quarts of orange concentrate. Each quart of orange juice requires 10 oranges, and each quart of concentrate requires 50 oranges. The company also anticipates using at least 200,000 oranges for these products. Each quart of orange juice costs the company 50¢ to produce, and each quart of concentrate costs \$2.00 to produce. How many quarts of each product should Succulent Citrus produce to meet the demand and minimize total costs?

30. ***Resource Allocation*** *Fancy Pineapple* produces pineapple juice and canned pineapple rings. This year the company anticipates a demand of at least 10,000 pints of pineapple juice and 1,000 cans of pineapple rings. Each pint of pineapple juice requires 2 pineapples, and each can of pineapple rings requires 1 pineapple. The company anticipates using at least 20,000 pineapples for these products. Each pint of pineapple juice costs the company 20¢ to produce, and each can of pineapple rings costs 50¢ to produce. How many pints of pineapple juice and cans of pineapple rings should Fancy Pineapple produce to meet the demand and minimize total costs?

31. ***Latin Music Sales (Digital)*** You are about to go live with a Latin music download service called *iYayay* that will compete head-to-head with Apple's *iTunes®* (good luck!). You will be selling digital albums of regional (Mexican/Tejano) music for \$5 each, pop/rock albums for \$4 each, and tropical (salsa/merengue/cumbia/bachata) at \$6 per album. Your servers can handle up to 40,000 downloaded albums per day, and you anticipate that, based on national sales,[30] revenues from regional music will be at least fives times those from tropical music. You also anticipate that that you will sell at least 10,000 pop/rock albums per day due to the very attractive \$4 price. Based on these assumptions, how many of each type of album should you sell for a maximum daily revenue, and what will your daily revenue be?

32. ***Latin Music Sales (Digital)*** It seems that your biggest rival, Lupita Pelogrande, has learned about your music store and has decided to launch *iRico*, a competitor Latin Music download service that will also offer regional (Mexican/Tejano) music albums for \$5 each and pop/rock albums for \$4 each. However, instead of tropical music, *iRico* will offer reggaeton albums at only \$3 per album. Lupita's servers are more robust than yours, and can handle up to 60,000 downloaded albums per day. She anticipates that revenues from regional music can total to up to double those from reggaeton, and that *iRico* can sell at least 50,000 albums per day, not even counting reggaeton. Based on these assumptions, how many of each type of album should *iRico* sell for a maximum daily revenue, and what will the daily revenue be?

33. ***Nutrition*** Gerber Products' Gerber Mixed Cereal for Baby contains, in each serving, 60 calories and no Vitamin C. Gerber Mango Tropical Fruit Dessert contains, in each serving, 80 calories and 45% of the U.S. Recommended Daily Allowance (RDA) of Vitamin C for infants. Gerber Apple Banana Juice contains, in each serving, 60 calories and 120% of the RDA of Vitamin C for infants.[31] The cereal costs 10¢/serving, the dessert costs 53¢/serving, and the juice costs 27¢/serving. If you want to provide your child with at least 120 calories and at least 120% of the RDA of Vitamin C, how can you do so at the least cost?

34. ***Nutrition*** Gerber Products' Gerber Mixed Cereal for Baby contains, in each serving, 60 calories, no Vitamin C, and 11 grams of carbohydrates. Gerber Mango Tropical Fruit Dessert contains, in each serving, 80 calories, 45% of the RDA of Vitamin C for infants, and 21 grams of carbohydrates. Gerber Apple Banana Juice contains, in each serving, 60 calories, 120% of the RDA of Vitamin C for infants, and 15 grams of carbohydrates.[32] Assume that the cereal costs 11¢/serving, the dessert costs 50¢/serving, and the juice costs 30¢/serving. If you want to provide your child with at least 180 calories, at least 120% of the RDA of Vitamin C, and at least 37 grams of carbohydrates, how can you do so at the least cost?

35. ***Purchasing*** *Cheapskate Electronics Store* needs to update its inventory of stereos, TVs, and DVD players. There are three suppliers it can buy from: Nadir offers a bundle consisting of 5 stereos, 10 TVs, and 15 DVD players for \$3,000. Blunt offers a bundle consisting of 10 stereos, 10 TVs, and 10 DVD players for \$4,000. Sonny offers a bundle consisting of 15 stereos, 10 TVs, and 10 DVD players for \$5,000. Cheapskate Electronics needs at least 150 stereos, 200 TVs, and 150 DVD players. How can it update its inventory at the least possible cost? What is the least possible cost?

36. ***Purchasing*** *Federal Rent-a-Car* is putting together a new fleet. It is considering package offers from three car manufacturers. Fred Motors is offering 5 small cars, 5 medium cars, and 10 large cars for \$500,000. Admiral Motors is offering 5 small, 10 medium, and 5 large cars for \$400,000. Chrysalis is offering 10 small, 5 medium, and 5 large cars for \$300,000. Federal would like to buy at least 550 small cars, at least 500 medium cars, and at least 550 large cars. How many packages should it buy from each car maker to keep the total cost as small as possible? What will be the total cost?

[30] In 2010, total U.S. revenues from regional music were about five times those from tropical music. Source: Recording Industry Association of America http://riaa.org

[31] Source: Nutrition information supplied with the products.

[32] *Ibid.*

Bodybuilding Supplements *Exercises 37 and 38 are based on the following data on four bodybuilding supplements. (Figures shown correspond to a single serving.)*[33]

	Creatine (g)	*Carbohydrates (g)*	*Taurine (g)*	*Alpha Lipoic Acid (mg)*	*Cost ($)*
Cell-Tech® (MuscleTech)	10	75	2	200	2.20
RiboForce HP® (EAS)	5	15	1	0	1.60
Creatine Transport® (Kaizen)	5	35	1	100	0.60
Pre-Load Creatine® (Optimum)	6	35	1	25	0.50

37. (Compare Exercise 29 in Section 5.2.) You are thinking of combining Cell-Tech, RiboForce HP, and Creatine Transport to obtain a 10-day supply that provides at least 80 grams of creatine and at least 10 grams of taurine, but no more than 750 grams of carbohydrates and 1,000 milligrams of alpha lipoic acid. How many servings of each supplement should you combine to meet your specifications for the least cost?

38. (Compare Exercise 30 in Section 5.2.) You are thinking of combining RiboForce HP, Creatine Transport, and Pre-Load Creatine to obtain a 10-day supply that provides at least 80 grams of creatine and at least 10 grams of taurine, but no more than 600 grams of carbohydrates and 2,000 milligrams of alpha lipoic acid. How many servings of each supplement should you combine to meet your specifications for the least cost?

39. ▼ ***Subsidies*** The Miami Beach City Council has offered to subsidize hotel development in Miami Beach, and it is hoping for at least two hotels with a total capacity of at least 1,400. Suppose that you are a developer interested in taking advantage of this offer by building a small group of hotels in Miami Beach. You are thinking of three prototypes: a convention-style hotel with 500 rooms costing $100 million, a vacation-style hotel with 200 rooms costing $20 million, and a small motel with 50 rooms costing $4 million. The City Council will approve your plans, provided you build at least one convention-style hotel and no more than two small motels.

a. How many of each type of hotel should you build to satisfy the city council's wishes and stipulations while minimizing your total cost?

b. Now assume that the city council will give developers 20 percent of the cost of building new hotels in Miami Beach, up to $50 million.[34] Will the city's $50 million subsidy be sufficient to cover 20 percent of your total costs?

40. ▼ ***Subsidies*** Refer back to the preceding exercise. You are about to begin the financial arrangements for your new hotels when the city council informs you that it has changed its mind and now requires at least two vacation-style hotels and no more than four small motels.

a. How many of each type of hotel should you build to satisfy the city council's wishes and stipulations while minimizing your total costs?

b. Will the city's $50 million subsidy limit still be sufficient to cover 20 percent of your total costs?

41. ▼ ***Transportation Scheduling*** We return to your exploits coordinating distribution for the Tubular Ride Boogie Board Company.[35] You will recall that the company has manufacturing plants in Tucson, Arizona, and Toronto, Ontario, and you have been given the job of coordinating distribution of their latest model, the Gladiator, to their outlets in Honolulu and Venice Beach. The Tucson plant can manufacture up to 620 boards per week, while the Toronto plant, beset by labor disputes, can produce no more than 410 Gladiator boards per week. The outlet in Honolulu orders 500 Gladiator boards per week, while Venice Beach orders 530 boards per week. Transportation costs are as follows: Tucson to Honolulu: $10/board; Tucson to Venice Beach: $5/board; Toronto to Honolulu: $20/board; Toronto to Venice Beach: $10/board. Your manager has said that you are to be sure to fill all orders and ship the boogie boards at a minimum total transportation cost. How will you do it?

42. ▼ ***Transportation Scheduling*** In the situation described in the preceding exercise, you have just been notified that workers at the Toronto boogie board plant have gone on strike, resulting in a total work stoppage. You are to come up with a revised delivery schedule by tomorrow with the understanding that the Tucson plant can push production to a maximum of 1,000 boards per week. What should you do?

43. ▼ ***Finance*** Senator Porkbarrel habitually overdraws his three bank accounts, at the *Congressional Integrity Bank, Citizens' Trust,* and *Checks R Us*. There are no penalties because the overdrafts are subsidized by the taxpayer. The Senate Ethics Committee tends to let slide irregular banking activities as long as they are not flagrant. At the moment (due to Congress's preoccupation with a Supreme Court nominee), a total overdraft of up to $10,000 will be overlooked. Porkbarrel's conscience makes him hesitate to overdraw accounts at banks whose names include expressions like "integrity" and "citizens' trust." The effect is that his overdrafts at the first two banks combined amount to no more than one quarter of the total. On the other hand, the financial officers at Integrity Bank, aware that Senator Porkbarrel is a member of the Senate Banking Committee, "suggest" that he overdraw at least $2,500 from their bank. Find the amount he should overdraw from each bank in order to avoid investigation by the Ethics Committee and overdraw his account at Integrity by as much as his sense of guilt will allow.

[33]Source: Nutritional information supplied by the manufacturers (www.netrition.com). Cost per serving is approximate.

[34]The Miami Beach City Council made such an offer in 1993. (*Chicago Tribune*, June 20, 1993, Section 7, p. 8).

[35]See Exercise 26 in Section 3.3 and also Exercise 41 in Section 5.3. This time, we will use the simplex method to solve the version of this problem we first considered in the chapter on systems of equations.

44. ▼ *Scheduling* Because Joe Slim's brother was recently elected to the State Senate, Joe's financial advisement concern, *Inside Information Inc.,* has been doing a booming trade, even though the financial counseling he offers is quite worthless. (None of his seasoned clients pays the slightest attention to his advice.) Slim charges different hourly rates to different categories of individuals: $5,000/hour for private citizens, $50,000/hour for corporate executives, and $10,000/hour for presidents of universities. Due to his taste for leisure, he feels that he can spend no more than 40 hours/week in consultation. On the other hand, Slim feels that it would be best for his intellect were he to devote at least 10 hours of consultation each week to university presidents. However, Slim always feels somewhat uncomfortable dealing with academics, so he would prefer to spend no more than half his consultation time with university presidents. Furthermore, he likes to think of himself as representing the interests of the common citizen, so he wishes to offer at least 2 more hours of his time each week to private citizens than to corporate executives and university presidents combined. Given all these restrictions, how many hours each week should he spend with each type of client in order to maximize his income?

45. ▼ *Transportation Scheduling* Your publishing company is about to start a promotional blitz for its new book, *Advanced Quantum Mechanics for the Liberal Arts.* You have 20 salespeople stationed in Chicago and 10 in Denver. You would like to fly at least 10 into Los Angeles and at least 15 into New York. A round-trip plane flight from Chicago to LA costs $200; from Chicago to NY costs $125; from Denver to LA costs $225; and from Denver to NY costs $280.[36] How many salespeople should you fly from each of Chicago and Denver to each of LA and NY to spend the least amount on plane flights?

46. ▼ *Transportation Scheduling* Repeat Exercise 45, but now suppose that you would like at least 15 salespeople in Los Angeles.

47. ▣ ▼ *Hospital Staffing* As the staff director of a new hospital, you are planning to hire cardiologists, rehabilitation specialists, and infectious disease specialists. According to recent data, each cardiology case averages $12,000 in revenue, each physical rehabilitation case $19,000, and each infectious disease case, $14,000.[37] You judge that each specialist you employ will expand the hospital caseload by about 10 patients per week. You already have 3 cardiologists on staff, and the hospital is equipped to admit up to 200 patients per week. Based on past experience, each cardiologist and rehabilitation specialist brings in one government research grant per year, while each infectious disease specialist brings in three. Your board of directors would like to see

a total of at least 30 grants per year and would like your weekly revenue to be as large as possible. How many of each kind of specialist should you hire?

48. ▣ ▼ *Hospital Staffing* Referring to Exercise 47, you completely misjudged the number of patients each type of specialist would bring to the hospital per week. It turned out that each cardiologist brought in 120 new patients per *year,* each rehabilitation specialist brought in 90 per year, and each infectious disease specialist brought in 70 per year.[38] It also turned out that your hospital could deal with no more than 1,960 new patients per year. Repeat the preceding exercise in light of this corrected data.

COMMUNICATION AND REASONING EXERCISES

49. Explain the need for Phase I in a nonstandard LP problem.

50. Explain the need for Phase II in a nonstandard LP problem.

51. Explain briefly why we would need to use Phase I in solving a linear programming problem with the constraint $x + 2y - z \geq 3$.

52. Which rows do we star, and why?

53. Consider the following linear programming problem:

Maximize $p = x + y$
subject to $\quad x - 2y \geq 0$
$\qquad\qquad 2x + y \leq 10$
$\qquad\qquad x \geq 0, y \geq 0.$

This problem

(A) must be solved using the techniques of Section 5.4.
(B) must be solved using the techniques of Section 5.3.
(C) can be solved using the techniques of either section.

54. Consider the following linear programming problem:

Maximize $p = x + y$
subject to $\quad x - 2y \geq 1$
$\qquad\qquad 2x + y \leq 10$
$\qquad\qquad x \geq 0, y \geq 0.$

This problem

(A) must be solved using the techniques of Section 5.4.
(B) must be solved using the techniques of Section 5.3.
(C) can be solved using the techniques of either section.

55. ▼ Find a linear programming problem in three variables that requires one pivot in Phase I.

56. ▼ Find a linear programming problem in three variables that requires two pivots in Phase I.

57. ▼ Find a linear programming problem in two or three variables with no optimal solution, and show what happens when you try to solve it using the simplex method.

58. ▼ Find a linear programming problem in two or three variables with more than one optimal solution, and investigate which solution is found by the simplex method.

---

[36]Approximate prices advertised on various Web sites in September 2011.

[37]These (rounded) figures are based on an Illinois survey of 1.3 million hospital admissions (*Chicago Tribune,* March 29, 1993, Section 4, p. 1). Source: Lutheran General Health System, Argus Associates, Inc.

[38]These (rounded) figures were obtained from the survey referenced in the preceding exercise by dividing the average hospital revenue per physician by the revenue per case.

5.5 The Simplex Method and Duality

We mentioned **standard minimization problems** in the last section. These problems have the following form.

Standard Minimization Problem

A **standard minimization problem** is an LP problem in which we are required to *minimize* (not maximize) a linear objective function

$$c = as + bt + cu + \cdots$$

of the variables $s, t, u, \ldots$ (in this section, we will always use the letters $s, t, u, \ldots$ for the unknowns in a standard minimization problem) subject to the constraints

$$s \geq 0, t \geq 0, u \geq 0, \ldots$$

and further constraints of the form

$$As + Bt + Cu + \cdots \geq N$$

where $A, B, C, \ldots$ and N are numbers with N nonnegative.

A **standard linear programming problem** is an LP problem that is either a standard maximization problem or a standard minimization problem. An LP problem satisfies the **nonnegative objective condition** if all the coefficients in the objective function are nonnegative.

Quick Examples

Standard Minimization and Maximization Problems

1. Minimize $c = 2s + 3t + 3u$
   subject to $2s + u \geq 10$
   $s + 3t - 6u \geq 5$
   $s \geq 0, t \geq 0, u \geq 0.$

   This is a standard minimization problem satisfying the nonnegative objective condition.

2. Maximize $p = 2x + 3y + 3z$
   subject to $2x + z \leq 7$
   $x + 3y - 6z \leq 6$
   $x \geq 0, y \geq 0, z \geq 0.$

   This is a standard maximization problem satisfying the nonnegative objective condition.

3. Minimize $c = 2s - 3t + 3u$
   subject to $2s + u \geq 10$
   $s + 3t - 6u \geq 5$
   $s \geq 0, t \geq 0, u \geq 0.$

   This is a standard minimization problem that does *not* satisfy the nonnegative objective condition.

We saw a way of solving minimization problems in Section 5.4, but a mathematically elegant relationship between maximization and minimization problems gives us another way of solving minimization problems that satisfy the nonnegative objective condition. This relationship is called **duality**.

To describe duality, we must first represent an LP problem by a matrix. This matrix is *not* the first tableau but something simpler: Pretend you forgot all about slack variables and also forgot to change the signs of the objective function.* As an example, consider the following two standard† problems:

Problem 1

$$\begin{aligned} \text{Maximize} \quad & p = 20x + 20y + 50z \\ \text{subject to} \quad & 2x + \ \ y + 3z \le 2{,}000 \\ & x + 2y + 4z \le 3{,}000 \\ & x \ge 0, y \ge 0, z \ge 0. \end{aligned}$$

We represent this problem by the matrix

$$\left[\begin{array}{ccc|c} 2 & 1 & 3 & 2{,}000 \\ 1 & 2 & 4 & 3{,}000 \\ \hline 20 & 20 & 50 & 0 \end{array}\right]. \quad \begin{array}{l} \text{Constraint 1} \\ \text{Constraint 2} \\ \text{Objective} \end{array}$$

Notice that the coefficients of the objective function go in the bottom row, and we place a zero in the bottom right corner.

Problem 2 (from Example 3 in Section 5.4)

$$\begin{aligned} \text{Minimize} \quad & c = 2{,}000s + 3{,}000t \\ \text{subject to} \quad & 2s + \ \ t \ge 20 \\ & s + 2t \ge 20 \\ & 3s + 4t \ge 50 \\ & s \ge 0, t \ge 0. \end{aligned}$$

Problem 2 is represented by

$$\left[\begin{array}{cc|c} 2 & 1 & 20 \\ 1 & 2 & 20 \\ 3 & 4 & 50 \\ \hline 2{,}000 & 3{,}000 & 0 \end{array}\right]. \quad \begin{array}{l} \text{Constraint 1} \\ \text{Constraint 2} \\ \text{Constraint 3} \\ \text{Objective} \end{array}$$

These two problems are related: The matrix for Problem 1 is the transpose of the matrix for Problem 2. (Recall that the transpose of a matrix is obtained by writing its rows as columns; see Section 4.1.) When we have a pair of LP problems related in this way, we say that the two are *dual* LP problems.

Dual Linear Programming Problems

Two LP problems, one a maximization and one a minimization problem, are **dual** if the matrix that represents one is the transpose of the matrix that represents the other.

Finding the Dual of a Given Problem

Given an LP problem, we find its dual as follows:

1. Represent the problem as a matrix (see above).

2. Take the transpose of the matrix.

3. Write down the dual, which is the LP problem corresponding to the new matrix. If the original problem was a maximization problem, its dual will be a minimization problem, and vice versa.

The original problem is called the **primal problem**, and its dual is referred to as the **dual problem**.

* Forgetting these things is exactly what happens to many students under test conditions!

† Although duality does not require the problems to be standard, it does require them to be written in so-called *standard form*: In the case of a maximization problem all constraints need to be (re)written using $\le$, while for a minimization problem all constraints need to be (re)written using $\ge$. It is least confusing to stick with standard problems, which is what we will do in this section.

Quick Example

Primal problem

$$\begin{array}{ll}\text{Minimize} & c = s + 2t \\ \text{subject to} & 5s + 2t \geq 60 \\ & 3s + 4t \geq 80 \\ & s + t \geq 20 \\ & s \geq 0, t \geq 0.\end{array} \xrightarrow{1} \begin{bmatrix} 5 & 2 & 60 \\ 3 & 4 & 80 \\ 1 & 1 & 20 \\ 1 & 2 & 0 \end{bmatrix}$$

$$\xrightarrow{2} \begin{bmatrix} 5 & 3 & 1 & 1 \\ 2 & 4 & 1 & 2 \\ 60 & 80 & 20 & 0 \end{bmatrix} \xrightarrow{3}$$

Dual problem

$$\begin{array}{ll}\text{Maximize} & p = 60x + 80y + 20z \\ \text{subject to} & 5x + 3y + z \leq 1 \\ & 2x + 4y + z \leq 2 \\ & x \geq 0, y \geq 0, z \geq 0.\end{array}$$

The following theorem justifies what we have been doing, and says that solving the dual problem of an LP problem is equivalent to solving the original problem.

Fundamental Theorem of Duality

a. If an LP problem has an optimal solution, then so does its dual. Moreover, the primal problem and the dual problem have the same optimal value for their objective functions.

b. Contained in the final tableau of the simplex method applied to an LP problem is the solution to its dual problem: It is given by the bottom entries in the columns associated with the slack variables, divided by the entry under the objective variable.

The theorem* gives us an alternative way of solving minimization problems that satisfy the nonnegative objective condition. Let's illustrate by solving Problem 2 above.

* The proof of the theorem is beyond the scope of this book but can be found in a textbook devoted to linear programming, like *Linear Programming* by Vašek Chvátal (San Francisco: W. H. Freeman and Co., 1983), which has a particularly well-motivated discussion.

EXAMPLE 1 Solving by Duality

$$\begin{array}{ll}\text{Minimize} & c = 2{,}000s + 3{,}000t \\ \text{subject to} & 2s + t \geq 20 \\ & s + 2t \geq 20 \\ & 3s + 4t \geq 50 \\ & s \geq 0, t \geq 0.\end{array}$$

Solution

Step 1 ***Find the dual problem.*** Write the primal problem in matrix form and take the transpose:

$$\begin{bmatrix} 2 & 1 & 20 \\ 1 & 2 & 20 \\ 3 & 4 & 50 \\ 2{,}000 & 3{,}000 & 0 \end{bmatrix} \rightarrow \begin{bmatrix} 2 & 1 & 3 & 2{,}000 \\ 1 & 2 & 4 & 3{,}000 \\ 20 & 20 & 50 & 0 \end{bmatrix}.$$

The dual problem is:

$$\begin{array}{ll}\text{Maximize} & p = 20x + 20y + 50z \\ \text{subject to} & 2x + y + 3z \leq 2{,}000 \\ & x + 2y + 4z \leq 3{,}000 \\ & x \geq 0, y \geq 0, z \geq 0.\end{array}$$

Step 2 ***Use the simplex method to solve the dual problem.*** Because we have a standard maximization problem, we do not have to worry about Phase I but go straight to Phase II.

	x	y	z	s	t	p	
s	2	1	[3]	1	0	0	2,000
t	1	2	4	0	1	0	3,000
p	−20	−20	−50	0	0	1	0

	x	y	z	s	t	p	
z	2	1	3	1	0	0	2,000
t	−5	[2]	0	−4	3	0	1,000
p	40	−10	0	50	0	3	100,000

	x	y	z	s	t	p	
z	9	0	6	6	−3	0	3,000
y	−5	2	0	−4	3	0	1,000
p	15	0	0	30	15	3	105,000

Note that the maximum value of the objective function is $p = 105{,}000/3 = 35{,}000$. By the theorem, this is also the optimal value of c in the primal problem!

Step 3 ***Read off the solution to the primal problem by dividing the bottom entries in the columns associated with the slack variables by the entry in the p column.*** Here is the final tableau again with the entries in question highlighted.

	x	y	z	s	t	p	
z	9	0	6	6	−3	0	3,000
y	−5	2	0	−4	3	0	1,000
p	15	0	0	**30**	**15**	**3**	**105,000**

The solution to the primal problem is

$$s = 30/3 = 10,\ t = 15/3 = 5,\ c = 105{,}000/3 = 35{,}000.$$

(Compare this with the method we used to solve Example 3 in the preceding section. Which method seems more efficient?)

➡ **Before we go on...** Can you now see the reason for using the variable names $s, t, u, \ldots$ in standard minimization problems? ■

Q: *Is the theorem also useful for solving problems that do not satisfy the nonnegative objective condition?*

A: Consider a standard minimization problem that does not satisfy the nonnegative objective condition, such as

$$\begin{aligned} \text{Minimize} \quad & c = 2s - t \\ \text{subject to} \quad & 2s + 3t \geq 2 \\ & s + 2t \geq 2 \\ & s \geq 0,\ t \geq 0. \end{aligned}$$

Its dual would be

$$\begin{aligned} &\text{Maximize} \quad p = 2x + 2y \\ &\text{subject to} \quad 2x + \ \ y \le 2 \\ &\qquad\qquad 3x + 2y \le -1 \\ &\qquad\qquad x \ge 0,\ y \ge 0. \end{aligned}$$

This is not a standard maximization problem because the right-hand side of the second constraint is negative. In general, if a problem does not satisfy the nonnegative objective condition, its dual is not standard. Therefore, to solve the dual by the simplex method will require using Phase I as well as Phase II, and we may as well just solve the primal problem that way to begin with. Thus, duality helps us solve problems only when the primal problem satisfies the nonnegative objective condition.

In many economic applications, the solution to the dual problem also gives us useful information about the primal problem, as we will see in the following example.

EXAMPLE 2 Shadow Costs

You are trying to decide how many vitamin pills to take. SuperV brand vitamin pills each contain 2 milligrams of vitamin X, 1 milligram of vitamin Y, and 1 milligram of vitamin Z. Topper brand vitamin pills each contain 1 milligram of vitamin X, 1 milligram of vitamin Y, and 2 milligrams of vitamin Z. You want to take enough pills daily to get at least 12 milligrams of vitamin X, 10 milligrams of vitamin Y, and 12 milligrams of vitamin Z. However, SuperV pills cost 4¢ each and Toppers cost 3¢ each, and you would like to minimize the total cost of your daily dosage. How many of each brand of pill should you take? How would changing your daily vitamin requirements affect your minimum cost?

Solution This is a straightforward minimization problem. The unknowns are

s = number of SuperV brand pills
t = number of Topper brand pills.

The linear programming problem is

$$\begin{aligned} &\text{Minimize} \quad c = 4s + 3t \\ &\text{subject to} \quad 2s + \ \ t \ge 12 \\ &\qquad\qquad s + \ \ t \ge 10 \\ &\qquad\qquad s + 2t \ge 12 \\ &\qquad\qquad s \ge 0,\ t \ge 0. \end{aligned}$$

We solve this problem by using the simplex method on its dual, which is

$$\begin{aligned} &\text{Maximize} \quad p = 12x + 10y + 12z \\ &\text{subject to} \quad 2x + y + \ \ z \le 4 \\ &\qquad\qquad x + y + 2z \le 3 \\ &\qquad\qquad x \ge 0,\ y \ge 0,\ z \ge 0. \end{aligned}$$

After pivoting three times, we arrive at the final tableau:

	x	y	z	s	t	p	
x	6	0	−6	6	−6	0	6
y	0	1	3	−1	2	0	2
p	0	0	6	2	8	1	32

Therefore, the answer to the original problem is that you should take two SuperV vitamin pills and eight Toppers at a cost of 32¢ per day.

Now, the key to answering the last question, which asks you to determine how changing your daily vitamin requirements would affect your minimum cost, is to look at the solution to the dual problem. From the tableau we see that $x = 1$, $y = 2$, and $z = 0$. To see what x, y, and z might tell us about the original problem, let's look at their units. In the inequality $2x + y + z \leq 4$, the coefficient 2 of x has units "mg of vitamin X/SuperV pill," and the 4 on the right-hand side has units "¢/SuperV pill." For $2x$ to have the same units as the 4 on the right-hand side, x must have units "¢/mg of vitamin X." Similarly, y must have units "¢/mg of vitamin Y" and z must have units "¢/mg of vitamin Z." One can show (although we will not do it here) that x gives the amount that would be added to the minimum cost for each increase* of 1 milligram of vitamin X in our daily requirement. For example, if we were to increase our requirement from 12 milligrams to 14 milligrams, an increase of 2 milligrams, the minimum cost would change by $2x = 2$¢, from 32¢ to 34¢. (Try it; you'll end up taking four SuperV pills and six Toppers.) Similarly, each increase of 1 milligram of vitamin Y in the requirements would increase the cost by $y = 2$¢. These costs are called the **marginal costs** or the **shadow costs** of the vitamins.

* To be scrupulously correct, this works only for relatively small changes in the requirements, not necessarily for very large ones.

What about $z = 0$? The shadow cost of vitamin Z is 0¢/mg, meaning that you can increase your requirement of vitamin Z without changing your cost. In fact, the solution $s = 2$ and $t = 8$ provides you with 18 milligrams of vitamin Z, so you can increase the required amount of vitamin Z up to 18 milligrams without changing the solution at all.

We can also interpret the shadow costs as the effective cost to you of each milligram of each vitamin in the optimal solution. You are paying 1¢/milligram of vitamin X, 2¢/milligram of vitamin Y, and getting the vitamin Z for free. This gives a total cost of $1 \times 12 + 2 \times 10 + 0 \times 12 = 32$¢, as we know. Again, if you change your requirements slightly, these are the amounts you will pay per milligram of each vitamin.

Game Theory

We return to a topic we discussed in Section 4.4: solving two-person zero-sum games. In that section, we described how to solve games that could be reduced to 2×2 games or smaller. It turns out that we can solve larger games using linear programming and duality. We summarize the procedure, work through an example, and then discuss why it works.

Solving a Matrix Game

Step 1 Reduce the payoff matrix by dominance.

Step 2 Add a fixed number k to each of the entries so that they all become nonnegative and no column is all zero.

Step 3 Write 1s to the right of and below the matrix, and then write down the associated standard maximization problem. Solve this primal problem using the simplex method.

Step 4 Find the optimal strategies and the expected value as follows:

Column Strategy

1. Express the solution to the primal problem as a column vector.
2. Normalize by dividing each entry of the solution vector by p (which is also the sum of all the entries).
3. Insert zeros in positions corresponding to the columns deleted during reduction.

Row Strategy

1. Express the solution to the dual problem as a row vector.
2. Normalize by dividing each entry by p, which will once again be the sum of all the entries.
3. Insert zeros in positions corresponding to the rows deleted during reduction.

Value of the Game

$$e = \frac{1}{p} - k$$

EXAMPLE 3 Restaurant Inspector

You manage two restaurants, Tender Steaks Inn (TSI) and Break for a Steak (BFS). Even though you run the establishments impeccably, the Department of Health has been sending inspectors to your restaurants on a daily basis and fining you for minor infractions. You've found that you can head off a fine if you're present, but you can cover only one restaurant at a time. The Department of Health, on the other hand, has two inspectors, who sometimes visit the same restaurant and sometimes split up, one to each restaurant. The average fines you have been getting are shown in the following matrix.

		Health Inspectors		
		Both at BFS	*Both at TSI*	*One at Each*
You go to	**TSI**	\$8,000	0	\$2,000
	BFS	0	\$10,000	\$4,000

How should you choose which restaurant to visit to minimize your expected fine?

Solution This matrix is not quite the payoff matrix because fines, being penalties, should be negative payoffs. Thus, the payoff matrix is the following:

$$P = \begin{bmatrix} -8{,}000 & 0 & -2{,}000 \\ 0 & -10{,}000 & -4{,}000 \end{bmatrix}.$$

We follow the steps above to solve the game using the simplex method.

Step 1 There are no dominated rows or columns, so this game does not reduce.

Step 2 We add $k = 10{,}000$ to each entry so that none are negative, getting the following new matrix (with no zero column):

$$\begin{bmatrix} 2{,}000 & 10{,}000 & 8{,}000 \\ 10{,}000 & 0 & 6{,}000 \end{bmatrix}.$$

Step 3 We write 1s to the right and below this matrix:

$$\begin{bmatrix} 2{,}000 & 10{,}000 & 8{,}000 & 1 \\ 10{,}000 & 0 & 6{,}000 & 1 \\ 1 & 1 & 1 & 0 \end{bmatrix}.$$

The corresponding standard maximization problem is the following:

$$\begin{aligned} &\text{Maximize} && p = x + y + z \\ &\text{subject to} && 2{,}000x + 10{,}000y + 8{,}000z \le 1 \\ &&& 10{,}000x + 6{,}000z \le 1 \\ &&& x \ge 0,\ y \ge 0,\ z \ge 0. \end{aligned}$$

Step 4 We use the simplex method to solve this problem. After pivoting twice, we arrive at the final tableau:

	x	y	z	s	t	p	
y	0	50,000	34,000	5	−1	0	4
x	10,000	0	6,000	0	1	0	1
p	0	0	14,000	5	4	50,000	9

Column Strategy The solution to the primal problem is

$$\begin{bmatrix} x \\ y \\ z \end{bmatrix} = \begin{bmatrix} \frac{1}{10{,}000} \\ \frac{4}{50{,}000} \\ 0 \end{bmatrix}.$$

We divide each entry by $p = 9/50{,}000$, which is also the sum of the entries. This gives the optimal column strategy:

$$C = \begin{bmatrix} \frac{5}{9} \\ \frac{4}{9} \\ 0 \end{bmatrix}.$$

Thus, the inspectors' optimal strategy is to stick together, visiting BFS with probability $5/9$ and TSI with probability $4/9$.

Row Strategy The solution to the dual problem is

$$[s \quad t] = \begin{bmatrix} \frac{5}{50{,}000} & \frac{4}{50{,}000} \end{bmatrix}.$$

Once again, we divide by $p = 9/50{,}000$ to find the optimal row strategy:

$$R = \begin{bmatrix} \frac{5}{9} & \frac{4}{9} \end{bmatrix}.$$

Thus, you should visit TSI with probability $5/9$ and BFS with probability $4/9$.

Value of the Game Your expected average fine is

$$e = \frac{1}{p} - k = \frac{50{,}000}{9} - 10{,}000 = -\frac{40{,}000}{9} \approx -\$4{,}444.$$

Before we go on... We owe you an explanation of why the procedure we used in Example 3 works. The main point is to understand how we turn a game into a linear programming problem. It's not hard to see that adding a fixed number k to all the payoffs will change only the payoff, increasing it by k, and not change the optimal strategies. So let's pick up Example 3 from the point where we were considering the following game:

$$P = \begin{bmatrix} 2{,}000 & 10{,}000 & 8{,}000 \\ 10{,}000 & 0 & 6{,}000 \end{bmatrix}.$$

We are looking for the optimal strategies R and C for the row and column players, respectively; if e is the value of the game, we will have $e = RPC$. Let's concentrate first on the column player's strategy $C = [u \;\; v \;\; w]^T$, where u, v, and w are the unknowns we want to find. Because e is the value of the game, if the column player uses the optimal strategy C and the row player uses any old strategy S, the expected value with these strategies has to be e or better for the column player, so $SPC \le e$. Let's write that out for two particular choices of S. First, consider $S = [1 \;\; 0]$:

$$[1 \;\; 0]\begin{bmatrix} 2{,}000 & 10{,}000 & 8{,}000 \\ 10{,}000 & 0 & 6{,}000 \end{bmatrix}\begin{bmatrix} u \\ v \\ w \end{bmatrix} \le e.$$

Multiplied out, this gives

$$2{,}000u + 10{,}000v + 8{,}000w \le e.$$

Next, do the same thing for $S = [0 \;\; 1]$:

$$[0 \;\; 1]\begin{bmatrix} 2{,}000 & 10{,}000 & 8{,}000 \\ 10{,}000 & 0 & 6{,}000 \end{bmatrix}\begin{bmatrix} u \\ v \\ w \end{bmatrix} \le e$$

$$10{,}000u + 6{,}000w \le e.$$

It turns out that if these two inequalities are true, then $SPC \le e$ for any S at all, which is what the column player wants. These are starting to look like constraints in a linear programming problem, but the e appearing on the right is in the way. We get around this by dividing by e, which we know to be positive because all of the payoffs are nonnegative and no column is all zero (so the column player can't force the value of the game to be 0; here is where we need these assumptions). We get the following inequalities:

$$\begin{aligned} 2{,}000\left(\frac{u}{e}\right) + 10{,}000\left(\frac{v}{e}\right) + 8{,}000\left(\frac{w}{e}\right) &\le 1 \\ 10{,}000\left(\frac{u}{e}\right) \qquad\qquad\qquad + 6{,}000\left(\frac{w}{e}\right) &\le 1. \end{aligned}$$

Now we're getting somewhere. To make these look even more like linear constraints, we replace our unknowns u, v, and w with new unknowns, $x = u/e$, $y = v/e$, and $z = w/e$. Our inequalities then become.

$$\begin{aligned} 2{,}000x + 10{,}000y + 8{,}000z &\le 1 \\ 10{,}000x \qquad\qquad + 6{,}000z &\le 1. \end{aligned}$$

What about an objective function? From the point of view of the column player, the objective is to find a strategy that will minimize the expected value e. In order to write e in terms of our new variables x, y, and z, we use the fact that our original variables, being the entries in the column strategy, have to add up to 1: $u + v + w = 1$. Dividing by e gives

$$\frac{u}{e} + \frac{v}{e} + \frac{w}{e} = \frac{1}{e}$$

or

$$x + y + z = \frac{1}{e}.$$

Now we notice that, if we *maximize* $p = x + y + z = 1/e$, it will have the effect of minimizing e, which is what we want. So, we get the following linear programming problem:

$$\begin{aligned} \text{Maximize} \quad & p = x + y + z \\ \text{subject to} \quad & 2{,}000x + 10{,}000y + 8{,}000z \le 1 \\ & 10{,}000x \qquad\qquad\quad + 6{,}000z \le 1 \\ & x \ge 0,\ y \ge 0,\ z \ge 0. \end{aligned}$$

Why can we say that x, y, and z should all be nonnegative? Because the unknowns u, v, w, and e must all be nonnegative.

So now, if we solve this linear programming problem to find x, y, z, and p, we can find the column player's optimal strategy by computing $u = xe = x/p$, $v = y/p$, and $w = z/p$. Moreover, the value of the game is $e = 1/p$. (If we added k to all the payoffs, we should now adjust by subtracting k again to find the correct value of the game.)

Turning now to the row player's strategy, if we repeat the above type of argument from the row player's viewpoint, we'll end up with the following linear programming problem to solve:

$$\begin{aligned} \text{Minimize} \quad & c = s + t \\ \text{subject to} \quad & 2{,}000s + 10{,}000t \ge 1 \\ & 10{,}000s \qquad\qquad \ge 1 \\ & 8{,}000s + \ 6{,}000t \ge 1 \\ & s \ge 0,\ t \ge 0. \end{aligned}$$

This is, of course, the dual to the problem we solved to find the column player's strategy, so we know that we can read its solution off of the same final tableau. The optimal value of c will be the same as the value of p, so $c = 1/e$ also. The entries in the optimal row strategy will be s/c and t/c. ■

FAQs

When to Use Duality

Q: *Given a minimization problem, when should I use duality, and when should I use the two-phase method in Section 5.4?*

A: If the original problem satisfies the nonnegative objective condition (none of the coefficients in the objective function are negative), then you can use duality to convert the problem to a standard maximization one, which can be solved with the one-phase method. If the original problem does not satisfy the nonnegative objective condition, then dualizing results in a nonstandard LP problem, so dualizing may not be worthwhile.

Q: *When is it absolutely necessary to use duality?*

A: Never. Duality gives us an efficient but not necessary alternative for solving standard minimization problems.

5.5 EXERCISES

▼ more advanced ◆ challenging

T indicates exercises that should be solved using technology

In Exercises 1–8, write down (without solving) the dual LP problem. HINT [See the Quick Example on page 371.]

1. Maximize $p = 2x + y$
subject to
$x + 2y \le 6$
$-x + y \le 2$
$x \ge 0, y \ge 0.$

2. Maximize $p = x + 5y$
subject to
$x + y \le 6$
$-x + 3y \le 4$
$x \ge 0, y \ge 0.$

3. Minimize $c = 2s + t + 3u$
subject to
$s + t + u \ge 100$
$2s + t \ge 50$
$s \ge 0, t \ge 0, u \ge 0.$

4. Minimize $c = 2s + 2t + 3u$
subject to
$s + u \ge 100$
$2s + t \ge 50$
$s \ge 0, t \ge 0, u \ge 0.$

5. Maximize $p = x + y + z + w$
subject to
$x + y + z \le 3$
$y + z + w \le 4$
$x + z + w \le 5$
$x + y + w \le 6$
$x \ge 0, y \ge 0, z \ge 0, w \ge 0.$

6. Maximize $p = x + y + z + w$
subject to
$x + y + z \le 3$
$y + z + w \le 3$
$x + z + w \le 4$
$x + y + w \le 4$
$x \ge 0, y \ge 0, z \ge 0, w \ge 0.$

7. Minimize $c = s + 3t + u$
subject to
$5s - t + v \ge 1{,}000$
$u - v \ge 2{,}000$
$s + t \ge 500$
$s \ge 0, t \ge 0, u \ge 0, v \ge 0.$

8. Minimize $c = 5s + 2u + v$
subject to
$s - t + 2v \ge 2{,}000$
$u + v \ge 3{,}000$
$s + t \ge 500$
$s \ge 0, t \ge 0, u \ge 0, v \ge 0.$

In Exercises 9–22, solve the standard minimization problems using duality. (You may already have seen some of them in earlier sections, but now you will be solving them using a different method.) HINT [See Example 1.]

9. Minimize $c = s + t$
subject to
$s + 2t \ge 6$
$2s + t \ge 6$
$s \ge 0, t \ge 0.$

10. Minimize $c = s + 2t$
subject to
$s + 3t \ge 30$
$2s + t \ge 30$
$s \ge 0, t \ge 0.$

11. Minimize $c = 6s + 6t$
subject to
$s + 2t \ge 20$
$2s + t \ge 20$
$s \ge 0, t \ge 0.$

12. Minimize $c = 3s + 2t$
subject to
$s + 2t \ge 20$
$2s + t \ge 10$
$s \ge 0, t \ge 0.$

13. Minimize $c = 0.2s + 0.3t$
subject to
$2s + t \ge 10$
$s + 2t \ge 10$
$s + t \ge 8$
$s \ge 0, t \ge 0.$

14. Minimize $c = 0.4s + 0.1t$
subject to
$3s + 2t \ge 60$
$s + 2t \ge 40$
$2s + 3t \ge 45$
$s \ge 0, t \ge 0.$

15. Minimize $c = 2s + t$
subject to
$3s + t \ge 30$
$s + t \ge 20$
$s + 3t \ge 30$
$s \ge 0, t \ge 0.$

16. Minimize $c = s + 2t$
subject to
$4s + t \ge 100$
$2s + t \ge 80$
$s + 3t \ge 150$
$s \ge 0, t \ge 0.$

17. Minimize $c = s + 2t + 3u$
subject to
$3s + 2t + u \ge 60$
$2s + t + 3u \ge 60$
$s \ge 0, t \ge 0, u \ge 0.$

18. Minimize $c = s + t + 2u$

subject to
$$\begin{aligned} s + 2t + 2u &\geq 60 \\ 2s + t + 3u &\geq 60 \\ s \geq 0, t \geq 0, u &\geq 0. \end{aligned}$$

19. Minimize $c = 2s + t + 3u$

subject to
$$\begin{aligned} s + t + u &\geq 100 \\ 2s + t \quad &\geq 50 \\ t + u &\geq 50 \\ s \geq 0, t \geq 0, u &\geq 0. \end{aligned}$$

20. Minimize $c = 2s + 2t + 3u$

subject to
$$\begin{aligned} s \quad + u &\geq 100 \\ 2s + t \quad &\geq 50 \\ t + u &\geq 50 \\ s \geq 0, t \geq 0, u &\geq 0. \end{aligned}$$

21. Minimize $c = s + t + u$

subject to
$$\begin{aligned} 3s + 2t + u &\geq 60 \\ 2s + t + 3u &\geq 60 \\ s + 3t + 2u &\geq 60 \\ s \geq 0, t \geq 0, u &\geq 0. \end{aligned}$$

22. Minimize $c = s + t + 2u$

subject to
$$\begin{aligned} s + 2t + 2u &\geq 60 \\ 2s + t + 3u &\geq 60 \\ s + 3t + 6u &\geq 60 \\ s \geq 0, t \geq 0, u &\geq 0. \end{aligned}$$

In Exercises 23–28, solve the games with the given payoff matrices. HINT [See Example 3.]

23. $P = \begin{bmatrix} -1 & 1 & 2 \\ 2 & -1 & -2 \end{bmatrix}$

24. $P = \begin{bmatrix} 1 & -1 & 2 \\ 1 & 2 & 0 \end{bmatrix}$

25. $P = \begin{bmatrix} -1 & 1 & 2 \\ 2 & -1 & -2 \\ 1 & 2 & 0 \end{bmatrix}$

26. $P = \begin{bmatrix} 1 & -1 & 2 \\ 1 & 2 & 0 \\ 0 & 1 & 1 \end{bmatrix}$

27. $P = \begin{bmatrix} -1 & 1 & 2 & -1 \\ 2 & -1 & -2 & -3 \\ 1 & 2 & 0 & 1 \\ 0 & 2 & 3 & 3 \end{bmatrix}$

28. $P = \begin{bmatrix} 1 & -1 & 2 & 0 \\ 1 & 2 & 0 & 1 \\ 0 & 1 & 1 & 0 \\ 2 & 0 & -2 & 2 \end{bmatrix}$

APPLICATIONS

Exercises 29–38 are similar to ones in preceding exercise sets. Use duality to answer them.

29. ***Nutrition*** Meow makes cat food out of fish and cornmeal. Fish has 8 grams of protein and 4 grams of fat per ounce, and cornmeal has 4 grams of protein and 8 grams of fat. A jumbo can of cat food must contain at least 48 grams of protein and 48 grams of fat. If fish and cornmeal both cost 5¢/ounce, how many ounces of each should Meow use in each can of cat food to minimize costs? What are the shadow costs of protein and of fat? HINT [See Example 2.]

30. ***Nutrition*** Oz makes lion food out of giraffe and gazelle meat. Giraffe meat has 18 grams of protein and 36 grams of fat per pound, while gazelle meat has 36 grams of protein and 18 grams of fat per pound. A batch of lion food must contain at least 36,000 grams of protein and 54,000 grams of fat. Giraffe meat costs \$2/pound and gazelle meat costs \$4/pound. How many pounds of each should go into each batch of lion food in order to minimize costs? What are the shadow costs of protein and fat? HINT [See Example 2.]

31. ***Nutrition*** *Ruff* makes dog food out of chicken and grain. Chicken has 10 grams of protein and 5 grams of fat/ounce, and grain has 2 grams of protein and 2 grams of fat/ounce. A bag of dog food must contain at least 200 grams of protein and at least 150 grams of fat. If chicken costs 10¢/ounce and grain costs 1¢/ounce, how many ounces of each should Ruff use in each bag of dog food in order to minimize cost? What are the shadow costs of protein and fat?

32. ***Purchasing*** The Enormous State University's Business School is buying computers. The school has two models to choose from, the Pomegranate and the iZac. Each Pomegranate comes with 400 GB of memory and 80 TB of disk space, while each iZac has 300 GB of memory and 100 TB of disk space. For reasons related to its accreditation, the school would like to be able to say that it has a total of at least 48,000 GB of memory and at least 12,800 TB of disk space. If both the Pomegranate and the iZac cost \$2,000 each, how many of each should the school buy to keep the cost as low as possible? What are the shadow costs of memory and disk space?

33. ***Nutrition*** Each serving of Gerber Mixed Cereal for Baby contains 60 calories and no vitamin C. Each serving of Gerber Mango Tropical Fruit Dessert contains 80 calories and 45 percent of the U.S. Recommended Daily Allowance (RDA) of vitamin C for infants. Each serving of Gerber Apple Banana Juice contains 60 calories and 120 percent of the U.S. RDA of vitamin C for infants.[39] The cereal costs 10¢/serving, the dessert costs 53¢/serving, and the juice costs 27¢/serving. If you want to provide your child with at least 120 calories and at least 120 percent of the U.S. RDA of vitamin C, how can you do so at the least cost? What are your shadow costs for calories and vitamin C?

34. ***Nutrition*** Each serving of Gerber Mixed Cereal for Baby contains 60 calories, no vitamin C, and 11 grams of carbohydrates. Each serving of Gerber Mango Tropical Fruit Dessert contains 80 calories, 45 percent of the U.S. Recommended Daily Allowance (RDA) of vitamin C for infants, and 21 grams of carbohydrates. Each serving of Gerber Apple Banana Juice contains 60 calories, 120 percent of the U.S. RDA of vitamin C for infants, and 15 grams of carbohydrates.[40]

[39] Source: Nutrition information supplied with the products.

[40] *Ibid.*

Assume that the cereal costs 11¢/serving, the dessert costs 50¢/serving, and the juice costs 30¢/serving. If you want to provide your child with at least 180 calories, at least 120 percent of the U.S. RDA of vitamin C, and at least 37 grams of carbohydrates, how can you do so at the least cost? What are your shadow costs for calories, vitamin C, and carbohydrates?

35. ***Politics*** The political pollster Canter is preparing for a national election. It would like to poll at least 1,500 Democrats and 1,500 Republicans. Each mailing to the East Coast gets responses from 100 Democrats and 50 Republicans. Each mailing to the Midwest gets responses from 100 Democrats and 100 Republicans. And each mailing to the West Coast gets responses from 50 Democrats and 100 Republicans. Mailings to the East Coast cost $40 each to produce and mail, mailings to the Midwest cost $60 each, and mailings to the West Coast cost $50 each. How many mailings should Canter send to each area of the country to get the responses it needs at the least possible cost? What will it cost? What are the shadow costs of a Democratic response and a Republican response?

36. ***Purchasing*** *Bingo's Copy Center* needs to buy white paper and yellow paper. Bingo's can buy from three suppliers. Harvard Paper sells a package of 20 reams of white and 10 reams of yellow for $60; Yale Paper sells a package of 10 reams of white and 10 reams of yellow for $40, and Dartmouth Paper sells a package of 10 reams of white and 20 reams of yellow for $50. If Bingo's needs 350 reams of white and 400 reams of yellow, how many packages should it buy from each supplier so as to minimize the cost? What is the lowest possible cost? What are the shadow costs of white paper and yellow paper?

37. ▼ ***Resource Allocation*** One day Gillian the Magician summoned the wisest of her women. "Devoted followers," she began, "I have a quandary: As you well know, I possess great expertise in sleep spells and shock spells, but unfortunately, these are proving to be a drain on my aural energy resources; each sleep spell costs me 500 pico-shirleys of aural energy, while each shock spell requires 750 pico-shirleys. Clearly, I would like to hold my overall expenditure of aural energy to a minimum, and still meet my commitments in protecting the Sisterhood from the ever-present threat of trolls. Specifically, I have estimated that each sleep spell keeps us safe for an average of 2 minutes, while every shock spell protects us for about 3 minutes. We certainly require enough protection to last 24 hours of each day, and possibly more, just to be safe. At the same time, I have noticed that each of my sleep spells can immobilize 3 trolls at once, while one of my typical shock spells (having a narrower range) can immobilize only 2 trolls at once. We are faced, my sisters, with an onslaught of 1,200 trolls per day! Finally, as you are no doubt aware, the bylaws dictate that for a Magician of the Order to remain in good standing, the number of shock spells must be between one quarter and one third the number of shock and sleep spells combined. What do I do, oh Wise Ones?"

38. ▼ ***Risk Management*** The Grand Vizier of the Kingdom of Um is being blackmailed by numerous individuals and is having a very difficult time keeping his blackmailers from going public. He has been keeping them at bay with two kinds of payoff: gold bars from the Royal Treasury and political favors. Through bitter experience, he has learned that each payoff in gold gives him peace for an average of about one month, and each political favor seems to earn him about a month and a half of reprieve. To maintain his flawless reputation in the court, he feels he cannot afford any revelations about his tainted past to come to light within the next year. Thus, it is imperative that his blackmailers be kept at bay for 12 months. Furthermore, he would like to keep the number of gold payoffs at no more than one quarter of the combined number of payoffs because the outward flow of gold bars might arouse suspicion on the part of the Royal Treasurer. The gold payoffs tend to deplete the Grand Vizier's travel budget. (The treasury has been subsidizing his numerous trips to the Himalayas.) He estimates that each gold bar removed from the treasury will cost him four trips. On the other hand, because the administering of political favors tends to cost him valuable travel time, he suspects that each political favor will cost him about two trips. Now, he would obviously like to keep his blackmailers silenced and lose as few trips as possible. What is he to do? How many trips will he lose in the next year?

39. ▼ ***Game Theory—Politics*** Incumbent Tax N. Spend and challenger Trick L. Down are running for county executive, and polls show them to be in a dead heat. The election hinges on three cities: Littleville, Metropolis, and Urbantown. The candidates have decided to spend the last weeks before the election campaigning in those three cities; each day each candidate will decide in which city to spend the day. Pollsters have determined the following payoff matrix, where the payoff represents the number of votes gained or lost for each one-day campaign trip.

		T. N. Spend		
		Littleville	*Metropolis*	*Urbantown*
T. L. Down	**Littleville**	−200	−300	300
	Metropolis	−500	500	−100
	Urbantown	−500	0	0

What percentage of time should each candidate spend in each city in order to maximize votes gained? If both candidates use their optimal strategies, what is the expected vote?

40. ▼ ***Game Theory—Marketing*** Your company's new portable phone/music player/PDA/bottle washer, the RunMan, will compete against the established market leader, the iNod, in a saturated market. (Thus, for each device you sell, one fewer iNod is sold.) You are planning to launch the RunMan with a traveling road show, concentrating on two cities,

New York and Boston. The makers of the iNod will do the same to try to maintain their sales. If, on a given day, you both go to New York, you will lose 1,000 units in sales to the iNod. If you both go to Boston, you will lose 750 units in sales. On the other hand, if you go to New York and your competitor to Boston, you will gain 1,500 units in sales from them. If you go to Boston and they to New York, you will gain 500 units in sales. What percentage of time should you spend in New York and what percentage in Boston, and how do you expect your sales to be affected?

41. ▼ ***Game Theory—Morra Games*** A three-finger *Morra game* is a game in which two players simultaneously show one, two, or three fingers at each round. The outcome depends on a predetermined set of rules. Here is an interesting example: If the numbers of fingers shown by A and B differ by 1, then A loses one point. If they differ by more than 1, the round is a draw. If they show the same number of fingers, A wins an amount equal to the sum of the fingers shown. Determine the optimal strategy for each player and the expected value of the game.

42. ▼ ***Game Theory—Morra Games*** Referring to the preceding exercise, consider the following rules for a three-finger Morra game: If the sum of the fingers shown is odd, then A wins an amount equal to that sum. If the sum is even, B wins the sum. Determine the optimal strategy for each player and the expected value of the game. HINT [Use technology to do the pivoting in the associated linear programming problem.]

43. ◆ ***Game Theory—Military Strategy*** Colonel Blotto is a well-known game in military strategy.[41] Here is a version of this game: Colonel Blotto has four regiments under his command, while his opponent, Captain Kije, has three. The armies are to try to occupy two locations, and each commander must decide how many regiments to send to each location. The army that sends more regiments to a location captures that location as well as the other army's regiments. If both armies send the same number of regiments to a location, then there is a draw. The payoffs are one point for each location captured and one point for each regiment captured. Find the optimum strategy for each commander and also the value of the game.

44. ◆ ***Game Theory—Military Strategy*** Referring to the preceding exercise, consider the version of Colonel Blotto with the same payoffs given there except that Captain Kije earns two points for each location captured, while Colonel Blotto continues to earn only one point. Find the optimum strategy for each commander and also the value of the game. Round all figures to two decimal places.

COMMUNICATION AND REASONING EXERCISES

45. Give one possible advantage of using duality to solve a standard minimization problem.

46. To ensure that the dual of a minimization problem will result in a standard maximization problem,

(A) the primal problem should satisfy the nonnegative objective condition.

(B) the primal problem should be a standard minimization problem.

(C) the primal problem should not satisfy the nonnegative objective condition.

47. Give an example of a standard minimization problem whose dual is *not* a standard maximization problem. How would you go about solving your problem?

48. Give an example of a nonstandard minimization problem whose dual is a standard maximization problem.

49. ▼ Given a minimization problem, when would you solve it by applying the simplex method to its dual, and when would you apply the simplex method to the minimization problem itself?

50. ▼ Create an interesting application that leads to a standard maximization problem. Solve it using the simplex method and note the solution to its dual problem. What does the solution to the dual tell you about your application?

---

[41]See Samuel Karlin, *Mathematical Methods and Theory in Games, Programming and Economics* (Addison-Wesley, 1959).

CHAPTER 5 REVIEW

KEY CONCEPTS

Website www.WanerMath.com

Go to the Website at www.WanerMath.com to find a comprehensive and interactive Web-based summary of Chapter 5.

5.1 Graphing Linear Inequalities

Inequalities, strict and nonstrict *p. 313*
Linear inequalities *p. 313*
Solution of an inequality *p. 313*
Sketching the region represented by a linear inequality in two variables *p. 315*
Bounded and unbounded regions *p. 318*
Feasible region *p. 318*

5.2 Solving Linear Programming Problems Graphically

Linear programming (LP) problem in two unknowns; objective function; constraints; optimal value; optimal solution *p. 322*
Feasible region *p. 323*
Fundamental Theorem of Linear Programming *p. 323*
Graphical method for solving an LP problem *p. 324*
Decision variables *p. 325*
Procedure for solving an LP problem with an unbounded feasible region *p. 328*

5.3 The Simplex Method: Solving Standard Maximization Problems

General linear programming problem in n unknowns *p. 339*
Standard maximization problem *p. 339*
Slack variable *p. 340*
Tableau *p. 341*
Active (or basic) variables; inactive (or nonbasic) variables; basic solution *p. 341*
Rules for selecting the pivot column *p. 342*
Rules for selecting the pivot; test ratios *p. 343*
Departing or exiting variable, entering variable *p. 343*

5.4 The Simplex Method: Solving General Linear Programming Problems

Surplus variable *p. 356*
Phase I and Phase II for solving general LP problems *p. 356*
Using the simplex method to solve a minimization problem *p. 361*

5.5 The Simplex Method and Duality

Standard minimization problem *p. 369*
Standard LP problem *p. 369*
Nonnegative objective condition *p. 369*
Dual LP problems; primal problem; dual problem *p. 370*
Fundamental Theorem of Duality *p. 371*
Shadow costs *p. 374*
Game theory: The LP problem associated with a two-person zero-sum game *p. 374*

REVIEW EXERCISES

In each of Exercises 1–4, sketch the region corresponding to the given inequalities, say whether it is bounded, and give the coordinates of all corner points.

1. $2x - 3y \le 12$

2. $x \le 2y$

3. $x + 2y \le 20$
$3x + 2y \le 30$
$x \ge 0, y \ge 0$

4. $3x + 2y \ge 6$
$2x - 3y \le 6$
$3x - 2y \ge 0$
$x \ge 0, y \ge 0$

In each of Exercises 5–8, solve the given linear programming problem graphically.

5. Maximize $p = 2x + y$
subject to $3x + y \le 30$
$x + y \le 12$
$x + 3y \le 30$
$x \ge 0, y \ge 0.$

6. Maximize $p = 2x + 3y$
subject to $x + y \ge 10$
$2x + y \ge 12$
$x + y \le 20$
$x \ge 0, y \ge 0.$

7. Minimize $c = 2x + y$
subject to $3x + y \ge 30$
$x + 2y \ge 20$
$2x - y \ge 0$
$x \ge 0, y \ge 0.$

8. Minimize $c = 3x + y$
subject to $3x + 2y \ge 6$
$2x - 3y \le 0$
$3x - 2y \ge 0$
$x \ge 0, y \ge 0.$

In each of Exercises 9–18, solve the given linear programming problem using the simplex method. If no optimal solution exists, indicate whether the feasible region is empty or the objective function is unbounded.

9. Maximize $p = x + y + 2z$
subject to $x + 2y + 2z \le 60$
$2x + y + 3z \le 60$
$x \ge 0, y \ge 0, z \ge 0.$

10. Maximize $p = x + y + 2z$
subject to $x + 2y + 2z \le 60$
$2x + y + 3z \le 60$
$x + 3y + 6z \le 60$
$x \ge 0, y \ge 0, z \ge 0.$

11. Maximize $p = x + y + 3z$
subject to $x + y + z \ge 100$
$y + z \le 80$
$x + z \le 80$
$x \ge 0, y \ge 0, z \ge 0.$

12. Maximize $p = 2x + y$
subject to $x + 2y \ge 12$
$2x + y \le 12$
$x + y \le 5$
$x \ge 0, y \ge 0.$

13. Minimize $c = x + 2y + 3z$
subject to $3x + 2y + z \geq 60$
$2x + y + 3z \geq 60$
$x \geq 0, y \geq 0, z \geq 0.$

14. Minimize $c = 5x + 4y + 3z$
subject to $x + y + 4z \geq 30$
$2x + y + 3z \geq 60$
$x \geq 0, y \geq 0, z \geq 0.$

15. T Minimize $c = x - 2y + 4z$
subject to $3x + 2y - z \geq 10$
$2x + y + 3z \geq 20$
$x + 3y - 2z \geq 30$
$x \geq 0, y \geq 0, z \geq 0.$

16. T Minimize $c = x + y - z$
subject to $3x + 2y + z \geq 60$
$2x + y + 3z \geq 60$
$x + 3y + 2z \geq 60$
$x \geq 0, y \geq 0, z \geq 0.$

17. Minimize $c = x + y + z + w$
subject to $x + y \geq 30$
$x + z \geq 20$
$x + y - w \leq 10$
$y + z - w \leq 10$
$x \geq 0, y \geq 0, z \geq 0, w \geq 0.$

18. Minimize $c = 4x + y + z + w$
subject to $x + y \geq 30$
$y - z \leq 20$
$z - w \leq 10$
$x \geq 0, y \geq 0, z \geq 0, w \geq 0.$

In each of Exercises 19–22, solve the given linear programming problem using duality.

19. Minimize $c = 2x + y$
subject to $3x + 2y \geq 60$
$2x + y \geq 60$
$x + 3y \geq 60$
$x \geq 0, y \geq 0.$

20. Minimize $c = 2x + y + 2z$
subject to $3x + 2y + z \geq 100$
$2x + y + 3z \geq 200$
$x \geq 0, y \geq 0, z \geq 0.$

21. Minimize $c = 2x + y$
subject to $3x + 2y \geq 10$
$2x - y \leq 30$
$x + 3y \geq 60$
$x \geq 0, y \geq 0.$

22. Minimize $c = 2x + y + 2z$
subject to $3x - 2y + z \geq 100$
$2x + y - 3z \leq 200$
$x \geq 0, y \geq 0, z \geq 0.$

In each of Exercises 23–26, solve the game with the given payoff matrix.

23. $P = \begin{bmatrix} -1 & 2 & -1 \\ 1 & -2 & 1 \\ 3 & -1 & 0 \end{bmatrix}$ **24.** $P = \begin{bmatrix} -3 & 0 & 1 \\ -4 & 0 & 0 \\ 0 & -1 & -2 \end{bmatrix}$

25. $P = \begin{bmatrix} -3 & -2 & 3 \\ 1 & 0 & 0 \\ -2 & 2 & 1 \end{bmatrix}$ **26.** $P = \begin{bmatrix} -4 & -2 & -3 \\ 1 & -3 & -2 \\ -3 & 1 & -4 \end{bmatrix}$

Exercises 27–30 are adapted from the Actuarial Exam on Operations Research.

27. You are given the following linear programming problem:

Minimize $c = x + 2y$
subject to $-2x + y \geq 1$
$x - 2y \geq 1$
$x \geq 0, y \geq 0.$

Which of the following is true?

(A) The problem has no feasible solutions.
(B) The objective function is unbounded.
(C) The problem has optimal solutions.

28. Repeat the preceding exercise with the following linear programming problem:

Maximize $p = x + y$
subject to $-2x + y \leq 1$
$x - 2y \leq 2$
$x \geq 0, y \geq 0.$

29. Determine the optimal value of the objective function. You are given the following linear programming problem.

Maximize $Z = x_1 + 4x_2 + 2x_3 - 10$
subject to $4x_1 + x_2 + x_3 \leq 45$
$-x_1 + x_2 + 2x_3 \leq 0$
$x_1, x_2, x_3 \geq 0.$

30. Determine the optimal value of the objective function. You are given the following linear programming problem.

Minimize $Z = x_1 + 4x_2 + 2x_3 + x_4 + 40$
subject to $4x_1 + x_2 + x_3 \leq 45$
$-x_1 + 2x_2 + x_4 \geq 40$
$x_1, x_2, x_3 \geq 0.$

APPLICATIONS: OHaganBooks.com

In Exercises 31–34, you are the buyer for OHaganBooks.com and are considering increasing stocks of romance and horror novels at the new OHaganBooks.com warehouse in Texas. You have offers from several publishers: Duffin House, Higgins Press, McPhearson Imprints, and O'Conell Books. Duffin offers a package of 5 horror novels and 5 romance novels for \$50, Higgins offers a package of 5 horror and 10 romance novels for \$80, McPhearson offers a package of 10 horror novels and 5 romance novels for \$80, and

O'Conell offers a package of 10 horror novels and 10 romance novels for $90.

31. How many packages should you purchase from Duffin House and Higgins Press to obtain at least 4,000 horror novels and 6,000 romance novels at minimum cost? What is the minimum cost?

32. How many packages should you purchase from McPhearson Imprints and O'Conell Books to obtain at least 5,000 horror novels and 4,000 romance novels at minimum cost? What is the minimum cost?

33. Refer to the scenario in Exercise 31. As it turns out, John O'Hagan promised Marjory Duffin that OHaganBooks.com would buy at least 20 percent more packages from Duffin as from Higgins, but you still want to obtain at least 4,000 horror novels and 6,000 romance novels at minimum cost.

a. *Without solving the problem,* say which of the following statements are possible:

(A) The cost will stay the same.
(B) The cost will increase.
(C) The cost will decrease.
(D) It will be impossible to meet all the conditions.
(E) The cost will become unbounded.

b. If you wish to meet all the requirements at minimum cost, how many packages should you purchase from each publisher? What is the minimum cost?

34. Refer to Exercise 32. You are about to place the order meeting the requirements of Exercise 32 when you are told that you can order no more than a total of 500 packages, and that at least half of the packages should be from McPhearson. Explain why this is impossible by referring to the feasible region for Exercise 32.

35. ***Investments*** Marjory Duffin's portfolio manager has suggested two high-yielding stocks: European Emerald Emporium (EEE) and Royal Ruby Retailers (RRR).[42] EEE shares cost $50, yield 4.5% in dividends, and have a risk index of 2.0 per share. RRR shares cost $55, yield 5% in dividends, and have a risk index of 3.0 per share. Marjory has up to $12,100 to invest and would like to earn at least $550 in dividends. How many shares of each stock should she purchase to meet her requirements and minimize the total risk index for her portfolio? What is the minimum total risk index?

36. ***Investments*** Marjory Duffin's other portfolio manager has suggested another two high-yielding stocks: Countrynarrow Mortgages (CNM) and Scotland Subprime (SS).[43] CNM shares cost $40, yield 5.5% in dividends, and have a risk index of 1.0 per share. SS shares cost $25, yield 7.5% in dividends, and have a risk index of 1.5 per share. Marjory can invest up to $30,000 in these stocks and would like to earn at least $1,650 in dividends. How many shares of each stock should she purchase in order to meet her requirements and minimize the total risk index for her portfolio?

37. ***Resource Allocation*** Billy-Sean O'Hagan has joined the Physics Society at Suburban State University, and the group is planning to raise money to support the dying space program by making and selling umbrellas. The society intends to make three models: the Sprinkle, the Storm, and the Hurricane. The amounts of cloth, metal, and wood used in making each model are given in this table:

	Sprinkle	***Storm***	***Hurricane***	***Total Available***
Cloth (sq. yd)	1	2	[illegible]	600
Metal (lbs)	2	1	3	600
Wood (lbs)	1	3	6	600
Profit ($)	1	1	2	

The table also shows the amo [illegible] of each material available in a given day and the profi [illegible] be made from each model. How many of each model [illegible] d the society make in order to maximize its profit?

38. ***Profit*** Duffin House, [illegible] s now the largest publisher of books sold at the OH [illegible] ooks.com site, prints three kinds of books: paperback [illegible] ty paperback, and hardcover. The amounts of paper, [illegible] d time on the presses required for each kind of book [illegible] ven in this table:

	[illegible]back	***Quality Paperback***	***Hardcover***	***Total Available***
Paper (pounds)	3	2	1	6,000
Ink (gallons)	2	1	3	6,000
Time (minute[illegible]	10	10	10	22,000
Profit [illegible]	1	2	3	

The tabl [illegible] so lists the total amounts of paper, ink, and time availabl [illegible] a given day and the profits made on each kind of book. [illegible] many of each kind of book should Duffin print to maxim [illegible] profit?

39. ***Purc[illegible]es*** You are just about to place book orders from Duff [illegible] and Higgins (see Exercise 31) when everything cha [illegible] : Duffin House informs you that, due to a global ron [illegible] ce crisis, its packages now each will contain 5 horror no [illegible] but only 2 romance novels and still cost $50 per packag [illegible] ackages from Higgins will now contain 10 of each type o [illegible] vel, but now cost $150 per package. Ewing Books en- t [illegible] the fray and offers its own package of 5 horror and 5 ro- [illegible] ce novels for $100. The sales manager now tells you that at least 50% of the packages must come from Higgins Press

[42] RRR and EEE happen to be, respectively, the ticker symbols of RSC Holdings (an equipment rental provider) and Evergreen Energy Inc. (a environmentally friendly energy technology company) and thus have nothing to do with rubies and emeralds.

[43] CNM is actually the ticker symbol of Carnegie Wave, whereas SS is not the ticker symbol of any U.S.-based company we are aware of.

and, as before, you want to obtain at least 4,000 horror novels and 6,000 romance novels at minimum cost. Taking all of this into account, how many packages should you purchase from each publisher? What is the minimum cost?

40. ***Purchases*** You are about to place book orders from McPhearson and O'Conell (see Exercise 32) when you get an e-mail from McPhearson Imprints saying that, sorry, but they have stopped publishing romance novels due to the global romance crisis and can now offer only packages of 10 horror novels for \$50. O'Conell is still offering packages of 10 horror novels and 10 romance novels for \$90, and now the United States Treasury, in an attempt to bolster the floundering romance industry, is offering its own package of 20 romance novels for \$120. Furthermore, Congress, in approving this measure, has passed legislation dictating that at least two thirds of the packages in every order must come from the U.S. Treasury. As before, you wish to obtain at least 5,000 horror novels and 4,000 romance novels at minimum cost. Taking all of this into account, how many packages should you purchase from each supplier? What is the minimum cost?

41. ***Degree Requirements*** During his lunch break, John O'Hagan decides to devote some time to assisting his son Billy-Sean, who continues to have a terrible time planning his college course schedule. The latest Bulletin of Suburban State University claims to have added new flexibility to its course requirements, but it remains as complicated as ever. It reads as follows:

> *All candidates for the degree of Bachelor of Arts at SSU must take at least 120 credits from the Sciences, Fine Arts, Liberal Arts, and Mathematics combined, including at least as many Science credits as Fine Arts credits, and at most twice as many Mathematics credits as Science credits, but with Liberal Arts credits exceeding Mathematics credits by no more than one third of the number of Fine Arts credits.*

Science and fine arts credits cost \$300 each, and liberal arts and mathematics credits cost \$200 each. John would like to have Billy-Sean meet all the requirements at a minimum total cost.

a. Set up (without solving) the associated linear programming problem.

b. T Use technology to determine how many of each type of credit Billy-Sean should take. What will the total cost be?

42. ***Degree Requirements*** No sooner had the "new and flexible" course requirement been released than the English Department again pressured the University Senate to include their vaunted "Verbal Expression" component in place of the fine arts requirement in all programs (including the sciences):

> *All candidates for the degree of Bachelor of Science at SSU must take at least 120 credits from the Liberal Arts, Sciences, Verbal Expression, and Mathematics, including at most as many Science credits as Liberal Arts credits, and at least twice as many Verbal Expression credits as Science credits and Liberal Arts credits combined, with Liberal Arts credits exceeding Mathematics credits by at least a quarter of the number of Verbal Expression credits.*

Science credits cost \$300 each, while each credit in the remaining subjects now costs \$400. John would like to have Billy-Sean meet all the requirements at a minimum total cost.

a. Set up (without solving) the associated linear programming problem.

b. T Use technology to determine how many of each type of credit Billy-Sean should take. What will the total cost be?

43. ***Shipping*** On the same day that the sales department at Duffin House received an order for 600 packages from the OHaganBooks.com Texas headquarters, it received an additional order for 200 packages from FantasyBooks.com, based in California. Duffin House has warehouses in New York and Illinois. The New York warehouse has 600 packages in stock, but the Illinois warehouse is closing down and has only 300 packages in stock. Shipping costs per package of books are as follows: New York to Texas: \$20; New York to California: \$50; Illinois to Texas: \$30; Illinois to California: \$40. What is the lowest total shipping cost for which Duffin House can fill the orders? How many packages should be sent from each warehouse to each online bookstore at a minimum shipping cost?

44. ***Transportation Scheduling*** Duffin House is about to start a promotional blitz for its new book, *Advanced String Theory for the Liberal Arts*. The company has 25 salespeople stationed in Austin and 10 in San Diego, and would like to fly at least 15 to sales fairs in each of Houston and Cleveland. A round-trip plane flight from Austin to Houston costs \$200; from Austin to Cleveland costs \$150; from San Diego to Houston costs \$400; and from San Diego to Cleveland costs \$200. How many salespeople should the company fly from each of Austin and San Diego to each of Houston and Cleveland for the lowest total cost in air fare?

45. ***Marketing*** Marjory Duffin, head of Duffin House, reveals to John O'Hagan that FantasyBooks.com is considering several promotional schemes: It may offer two books for the price of one, three books for the price of two, or possibly a free copy of *Brain Surgery for Klutzes* with each order. OHaganBooks.com's marketing advisers Floody and O'Lara seem to have different ideas as to how to respond. Floody suggests offering *three* books for the price of one, while O'Lara suggests instead offering a free copy of the *Finite Mathematics Student Solutions Manual* with every purchase. After a careful analysis, O'Hagan comes up with the following payoff matrix, where the payoffs represent the number of customers, in thousands, O'Hagan expects to gain from FantasyBooks.com.

		FantasyBooks.com			
		No Promo	2 for Price of 1	3 for Price of 2	Brain Surgery
OHaganBooks.com	No Promo	0	−60	−40	10
	3 for Price of 1	30	20	10	15
	Finite Math	20	0	15	10

Find the optimal strategies for both companies and the expected shift in customers.

46. ***Study Techniques*** Billy-Sean's friend Pat from college has been spending all of his time in fraternity activities, and thus knows absolutely nothing about any of the three topics on tomorrow's math test. He has turned to Billy-Sean for advice as to how to spend his "all-nighter." The table below shows the scores Pat could expect to earn if the entire test were to be in a specific subject. (Because he knows no linear programming or matrix algebra, the table shows, for instance, that studying game theory all night will not be much use in preparing him for this topic.)

	Test		
Pat's Strategies ↓	**Game Theory**	**Linear Programming**	**Matrix Algebra**
Study Game Theory	30	0	20
Study Linear Programming	0	70	0
Study Matrix Algebra	0	0	70

What percentage of the night should Pat spend on each topic, assuming the principles of game theory, and what score can he expect to get?

Image Studios/UpperCut Images/Getty Images

The Diet Problem

The Galaxy Nutrition health-food mega-store chain provides free online nutritional advice and support to its customers. As Web site technical consultant, you are planning to construct an interactive Web page to assist customers in preparing a diet tailored to their nutritional and budgetary requirements. Ideally, the customer would select foods to consider and specify nutritional and/or budgetary constraints, and the tool should return the optimal diet meeting those requirements. You would also like the Web page to allow the customer to decide whether, for instance, to find the cheapest possible diet meeting the requirements, the diet with the lowest number of calories, or the diet with the least total carbohydrates.

After doing a little research, you notice that the kind of problem you are trying is solve is quite well known and referred to as the *diet problem*, and that solving the diet problem is a famous example of linear programming. Indeed, there are already some online pages that solve versions of the problem that minimize total cost, so you have adequate information to assist you as you plan the page.*

✱ See, for instance, the Diet Problem Demo at the NEOS Wiki: www.neos-guide.org/NEOS/index.php/Diet_Problem_Demo

You decide to start on a relatively small scale, starting with a program that uses a list of 10 foods, and minimizes either total caloric intake or total cost and satisfies a small list of requirements. Following is a small part of a table of nutritional information from the demo at the NEOS Wiki (all the values shown are for a single serving) as well as approximate minimum daily requirements:

	Price per Serving	*Calories*	*Total Fat g*	*Carbs g*	*Dietary Fiber g*	*Protein g*	*Vit C IU*
Tofu	$0.31	88.2	5.5	2.2	1.4	9.4	0.1
Roast Chicken	$0.84	277.4	10.8	0	0	42.2	0
Spaghetti w/Sauce	$0.78	358.2	12.3	58.3	11.6	8.2	27.9
Tomato	$0.27	25.8	0.4	5.7	1.4	1.0	23.5
Oranges	$0.15	61.6	0.2	15.4	3.1	1.2	69.7
Wheat Bread	$0.05	65.0	1.0	12.4	1.3	2.2	0
Cheddar Cheese	$0.25	112.7	9.3	0.4	0	7.0	0
Oatmeal	$0.82	145.1	2.3	25.3	4.0	6.1	0
Peanut Butter	$0.07	188.5	16.0	6.9	2.1	7.7	0
White Tuna in Water	$0.69	115.6	2.1	0	0	22.7	0
Minimum Requirements		2,200	20	80	25	60	90

Source: www.neos-guide.org/NEOS/index.php/Diet_Problem_Demo

Now you get to work. As always, you start by identifying the unknowns. Since the output of the Web page will consist of a recommended diet, the unknowns should logically be the number of servings of each item of food selected by the user. In your first trial run, you decide to include all the 10 food items listed, so you take

x_1 = Number of servings of tofu

x_2 = Number of servings of roast chicken

$\vdots$

x_{10} = Number of servings of white tuna in water.

You now set up a linear programming problem for two sample scenarios:

Scenario 1 (Minimum Cost): Satisfy all minimum nutritional requirements at a minimum cost. Here the linear programming problem is:

Minimize

$$c = 0.31x_1 + 0.84x_2 + 0.78x_3 + 0.27x_4 + 0.15x_5 + 0.05x_6 + 0.25x_7 + 0.82x_8 + 0.07x_9 + 0.69x_{10}$$

subject to

$$88.2x_1 + 277.4x_2 + 358.2x_3 + 25.8x_4 + 61.6x_5 + 65x_6 + 112.7x_7 + 145.1x_8 + 188.5x_9 + 115.6x_{10} \geq 2{,}200$$

$$5.5x_1 + 10.8x_2 + 12.3x_3 + 0.4x_4 + 0.2x_5 + 1x_6 + 9.3x_7 + 2.3x_8 + 16x_9 + 2.1x_{10} \geq 20$$

$$2.2x_1 + 58.3x_3 + 5.7x_4 + 15.4x_5 + 12.4x_6 + 0.4x_7 + 25.3x_8 + 6.9x_9 \geq 80$$

$$1.4x_1 + 11.6x_3 + 1.4x_4 + 3.1x_5 + 1.3x_6 + 4x_8 + 2.1x_9 \geq 25$$

$$9.4x_1 + 42.2x_2 + 8.2x_3 + 1x_4 + 1.2x_5 + 2.2x_6 + 7x_7 + 6.1x_8 + 7.7x_9 + 22.7x_{10} \geq 60$$

$$0.1x_1 + 27.9x_3 + 23.5x_4 + 69.7x_5 \geq 90.$$

This is clearly the kind of linear programming problem no one in their right mind would like to do by hand (solving it requires 16 tableaus!) so you decide to use the online simplex method tool at the Website (www.WanerMath.com → Student Web Site → On Line Utilities → Simplex Method Tool).

Here is a picture of the input, entered almost exactly as written above (you need to enter each constraint on a new line, and "`Minimize c = 0.31x1 + ··· Subject to`" must be typed on a single line):

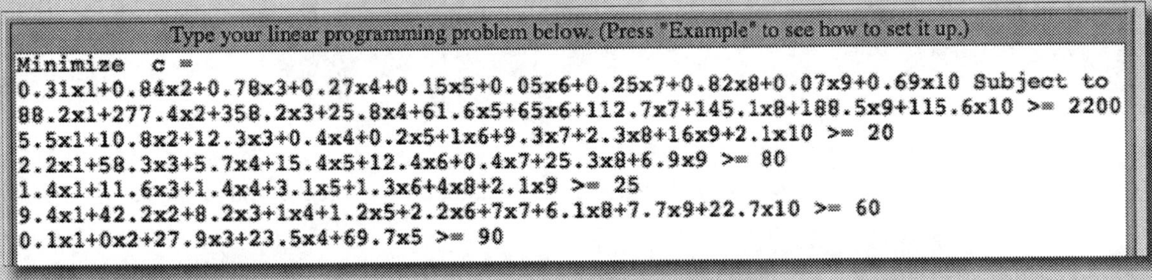
Type your linear programming problem below. (Press "Example" to see how to set it up.)
Minimize c =
0.31x1+0.84x2+0.78x3+0.27x4+0.15x5+0.05x6+0.25x7+0.82x8+0.07x9+0.69x10 Subject to
88.2x1+277.4x2+358.2x3+25.8x4+61.6x5+65x6+112.7x7+145.1x8+188.5x9+115.6x10 >= 2200
5.5x1+10.8x2+12.3x3+0.4x4+0.2x5+1x6+9.3x7+2.3x8+16x9+2.1x10 >= 20
2.2x1+58.3x3+5.7x4+15.4x5+12.4x6+0.4x7+25.3x8+6.9x9 >= 80
1.4x1+11.6x3+1.4x4+3.1x5+1.3x6+4x8+2.1x9 >= 25
9.4x1+42.2x2+8.2x3+1x4+1.2x5+2.2x6+7x7+6.1x8+7.7x9+22.7x10 >= 60
0.1x1+0x2+27.9x3+23.5x4+69.7x5 >= 90

Clicking "Solve" results in the following solution:

$$c = 0.981126;\ x_1 = 0,\ x_2 = 0,\ x_3 = 0,\ x_4 = 0,\ x_5 = 1.29125,\ x_6 = 0,\ x_7 = 0,\ x_8 = 0,\ x_9 = 11.2491,\ x_{10} = 0.$$

This means that you can satisfy all the daily requirements for less than $1 on a diet of 1.3 servings of orange juice and 11.2 servings of peanut butter! Although you enjoy peanut butter, 11.2 servings seems a little over the top, so you modify the LP problem by adding a new constraint (which also suggests to you that some kind of flexibility needs to be built into the site to allow users to set limits on the number of servings of any one item):

$$x_9 \le 3.$$

This new constraint results in the following solution:

$$c = 1.59981; x_1 = 0, x_2 = 0, x_3 = 0, x_4 = 0, x_5 = 1.29125, x_6 = 23.9224,$$
$$x_7 = 0, x_8 = 0, x_9 = 3, x_{10} = 0.$$

Because wheat bread is cheap and, in large enough quantities, supplies ample protein, the program has now substituted 23.9 servings of wheat bread for the missing peanut butter for a total cost of $1.60.

Unfettered, you now add

$$x_6 \le 4$$

and obtain the following spaghetti, bread, and peanut butter diet for $3.40 per day:

$$c = 3.40305; x_1 = 0, x_2 = 0, x_3 = 3.83724, x_4 = 0, x_5 = 0, x_6 = 4, x_7 = 0,$$
$$x_8 = 0, x_9 = 3, x_{10} = 0.$$

Scenario 2 (Minimum Calories): Minimize total calories and satisfy all minimum nutritional requirements (except for caloric intake).

Here, the linear programming problem is

Minimize

$$c = 88.2x_1 + 277.4x_2 + 358.2x_3 + 25.8x_4 + 61.6x_5 + 65x_6 + 112.7x_7$$
$$+ 145.1x_8 + 188.5x_9 + 115.6x_{10}$$

subject to

$$5.5x_1 + 10.8x_2 + 12.3x_3 + 0.4x_4 + 0.2x_5 + 1x_6 + 9.3x_7 + 2.3x_8 + 16x_9$$
$$+ 2.1x_{10} \ge 20$$
$$2.2x_1 + 58.3x_3 + 5.7x_4 + 15.4x_5 + 12.4x_6 + 0.4x_7 + 25.3x_8 + 6.9x_9 \ge 80$$
$$1.4x_1 + 11.6x_3 + 1.4x_4 + 3.1x_5 + 1.3x_6 + 4x_8 + 2.1x_9 \ge 25$$
$$9.4x_1 + 42.2x_2 + 8.2x_3 + 1x_4 + 1.2x_5 + 2.2x_6 + 7x_7 + 6.1x_8 + 7.7x_9$$
$$+ 22.7x_{10} \ge 60$$
$$0.1x_1 + 27.9x_3 + 23.5x_4 + 69.7x_5 \ge 90.$$

You obtain the following 716-calorie tofu, tomato, and tuna diet:

$$x_1 = 2.07232, x_2 = 0, x_3 = 0, x_4 = 15.7848, x_5 = 0, x_6 = 0, x_7 = 0, x_8 = 0,$$
$$x_9 = 0, x_{10} = 1.08966.$$

As 16 servings of tomatoes seems a little over the top, you add the new constraint $x_4 \le 3$ and obtain a 783-calorie tofu, tomato, orange, and tuna diet:

$$x_1 = 2.81682, x_2 = 0, x_3 = 0, x_4 = 3, x_5 = 5.43756, x_6 = 0, x_7 = 0, x_8 = 0,$$
$$x_9 = 0, x_{10} = 1.05713.$$

What the trial runs have shown you is that your Web site will need to allow the user to set reasonable upper bounds for the number of servings of each kind of food considered. You now get to work writing the algorithm, which appears here:

www.WanerMath.com → Student Web Site → On Line Utilities → Diet Problem Solver

EXERCISES

1. Briefly explain why roast chicken, which supplies protein more cheaply either tofu or tuna, does not appear in the optimal solution in either scenario.

2. Consider the optimal solution obtained in Scenario 1 when peanut butte bread were restricted. Experiment on the Simplex Method Tool by increasing the pro equirement 10 grams at a time until chicken appears in the optimal diet. At what level otein does the addition of chicken first become necessary?

3. What constraints would you add for a person who wants to eat at most tv vings of chicken a day and is allergic to tomatoes and peanut butter? What is the res diet for Scenario 2?

4. What is the linear programming problem for someone who wants as much prot possible at a cost of no more than \$6 per day with no more than 50 g of carbohydra r day assuming they want to satisfy the minimum requirements for all the remaining nts? What is the resulting diet?

5. Is it possible to obtain a diet with no bread or peanut butter in Scenario 1 costing an \$4 per day?

TI-83/84 Plus Technology Guide

Section 5.1

Some calculators, including the TI-83/84 Plus, will shade one side of a graph, but you need to tell the calculator which side to shade. For instance, to obtain the solution set of $2x + 3y \le 6$ shown in Figure 4:

1. Solve the corresponding equation $2x + 3y = 6$ for y and use the input shown below:

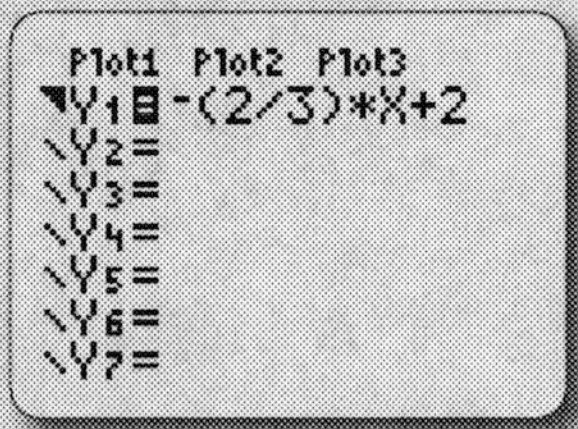

2. The icon to the left of "Y_1" tells the calculator to shade above the line. You can cycle through the various shading options by positioning the cursor to the left of Y_1 and pressing ENTER until you see the one you want. Here's what the graph will look like:

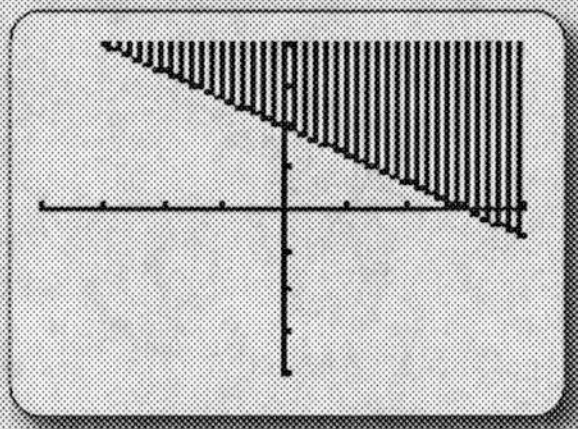

Section 5.3

Example 3 (page 346) The Acme Baby Foods example in the text leads to the following linear programming problem:

$$\begin{aligned} \text{Maximize} \quad & p = 10x + 7y \\ \text{subject to} \quad & x \le 600 \\ & 2x + 3y \le 3{,}600 \\ & 5x + 3y \le 4{,}500 \\ & x \ge 0,\ y \ge 0. \end{aligned}$$

Solve it using technology.

Solution with Technology

When we introduce slack variables, we get the following system of equations:

$$\begin{aligned} x \quad\quad + s \quad\quad\quad\quad &= 600 \\ 2x + 3y \quad\quad + t \quad\quad\quad &= 3{,}600 \\ 5x + 3y \quad\quad\quad\quad + u \quad &= 4{,}500 \\ -10x - 7y \quad\quad\quad\quad\quad + p &= 0. \end{aligned}$$

We use the PIVOT program for the TI-83/84 Plus to help with the simplex method. This program is available at the Website by following

Everything → Math Tools for Chapter 5.

Because the calculator handles decimals as easily as integers, there is no need to avoid them, except perhaps to save limited screen space. If we don't need to avoid decimals, we can use the traditional Gauss-Jordan method (see the discussion at the end of Section 3.2): After selecting your pivot, and prior to clearing the pivot column, *divide the pivot row by the value of the pivot, thereby turning the pivot into a 1.*

The main drawback to using the TI-83/84 Plus is that we can't label the rows and columns. We can mentally label them as we go, but we can do without labels entirely if we wish. We begin by entering the initial tableau as the matrix [A]. (Another drawback to using the TI-83/84 Plus is that it can't show the whole tableau at once. Here and below we show tableaux across several screens. Use the TI-83/84 Plus's arrow keys to scroll a matrix left and right so you can see all of it.)

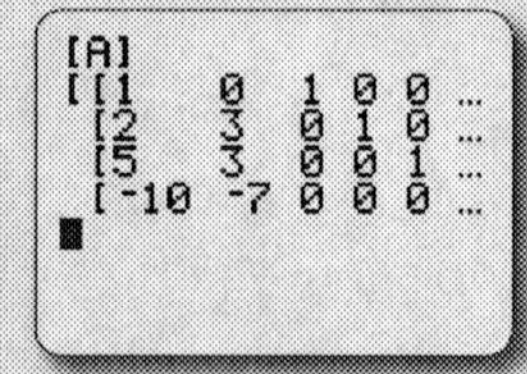

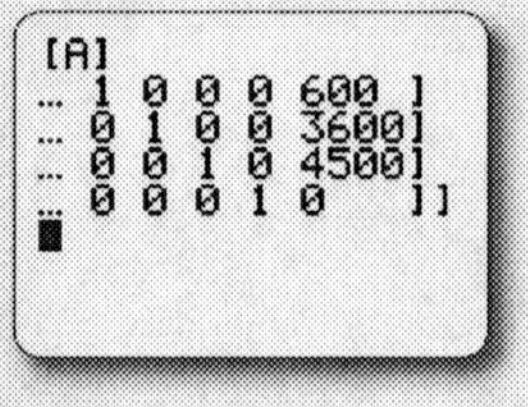

The following is the sequence of tableaux we get while using the simplex method with the help of the PIVOT program.

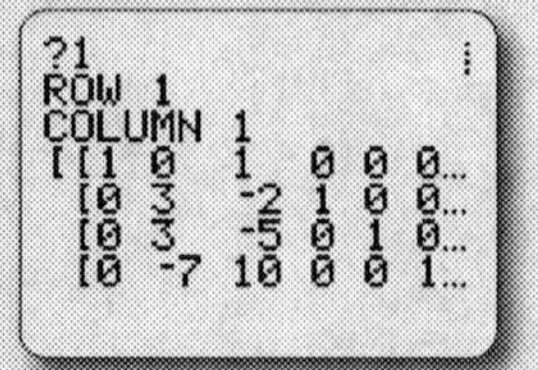

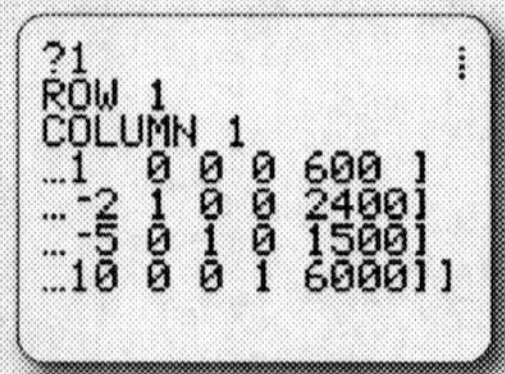

After determining that the next pivot is in the third row and second column, we divide the third row by the pivot, 3, and then pivot:

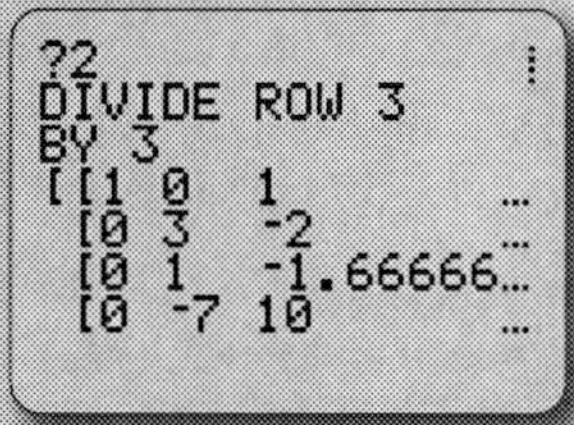

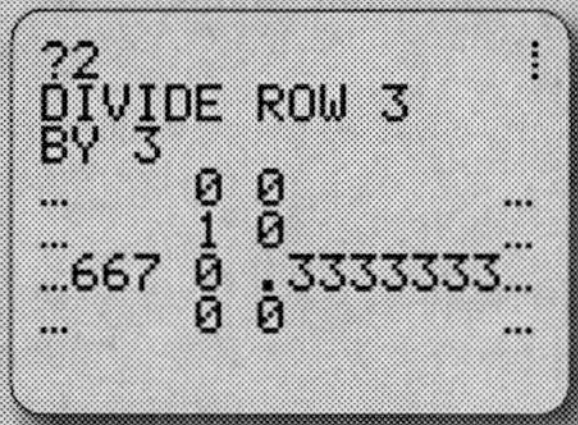

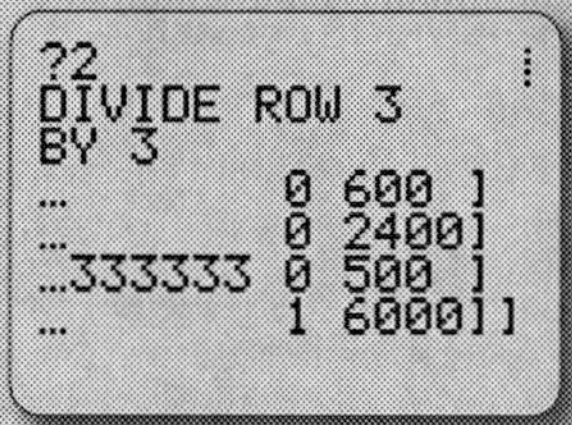

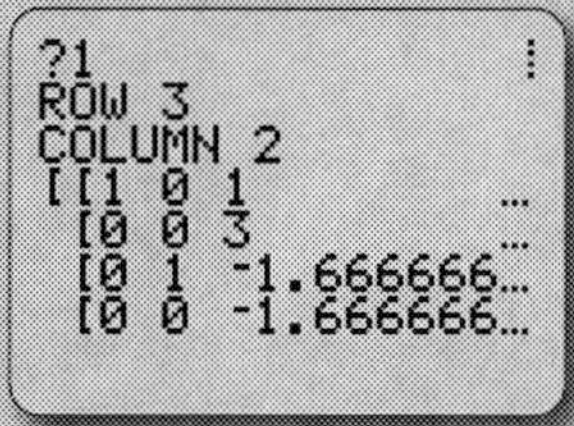

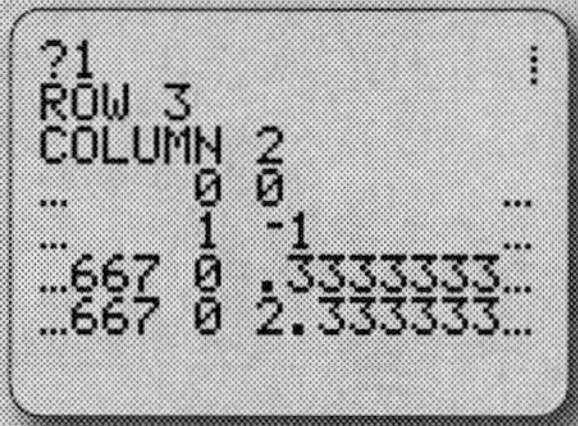

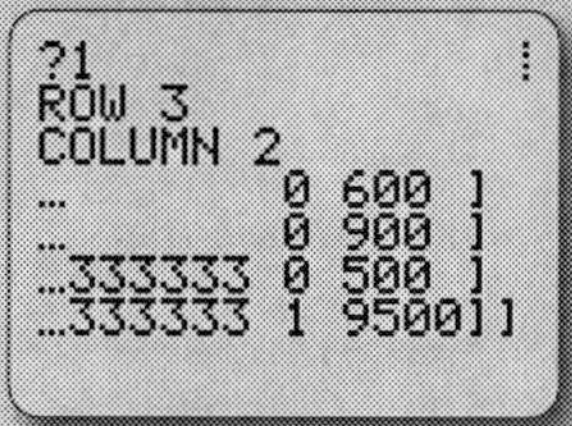

The next pivot is the 3 in the second row, third column. We divide its row by 3 and pivot:

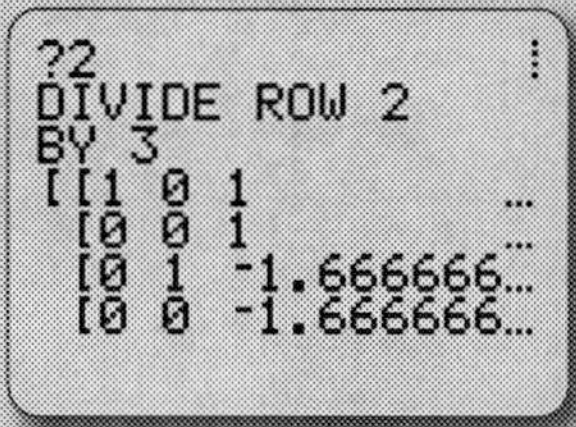

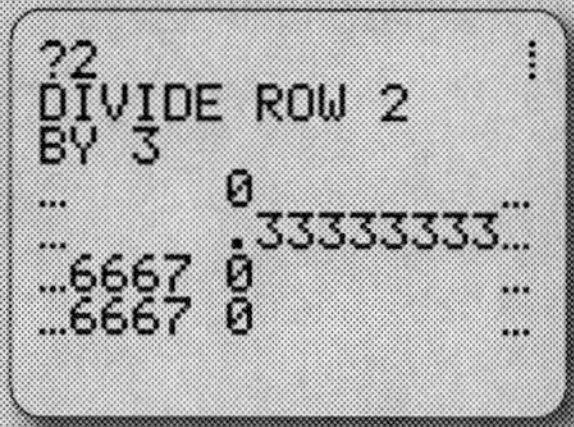

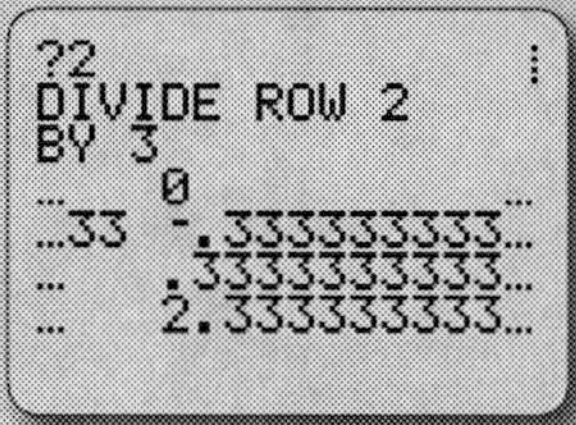

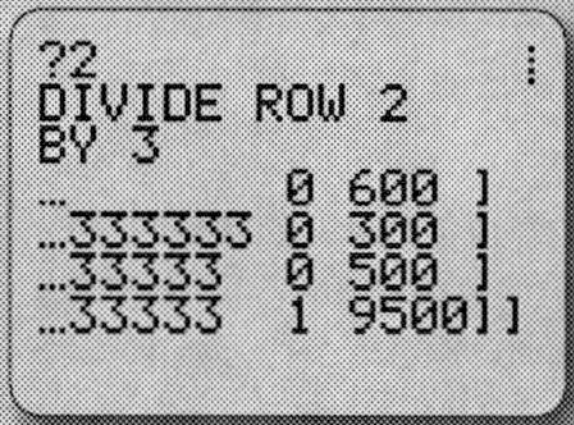

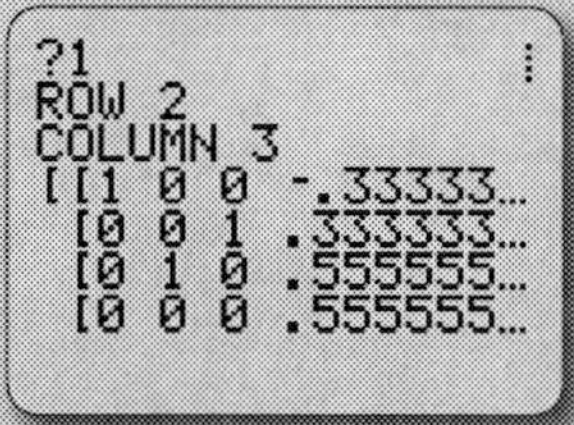

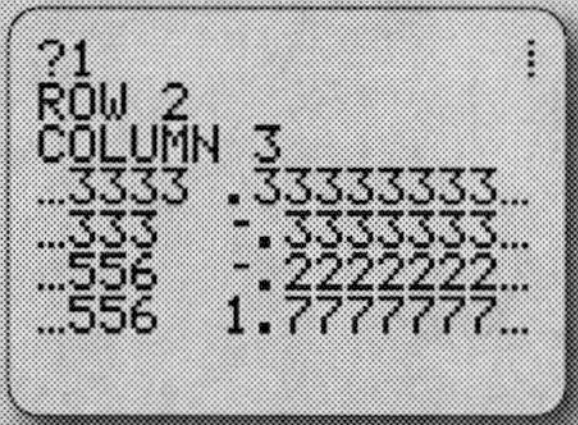

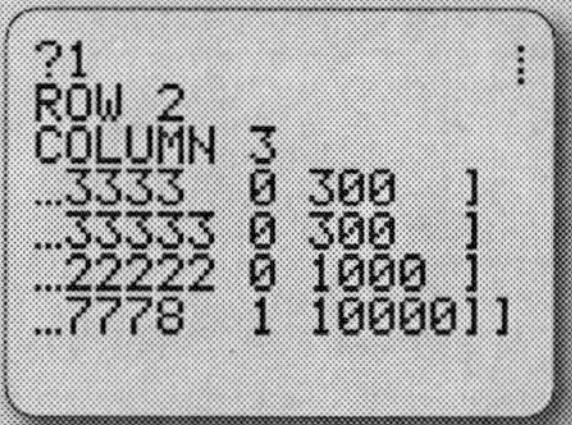

There are no negative numbers in the bottom r[illegible] we're finished. How do we read off the optimal s[illegible]s if we don't have labels, though? Look at the colu[illegible]ontaining one 1 and three 0s. They are the x colum[illegible] y column, the s column, and the p column. Thi[illegible]f the 1 that appears in each of these columns as a p[illegible] whose column has been cleared. If we had labels, t[illegible]ow containing a pivot would have the same label as t[illegible]olumn containing that pivot. We can now read off t[illegible]olution as follows:

x column: The pivot is in th[illegible]st row, so row 1 would have been labeled w[illegible]. We look at the rightmost column to read[illegible]the value $x = 300$.

y column: The pivot is in row 3, so we look at the rightmost column to read off the value $y = 1{,}000$.

s column: The pivot is in row 2, so we look at the rightmost column to read off the value $s = 300$.

p column: The pivot is in row 3, so we look at the rightmost column to read off the value $p = 10{,}000$.

Thus, the maximum value of p is 10,000¢ = \$100, which occurs when $x = 300$ and $y = 1{,}000$. The values of the slack variables are $s = 300$ and $t = u = 0$. (Look at the t and u columns to see that they must be inactive.)

SPREAD[illegible]ET Technology Guide

Sectio[illegible]

Exce[illegible]articularly good tool for graphing linear in[illegible]ecause it cannot easily shade one side of a [illegible] solution available in Excel, for instance, is to [illegible] "error bar" feature to indicate which side of the [illegible] *should* be shaded. For example, here is how we [illegible]ight graph the inequality $2x + 3y \le 6$.

1. Create a scatter graph using two points to construct a line segment (as in Chapter 1). (Notice that we had to solve the equation $2x + 3y = 6$ for y.)

	A	B
1	x	y
2	-10	=-(2/3)*A2 + 2
3	10	

2. Double-click on the line segment, and use the "X-Error Bars" feature to obtain a diagram similar to the one on the left below, where the error bars indicate the direction of shading.

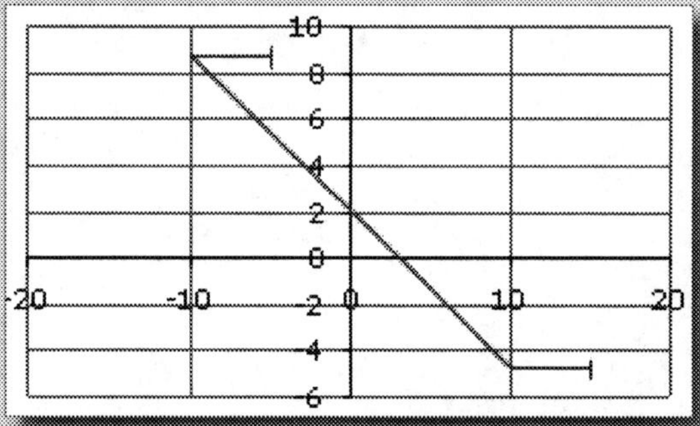

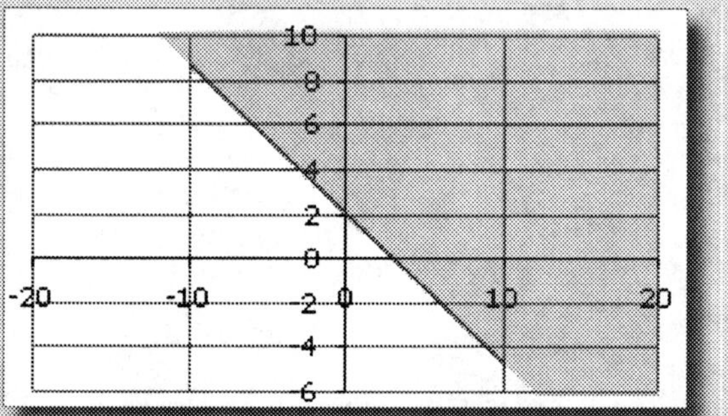

Alternatively, you can use the Drawing Palette to create a polygon with a semi-transparent fill, as shown above.

CHAPTER 5 QUIZ

1. Eddy's Energy Emulsion is a "sport slurpee" that is made up of a combination of two different concoctions, which are called Mixit 1 and Mixit 2. Mixit 1 is a liquid that is 50% carbohydrates, 30% protein, and 20% fat. Mixit 2 is a sludge that is 75% carbohydrates, 20% protein, and 5% fat. Mixit 1 costs \$2 per gallon to make, while Mixit 2 costs \$2.50 per pound to make. How many gallons of each concoction should be combined in order to produce a batch of EEE that contains at least 3 gallons of carbohydrates, 1.5 gallons of protein, and 0.50 gallons of fat at the minimum possible cost? Set up and solve a linear program to solve this problem. Declare what all variables represent, and show all relevant work (graphs, etc.) to support your conclusion.

2. Maximize and minimize

$$Q = 5x + 8y$$

subject to

$$2x + y \geq 8$$
$$4x + 5y \leq 13$$
$$y \leq 10$$
$$x \geq 0, y \geq 0$$

Show all relevant supporting work. If you believe either the maximum or minimum value does not exist, explain why.

3. The maximum daily production of an oil refinery is 1900 barrels. The refinery can produce three types of fuel: gasoline, diesel, and heating oil. The production cost per barrel is \$8 for gasoline, \$6 for diesel, and \$5 for heating oil. The daily production budget is \$13,400. The profit is \$9 per barrel on gasoline, \$8 per barrel on diesel, and \$6 per barrel on heating oil. Management wishes to know how many barrels of each type of fuel to produce to maximize daily profit. Write an objective function and all constraints for this linear programming problem. Declare what all variables represent.

4. Consider the objective function $z = 8x + y$. Assume that $x, y \geq 0$.

a. Sketch a possible feasible region where z has only a minimum value.

b. Sketch a possible feasible region where z has both a maximum value and a minimum value but the minimum value does not occur at the origin.

c. Write a system of constraints so that z attains a maximum value at the point (4,6). Verify the validity of your system.

5. Silica Express manufactures computer chips. Its two main customers, Geo Computers and Engage Technologies, have just submitted orders that need to be filled immediately. Geo needs at least 120 cases of chips and Engage needs at least 160 cases of chips. Due to limited silicon supply, Silica cannot send more than 400 cases in total. It costs \$150 per case to ship to Geo, and it costs \$100 per case to ship to Engage. Silica needs to know how many cases to ship to each customer in order to minimize shipping costs.
   a. Write an objective function and all constraints for this linear program. Declare what variables represent, and indicate if you are to maximize or minimize the objective function.

   b. Sketch the appropriate feasible region, label all corner points with exact coordinates, and solve the linear program. State your conclusion in a complete sentence.

9

Nonlinear Functions and Models

Website
www.WanerMath.com
At the Website you will find:

- Section-by-section tutorials, including game tutorials with randomized quizzes
- A detailed chapter summary
- A true/false quiz
- Additional review exercises
- Graphers, Excel tutorials, and other resources
- The following extra topics:
  - Inverse functions
  - Using and deriving algebraic properties of logarithms

Case Study Checking up on Malthus

In 1798 Thomas R. Malthus (1766–1834) published an influential pamphlet, later expanded into a book, titled *An Essay on the Principle of Population as It Affects the Future Improvement of Society*. One of his main contentions was that population grows geometrically (exponentially), while the supply of resources such as food grows only arithmetically (linearly). Some 200+ years later, you have been asked to check the validity of Malthus's contention. **How do you go about doing so?**

Robert Nickelsberg/Getty Images

Introduction

To see if Malthus was right, we need to see if the data fit the models (linear and exponential) that he suggested or if other models would be better. We saw in Chapter 1 how to fit a linear model. In this chapter we discuss how to construct models that use various *nonlinear* functions.

The nonlinear functions we consider in this chapter are the *quadratic* functions, the simplest nonlinear functions; the *exponential* functions, essential for discussing many kinds of growth and decay, including the growth (and decay) of money in finance and the initial growth of an epidemic; the *logarithmic* functions, needed to fully understand the exponential functions; and the *logistic* functions, used to model growth with an upper limit, such as the spread of an epidemic.

algebra Review
For this chapter, you should be familiar with the algebra reviewed in **Chapter 0, Section 2.**

9.1 Quadratic Functions and Models

In Chapter 1 we studied linear functions. Linear functions are useful, but in real-life applications, they are often accurate for only a limited range of values of the variables. The relationship between two quantities is often best modeled by a curved line rather than a straight line. The simplest function with a graph that is not a straight line is a *quadratic* function.

Quadratic Function

A **quadratic function** of the variable x is a function that can be written in the form

$$f(x) = ax^2 + bx + c \qquad \text{Function form}$$

or

$$y = ax^2 + bx + c \qquad \text{Equation form}$$

where a, b, and c are fixed numbers (with $a \neq 0$).

Quick Examples

1. $f(x) = 3x^2 - 2x + 1$ — $a = 3, b = -2, c = 1$
2. $g(x) = -x^2$ — $a = -1, b = 0, c = 0$
3. $R(p) = -5{,}600p^2 + 14{,}000p$ — $a = -5{,}600, b = 14{,}000, c = 0$

Every quadratic function $f(x) = ax^2 + bx + c$ $(a \neq 0)$ has a **parabola** as its graph. Following is a summary of some features of parabolas that we can use to sketch the graph of any quadratic function.*

* We shall not fully justify the formula for the vertex and the axis of symmetry until we have studied some calculus, although it is possible to do so with just algebra.

Features of a Parabola

The graph of $f(x) = ax^2 + bx + c\ (a \neq 0)$ is a **parabola**. If $a > 0$ the parabola opens upward (concave up) and if $a < 0$ it opens downward (concave down):

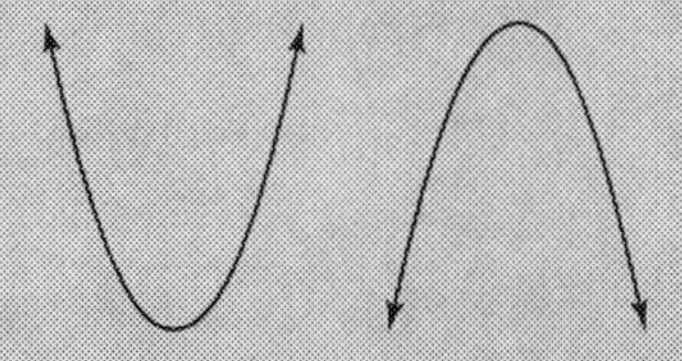

Vertex, Intercepts, and Symmetry

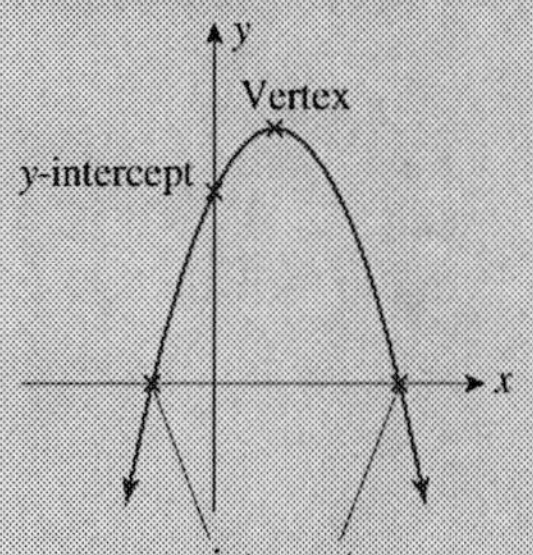

Vertex The vertex is the highest or lowest point of the parabola (see the figure above). Its x-coordinate is $-\dfrac{b}{2a}$. Its y-coordinate is $f\left(-\dfrac{b}{2a}\right)$.

***x*-Intercepts** (if any) These occur when $f(x) = 0$; that is, when

$$ax^2 + bx + c = 0.$$

Solve this equation for x by either factoring or using the quadratic formula. The x-intercepts are

$$x = \frac{-b \pm \sqrt{b^2 - 4ac}}{2a}.$$

If the **discriminant** $b^2 - 4ac$ is positive, there are two x-intercepts. If it is zero, there is a single x-intercept (at the vertex). If it is negative, there are no x-intercepts (so the parabola doesn't touch the x-axis at all).

***y*-Intercept** This occurs when $x = 0$, so

$$y = a(0)^2 + b(0) + c = c.$$

Symmetry The parabola is symmetric with respect to the vertical line through the vertex, which is the line $x = -\dfrac{b}{2a}$.

Note that the x-intercepts can also be written as

$$x = -\frac{b}{2a} \pm \frac{\sqrt{b^2 - 4ac}}{2a},$$

making it clear that they are located symmetrically on either side of the line $x = -b/(2a)$. This partially justifies the claim that the whole parabola is symmetric with respect to this line.

EXAMPLE 1 Sketching the Graph of a Quadratic Function

Sketch the graph of $f(x) = x^2 + 2x - 8$ by hand.

Solution Here, $a = 1$, $b = 2$, and $c = -8$. Because $a > 0$, the parabola is concave up (Figure 1).

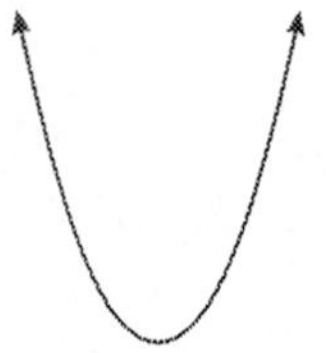

Figure 1

Vertex: The x coordinate of the vertex is

$$x = -\frac{b}{2a} = -\frac{2}{2} = -1.$$

To get its y coordinate, we substitute the value of x back into $f(x)$ to get

$$y = f(-1) = (-1)^2 + 2(-1) - 8 = 1 - 2 - 8 = -9.$$

Thus, the coordinates of the vertex are $(-1, -9)$.

x-Intercepts: To calculate the x-intercepts (if any), we solve the equation

$$x^2 + 2x - 8 = 0.$$

Luckily, this equation factors as $(x + 4)(x - 2) = 0$. Thus, the solutions are $x = -4$ and $x = 2$, so these values are the x-intercepts. (We could also have used the quadratic formula here.)

y-Intercept: The y-intercept is given by $c = -8$.

Symmetry: The graph is symmetric around the vertical line $x = -1$.

Now we can sketch the curve as in Figure 2. (As we see in the figure, it is helpful to plot additional points by using the equation $y = x^2 + 2x - 8$, and to use symmetry to obtain others.)

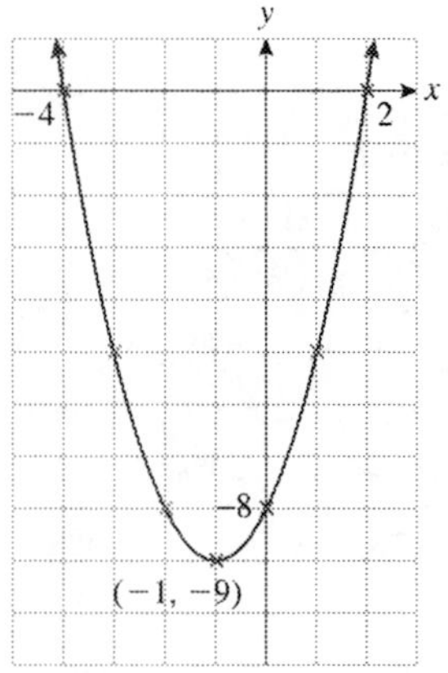

$y = x^2 + 2x - 8$

Figure 2

EXAMPLE 2 One *x*-Intercept and No *x*-Intercepts

Sketch the graph of each quadratic function, showing the location of the vertex and intercepts.

a. $f(x) = 4x^2 - 12x + 9$

b. $g(x) = -\frac{1}{2}x^2 + 4x - 12$

Solution

a. We have $a = 4$, $b = -12$, and $c = 9$. Because $a > 0$, this parabola is concave up.

Vertex: $x = -\frac{b}{2a} = \frac{12}{8} = \frac{3}{2}$ — *x coordinate of vertex*

$y = f\left(\frac{3}{2}\right) = 4\left(\frac{3}{2}\right)^2 - 12\left(\frac{3}{2}\right) + 9 = 0$ — *y coordinate of vertex*

Thus, the vertex is at the point $(3/2, 0)$.

x-Intercepts: $4x^2 - 12x + 9 = 0$

$(2x - 3)^2 = 0$

The only solution is $2x - 3 = 0$, or $x = 3/2$. Note that this coincides with the vertex, which lies on the x-axis.

y-Intercept: $c = 9$

Symmetry: The graph is symmetric around the vertical line $x = 3/2$.

The graph is the narrow parabola shown in Figure 3. (As we remarked in Example 1, plotting additional points and using symmetry helps us obtain an accurate sketch.)

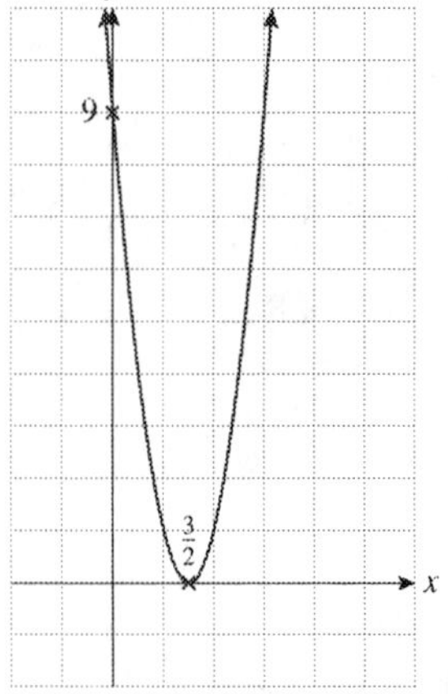

$y = 4x^2 - 12x + 9$

Figure 3

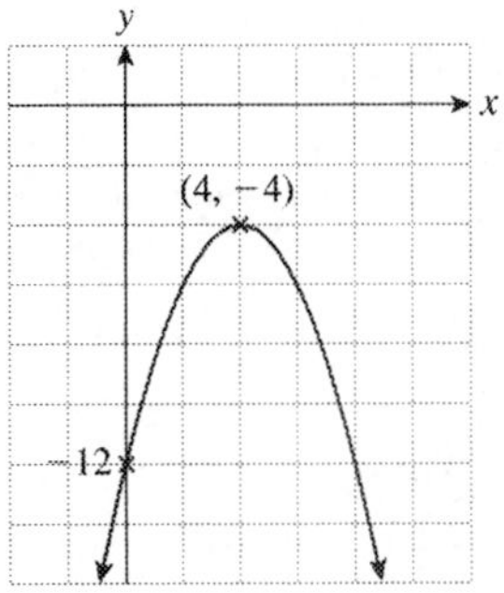

$y = -\frac{1}{2}x^2 + 4x - 12$

Figure 4

b. Here, $a = -1/2, b = 4$, and $c = -12$. Because $a < 0$, the parabola is concave down. The vertex has x coordinate $-b/(2a) = 4$, with corresponding y coordinate $f(4) = -\frac{1}{2}(4)^2 + 4(4) - 12 = -4$. Thus, the vertex is at $(4, -4)$.

For the x-intercepts, we must solve $-\frac{1}{2}x^2 + 4x - 12 = 0$. If we try to use the quadratic formula, we discover that the discriminant is $b^2 - 4ac = 16 - 24 = -8$. Because the discriminant is negative, there are no solutions of the equation, so there are no x-intercepts.

The y-intercept is given by $c = -12$, and the graph is symmetric around the vertical line $x = 4$.

Because there are no x-intercepts, the graph lies entirely below the x-axis, as shown in Figure 4. (Again, you should plot additional points and use symmetry to ensure that your sketch is accurate.)

using Technology

To automate the computations in Example 2 using a graphing calculator or a spreadsheet, see the Technology Guides at the end of the chapter. Outline:

TI-83/84 Plus

```
Y1=AX^2+BX+C
4→A:-12→B:9→C
[WINDOW] Xmin=0, Xmax=3
[ZOOM] [0]
```

[More details on page 680.]

Spreadsheet

Enter x values in column A.
Compute the corresponding y values in column B.
Graph the data in columns A and B.
[More details on page 682.]

Website

www.WanerMath.com

In the Function Evaluator and Grapher, enter `4x^2-12x+9` for y_1. For a table of values, enter the various x-values in the Evaluator box, and press "Evaluate".

APPLICATIONS

Recall that the **revenue** resulting from one or more business transactions is the total payment received. Thus, if q units of some item are sold at p dollars per unit, the revenue resulting from the sale is

$$\text{revenue} = \text{price} \times \text{quantity}$$
$$R = pq.$$

EXAMPLE 3 Demand and Revenue

Alien Publications, Inc. predicts that the demand equation for the sale of its latest illustrated sci-fi novel *Episode 93: Yoda vs. Alien* is

$$q = -2{,}000p + 150{,}000$$

where q is the number of books it can sell each year at a price of \$$p$ per book. What price should Alien Publications, Inc., charge to obtain the maximum annual revenue?

Solution The total revenue depends on the price, as follows:

$$\begin{aligned} R &= pq && \text{Formula for revenue} \\ &= p(-2{,}000p + 150{,}000) && \text{Substitute for } q \text{ from demand equation.} \\ &= -2{,}000p^2 + 150{,}000p. && \text{Simplify.} \end{aligned}$$

We are after the price p that gives the maximum possible revenue. Notice that what we have is a quadratic function of the form $R(p) = ap^2 + bp + c$, where $a = -2{,}000$, $b = 150{,}000$, and $c = 0$. Because a is negative, the graph of the function is a parabola, concave down, so its vertex is its highest point (Figure 5). The p coordinate of the vertex is

$$p = -\frac{b}{2a} = -\frac{150{,}000}{-4{,}000} = 37.5.$$

This value of p gives the highest point on the graph and thus gives the largest value of $R(p)$. We may conclude that Alien Publications, Inc., should charge \$37.50 per book to maximize its annual revenue.

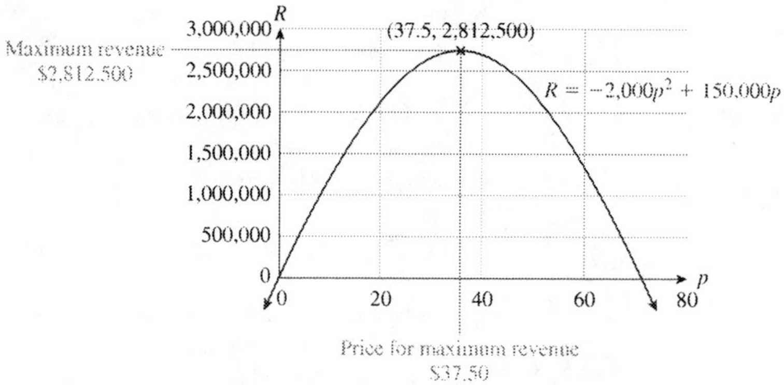

Figure 5

Before we go on... You might ask what the maximum annual revenue is for the publisher in Example 3. Because $R(p)$ gives us the revenue at a price of \$$p$, the answer is $R(37.5) = -2{,}000\,(37.5)^2 + 150{,}000(37.5) = 2{,}812{,}500$. In other words, the company will earn total annual revenues from this book amounting to \$2,812,500. ■

EXAMPLE 4 Demand, Revenue, and Profit

As the operator of *YSport Fitness* gym, you calculate your demand equation to be

$$q = -0.06p + 84,$$

where q is the number of members in the club and p is the annual membership fee you charge.

a. Your annual operating costs are a fixed cost of \$20,000 per year plus a variable cost of \$20 per member. Find the annual revenue and profit as functions of the membership price p.

b. At what price should you set the annual membership fee to obtain the maximum revenue? What is the maximum possible revenue?

c. At what price should you set the annual membership fee to obtain the maximum profit? What is the maximum possible profit? What is the corresponding revenue?

Solution

a. The annual revenue is given by

$$R = pq \quad \text{Formula for revenue}$$
$$= p(-0.06p + 84) \quad \text{Substitute for } q \text{ from demand equation.}$$
$$= -0.06p^2 + 84p. \quad \text{Simplify.}$$

The annual cost C is given by

$$C = 20{,}000 + 20q. \quad \text{\$20,000 plus \$20 per member}$$

However, this is a function of q, and not p. To express C as a function of p we substitute for q using the demand equation $q = -0.06p + 84$:

$$C = 20{,}000 + 20(-0.06p + 84)$$
$$= 20{,}000 - 1.2p + 1{,}680$$
$$= -1.2p + 21{,}680.$$

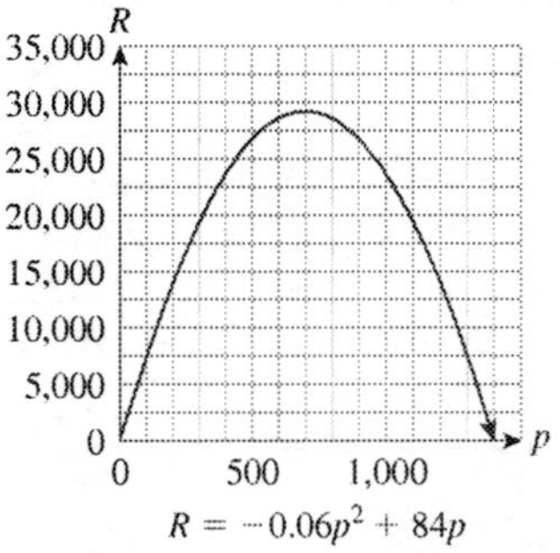

Figure 6

Thus, the profit function is:

$$
\begin{aligned}
P &= R - C && \text{Formula for profit} \\
&= -0.06p^2 + 84p - (-1.2p + 21{,}680) && \text{Substitute for revenue and cost.} \\
&= -0.06p^2 + 85.2p - 21{,}680.
\end{aligned}
$$

b. From part (a) the revenue function is given by

$$R = -0.06p^2 + 84p.$$

This is a quadratic function ($a = -0.06, b = 84, c = 0$) whose graph is a concave-down parabola (Figure 6). The maximum revenue corresponds to the highest point of the graph: the vertex, of which the p coordinate is

$$p = -\frac{b}{2a} = -\frac{84}{2(-0.06)} \approx \$700.$$

This is the membership fee you should charge for the maximum revenue. The corresponding maximum revenue is given by the y coordinate of the vertex in Figure 6:

$$R(700) = -0.06(700)^2 + 84(700) = \$29{,}400.$$

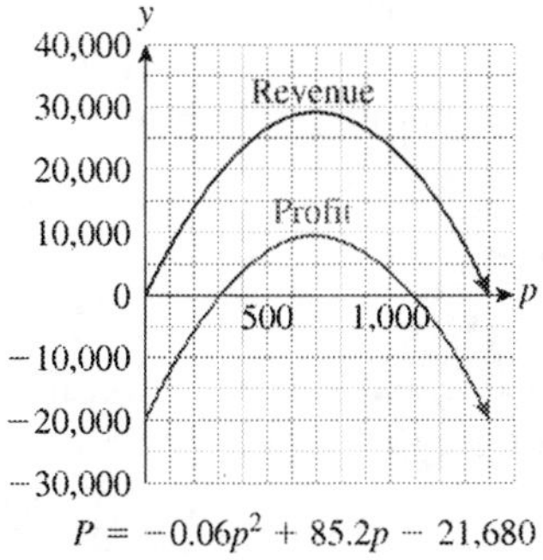

Figure 7

c. From part (a), the profit function is given by

$$P = -0.06p^2 + 85.2p - 21{,}680.$$

Like the revenue function, the profit function is quadratic ($a = -0.06$, $b = 85.2$, $c = -21{,}680$). Figure 7 shows both the revenue and profit functions. The maximum profit corresponds to the vertex, whose p coordinate is

$$p = -\frac{b}{2a} = -\frac{85.2}{2(-0.06)} \approx \$710.$$

This is the membership fee you should charge for the maximum profit. The corresponding maximum profit is given by the y coordinate of the vertex of the profit curve in Figure 7:

$$P(710) = -0.06(710)^2 + 85.2(710) - 21{,}680 = \$8{,}566.$$

The corresponding revenue is

$$R(710) = -0.06(710)^2 + 84(710) = \$29{,}394,$$

slightly less than the maximum possible revenue of $29,400.

Before we go on... The result of part (c) of Example 4 tells us that the vertex of the profit curve in Figure 7 is slightly to the right of the vertex in the revenue curve. However, the difference is tiny compared to the scale of the graphs, so the graphs appear to be parallel. ■

Q: *Charging \$710 membership brings in less revenue than charging \$700. So why charge \$710?*

A: A membership fee of \$700 does bring in slightly larger revenue than a fee of \$710, but it also brings in a slightly larger membership, which in turn raises the operating expense and has the effect of *lowering* the profit slightly (to \$8,560). In other words, the slightly higher fee, while bringing in less revenue, also lowers the cost, and the net result is a larger profit.

Fitting a Quadratic Function to Data: Quadratic Regression

In Section 1.4 we saw how to fit a regression line to a collection of data points. Here, we see how to use technology to obtain the **quadratic regression curve** associated with a set of points. The quadratic regression curve is the quadratic curve $y = ax^2 + bx + c$ that best fits the data points in the sense that the associated sum-of-squares error (SSE—see Section 1.4) is a minimum. Although there are algebraic methods for obtaining the quadratic regression curve, it is normal to use technology to do this.

EXAMPLE 5 Carbon Dioxide Concentration

The following table shows the annual mean carbon dioxide concentration measured at Mauna Loa Observatory in Hawaii, in parts per million, every 10 years from 1960 through 2010 ($t = 0$ represents 1960).[1]

Year t	0	10	20	30	40	50
PPM CO_2 C	317	326	339	354	369	390

a. Is a linear model appropriate for these data?

b. Find the quadratic model

$$C(t) = at^2 + bt + c$$

that best fits the data.

Solution

a. To see whether a linear model is appropriate, we plot the data points and the regression line using one of the methods of Example 2 in Section 1.4 (Figure 8).

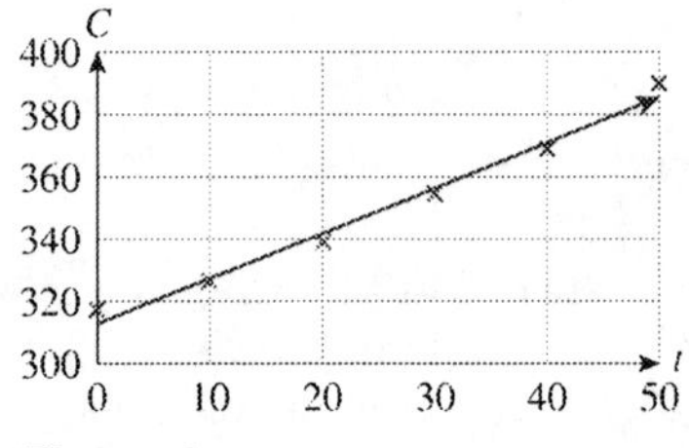

Figure 8

[1]Figures are approximate. Source: U.S. Department of Commerce/National Oceanic and Atmospheric Administration (NOAA) Earth System Research Laboratory, data downloaded from www.esrl.noaa.gov/gmd/ccgg/trends/ on March 13, 2011.

using Technology

For detailed instructions on how to find and graph the regression curve in Example 5 using a graphing calculator or a spreadsheet, see the Technology Guides at the end of the chapter. Outline:

TI-83/84 Plus

STAT EDIT values of t in L_1 and values of C in L_2
Regression curve: STAT CALC option 5
QuadReg ENTER
Graph: Y= VARS 5 EQ 1, then ZOOM 9
[More details on page 680.]

Spreadsheet

t- and C-values in Columns A and B.
Graph: Highlight data and insert a Scatter chart.
Regression curve: Right-click a datapoint and add polynomial order 2 trendline with option to show equation on chart.
[More details on page 683.]

Website

www.WanerMath.com
In the Simple Regression utility, enter the data in the x- and y-columns and press "y=ax^2+bx+c".

From the graph, we can see that the given data suggest a curve and not a straight line: The observed points are above the regression line at the ends but below in the middle. (We would expect the data points from a linear relation to fall randomly above and below the regression line.)

b. The quadratic model that best fits the data is the quadratic regression model. As with linear regression, there are algebraic formulas to compute a, b, and c, but they are rather involved. However, we exploit the fact that these formulas are built into graphing calculators, spreadsheets, and other technology and obtain the regression curve using technology (see Figure 9):

$$C(t) = 0.012t^2 + 0.85t + 320. \quad \text{Coefficients rounded to two significant digits}$$

Notice from the graphs that the quadratic regression model appears to give a better fit than the linear regression model. This impression is supported by the values of SSE: For the linear regression model, SSE $\approx$ 58, while for the quadratic regression model, SSE is much smaller, approximately 2.6, indicating a much better fit.

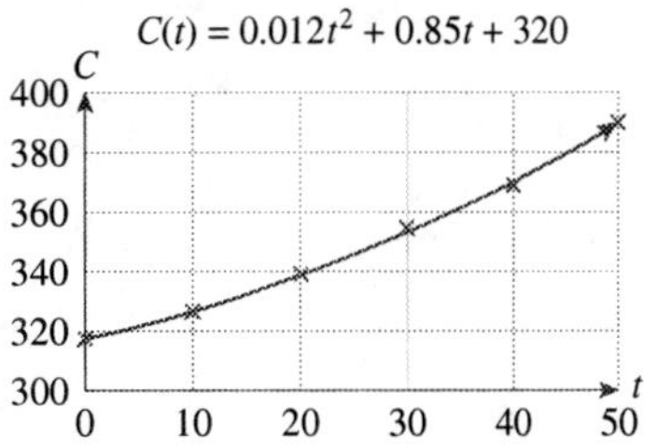

Figure 9

9.1 EXERCISES

▼ more advanced ◆ challenging

indicates exercises that should be solved using technology

In Exercises 1–10, sketch the graphs of the quadratic functions, indicating the coordinates of the vertex, the y-intercept, and the x-intercepts (if any). HINT [See Example 1.]

1. $f(x) = x^2 + 3x + 2$
2. $f(x) = -x^2 - x$
3. $f(x) = -x^2 + 4x - 4$
4. $f(x) = x^2 + 2x + 1$
5. $f(x) = -x^2 - 40x + 500$
6. $f(x) = x^2 - 10x - 600$
7. $f(x) = x^2 + x - 1$
8. $f(x) = x^2 + \sqrt{2}x + 1$
9. $f(x) = x^2 + 1$
10. $f(x) = -x^2 + 5$

In Exercises 11–14, for each demand equation, express the total revenue R as a function of the price p per item, sketch the graph of the resulting function, and determine the price p that maximizes total revenue in each case. HINT [See Example 3.]

11. $q = -4p + 100$
12. $q = -3p + 300$
13. $q = -2p + 400$
14. $q = -5p + 1{,}200$

In Exercises 15–18, use technology to find the quadratic regression curve through the given points. (Round all coefficients to four decimal places.) HINT [See Example 5.]

15. $\{(1, 2), (3, 5), (4, 3), (5, 1)\}$

16. $\{(-1, 2), (-3, 5), (-4, 3), (-5, 1)\}$

17. $\{(-1, 2), (-3, 5), (-4, 3)\}$

18. $\{(2, 5), (3, 5), (5, 3)\}$

APPLICATIONS

19. ***World Military Expenditure*** The following chart shows total military and arms trade expenditure from 1990 to 2008 ($t = 0$ represents 1990).[2]

[2] Approximate figures in constant 2005 dollars. The 2008 figure is an estimate, based on the increase in U.S. military expenditure.

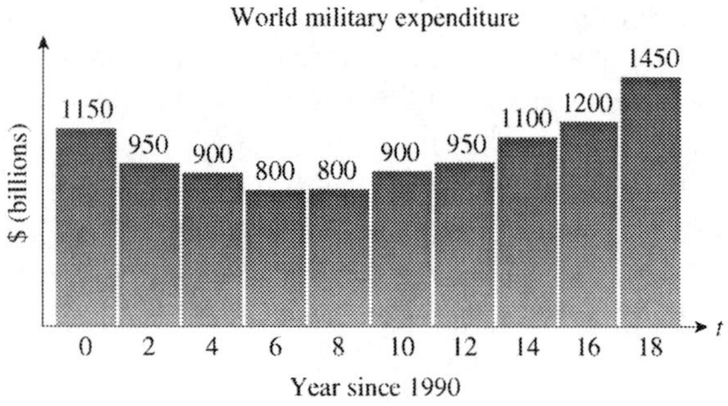

Source: www.globalissues.org/Geopolitics/ArmsTrade/Spending.asp

a. If you want to model the expenditure figures with a function of the form

$$f(t) = at^2 + bt + c,$$

would you expect the coefficient a to be positive or negative? Why? HINT [See "Features of a Parabola," page 621.]

b. Which of the following models best approximates the data given? (Try to answer this without actually computing values.)

(A) $f(t) = 5t^2 - 80t - 1,150$
(B) $f(t) = -5t^2 - 80t + 1,150$
(C) $f(t) = 5t^2 - 80t + 1,150$
(D) $f(t) = -5t^2 - 80t - 1,150$

c. What is the nearest year that would correspond to the vertex of the graph of the correct model from part (b)? What is the danger of extrapolating the data in either direction?

20. ***Education Expenditure*** The following chart shows the percentage of the U.S. Discretionary Budget allocated to education from 2003 to 2009 ($t = 3$ represents the start of 2003).

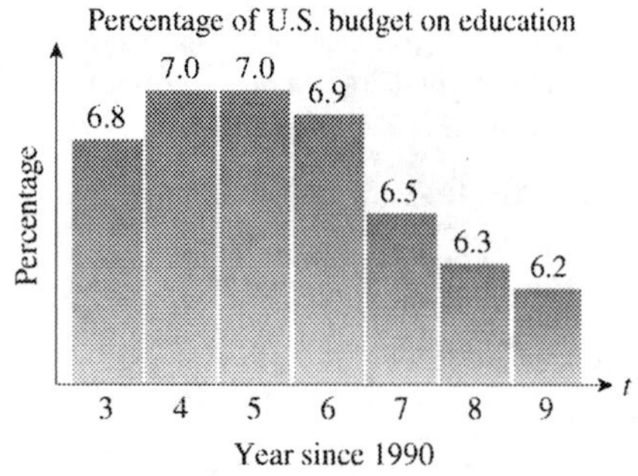

Source: www.globalissues.org/Geopolitics/ArmsTrade/Spending.asp

a. If you want to model the percentage figures with a function of the form

$$f(t) = at^2 + bt + c,$$

would you expect the coefficient a to be positive or negative? Why? HINT [See "Features of a Parabola," page 621.]

b. Which of the following models best approximates the data given? (Try to answer this without actually computing values)

(A) $f(t) = 0.04t^2 + 0.3t - 6$
(B) $f(t) = -0.04t^2 + 0.3t + 6$
(C) $f(t) = 0.04t^2 + 0.3t + 6$
(D) $f(t) = -0.04t^2 + 0.3t - 6$

c. What is the nearest year that would correspond to the vertex of the graph of the correct model from part (b)? What is the danger of extrapolating the data in either direction?

21. ***Oil Imports from Mexico*** Daily oil imports to the United States from Mexico can be approximated by

$$I(t) = -0.015t^2 + 0.1t + 1.4 \text{ million barrels/day } (0 \le t \le 8)$$

where t is time in years since the start of 2000.[3] According to the model, in what year were oil imports to the United States greatest? How many barrels per day were imported that year? HINT [See Example 1.]

22. ***Oil Production in Mexico*** Daily oil production by Pemex, Mexico's national oil company, for 2001–2009 can be approximated by

$$P(t) = -0.022t^2 + 0.2t + 2.9 \text{ million barrels/day } (1 \le t \le 9)$$

where t is time in years since the start of 2000.[4] According to the model, in what year was oil production by Pemex greatest? How many barrels per day were produced that year?

23. ***Net Income*** The annual net income of General Electric for the period 2005–2010 could be approximated by

$$P(t) = -2.0t^2 + 6.6t + 16 \text{ billion dollars } (0 \le t \le 5)$$

where t is time in years since 2005.[5] According to the model, in what year in this period was General Electric's net income highest? What was its net income that year? Would you trust this model to continue to be valid long past this period? Why?

24. ***Net Income*** The annual net income of General Electric for the period 2007–2012 could be approximated by

$$P(t) = 3.0t^2 - 24t + 59 \text{ billion dollars } (2 \le t \le 7)$$

where t is time in years since 2005.[6] According to the model, in what year in this period was General Electric's net income lowest? What was its net income that year? Would you trust this model to continue to be valid long past this period? Why?

[3]Source: Energy Information Administration/Pemex/www.eia.gov

[4]Figures are approximate, and 2008–2009 figures are projections by the Department of Energy. Source: Energy Information Administration: Pemex.

[5]Source for data: www.wikinvest.com/

[6]*Ibid.* 2011 net income is projected.

a. Find a quadratic regression model for these data. (Round coefficients to two significant digits.) Graph the model together with the data.
b. What does the model predict for iPod sales in the third quarter of 2010 ($t = 7$), to the nearest million? Comment on the answer.

COMMUNICATION AND REASONING EXERCISES

41. What can you say about the graph of $f(x) = ax^2 + bx + c$ if $a = 0$?

42. What can you say about the graph of $f(x) = ax^2 + bx + c$ if $c = 0$?

43. Multiple choice: Following is the graph of $f(x) = ax^2 + bx + c$:

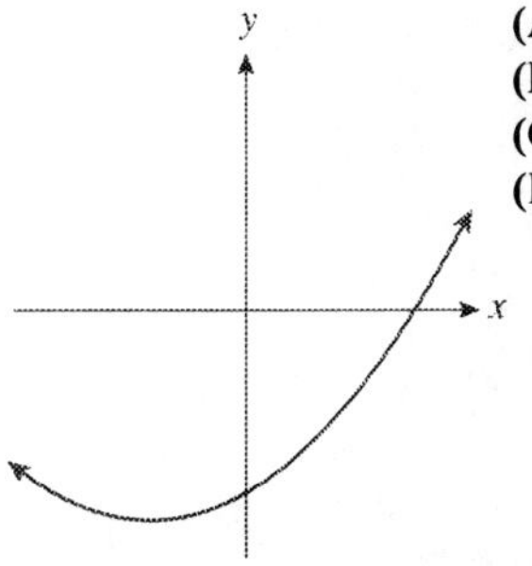

(A) a is positive and c is positive.
(B) a is negative and c is positive.
(C) a is positive and c is negative.
(D) a is negative and c is negative.

44. Multiple choice: Following is the graph of $f(x) = ax^2 + bx + c$:

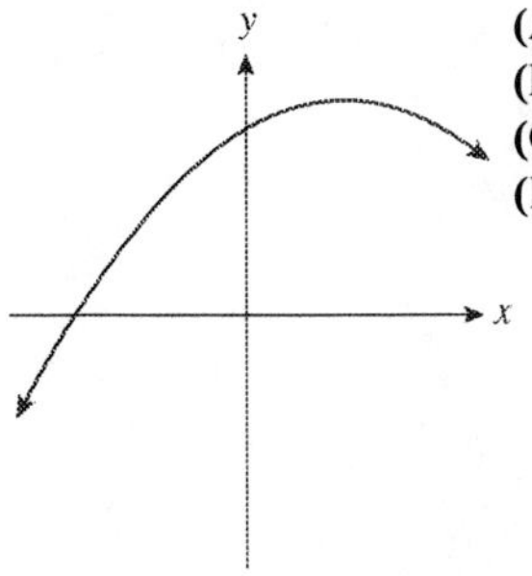

(A) a is positive and c is positive.
(B) a is negative and c is positive.
(C) a is positive and c is negative.
(D) a is negative and c is negative.

45. ▼ Refer to the graph of $f(x) = ax^2 + bx + c$ in Exercise 43. Is b positive or negative? Why?

46. ▼ Refer to the graph of $f(x) = ax^2 + bx + c$ in Exercise 44. Is b positive or negative? Why?

47. Suppose the graph of revenue as a function of unit price is a parabola that is concave down. What is the significance of the coordinates of the vertex, the x-intercepts, and the y-intercept?

48. Suppose the height of a stone thrown vertically upward is given by a quadratic function of time. What is the significance of the coordinates of the vertex, the (possible) x-intercepts, and the y-intercept?

49. How might you tell, roughly, whether a set of data should be modeled by a quadratic rather than by a linear equation?

50. A member of your study group tells you that, because the following set of data does not suggest a straight line, the data are best modeled by a quadratic.

x	0	2	4	6	8
y	1	2	1	0	1

Comment on her suggestion.

51. Is a quadratic model useful for long-term prediction of sales of an item? Why?

52. Of what use is a quadratic model, if not for long-term prediction?

53. ▼ Explain why, if demand is a linear function of unit price p (with negative slope), then there must be a *single value of* p that results in the maximum revenue.

54. ▼ Explain why, if the average cost of a commodity is given by $y = 0.1x^2 - 4x - 2$, where x is the number of units sold, there is a single choice of x that results in the lowest possible average cost.

55. ▼ If the revenue function for a particular commodity is $R(p) = -50p^2 + 60p$, what is the (linear) demand function? Give a reason for your answer.

56. ▼ If the revenue function for a particular commodity is $R(p) = -50p^2 + 60p + 50$, can the demand function be linear? What is the associated demand function?

Practice Problems 9.1, Part 1

When a popular style of running shoe is priced at \$80, Runner's Emporium sells an average of 96 pairs per week. Based on comparative research, management believes that for each decrease of \$2.50 in price, four additional pairs of shoes could be sold weekly.

1. Let n denote the number of \$2.50 decreases in price and let q denote the number of pairs of shoes sold. Write an equation that gives n in terms of q.

2. Write a function R that gives the expected weekly revenue from sales of this particular style of shoe as a function of p, the price per pair (in dollars).

3. Determine the selling price per pair that will result in maximum possible revenue, as well as the maximum possible revenue.

4. Determine the lowest price (to the nearest cent) that will result in weekly revenue of at least \$7000 from sales of the shoes.

Practice Problems 9.1, Part 2

Suppose that the price at which q **thousand** flash drives can be sold is given by the demand equation

$$p = 12 - 0.4q \quad \text{dollars per drive,}$$

where $0 \le q \le 22$. In addition, the cost of producing q **thousand** drives is given by the cost function

$$C(q) = 26 + 0.85q \quad \text{thousand dollars.}$$

1. Let $R(q)$ denote the corresponding revenue function. Sketch a graph of both $R(q)$ and $C(q)$ on the same set of axes. Show only what is relevant.

2. Find the level of production (to the nearest flash drive) that maximizes revenue.

3. What is the selling price (per flash drive) that generates maximum revenue?

4. What is the maximum possible revenue?

5. Find all break-even production levels, to the nearest flash drive.

6. Determine the level of sales that results in revenue of at least $85,000. Illustrate your results graphically.

Practice Problems 9.1, Part 3

The arch of a bridge is in the shape of a parabola and is 16 feet high at the center and 24 feet wide at the base.

1. What is the tallest 8-foot wide truck that can pass through the arch? Give the height accurate to two decimal places.

2. What is the widest 14-foot high truck that can pass through the arch? Give the width accurate to two decimal places.

9.2 Exponential Functions and Models

The quadratic functions we discussed in Section 9.1 can be used to model many nonlinear situations. However, exponential functions give better models in some applications, including population growth, radioactive decay, the growth or depreciation of financial investments, and many other phenomena. (We already saw some of these applications in Section 1.2.)

To work effectively with exponential functions, we need to know the laws of exponents. The following list, taken from the algebra review in Chapter 0, gives the laws of exponents we will be using.

The Laws of Exponents

If b and c are positive and x and y are any real numbers, then the following laws hold:

Law	Quick Examples	
1. $b^x b^y = b^{x+y}$	$2^3 2^2 = 2^5 = 32$	$2^{3-x} = 2^3 2^{-x}$
2. $\dfrac{b^x}{b^y} = b^{x-y}$	$\dfrac{4^3}{4^2} = 4^{3-2} = 4^1 = 4$	$3^{x-2} = \dfrac{3^x}{3^2} = \dfrac{3^x}{9}$
3. $\dfrac{1}{b^x} = b^{-x}$	$9^{-0.5} = \dfrac{1}{9^{0.5}} = \dfrac{1}{3}$	$2^{-x} = \dfrac{1}{2^x}$
4. $b^0 = 1$	$(3.3)^0 = 1$	$x^0 = 1$ if $x \neq 0$
5. $(b^x)^y = b^{xy}$	$(2^3)^2 = 2^6 = 64$	$\left(\dfrac{1}{2}\right)^x = (2^{-1})^x = 2^{-x}$
6. $(bc)^x = b^x c^x$	$(4 \cdot 2)^2 = 4^2 2^2 = 64$	$10^x = 5^x 2^x$
7. $\left(\dfrac{b}{c}\right)^x = \dfrac{b^x}{c^x}$	$\left(\dfrac{4}{3}\right)^2 = \dfrac{4^2}{3^2} = \dfrac{16}{9}$	$\left(\dfrac{1}{2}\right)^x = \dfrac{1^x}{2^x} = \dfrac{1}{2^x}$

Here are the functions we will study in this section.

Exponential Function

An **exponential function** has the form

$$f(x) = Ab^x, \qquad \text{Technology: A*b^x}$$

where A and b are constants with $A \neq 0$ and b positive and not equal to 1. We call b the **base** of the exponential function.

Quick Examples

1. $f(x) = 2^x$ — $A = 1, b = 2$; Technology: 2^x

   $f(1) = 2^1 = 2$ — 2^1

   $f(-3) = 2^{-3} = \dfrac{1}{8}$ — 2^(-3)

   $f(0) = 2^0 = 1$ — 2^0

2. $g(x) = 20(3^x)$ — $A = 20, b = 3$; Technology: 20*3^x

   $g(2) = 20(3^2) = 20(9) = 180$ — 20*3^2

   $g(-1) = 20(3^{-1}) = 20\left(\dfrac{1}{3}\right) = 6\dfrac{2}{3}$ — 20*3^(-1)

3. $h(x) = 2^{-x} = \left(\frac{1}{2}\right)^x$ — $A = 1, b = \frac{1}{2}$; Technology: `2^(-x)` or `(1/2)^x`

$h(1) = 2^{-1} = \frac{1}{2}$ — `2^(-1)` or `(1/2)^1`

$h(2) = 2^{-2} = \frac{1}{4}$ — `2^(-2)` or `(1/2)^2`

4. $k(x) = 3 \cdot 2^{-4x} = 3(2^{-4})^x$ — $A = 3, b = 2^{-4}$; Technology: `3*2^(-4*x)`

$k(-2) = 3 \cdot 2^{-4(-2)}$ — `3*2^(-4*(-2))`

$= 3 \cdot 2^8 = 3 \cdot 256 = 768$

Exponential Functions from the Numerical and Graphical Points of View

The following table shows values of $f(x) = 3(2^x)$ for some values of x ($A = 3$, $b = 2$):

x	−3	−2	−1	0	1	2	3
$f(x)$	$\frac{3}{8}$	$\frac{3}{4}$	$\frac{3}{2}$	3	6	12	24

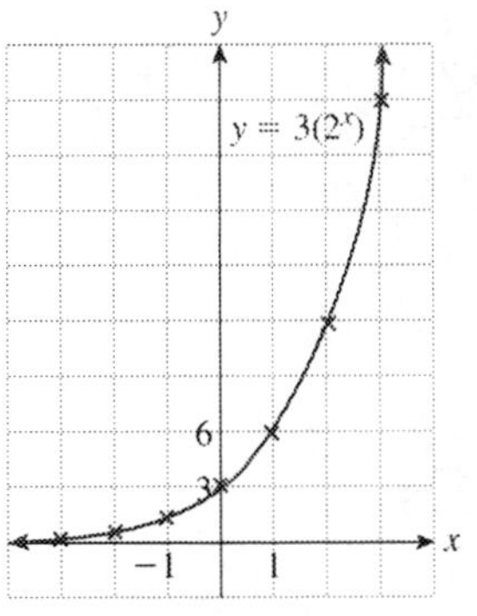

Figure 10

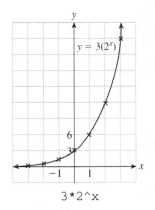

The graph of f is shown in Figure 10.

Notice that the y-intercept is $A = 3$ (obtained by setting $x = 0$). In general:

In the graph of $f(x) = Ab^x$, A is the y-intercept, or the value of y when $x = 0$.

What about b? Notice from the table that the value of y is multiplied by $b = 2$ for every increase of 1 in x. If we decrease x by 1, the y coordinate gets *divided* by $b = 2$.

The value of y is multiplied by b for every one-unit increase of x.

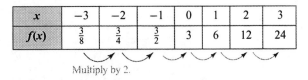

x	−3	−2	−1	0	1	2	3
$f(x)$	$\frac{3}{8}$	$\frac{3}{4}$	$\frac{3}{2}$	3	6	12	24

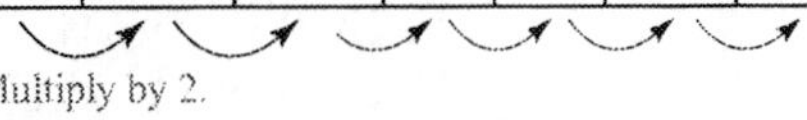

Multiply by 2.

On the graph, if we move one unit to the right from any point on the curve, the y coordinate doubles. Thus, the curve becomes dramatically steeper as the value of x increases. This phenomenon is called **exponential growth**. (See Section 1.2.)

Exponential Function Numerically and Graphically

For the exponential function $f(x) = Ab^x$:

Role of *A*

$f(0) = A$, so A is the y-intercept of the graph of f.

Role of *b*

If x increases by 1, $f(x)$ is multiplied by b.

If x increases by 2, $f(x)$ is multiplied by b^2.

⋮

If x increases by Δx, $f(x)$ is multiplied by $b^{\Delta x}$.

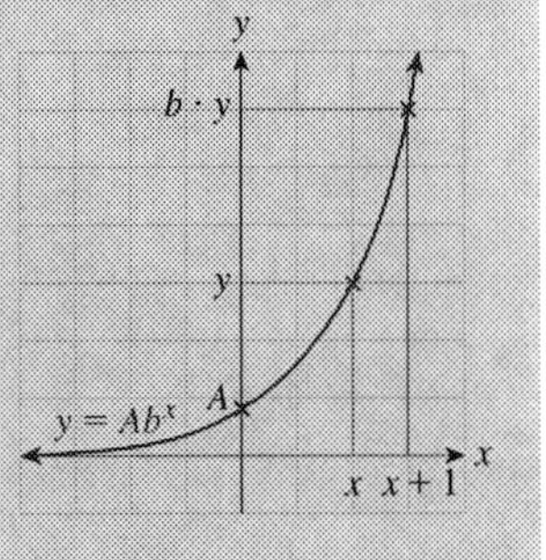

If x increases by 1, y is multiplied by b.

Quick Examples

1. $f_1(x) = 2^x$, $f_2(x) = \left(\frac{1}{2}\right)^x = 2^{-x}$

	A	B	C
1	x	2^x	2^(-x)
2	-3	1/8	8
3	-2	1/4	4
4	-1	1/2	2
5	0	1	1
6	1	2	1/2
7	2	4	1/4
8	3	8	1/8

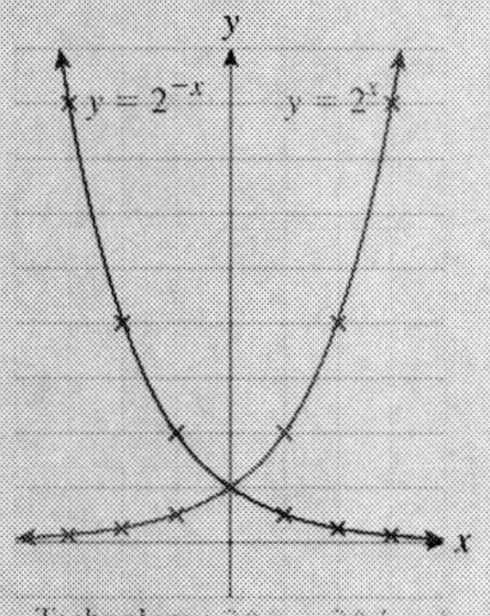

Technology: 2^x; 2^(-x)

When x increases by 1, $f_2(x)$ is multiplied by $\frac{1}{2}$. The function $f_1(x) = 2^x$ illustrates exponential growth, while $f_2(x) = \left(\frac{1}{2}\right)^x$ illustrates the opposite phenomenon: **exponential decay.**

2. $f_1(x) = 2^x$, $f_2(x) = 3^x$, $f_3(x) = 1^x$ (Can you see why f_3 is not an exponential function?)

	A	B	C	D
1	x	2^x	3^x	1^x
2	-3	1/8	1/27	1
3	-2	1/4	1/9	1
4	-1	1/2	1/3	1
5	0	1	1	1
6	1	2	3	1
7	2	4	9	1
8	3	8	27	1

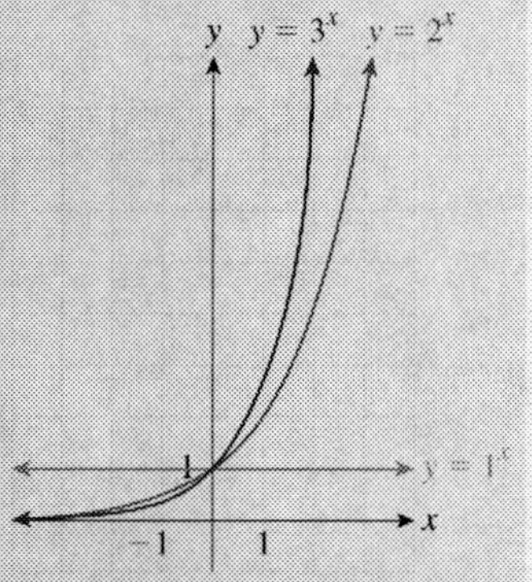

If x increases by 1, 3^x is multiplied by 3. Note also that all the graphs pass through (0, 1). (Why?)

EXAMPLE 1 Recognizing Exponential Data Numerically and Graphically

Some of the values of two functions, f and g, are given in the following table:

x	-2	-1	0	1	2
$f(x)$	-7	-3	1	5	9
$g(x)$	$\frac{2}{9}$	$\frac{2}{3}$	2	6	18

One of these functions is linear, and the other is exponential. Which is which?

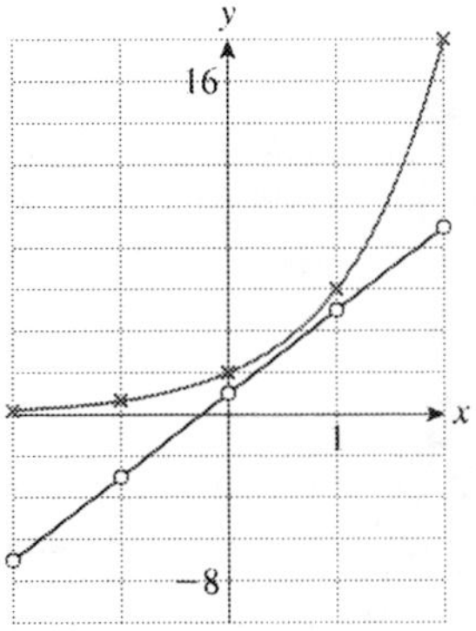

Figure 11

Solution Remember that a linear function increases (or decreases) by the same amount every time x increases by 1. The values of f behave this way: Every time x increases by 1, the value of $f(x)$ increases by 4. Therefore, f is a linear function with a *slope* of 4. Because $f(0) = 1$, we see that

$$f(x) = 4x + 1$$

is a linear formula that fits the data.

On the other hand, every time x increases by 1, the value of $g(x)$ is *multiplied* by 3. Because $g(0) = 2$, we find that

$$g(x) = 2(3^x)$$

is an exponential function fitting the data.

We can visualize the two functions f and g by plotting the data points (Figure 11). The data points for $f(x)$ clearly lie along a straight line, whereas the points for $g(x)$ lie along a curve. The y coordinate of each point for $g(x)$ is 3 times the y coordinate of the preceding point, demonstrating that the curve is an exponential one.

In Section 1.3, we discussed a method for calculating the equation of the line that passes through two given points. In the following example, we show a method for calculating the equation of the exponential curve through two given points.

EXAMPLE 2 Finding the Exponential Curve through Two Points

Find an equation of the exponential curve through (1, 6.3) and (4, 170.1).

Solution We want an equation of the form

$$y = Ab^x \quad (b > 0).$$

Substituting the coordinates of the given points, we get

$$6.3 = Ab^1 \qquad \text{Substitute } (1, 6.3).$$
$$170.1 = Ab^4. \qquad \text{Substitute } (4, 170.1).$$

If we now divide the second equation by the first, we get

$$\frac{170.1}{6.3} = \frac{Ab^4}{Ab} = b^3$$
$$b^3 = 27$$
$$b = 27^{1/3} \qquad \text{Take reciprocal power of both sides.}$$
$$b = 3.$$

Now that we have b, we can substitute its value into the first equation to obtain

$$6.3 = 3A \qquad \text{Substitute } b = 3 \text{ into the equation } 6.3 = Ab^1.$$
$$A = \frac{6.3}{3} = 2.1.$$

We have both constants, $A = 2.1$ and $b = 3$, so the model is

$$y = 2.1(3^x).$$

Example 6 will show how to use technology to fit an exponential function to two or more data points.

APPLICATIONS

Recall some terminology we mentioned earlier: A quantity y experiences **exponential growth** if $y = Ab^t$ with $b > 1$. (Here we use t for the independent variable, thinking of time.) It experiences **exponential decay** if $y = Ab^t$ with $0 < b < 1$. We already saw several examples of exponential growth and decay in Section 1.2.

EXAMPLE 3 Exponential Growth and Decay

a. Compound Interest (See Section 1.2 Example 6.) If \$2,000 is invested in a mutual fund with an annual yield of 12.6% and the earnings are reinvested each month, then the future value after t years is

$$A(t) = P\left(1 + \frac{r}{m}\right)^{mt} = 2{,}000\left(1 + \frac{0.126}{12}\right)^{12t} = 2{,}000(1.0105)^{12t},$$

which can be written as $2{,}000(1.0105^{12})^t$, so $A = 2{,}000$ and $b = 1.0105^{12}$. This is an example of exponential growth, because $b > 1$.

b. Carbon Decay (See Section 1.2 Example 7.) The amount of carbon 14 remaining in a sample that originally contained A grams is approximately

$$C(t) = A(0.999879)^t.$$

This is an instance of exponential decay, because $b < 1$.

➡ **Before we go on...** Refer again to part (a). In Example 6(b) of Section 1.2 we showed how to use technology to answer questions such as the following: "When, to the nearest year, will the value of your investment reach \$5,000?" ■

The next example shows an application to public health.

EXAMPLE 4 Exponential Growth: Epidemics

In the early stages of the AIDS epidemic during the 1980s, the number of cases in the United States was increasing by about 50% every 6 months. By the start of 1983, there were approximately 1,600 AIDS cases in the United States.[14]

a. Assuming an exponential growth model, find a function that predicts the number of people infected t years after the start of 1983.

b. Use the model to estimate the number of people infected by October 1, 1986, and also by the end of that year.

Solution

a. One way of finding the desired exponential function is to reason as follows: At time $t = 0$ (January 1, 1983), the number of people infected was 1,600, so $A = 1{,}600$. Every 6 months, the number of cases increased to 150% of the number 6 months earlier—that is, to 1.50 times that number. Each year, it therefore increased to $(1.50)^2 = 2.25$ times the number one year earlier. Hence, after t years, we need to multiply the original 1,600 by 2.25^t, so the model is

$$y = 1{,}600(2.25^t) \text{ cases.}$$

[14]Data based on regression of the 1982–1986 figures. Source for data: Centers for Disease Control and Prevention. HIV/AIDS Surveillance Report, 2000;12 (No. 2).

Alternatively, if we wish to use the method of Example 2, we need two data points. We are given one point: (0, 1,600). Because y increased by 50% every 6 months, 6 months later it reached $1{,}600 + 800 = 2{,}400$ ($t = 0.5$). This information gives a second point: (0.5, 2,400). We can now apply the method in Example 2 to find the model above.

b. October 1, 1986, corresponds to $t = 3.75$ (because October 1 is 9 months, or $9/12 = 0.75$ of a year after January 1). Substituting this value of t in the model gives

$$y = 1{,}600(2.25^{3.75}) \approx 33{,}481 \text{ cases}$$ 1600*2.25^3.75

By the end of 1986, the model predicts that

$$y = 1{,}600(2.25^4) = 41{,}006 \text{ cases.}$$

(The actual number of cases was around 41,700.)

Before we go on... Increasing the number of cases by 50% every 6 months couldn't continue for very long and this is borne out by observations. If increasing by 50% every 6 months did continue, then by January 2003 ($t = 20$), the number of infected people would have been

$$1{,}600(2.25^{20}) \approx 17{,}700{,}000{,}000$$

a number that is more than 50 times the size of the U.S. population! Thus, although the exponential model is fairly reliable in the early stages of the epidemic, it is unreliable for predicting long-term trends. ■

Epidemiologists use more sophisticated models to measure the spread of epidemics, and these models predict a leveling-off phenomenon as the number of cases becomes a significant part of the total population. We discuss such a model, the **logistic function**, in Section 9.4.

The Number e and More Applications

In nature we find examples of growth that occurs *continuously*, as though "interest" is being added more often than every second or fraction of a second. To model this, we need to see what happens to the compound interest formula of Section 1.2 as we let m (the number of times interest is added per year) become extremely large. Something very interesting does happen: We end up with a more compact and elegant formula than we began with. To see why, let's look at a very simple situation.

Suppose we invest \$1 in the bank for 1 year at 100% interest, compounded m times per year. If $m = 1$, then 100% interest is added every year, and so our money doubles at the end of the year. In general, the accumulated capital at the end of the year is

$$A = 1\left(1 + \frac{1}{m}\right)^m = \left(1 + \frac{1}{m}\right)^m.$$ (1+1/m)^m

	A	B
1	m	(1+1/m)^m
2	1	2
3	10	2.59374246
4	100	2.704813829
5	1000	2.716923932
6	10000	2.718145927
7	100000	2.718268237
8	1000000	2.718280469
9	10000000	2.718281694
10	100000000	2.718281786
11	1000000000	2.718282031

Now, we are interested in what A becomes for large values of m. On the left is a spreadsheet showing the quantity $\left(1 + \frac{1}{m}\right)^m$ for larger and larger values of m.

Something interesting *does* seem to be happening! The numbers appear to be getting closer and closer to a specific value. In mathematical terminology, we say that the numbers **converge** to a fixed number, 2.71828..., called the **limiting value*** of the quantities $\left(1 + \frac{1}{m}\right)^m$. This number, called e, is one of the most important in mathematics. The number e is irrational, just as the more familiar number π is, so we cannot write down its exact numerical value. To 20 decimal places,

$$e = 2.71828182845904523536\ldots.$$

* See Chapter 10 for more on limits.

We now say that, if \$1 is invested for 1 year at 100% interest **compounded continuously**, the accumulated money at the end of that year will amount to $\$e = \$2.72$ (to the nearest cent). But what about the following more general question?

Q: *What about a more general scenario: If we invest an amount \$P for t years at an interest rate of r, compounded continuously, what will be the accumulated amount A at the end of that period?*

A: In the special case above (P, t, and r all equal 1), we took the compound interest formula and let m get larger and larger. We do the same more generally, after a little preliminary work with the algebra of exponentials.

$$A = P\left(1 + \frac{r}{m}\right)^{mt}$$

$$= P\left(1 + \frac{1}{(m/r)}\right)^{mt} \qquad \text{Substituting } \frac{r}{m} = \frac{1}{(m/r)}$$

$$= P\left(1 + \frac{1}{(m/r)}\right)^{(m/r)rt} \qquad \text{Substituting } m = \left(\frac{m}{r}\right)r$$

$$= P\left[\left(1 + \frac{1}{(m/r)}\right)^{(m/r)}\right]^{rt} \qquad \text{Using the rule } a^{bc} = (a^b)^c$$

For continuous compounding of interest, we let m, and hence m/r, get very large. This affects only the term in brackets, which converges to e, and we get the formula

$$A = Pe^{rt}.$$

Q: *How do I obtain powers of e or e itself on a TI-83/84 Plus or in a spreadsheet?*

A: On the TI-83/84 Plus, enter e^x as `e^(x)`, where `e^(` can be obtained by pressing [2ND] [LN]. To obtain the number e on the TI-83/84 Plus, enter `e^(1)`. Spreadsheets have a built-in function called `EXP`; `EXP(x)` gives the value of e^x. To obtain the number e in a spreadsheet, enter `=EXP(1)`.

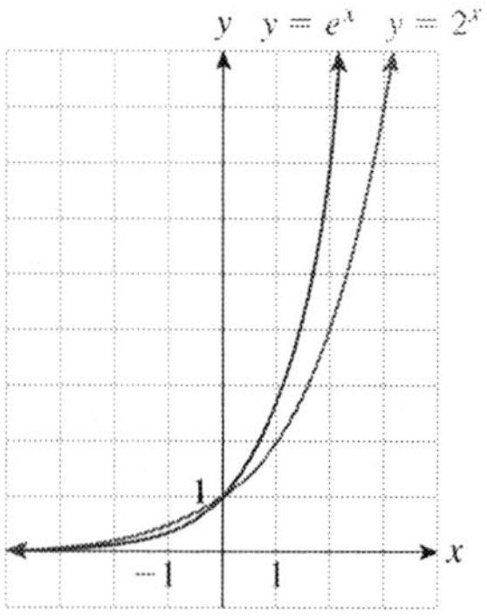

Technology formula: `e^(x)` or `EXP(x)`

Figure 12

Figure 12 shows the graph of $y = e^x$ with that of $y = 2^x$ for comparison.

The Number e and Continuous Compounding

The number e is the limiting value of the quantities $\left(1 + \frac{1}{m}\right)^m$ as m gets larger and larger, and has the value 2.71828182845904523536 . . .

If \$$P$ is invested at an annual interest rate r compounded continuously, the accumulated amount after t years is

$$A(t) = Pe^{rt}. \qquad \texttt{P*e^(r*t)} \text{ or } \texttt{P*EXP(r*t)}$$

Quick Examples

1. If \$100 is invested in an account that bears 15% interest compounded continuously, at the end of 10 years the investment will be worth

$$A(10) = 100e^{(0.15)(10)} = \$448.17. \qquad \texttt{100*e^(0.15*10)} \text{ or } \texttt{100*EXP(0.15*10)}$$

2. If \$1 is invested in an account that bears 100% interest compounded continuously, at the end of x years the investment will be worth

$$A(x) = e^x \text{ dollars.}$$

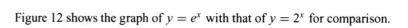

EXAMPLE 5 Continuous Compounding

a. You invest \$10,000 at *Fastrack Savings & Loan,* which pays 6% compounded continuously. Express the balance in your account as a function of the number of years t and calculate the amount of money you will have after 5 years.

b. Your friend has just invested \$20,000 in *Constant Growth Funds,* whose stocks are continuously *declining* at a rate of 6% per year. How much will her investment be worth in 5 years?

c. During which year will the value of your investment first exceed that of your friend?

Solution

a. We use the continuous growth formula with $P = 10{,}000$, $r = 0.06$, and t variable, getting

$$A(t) = Pe^{rt} = 10{,}000e^{0.06t}.$$

In 5 years,

$$\begin{aligned} A(5) &= 10{,}000e^{0.06(5)} \\ &= 10{,}000e^{0.3} \\ &\approx \$13{,}498.59. \end{aligned}$$

b. Because the investment is depreciating, we use a negative value for r and take $P = 20{,}000$, $r = -0.06$, and $t = 5$, getting

$$\begin{aligned} A(t) &= Pe^{rt} = 20{,}000e^{-0.06t} \\ A(5) &= 20{,}000e^{-0.06(5)} \\ &= 20{,}000e^{-0.3} \\ &\approx \$14{,}816.36. \end{aligned}$$

c. We can answer the question now using a graphing calculator, a spreadsheet, or the Function Evaluator and Grapher tool at the Website. Just enter the exponential models of parts (a) and (b) and create tables to compute the values at the end of several years:

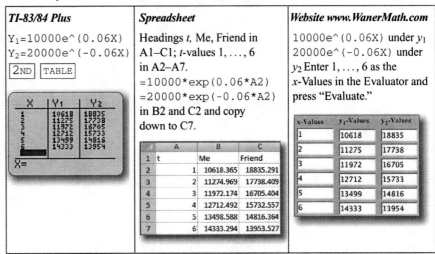

TI-83/84 Plus

`Y1=10000e^(0.06X)`
`Y2=20000e^(-0.06X)`
`2ND` `TABLE`

X	Y1	Y2
1	10618	18835
2	11275	17738
3	11972	16705
4	12712	15733
5	13499	14816
6	14333	13954

X=

Spreadsheet

Headings t, Me, Friend in A1–C1; t-values 1, . . . , 6 in A2–A7.
`=10000*exp(0.06*A2)`
`=20000*exp(-0.06*A2)`
in B2 and C2 and copy down to C7.

	A	B	C
1	t	Me	Friend
2	1	10618.365	18835.291
3	2	11274.969	17738.409
4	3	11972.174	16705.404
5	4	12712.492	15732.557
6	5	13498.588	14816.364
7	6	14333.294	13953.527

Website www.WanerMath.com

`10000e^(0.06X)` under y_1
`20000e^(-0.06X)` under y_2 Enter 1, . . . , 6 as the x-Values in the Evaluator and press "Evaluate."

x-Values	y_1-Values	y_2-Values
1	10618	18835
2	11275	17738
3	11972	16705
4	12712	15733
5	13499	14816
6	14333	13954

From the table, we see that the value of your investment overtakes that of your friend after $t = 5$ (the end of year 5) and before $t = 6$ (the end of year 6). Thus your investment first exceeds that of your friend sometime during year 6.

Before we go on...

Q: *How does continuous compounding compare with monthly compounding?*

A: To repeat the calculation in part (a) of Example 5 using monthly compounding instead of continuous compounding, we use the compound interest formula with $P = 10{,}000$, $r = 0.06$, $m = 12$, and $t = 5$ and find

$$A(5) = 10{,}000(1 + 0.06/12)^{60} \approx \$13{,}488.50.$$

Thus, continuous compounding earns you approximately \$10 more than monthly compounding on a 5-year, \$10,000 investment. This is little to get excited about.

■

If we write the continuous compounding formula $A(t) = Pe^{rt}$ as $A(t) = P(e^r)^t$, we see that $A(t)$ is an exponential function of t, where the base is $b = e^r$, so we have really not introduced a new kind of function. In fact, exponential functions are often written in this way:

Exponential Functions: Alternative Form

We can write any exponential function in the following alternative form:

$$f(x) = Ae^{rx}$$

where A and r are constants. If r is positive, f models exponential growth; if r is negative, f models exponential decay.

Quick Examples

1. $f(x) = 100e^{0.15x}$ — Exponential growth $A = 100$, $r = 0.15$
2. $f(t) = Ae^{-0.000\,121\,01t}$ — Exponential decay of carbon 14; $r = -0.000\,121\,01$
3. $f(t) = 100e^{0.15t} = 100\left(e^{0.15}\right)^t = 100(1.1618)^t$ — Converting Ae^{rt} to the form Ab^t

We will see in Chapter 11 that the exponential function with base e exhibits some interesting properties when we measure its rate of change, and this is the real mathematical importance of e.

Exponential Regression

Starting with a set of data that suggests an exponential curve, we can use technology to compute the exponential regression curve in much the same way as we did for the quadratic regression curve in Example 5 of Section 9.1.

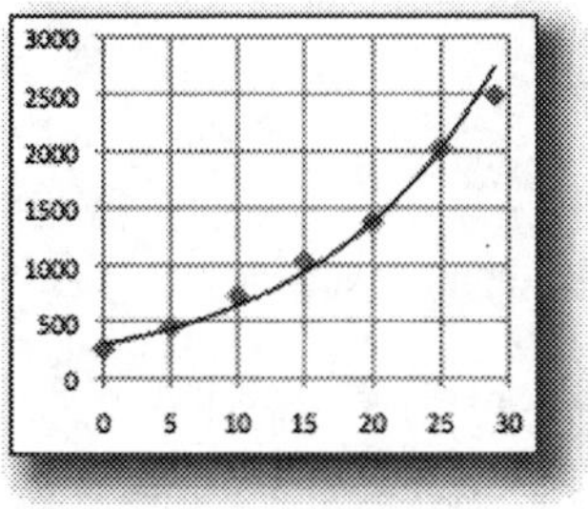

Figure 13

using Technology

See the Technology Guides at the end of the chapter for detailed instructions on how to obtain the regression curve and graph for Example 6 using a graphing calculator or spreadsheet. Outline:

TI-83/84 Plus

[STAT] EDIT values of t in L_1 and values of C in L_2
Regression curve: [STAT] CALC option #0 `ExpReg` [ENTER]
Graph: [Y=] [VARS] [5] EQ [1], then [ZOOM] [9]
[More details on page 681.]

Spreadsheet

t- and C-values in Columns A and B, graph these data. Regression curve: Add exponential Trendline with option to show equation.
[More details on page 684.]

Website

www.WanerMath.com
In the Simple Regression utility, enter the data in the x and y columns and press "y=a(b^x)".

EXAMPLE 6 Exponential Regression: Health Expenditures

The following table shows annual expenditure on health in the U.S. from 1980 through 2009 ($t = 0$ represents 1980).[15]

Year t	0	5	10	15	20	25	29
Expenditure ($ billion)	256	444	724	1,030	1,380	2,020	2,490

a. Find the exponential regression model

$$C(t) = Ab^t$$

for the annual expenditure.

b. Use the regression model to estimate the expenditure in 2002 ($t = 22$; the actual expenditure was approximately \$1,640 billion).

Solution

a. We use technology to obtain the exponential regression curve (See Figure 13):

$$C(t) \approx 296(1.08)^t. \qquad \text{Coefficients rounded}$$

b. Using the model $C(t) \approx 296(1.08)^t$ we find that

$$C(22) \approx 296(1.08)^{22} \approx \$1,609 \text{ billion},$$

which is close to the actual number of about \$1,640 billion.

Before we go on... We said in the preceding section that the regression curve gives the smallest value of the sum-of-squares error, SSE (the sum of the squares of the residuals). However, exponential regression as computed via technology generally minimizes the sum of the squares of the residuals of the *logarithms* (logarithms are discussed in the next section). Using logarithms allows one easily to convert an exponential function into a linear one and then use linear regression formulas. However, in Section 9.4, we will discuss a way of using Excel's Solver to minimize SSE directly, which allows us to find the best-fit exponential curve directly without the need for devices to simplify the mathematics. If we do this, we obtain a very different equation:

$$C(t) \approx 353(1.07)^t.$$

If you plot this function, you will notice that it seems to fit the data more closely than the regression curve. ■

FAQs

When to Use an Exponential Model for Data Points, and when to Use *e* in Your Model

Q: *Given a set of data points that appear to be curving upward, how can I tell whether to use a quadratic model or an exponential model?*

[15]Data are rounded. Source: U.S. Department of Health & Human Services/Centers for Medicare & Medicaid Services, National Health Expenditure Data, downloaded April 2011 from www.cms.gov.

A: Here are some things to look for:

- Do the data values appear to double at regular intervals? (For example, do the values approximately double every 5 units?) If so, then an exponential model is appropriate. If it takes longer and longer to double, then a quadratic model may be more appropriate.
- Do the values first decrease to a low point and then increase? If so, then a quadratic model is more appropriate.

It is also helpful to use technology to graph both the regression quadratic and exponential curves and to visually inspect the graphs to determine which gives the closest fit to the data.

Q: *We have two ways of writing exponential functions: $f(x) = Ab^x$ and $f(x) = Ae^{rx}$. How do we know which one to use?*

A: The two forms are equivalent, and it is always possible to convert from one form to the other.* So, use whichever form seems to be convenient for a particular situation. For instance, $f(t) = A(3^t)$ conveniently models exponential growth that is tripling every unit of time, whereas $f(t) = Ae^{0.06t}$ conveniently models an investment with continuous compounding at 6%.

* Quick Example 3 on page 640 shows how to convert Ae^{rx} to Ab^x. Conversion from Ab^x to Ae^{rx} involves logarithms: $r = \ln b$.

9.2 EXERCISES

▼ more advanced ◆ challenging

T indicates exercises that should be solved using technology

For each function in Exercises 1–12, compute the missing values in the following table and supply a valid technology formula for the given function: HINT [See Quick Examples on page 632.]

x	−3	−2	−1	0	1	2	3
$f(x)$							

1. $f(x) = 4^x$ **2.** $f(x) = 3^x$

3. $f(x) = 3^{-x}$ **4.** $f(x) = 4^{-x}$

5. $g(x) = 2(2^x)$ **6.** $g(x) = 2(3^x)$

7. $h(x) = -3(2^{-x})$ **8.** $h(x) = -2(3^{-x})$

9. $r(x) = 2^x - 1$ **10.** $r(x) = 2^{-x} + 1$

11. $s(x) = 2^{x-1}$ **12.** $s(x) = 2^{1-x}$

Using a chart of values, graph each of the functions in Exercises 13–18. (Use $-3 \le x \le 3$.)

13. $f(x) = 3^{-x}$ **14.** $f(x) = 4^{-x}$

15. $g(x) = 2(2^x)$ **16.** $g(x) = 2(3^x)$

17. $h(x) = -3(2^{-x})$ **18.** $h(x) = -2(3^{-x})$

In Exercises 19–24, the values of two functions, f and g, are given in a table. One, both, or neither of them may be exponential. Decide which, if any, are exponential, and give the exponential models for those that are. HINT [See Example 1.]

19.

x	−2	−1	0	1	2
$f(x)$	0.5	1.5	4.5	13.5	40.5
$g(x)$	8	4	2	1	$\frac{1}{2}$

20.

x	−2	−1	0	1	2
$f(x)$	$\frac{1}{2}$	1	2	4	8
$g(x)$	3	0	−1	0	3

21.

x	−2	−1	0	1	2
$f(x)$	22.5	7.5	2.5	7.5	22.5
$g(x)$	0.3	0.9	2.7	8.1	16.2

22.

x	−2	−1	0	1	2
$f(x)$	0.3	0.9	2.7	8.1	24.3
$g(x)$	3	1.5	0.75	0.375	0.1875

23.

x	−2	−1	0	1	2
$f(x)$	100	200	400	600	800
$g(x)$	100	20	4	0.8	0.16

24.

x	−2	−1	0	1	2
$f(x)$	0.8	0.2	0.1	0.05	0.025
$g(x)$	80	40	20	10	2

For each function in Exercises 25–30, supply a valid technology formula and then use technology to compute the missing values in the following table: HINT [See Quick Examples on page 632.]

x	−3	−2	−1	0	1	2	3
$f(x)$							

25. $f(x) = e^{-2x}$

26. $g(x) = e^{x/5}$

27. $h(x) = 1.01(2.02^{-4x})$

28. $h(x) = 3.42(3^{-x/5})$

29. $r(x) = 50\left(1+\frac{1}{3.2}\right)^{2x}$

30. $r(x) = 0.043\left(4.5 - \frac{5}{1.2}\right)^{-x}$

In Exercises 31–38, supply a valid technology formula for the given function.

31. 2^{x-1}

32. 2^{-4x}

33. $\frac{2}{1-2^{-4x}}$

34. $\frac{2^{3-x}}{1-2^x}$

35. $\frac{(3+x)^{3x}}{x+1}$

36. $\frac{20.3^{3x}}{1+20.3^{2x}}$

37. $2e^{(1+x)/x}$

38. $\frac{2e^{2/x}}{x}$

On the same set of axes, use technology to graph the pairs of functions in Exercises 39–46 with $-3 \le x \le 3$. Identify which graph corresponds to which function. HINT [See Quick Examples on page 633.]

39. $f_1(x) = 1.6^x$, $f_2(x) = 1.8^x$

40. $f_1(x) = 2.2^x$, $f_2(x) = 2.5^x$

41. $f_1(x) = 300(1.1^x)$, $f_2(x) = 300(1.1^{2x})$

42. $f_1(x) = 100(1.01^{2x})$, $f_2(x) = 100(1.01^{3x})$

43. $f_1(x) = 2.5^{1.02x}$, $f_2(x) = e^{1.02x}$

44. $f_1(x) = 2.5^{-1.02x}$, $f_2(x) = e^{-1.02x}$

45. $f_1(x) = 1{,}000(1.045^{-3x})$, $f_2(x) = 1{,}000(1.045^{3x})$

46. $f_1(x) = 1{,}202(1.034^{-3x})$, $f_2(x) = 1{,}202(1.034^{3x})$

For Exercises 47–54, model the data using an exponential function $f(x) = Ab^x$. HINT [See Example 1.]

47.

x	0	1	2
$f(x)$	500	250	125

48.

x	0	1	2
$f(x)$	500	1,000	2,000

49.

x	0	1	2
$f(x)$	10	30	90

50.

x	0	1	2
$f(x)$	90	30	10

51.

x	0	1	2
$f(x)$	500	225	101.25

52.

x	0	1	2
$f(x)$	5	3	1.8

53.

x	1	2
$f(x)$	−110	−121

54.

x	1	2
$f(x)$	−41	−42.025

Find equations for exponential functions that pass through the pairs of points given in Exercises 55–62. (Round all coefficients to 4 decimal places when necessary.) HINT [See Example 2.]

55. Through (2, 36) and (4, 324)

56. Through (2, −4) and (4, −16)

57. Through (−2, −25) and (1, −0.2)

58. Through (1, 1.2) and (3, 0.108)

59. Through (1, 3) and (3, 6)

60. Through (1, 2) and (4, 6)

61. Through (2, 3) and (6, 2)

62. Through (−1, 2) and (3, 1)

Obtain exponential functions in the form $f(t) = Ae^{rt}$ in Exercises 63–66. HINT [See Example 5.]

63. $f(t)$ is the value after t years of a \$5,000 investment earning 10% interest compounded continuously.

64. $f(t)$ is the value after t years of a \$2,000 investment earning 5.3% interest compounded continuously.

65. $f(t)$ is the value after t years of a \$1,000 investment depreciating continuously at an annual rate of 6.3%.

66. $f(t)$ is the value after t years of a \$10,000 investment depreciating continuously at an annual rate of 60%.

In Exercises 67–70, use technology to find the exponential regression function through the given points. (Round all coefficients to 4 decimal places.) HINT [See Example 6.]

67. {(1, 2), (3, 5), (4, 9), (5, 20)}

68. {(−1, 2), (−3, 5), (−4, 9), (−5, 20)}

69. {(−1, 10), (−3, 5), (−4, 3)}

70. {(3, 3), (4, 5), (5, 10)}

APPLICATIONS

71. ***Aspirin*** Soon after taking an aspirin, a patient has absorbed 300 mg of the drug. After 2 hours, only 75 mg remain. Find an exponential model for the amount of aspirin in the bloodstream after t hours, and use your model to find the amount of aspirin in the bloodstream after 5 hours. HINT [See Example 2.]

72. ***Alcohol*** After a large number of drinks, a person has a blood alcohol level of 200 mg/dL (milligrams per deciliter). If the amount of alcohol in the blood decays exponentially, and after 2 hours, 112.5 mg/dL remain, find an exponential model for the person's blood alcohol level, and use your model to estimate the person's blood alcohol level after 4 hours. HINT [See Example 2.]

73. ***Freon Production*** The production of ozone-layer-damaging Freon 22 (chlorodifluoromethane) in developing countries rose from 200 tons in 2004 to a projected 590 tons in 2010.[16]

[16]Figures are approximate. Source: Lampert Kuijpers (Panel of the Montreal Protocol), National Bureau of Statistics in China, via CEIC Data/*New York Times*, February 23, 2007, p. C1.

a. Use this information to find both a linear model and an exponential model for the amount F of Freon 22 (in tons) as a function of time t in years since 2000. (Round all coefficients to three significant digits.) HINT [See Example 2.] Which of these models would you judge to be more appropriate to the data shown below?

t (year since 2000)	0	2	4	6	8	10
F (tons of Freon 22)	100	140	200	270	400	590

b. Use the better of the two models from part (a) to predict the 2008 figure and compare it with the projected figure above.

74. ***Revenue*** The annual revenue of Amazon.com rose from approximately $10.7 billion in 2006 to $34.2 billion in 2010.[17]

a. Use this information to find both a linear model and an exponential model for Amazon.com's annual revenue I (in billions of dollars) as a function of time t in years since 2000. (Round all coefficients to three significant digits.) HINT [See Example 2.] Which of these models would you judge to be more appropriate to the data shown below?

t (Year since 2000)	6	7	8	9	10
I ($ billions)	10.7	14.8	19.2	24.5	34.2

b. Use the better of the two models from part (a) to predict the 2008 figure and compare it with the actual figure above.

75. ▼ ***U.S. Population*** The U.S. population was 180 million in 1960 and 309 million in 2010.[18]

a. Use these data to give an exponential growth model showing the U.S. population P as a function of time t in years since 1960. Round coefficients to 6 significant digits. HINT [See Example 2.]

b. By experimenting, determine the smallest number of significant digits to which you should round the coefficients in part (a) in order to obtain the correct 2010 population figure accurate to 3 significant digits.

c. Using the model in part (a), predict the population in 2020.

76. ▼ ***World Population*** World population was estimated at 2.56 billion people in 1950 and 6.91 billion people in 2011.[19]

a. Use these data to give an exponential growth model showing the world population P as a function of time t in years since 1950. Round coefficients to 6 significant digits. HINT [See Example 2.]

b. By experimenting, determine the smallest number of significant digits to which you should round the coefficients in part (a) in order to obtain the correct 2011 population figure to 3 significant digits.

c. Assuming the exponential growth model from part (a), estimate the world population in the year 1000. Comment on your answer.

77. ▼ ***Frogs*** Frogs have been breeding like flies at the Enormous State University (ESU) campus! Each year, the pledge class of the Epsilon Delta fraternity is instructed to tag all the frogs residing on the ESU campus. Two years ago they managed to tag all 50,000 of them (with little Epsilon Delta Fraternity tags). This year's pledge class discovered that last year's tags had all fallen off, and they wound up tagging a total of 75,000 frogs.

a. Find an exponential model for the frog population.

b. Assuming exponential population growth, and that all this year's tags have fallen off, how many tags should Epsilon Delta order for next year's pledge class?

78. ▼ ***Flies*** Flies in Suffolk County have been breeding like frogs! Three years ago the Health Commission caught 4,000 flies in a trap in 1 hour. This year it caught 7,000 flies in 1 hour.

a. Find an exponential model for the fly population.

b. Assuming exponential population growth, how many flies should the commission expect to catch next year?

79. ***Bacteria*** A bacteria culture starts with 1,000 bacteria and doubles in size every 3 hours. Find an exponential model for the size of the culture as a function of time t in hours and use the model to predict how many bacteria there will be after 2 days. HINT [See Example 4.]

80. ***Bacteria*** A bacteria culture starts with 1,000 bacteria. Two hours later there are 1,500 bacteria. Find an exponential model for the size of the culture as a function of time t in hours, and use the model to predict how many bacteria there will be after 2 days. HINT [See Example 4.]

81. ***SARS*** In the early stages of the deadly SARS (Severe Acute Respiratory Syndrome) epidemic in 2003, the number of cases was increasing by about 18% each day.[20] On March 17, 2003 (the first day for which statistics were reported by the World Health Organization), there were 167 cases. Find an exponential model that predicts the number of cases t days after March 17, 2003, and use it to estimate the number of cases on March 31, 2003. (The actual reported number of cases was 1,662.)

82. ***SARS*** A few weeks into the deadly SARS (Severe Acute Respiratory Syndrome) epidemic in 2003, the number of cases was increasing by about 4% each day.[21] On April 1,

[17] Source for data: www.wikinvest.com/

[18] Figures are rounded to 3 significant digits. Source: U.S. Census Bureau, www.census.gov.

[19] *Ibid.*

[20] Source: World Health Organization, www.who.int.

[21] *Ibid.*

2003 there were 1,804 cases. Find an exponential model that predicts the number of cases t days after April 1, 2003, and use it to estimate the number of cases on April 30, 2003. (The actual reported number of cases was 5,663.)

83. ***Investments*** In November 2010, E*TRADE Financial was offering only 0.3% interest on its online savings accounts, with interest reinvested monthly.[22] Find the associated exponential model for the value of a \$5,000 deposit after t years. Assuming this rate of return continued for seven years, how much would a deposit of \$5,000 in November 2010 be worth in November 2017? (Answer to the nearest \$1.) HINT [See Example 3; you saw this exercise before in Section 1.2.]

84. ***Investments*** In November 2010, ING Direct was offering 2.4% interest on its Orange Savings Account, with interest reinvested quarterly.[23] Find the associated exponential model for the value of a \$4,000 deposit after t years. Assuming this rate of return continued for 8 years, how much would a deposit of \$4,000 in November 2010 be worth in November 2018? (Answer to the nearest \$1.) HINT [See Example 3; you saw this exercise before in Section 1.2.]

85. ***Investments*** Refer to Exercise 83. In November of which year will an investment of \$5,000 made in November of 2010 first exceed \$5,200? HINT [See Example 5; you saw this exercise before in Section 1.2.]

86. ***Investments*** Refer to Exercise 84. In November of which year will an investment of \$4,000 made in November of 2010 first exceed \$5,200? HINT [See Example 5; you saw this exercise before in Section 1.2.]

87. ***Investments*** *Rock Solid Bank & Trust* is offering a CD (certificate of deposit) that pays 4% compounded continuously. How much interest would a \$1,000 deposit earn over 10 years? HINT [See Example 5.]

88. ***Savings*** *FlybynightSavings.com* is offering a savings account that pays 31% interest compounded continuously. How much interest would a deposit of \$2,000 earn over 10 years?

89. ***Home Sales*** Sales of existing homes in the U.S. rose continuously over the period 2008–2011 at the rate of 3.2% per year from 4.9 million in 2008.[24] Write down a formula that predicts sales of existing homes t years after 2008. Use your model to estimate, to the nearest 0.1 million, sales of existing homes in 2010 and 2012.

90. ***Home Prices*** The median selling price of an existing home in the U.S. declined continuously over the period 2008–2011 at the rate of 7.6% per year from approximately \$198 thousand in 2008.[25] Write down a formula that predicts the median selling price of an existing home t years after 2008. Use your model to estimate, to the nearest \$1,000, the median selling price of an existing home in 2011 and 2013.

91. ***Global Warming*** The most abundant greenhouse gas is carbon dioxide. According to figures from the Intergovernmental Panel on Climate Change (IPCC), the amount of carbon dioxide in the atmosphere (in parts of volume per million) can be approximated by

$$C(t) \approx 280e^{0.00119t} \text{ parts per million}$$

where t is time in years since 1750.[26]

a. Use the model to estimate the amount of carbon dioxide in the atmosphere in 1950, 2000, 2050, and 2100.

b. According to the model, when, to the nearest decade, will the level surpass 390 parts per million?

92. ***Global Warming*** Another greenhouse gas is methane. According to figures from the Intergovernmental Panel on Climate Change (IPCC), the amount of methane in the atmosphere (in parts of volume per billion) can be approximated by

$$C(t) \approx 715e^{0.00356t} \text{ parts per billion}$$

where t is time in years since 1750.[27]

a. Use the model to estimate the amount of methane in the atmosphere in 1950, 2000, 2050, and 2100. (Round your answers to the nearest 10 parts per billion.)

b. According to the model, when, to the nearest decade, will the level surpass 2,000 parts per billion?

93. ***New York City Housing Costs: Downtown*** The following table shows the average price of a two-bedroom apartment in downtown New York City during the real estate boom from 1994 to 2004.[28]

t	0 (1994)	2	4	6	8	10 (2004)
Price (\$ million)	0.38	0.40	0.60	0.95	1.20	1.60

a. Use exponential regression to model the price $P(t)$ as a function of time t since 1994. Include a sketch of the points and the regression curve. (Round the coefficients to 3 decimal places.) HINT [See Example 6.]

b. Extrapolate your model to estimate the cost of a two-bedroom downtown apartment in 2005.

94. ***New York City Housing Costs: Uptown*** The following table shows the average price of a two-bedroom apartment in uptown New York City during the real estate boom from 1994 to 2004.[29]

t	0 (1994)	2	4	6	8	10 (2004)
Price (\$ million)	0.18	0.18	0.19	0.2	0.35	0.4

[22] Interest rate based on annual percentage yield. Source: us.etrade.com, November 2010.

[23] Interest rate based on annual percentage yield. Source: home .ingdirect.com, November 2010.

[24] Source: National Association of Realtors, www.realtor.org.

[25] *Ibid.*

[26] Authors' exponential model based on the 1750 and 2005 figures. Source for data: IPCC Fourth Assessment Report: Climate Change 2007, www.ipcc.ch.

[27] *Ibid.*

[28] Data are rounded and 2004 figure is an estimate. Source: Miller Samuel/*New York Times*, March 28, 2004, p. RE 11.

[29] *Ibid.*

a. Use exponential regression to model the price $P(t)$ as a function of time t since 1994. Include a sketch of the points and the regression curve. (Round the coefficients to 3 decimal places.)

b. Extrapolate your model to estimate the cost of a two-bedroom uptown apartment in 2005.

95. ⚄ *Facebook* The following table gives the approximate numbers of Facebook members at various times early in its history.[30]

Year t (Since start of 2005)	0	0.5	1	1.5	2	2.5	3	3.5
Facebook Members n (millions)	1	2	5.5	7	12	30	58	80

a. Use exponential regression to model Facebook membership as a function of time in years since the start of 2005, and graph the data points and regression curve. (Round coefficients to 3 decimal places.)

b. Fill in the missing quantity: According to the model, Facebook membership each year was ____ times that of the year before.

c. Use your model to estimate Facebook membership in early 2009 to the nearest million.

96. ⚄ *Freon Production* The following table shows Freon 22 production in developing countries in various years since 2000.[31]

t (Year since 2000)	0	2	4	6	8	10
F (Tons of Freon 22)	100	140	200	270	400	590

a. Use exponential regression to model Freon production as a function of time in years since 2000, and graph the data points and regression curve. (Round coefficients to 3 decimal places.)

b. Fill in the missing quantity: According to the model, Freon production each year was ____ times that of the year before.

c. Use your model to estimate freon production in 2009 to the nearest ton.

COMMUNICATION AND REASONING EXERCISES

97. Which of the following three functions will be largest for large values of x?

(A) $f(x) = x^2$ (B) $r(x) = 2^x$ (C) $h(x) = x^{10}$

98. Which of the following three functions will be smallest for large values of x?

(A) $f(x) = x^{-2}$ (B) $r(x) = 2^{-x}$ (C) $h(x) = x^{-10}$

99. What limitations apply to using an exponential function to model growth in real-life situations? Illustrate your answer with an example.

100. Explain in words why 5% per year compounded continuously yields more interest than 5% per year compounded monthly.

101. ▼ The following commentary and graph appeared in politicalcalculations.blogspot.com on August 30, 2005:[32]

> One of the neater blogs I've recently encountered is The Real Returns, which offers a wealth of investing, market and economic data. Earlier this month, The Real Returns posted data related to the recent history of U.S. median house prices over the period from 1963 to 2004. The original source of the housing data is the U.S. Census Bureau.
>
> Well, that kind of data deserves some curve-fitting and a calculator to estimate what the future U.S. median house price might be, so Political Calculations has extracted the data from 1973 onward to create the following chart:

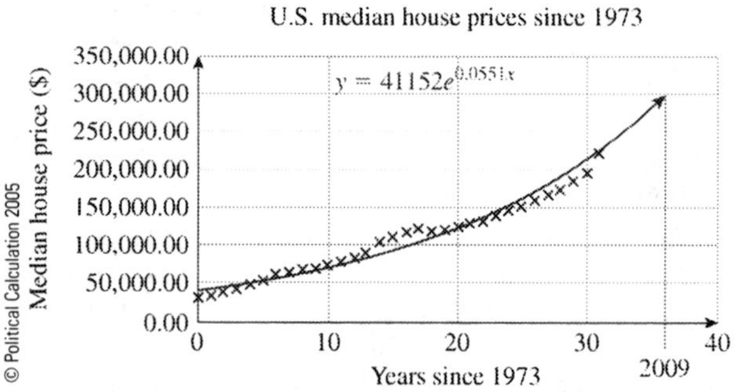

U.S. median house prices since 1973

$y = 41152e^{0.0551x}$

Comment on the article and graph. HINT **[See Exercise 90.]**

102. ▼ Refer to Exercise 101. Of what possible predictive use, then, is the kind of exponential model given by the blogger in the article referred to?

103. ▼ Describe two real-life situations in which a linear model would be more appropriate than an exponential model, and two situations in which an exponential model would be more appropriate than a linear model.

104. ▼ Describe a real-life situation in which a quadratic model would be more appropriate than an exponential model and one in which an exponential model would be more appropriate than a quadratic model.

105. How would you check whether data points of the form $(1, y_1), (2, y_2), (3, y_3)$ lie on an exponential curve?

[30]Sources: www.facebook.com, www.insidehighered.com. (Some data are interpolated.)

[31]Figures are approximate. Source: Lampert Kuijpers (Panel of the Montreal Protocol), National Bureau of Statistics in China, via CEIC Data/*New York Times*, February 23, 2007, p. C1.

[32]The graph was re-created by the authors using the blog author's data source.
Source for article: politicalcalculations.blogspot.com/2005/08/projecting-us-median-housing-prices.html.
Source for data: therealreturns.blogspot.com/2005_08_01_archive.html.

106. ▼ You are told that the points $(1, y_1)$, $(2, y_2)$, $(3, y_3)$ lie on an exponential curve. Express y_3 in terms of y_1 and y_2.

107. ▼ Your local banker tells you that the reason his bank doesn't compound interest continuously is that it would be too demanding of computer resources because the computer would need to spend a great deal of time keeping all accounts updated. Comment on his reasoning.

108. ▼ Your other local banker tells you that the reason *her* bank doesn't offer continuously compounded interest is that it is equivalent to offering a fractionally higher interest rate compounded daily. Comment on her reasoning.

Practice Problems 9.2, Part 1

1. The population of Cesspool Villa is currently 5000 people and is growing at a rate of about 300 people per year. The population of Armpit Junction is currently 1800 people and is growing at a rate of about 4% per year. Assuming that these rates of population growth continue to hold, is there a point in the future where the population of Armpit Junction will match the population of Cesspool Villa? If so, find that time. If not, then explain why.

2. Five years ago, Wendy invested $12,000 into a mutual fund, and now the fund is worth $15,000. Let $V(t)$ denote the value of the mutual fund after t years, with $t = 0$ corresponding to the time the fund was originally purchased.

a. Assume that the value of the fund has been changing linearly. Write a formula for $V(t)$. What annual growth rate does this model indicate? Label appropriately.

b. Assume that the value of the fund has been changing exponentially. Write a formula for $V(t)$. What approximate annual percentage growth rate does this model indicate? Give your percentage accurate to two decimal places.

Practice Problems 9.2, Part 2

1. The following formulas give the populations of four different bacteria cultures, *A*, *B*, *C*, and *D*, with *t* representing the number of days from now.

$$P_A = 3600e^{-0.12t} \qquad P_B = 2800e^{0.09t} \qquad P_C = 5560e^{-0.06t} \qquad P_D = 4200e^{0.02t}$$

a. Which culture is growing the fastest (has the largest percentage growth rate)?

b. Which culture is the largest now?

c. Which culture is shrinking the fastest (has the largest percentage rate of decrease)?

2. The population of a city is 18,000 and is growing at an annual rate of 7.5%.

a. Find a formula for the population *P* of the city at time *t* years from now assuming that the 7.5% per year is an incremental rate.

b. Find a formula for the population *P* of the city at time *t* years from now assuming that the 7.5% per year is a continuous rate.

c. In each of the above cases, estimate the population of the city in 10 years.

Practice Problems 9.2, Part 3

1. Suppose that the value of a piece of property has been decreasing at a continuous rate of 5% per year and is expected to continue to decrease in that manner. Right now, the property is worth \$160,000. Let $V(t)$ give the value of the property t years from now.

a. Write a formula for $V(t)$.

b. Determine how long it will take for the property value to drop to half of its current value. Give the time accurate to two decimal places and illustrate your result graphically.

2. Convert each of the following to the form $f(x) = Ab^x$. Round all constants to four decimal places.

a. $f(x) = 48e^{-0.1x}$

b. $f(x) = 136e^{0.29x}$

c. $f(x) = 450e^{3+0.06x}$

9.3 Logarithmic Functions and Models

Logarithms were invented by John Napier (1550–1617) in the late sixteenth century as a means of aiding calculation. His invention made possible the prodigious hand calculations of astronomer Johannes Kepler (1571–1630), who was the first to describe accurately the orbits and the motions of the planets. Today, computers and calculators have done away with that use of logarithms, but many other uses remain. In particular, the logarithm is used to model real-world phenomena in numerous fields, including physics, finance, and economics.

From the equation

$$2^3 = 8$$

we can see that the power to which we need to raise 2 in order to get 8 is 3. We abbreviate the phrase "the power to which we need to raise 2 in order to get 8" as "$\log_2 8$." Thus, another way of writing the equation $2^3 = 8$ is

$$\log_2 8 = 3.$$ The power to which we need to raise 2 in order to get 8 is 3.

This is read "the base 2 logarithm of 8 is 3" or "the log, base 2, of 8 is 3."

Here is the general definition.

Base *b* Logarithm

The **base *b* logarithm of *x***, $\log_b x$, is the power to which we need to raise b in order to get x. Symbolically,

$\log_b x = y$ means $b^y = x$.

Logarithmic form — *Exponential form*

Quick Examples

1. The following table lists some exponential equations and their equivalent logarithmic forms:

Exponential Form	$10^3 = 1000$	$4^2 = 16$	$3^3 = 27$	$5^1 = 5$	$7^0 = 1$	$4^{-2} = \frac{1}{16}$	$25^{1/2} = 5$
Logarithmic Form	$\log_{10} 1000 = 3$	$\log_4 16 = 2$	$\log_3 27 = 3$	$\log_5 5 = 1$	$\log_7 1 = 0$	$\log_4 \frac{1}{16} = -2$	$\log_{25} 5 = \frac{1}{2}$

2. $\log_3 9 =$ the power to which we need to raise 3 in order to get 9. Because $3^2 = 9$, this power is 2, so $\log_3 9 = 2$.

3. $\log_{10}10{,}000$ = the power to which we need to raise 10 in order to get 10,000. Because $10^4 = 10{,}000$, this power is 4, so $\log_{10}10{,}000 = 4$.

4. $\log_3 \frac{1}{27}$ is the power to which we need to raise 3 in order to get $\frac{1}{27}$. Because $3^{-3} = \frac{1}{27}$ this power is -3, so $\log_3 \frac{1}{27} = -3$.

5. $\log_b 1 = 0$ for every positive number b other than 1 because $b^0 = 1$.

Note The number $\log_b x$ is defined only if b and x are both positive and $b \neq 1$. Thus, it is impossible to compute, say, $\log_3(-9)$ (because there is no power of 3 that equals -9), or $\log_1(2)$ (because there is no power of 1 that equals 2). ■

Logarithms with base 10 and base e are frequently used, so they have special names and notations.

Common Logarithm, Natural Logarithm

The following are standard abbreviations.

		TI-83/84 Plus & Spreadsheet Formula
Base 10: $\log_{10} x = \log x$	*Common Logarithm*	log(x)
Base e: $\log_e x = \ln x$	*Natural Logarithm*	ln(x)

Quick Examples

Logarithmic Form	Exponential Form
1. $\log 10{,}000 = 4$	$10^4 = 10{,}000$
2. $\log 10 = 1$	$10^1 = 10$
3. $\log \dfrac{1}{10{,}000} = -4$	$10^{-4} = \dfrac{1}{10{,}000}$
4. $\ln e = 1$	$e^1 = e$
5. $\ln 1 = 0$	$e^0 = 1$
6. $\ln 2 = 0.69314718\ldots$	$e^{0.69314718\ldots} = 2$

Some technologies (such as calculators) do not permit direct calculation of logarithms other than common and natural logarithms. To compute logarithms with other bases with these technologies, we can use the following formula:

Change-of-Base Formula

$$\log_b a = \frac{\log a}{\log b} = \frac{\ln a}{\ln b}$$ Change-of-base formula*

Quick Examples

1. $\log_{11} 9 = \dfrac{\log 9}{\log 11} \approx 0.91631$ log(9)/log(11)

2. $\log_{11} 9 = \dfrac{\ln 9}{\ln 11} \approx 0.91631$ ln(9)/ln(11)

3. $\log_{3.2}\left(\dfrac{1.42}{3.4}\right) \approx -0.75065$ log(1.42/3.4)/log(3.2)

* Here is a quick explanation of why this formula works: To calculate $\log_b a$, we ask, "to what power must we raise b to get a?" To check the formula, we try using $\log a/\log b$ as the exponent.

$$b^{\frac{\log a}{\log b}} = (10^{\log b})^{\frac{\log a}{\log b}} \quad (\text{because } b = 10^{\log b})$$
$$= 10^{\log a} = a$$

so this exponent works!

Using Technology to Compute Logarithms

To compute $\log_b x$ using technology, use the following formulas:

TI-83/84 Plus	`log(x)/log(b)`	Example: $\log_2(16)$ is `log(16)/log(2)`
Spreadsheet:	`=LOG(x,b)`	Example: $\log_2(16)$ is `=LOG(16,2)`

One important use of logarithms is to solve equations in which the unknown is in the exponent.

EXAMPLE 1 Solving Equations with Unknowns in the Exponent

Solve the following equations.

a. $5^{-x} = 125$ **b.** $3^{2x-1} = 6$ **c.** $100(1.005)^{3x} = 200$

Solution

a. Write the given equation $5^{-x} = 125$ in logarithmic form:

$$-x = \log_5 125$$

This gives $x = -\log_5 125 = -3$.

b. In logarithmic form, $3^{2x-1} = 6$ becomes

$$2x - 1 = \log_3 6$$
$$2x = 1 + \log_3 6$$

giving

$$x = \frac{1 + \log_3 6}{2} \approx \frac{1 + 1.6309}{2} \approx 1.3155.$$

c. We cannot write the given equation, $100(1.005)^{3x} = 200$, directly in logarithmic form. We must first divide both sides by 100:

$$1.005^{3x} = \frac{200}{100} = 2$$
$$3x = \log_{1.005} 2$$
$$x = \frac{\log_{1.005} 2}{3} \approx \frac{138.9757}{3} \approx 46.3252.$$

Now that we know what logarithms are, we can talk about functions based on logarithms:

Logarithmic Function

A **logarithmic function** has the form

$$f(x) = \log_b x + C \quad (b \text{ and } C \text{ are constants with } b > 0, b \neq 1)$$

or, alternatively,

$$f(x) = A \ln x + C. \quad (A, C \text{ constants with } A \neq 0)$$

Quick Examples

1. $f(x) = \log x$
2. $g(x) = \ln x - 5$
3. $h(x) = \log_2 x + 1$
4. $k(x) = 3.2 \ln x + 7.2$

Q: *What is the difference between the two forms of the logarithmic function?*

A: None, really—they're equivalent: We can start with an equation in the first form and use the change-of-base formula to rewrite it:

$$\begin{aligned} f(x) &= \log_b x + C \\ &= \frac{\ln x}{\ln b} + C \qquad \text{Change-of-base formula} \\ &= \left(\frac{1}{\ln b}\right) \ln x + C. \end{aligned}$$

Our function now has the form $f(x) = A \ln x + C$, where $A = 1/\ln b$. We can go the other way as well, to rewrite $A \ln x + C$ in the form $\log_b x + C$.

EXAMPLE 2 Graphs of Logarithmic Functions

a. Sketch the graph of $f(x) = \log_2 x$ by hand.

b. Use technology to compare the graph in part (a) with the graphs of $\log_b x$ for $b = 1/4, 1/2$, and 4.

Solution

a. To sketch the graph of $f(x) = \log_2 x$ by hand, we begin with a table of values. Because $\log_2 x$ is not defined when $x = 0$, we choose several values of x close to zero and also some larger values, all chosen so that their logarithms are easy to compute:

x	$\frac{1}{8}$	$\frac{1}{4}$	$\frac{1}{2}$	1	2	4	8
$f(x) = \log_2 x$	−3	−2	−1	0	1	2	3

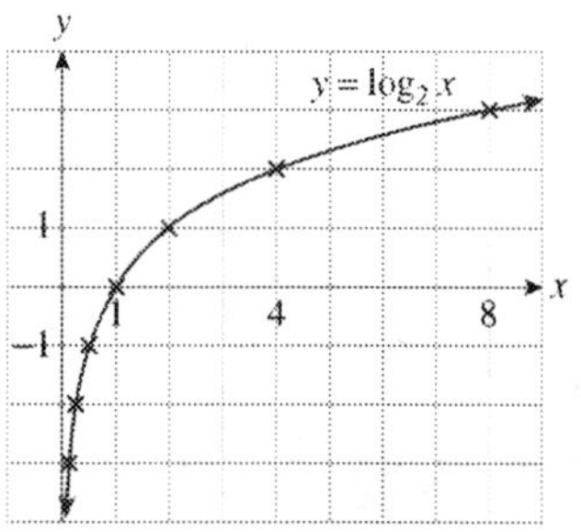

Figure 14

Graphing these points and joining them by a smooth curve gives us Figure 14.

b. We enter the logarithmic functions in graphing utilities as follows (note the use of the change-of-base formula in the TI-83/84 Plus version):

TI-83/84 Plus	Spreadsheet
`Y1=log(X)/log(0.25)`	`=LOG(x,0.25)`
`Y2=log(X)/log(0.5)`	`=LOG(x,0.5)`
`Y3=log(X)/log(2)`	`=LOG(x,2)`
`Y4=log(X)/log(4)`	`=LOG(x,4)`

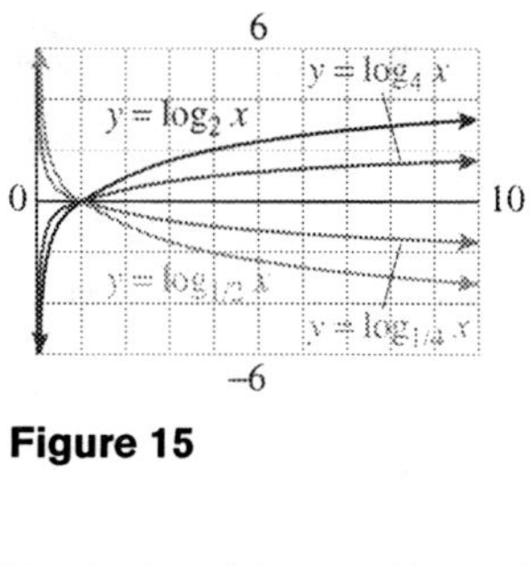

Figure 15

Figure 15 shows the resulting graphs.

Before we go on... Notice that the graphs of the logarithmic functions in Example 2 all pass through the point (1, 0). (Why?) Notice further that the graphs of the logarithmic functions with bases less than 1 are upside-down versions of the others. Finally, how are these graphs related to the graphs of exponential functions? ■

Below are some important algebraic properties of logarithms we shall use throughout the rest of this section.

Website
www.WanerMath.com
Follow the path
Chapter 9
→ Using and Deriving Algebraic Properties of Logarithms
to find a list of logarithmic identities and a discussion on where they come from.
Follow the path
Chapter 9
→ Inverse Functions
for a general discussion of inverse functions, including further discussion of the relationship between logarithmic and exponential functions.

Logarithm Identities

The following identities hold for all positive bases $a \neq 1$ and $b \neq 1$, all positive numbers x and y, and every real number r. These identities follow from the laws of exponents.

Identity	Quick Examples
1. $\log_b(xy) = \log_b x + \log_b y$	$\log_2 16 = \log_2 8 + \log_2 2$
2. $\log_b\left(\dfrac{x}{y}\right) = \log_b x - \log_b y$	$\log_2\left(\dfrac{5}{3}\right) = \log_2 5 - \log_2 3$
3. $\log_b(x^r) = r \log_b x$	$\log_2(6^5) = 5 \log_2 6$
4. $\log_b b = 1$; $\log_b 1 = 0$	$\log_2 2 = 1$; $\ln e = 1$; $\log_{11} 1 = 0$
5. $\log_b\left(\dfrac{1}{x}\right) = -\log_b x$	$\log_2\left(\dfrac{1}{3}\right) = -\log_2 3$
6. $\log_b x = \dfrac{\log_a x}{\log_a b}$	$\log_2 5 = \dfrac{\log_{10} 5}{\log_{10} 2} = \dfrac{\log 5}{\log 2}$

Relationship with Exponential Functions

The following two identities demonstrate that the operations of taking the base b logarithm and raising b to a power are *inverse* to each other.

Identity	Quick Examples
1. $\log_b(b^x) = x$ *In words:* The power to which you raise b in order to get b^x is x. (!)	$\log_2(2^7) = 7$
2. $b^{\log_b x} = x$ *In words:* Raising b to the power to which it must be raised to get x yields x. (!)	$5^{\log_5 8} = 8$

APPLICATIONS

EXAMPLE 3 Investments: How Long?

Global bonds sold by Mexico are yielding an average of 2.51% per year.[33] At that interest rate, how long will it take a $1,000 investment to be worth $1,200 if the interest is compounded monthly?

[33]In 2011 (Bonds maturing 03/03/2015). Source: www.bloomberg.com.

Solution Substituting $A = 1{,}200$, $P = 1{,}000$, $r = 0.0251$, and $m = 12$ in the compound interest equation gives

$$A(t) = P\left(1 + \frac{r}{m}\right)^{mt}$$

$$1{,}200 = 1{,}000\left(1 + \frac{0.0251}{12}\right)^{12t}$$

$$\approx 1{,}000(1.002092)^{12t}$$

and we must solve for t. We first divide both sides by 1,000, getting an equation in exponential form:

$$1.2 = 1.002092^{12t}.$$

In logarithmic form, this becomes

$$12t = \log_{1.002092}(1.2).$$

We can now solve for t:

$$t = \frac{\log_{1.002092}(1.2)}{12} \approx 7.3 \text{ years.}$$ `log(1.2)/(log(1.002092)*12)`

Thus, it will take approximately 7.3 years for a $1,000 investment to be worth $1,200.

Before we go on... We can use the logarithm identities to solve the equation

$$1.2 = 1.002092^{12t}$$

that arose in Example 3 (and also more general equations with unknowns in the exponent) by taking the natural logarithm of both sides:

$$\ln 1.2 = \ln(1.002092^{12t})$$

$$= 12t \ln 1.002092. \qquad \text{By Identity 3}$$

We can now solve this for t to get

$$t = \frac{\ln 1.2}{12 \ln 1.002092},$$

which, by the change-of-base formula, is equivalent to the answer we got in Example 3. ■

EXAMPLE 4 Half-Life

a. The weight of carbon 14 that remains in a sample that originally contained A grams is given by

$$C(t) = A(0.999879)^t$$

where t is time in years. Find the **half-life**, the time it takes half of the carbon 14 in a sample to decay.

b. Repeat part (a) using the following alternative form of the exponential model in part (a):

$$C(t) = Ae^{-0.000\,121\,01t}$$ See Quick Examples, page 640.

c. Another radioactive material has a half-life of 7,000 years. Find an exponential decay model in the form

$$R(t) = Ae^{-kt}$$

for the amount of undecayed material remaining. (The constant k is called the **decay constant**.)

d. How long will it take for 99.95% of the substance in a sample of the material in part (c) to decay?

Solution

a. We want to find the value of t for which $C(t)$ = the weight of undecayed carbon 14 left = half the original weight = $0.5A$. Substituting, we get

$$0.5A = A(0.999879)^t.$$

Dividing both sides by A gives

$$0.5 = 0.999879^t \quad \text{Exponential form}$$

$$t = \log_{0.999879} 0.5 \approx 5{,}728 \text{ years.} \quad \text{Logarithmic form}$$

b. This is similar to part (a): We want to solve the equation

$$0.5A = Ae^{-0.000\,121\,01t}$$

for t. Dividing both sides by A gives

$$0.5 = e^{-0.000\,121\,01t}.$$

Taking the natural logarithm of both sides gives

$$\ln(0.5) = \ln(e^{-0.000\,121\,01t}) = -0.000\,121\,01t \quad \text{Identity 3: } \ln(e^a) = a \ln e = a$$

$$t = \frac{\ln(0.5)}{-0.000\,121\,01} \approx 5{,}728 \text{ years,}$$

as we obtained in part (a).

c. This time we are given the half-life, which we can use to find the exponential model $R(t) = Ae^{-kt}$. At time $t = 0$, the amount of radioactive material is

$$R(0) = Ae^0 = A.$$

Because half of the sample decays in 7,000 years, this sample will decay to $0.5A$ grams in 7,000 years ($t = 7{,}000$). Substituting this information gives

$$0.5A = Ae^{-k(7{,}000)}.$$

Canceling A and taking natural logarithms (again using Identity 3) gives

$$\ln(0.5) = -7{,}000k$$

so the decay constant k is

$$k = -\frac{\ln(0.5)}{7{,}000} \approx 0.000\,099\,021.$$

Therefore, the model is

$$R(t) = Ae^{-0.000\,099\,021t}.$$

d. If 99.95% of the substance in a sample has decayed, then the amount of undecayed material left is 0.05% of the original amount, or $0.0005A$. We have

$$0.0005A = Ae^{-0.000\,099\,021t}$$
$$0.0005 = e^{-0.000\,099\,021t}$$
$$\ln(0.0005) = -0.000\,099\,021t$$
$$t = \frac{\ln(0.0005)}{-0.000\,099\,021} \approx 76{,}760 \text{ years.}$$

Before we go on...

Q: *In parts (a) and (b) of Example 4 we were given two different forms of the model for carbon 14 decay. How do we convert an exponential function in one form to the other?*

A: We have already seen (See Quick Example 3 on page 640) how to convert from the form $f(t) = Ae^{rt}$ in part (b) to the form $f(t) = Ab^t$ in part (a). To go the other way, start with the model in part (a), and equate it to the desired form:

$$C(t) = A(0.999\,879)^t = Ae^{rt}.$$

To solve for r, cancel the As and take the natural logarithm of both sides:

$$t\ln(0.999\,879) = rt\ln e = rt$$

so $r = \ln(0.999\,879) \approx -0.000\,121\,007$,

giving

$$C(t) = Ae^{-0.000\,121\,01t}$$

as in part (b).

■

We can use the work we did in parts (b) and (c) of the above example to obtain a formula for the decay constant in an exponential decay model for any radioactive substance when we know its half-life. Write the half-life as t_h. Then the calculation in part (b) gives

$$k = -\frac{\ln(0.5)}{t_h} = \frac{\ln 2}{t_h}. \qquad -\ln(0.5) = -\ln\left(\frac{1}{2}\right) = \ln 2$$

Multiplying both sides by t_h gives us the relationship $t_hk = \ln 2$.

Exponential Decay Model and Half-Life

An **exponential decay function** has the form

$$Q(t) = Q_0e^{-kt}. \qquad Q_0,\ k \text{ both positive}$$

Q_0 represents the value of Q at time $t = 0$, and k is the **decay constant.** The decay constant k and half-life t_h for Q are related by

$$t_hk = \ln 2.$$

Quick Examples

1. $Q(t) = Q_0e^{-0.000\,121\,01t}$ is the decay function for carbon 14 (see Example 4b).
2. If $t_h = 10$ years, then $10k = \ln 2$, so $k = \frac{\ln 2}{10} \approx 0.06931$ and the decay model is

   $$Q(t) = Q_0e^{-0.06931t}.$$
3. If $k = 0.0123$, then $t_h(0.0123) = \ln 2$, so the half-life is

   $$t_h = \frac{\ln 2}{0.0123} \approx 56.35 \text{ years.}$$

We can repeat the analysis above for exponential growth models:

Exponential Growth Model and Doubling Time

An **exponential growth function** has the form

$$Q(t) = Q_0e^{kt}. \qquad Q_0, k \text{ both positive}$$

Q_0 represents the value of Q at time $t = 0$, and k is the **growth constant.** The growth constant k and doubling time t_d for Q are related by

$$t_dk = \ln 2.$$

Quick Examples

1. $P(t) = 1{,}000e^{0.05t}$ — $1,000 invested at 5% annually with interest compounded continuously
2. If $t_d = 10$ years, then $10k = \ln 2$, so $k = \frac{\ln 2}{10} \approx 0.06931$ and the growth model is

   $$Q(t) = Q_0e^{0.06931t}.$$
3. If $k = 0.0123$, then $t_d(0.0123) = \ln 2$, so the doubling time is

   $$t_d = \frac{\ln 2}{0.0123} \approx 56.35 \text{ years.}$$

using Technology

To obtain the regression curve and graph for Example 5 using a graphing calculator or a spreadsheet, see the Technology Guides at the end of the chapter. Outline:

TI-83/84 Plus

[STAT] EDIT values of t in L_1 and values of S in L_2

Regression curve: [STAT] CALC option #9 LnReg [ENTER]

Graph: [Y=] [VARS] [5] EQ [1], then [ZOOM] [9]

[More details on page 681.]

Spreadsheet

t- and S-values in Columns A and B

Graph: Highlight data and insert a Scatter chart.

Regression curve: Right-click a datapoint and add logarithmic Trendline with option to show equation on chart.

[More details on page 684.]

Website

www.WanerMath.com

In the Function Evaluator and Grapher, enter the data as shown, press "Examples" until the logarithmic model `$1*ln(x)+$2` shows in the first box, and press "Fit Curve".

Logarithmic Regression

If we start with a set of data that suggests a logarithmic curve we can, by repeating the methods from previous sections, use technology to find the logarithmic regression curve $y = \log_b x + C$ approximating the data.

EXAMPLE 5 Research & Development

The following table shows the total spent on research and development by universities and colleges in the U.S., in billions of dollars, for the period 1998–2008 (t is the number of years since 1990).[34]

[34] 2008 data is preliminary. Source: National Science Foundation, Division of Science Resources Statistics. 2010. *National Patterns of R&D Resources: 2008 Data Update.* NSF 10-314. Arlington, VA. www.nsf.gov/statistics/nsf10314/.

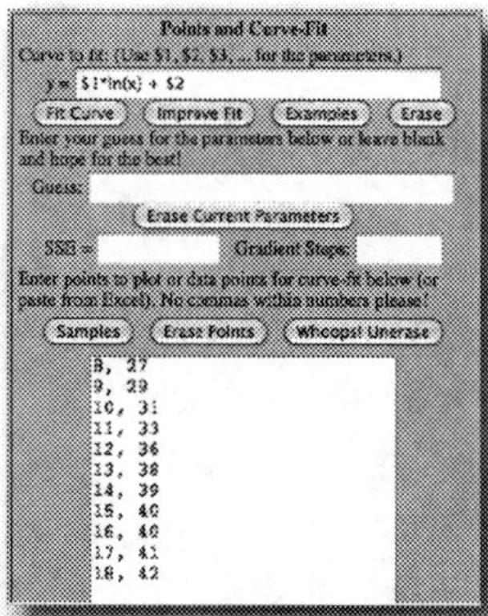

Year t	8	9	10	11	12	13	14	15	16	17	18
Spending ($ billions)	27	29	31	33	36	38	39	40	40	41	42

Find the best-fit logarithmic model of the form

$$S(t) = A \ln t + C$$

and use the model to project total spending on research by universities and colleges in 2012, assuming the trend continues.

Solution We use technology to get the following regression model:

$$S(t) = 19.3 \ln t - 12.8.$$ Coefficients rounded

Because 2012 is represented by $t = 22$, we have

$$S(22) = 19.3 \ln(22) - 12.8 \approx 47.$$ Why did we round the result to two significant digits?

So, research and development spending by universities and colleges is projected to be around $47 billion in 2012.

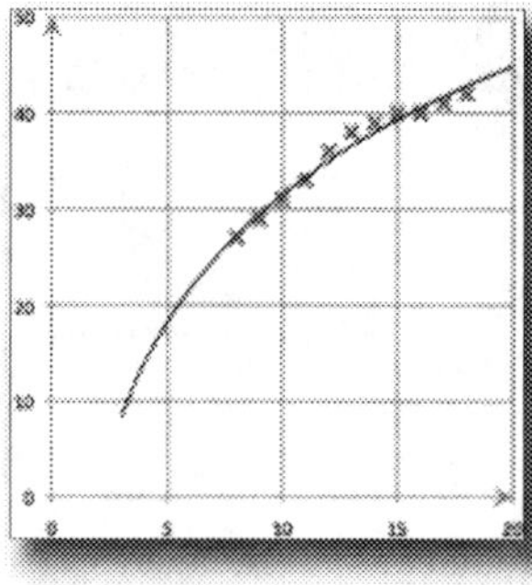
Figure 16

➡ **Before we go on...** The model in Example 5 seems to give reasonable estimates when we extrapolate forward, but extrapolating backward is quite another matter: The logarithm curve drops sharply to the left of the given range and becomes negative for small values of t (Figure 16). ■

9.3 EXERCISES

▼ more advanced ◆ challenging

T indicates exercises that should be solved using technology

In Exercises 1–4, complete the given tables. HINT [See Quick Examples on page 647.]

1.

Exponential Form	$10^4 = 10{,}000$	$4^2 = 16$	$3^3 = 27$	$5^1 = 5$	$7^0 = 1$	$4^{-2} = \frac{1}{16}$
Logarithmic Form						

2.

Exponential Form	$4^3 = 64$	$10^{-1} = 0.1$	$2^8 = 256$	$5^0 = 1$	$(0.5)^2 = 0.25$	$6^{-2} = \frac{1}{36}$
Logarithmic Form						

3.

Exponential Form						
Logarithmic Form	$\log_{0.5} 0.25 = 2$	$\log_5 1 = 0$	$\log_{10} 0.1 = -1$	$\log_4 64 = 3$	$\log_2 256 = 8$	$\log_2 \frac{1}{4} = -2$

4.

Exponential Form						
Logarithmic Form	$\log_5 5 = 1$	$\log_4 \frac{1}{16} = -2$	$\log_4 16 = 2$	$\log_{10} 10{,}000 = 4$	$\log_3 27 = 3$	$\log_7 1 = 0$

In Exercises 5–12, use logarithms to solve the given equation. (Round answers to 4 decimal places.) HINT [See Example 1.]

5. $3^x = 5$ **6.** $4^x = 3$

7. $5^{-2x} = 40$ **8.** $6^{3x+1} = 30$

9. $4.16e^x = 2$ **10.** $5.3(10^x) = 2$

11. $5(1.06^{2x+1}) = 11$ **12.** $4(1.5^{2x-1}) = 8$

In Exercises 13–18, graph the given function. HINT [See Example 2.]

13. $f(x) = \log_4 x$ **14.** $f(x) = \log_5 x$

15. $f(x) = \log_4(x-1)$ **16.** $f(x) = \log_5(x+1)$

17. $f(x) = \log_{1/4} x$ **18.** $f(x) = \log_{1/5} x$

In Exercises 19–22 find the associated exponential decay or growth model. HINT [See Quick Examples on page 655.]

19. $Q = 1{,}000$ when $t = 0$; half-life $= 1$

20. $Q = 2{,}000$ when $t = 0$; half-life $= 5$

21. $Q = 1{,}000$ when $t = 0$; doubling time $= 2$

22. $Q = 2{,}000$ when $t = 0$; doubling time $= 5$

In Exercises 23–26 find the associated half-life or doubling time. HINT [See Quick Examples on page 655.]

23. $Q = 1{,}000e^{0.5t}$ **24.** $Q = 1{,}000e^{-0.025t}$

25. $Q = Q_0e^{-4t}$ **26.** $Q = Q_0e^{t}$

In Exercises 27–32 convert the given exponential function to the form indicated. Round all coefficients to 4 significant digits. HINT [See Example 4 "Before we go on."]

27. $f(x) = 4e^{2x}$; $f(x) = Ab^x$

28. $f(x) = 2.1e^{-0.1x}$; $f(x) = Ab^x$

29. $f(t) = 2.1(1.001)^t$; $f(t) = Q_0e^{kt}$

30. $f(t) = 23.4(0.991)^t$; $f(t) = Q_0e^{-kt}$

31. $f(t) = 10(0.987)^t$; $f(t) = Q_0e^{-kt}$

32. $f(t) = 2.3(2.2)^t$; $f(t) = Q_0e^{kt}$

APPLICATIONS

33. ***Investments*** How long will it take a \$500 investment to be worth \$700 if it is continuously compounded at 10% per year? (Give the answer to two decimal places.) HINT [See Example 3.]

34. ***Investments*** How long will it take a \$500 investment to be worth \$700 if it is continuously compounded at 15% per year? (Give the answer to two decimal places.) HINT [See Example 3.]

35. ***Investments*** How long, to the nearest year, will it take an investment to triple if it is continuously compounded at 10% per year? HINT [See Example 3.]

36. ***Investments*** How long, to the nearest year, will it take me to become a millionaire if I invest \$1,000 at 10% interest compounded continuously? HINT [See Example 3.]

37. ***Investments*** I would like my investment to double in value every 3 years. At what rate of interest would I need to invest it, assuming the interest is compounded continuously? HINT [See Quick Examples page 655.]

38. ***Depreciation*** My investment in OHaganBooks.com stocks is losing half its value every 2 years. Find and interpret the associated decay rate. HINT [See Quick Examples page 655.]

39. ***Carbon Dating*** The amount of carbon 14 remaining in a sample that originally contained A grams is given by

$$C(t) = A(0.999879)^t$$

where t is time in years. If tests on a fossilized skull reveal that 99.95% of the carbon 14 has decayed, how old, to the nearest 1,000 years, is the skull? HINT [See Example 4.]

40. ***Carbon Dating*** Refer back to Exercise 39. How old, to the nearest 1,000 years, is a fossil in which only 30% of the carbon 14 has decayed? HINT [See Example 4.]

Long-Term Investments *Exercises 41–48 are based on the following table, which lists interest rates on long-term investments (based on 10-year government bonds) in several countries in 2011.*[35] HINT [See Example 3.]

Country	U.S.	Japan	Germany	Australia	Brazil
Yield	3.4%	1.2%	3.3%	5.5%	12.7%

41. Assuming that you invest \$10,000 in the U.S., how long (to the nearest year) must you wait before your investment is worth \$15,000 if the interest is compounded annually?

42. Assuming that you invest \$10,000 in Japan, how long (to the nearest year) must you wait before your investment is worth \$15,000 if the interest is compounded annually?

43. If you invest \$10,400 in Germany and the interest is compounded monthly, when, to the nearest month, will your investment be worth \$20,000?

44. If you invest \$10,400 in the U.S., and the interest is compounded monthly, when, to the nearest month, will your investment be worth \$20,000?

45. How long, to the nearest year, will it take an investment in Australia to double its value if the interest is compounded every 6 months?

46. How long, to the nearest year, will it take an investment in Brazil to double its value if the interest is compounded every 6 months?

47. If the interest on a long-term U.S. investment is compounded continuously, how long will it take the value of an investment to double? (Give the answer correct to 2 decimal places.)

[35]Approximate interest rates based on 10-year government bonds. Source: www.bloomberg.com.

48. If the interest on a long-term Australia investment is compounded continuously, how long will it take the value of an investment to double? (Give an answer correct to 2 decimal places.)

49. ***Half-Life*** The amount of radium 226 remaining in a sample that originally contained A grams is approximately

$$C(t) = A(0.999\,567)^t$$

where t is time in years. Find the half-life to the nearest 100 years. HINT [See Example 4a.]

50. ***Half-Life*** The amount of iodine 131 remaining in a sample that originally contained A grams is approximately

$$C(t) = A(0.9175)^t$$

where t is time in days. Find the half-life to 2 decimal places. HINT [See Example 4a.]

51. ***Automobiles*** The rate of auto thefts triples every 6 months.

a. Determine, to 2 decimal places, the base b for an exponential model $y = Ab^t$ of the rate of auto thefts as a function of time in months.

b. Find the doubling time to the nearest tenth of a month. HINT [(a) See Section 9.2 Example 2. (b) See Quick Examples page 655.]

52. ***Televisions*** The rate of television thefts is doubling every 4 months.

a. Determine, to 2 decimal places, the base b for an exponential model $y = Ab^t$ of the rate of television thefts as a function of time in months.

b. Find the tripling time to the nearest tenth of a month. HINT [(a) See Section 9.2 Example 2. (b) See Quick Examples page 655.]

53. ***Half-Life*** The half-life of cobalt 60 is 5 years.

a. Obtain an exponential decay model for cobalt 60 in the form $Q(t) = Q_0e^{-kt}$. (Round coefficients to 3 significant digits.)

b. Use your model to predict, to the nearest year, the time it takes one third of a sample of cobalt 60 to decay.

54. ***Half-Life*** The half-life of strontium 90 is 28 years.

a. Obtain an exponential decay model for strontium 90 in the form $Q(t) = Q_0e^{-kt}$. (Round coefficients to 3 significant digits.)

b. Use your model to predict, to the nearest year, the time it takes three fifths of a sample of strontium 90 to decay.

55. ***Radioactive Decay*** Uranium 235 is used as fuel for some nuclear reactors. It has a half-life of 710 million years. How long will it take 10 grams of uranium 235 to decay to 1 gram? (Round your answer to 3 significant digits.)

56. ***Radioactive Decay*** Plutonium 239 is used as fuel for some nuclear reactors, and also as the fissionable material in atomic bombs. It has a half-life of 24,400 years. How long would it take 10 grams of plutonium 239 to decay to 1 gram? (Round your answer to 3 significant digits.)

57. ▼ ***Aspirin*** Soon after taking an aspirin, a patient has absorbed 300 mg of the drug. If the amount of aspirin in the bloodstream decays exponentially, with half being removed every 2 hours, find, to the nearest 0.1 hour, the time it will take for the amount of aspirin in the bloodstream to decrease to 100 mg.

58. ▼ ***Alcohol*** After a large number of drinks, a person has a blood alcohol level of 200 mg/dL (milligrams per deciliter). If the amount of alcohol in the blood decays exponentially, with one fourth being removed every hour, find the time it will take for the person's blood alcohol level to decrease to 80 mg/dL. HINT [See Example 4.]

59. ▼ ***Radioactive Decay*** You are trying to determine the half-life of a new radioactive element you have isolated. You start with 1 gram, and 2 days later you determine that it has decayed down to 0.7 grams. What is its half-life? (Round your answer to 3 significant digits.) HINT [First find an exponential model, then see Example 4.]

60. ▼ ***Radioactive Decay*** You have just isolated a new radioactive element. If you can determine its half-life, you will win the Nobel Prize in physics. You purify a sample of 2 grams. One of your colleagues steals half of it, and 3 days later you find that 0.1 grams of the radioactive material is still left. What is the half-life? (Round your answer to 3 significant digits.) HINT [First find an exponential model, then see Example 4.]

61. ***Population Aging*** The following table shows the percentage of U.S. residents over the age of 65 in 1950, 1960, . . . , 2010 (t is time in years since 1900):[36]

t (Year since 1900)	50	60	70	80	90	100	110
P (% over 65)	8.2	9.2	9.9	11.3	12.6	12.6	13

a. Find the logarithmic regression model of the form $P(t) = A \ln t + C$. (Round the coefficients to 4 significant digits). HINT [See Example 5.]

b. In 1940, 6.9% of the population was over 65. To how many significant digits does the model reflect this figure?

c. Which of the following is correct? The model, if extrapolated into the indefinite future, predicts that

(A) The percentage of U.S. residents over the age of 65 will increase without bound.

(B) The percentage of U.S. residents over the age of 65 will level off at around 14.2%.

(C) The percentage of U.S. residents over the age of 65 will eventually decrease.

62. ***Population Aging*** The following table shows the percentage of U.S. residents over the age of 85 in 1950, 1960, . . . , 2010 (t is time in years since 1900):[37]

t (Year since 1900)	50	60	70	80	90	100	110
P (% over 85)	0.4	0.5	0.7	1	1.2	1.6	1.9

a. Find the logarithmic regression model of the form $P(t) = A \ln t + C$. (Round the coefficients to 4 significant digits). HINT [See Example 5.]

[36]Source: U.S. Census Bureau.

[37]*Ibid.*

b. In 2020, 2.1% of the population is projected to be over 85. To how many significant digits does the model reflect this figure?

c. Which of the following is correct? If you increase A by 0.1 and decrease C by 0.1 in the logarithmic model, then

(A) The new model predicts eventually lower percentages.

(B) The long-term prediction is essentially the same.

(C) The new model predicts eventually higher percentages.

63. ***Research & Development: Industry*** The following table shows the total spent on research and development by industry in the United States, in billions of dollars, for the period 1998–2008 (t is the year since 1990).[38]

Year t	8	9	10	11	12	13	14	15	16	17	18
Spending ($ billions)	150	165	183	181	170	172	172	181	191	203	215

Find the logarithmic regression model of the form $S(t) = A \ln t + C$ with coefficients A and C rounded to 2 decimal places. Also obtain a graph showing the data points and the regression curve. In which direction is it more reasonable to extrapolate the model? Why?

64. ***Research & Development: Federal*** The following table shows the total spent on research and development by the federal government in the United States, in billions of dollars, for the period 1998–2008 (t is the year since 1990).[39]

Year t	8	9	10	11	12	13	14	15	16	17	18
Spending ($ billions)	18	18	18	20	21	21	21	22	22	21	22

Find the logarithmic regression model of the form $S(t) = A \ln t + C$ with coefficients A and C rounded to 2 decimal places. Also obtain a graph showing the data points and the regression curve. In which direction is it more reasonable to extrapolate the model? Why?

65. ***Richter Scale*** The **Richter scale** is used to measure the intensity of earthquakes. The Richter scale rating of an earthquake is given by the formula

$$R = \frac{2}{3}(\log E - 11.8)$$

where E is the energy released by the earthquake (measured in ergs[40]).

a. The San Francisco earthquake of 1906 is estimated to have registered $R = 7.9$ on the Richter scale. How many ergs of energy were released?

b. The Japan earthquake of 2011 registered 9.0 on the Richter scale. Compare the two: The energy released in the 1906 earthquake was what percentage of the energy released in the 2011 quake?

c. Solve the equation given above for E in terms of R.

d. Use the result of part (c) to show that if two earthquakes registering R_1 and R_2 on the Richter scale release E_1 and E_2 ergs of energy, respectively, then

$$\frac{E_2}{E_1} = 10^{1.5(R_2 - R_1)}.$$

e. Fill in the blank: If one earthquake registers 2 points more on the Richter scale than another, then it releases ___ times the amount of energy.

66. ***Sound Intensity*** The loudness of a sound is measured in **decibels**. The decibel level of a sound is given by the formula

$$D = 10 \log \frac{I}{I_0},$$

where D is the decibel level (dB), I is its intensity in watts per square meter (W/m^2), and $I_0 = 10^{-12}$ W/m^2 is the intensity of a barely audible "threshold" sound. A sound intensity of 90 dB or greater causes damage to the average human ear.

a. Find the decibel levels of each of the following, rounding to the nearest decibel:

Whisper:	115×10^{-12} W/m^2
TV (average volume from 10 feet):	320×10^{-7} W/m^2
Loud music:	900×10^{-3} W/m^2
Jet aircraft (from 500 feet):	100 W/m^2

b. Which of the sounds above damages the average human ear?

c. Solve the given equation to express I in terms of D.

d. Use the answer to part (c) to show that if two sounds of intensity I_1 and I_2 register decibel levels of D_1 and D_2, respectively, then

$$\frac{I_2}{I_1} = 10^{0.1(D_2 - D_1)}.$$

e. Fill in the blank: If one sound registers one decibel more than another, then it is ___ times as intense.

67. ***Sound Intensity*** The decibel level of a TV set decreases with the distance from the set according to the formula

$$D = 10 \log\left(\frac{320 \times 10^7}{r^2}\right)$$

[38] Excludes Federal funding; 2008 data is preliminary. Source: National Science Foundation, Division of Science Resources Statistics. 2010. *National Patterns of R&D Resources: 2008 Data Update.* NSF 10-314. Arlington, VA. www.nsf.gov/statistics/nsf10314/.

[39] Excludes Federal funding to industry and nonprofit organizations; 2008 data is preliminary. Source: National Science Foundation, Division of Science Resources Statistics. 2010. *National Patterns of R&D Resources: 2008 Data Update.* NSF 10-314. Arlington, VA. www.nsf.gov/statistics/nsf10314/.

[40] An erg is a unit of energy. One erg is the amount of energy it takes to move a mass of one gram one centimeter in one second. The term "Richter scale" is used loosely to refer to several ways of measuring earthquake magnitudes, calibrated to agree where they overlap.

where D is the decibel level (dB) and r is the distance from the TV set in feet.

a. Find the decibel level (to the nearest decibel) at distances of 10, 20, and 50 feet.
b. Express D in the form $D = A + B \log r$ for suitable constants A and B. (Round A and D to 2 significant digits.)
c. How far must a listener be from a TV so that the decibel level drops to 0 dB? (Round the answer to two significant digits.)

68. ▼ ***Acidity*** The acidity of a solution is measured by its pH, which is given by the formula

$$pH = -\log(H^+)$$

where H^+ measures the concentration of hydrogen ions in moles per liter.[41] The pH of pure water is 7. A solution is referred to as *acidic* if its pH is below 7 and as *basic* if its pH is above 7.

a. Calculate the pH of each of the following substances.

Blood:	3.9×10^{-8} moles/liter
Milk:	4.0×10^{-7} moles/liter
Soap solution:	1.0×10^{-11} moles/liter
Black coffee:	1.2×10^{-7} moles/liter

b. How many moles of hydrogen ions are contained in a liter of acid rain that has a pH of 5.0?
c. Complete the following sentence: If the pH of a solution increases by 1.0, then the concentration of hydrogen ions ________.

COMMUNICATION AND REASONING EXERCISES

69. On the same set of axes, graph $y = \ln x$, $y = A \ln x$, and $y = A \ln x + C$ for various choices of *positive* A and C. What is the effect on the graph of $y = \ln x$ of multiplying by A? What is the effect of then adding C?

[41]A mole corresponds to about 6.0×10^{23} hydrogen ions. (This number is known as Avogadro's number.)

70. On the same set of axes, graph $y = -\ln x$, $y = A \ln x$, and $y = A \ln x + C$ for various choices of *negative* A and C. What is the effect on the graph of $y = \ln x$ of multiplying by A? What is the effect of then adding C?

71. Why is the logarithm of a negative number not defined?

72. Of what use are logarithms, now that they are no longer needed to perform complex calculations?

73. Your company's market share is undergoing steady growth. Explain why a logarithmic function is *not* appropriate for long-term future prediction of your market share.

74. Your company's market share is undergoing steady growth. Explain why a logarithmic function is *not* appropriate for long-term backward extrapolation of your market share.

75. If $y = 4^x$, then $x =$ ________.

76. If $y = \log_6 x$, then $x =$ ________.

77. Simplify: $2^{\log_2 8}$.

78. Simplify: $e^{\ln x}$.

79. Simplify: $\ln(e^x)$.

80. Simplify: $\ln\sqrt{a}$.

81. ▼ If a town's population is increasing exponentially with time, how is time increasing with population? Explain.

82. ▼ If a town's population is increasing logarithmically with time, how is time increasing with population? Explain.

83. ▼ If two quantities Q_1 and Q_2 are logarithmic functions of time t, show that their sum, $Q_1 + Q_2$, is also a logarithmic function of time t.

84. ▼ In Exercise 83 we saw that the sum of two logarithmic functions is a logarithmic function. In Exercises 63 and 64 you modeled research and development expenditure by industry and government. Now do a logarithmic regression on the sum of the two sets of figures. Does the result coincide with the sum of the two individual regression models? What does your answer tell you about the sum of logarithmic regression models?

Practice Problems 9.3, Part 1

1. Convert the given exponential functions to the form $P = Ae^{rt}$. Round constants to four decimal places.
   a. $P = 85(1.45)^t$

   b. $P = 19(0.75)^t$

   c. $P = 19(3)^{\frac{t}{5}}$

2. Assume that u and v are positive numbers. Simplify $e^{3\ln u - 2\ln v}$.

3. Solve for x: $2^x = 5^{3x-1}$. Give the exact solution in terms of common logarithms.

Practice Problems 9.3, Part 2

The quantity of an exponentially decaying substance decreases by 48% in 10 hours.

1. Calculate both the incremental hourly percentage rate of decay and the continuous hourly rate of decay. Give both as a percentage, correct to two decimal places.

2. Determine the half-life of the substance, accurate to two decimal places.

Practice Problems 9.3, Part 3

1. For some airplanes, the minimum runway length (in thousands of feet) required for takeoff is given by $L(x) = 3\log x$, where x is the weight of the airplane, in pounds.

a. What is the heaviest such an airplane can be to be able to take off using a 15,000-foot runway? Give your result to the nearest pound.

b. Let w denote the weight of such an airplane, in **thousands** of pounds. Let R be a function that gives the minimum runway length (in thousands of feet) for an airplane of weight w. Write an equation for R in terms of $\log w$.

2. One way of describing the brightness of a star is by a magnitude, *m*, given by

$$m = 6 - 2.5\log\left(\frac{l}{l_0}\right)$$

where l is the light flux (apparent brightness) of the star and l_0 is the light flux of the dimmest stars still visible to the naked eye. Which is brighter: a magnitude 1 star, or a magnitude 6 star? How many times brighter than the dimmer star is the brighter star?

Practice Problems 9.3, Part 4

1. Bacteria culture A currently numbers 9600 organisms and is increasing in size at a rate of 8.4% per hour. Bacteria culture B currently numbers 800 organisms and is increasing in size at a continuous rate of 13% per hour. Determine how long it will take for the size of culture A to overtake that of culture B. Give the result accurate to two decimal places.

2. A class in underwater basket weaving is tested at the end of the semester and weekly thereafter on the same material. The average score on the exam taken after t weeks is given by the "forgetting function" $g(t) = 84 - 10 \cdot \ln(t+1)$.

a. What was the average score on the original exam?

b. What was the average score after 6 weeks, accurate to one decimal place?

c. When did the average score drop below 50?

9.4 Logistic Functions and Models

Figure 17 shows wired broadband penetration in the United States as a function of time t in years ($t = 0$ represents 2000).[42]

The left-hand part of the curve in Figure 17, from $t = 2$ to, say, $t = 6$, looks roughly like exponential growth: P behaves (roughly) like an exponential function, with the y-coordinates growing by a factor of around 1.5 per year. Then, as the market starts to become saturated, the growth of P slows and its value approaches a "saturation" point that appears to be around 30%. **Logistic** functions have just this

[42] Broadband penetration is the number of broadband installations divided by the total population. Source for data: Organisation for Economic Co-operation and Development (OECD) Directorate for Science, Technology, and Industry, table of Historical Penetration Rates, June 2010, downloaded April 2011 from www.oecd.org/sti/ict/broadband.

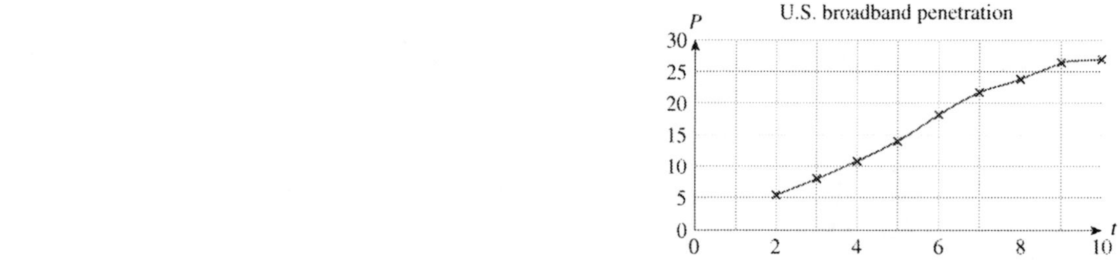

Figure 17

kind of behavior, growing exponentially at first and then leveling off. In addition to modeling the demand for a new technology or product, logistic functions are often used in epidemic and population modeling. In an epidemic, the number of infected people often grows exponentially at first and then slows when a significant proportion of the entire susceptible population is infected and the epidemic has "run its course." Similarly, populations may grow exponentially at first and then slow as they approach the capacity of the available resources.

Logistic Function

A **logistic function** has the form

$$f(x) = \frac{N}{1 + Ab^{-x}}$$

for nonzero constants N, A, and b (A and b positive and $b \neq 1$).

Quick Example

$N = 6, A = 2, b = 1.1$ gives $f(x) = \dfrac{6}{1 + 2(1.1^{-x})}$ 6/(1+2*1.1^-x)

$f(0) = \dfrac{6}{1+2} = 2$ The y-intercept is $N/(1 + A)$.

$f(1{,}000) = \dfrac{6}{1 + 2(1.1^{-1{,}000})} \approx \dfrac{6}{1+0} = 6 = N$ When x is large, $f(x) \approx N$.

Graph of a Logistic Function

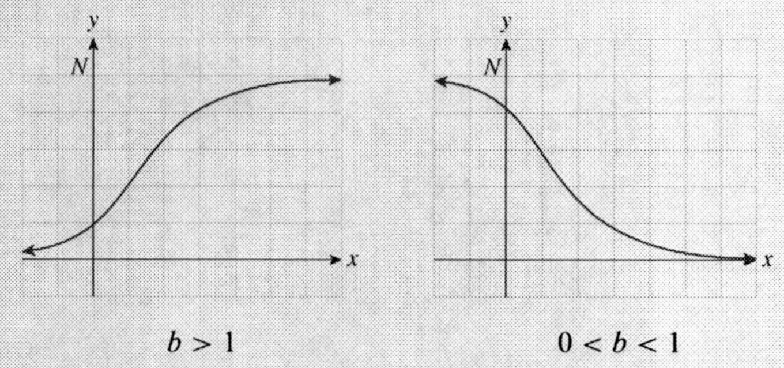

$$y = \frac{N}{1 + Ab^{-x}}$$

Properties of the Logistic Curve $y = \dfrac{N}{1 + Ab^{-x}}$

- The graph is an S-shaped curve sandwiched between the horizontal lines $y = 0$ and $y = N$. N is called the **limiting value** of the logistic curve.
- If $b > 1$ the graph rises; if $b < 1$, the graph falls.
- The y-intercept is $\dfrac{N}{1+A}$.
- The curve is steepest when $t = \dfrac{\ln A}{\ln b}$. We will see why in Chapter 12.

Note If we write b^{-x} as e^{-kx} (so that $k = \ln b$), we get the following alternative form of the logistic function:

$$f(x) = \frac{N}{1 + Ae^{-kx}}.$$

■

Q: *How does the constant b affect the graph?*

A: To understand the role of b, we first rewrite the logistic function by multiplying top and bottom by b^x:

$$\begin{aligned} f(x) &= \frac{N}{1 + Ab^{-x}} \\ &= \frac{Nb^x}{(1 + Ab^{-x})b^x} \\ &= \frac{Nb^x}{b^x + A} \qquad \text{Because } b^{-x}b^x = 1 \end{aligned}$$

For values of x close to 0, the quantity b^x is close to 1, so the denominator is approximately $1 + A$, giving

$$f(x) \approx \frac{Nb^x}{1 + A} = \left(\frac{N}{1 + A}\right) b^x.$$

In other words, $f(x)$ is approximately exponential with base b for values of x close to 0. Put another way, if x represents time, then initially the logistic function behaves like an exponential function.

To summarize:

Logistic Function for Small *x* and the Role of *b*

For small values of x, we have

$$\frac{N}{1 + Ab^{-x}} \approx \left(\frac{N}{1 + A}\right) b^x.$$

Thus, for small x, the logistic function grows approximately exponentially with base b.

Quick Example

Let

$$f(x) = \frac{50}{1 + 24(3^{-x})}. \qquad N = 50, A = 24, b = 3$$

Then

$$f(x) \approx \left(\frac{50}{1 + 24}\right)(3^x) = 2(3^x)$$

for small values of x. The following figure compares their graphs:

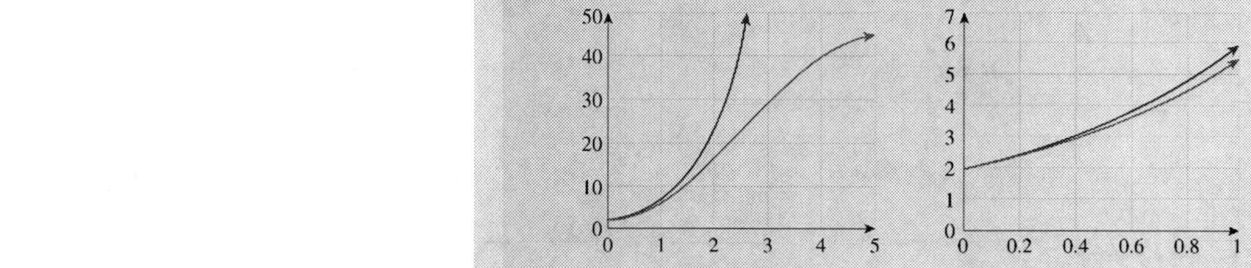

The upper curve is the exponential curve.

Modeling with the Logistic Function

EXAMPLE 1 Epidemics

A flu epidemic is spreading through the U.S. population. An estimated 150 million people are susceptible to this particular strain, and it is predicted that all susceptible people will eventually become infected. There are 10,000 people already infected, and the number is doubling every 2 weeks. Use a logistic function to model the number of people infected. Hence predict when, to the nearest week, 1 million people will be infected.

Solution Let t be time in weeks, and let $P(t)$ be the total number of people infected at time t. We want to express P as a logistic function of t, so that

$$P(t) = \frac{N}{1 + Ab^{-t}}.$$

We are told that, in the long run, 150 million people will be infected, so that

$$N = 150{,}000{,}000. \qquad \text{Limiting value of } P$$

At the current time ($t = 0$), 10,000 people are infected, so

$$10{,}000 = \frac{N}{1 + A} = \frac{150{,}000{,}000}{1 + A}. \qquad \text{Value of } P \text{ when } t = 0$$

Solving for A gives

$$\begin{aligned} 10{,}000(1 + A) &= 150{,}000{,}000 \\ 1 + A &= 15{,}000 \\ A &= 14{,}999. \end{aligned}$$

What about b? At the beginning of the epidemic (t near 0), P is growing approximately exponentially, doubling every 2 weeks. Using the technique of Section 9.2, we find that the exponential curve passing through the points (0, 10,000) and (2, 20,000) is

$$y = 10{,}000(\sqrt{2})^t$$

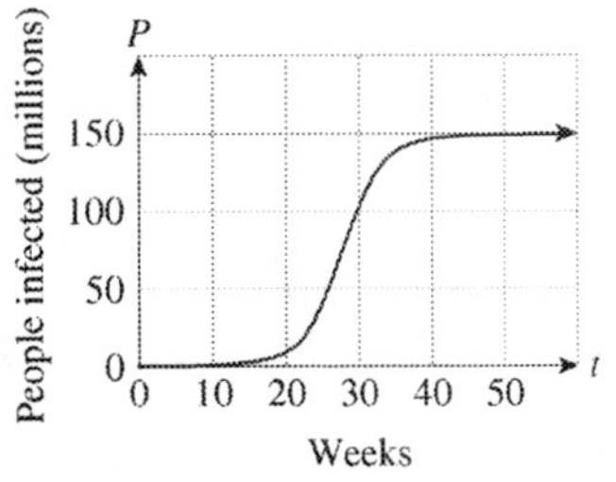

Figure 18

giving us $b = \sqrt{2}$. Now that we have the constants N, A, and b, we can write down the logistic model:

$$P(t) = \frac{150{,}000{,}000}{1 + 14{,}999(\sqrt{2})^{-t}}.$$

The graph of this function is shown in Figure 18.

Now we tackle the question of prediction: When will 1 million people be infected? In other words: When is $P(t) = 1{,}000{,}000$?

$$1{,}000{,}000 = \frac{150{,}000{,}000}{1 + 14{,}999(\sqrt{2})^{-t}}$$

$$1{,}000{,}000[1 + 14{,}999(\sqrt{2})^{-t}] = 150{,}000{,}000$$

$$1 + 14{,}999(\sqrt{2})^{-t} = 150$$

$$14{,}999(\sqrt{2})^{-t} = 149$$

$$(\sqrt{2})^{-t} = \frac{149}{14{,}999}$$

$$-t = \log_{\sqrt{2}}\left(\frac{149}{14{,}999}\right) \approx -13.31 \quad \text{Logarithmic form}$$

Thus, 1 million people will be infected by about the thirteenth week.

Before we go on... We said earlier that the logistic curve is steepest when $t = \frac{\ln A}{\ln b}$. In Example 1, this occurs when $t = \frac{\ln 14{,}999}{\ln\sqrt{2}} \approx 28$ weeks into the epidemic. At that time, the number of cases is growing most rapidly (look at the apparent slope of the graph at the corresponding point). ■

Logistic Regression

Let's go back to the data on broadband penetration in the United States with which we began this section and try to determine the long-term percentage of broadband penetration. In order to be able to make predictions such as this, we require a model for the data, so we will need to do some form of regression.

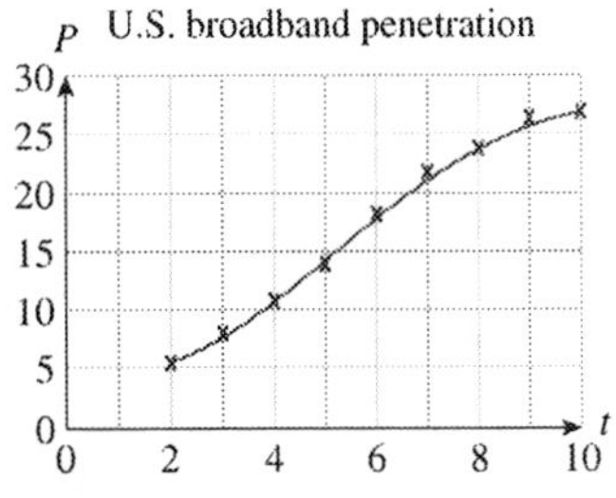

Figure 19

EXAMPLE 2 Broadband Penetration

Here are the data graphed in Figure 17:

Year (t)	2	3	4	5	6	7	8	9	10
Penetration (%) (P)	5.5	7.9	10.9	14.2	18.2	21.9	23.9	26.5	27.1

using Technology

See the Technology Guide at the end of the chapter for detailed instructions on how to obtain the regression curve and graph for Example 2 using a graphing calculator or spreadsheet. Outline:

TI-83/84 Plus

[STAT] EDIT values of t in L_1 and values of P in L_2

Regression curve: [STAT]

CALC option #B Logistic [ENTER]

Graph: [Y=] [VARS] [5] EQ [1], then [ZOOM] [9] [More details on page 682.]

Spreadsheet

Use the Solver Add-in to obtain the best-fit logistic curve. [More details on page 684.]

Website

www.WanerMath.com

In the Function Evaluator and Grapher, enter the data as shown, press "Examples" until the logistic model `$1/(1+$2*$3^(-x))` shows in the first box, and press "Fit Curve".

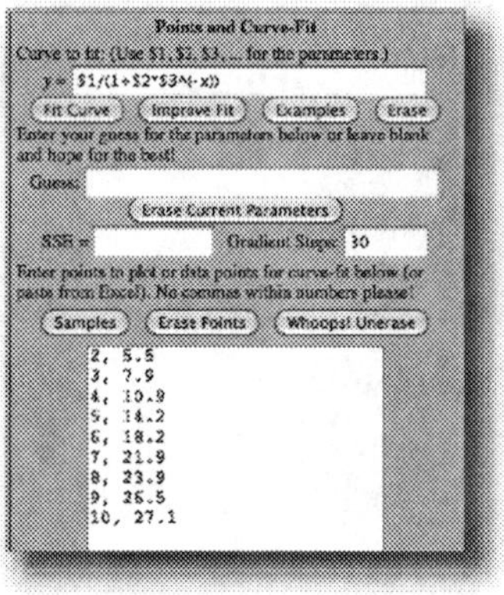

Find a logistic regression curve of the form

$$P(t) = \frac{N}{1 + Ab^{-t}}.$$

In the long term, what percentage of broadband penetration in the United States does the model predict?

Solution We can use technology to obtain the following regression model:

$$P(t) \approx \frac{29.842}{1 + 12.502(1.642)^{-t}}. \qquad \text{Coefficients rounded to 3 decimal places}$$

Its graph and the original data are shown in Figure 19. Because $N = 29.842$, this model predicts that, in the long term, the percentage of broadband penetration in the United States will be 29.842%, or about 30%.

Before we go on... Logistic regression programs generally estimate all three constants N, A, and b for a model $y = \frac{N}{1 + Ab^{-x}}$. However, there are times, as in Example 1, when we already know the limiting value N and require estimates of only A and b. In such cases, we can use technology like Excel Solver to find A and b for the best-fit curve with N fixed. Alternatively, we can use exponential regression to compute estimates of A and b as follows: First rewrite the logistic equation as

$$\frac{N}{y} = 1 + Ab^{-x},$$

so that

$$\frac{N}{y} - 1 = Ab^{-x} = A(b^{-1})^x.$$

This equation gives $N/y - 1$ as an exponential function of x. Thus, if we do exponential regression using the data points $(x, N/y - 1)$, we can obtain estimates for A and b^{-1} (and hence b). This is done in Exercises 35 and 36.

It is important to note that the resulting curve is not the best-fit curve (in the sense of minimizing SSE; see the "Before we go on" discussion on page 641 after Example 6 in Section 9.2) and will be thus be different from that obtained using the method in Example 2. ■

9.4 EXERCISES

▼ more advanced ◆ challenging

T indicates exercises that should be solved using technology

In Exercises 1–6, find N, A, and b, give a technology formula for the given function, and use technology to sketch its graph for the given range of values of x. HINT [See Quick Examples on page 661.]

1. $f(x) = \frac{7}{1 + 6(2^{-x})}$; $[0, 10]$

2. $g(x) = \frac{4}{1 + 0.333(4^{-x})}$; $[0, 2]$

3. $f(x) = \frac{10}{1 + 4(0.3^{-x})}$; $[-5, 5]$

4. $g(x) = \frac{100}{1 + 5(0.5^{-x})}$; $[-5, 5]$

5. $h(x) = \frac{2}{0.5 + 3.5(1.5^{-x})}$; $[0, 15]$

(First divide top and bottom by 0.5.)

6. $k(x) = \dfrac{17}{2 + 6.5(1.05^{-x})}$; [0, 100]
(First divide top and bottom by 2.)

In Exercises 7–10, find the logistic function f with the given properties. HINT [See Example 1.]

7. $f(0) = 10$, f has limiting value 200, and for small values of x, f is approximately exponential and doubles with every increase of 1 in x.

8. $f(0) = 1$, f has limiting value 10, and for small values of x, f is approximately exponential and grows by 50% with every increase of 1 in x.

9. f has limiting value 6 and passes through (0, 3) and (1, 4). HINT [First find A, then substitute.]

10. f has limiting value 4 and passes through (0, 1) and (1, 2). HINT [First find A, then substitute.]

In Exercises 11–16, choose the logistic function that best approximates the given curve.

11.

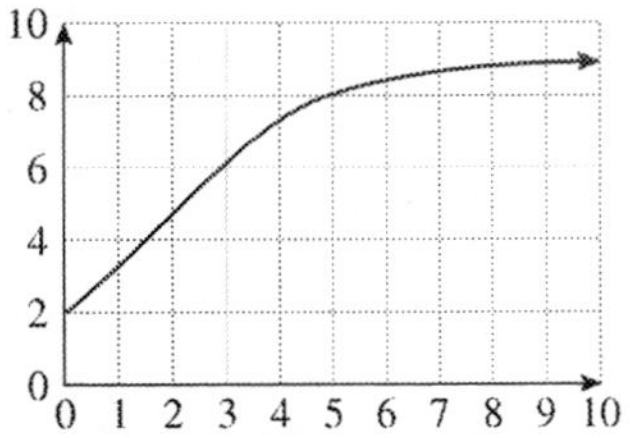

(A) $f(x) = \dfrac{6}{1 + 0.5(3^{-x})}$

(B) $f(x) = \dfrac{9}{1 + 3.5(2^{-x})}$

(C) $f(x) = \dfrac{9}{1 + 0.5(1.01)^{-x}}$

12.

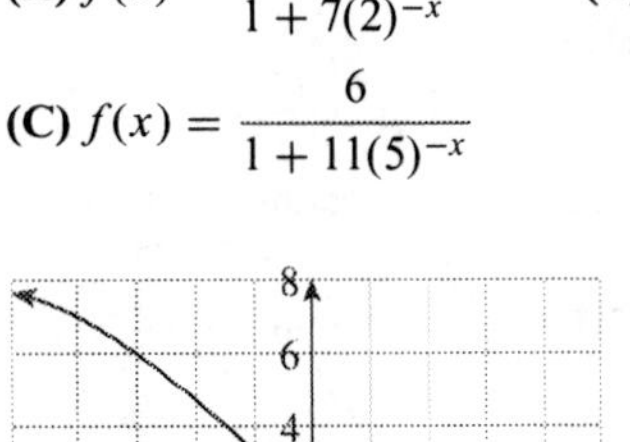

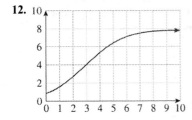

(A) $f(x) = \dfrac{8}{1 + 7(2)^{-x}}$ **(B)** $f(x) = \dfrac{8}{1 + 3(2)^{-x}}$

(C) $f(x) = \dfrac{6}{1 + 11(5)^{-x}}$

13.

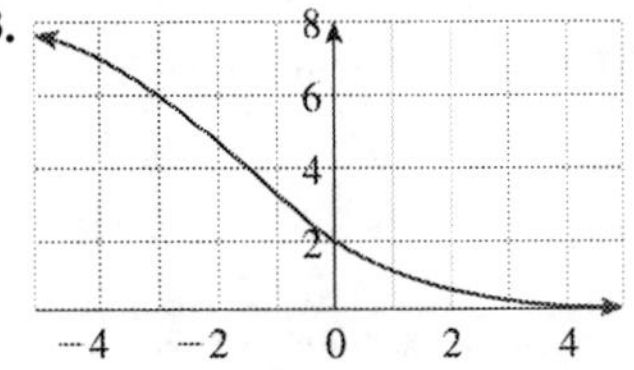

(A) $f(x) = \dfrac{8}{1 + 7(0.5)^{-x}}$ **(B)** $f(x) = \dfrac{8}{1 + 3(0.5)^{-x}}$

(C) $f(x) = \dfrac{8}{1 + 3(2)^{-x}}$

14.

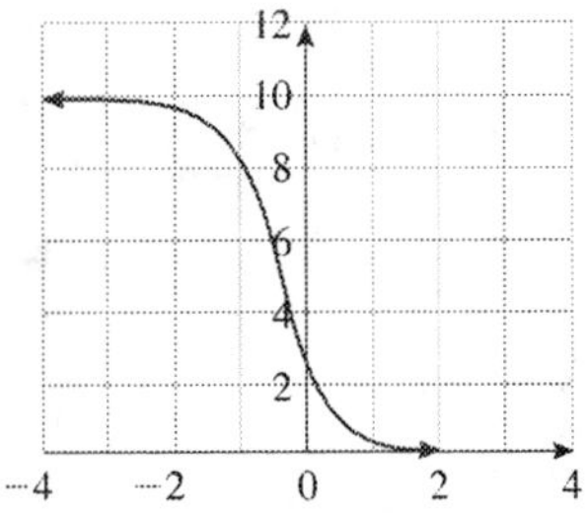

(A) $f(x) = \dfrac{10}{1 + 3(1.01)^{-x}}$ **(B)** $f(x) = \dfrac{8}{1 + 7(0.1)^{-x}}$

(C) $f(x) = \dfrac{10}{1 + 3(0.1)^{-x}}$

15.

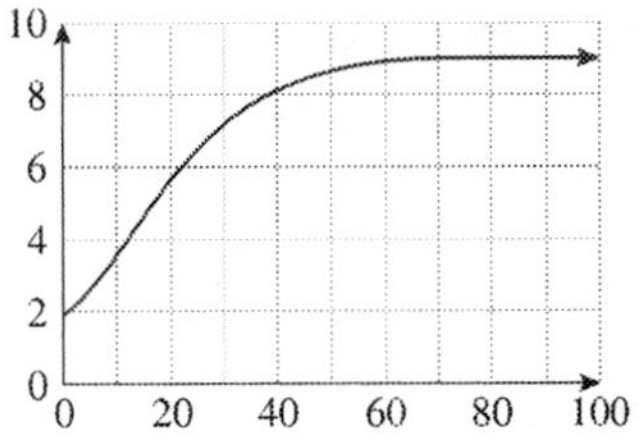

(A) $f(x) = \dfrac{18}{2 + 7(5)^{-x}}$ **(B)** $f(x) = \dfrac{18}{2 + 3(1.1)^{-x}}$

(C) $f(x) = \dfrac{18}{2 + 7(1.1)^{-x}}$

16.

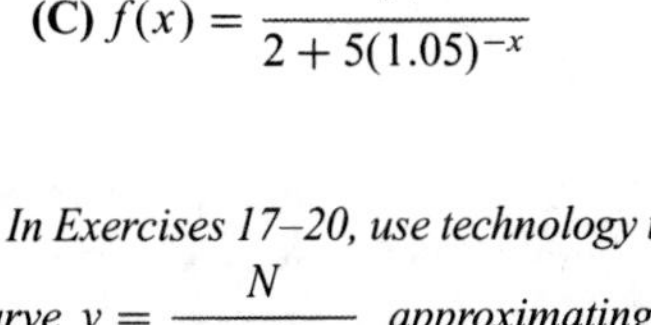

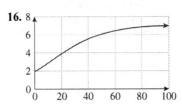

(A) $f(x) = \dfrac{14}{2 + 5(15)^{-x}}$ **(B)** $f(x) = \dfrac{14}{1 + 13(1.05)^{-x}}$

(C) $f(x) = \dfrac{14}{2 + 5(1.05)^{-x}}$

In Exercises 17–20, use technology to find a logistic regression curve $y = \dfrac{N}{1 + Ab^{-x}}$ *approximating the given data. Draw a graph showing the data points and regression curve. (Round b to 3 significant digits and A and N to 2 significant digits.)* HINT [See Example 2.]

17.

x	0	20	40	60	80	100
y	2.1	3.6	5.0	6.1	6.8	6.9

18.

x	0	30	60	90	120	150
y	2.8	5.8	7.9	9.4	9.7	9.9

19.

x	0	20	40	60	80	100
y	30.1	11.6	3.8	1.2	0.4	0.1

20.

x	0	30	60	90	120	150
y	30.1	20	12	7.2	3.8	2.4

APPLICATIONS

21. ***Subprime Mortgages during the Housing Bubble*** The following graph shows the approximate percentage of mortgages issued in the United States during the real-estate run-up in 2000–2008 that were subprime (normally classified as risky) as well as the logistic regression curve:[43]

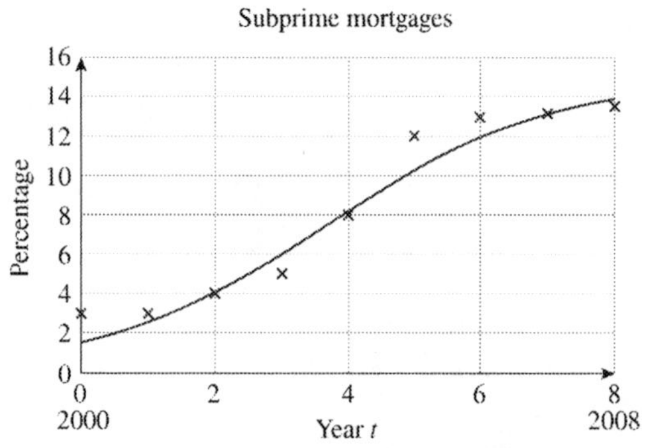

a. Which of the following logistic functions best approximates the curve? (t is the number of years since the start of 2000.) Try to determine the correct model without actually computing data points. HINT [See Properties of the Logistic Curve on page 662.]

(A) $A(t) = \dfrac{15.0}{1 + 8.6(1.8)^{-t}}$

(B) $A(t) = \dfrac{2.0}{1 + 6.8(0.8)^{-t}}$

(C) $A(t) = \dfrac{2.0}{1 + 6.8(1.8)^{-t}}$

(D) $A(t) = \dfrac{15.0}{1 + 8.6(0.8)^{-t}}$

b. According to the model you selected, during which year was the percentage growing fastest? HINT [See the "Before we go on" discussion after Example 1.]

22. ***Subprime Mortgage Debt during the Housing Bubble*** The following graph shows the approximate value of subprime (normally classified as risky) mortgage debt outstanding in the United States during the real-estate run-up in 2000–2008 as well as the logistic regression curve:[44]

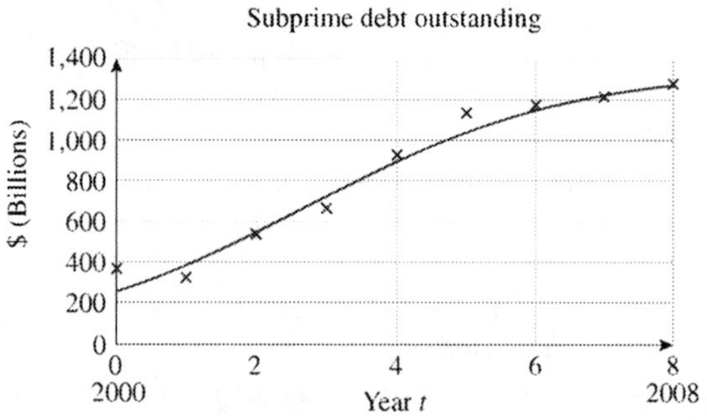

a. Which of the following logistic functions best approximates the curve? (t is the number of years since the start of 2000.) Try to determine the correct model without actually computing data points. HINT [See Properties of the Logistic Curve on page 662.]

(A) $A(t) = \dfrac{1{,}850}{1 + 5.36(1.8)^{-t}}$

(B) $A(t) = \dfrac{1{,}350}{1 + 4.2(1.7)^{-t}}$

(C) $A(t) = \dfrac{1{,}020}{1 + 5.3(1.8)^{-t}}$

(D) $A(t) = \dfrac{1{,}300}{1 + 4.2(0.9)^{-t}}$

b. According to the model you selected, during which year was outstanding debt growing fastest? HINT [See the "Before we go on" discussion after Example 1.]

23. ***Scientific Research*** The following graph shows the number of research articles in the prominent journal *Physical Review* that were written by researchers in Europe during 1983–2003 ($t = 0$ represents 1983).[45]

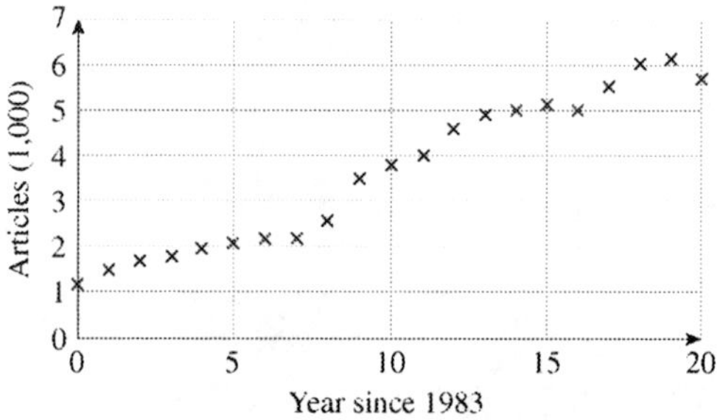

a. Which of the following logistic functions best models the data? (t is the number of years since 1983.) Try to determine the correct model without actually computing data points.

[43] 2008 figure is an estimate. Sources: Mortgage Bankers Association, UBS.

[44] 2008–2009 figures are estimates. Source: www.data360.org/dataset.aspx?Data_Set_Id=9549.

[45] Source: The American Physical Society/*New York Times* May 3, 2003, p. A1.

(A) $A(t) = \dfrac{7.0}{1 + 5.4(1.2)^{-t}}$

(B) $A(t) = \dfrac{4.0}{1 + 3.4(1.2)^{-t}}$

(C) $A(t) = \dfrac{4.0}{1 + 3.4(0.8)^{-t}}$

(D) $A(t) = \dfrac{7.0}{1 + 5.4(6.2)^{-t}}$

b. According to the model you selected, at what percentage was the number of articles growing around 1985?

24. ***Scientific Research*** The following graph shows the percentage, above 25%, of research articles in the prominent journal *Physical Review* that were written by researchers in the United States during 1983–2003 ($t = 0$ represents 1983).[46]

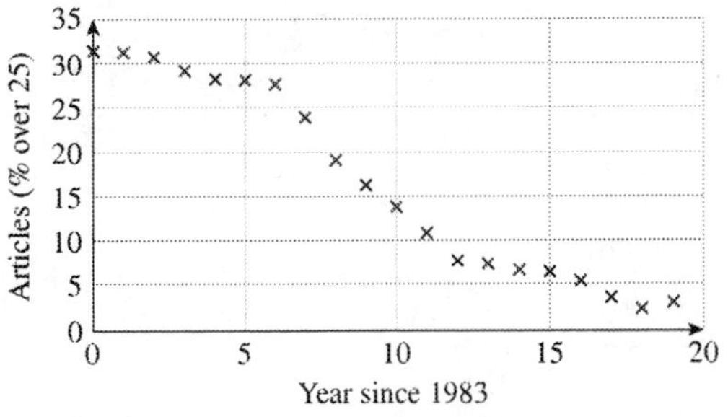

a. Which of the following logistic functions best models the data? (t is the number of years since 1983 and P is the actual percentage.) Try to determine the correct model without actually computing data points.

(A) $P(t) = \dfrac{36}{1 + 0.06(0.02)^{-t}}$

(B) $P(t) = \dfrac{12}{1 + 0.06(1.7)^{-t}}$

(C) $P(t) = \dfrac{12}{1 + 0.06(0.7)^{-t}}$

(D) $P(t) = \dfrac{36}{1 + 0.06(0.7)^{-t}}$

b. According to the model you selected, how fast was the value of P declining around 1985?

25. ***Internet Use*** The following graph shows the percentage of U.S. households using the Internet at home in 2010 as a function of household income (the data points) and a logistic model of these data (the curve).[47]

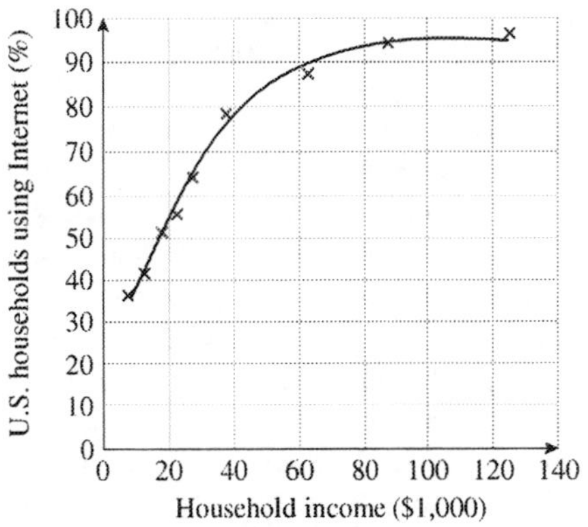

The logistic model is

$$P(x) = \frac{95.0}{1 + 2.78(1.064)^{-x}} \text{ percent}$$

where x is the household income in thousands of dollars.

a. According to the model, what percentage of extremely wealthy households used the Internet?

b. For low incomes, the logistic model is approximately exponential. Which exponential model best approximates $P(x)$ for small x?

c. According to the model, 50% of households of what income used the Internet in 2010? (Round the answer to the nearest $1,000.)

26. ***Internet Use*** The following graph shows the percentage of U.S. residents who used the Internet at home in 2010 as a function of income (the data points) and a logistic model of these data (the curve).[48]

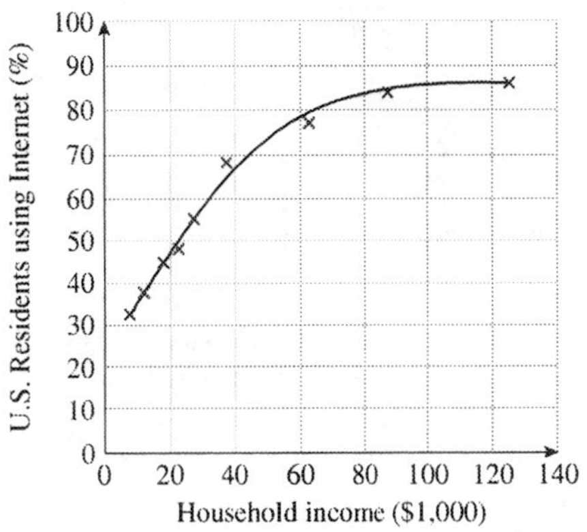

The logistic model is given by

$$P(x) = \frac{86.2}{1 + 2.49(1.054)^{-x}} \text{ percent}$$

where x is the household income in thousands of dollars.

[46] Source: The American Physical Society/*New York Times* May 3, 2003, p. A1.

[47] Income levels are midpoints of income brackets. Source: *Current Population Survey (CPS) Internet Use 2010,* National Telecommunications and Information Administration, www.ntia.doc.gov, January 2011.

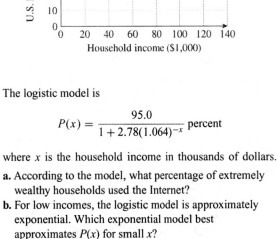

[48] *Ibid.*

a. According to the model, what percentage of extremely wealthy people used the Internet at home?

b. For low incomes, the logistic model is approximately exponential. Which exponential model best approximates $P(x)$ for small x?

c. According to the model, 50% of individuals with what household income used the Internet at home in 2010? (Round the answer to the nearest $1,000.)

27. ***Epidemics*** There are currently 1,000 cases of Venusian flu in a total susceptible population of 10,000 and the number of cases is increasing by 25% each day. Find a logistic model for the number of cases of Venusian flu and use your model to predict the number of flu cases a week from now. HINT [See Example 1.]

28. ***Epidemics*** Last year's epidemic of Martian flu began with a single case in a total susceptible population of 10,000. The number of cases was increasing initially by 40% per day. Find a logistic model for the number of cases of Martian flu and use your model to predict the number of flu cases 3 weeks into the epidemic. HINT [See Example 1.]

29. ***Sales*** You have sold 100 "I ♥ Calculus" T-shirts and sales appear to be doubling every 5 days. You estimate the total market for "I ♥ Calculus" T-shirts to be 3,000. Give a logistic model for your sales and use it to predict, to the nearest day, when you will have sold 700 T-shirts.

30. ***Sales*** In Russia the average consumer drank two servings of Coca-Cola® in 1993. This amount appeared to be increasing exponentially with a doubling time of 2 years.[49] Given a long-range market saturation estimate of 100 servings per year, find a logistic model for the consumption of Coca-Cola in Russia and use your model to predict when, to the nearest year, the average consumption reached 50 servings per year.

31. ***Scientific Research*** The following chart shows some the data shown in the graph in Exercise 23 ($t = 0$ represents 1983).[50]

Year t	0	5	10	15	20
Research Articles A (1,000)	1.2	2.1	3.8	5.1	5.7

a. What is the logistic regression model for the data? (Round all coefficients to 2 significant digits.) At what value does the model predict that the number of research articles will level off? HINT [See Example 2.]

b. According to the model, how many *Physical Review* articles were published by U.S. researchers in 2000 ($t = 17$)? (The actual number was about 5,500 articles.)

32. ***Scientific Research*** The following chart shows some the data shown in the graph in Exercise 24 ($t = 0$ represents 1983).[51]

Year t	0	5	10	15	20
Percentage P (over 25)	36	28	16	7	3

a. What is the logistic regression model for the data? (Round all coefficients to 2 significant digits.) HINT [See Example 2.]

b. According to the model, what percentage of *Physical Review* articles were published by researchers in the United States in 2000 ($t = 17$)? (The actual figure was about 30.1%.)

33. ***College Basketball: Men*** The following table shows the number of NCAA men's college basketball teams in the U.S. for various years since 1990.[52]

t (Year since 1990)	0	5	10	11	12	13	14
Teams	767	868	932	937	936	967	981
t (Year since 1990)	15	16	17	18	19	20	
Teams	983	984	982	1,017	1,017	1,011	

a. What is the logistic regression model for the data? (Round all coefficients to 3 significant digits.) At what value does the model predict that the number of basketball teams will level off?

b. According to the model, for what value of t is the regression curve steepest? Interpret the answer.

c. Interpret the coefficient b in the context of the number of men's basketball teams.

34. ***College Basketball: Women*** The following table shows the number of NCAA women's college basketball teams in the U.S. for various years since 1990.[53]

t (Year since 1990)	0	5	10	11	12	13	14
Teams	782	864	956	958	975	1,009	1,008
t (Year since 1990)	15	16	17	18	19	20	
Teams	1,036	1,018	1,003	1,013	1,032	1,036	

a. What is the logistic regression model for the data? (Round all coefficients to 3 significant digits.) At what value does the model predict that the number of basketball teams will level off?

[49] The doubling time is based on retail sales of Coca-Cola products in Russia. Sales in 1993 were double those in 1991, and were expected to double again by 1995. Source: *New York Times*, September 26, 1994, p. D2.

[50] Source: The American Physical Society/*New York Times* May 3, 2003, p. A1.

[51] *Ibid.*

[52] 2010 figure is an estimate. Source: www.census.gov.

[53] *Ibid.*

b. According to the model, for what value of t is the regression curve steepest? Interpret the answer.

c. Interpret the coefficient b in the context of the number of women's basketball teams.

Exercises 35 and 36 are based on the discussion following Example 2. If the limiting value N is known, then

$$\frac{N}{y} - 1 = A(b^{-1})^x$$

and so $N/y - 1$ is an exponential function of x. In Exercises 35 and 36, use the given value of N and the data points $(x, N/y - 1)$ to obtain A and b, and hence a logistic model.

35. ◆ ***Population: Puerto Rico*** The following table and graph show the population of Puerto Rico in thousands from 1950 to 2025.[54]

t (year since 1950)	0	10	20	30	40	50
Population (thousands)	2,220	2,360	2,720	3,210	3,540	3,820
t (year since 1950)	55	60	65	70	75	
Population (thousands)	3,910	3,990	4,050	4,080	4,100	

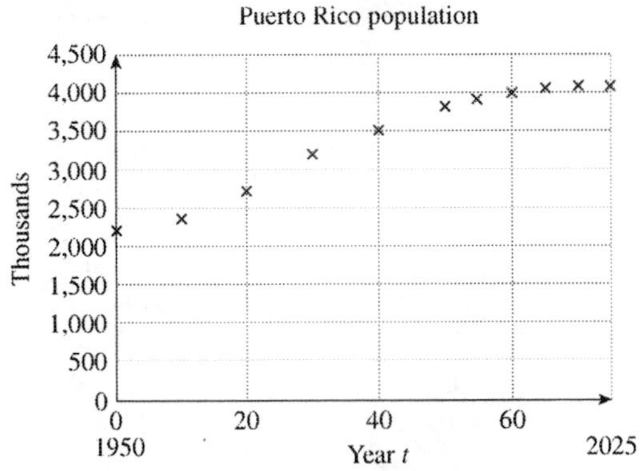

Take t to be the number of years since 1950, and find a logistic model based on the assumption that, eventually, the population of Puerto Rico will grow to 4.5 million. (Round coefficients to 4 decimal places.) In what year does your model predict the population of Puerto Rico will first reach 4.0 million?

36. ◆ ***Population: Virgin Islands*** The following table and graph show the population of the Virgin Islands in thousands from 1950 to 2025.[55]

t (year since 1950)	0	10	20	30	40	50
Population (thousands)	27	33	63	98	104	106
t (year since 1950)	55	60	65	70	75	
Population (thousands)	108	108	107	107	108	

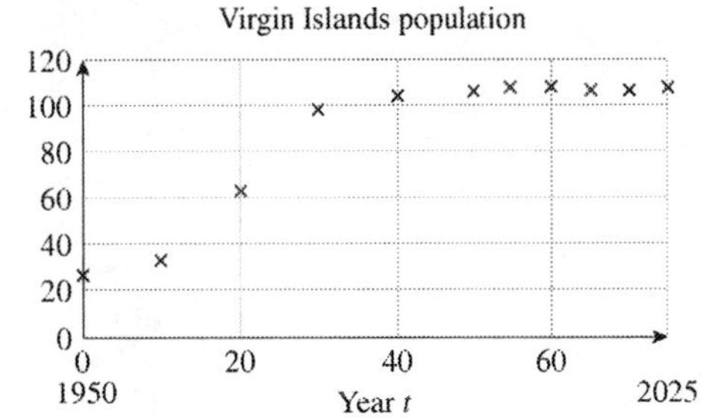

Take t to be the number of years since 1950, and find a logistic model based on the assumption that, eventually, the population of the Virgin Islands will grow to 110,000. (Round coefficients to 4 decimal places.) In what year does your model predict the population of the Virgin Islands first reached 80,000?

COMMUNICATION AND REASONING EXERCISES

37. Logistic functions are commonly used to model the spread of epidemics. Given this fact, explain why a logistic function is also useful to model the spread of a new technology.

38. Why is a logistic function more appropriate than an exponential function for modeling the spread of an epidemic?

39. Give one practical use for logistic regression.

40. Refer to an exercise or example in this section to find a scenario in which a logistic model may not be a good predictor of long-term behavior.

41. What happens to the function $P(t) = \dfrac{N}{1 + Ab^{-t}}$ if we replace b^{-t} by b^t when $b > 1$? When $b < 1$?

42. ▼ What happens to the function $P(t) = \dfrac{N}{1 + Ab^{-t}}$ if $A = 0$? If $A < 0$?

43. ▼ We said that the logistic curve $y = \dfrac{N}{1 + Ab^{-t}}$ is steepest when $t = \dfrac{\ln A}{\ln b}$. Show that the corresponding value of y is $N/2$. HINT [Use the fact that $\dfrac{\ln A}{\ln b} = \log_b A$.]

44. ▼ We said that the logistic curve $y = \dfrac{N}{1 + Ab^{-t}}$ is steepest when $t = \dfrac{\ln A}{\ln b}$. For which values of A and b is this value of t positive, zero, and negative?

[54]Figures from 2010 on are U.S. census projections. Source: The 2008 Statistical Abstract, www.census.gov.

[55]*Ibid.*

CHAPTER 9 REVIEW

KEY CONCEPTS

WW Website www.WanerMath.com

Go to the Website at www.WanerMath.com to find a comprehensive and interactive Web-based summary of Chapter 9.

9.1 Quadratic Functions and Models

A **quadratic function** has the form $f(x) = ax^2 + bx + c$. *p. 620*

The graph of $f(x) = ax^2 + bx + c$ $(a \neq 0)$ is a **parabola.** *p. 621*

The x-coordinate of the **vertex** is $-\frac{b}{2a}$. The y-coordinate is $f\left(-\frac{b}{2a}\right)$. *p. 621*

x-intercepts (if any) occur at $x = \frac{-b \pm \sqrt{b^2 - 4ac}}{2a}$. *p. 621*

The **y-intercept** occurs at $y = c$. *p. 621*

The parabola is **symmetric** with respect to the vertical line through the vertex. *p. 621*

Sketching the graph of a quadratic function *p. 622*

Application to maximizing revenue *p. 624*

Application to maximizing profit *p. 624*

Finding the quadratic regression curve *p. 626*

9.2 Exponential Functions and Models

An **exponential function** has the form $f(x) = Ab^x$. *p. 632*

Roles of the constants A and b in an exponential function $f(x) = Ab^x$ *p. 633*

Recognizing exponential data *p. 634*

Finding the exponential curve through two points *p. 635*

Application to compound interest *p. 636*

Application to exponential decay (carbon dating) *p. 636*

Application to exponential growth (epidemics) *p. 636*

The number e and continuous compounding *p. 638*

Alternative form of an exponential function: $f(x) = Ae^{rx}$ *p. 640*

Finding the exponential regression curve *p. 640*

9.3 Logarithmic Functions and Models

The **base b logarithm of x**: $y = \log_b x$ means $b^y = x$ *p. 647*

Common logarithm, $\log x = \log_{10} x$, and **natural logarithm**, $\ln x = \log_e x$ *p. 648*

Change-of-base formula *p. 648*

Solving equations with unknowns in the exponent *p. 649*

A **logarithmic function** has the form $f(x) = \log_b x + C$ or $f(x) = A \ln x + C$. *p. 649*

Graphs of logarithmic functions *p. 650*

Logarithm identities *p. 651*

Application to investments (How long?) *p. 651*

Application to half-life *p. 652*

Exponential decay models and half-life *p. 654*

Exponential growth models and doubling time *p. 655*

Finding the logarithmic regression curve *p. 655*

9.4 Logistic Functions and Models

A **logistic function** has the form $f(x) = \frac{N}{1 + Ab^{-x}}$. *p. 661*

Properties of the logistic curve, point where curve is steepest *p. 662*

Logistic function for small x, the role of b *p. 662*

Application to epidemics *p. 663*

Finding the logistic regression curve *p. 664*

REVIEW EXERCISES

Sketch the graph of the quadratic functions in Exercises 1 and 2, indicating the coordinates of the vertex, the y-intercept, and the x-intercepts (if any).

1. $f(x) = x^2 + 2x - 3$

2. $f(x) = -x^2 - x - 1$

In Exercises 3 and 4, the values of two functions, f and g, are given in a table. One, both, or neither of them may be exponential. Decide which, if any, are exponential, and give the exponential models for those that are.

3.

x	−2	−1	0	1	2
$f(x)$	20	10	5	2.5	1.25
$g(x)$	8	4	2	1	0

4.

x	−2	−1	0	1	2
$f(x)$	8	6	4	2	1
$g(x)$	$\frac{3}{4}$	$\frac{3}{2}$	3	6	12

In Exercises 5 and 6, graph the given pairs of functions on the same set of axes with $-3 \le x \le 3$.

5. $f(x) = \frac{1}{2}(3^x)$; $g(x) = \frac{1}{2}(3^{-x})$

6. $f(x) = 2(4^x)$; $g(x) = 2(4^{-x})$

T *On the same set of axes, use technology to graph the pairs of functions in Exercises 7 and 8 for the given range of x. Identify which graph corresponds to which function.*

7. $f(x) = e^x$; $g(x) = e^{0.8x}$; $-3 \le x \le 3$

8. $f(x) = 2(1.01)^x$; $g(x) = 2(0.99)^x$; $-100 \le x \le 100$

In Exercises 9–14, compute the indicated quantity.

9. A \$3,000 investment earns 3% interest, compounded monthly. Find its value after 5 years.

10. A \$10,000 investment earns 2.5% interest, compounded quarterly. Find its value after 10 years.

11. An investment earns 3% interest, compounded monthly, and is worth \$5,000 after 10 years. Find its initial value.

12. An investment earns 2.5% interest, compounded quarterly, and is worth \$10,000 after 10 years. Find its initial value.

13. A \$3,000 investment earns 3% interest, compounded continuously. Find its value after 5 years.

14. A \$10,000 investment earns 2.5% interest, compounded continuously. Find its value after 10 years.

In Exercises 15–18, find a formula of the form $f(x) = Ab^x$ using the given information.

15. $f(0) = 4.5$; the value of f triples for every half-unit increase in x.

16. $f(0) = 5$; the value of f decreases by 75% for every 1-unit increase in x.

17. $f(1) = 2$, $f(3) = 18$.

18. $f(1) = 10$, $f(3) = 5$.

In Exercises 19–22, use logarithms to solve the given equation for x.

19. $3^{-2x} = 4$

20. $2^{2x^2-1} = 2$

21. $300(10^{3x}) = 315$

22. $P(1+i)^{mx} = A$

On the same set of axes, graph the pairs of functions in Exercises 23 and 24.

23. $f(x) = \log_3 x$; $g(x) = \log_{(1/3)} x$

24. $f(x) = \log x$; $g(x) = \log_{(1/10)} x$

In Exercises 25–28, use the given information to find an exponential model of the form $Q = Q_0e^{-kt}$ or $Q = Q_0e^{kt}$, as appropriate. Round all coefficients to 3 significant digits when rounding is necessary.

25. Q is the amount of radioactive substance with a half-life of 100 years in a sample originally containing 5 g (t is time in years).

26. Q is the number of cats on an island whose cat population was originally 10,000 but is being cut in half every 5 years (t is time in years).

27. Q is the diameter (in cm) of a circular patch of mold on your roommate's damp towel you have been monitoring with morbid fascination. You measured the patch at 2.5 cm across 4 days ago, and have observed that it is doubling in diameter every 2 days (t is time in days).

28. Q is the population of cats on another island whose cat population was originally 10,000 but is doubling every 15 months (t is time in months).

In Exercises 29–32, find the time required, to the nearest 0.1 year, for the investment to reach the desired goal.

29. \$2,000 invested at 4%, compounded monthly; goal: \$3,000

30. \$2,000 invested at 6.75%, compounded daily; goal: \$3,000

31. \$2,000 invested at 3.75%, compounded continuously; goal: \$3,000

32. \$1,000 invested at 100%, compounded quarterly; goal: \$1,200

In Exercises 33–36, find equations for the logistic functions of x with the stated properties.

33. Through (0, 100), initially increasing by 50% per unit of x, and limiting value 900.

34. Initially exponential of the form $y = 5(1.1)^x$ with limiting value 25.

35. Passing through (0, 5) and decreasing from a limiting value of 20 to 0 at a rate of 20% per unit of x when x is near 0.

36. Initially exponential of the form $y = 2(0.8)^x$ with a value close to 10 when $x = -60$.

APPLICATIONS: OHaganBooks.com

37. ***Web Site Traffic*** The daily traffic ("hits per day") at OHaganBooks.com apparently depends on the monthly expenditure on Internet advertising. The following model is based on information collected over the past few months:

$$h = -0.000005c^2 + 0.085c + 1{,}750.$$

Here, h is the average number of hits per day at OHaganBooks.com, and c is the monthly advertising expenditure.

a. According to the model, what monthly advertising expenditure will result in the largest volume of traffic at OHaganBooks.com? What is that volume?

b. In addition to predicting a maximum volume of traffic, the model predicts that the traffic will eventually drop to zero if the advertising expenditure is increased too far. What expenditure (to the nearest dollar) results in no Web site traffic?

c. What feature of the formula for this quadratic model indicates that it will predict an eventual decline in traffic as advertising expenditure increases?

38. ***Broadband Access*** Pablo Pelogrande, a new summer intern at OHaganBooks.com in 2013, was asked by John O'Hagan to research the extent of broadband access in the United States. Pelogrande found some very old data online on broadband access from the start of 2001 to the end of 2003 and used it to construct the following quadratic model of the growth rate of broadband access:

$n(t) = 2t^2 - 6t + 12$ million new American adults with broadband per year

(t is time in years; $t = 0$ represents the start 2000).[56]

a. What is the appropriate domain of n?

b. According to the model, when was the growth rate at a minimum?

c. Does the model predict a zero growth rate at any particular time? If so, when?

d. What feature of the formula for this quadratic model indicates that the growth rate eventually increases?

e. Does the fact that $n(t)$ decreases for $t \le 1.5$ suggest that the number of broadband users actually declined before June 2001? Explain.

[56]Based on data for 2001–2003. Source for data: Pew Internet and American Life Project data memos dated May 18, 2003 and April 19, 2004, downloaded from www.pewinternet.org.

f. Pelogande extrapolated the model in order to estimate the growth rate at the beginning of 2013 and 2014. What did he find? Comment on the answer.

39. ***Revenue and Profit*** Some time ago, a consultant formulated the following linear model of demand for online novels:

$$q = -60p + 950$$

where q is the monthly demand for OHaganBooks.com's online novels at a price of p dollars per novel.

a. Use this model to express the monthly revenue as a function of the unit price p, and hence determine the price you should charge for a maximum monthly revenue.

b. Author royalties and copyright fees cost the company an average of \$4 per novel, and the monthly cost of operating and maintaining the online publishing service amounts to \$900 per month. Express the monthly profit P as a function of the unit price p, and hence determine the unit price you should charge for a maximum monthly profit. What is the resulting profit (or loss)?

40. ***Revenue and Profit*** Billy-Sean O'Hagan is John O'Hagan's son and a freshman in college. He notices that the demand for the college newspaper was 2,000 copies each week when the paper was given away free of charge, but dropped to 1,000 each week when the college started charging 10¢/copy.

a. Write down the associated linear demand function.

b. Use your demand function to express the revenue as a function of the unit price p, and hence determine the price the college should charge for a maximum revenue. At that price, what is the revenue from sales of one edition of the newspaper?

c. It costs the college 4¢ to produce each copy of the paper, plus an additional fixed cost of \$200. Express the profit P as a function of the unit price p, and hence determine the unit price the college should charge for a maximum monthly profit (or minimum loss). What is the resulting profit (or loss)?

41. ***Lobsters*** Marjory Duffin, CEO of Duffin House, is particularly fond of having steamed lobster at working lunches with executives from OHaganBooks.com and is therefore alarmed by the fact that the yearly lobster harvest from New York's Long Island Sound has been decreasing dramatically since 1997. Indeed, the size of the annual harvest can be approximated by

$$n(t) = 9.1(0.81^t) \text{ million pounds}$$

where t is time in years since 1997.[57]

a. The model tells us that the harvest was ____ million pounds in 1997 and decreasing by ___% each year.

b. What does the model predict for the 2013 harvest?

42. ***Stock Prices*** In the period immediately following its initial public offering (IPO), OHaganBooks.com's stock was doubling in value every 3 hours. If you bought \$10,000 worth of the stock when it was first offered, how much was your stock worth after 8 hours?

[57]Authors' regression model. Source for data: Long Island Sound Study, data downloaded May 2011 from longislandsoundstudy.net/2010/07/lobster-landings/.

43. ***Lobsters*** (See Exercise 41.) Marjory Duffin has just left John O'Hagan, CEO of OHaganBooks.com, a frantic phone message to the effect that this year's lobster harvest from New York's Long Island Sound is predicted to dip below 200,000 pounds, making that planned lobster working lunch more urgent than ever. What year is it?

44. ***Stock Prices*** We saw in Exercise 42 that OHaganBooks.com's stock was doubling in value every 3 hours, following its IPO. If you bought \$10,000 worth of the stock when it was first offered, how long from the initial offering did it take your investment to reach \$50,000?

45. ***Lobsters*** We saw in Exercise 41 that the Long Island Sound lobster harvest was given by $n(t) = 9.1(0.81^t)$ million pounds t years after 1997. However, in 2010, thanks to the efforts of Duffin House, Inc. it turned around and started increasing by 24% each year.[58] What, to the nearest 10,000 pounds, was the actual size of the harvest in 2013?

46. ***Stock Prices*** We saw in Exercise 42 that OHaganBooks.com's stock was doubling in value every 3 hours, following its IPO. After 10 hours of trading, the stock turns around and starts losing one third of its value every 4 hours. How long (from the initial offering) will it be before your stock is once again worth \$10,000?

47. ***Lobsters*** The following chart shows some of the data that went into the model in Exercise 41:

Annual Lobster Harvest from Long Island Sound

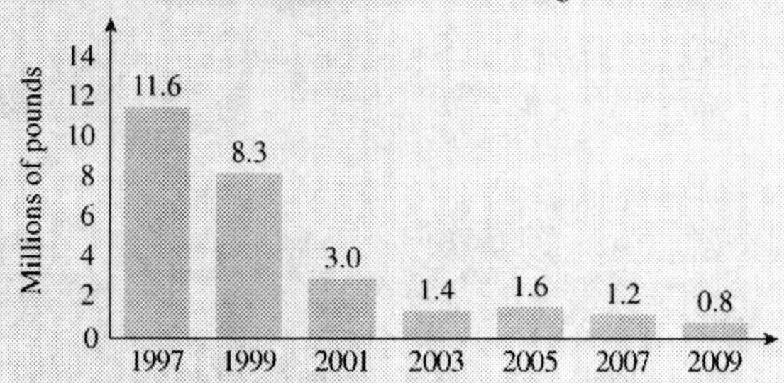

Use these data to obtain an exponential regression curve of the form $n(t) = Ab^t$, with $t = 0$ corresponding to 1997 and coefficients rounded to 2 significant digits.

48. ***Stock Prices*** The actual stock price of OHaganBooks.com in the hours following its IPO is shown in the following chart:

OHaganBooks.com stock price

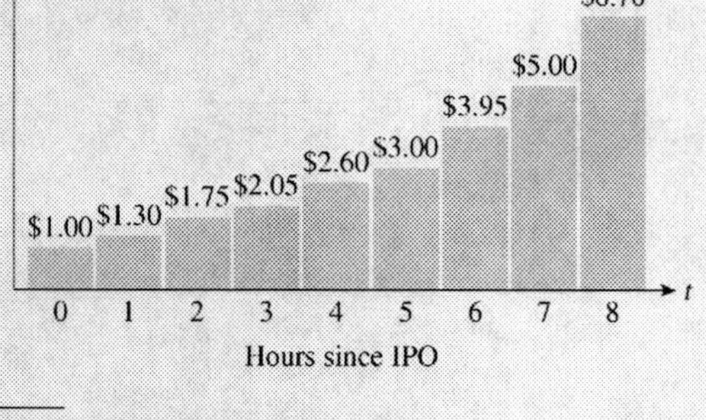

Hours since IPO

[58]This claim, like Duffin House, is fiction.

Use the data to obtain an exponential regression curve of the form $P(t) = Ab^t$, with $t = 0$ the time in hours since the IPO and coefficients rounded to 3 significant digits. At the end of which hour will the stock price first be above \$10?

49. ***Hardware Life*** *(Based on a question from the GRE economics exam)* To estimate the rate at which new computer hard drives will have to be retired, OHaganBooks.com uses the "survivor curve":

$$L_x = L_0 e^{-x/t}$$

where

L_x = number of surviving hard drives at age x
L_0 = number of hard drives initially
t = average life in years.

All of the following are implied by the curve *except:*

(A) Some of the equipment is retired during the first year of service.
(B) Some equipment survives three average lives.
(C) More than half the equipment survives the average life.
(D) Increasing the average life of equipment by using more durable materials would increase the number surviving at every age.
(E) The number of survivors never reaches zero.

50. ***Sales*** OHaganBooks.com modeled its weekly sales over a period of time with the function

$$s(t) = 6{,}050 + \frac{4{,}470}{1 + 14(1.73^{-t})}$$

as shown in the following graph (t is measured in weeks):

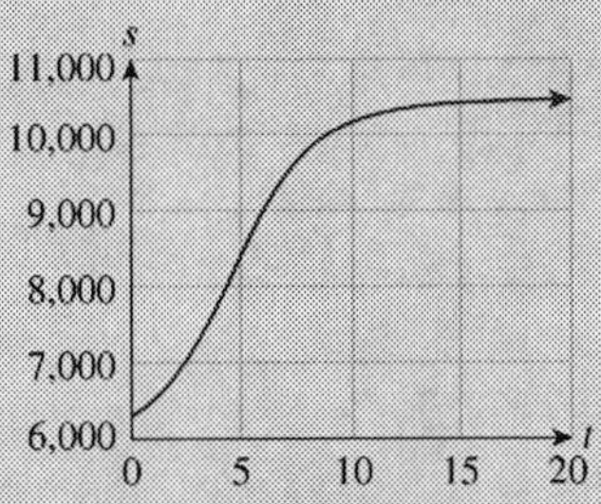

a. As time goes on, it appears that weekly sales are leveling off. At what value are they leveling off?
b. When did weekly sales rise above 10,000?
c. When, to the nearest week, were sales rising most rapidly?

Robert Nickelsberg/Getty Images

Checking up on Malthus

In 1798 Thomas R. Malthus (1766–1834) published an influential pamphlet, later expanded into a book, titled *An Essay on the Principle of Population As It Affects the Future Improvement of Society.* One of his main contentions was that population grows geometrically (exponentially) while the supply of resources such as food grows only arithmetically (linearly). This led him to the pessimistic conclusion that population would always reach the limits of subsistence and precipitate famine, war, and ill health, unless population could be checked by other means. He advocated "moral restraint," which includes the pattern of late marriage common in Western Europe at the time and now common in most developed countries and which leads to a lower reproduction rate.

Two hundred years later, you have been asked to check the validity of Malthus's contention. That population grows geometrically, at least over short periods of time, is commonly assumed. That resources grow linearly is more questionable. You decide to check the actual production of a common crop, wheat, in the United States. Agricultural statistics like these are available from the U.S. government on the Internet, through the U.S. Department of Agriculture's National Agricultural Statistics Service (NASS). As of 2011, this service was available at www.nass.usda.gov. Looking through this site, you locate data on the annual production of all wheat in the United States from 1900 through 2010.

Website
www.WanerMath.com
To download an Excel sheet with the data used in the case study, go to Everything, scroll down to the case study for Chapter 9, and click on "Wheat Production Data (Excel)".

Year	1900	1901	...	2009	2010
Thousands of Bushels	599,315	762,546	...	2,218,061	2,208,391

Graphing these data (using Excel, for example), you obtain the graph in Figure 20.

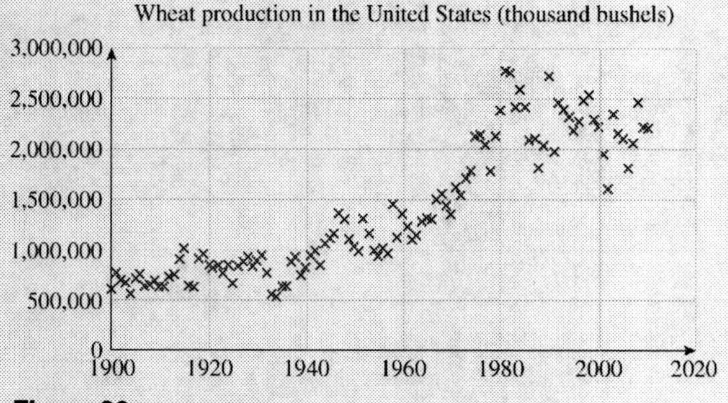

Figure 20

This does not look very linear, particularly in the last half of the twentieth century, but you continue checking the mathematics. Using Excel's built-in linear regression capabilities, you find that the line that best fits these data, shown in Figure 21, has $r^2 = 0.8039$. (Recall the discussion of the correlation coefficient r in Section 1.4. A similar statistic is available for other types of regression as well.)

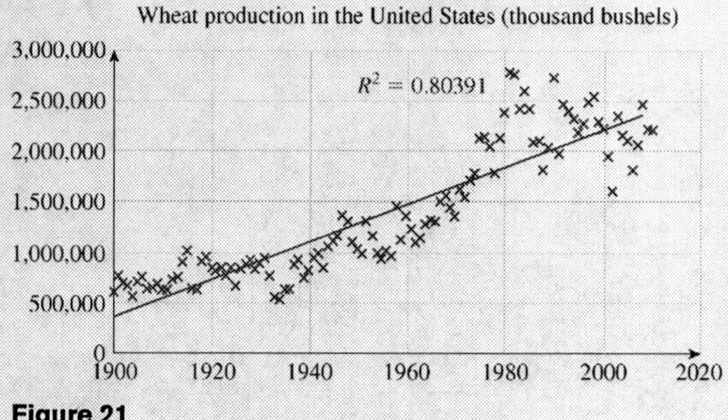

Figure 21

* Recall that the residuals are defined as $y_{\text{Observed}} - y_{\text{Predicted}}$ (see Section 1.4) and are the vertical distances between the observed data points and the regression line.

Although that is a fairly high correlation, you notice that the residuals* are not distributed randomly: The actual wheat production starts out higher than the line, dips below the line from about 1920 to about 1970, then rises above the line, and finally appears to dip below the line around 2002. This behavior seems to suggest a logistic curve or perhaps a cubic curve. On the other hand, it is also possible that the apparent dip at the end of the data is not statistically significant—it could be nothing more than a transitory fluctuation in the wheat production industry—so perhaps we should also consider models that do not bend downward, like exponential and quadratic models.

Following is a comparison of the four proposed models (with coefficients rounded to 3 significant digits). For the independent variable, we used t = time in years since 1900. SSE is the sum-of-squares error.

Quadratic

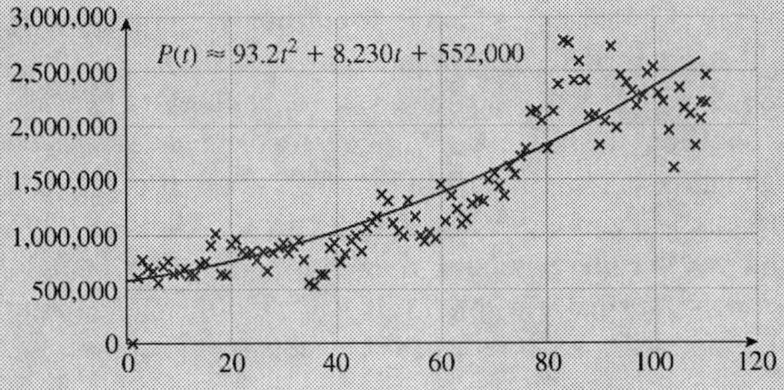

SSE $\approx 8.68 \times 10^{12}$

Cubic

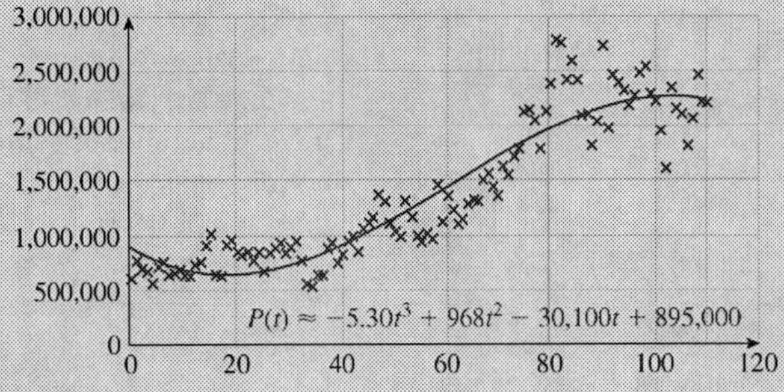

SSE $\approx 6.60 \times 10^{12}$

Exponential

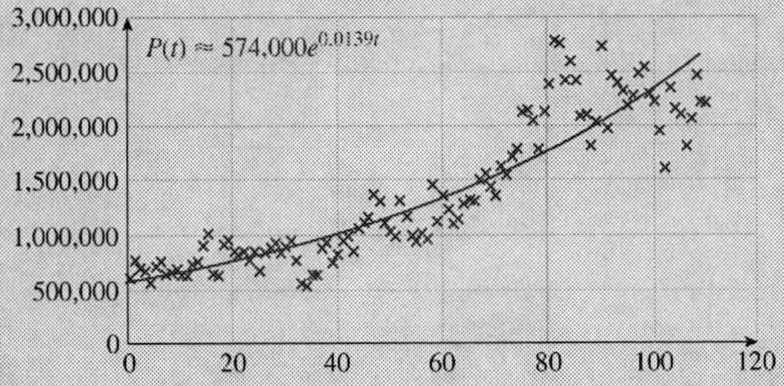

SSE $\approx 9.34 \times 10^{12}$

Logistic

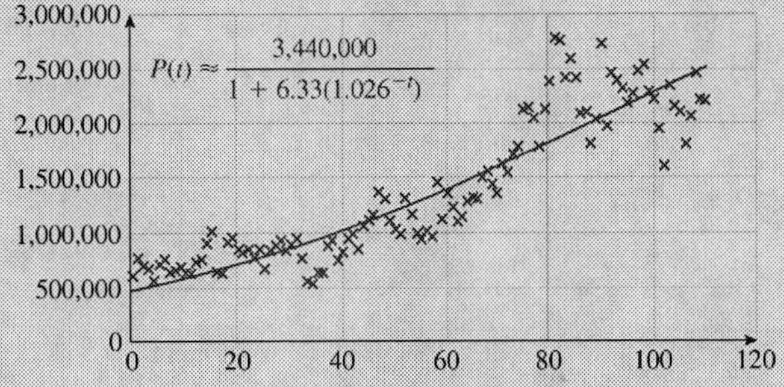

SSE $\approx 8.26 \times 10^{12}$

The model that appears to best fit the data seems to be the cubic model; both visually and by virtue of SSE. Notice also that the cubic model predicts a *decrease* in the production of wheat in the near term (see Figure 22).

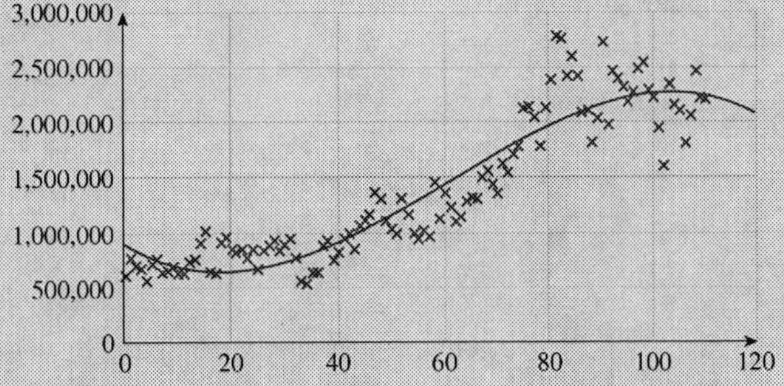

Figure 22

So you prepare a report that documents your findings and concludes that things are even worse than Malthus predicted, at least as far as wheat production in the United States is concerned: The supply is deceasing while the population is still increasing more-or-less exponentially. (See Exercise 75 in Section 9.2.)

You are about to hit "Send," which will dispatch copies of your report to a significant number of people on whom the success of your career depends, when you notice something strange about the pattern of data in Figure 22: The observed data points appear to hug the regression curve quite closely for small values of t, but appear to become more and more scattered as the value of t increases. In the language of residuals, the residuals are small for small values of t but then tend to get larger with increasing t. Figure 23 shows a plot of the residuals that shows this trend even more clearly.

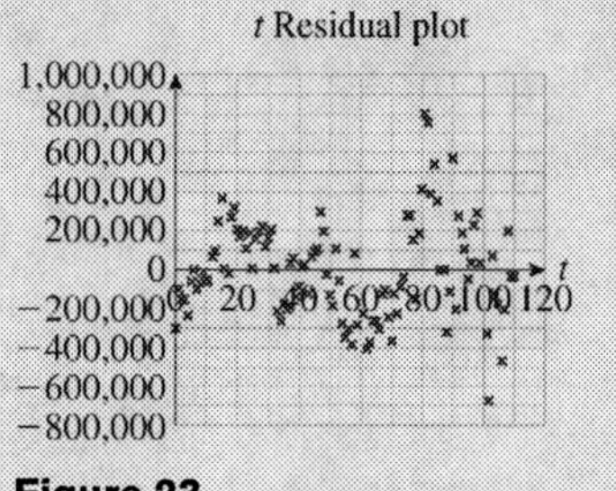

Figure 23

This reminds you vaguely of something that came up in your college business statistics course, so you consult the textbook from that class that (fortunately) you still own and discover that a pattern of residuals with increasing magnitude suggests that, instead of modeling y versus t directly, you instead model ln y versus t. (The residuals for large values of t will then be scaled down by the logarithm.)

Figure 24 shows the resulting plot together with the regression line (what we call the "linear transformed model").

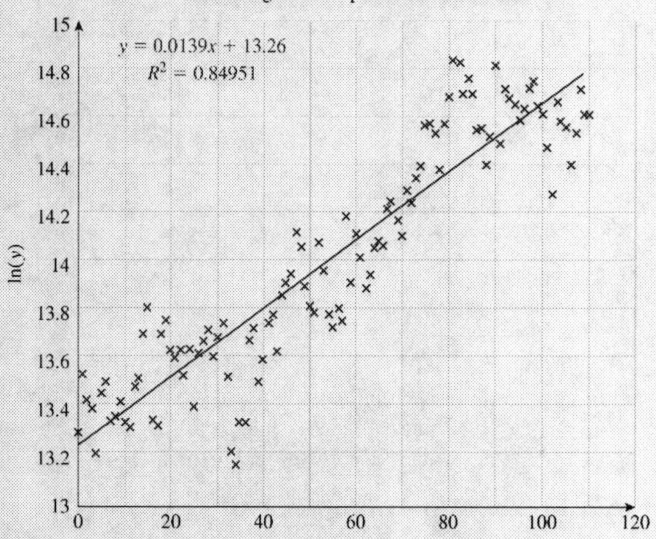

SSE $\approx$ 3.89

Linear Transformed Model

Figure 24

Notice that this time, the regression patterns no longer suggest an obvious curve. Further, they no longer appear to grow with increasing t. Although SSE is dramatically lower than the values for the earlier models, the contrast is a false one; the units of y are now different, and comparing SSE with that of the earlier models is like comparing apples and oranges. While SSE depends on the units of measurement used, the coefficient of determination r^2 discussed in Section 1.4 is independent of the units used. A similar statistic is available for other types of regression as well, as well as something called "adjusted r^2."

The value of r^2 for the transformed model is approximately 0.850, while r^2 for the cubic model* is about 0.861, which is fairly close.

* The "adjusted r^2" from statistics that corrects for model size.

Q: *If the cubic model and the linear transformed model have similar values of r^2, how do I decide which is more appropriate?*

A: The cubic model, if extrapolated, predicts unrealistically that the production of wheat will plunge in the near future, but the linear transformed model sees the recent drop-off as just one of several market fluctuations that show up in the residuals. You should therefore favor the more reasonable linear transformed model.

Q: *The linear transformed model gives us ln y versus t. What does it say about y versus t?*

A: Accurately write down the equation of the transformed linear model, being careful to replace y by $\ln y$:

$$\ln y = 0.0139t + 13.26.$$

Rewriting this in exponential form gives

$$\begin{aligned} y &= e^{0.0139t+13.26} \\ &= e^{13.26}e^{0.0139t} \\ &\approx 574{,}000e^{0.0139t}, \quad \text{Coefficients rounded to 3 digits} \end{aligned}$$

which is exactly the exponential model we found earlier! (In fact, using the natural logarithm transformation is the standard method of computing the regression exponential curve.)

Q: *What of the logistic model; should that not be the most realistic?*

A: The logistic model seems as though it *ought* to be the most appropriate, because wheat production cannot reasonably be expected to continue increasing exponentially forever; eventually resource limitations must lead to a leveling off of wheat production. Such a leveling off, if it occurred before the population started to level off, would seem to vindicate Malthus's pessimistic predictions. However, the logistic regression model has the same problem as the cubic model: It is trying to interpret the recent large fluctuations in the data as evidence of leveling off, but we really do not yet have significant evidence that that is occurring. Wheat production—even if it is logistic—appears still in the early (exponential) stage of growth. In general, for a logistic model to be reliable in its prediction of the leveling-off value N, we would need to see significant evidence of leveling off in the data. (See, however, Exercise 2 following.)

You now conclude that wheat production for the past 100 years is better described as increasing exponentially than linearly, contradicting Malthus, and moreover that it shows no sign of leveling off as yet.

EXERCISES

1. Use the wheat production data starting at 1950 to construct the exponential regression model in two ways: directly, and using a linear transformed model as above. (Round coefficients to 3 digits.) Compare the growth constant k of your model with that of the exponential model based on the data from 1900 on. How would you interpret the difference?
2. Compute the least-squares logistic model for the data in the preceding exercise. (Round coefficients to 3 significant digits.) At what level does it predict that wheat production will level off? (Note on using Excel Solver for logistic regression: Before running Solver, press Options in the Solver window and turn "Automatic Scaling" on. This adjusts the algorithm for the fact that the constants A, N, and b have vastly different orders of magnitude.) Give

two graphs: one showing the data with the exponential regression model, and the other showing the data with the logistic regression model. Which model gives a better fit visually? Justify your observation by computing SSE directly for both models. Comment on your answer in terms of Malthus's assertions.

3. Find the production figures for another common crop grown in the United States. Compare the linear, quadratic, cubic, exponential, and logistic models. What can you conclude?

4. Below are the census figures for the population of the U.S. (in thousands) from 1820 to 2010.[59] Compare the linear, quadratic, and exponential models. What can you conclude?

Year	1820	1830	1840	1850	1860	1870	1880	1890	1900	1910
Population (1000s)	9,638	12,861	17,063	23,192	31,443	38,558	50,189	62,980	76,212	92,228
Year	1920	1930	1940	1950	1960	1970	1980	1990	2000	2010
Population (1000s)	106,022	123,203	132,165	151,326	179,323	203,302	226,542	248,710	281,422	308,746

[59]Source: Bureau of the Census, U.S. Department of Commerce.

TI-83/84 Plus Technology Guide

Section 9.1

Example 2 (page 622) Sketch the graph of each quadratic function, showing the location of the vertex and intercepts.

a. $f(x) = 4x^2 - 12x + 9$ **b.** $g(x) = -\frac{1}{2}x^2 + 4x - 12$

Solution with Technology

We will do part (a).

1. Start by storing the coefficients a, b, c using

   `4→A:-12→B:9→C`

   [STO>] gives the arrow [ALPHA] [.] gives the colon

2. Save your quadratic as Y_1 using the Y = screen:

   `Y1=AX^2+BX+C`

3. To obtain the x-coordinate of the vertex, enter its formula as shown below on the left.

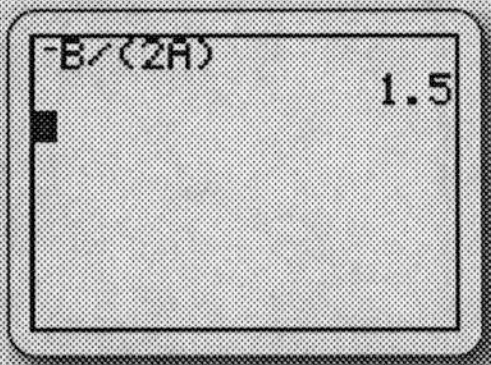

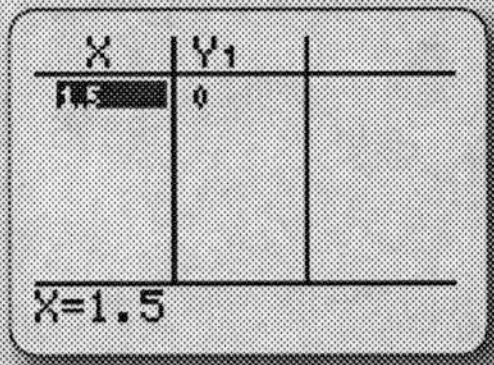

4. The y-coordinate of the vertex can be obtained from the Table screen by entering $x = 1.5$ as shown above on the right. (If you can't enter values of x, press [2ND] [TBLSET], and set `Indpnt` to Ask.) From the table, we see that the vertex is at the point (1.5, 0).

5. To obtain the x-intercepts, enter the quadratic formula on the home screen as shown:

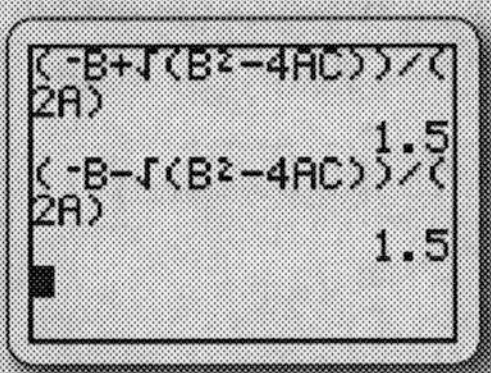

   Because both intercepts agree, we conclude that the graph intersects the x-axis on a single point (at the vertex).

6. To graph the function, we need to select good values for Xmin and Xmax. In general, we would like our graph to show the vertex as well as all the intercepts. To see the vertex, make sure that its x coordinate (1.5) is between Xmin and Xmax. To see the x-intercepts, make sure that they are also between Xmin and Xmax. To see the y-intercept, make sure that $x = 0$ is between Xmin and Xmax. Thus, to see everything, choose Xmin and Xmax so that the interval [xMin, xMax] contains the x coordinate of the vertex, the x-intercepts, and 0. For this example, we can choose an interval like $[-1, 3]$.

7. Once xMin and xMax are chosen, you can obtain convenient values of yMin and yMax by pressing [ZOOM] and selecting the option `ZoomFit`. (Make sure that your quadratic equation is entered in the `Y=` screen before doing this!)

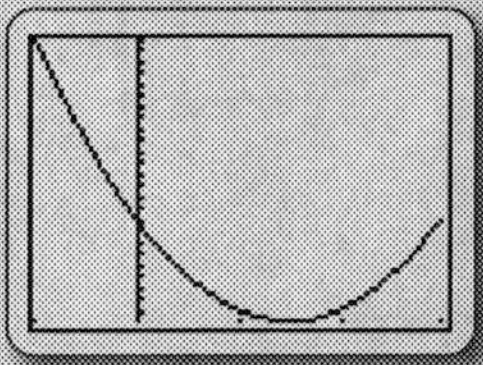

Example 5 (page 626) The following table shows the annual mean carbon dioxide concentration measured at Mauna Loa Observatory in Hawaii, in parts per million, every 10 years from 1960 through 2010 ($t = 0$ represents 1960).

Year t	0	10	20	30	40	50
PPM CO_2 C	317	326	339	354	369	390

Find the quadratic model

$$C(t) = at^2 + bt + c$$

that best fits the data.

Solution with Technology

1. Using [STAT] `EDIT` enter the data with the x-coordinates (values of t) in L_1 and the y-coordinates (values of C) in L_2, just as in Section 1.4:

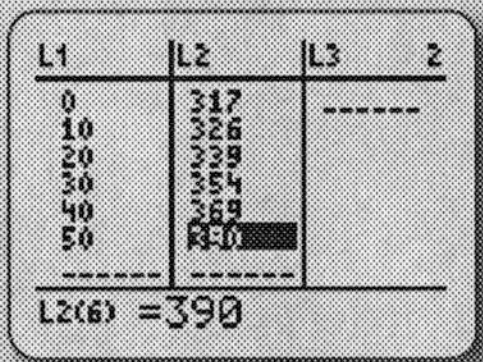

2. Press STAT, select CALC, and choose option #5 QuadReg. Pressing ENTER gives the quadratic regression curve in the home screen:

$$y \approx 0.01214x^2 + 0.8471x + 316.9.$$ Coefficients rounded to 4 decimal places

3. Now go to the Y= window and turn Plot1 on by selecting it and pressing ENTER. (You can also turn it on in the 2ND STAT PLOT screen.)
4. Next, enter the regression equation in the Y= screen by pressing Y=, clearing out whatever function is there, and pressing VARS 5 and selecting EQ option #1: RegEq as shown below left.

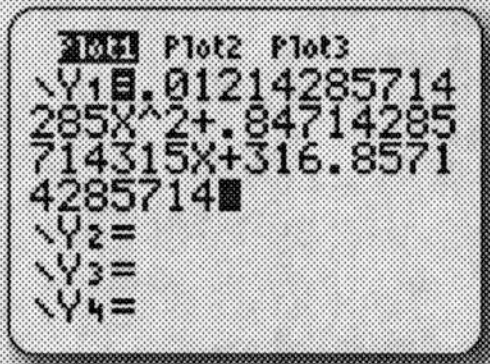

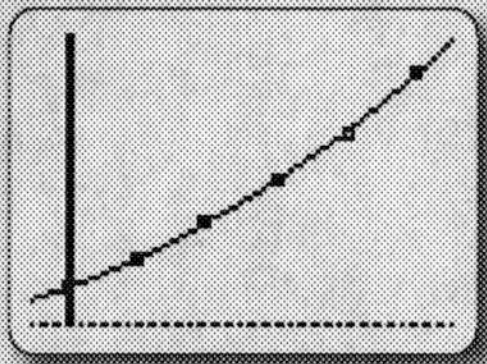

5. To obtain a convenient window showing all the points and the lines, press ZOOM and choose option #9: ZoomStat as shown above on the right.

Note When you are done viewing the graph, it is a good idea to turn Plot1 off again to avoid errors in graphing or data points showing up in your other graphs. ■

Section 9.2

Example 6(a) (page 641) The following table shows annual expenditure on health in the U.S. from 1980 through 2009 ($t = 0$ represents 1980).

Year t	0	5	10	15	20	25	29
Expenditure ($ billion)	256	444	724	1,030	1,380	2,020	2,490

Find the exponential regression model

$$C(t) = Ab^t$$

for the annual expenditure.

Solution with Technology

This is very similar to Example 5 in Section 9.1 (see the Technology Guide for Section 9.1):

1. Use STAT EDIT to enter the table of values.

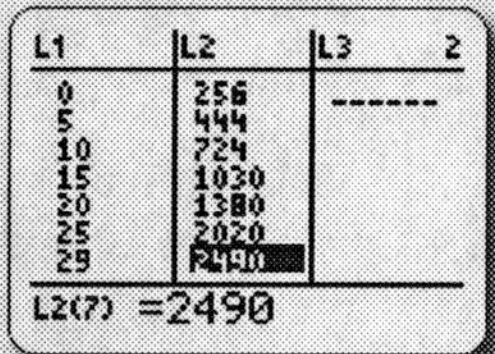

2. Press STAT, select CALC, and choose option #0 ExpReg. Pressing ENTER gives the exponential regression curve in the home screen:

$$C(t) \approx 296.25(1.0798)^t.$$ Coefficients rounded

3. To graph the points and regression line in the same window, turn Plot1 on (see the Technology Guide for Example 5 in Section 9.1) and enter the regression equation in the Y= screen by pressing Y=, clearing out whatever function is there, and pressing VARS 5 and selecting EQ option #1: RegEq. Then press ZOOM and choose option #9: ZoomStat to see the graph.

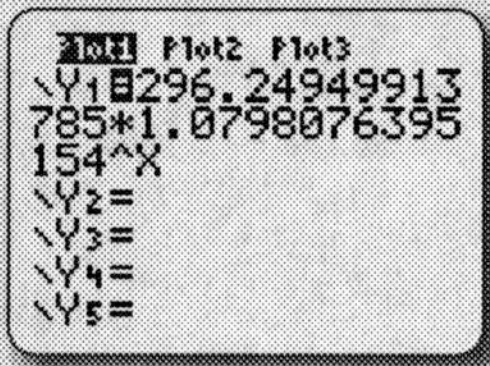

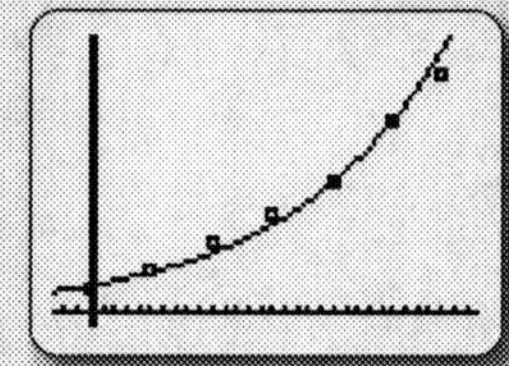

Note When you are done viewing the graph, it is a good idea to turn Plot1 off again to avoid errors in graphing or data points showing up in your other graphs. ■

Section 9.3

Example 5 (page 655) The following table shows the total spent on research and development by universities and colleges in the U.S., in billions of dollars, for the period 1998–2008 (t is the year since 1990).

Year t	8	9	10	11	12	13
Spending ($ billions)	27	29	31	33	36	38
Year t	14	15	16	17	18	
Spending ($ billions)	39	40	40	41	42	

Find the best-fit logarithmic model of the form

$$S(t) = A \ln t + C$$

and use the model to project total spending on research by universities and colleges in 2012, assuming the trend continues.

Solution with Technology

This is very similar to Example 5 in Section 9.1 (see the Technology Guide for Section 9.1):

1. Use STAT EDIT to enter the table of values.
2. Press STAT, select CALC, and choose option #9 LnReg. Pressing ENTER gives the logarithmic regression curve in the home screen:

$$S(t) \approx 19.25 \ln t - 12.78. \qquad \text{Coefficients rounded}$$

3. To graph the points and regression line in the same window, turn Plot1 on (see the Technology Guide for Example 5 in Section 9.1) and enter the regression equation in the Y= screen by pressing Y=, clearing out whatever function is there, and pressing VARS 5 and selecting EQ option #1: RegEq. Then press ZOOM and choose option #9: ZoomStat to see the graph.

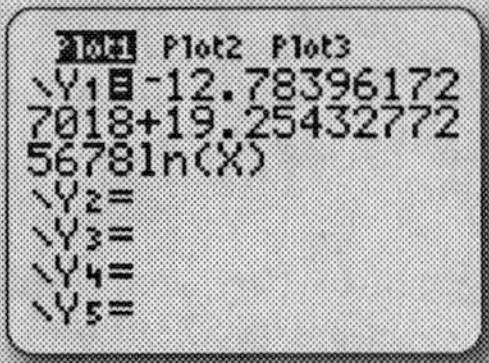

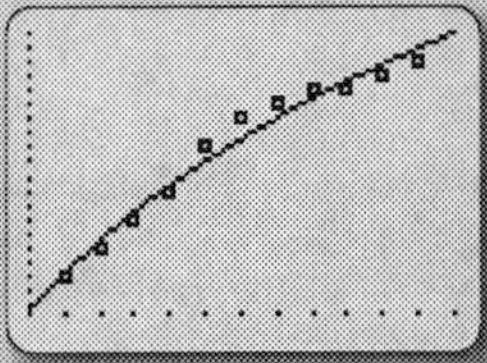

Section 9.4

Example 2 (page 664) The following table shows wired broadband penetration in the United States as a function of time t in years ($t = 0$ represents 2000).

Year (t)	2	3	4	5	6	7	8	9	10
Penetration (%) (P)	5.5	7.9	10.9	14.2	18.2	21.9	23.9	26.5	27.1

Find a logistic regression curve of the form

$$P(t) = \frac{N}{1 + Ab^{-t}}.$$

Solution with Technology

This is very similar to Example 5 in Section 9.1 (see the Technology Guide for Section 9.1):

1. Use STAT EDIT to enter the table of values.
2. Press STAT, select CALC, and choose option #B Logistic. Pressing ENTER gives the logistic regression curve in the home screen:

$$P(t) \approx \frac{29.842}{1 + 12.502e^{-0.49592t}}. \qquad \text{Coefficients rounded}$$

This is not exactly the form we are seeking, but we can convert it to that form by writing

$$e^{-0.49592t} = (e^{0.49592})^{-t} \approx 1.642^{-t}$$

so

$$P(t) \approx \frac{29.842}{1 + 12.502(1.642)^{-t}}.$$

3. To graph the points and regression line in the same window, turn Plot1 on (see the Technology Guide for Example 5 in Section 9.1) and enter the regression equation in the Y= screen by pressing Y=, clearing out whatever function is there, and pressing VARS 5 and selecting EQ option #1: RegEq. Then press ZOOM and choose option #9: ZoomStat to see the graph.

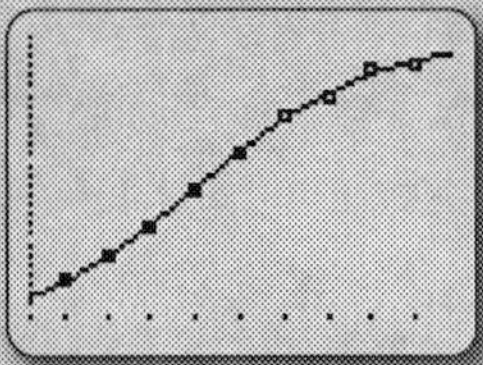

SPREADSHEET Technology Guide

Section 9.1

Example 2 (page 622) Sketch the graph of each quadratic function, showing the location of the vertex and intercepts.

a. $f(x) = 4x^2 - 12x + 9$

b. $g(x) = -\frac{1}{2}x^2 + 4x - 12$

Solution with Technology

We can set up a worksheet so that all we have to enter are the coefficients a, b, and c, and a range of x-values for the graph. Here is a possible layout that will plot 101 points using the coefficients for part (a).

1. First, we compute the x coordinates:

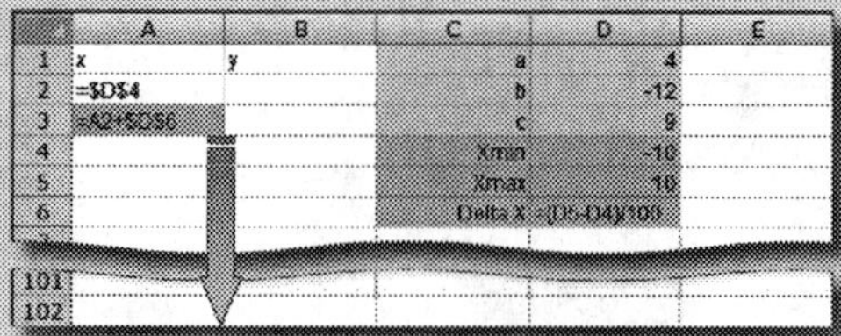

2. To add the y coordinates, we use the technology formula

```
a*x^2+b*x+c
```

replacing a, b, and c with (absolute) references to the cells containing their values.

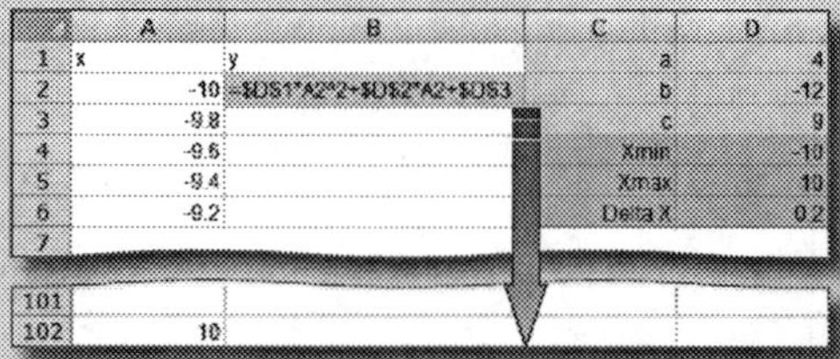

3. Graphing the data in columns A and B gives the graph shown here:

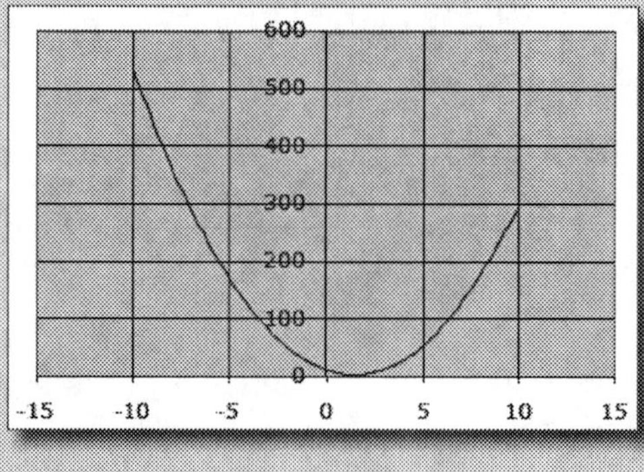

$$y = 4x^2 - 12x + 9$$

4. We can go further and compute the exact coordinates of the vertex and intercepts:

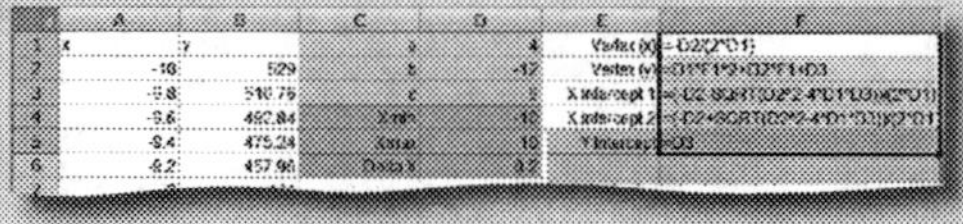

The completed sheet should look like this:

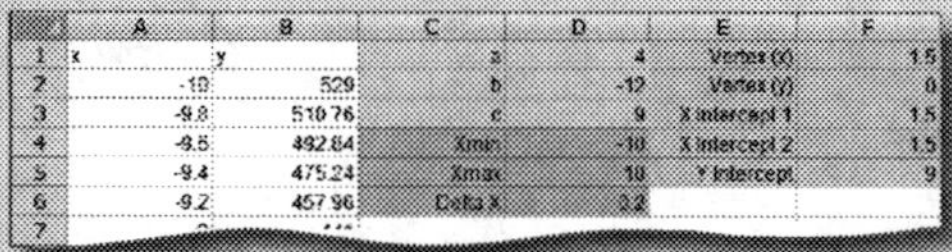

We can now save this sheet as a template to handle all quadratic functions. For instance, to do part (b), we just change the values of a, b, and c in column D to $a = -1/2$, $b = 4$, and $c = -12$.

Example 5 (page 626) The following table shows the annual mean carbon dioxide concentration measured at Mauna Loa Observatory in Hawaii, in parts per million, every 10 years from 1960 through 2010 ($t = 0$ represents 1960).

Year t	0	10	20	30	40	50
PPM CO_2 C	317	326	339	354	369	390

Find the quadratic model

$$C(t) = at^2 + bt + c$$

that best fits the data.

Solution with Technology

As in Section 1.4, Example 2, we start with a scatter plot of the original data, and add a trendline:

1. Start with the original data and a "Scatter plot" (see Section 1.2 Example 5).

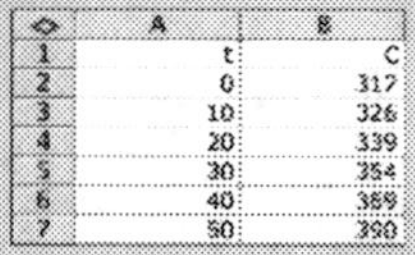

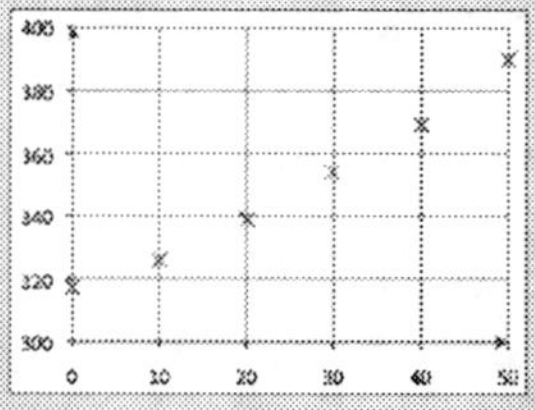

2. Add a quadratic trend line. (As of the time of this writing, among the common spreadsheets only Excel has the ability to add a polynomial trendline.) Right-click on any data point in the chart and select "Add Trendline," then select a "Polynomial" type of order 2 and check the option to "Display Equation on chart."

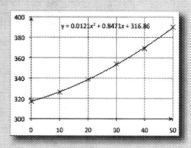

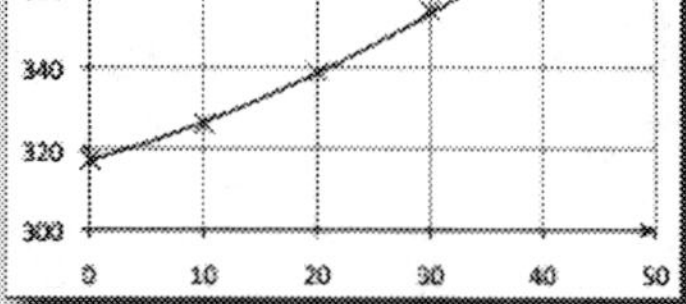

Section 9.2

Example 6(a) (page 641) The following table shows annual expenditure on health in the U.S. from 1980 through 2009 ($t = 0$ represents 1980).

Year t	0	5	10	15	20	25	29
Expenditure ($ billion)	256	444	724	1,030	1,380	2,020	2,490

Find the exponential regression model

$$C(t) = Ab^t$$

for the annual expenditure.

Solution with Technology

This is very similar to Example 5 in Section 9.1 (see the Technology Guide for Section 9.1):

1. Start with a "Scatter plot" of the observed data.
2. Add an exponential trendline:[60] The details vary from spreadsheet to spreadsheet—in OpenOffice, first double-click on the graph. Right-click on any data point in the chart and select "Add Trendline," then select an "Exponential" type and check the option to "Display Equation on chart."

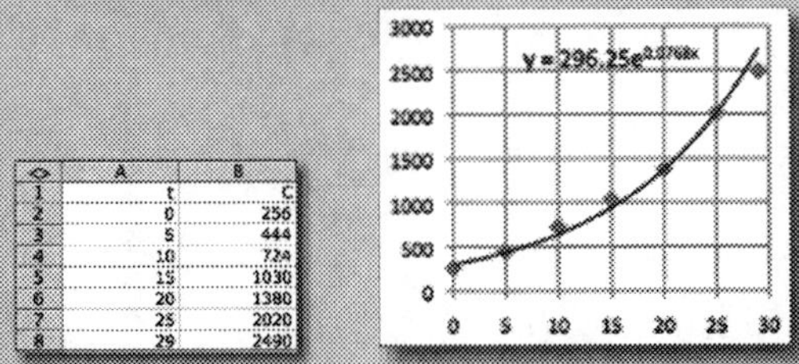

A	B
t	C
0	256
5	444
10	724
15	1030
20	1380
25	2020
29	2490

Notice that the regression curve is given in the form Ae^{kt} rather than Ab^t. To transform it, write

$$296.25e^{0.0768t} = 296.25(e^{0.0768})^t$$
$$\approx 296.25(1.0798)^t. \qquad e^{0.0768} \approx 1.0798$$

Section 9.3

Example 5 (page 655) The following table shows the total spent on research and development by universities and colleges in the U.S., in billions of dollars, for the period 1998–2008 (t is the year since 1990).

Year t	8	9	10	11	12	13
Spending ($ billions)	27	29	31	33	36	38
Year t	14	15	16	17	18	
Spending ($ billions)	39	40	40	41	42	

Find the best-fit logarithmic model of the form

$$S(t) = A \ln t + C$$

and use the model to project total spending on research by universities and colleges in 2012, assuming the trend continues.

Solution with Technology

This is very similar to Example 5 in Section 9.1 (see the Technology Guide for Section 9.1): We start, as usual, with a "Scatter plot" of the observed data and add a Logarithmic trendline. Here is the result:

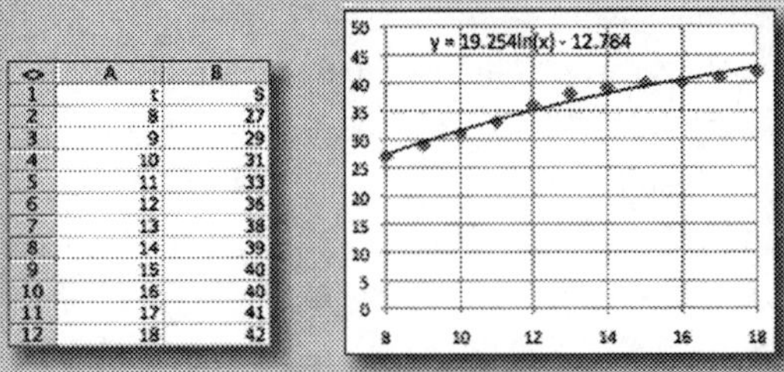

A	B
t	S
8	27
9	29
10	31
11	33
12	36
13	38
14	39
15	40
16	40
17	41
18	42

Section 9.4

Example 2 (page 664) The following table shows wired broadband penetration in the United States as a function of time t in years ($t = 0$ represents 2000).

Year (t)	2	3	4	5	6	7	8	9	10
Penetration (%) (P)	5.5	7.9	10.9	14.2	18.2	21.9	23.9	26.5	27.1

Find a logistic regression curve of the form

$$P(t) = \frac{N}{1 + Ab^{-t}}.$$

Solution with Technology

At the time of this writing, available spreadsheets did not have a built-in logistic regression calculation, so we use an alternative method that works for any type of regression curve. The Solver included with Windows versions of Excel and some Mac versions can find logistic regression curves while the Solver included with some other spreadsheets is not yet capable of this, so the instructions here are specific to Excel.

[60] At the time of this writing, Google Docs has no trendline feature for its spreadsheet.

1. First use rough estimates for N, A, and b, and compute the sum-of-squares error (SSE; see Section 1.4) directly:

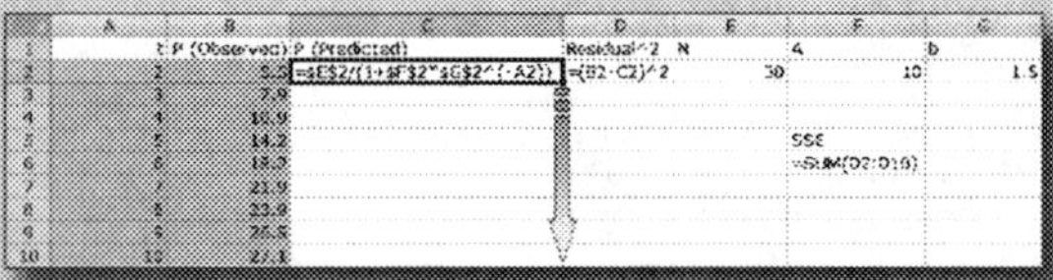

Cells E2:G2 contain our initial rough estimates of N, A, and b. For N, we used 30 (notice that the y-coordinates do appear to level off around 30). For A, we used the fact that the y-intercept is $N/(1 + A)$ and the y-intercept appears to be approximately 3. In other words,

$$3 = \frac{30}{1 + A}.$$

Because a very rough estimate is all we are after, using $A = 10$ will do just fine. For b, we chose 1.5 as the values of P appear to be increasing by around 50% per year initially (again, this is rough).

2. Cell C2 contains the formula for $P(t)$, and the square of the resulting residual is computed in D2.

3. Cell F6 will contain SSE. The completed spreadsheet should look like this:

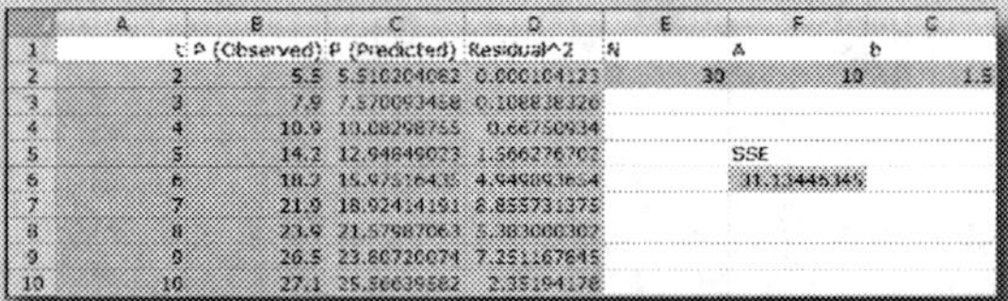

The best-fit curve will result from values of N, A, and b that give a minimum value for SSE. We shall use Excel's "Solver," found in the "Analysis" group on the "Data" tab. (If "Solver" does not appear in the Analysis group, you will have to install the Solver Add-in using the Excel Options dialogue.) The Solver dialogue box with the necessary fields completed to solve the problem looks like this:

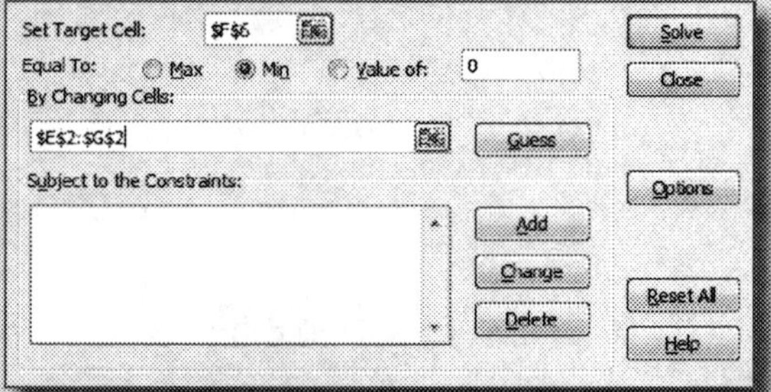

- The Target Cell refers to the cell that contains SSE.
- "Min" is selected because we are minimizing SSE.
- "Changing Cells" are obtained by selecting the cells that contain the current values of N, A, and b.

4. When you have filled in the values for the three items above, press "Solve" and tell Solver to Keep Solver Solution when done. You will find $N \approx 29.842$, $A \approx 12.501$, and $b \approx 1.642$ so that

$$P(t) \approx \frac{29.842}{1 + 12.501(1.642)^{-t}}.$$

If you use a scatter plot to graph the data in columns A, B and C, you will obtain the following graph:

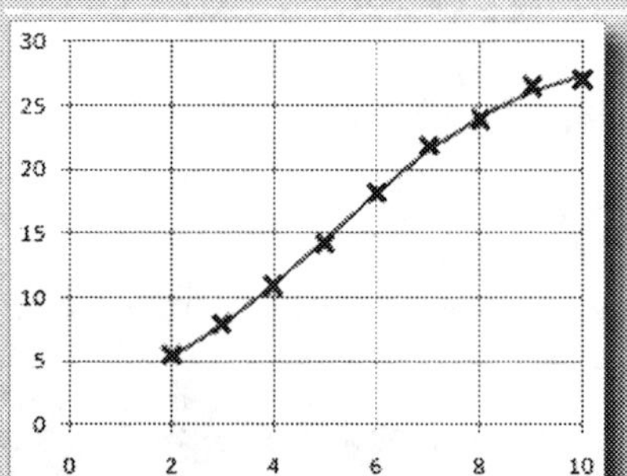

CHAPTER 9 QUIZ

1. Suppose that the population of a region at the start of 2010 was 2.8 million people and at the start of 2013 the population was 3.5 million people. Let $P(t)$ denote the population of the region (in millions) at time t, with $t = 0$ corresponding to the beginning of 2010. Assume that the population is growing exponentially.

   a. Write a formula for $P(t)$ in the form $P(t) = Ab^t$. Use the exact values of A and b.

   b. Write a formula for $P(t)$ in the form $P(t) = Ae^{rt}$. Use the exact value of A and give the value of r accurate to five decimal places.

   c. Determine how long it will take for the population of the region to reach 4.2 million people, accurate to two decimal places.

2. A beaker of a solution is being heated in such a way that the volume of liquid in the beaker is decreasing exponentially. Over the course of six minutes, the volume decreased by 25%. How long does it take for the volume to decrease by 50%? Give your result accurate to two decimal places.

3. Fill in the missing entries in the table below.

x		$\frac{1}{9}$		243	6561
$f(x) = \log_3 x$	-4		0		

4. Suppose that $\log_b 3 \approx 1.585$, $\log_b 5 \approx 2.322$, and $\log_b 7 \approx 2.807$. Estimate $\log_b \sqrt{15/7}$ without attempting to find b.

5. Fill in the blanks. Give results accurate to two decimal places.

a. An incremental growth rate of 10.2% per year corresponds to a continuous growth rate of ____________% per year.

b. An incremental decay rate of 22% per hour corresponds to a continuous decay rate of ____________% per hour.

c. A continuous growth rate of 9.8% per second corresponds to an incremental growth rate of ____________% per second.

d. A continuous decay rate of 27.4% per minute corresponds to an incremental decay rate of ____________% per minute.

6. Fill in the blanks.

a. If $\log\left(\frac{A}{\alpha}\right) = 3$ and $\log\left(\frac{B}{\alpha}\right) = 5$, then the value of B is ____________ times the value of A.

b. If $\log_2(3x) = 9$ and $\log_2(3y) = 4$, then the value of x is ____________ times the value of y.

10

Introduction to the Derivative

Website
www.WanerMath.com
At the Website you will find:

- Section-by-section tutorials, including game tutorials with randomized quizzes
- A detailed chapter summary
- A true/false quiz
- Additional review exercises
- Graphers, Excel tutorials, and other resources
- The following extra topics:
  - Sketching the graph of the derivative
  - Continuity and differentiability

Case Study Reducing Sulfur Emissions

The Environmental Protection Agency (EPA) wants to formulate a policy that will encourage utilities to reduce sulfur emissions. Its goal is to reduce annual emissions of sulfur dioxide by a total of 10 million tons from the current level of 25 million tons by imposing a fixed charge for every ton of sulfur released into the environment per year. The EPA has some data showing the marginal cost to utilities of reducing sulfur emissions. As a consultant to the EPA, you must determine the amount to be charged per ton of sulfur emissions in light of these data.

Norbert Schaefer/CORBIS

Introduction

In the world around us, everything is changing. The mathematics of change is largely about the rate of change: how fast and in which direction the change is occurring. Is the Dow Jones average going up, and if so, how fast? If I raise my prices, how many customers will I lose? If I launch this missile, how fast will it be traveling after two seconds, how high will it go, and where will it come down?

We have already discussed the concept of rate of change for linear functions (straight lines), where the slope measures the rate of change. But this works only because a straight line maintains a constant rate of change along its whole length. Other functions rise faster here than there—or rise in one place and fall in another—so that the rate of change varies along the graph. The first achievement of calculus is to provide a systematic and straightforward way of calculating (hence the name) these rates of change. To describe a changing world, we need a language of change, and that is what calculus is.

The history of calculus is an interesting story of personalities, intellectual movements, and controversy. Credit for its invention is given to two mathematicians: Isaac Newton (1642–1727) and Gottfried Leibniz (1646–1716). Newton, an English mathematician and scientist, developed calculus first, probably in the 1660s. We say "probably" because, for various reasons, he did not publish his ideas until much later. This allowed Leibniz, a German mathematician and philosopher, to publish his own version of calculus first, in 1684. Fifteen years later, stirred up by nationalist fervor in England and on the continent, controversy erupted over who should get the credit for the invention of calculus. The debate got so heated that the Royal Society (of which Newton and Leibniz were both members) set up a commission to investigate the question. The commission decided in favor of Newton, who happened to be president of the society at the time. The consensus today is that both mathematicians deserve credit because they came to the same conclusions working independently. This is not really surprising: Both built on well-known work of other people, and it was almost inevitable that someone would put it all together at about that time.

algebra Review
For this chapter, you should be familiar with the algebra reviewed in **Chapter 0, Section 2.**

10.1 Limits: Numerical and Graphical Viewpoints

Rates of change are calculated by derivatives, but an important part of the definition of the derivative is something called a **limit**. Arguably, much of mathematics since the eighteenth century has revolved around understanding, refining, and exploiting the idea of the limit. The basic idea is easy, but getting the technicalities right is not.

Evaluating Limits Numerically

Start with a very simple example: Look at the function $f(x) = 2 + x$ and ask: What happens to $f(x)$ as x approaches 3? The following table shows the value of $f(x)$ for values of x close to and on either side of 3:

	x approaching 3 from the left →					← x approaching 3 from the right			
x	2.9	2.99	2.999	2.9999	3	3.0001	3.001	3.01	3.1
$f(x) = 2 + x$	4.9	4.99	4.999	4.9999		5.0001	5.001	5.01	5.1

We have left the entry under 3 blank to emphasize that when calculating the limit of $f(x)$ as *x approaches* 3, we are not interested in its value when *x equals* 3.

Notice from the table that the closer x gets to 3 from either side, the closer $f(x)$ gets to 5. We write this as

$$\lim_{x\to 3} f(x) = 5. \qquad \text{The limit of } f(x) \text{, as } x \text{ approaches 3, equals 5.}$$

Q: *Why all the fuss? Can't we simply substitute $x = 3$ and avoid having to use a table?*

A: This happens to work for *some* functions, but not for *all* functions. The following example illustrates this point.

EXAMPLE 1 Estimating a Limit Numerically

Use a table to estimate the following limits:

a. $\displaystyle\lim_{x\to 2} \frac{x^3-8}{x-2}$ **b.** $\displaystyle\lim_{x\to 0} \frac{e^{2x}-1}{x}$

Solution

a. We cannot simply substitute $x = 2$, because the function $f(x) = \dfrac{x^3-8}{x-2}$ is not defined at $x = 2$. (Why?)* Instead, we use a table of values as we did above, with x approaching 2 from both sides.

* However, if you factor $x^3 - 8$, you will find that $f(x)$ can be simplified to a function that *is* defined at $x = 2$. This point will be discussed (and this example redone) in Section 10.3. The function in part (b) cannot be simplified by factoring.

x approaching 2 from the left → ← x approaching 2 from the right

x	1.9	1.99	1.999	1.9999	2	2.0001	2.001	2.01	2.1
$f(x) = \dfrac{x^3-8}{x-2}$	11.41	11.9401	11.9940	11.9994		12.0006	12.0060	12.0601	12.61

We notice that as x approaches 2 from either side, $f(x)$ appears to be approaching 12. This suggests that the limit is 12, and we write

$$\lim_{x\to 2} \frac{x^3-8}{x-2} = 12.$$

b. The function $g(x) = \dfrac{e^{2x}-1}{x}$ is not defined at $x = 0$ (nor can it even be simplified to one which *is* defined at $x = 0$). In the following table, we allow x to approach 0 from both sides:

x approaching 0 from the left → ← x approaching 0 from the right

x	−0.1	−0.01	−0.001	−0.0001	0	0.0001	0.001	0.01	0.1
$g(x) = \dfrac{e^{2x}-1}{x}$	1.8127	1.9801	1.9980	1.9998		2.0002	2.0020	2.0201	2.2140

The table suggests that $\displaystyle\lim_{x\to 0} \frac{e^{2x}-1}{x} = 2.$

using Technology

To automate the computations in Example 1 using a graphing calculator or a spreadsheet, see the Technology Guides at the end of the chapter. Outline for part (a):

TI-83/84 Plus
Home screen: Y1=(X^3-8)/(X-2)
[2ND] [TBLSET] Indpnt set to Ask
[2ND] [TABLE] Enter some values of x from the example: 1.9, 1.99, 1.999 . . .
[More details on page 778.]

Spreadsheet
Headings x, $f(x)$ in A1–B1 and again in C1–D1.
In A2–A5 enter 1.9, 1.99, 1.999, 1.9999.
In C1–C5 enter 2.1, 2.01, 2.001, 2.0001. Enter
`=(A2^3-8)/(A2-2)`
in B2 and copy down to B5. Copy and paste the same formula in D2–D5.
[More details on page 780.]

Website
www.WanerMath.com
In the Function Evaluator and Grapher, enter `(x^3-8)/(x-2)` for y_1. For a table of values, enter the various x-values in the Evaluator box, and press "Evaluate".

Before we go on... Although the table *suggests* that the limit in Example 1 part (b) is 2, it by no means establishes that fact conclusively. It is *conceivable* (though not in fact the case here) that putting $x = 0.000000087$ could result in, say, $g(x) = 426$. Using a table can only *suggest* a value for the limit. In the next two sections we shall discuss algebraic techniques to allow us to actually *calculate* limits. ■

Before we continue, let us make a more formal definition.

Definition of a Limit

If $f(x)$ approaches the number L as x approaches (but is not equal to) a from both sides, then we say that $f(x)$ **approaches** L **as** $x \to a$ ("x approaches a") or that the **limit** of $f(x)$ as $x \to a$ is L. More precisely, *we can make* $f(x)$ *be as close to L as we like by choosing any x sufficiently close to (but not equal to) a on either side.* We write

$$\lim_{x\to a} f(x) = L$$

or

$$f(x) \to L \text{ as } x \to a.$$

If $f(x)$ *fails* to approach *a single fixed number* as x approaches a from both sides, then we say that $f(x)$ **has no limit** as $x \to a$, or

$$\lim_{x\to a} f(x) \textbf{ does not exist.}$$

Quick Examples

1. $\lim_{x\to 3}(2+x) = 5$ — See discussion before Example 1.
2. $\lim_{x\to -2}(3x) = -6$ — As x approaches -2, $3x$ approaches -6.
3. $\lim_{x\to 0}(x^2 - 2x + 1)$ exists. — In fact, the limit is 1.
4. $\lim_{x\to 5}\frac{1}{x} = \frac{1}{5}$ — As x approaches 5, $\frac{1}{x}$ approaches $\frac{1}{5}$.
5. $\lim_{x\to 2}\frac{x^3-8}{x-2} = 12$ — See Example 1. (We cannot just put $x = 2$ here.)

(For examples where the limit does not exist, see Example 2.)

Notes

1. It is important that $f(x)$ approach the same number as x approaches a from *both sides*. For instance, if $f(x)$ approaches 5 for $x = 1.9, 1.99, 1.999, \ldots$, but approaches 4 for $x = 2.1, 2.01, 2.001, \ldots$, then the limit as $x \to 2$ does not exist. (See Example 2 for such a situation.)
2. It may happen that $f(x)$ does not approach any fixed number at all as $x \to a$ from either side. In this case, we also say that the limit does not exist.
3. If a happens to be an endpoint of the domain of f, then the function is only defined on one side of a, and so the limit as $x \to a$ does not exist. For example, the natural domain of $f(x) = \sqrt{x}$ is $[0, +\infty)$, so the limit of $f(x)$ as $x \to 0$ does not exist. The appropriate kind of limit to consider in such a case is a **one-sided limit** (see Example 2). ■

The next example gives instances in which a stated limit does not exist.

EXAMPLE 2 Limits Do Not Always Exist

Do the following limits exist?

a. $\lim_{x \to 0} \frac{1}{x^2}$ **b.** $\lim_{x \to 0} \frac{|x|}{x}$ **c.** $\lim_{x \to 2} \frac{1}{x-2}$ **d.** $\lim_{x \to 1} \sqrt{x-1}$

Solution

a. Here is a table of values for $f(x) = \frac{1}{x^2}$, with x approaching 0 from both sides.

x approaching 0 from the left → ← x approaching 0 from the right

x	−0.1	−0.01	−0.001	−0.0001	0	0.0001	0.001	0.01	0.1
$f(x) = \frac{1}{x^2}$	100	10,000	1,000,000	100,000,000		100,000,000	1,000,000	10,000	100

The table shows that as x gets closer to zero on either side, $f(x)$ gets larger and larger **without bound**—that is, if you name any number, no matter how large, $f(x)$ will be even larger than that if x is sufficiently close to 0. Because $f(x)$ is not approaching any real number, we conclude that $\lim_{x \to 0} \frac{1}{x^2}$ does not exist. Because $f(x)$ is becoming arbitrarily large, we also say that $\lim_{x \to 0} \frac{1}{x^2}$ **diverges to** $+\infty$, or just

$$\lim_{x \to 0} \frac{1}{x^2} = +\infty.$$

Note This is not meant to imply that the limit exists; the symbol $+\infty$ does not represent any real number. We write $\lim_{x \to a} f(x) = +\infty$ to indicate two things: (1) The limit does not exist and (2) the function gets large without bound as x approaches a. ■

b. Here is a table of values for $f(x) = \frac{|x|}{x}$, with x approaching 0 from both sides.

x approaching 0 from the left → ← x approaching 0 from the right

x	−0.1	−0.01	−0.001	−0.0001	0	0.0001	0.001	0.01	0.1
$f(x) = \frac{\lvert x \rvert}{x}$	−1	−1	−1	−1		1	1	1	1

The table shows that $f(x)$ does not approach the same limit as x approaches 0 from both sides. There appear to be two *different* limits: the limit as we approach 0 from the left and the limit as we approach from the right. We write

$$\lim_{x \to 0^-} f(x) = -1$$

read as "the limit as x approaches 0 from the left (or from below) is −1" and

$$\lim_{x \to 0^+} f(x) = 1$$

read as "the limit as x approaches 0 from the right (or from above) is 1." These are called the **one-sided limits** of $f(x)$. In order for f to have a **two-sided limit**, the two one-sided limits must be equal. Because they are not, we conclude that $\lim_{x \to 0} f(x)$ does not exist.

c. Near $x = 2$, we have the following table of values for $f(x) = \dfrac{1}{x-2}$:

	x approaching 2 from the left →					← x approaching 2 from the right			
x	1.9	1.99	1.999	1.9999	2	2.0001	2.001	2.01	2.1
$f(x) = \dfrac{1}{x-2}$	−10	−100	−1,000	−10,000		10,000	1,000	100	10

Because $f(x)$ is approaching no (single) real number as $x \to 2$, we see that $\lim_{x\to 2} \dfrac{1}{x-2}$ does not exist. Notice also that $\dfrac{1}{x-2}$ diverges to $+\infty$ as $x \to 2$ from the positive side (right half of the table) and to $-\infty$ as $x \to 2$ from the left (left half of the table). In other words,

$$\lim_{x\to 2^-} \frac{1}{x-2} = -\infty$$

$$\lim_{x\to 2^+} \frac{1}{x-2} = +\infty$$

$$\lim_{x\to 2} \frac{1}{x-2} \text{ does not exist.}$$

d. The natural domain of $f(x) = \sqrt{x-1}$ is $[1, +\infty)$, as $f(x)$ is defined only when $x \geq 1$. Thus we cannot evaluate $f(x)$ if x is to the left of 1. This means that

$$\lim_{x\to 1^-} \sqrt{x-1} \text{ does not exist,}$$

and our table looks like this:

		← x approaching 1 from the right				
x	1	1.00001	1.0001	1.001	1.01	1.1
$f(x) = \sqrt{x-1}$		0.0032	0.0100	0.0316	0.1000	0.3162

The values suggest that

$$\lim_{x\to 1^+} \sqrt{x-1} = 0.$$

In fact, we can obtain this limit by substituting $x = 1$ in the formula for $f(x)$ (see the comments after the example).

Q: *In Example 2(d) (and also in some of the Quick Examples before that) we could find a limit of an algebraically specified function by simply substituting the value of x in the formula for f(x). Does this always work?*

A: Short answer: Yes, when it makes sense. If the function is specified by a *single* algebraic formula and if $x = a$ is in the domain of f, then the limit can be obtained by substituting. We will say more about this when we discuss the algebraic approach to limits in Section 10.3. Remember, however, that, by definition, the limit of a function as $x \to a$ has nothing to do with its value at $x = a$, but rather its values for *x close to a*.

Q: *If f(x) is undefined when x = a, then the limit does not exist, right?*

A: Wrong. If *f*(*a*) is not defined, then the limit may or may not exist. Example 1 shows instances where the limit *does* exist, and Example 2 shows instances where it does not. Again, the limit of a function as $x \to a$ has nothing to do with its value at $x = a$, but rather its values for *x close to a*.

In another useful kind of limit, we let x approach either $+\infty$ or $-\infty$, by which we mean that we let x get arbitrarily large or let x become an arbitrarily large negative number. The next example illustrates this.

EXAMPLE 3 Limits at Infinity

Use a table to estimate: **a.** $\lim_{x\to+\infty} \dfrac{2x^2-4x}{x^2-1}$ and **b.** $\lim_{x\to-\infty} \dfrac{2x^2-4x}{x^2-1}$.

Solution

a. By saying that x is "approaching $+\infty$," we mean that x is getting larger and larger without bound, so we make the following table:

x approaching $+\infty$ →

x	10	100	1,000	10,000	100,000
$f(x) = \dfrac{2x^2-4x}{x^2-1}$	1.6162	1.9602	1.9960	1.9996	2.0000

(Note that we are only approaching $+\infty$ from the left because we can hardly approach it from the right!) What seems to be happening is that $f(x)$ is approaching 2. Thus we write

$$\lim_{x\to+\infty} f(x) = 2.$$

b. Here, x is approaching $-\infty$, so we make a similar table, this time with x assuming negative values of greater and greater magnitude (read this table from right to left):

← x approaching $-\infty$

x	−100,000	−10,000	−1,000	−100	−10
$f(x) = \dfrac{2x^2-4x}{x^2-1}$	2.0000	2.0004	2.0040	2.0402	2.4242

Once again, $f(x)$ is approaching 2. Thus, $\lim_{x\to-\infty} f(x) = 2$.

Estimating Limits Graphically

We can often estimate a limit from a graph, as the next example shows.

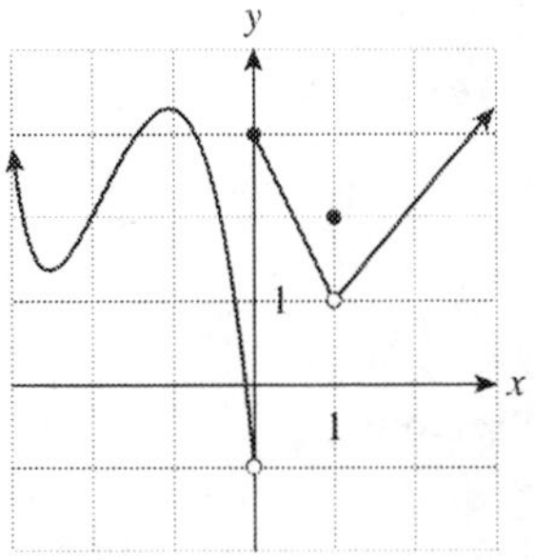

Figure 1

EXAMPLE 4 Estimating Limits Graphically

The graph of a function f is shown in Figure 1. (Recall that the solid dots indicate points on the graph, and the hollow dots indicate points not on the graph.) From the graph, analyze the following limits.

a. $\lim_{x\to-2} f(x)$ **b.** $\lim_{x\to 0} f(x)$ **c.** $\lim_{x\to 1} f(x)$ **d.** $\lim_{x\to+\infty} f(x)$

Solution Since we are given only a graph of f, we must analyze these limits graphically.

a. Imagine that Figure 1 was drawn on a graphing calculator equipped with a trace feature that allows us to move a cursor along the graph and see the coordinates as we go. To simulate this, place a pencil point on the graph to the left of $x = -2$, and move it along the curve so that the x-coordinate approaches -2. (See Figure 2.) We evaluate the limit numerically by noting the behavior of the y-coordinates.*

However, we can see directly from the graph that the y-coordinate approaches 2. Similarly, if we place our pencil point to the right of $x = -2$ and move it to the left, the y coordinate will approach 2 from that side as well (Figure 3). Therefore, as x approaches -2 from either side, $f(x)$ approaches 2, so

$$\lim_{x \to -2} f(x) = 2.$$

* For a visual animation of this process, look at the online tutorial for this section at the Website.

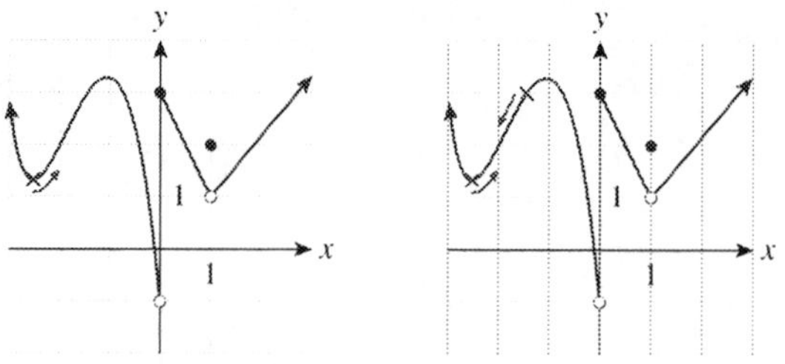

Figure 2 **Figure 3**

b. This time we move our pencil point toward $x = 0$. Referring to Figure 4, if we start from the left of $x = 0$ and approach 0 (by moving right), the y-coordinate approaches -1. However, if we start from the right of $x = 0$ and approach 0 (by moving left), the y-coordinate approaches 3. Thus (see Example 2),

$$\lim_{x \to 0^-} f(x) = -1$$

and

$$\lim_{x \to 0^+} f(x) = 3.$$

Because these limits are not equal, we conclude that

$$\lim_{x \to 0} f(x) \text{ does not exist.}$$

In this case there is a "break" in the graph at $x = 0$, and we say that the function is **discontinuous** at $x = 0$ (see Section 10.2).

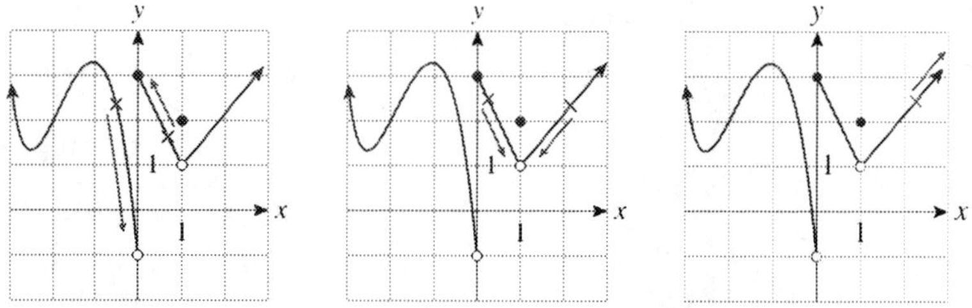

Figure 4 **Figure 5** **Figure 6**

c. Once more we think about a pencil point moving along the graph with the x-coordinate this time approaching $x = 1$ from the left and from the right (Figure 5).

As the x-coordinate of the point approaches 1 from either side, the y-coordinate approaches 1 also. Therefore,

$$\lim_{x \to 1} f(x) = 1.$$

d. For this limit, x is supposed to approach infinity. We think about a pencil point moving along the graph further and further to the right as shown in Figure 6.

As the x-coordinate gets larger, the y-coordinate also gets larger and larger without bound. Thus, $f(x)$ diverges to $+\infty$:

$$\lim_{x \to +\infty} f(x) = +\infty.$$

Similarly,

$$\lim_{x \to -\infty} f(x) = +\infty.$$

Before we go on... In Example 4(c) $\lim_{x \to 1} f(x) = 1$ but $f(1) = 2$ (why?). Thus, $\lim_{x \to 1} f(x) \neq f(1)$. In other words, the limit of $f(x)$ as x *approaches* 1 is not the same as the value of f *at* $x = 1$. Always keep in mind that when we evaluate a limit as $x \to a$, *we do not care about the value of the function at* $x = a$. We only care about the value of $f(x)$ as x *approaches* a. In other words, $f(a)$ may or may not equal $\lim_{x \to a} f(x)$. ■

Here is a summary of the graphical method we used in Example 4, together with some additional information:

Evaluating Limits Graphically

To decide whether $\lim_{x \to a} f(x)$ exists and to find its value if it does:

1. Draw the graph of $f(x)$ by hand or with graphing technology.
2. Position your pencil point (or the Trace cursor) on a point of the graph to the right of $x = a$.
3. Move the point *along the graph* toward $x = a$ from the right and read the y-coordinate as you go. The value the y-coordinate approaches (if any) is the limit $\lim_{x \to a^+} f(x)$.
4. Repeat Steps 2 and 3, this time starting from a point on the graph to the left of $x = a$, and approaching $x = a$ along the graph from the left. The value the y-coordinate approaches (if any) is $\lim_{x \to a^-} f(x)$.
5. If the left and right limits both exist and have the same value L, then $\lim_{x \to a} f(x) = L$. Otherwise, the limit does not exist. The value $f(a)$ has no relevance whatsoever.
6. To evaluate $\lim_{x \to +\infty} f(x)$, move the pencil point toward the far right of the graph and estimate the value the y-coordinate approaches (if any). For $\lim_{x \to -\infty} f(x)$, move the pencil point toward the far left.
7. If $x = a$ happens to be an endpoint of the domain of f, then only a one-sided limit is possible at $x = a$. For instance, if the domain is $(-\infty, 4]$, then $\lim_{x \to 4^-} f(x)$ may exist, but neither $\lim_{x \to 4^+} f(x)$ nor $\lim_{x \to 4} f(x)$ exists.

In the next example we use both the numerical and graphical approaches.

EXAMPLE 5 Infinite Limit

Does $\lim_{x\to 0^+} \frac{1}{x}$ exist?

Solution

Numerical Method Because we are asked for only the right-hand limit, we need only list values of x approaching 0 from the right.

← x approaching 0 from the right

x	0	0.0001	0.001	0.01	0.1
$f(x) = \frac{1}{x}$		10,000	1,000	100	10

What seems to be happening as x approaches 0 from the right is that $f(x)$ is increasing without bound, as in Example 4(d). That is, if you name any number, no matter how large, $f(x)$ will be even larger than that if x is sufficiently close to zero. Thus, the limit diverges to $+\infty$, so

$$\lim_{x\to 0^+} \frac{1}{x} = +\infty$$

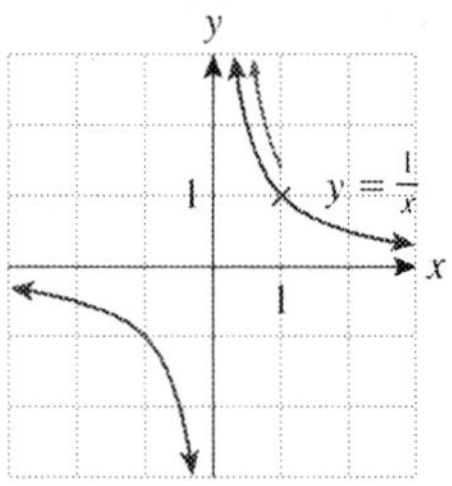

Figure 7

Graphical Method Recall that the graph of $f(x) = \frac{1}{x}$ is the standard hyperbola shown in Figure 7. The figure also shows the pencil point moving so that its x-coordinate approaches 0 from the right. Because the point moves along the graph, it is forced to go higher and higher. In other words, its y-coordinate becomes larger and larger, approaching $+\infty$. Thus, we conclude that

$$\lim_{x\to 0^+} \frac{1}{x} = +\infty.$$

➡ **Before we go on...** In Example 5 you should check that

$$\lim_{x\to 0^-} \frac{1}{x} = -\infty. \qquad \frac{1}{x} \text{ diverges to } -\infty \text{ as } x \to 0^-.$$

Also, check that

$$\lim_{x\to +\infty} \frac{1}{x} = \lim_{x\to -\infty} \frac{1}{x} = 0. \blacksquare$$

APPLICATION

EXAMPLE 6 Broadband Penetration

Wired broadband penetration in the United States can be modeled by

$$P(t) = \frac{29.842}{1 + 12.502(1.642)^{-t}} \quad (t \geq 0),$$

where t is time in years since 2000.[1]

[1] See Example 2 in Section 9.4. Broadband penetration is the number of broadband installations divided by the total population. Source for data: Organization for Economic Cooperation and Development (OECD) Directorate for Science, Technology, and Industry, table of Historical Penetration Rates, June 2010, downloaded April 2011 from www.oecd.org/sti /ict/broadband.

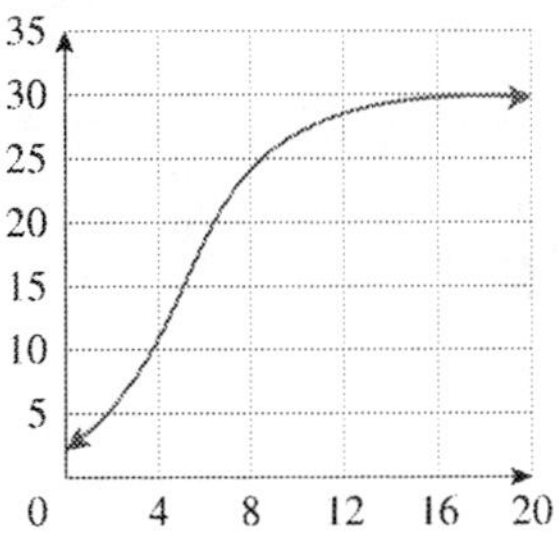

Figure 8

a. Estimate $\lim_{t \to +\infty} P(t)$ and interpret the answer.

b. Estimate $\lim_{t \to 0^+} P(t)$ and interpret the answer.

Solution

a. Figure 8 shows a plot of $P(t)$ for $0 \le t \le 20$. Using either the numerical or the graphical approach, we find

$$\lim_{t \to +\infty} P(t) = \lim_{t \to +\infty} \frac{29.842}{1 + 12.502(1.642)^{-t}} \approx 30.$$

(The actual limit is 29.842. Why?) Thus, in the long term (as t gets larger and larger), broadband penetration in the United States is expected to approach 30%; that is, the number of installations is expected to approach 30% of the total population.

b. The limit here is

$$\lim_{t \to 0^+} P(t) = \lim_{t \to 0^+} \frac{29.842}{1 + 12.502(1.642)^{-t}} \approx 2.21.$$

(Notice that in this case, we can simply put $t = 0$ to evaluate this limit.) Thus, the closer t gets to 0 (representing 2000) from the right, the closer $P(t)$ gets to 2.21%, meaning that, in 2000, broadband penetration was about 2.2% of the population.

FAQs

Determining when a Limit Does or Does Not Exist

Q: *If I substitute $x = a$ in the formula for a function and find that the function is defined there, it means that $\lim_{x \to a} f(x)$ exists and equals $f(a)$, right?*

A: Correct, provided the function is specified by *a single algebraic formula* and is not, say, piecewise-defined. We shall say more about this in the next two sections.

Q: *If I substitute $x = a$ in the formula for a function and find that the function is* not *defined there, it means that $\lim_{x \to a} f(x)$ does not exist, right?*

A: Wrong. The limit may still exist, as in Example 1, or may not exist, as in Example 2. In general, whether or not $\lim_{x \to a} f(x)$ exists has nothing to do with $f(a)$, but rather the values of f when x is *very close to, but not equal to a.*

Q: *Is there a quick and easy way of telling from a graph whether $\lim_{x \to a} f(x)$ exists?*

A: Yes. If you cover up the portion of the graph corresponding to $x = a$ and it appears as though the visible part of the graph could be made into a continuous curve by filling in a suitable point at $x = a$, then the limit exists. (The "suitable point" need not be $(a, f(a))$.) Otherwise, it does not. Try this method with the curves in Example 4.

10.1 EXERCISES

▼ more advanced ◆ challenging

indicates exercises that should be solved using technology

Estimate the limits in Exercises 1–20 numerically.
HINT [See Examples 1–3.]

1. $\lim_{x \to 0} \frac{x^2}{x+1}$

2. $\lim_{x \to 0} \frac{x-3}{x-1}$

3. $\lim_{x \to 2} \frac{x^2-4}{x-2}$

4. $\lim_{x \to 2} \frac{x^2-1}{x-2}$

5. $\lim_{x \to -1} \frac{x^2+1}{x+1}$

6. $\lim_{x \to -1} \frac{x^2+2x+1}{x+1}$

7. $\lim_{x \to +\infty} \frac{3x^2+10x-1}{2x^2-5x}$

8. $\lim_{x \to +\infty} \frac{6x^2+5x+100}{3x^2-9}$

9. $\lim_{x \to -\infty} \frac{x^5-1{,}000x^4}{2x^5+10{,}000}$

10. $\lim_{x \to -\infty} \frac{x^6+3{,}000x^3+1{,}000{,}000}{2x^6+1{,}000x^3}$

11. $\lim_{x \to +\infty} \frac{10x^2+300x+1}{5x+2}$

12. $\lim_{x \to +\infty} \frac{2x^4+20x^3}{1{,}000x^6+6}$

13. $\lim_{x \to +\infty} \frac{10x^2+300x+1}{5x^3+2}$

14. $\lim_{x \to +\infty} \frac{2x^4+20x^3}{1{,}000x^3+6}$

15. $\lim_{x \to 2} e^{x-2}$

16. $\lim_{x \to +\infty} e^{-x}$

17. $\lim_{x \to +\infty} xe^{-x}$

18. $\lim_{x \to -\infty} xe^{x}$

19. $\lim_{x \to -\infty} (x^{10}+2x^5+1)e^x$

20. $\lim_{x \to +\infty} (x^{50}+x^{30}+1)e^{-x}$

In each of Exercises 21–34, the graph of f is given. Use the graph to compute the quantities asked for. HINT [See Examples 4–5.]

21. a. $\lim_{x \to 1} f(x)$ b. $\lim_{x \to -1} f(x)$

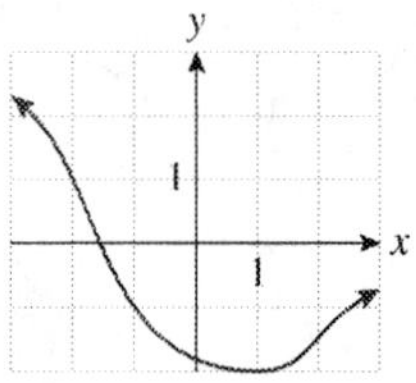

22. a. $\lim_{x \to -1} f(x)$ b. $\lim_{x \to 1} f(x)$

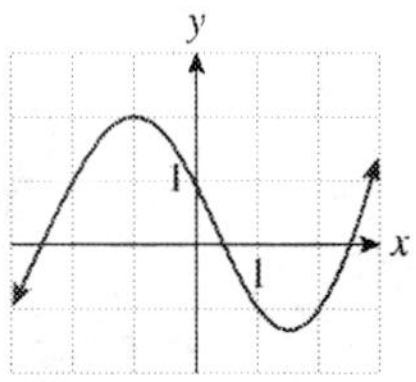

23. a. $\lim_{x \to 0} f(x)$ b. $\lim_{x \to 2} f(x)$ c. $\lim_{x \to -\infty} f(x)$ d. $\lim_{x \to +\infty} f(x)$

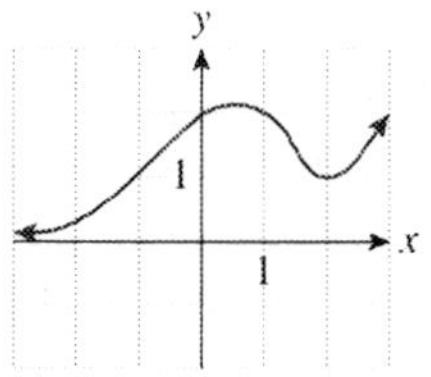

24. a. $\lim_{x \to -1} f(x)$ b. $\lim_{x \to 1} f(x)$ c. $\lim_{x \to +\infty} f(x)$ d. $\lim_{x \to -\infty} f(x)$

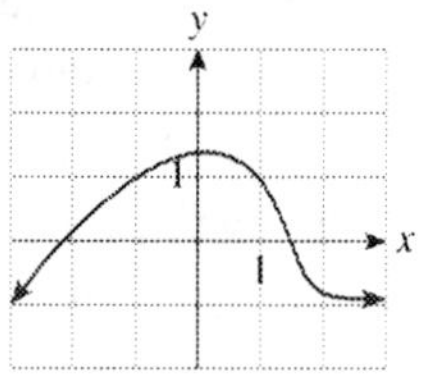

25. a. $\lim_{x \to 2} f(x)$ b. $\lim_{x \to 0^+} f(x)$ c. $\lim_{x \to 0^-} f(x)$
d. $\lim_{x \to 0} f(x)$ e. $f(0)$ f. $\lim_{x \to -\infty} f(x)$

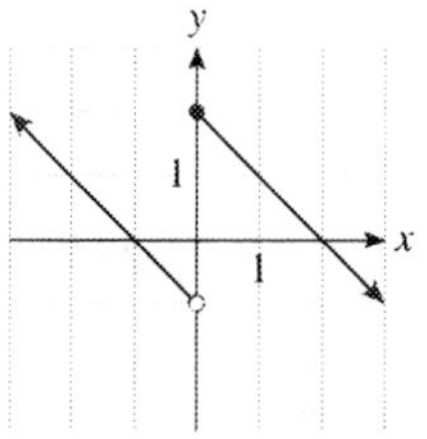

26. a. $\lim_{x \to 3} f(x)$ b. $\lim_{x \to 1^+} f(x)$ c. $\lim_{x \to 1^-} f(x)$
d. $\lim_{x \to 1} f(x)$ e. $f(1)$ f. $\lim_{x \to +\infty} f(x)$

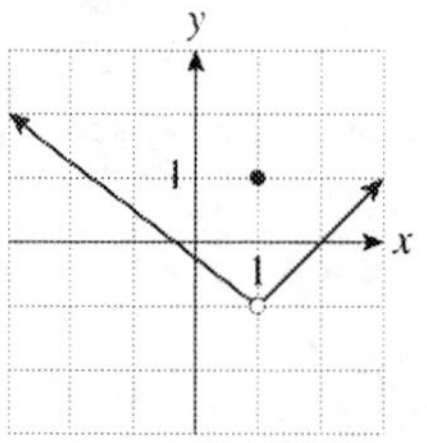

27. a. $\lim_{x \to -2} f(x)$ b. $\lim_{x \to -1^+} f(x)$ c. $\lim_{x \to -1^-} f(x)$
d. $\lim_{x \to -1} f(x)$ e. $f(-1)$ f. $\lim_{x \to +\infty} f(x)$

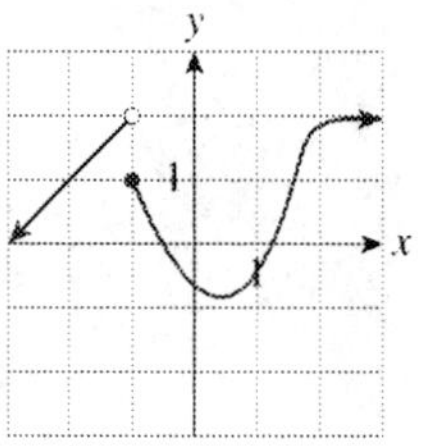

28. a. $\lim_{x\to -1} f(x)$ **b.** $\lim_{x\to 0^+} f(x)$ **c.** $\lim_{x\to 0^-} f(x)$

d. $\lim_{x\to 0} f(x)$ **e.** $f(0)$ **f.** $\lim_{x\to -\infty} f(x)$

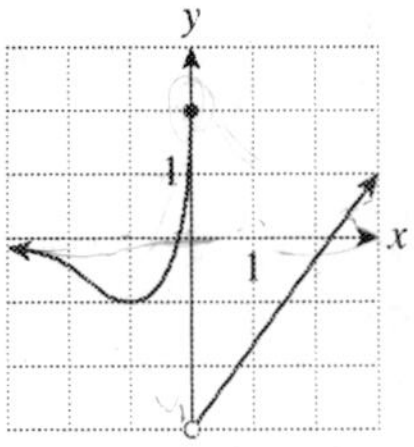

29. a. $\lim_{x\to -1^+} f(x)$ **b.** $\lim_{x\to -1^-} f(x)$ **c.** $\lim_{x\to -1} f(x)$ **d.** $f(-1)$

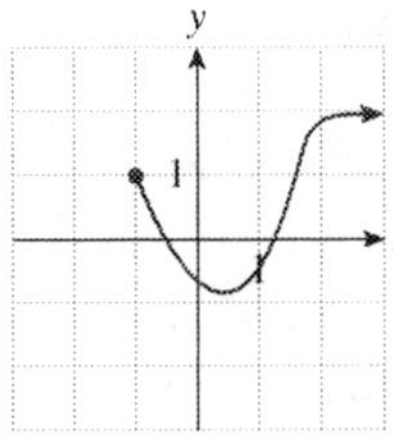

30. a. $\lim_{x\to 0^+} f(x)$ **b.** $\lim_{x\to 0^-} f(x)$ **c.** $\lim_{x\to 0} f(x)$ **d.** $f(0)$

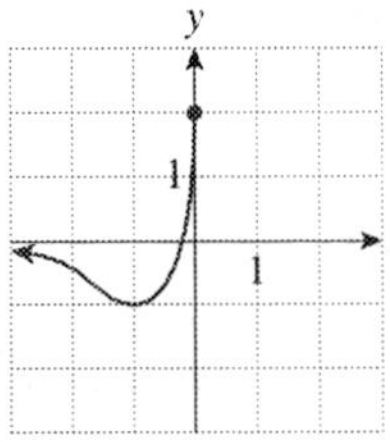

31. a. $\lim_{x\to -1} f(x)$ **b.** $\lim_{x\to 0^+} f(x)$ **c.** $\lim_{x\to 0^-} f(x)$

d. $\lim_{x\to 0} f(x)$ **e.** $f(0)$ **f.** $\lim_{x\to +\infty} f(x)$

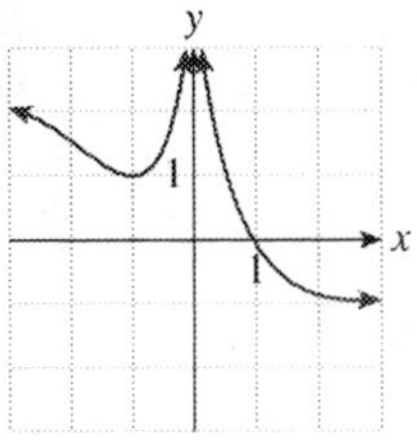

32. a. $\lim_{x\to 1} f(x)$ **b.** $\lim_{x\to 0^+} f(x)$ **c.** $\lim_{x\to 0^-} f(x)$

d. $\lim_{x\to 0} f(x)$ **e.** $f(0)$ **f.** $\lim_{x\to -\infty} f(x)$

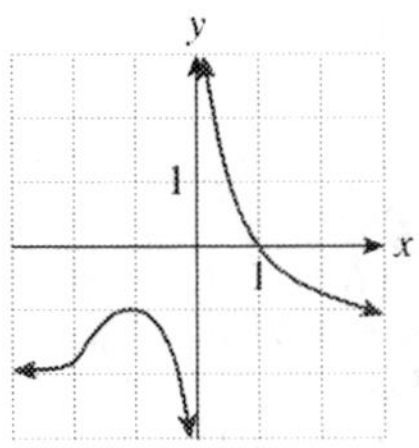

33. a. $\lim_{x\to -1} f(x)$ **b.** $\lim_{x\to 0^+} f(x)$ **c.** $\lim_{x\to 0^-} f(x)$

d. $\lim_{x\to 0} f(x)$ **e.** $f(0)$ **f.** $f(-1)$

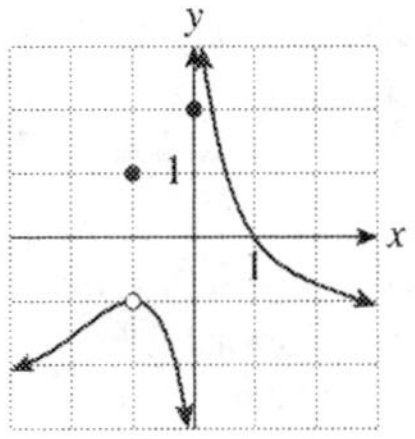

34. a. $\lim_{x\to 0^-} f(x)$ **b.** $\lim_{x\to 1^+} f(x)$ **c.** $\lim_{x\to 0} f(x)$

d. $\lim_{x\to 1} f(x)$ **e.** $f(0)$ **f.** $f(1)$

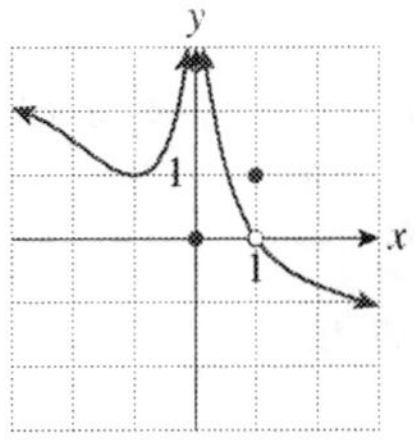

APPLICATIONS

35. ***Economic Growth*** The value of sold goods in Mexico can be approximated by

$$v(t) = 210 - 62e^{-0.05t} \text{ trillion pesos per month} \quad (t \geq 0),$$

where t is time in months since January 2005.[2] Numerically estimate $\lim_{t\to +\infty} v(t)$ and interpret the answer. HINT [See Example 6.]

36. ***Economic Growth*** The number of housing starts for single family homes in the U.S. can be approximated by

$$n(t) = 400 + 1{,}420e^{-0.48t} \text{ thousand housing starts per year} \quad (t \geq 0),$$

where t is time in years since January 2005.[3] Numerically estimate $\lim_{t\to +\infty} n(t)$ and interpret the answer.

37. ***Revenue*** The annual revenue of Amazon.com for the period 2006–2010 could be approximated by

$$P(t) = 870t^2 + 2{,}200t + 11{,}000 \text{ million dollars } (0 \leq t \leq 4),$$

where t is time in years since 2006.[4] If one extrapolates the function and numerically estimates $\lim_{t\to +\infty} P(t)$, what does the answer suggest about Amazon's revenue?

[2]Source: Instituto Nacional de Estadística y Geografía (INEGI), www.inegi.org.mx.

[3]Source for data: www.census.gov.

[4]Source for data: www.wikinvest.com.

38. ***Net Income*** The annual net income of General Electric for the period 2005–2010 could be approximated by

$$P(t) = -2.0t^2 + 6.6t + 16 \text{ billion dollars} \quad (0 \le t \le 5),$$

where t is time in years since 2005.[5] If one extrapolates the function and numerically estimates $\lim_{t\to+\infty} P(t)$, what does the answer suggest about General Electric's net income?

39. ***Scientific Research*** The number of research articles per year, in thousands, in the prominent journal *Physical Review* written by researchers in Europe can be modeled by

$$A(t) = \frac{7.0}{1 + 5.4(1.2)^{-t}},$$

where t is time in years ($t = 0$ represents 1983).[6] Numerically estimate $\lim_{t\to+\infty} A(t)$ and interpret the answer.

40. ***Scientific Research*** The percentage of research articles in the prominent journal *Physical Review* written by researchers in the United States can be modeled by

$$A(t) = 25 + \frac{36}{1 + 0.6(0.7)^{-t}},$$

where t is time in years ($t = 0$ represents 1983).[7] Numerically estimate $\lim_{t\to+\infty} A(t)$ and interpret the answer.

41. ***SAT Scores by Income*** The following bar graph shows U.S. math SAT scores as a function of household income:[8]

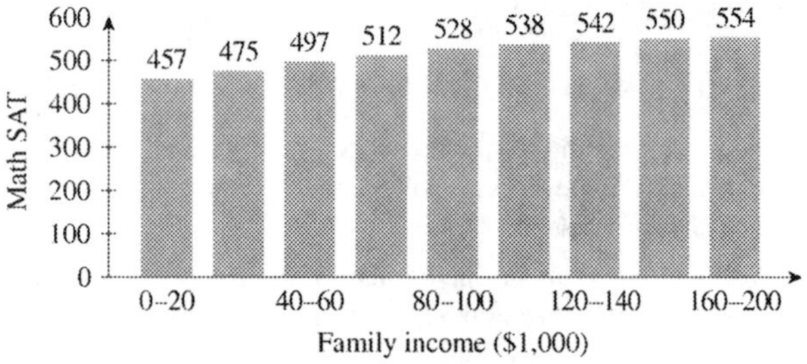

These data can be modeled by

$$S(x) = 573 - 133(0.987)^x,$$

where $S(x)$ is the average math SAT score of students whose household income is x thousand dollars per year. Numerically estimate $\lim_{x\to+\infty} S(x)$ and interpret the answer.

42. ***SAT Scores by Income*** The following bar graph shows U.S. critical reading SAT scores as a function of household income:[9]

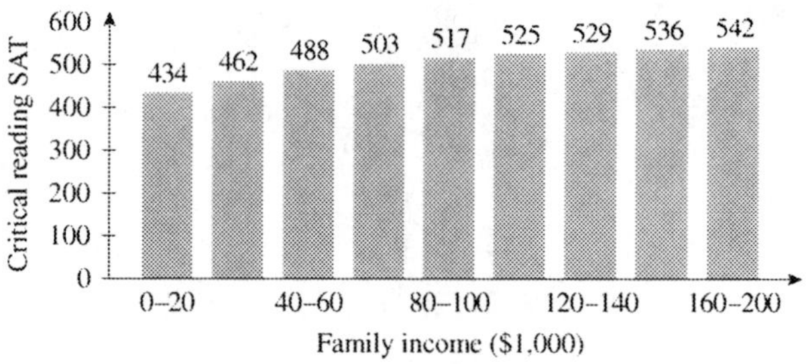

These data can be modeled by

$$S(x) = 550 - 136(0.985)^x,$$

where $S(x)$ is the average critical reading SAT score of students whose household income is x thousand dollars per year. Numerically estimate $\lim_{x\to+\infty} S(x)$ and interpret the answer.

43. ***Flash Crash*** The graph shows a rough representation of what happened to the Russel 1000 Growth Index Fund (IWF) stock price on the day of the U.S. stock market crash at 2:45 pm on May 6, 2010 (the "Flash Crash"; t is the time of the day in hours, and $r(t)$ is the price of the stock in dollars).[10]

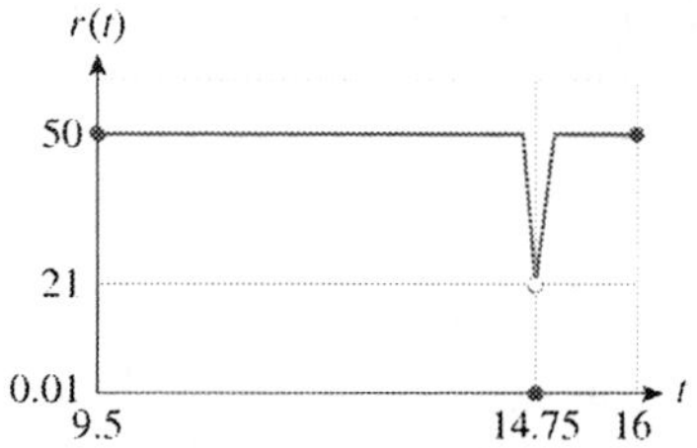

a. Compute the following (if a limit does not exist, say why):

$$\lim_{t\to 14.75^-} r(t), \quad \lim_{t\to 14.75^+} r(t), \quad \lim_{t\to 14.75} r(t), \quad r(14.75).$$

b. What do the answers to part (a) tell you about the IWF stock price?

44. ***Flash Crash*** The graph shows a rough representation of the (aggregate) market depth[11] of the stocks comprising the S&P 500 on the day of the U.S. stock market crash at 2:45 pm on May 6, 2010 (the "Flash Crash"; t is the time of the day in hours, and $m(t)$ is the market depth in millions of shares).

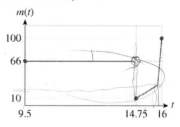

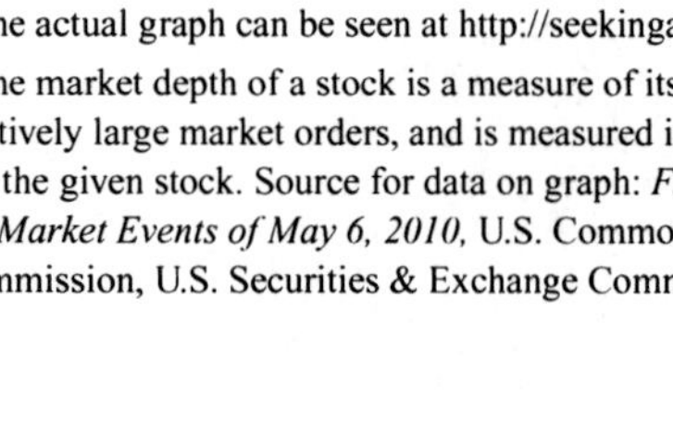

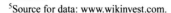

[5]Source for data: www.wikinvest.com.

[6]Based on data from 1983 to 2003. Source: The American Physical Society/*New York Times*, May 3, 2003, p. A1.

[7]*Ibid.*

[8]2009 data. Source: College Board/*New York Times* http://economix.blogs.nytimes.com.

[9]*Ibid.*

[10]The actual graph can be seen at http://seekingalpha.com.

[11]The market depth of a stock is a measure of its ability to withstand relatively large market orders, and is measured in orders to buy or sell the given stock. Source for data on graph: *Findings Regarding the Market Events of May 6, 2010*, U.S. Commodity Futures Trading Commission, U.S. Securities & Exchange Commission.

a. Compute the following (if a limit does not exist, say why):
$\lim_{t\to 14.75^-} m(t)$, $\lim_{t\to 14.75^+} m(t)$, $\lim_{t\to 14.75} m(t)$, $m(14.75)$.

b. What do the answers to part (a) tell you about the market depth?

45. ***Home Prices*** The following graph shows the values of the home price index[12] for 2000–2010 together with a mathematical model I extrapolating the data.

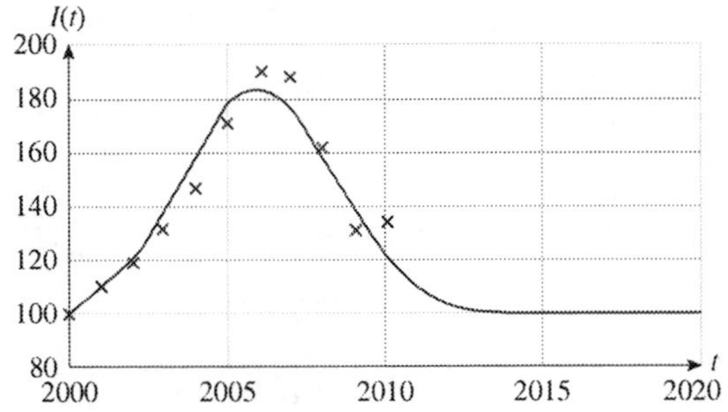

Estimate and interpret $\lim_{t\to+\infty} I(t)$.

46. ***Home Prices: Optimist Projection*** The following graph shows the values of the home price index[13] for 2000–2010 together with another mathematical model I extrapolating the data.

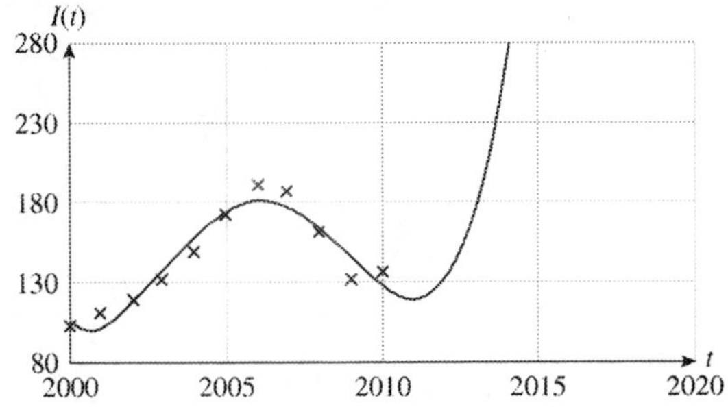

Estimate and interpret $\lim_{t\to+\infty} I(t)$.

47. ***Electric Rates*** The cost of electricity in Portland, Oregon, for residential customers increased suddenly on October 1, 2001, from around \$0.06 to around \$0.08 per kilowatt hour.[14] Let $C(t)$ be this cost at time t, and take $t = 1$ to represent October 1, 2001. What does the given information tell you about $\lim_{t\to 1} C(t)$?

48. ***Airline Stocks*** Prior to the September 11, 2001 attacks, United Airlines stock was trading at around \$35 per share. Immediately following the attacks, the share price dropped by \$15.[15] Let $U(t)$ be this cost at time t, and take $t = 11$ to represent September 11, 2001. What does the given information tell you about $\lim_{t\to 11} U(t)$?

[12]The index is the Standard & Poor/Case-Shiller Home Price Index. Source for data: www.standardandpoors.com.

[13]*Ibid.*

[14]Source: Portland General Electric/*New York Times*, February 2, 2002, p. C1.

[15]Stock prices are approximate.

Foreign Trade *Annual U.S. imports from China in the years 1996 through 2003 can be approximated by*

$$I(t) = t^2 + 3.5t + 50 \qquad (1 \le t \le 9)$$

billion dollars, where t represents time in years since 1995. Annual U.S. exports to China in the same years can be approximated by

$$E(t) = 0.4t^2 - 1.6t + 14$$

billion dollars.[16] *Exercises 49 and 50 are based on these models.*

49. ▼ Assuming the trends shown in the above models continued indefinitely, numerically estimate

$$\lim_{t\to+\infty} I(t) \text{ and } \lim_{t\to+\infty} \frac{I(t)}{E(t)},$$

interpret your answers, and comment on the results.

50. ▼ Repeat Exercise 49, this time calculating

$$\lim_{t\to+\infty} E(t) \text{ and } \lim_{t\to+\infty} \frac{E(t)}{I(t)}.$$

COMMUNICATION AND REASONING EXERCISES

51. Describe the method of evaluating limits numerically. Give at least one disadvantage of this method.

52. Describe the method of evaluating limits graphically. Give at least one disadvantage of this method.

53. Your friend Dion, a business student, claims that the study of limits that do not exist is completely unrealistic and has nothing to do with the world of business. Give two examples from the world of business that might convince him that he is wrong.

54. Your other friend Fiona claims that the study of limits is a complete farce; all you ever need to do to find the limit as x approaches a is substitute $x = a$. Give two examples that show she is wrong.

55. ▼ What is wrong with the following statement? "Because $f(a)$ is not defined, $\lim_{x\to a} f(x)$ does not exist." Illustrate your claim with an example.

56. ▼ What is wrong with the following statement? "Because $f(a)$ is defined, $\lim_{x\to a} f(x)$ exists." Illustrate your claim with an example.

57. ◆ Give an example of a function f with $\lim_{x\to 1} f(x) = f(2)$.

58. ◆ If $S(t)$ represents the size of the universe in billions of light years at time t years since the big bang and $\lim_{t\to+\infty} S(t) = 130{,}000$, is it possible that the universe will continue to expand forever?

59. ◆ Investigate $\lim_{x\to+\infty} x^n e^{-x}$ for some large values of n. What do you find? What do you think is the value of $\lim_{x\to+\infty} p(x)e^{-x}$ if $p(x)$ is any polynomial?

60. ◆ Investigate $\lim_{x\to-\infty} x^n e^{x}$ for some large values of n. What do you find? What do you think is the value of $\lim_{x\to-\infty} p(x)e^{x}$ if $p(x)$ is any polynomial?

[16]Based on quadratic regression using data from the U.S. Census Bureau Foreign Trade Division Web site www.census.gov/foreign-trade/sitc1/ as of December 2004.

Practice Problems 10.1, Part 1

1. I was hanging around an internet chat room the other day and somebody proposed the following: $\lim_{x \to 0} \frac{7^x - 1}{x} = \ln 7$. Should I believe this person? Fill in the following table (round results to five decimal places) and sketch a graph in the provided space to support your recommendation. If you believe the claim is incorrect, then include in your recommendation an appropriate correction.

x	−0.01	−0.001	−0.0001	0.0001	0.001	0.01
$\frac{7^x - 1}{x}$						

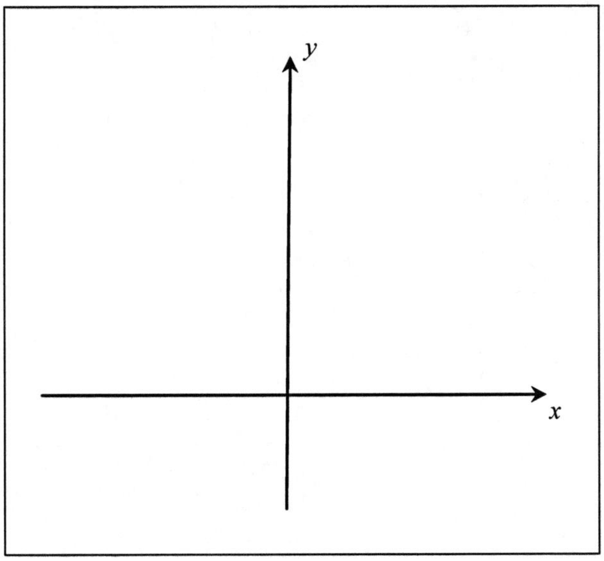

Recommendation:

Practice Problems 10.1, Part 2

1. Consider $\lim_{x \to 9} \frac{3-\sqrt{x}}{x-9}$. Determine whether or not the limit exists. If the limit exists, then propose a value for the limit. Support your conclusion with appropriate graphical **and** numerical evidence (use the table and space provided).

x	8.99	8.999	8.9999	9.0001	9.001	9.01
$\frac{3-\sqrt{x}}{x-9}$	-.16671	-.16667	-.166667	-0.1666662	-0.166662	-0.1666662

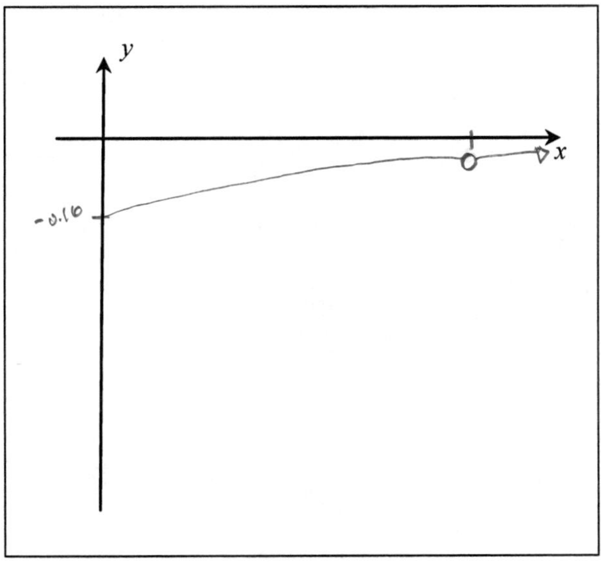

-0.16

Proposal:

LIMIT EXISTS

f(x) IS NOT DEFINED AT X=9

BUT $\lim_{x \to 9} f(x)$ EXISTS

X=9 IS NOT IN DOMAIN OF f(x)

Practice Problems 10.1, Part 3

A slip of paper was found on a table in one of the classrooms on campus. Written upon this slip of paper was the following tidbit.

$$\lim_{x\to 0}\frac{e^{8x}-1}{10x}=\frac{e^{0}-1}{10(0)}=\frac{1-1}{0}=\frac{0}{0},\text{ so the limit does not exist.}$$

Is the conclusion that was drawn correct? If so, explain why. If not, explain why not. If you believe the limit in question exists, then propose a value for the limit and support for your contention (use numerical and graphical evidence).

10.2 Limits and Continuity

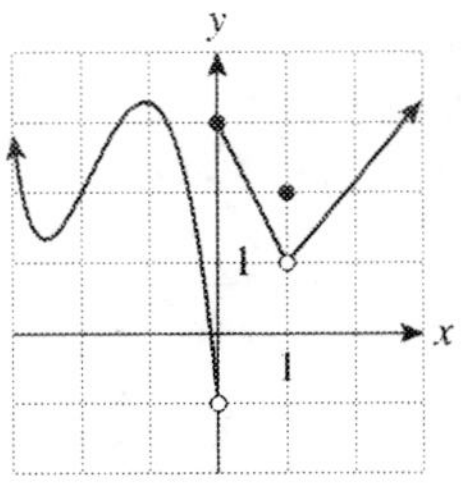

Figure 9

In the last section we saw examples of graphs that had various kinds of "breaks" or "jumps." For instance, in Example 4 we looked at the graph in Figure 9. This graph appears to have breaks, or **discontinuities**, at $x = 0$ and at $x = 1$. At $x = 0$ we saw that $\lim_{x\to 0} f(x)$ does not exist because the left- and right-hand limits are not the same. Thus, the discontinuity at $x = 0$ seems to be due to the fact that the limit does not exist there. On the other hand, at $x = 1$, $\lim_{x\to 1} f(x)$ *does* exist (it is equal to 1), but is not equal to $f(1) = 2$.

Thus, we have identified two kinds of discontinuity:

1. Points where the limit of the function does not exist. — $x = 0$ in Figure 9 because $\lim_{x\to 0} f(x)$ does not exist.
2. Points where the limit exists but does not equal the value of the function. — $x = 1$ in Figure 9 because $\lim_{x\to 1} f(x) = 1 \neq f(1)$

On the other hand, there is no discontinuity at, say, $x = -2$, where we find that $\lim_{x\to -2} f(x)$ exists and equals 2 and $f(-2)$ is also equal to 2. In other words,

$$\lim_{x\to -2} f(x) = 2 = f(-2).$$

The point $x = -2$ is an example of a point where f is **continuous**. (Notice that you can draw the portion of the graph near $x = -2$ without lifting your pencil from the paper.) Similarly, f is continuous at *every* point other than $x = 0$ and $x = 1$. Here is the mathematical definition.

Continuous Function

Let f be a function and let a be a number in the domain of f. Then f is **continuous at a** if

a. $\lim_{x\to a} f(x)$ exists, and

b. $\lim_{x\to a} f(x) = f(a)$.

If the number a is an endpoint of the domain, we will understand that the limit is the left or right limit, as appropriate.

The function f is said to be **continuous on its domain** if it is continuous at each point in its domain.

If f is not continuous at a particular a in its domain, we say that f is **discontinuous** at a or that f has a **discontinuity** at a. Thus, a discontinuity can occur at $x = a$ if either

a. $\lim_{x\to a} f(x)$ does not exist, or

b. $\lim_{x\to a} f(x)$ exists but is not equal to $f(a)$.

Quick Examples

1. The function shown in Figure 9 is continuous at $x = -1$ and $x = 2$. It is discontinuous at $x = 0$ and $x = 1$, and so is not continuous on its domain.
2. The function $f(x) = x^2$ is continuous on its domain. (Think of its graph, which contains no breaks.)

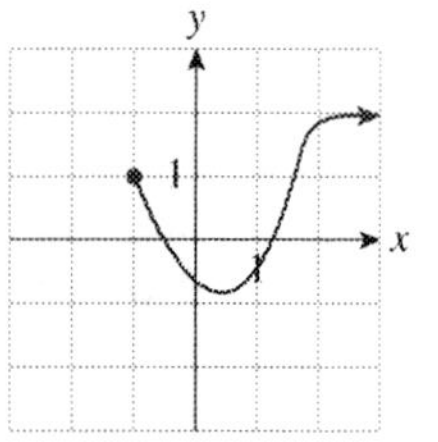

Figure 10

3. The function shown in Figure 10 is continuous on its domain. In particular, it is continuous at the left endpoint $x = -1$ of its domain, because $\lim_{x \to -1^+} f(x) = 1 = f(-1)$ (recall that we use only a one-sided limit at an endpoint of the domain).
4. The function f whose graph is shown on the left in the following figure is continuous on its domain. (Although the graph breaks at $x = 2$, that is not a point of its domain.) The function g whose graph is shown on the right is not continuous on its domain because it has a discontinuity at $x = 2$. (Here, $x = 2$ is a point of the domain of g.)

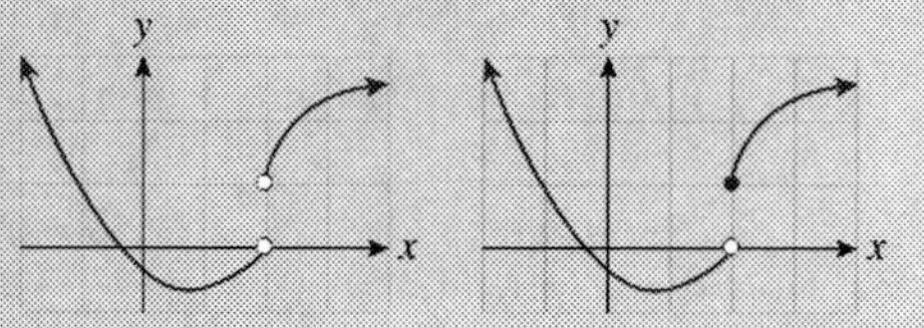

$y = f(x)$: Continuous on its domain

$y = g(x)$: Not continuous on its domain

Note Continuity and discontinuity of a function are defined only for points in a function's domain; a function cannot be continuous at a point not in its domain, and it cannot be discontinuous there either. So, if a is not in the domain of f—that is, if $f(a)$ is not defined—then it is meaningless to talk about whether f is continuous or discontinuous at a. ■

EXAMPLE 1 Continuous and Discontinuous Functions

Which of the following functions are continuous on their domains?

a. $h(x) = \begin{cases} x + 3 & \text{if } x \le 1 \\ 5 - x & \text{if } x > 1 \end{cases}$ **b.** $k(x) = \begin{cases} x + 3 & \text{if } x \le 1 \\ 1 - x & \text{if } x > 1 \end{cases}$

c. $f(x) = \dfrac{1}{x}$ **d.** $g(x) = \begin{cases} \dfrac{1}{x} & \text{if } x \ne 0 \\ 0 & \text{if } x = 0 \end{cases}$

Solution

a and **b.** The graphs of h and k are shown in Figure 11.

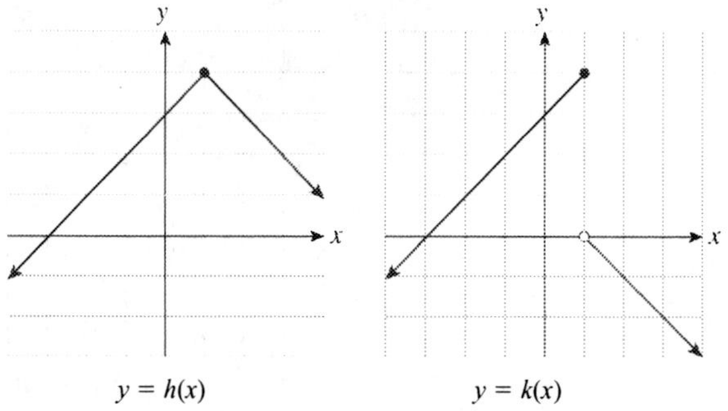

Figure 11

Even though the graph of h is made up of two different line segments, it is continuous at every point of its domain, including $x = 1$ because

$$\lim_{x\to 1} h(x) = 4 = h(1).$$

On the other hand, $x = 1$ is also in the domain of k, but $\lim_{x\to 1} k(x)$ does not exist. Thus, k is discontinuous at $x = 1$ and thus not continuous on its domain.

c and **d.** The graphs of f and g are shown in Figure 12.

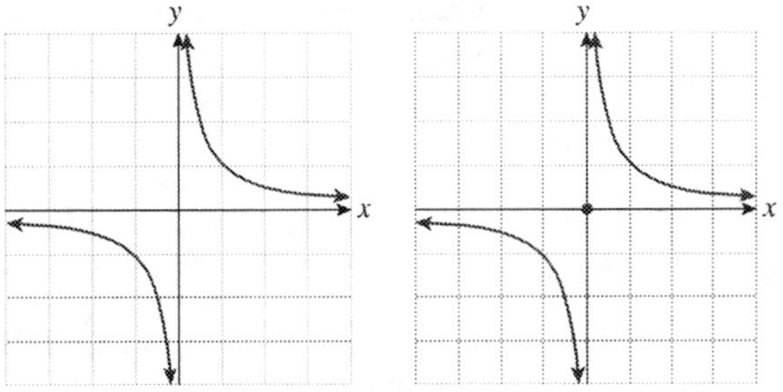

$y = f(x)$ $y = g(x)$

Figure 12

The domain of f consists of all real numbers except 0 and f is continuous at all such numbers. (Notice that 0 is not in the domain of f, so the question of continuity at 0 does not arise.) Thus, f is continuous on its domain.

The function g, on the other hand, has its domain expanded to include 0, so we now need to check whether g is continuous at 0. From the graph, it is easy to see that g is discontinuous there because $\lim_{x\to 0} g(x)$ does not exist. Thus, g is not continuous on its domain because it is discontinuous at 0.

using Technology

We can use technology to draw (approximate) graphs of the functions in Example 1(a), (b), and (c). Here are the technology formulas that will work for the TI-83/84 Plus, spreadsheets, and Website function evaluator and grapher. (In the TI-83/84 Plus, replace <= by ≤. In spreadsheets, replace x by a cell reference and insert an equals sign in front of the formula.)

a. `(x+3)*(x<=1)`
`+(5-x)*(x>1)`

b. `(x+3)*(x<=1)`
`+(1-x)*(x>1)`

c. `(1/x)`

Observe in each case how technology handles the breaks in the curves.

Before we go on...

Q: *Wait a minute! How can a function like $f(x) = 1/x$ be continuous when its graph has a break in it?*

A: We are not claiming that f is continuous *at every real number.* What we are saying is that f is continuous *on its domain;* the break in the graph occurs at a point not in the domain of f. In other words, f is continuous on the set of all nonzero real numbers; it is not continuous on the set of *all* real numbers because it is not even defined on that set.

EXAMPLE 2 Continuous Except at a Point

In each case, say what, if any, value of $f(a)$ would make f continuous at a.

a. $f(x) = \dfrac{x^3 - 8}{x - 2}$; $a = 2$ **b.** $f(x) = \dfrac{e^{2x} - 1}{x}$; $a = 0$ **c.** $f(x) = \dfrac{|x|}{x}$; $a = 0$

Solution

a. In Figure 13 we see the graph of $f(x) = \dfrac{x^3 - 8}{x - 2}$. The point corresponding to $x = 2$ is missing because f is not (yet) defined there. (Your graphing utility will probably miss this subtlety and render a continuous curve. See the technology note in the margin.) To turn f into a function that is continuous at $x = 2$, we need

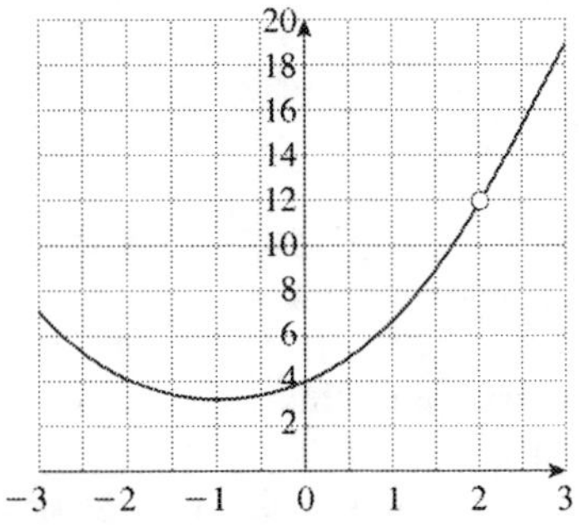

Figure 13

to "fill in the gap" so as to obtain a continuous curve. Since the graph suggests that the missing point is (2, 12), let us define $f(2) = 12$.

Does f now become continuous if we take $f(2) = 12$? From the graph, or Example 1(a) of Section 10.1,

$$\lim_{x\to 2} f(x) = \lim_{x\to 2} \frac{x^3 - 8}{x - 2} = 12,$$

which is now equal to $f(2)$. Thus, $\lim_{x\to 2} f(x) = f(2)$, showing that f is now continuous at $x = 2$.

b. In Example 1(b) of the preceding section, we saw that

$$\lim_{x\to 0} f(x) = \lim_{x\to 0} \frac{e^{2x} - 1}{x} = 2,$$

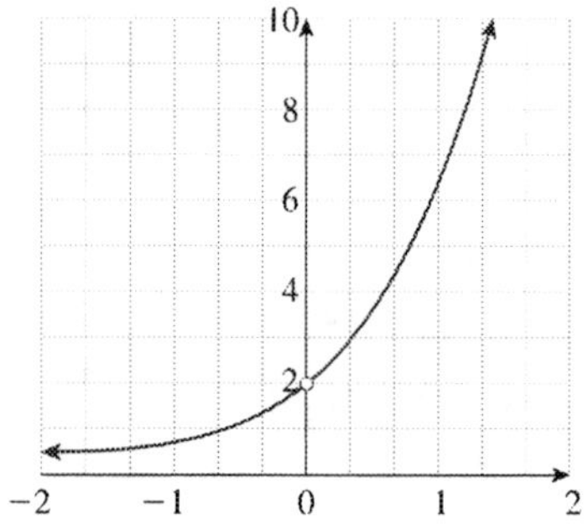

Figure 14

and so, as in part (a), we must define $f(0) = 2$. This is confirmed by the graph, shown in Figure 14.

c. We considered the function $f(x) = |x|/x$ in Example 2 in Section 10.1. Its graph is shown in Figure 15.

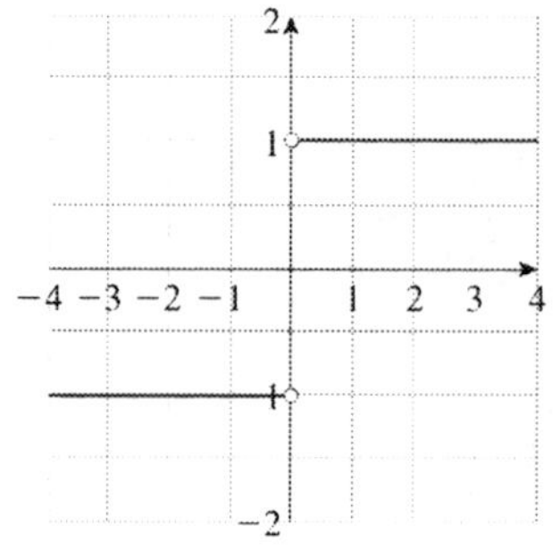

Figure 15

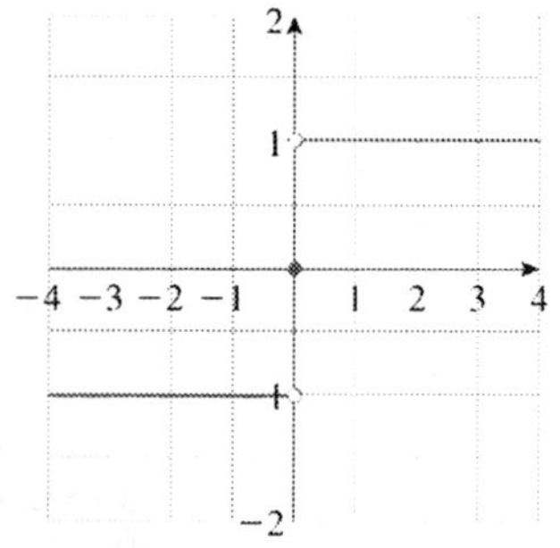

Figure 16

Now we encounter a problem: No matter how we try to fill in the gap at $x = 0$, the result will be a discontinuous function. For example, setting $f(0) = 0$ will result in the discontinuous function shown in Figure 16. We conclude that it is impossible to assign any value to $f(0)$ to turn f into a function that is continuous at $x = 0$.

We can also see this result algebraically: In Example 2 of Section 10.1, we saw that $\lim_{x\to 0} \frac{|x|}{x}$ does not exist. Thus, the resulting function will fail to be continuous at 0, no matter how we define $f(0)$.

using Technology

It is instructive to see how technology handles the functions in Example 2. Here are the technology formulas that will work for the TI-83/84 Plus, spreadsheets, and Website function evaluator and grapher. (In spreadsheets, replace `x` by a cell reference and insert an equal sign in front of the formula.)

a. `(x^3-8)/(x-2)`

b. `(e^(2x)-1)/x`

Spreadsheet:
`=(exp(2*A2)-1)/A2`

c. `abs(x)/x`

In each case, compare the graph rendered by technology with the corresponding figure in Example 2.

A function not defined at an isolated point is said to have a **singularity** at that point. The function in part (a) of Example 2 has a singularity at $x = 2$, and the functions in parts (b) and (c) have singularities at $x = 0$. The functions in parts (a) and (b) have **removable singularities** because we can make these functions continuous at $x = a$ by properly defining $f(a)$. The function in part (c) has an **essential singularity** because we cannot make f continuous at $x = a$ just by defining $f(a)$ properly.

10.2 EXERCISES

▼ more advanced ◆ challenging

T indicates exercises that should be solved using technology

In Exercises 1–14, the graph of a function f is given. Determine whether f is continuous on its domain. If it is not continuous on its domain, say why. HINT [See Quick Examples page 702.]

1.
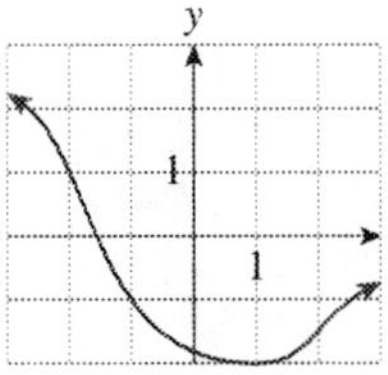

2.
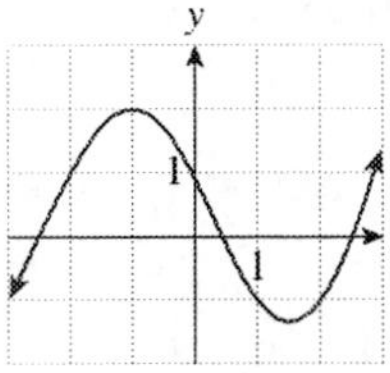

3.
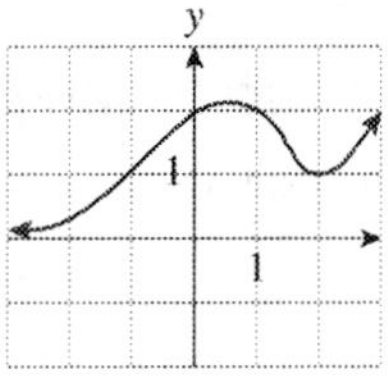

4.
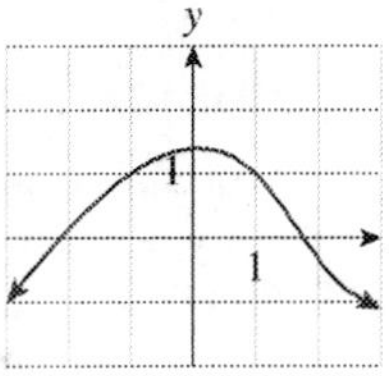

5.
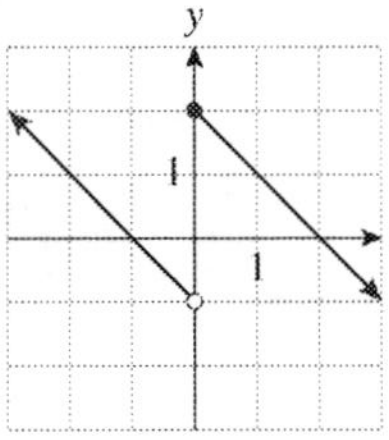

6.
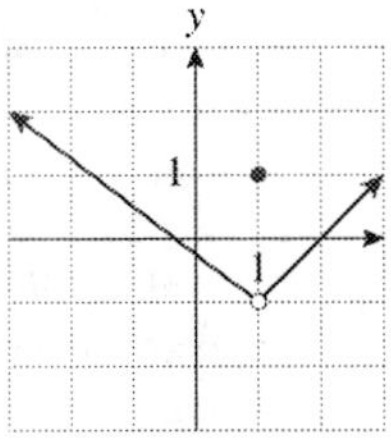

7.
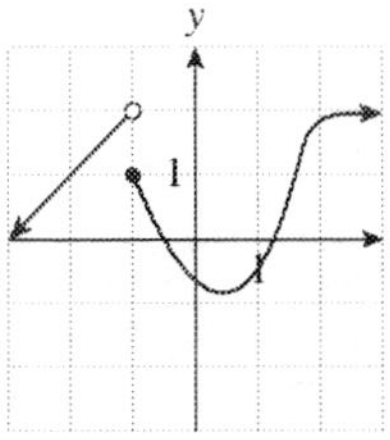

8.
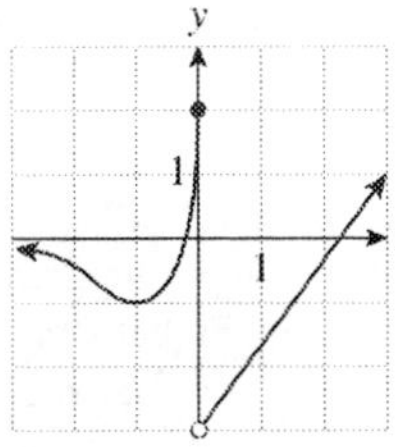

9.
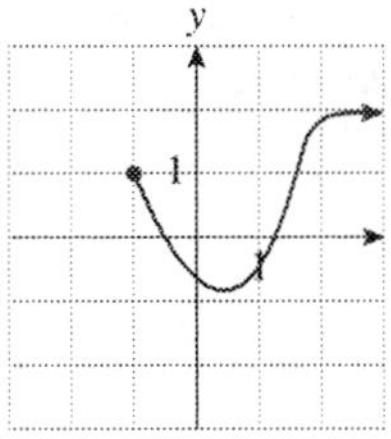

10.
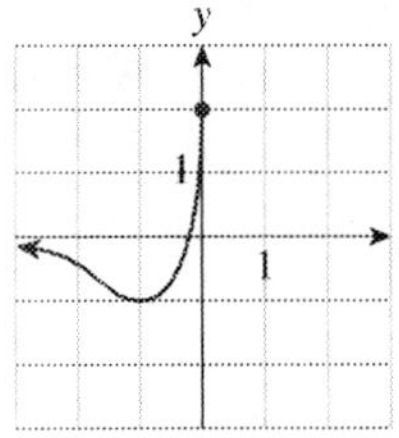

11.
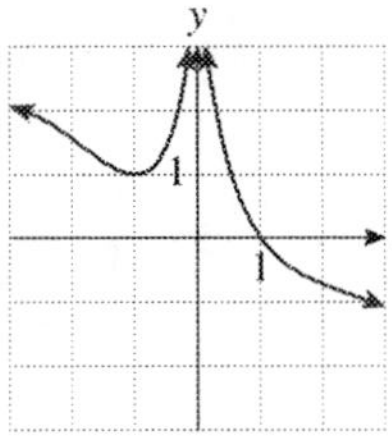

12.
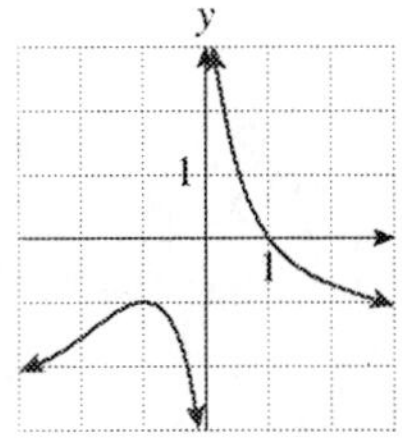

13.
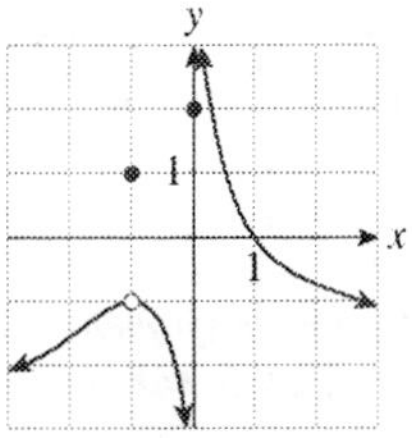

14.
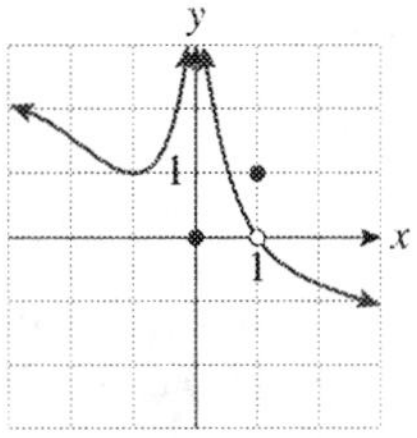

In Exercises 15 and 16, identify which (if any) of the given graphs represent functions continuous on their domains. HINT [See Quick Examples page 702.]

15. **(A)**
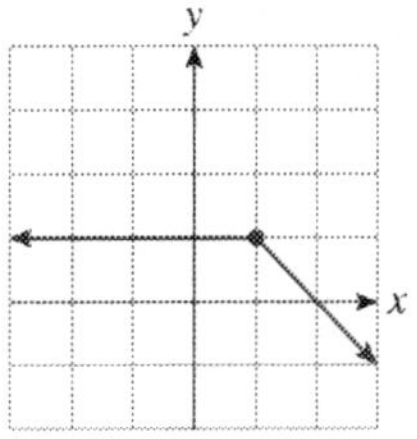

(B)
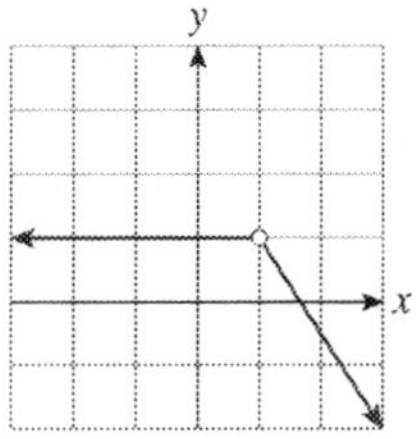

(C)
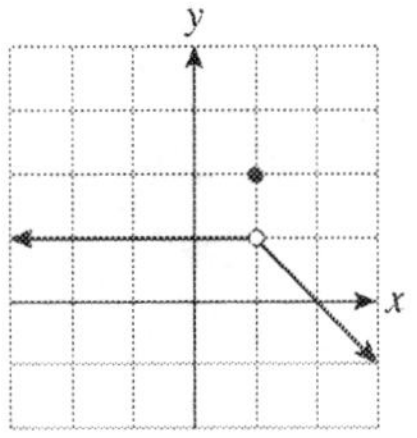

(D)
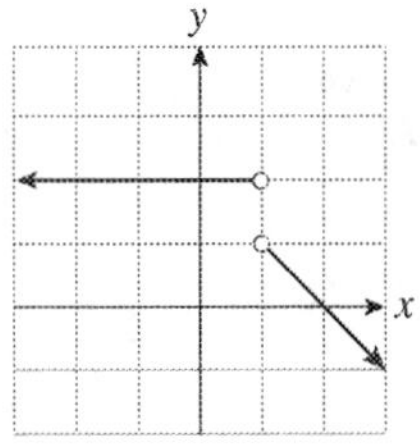

(E)
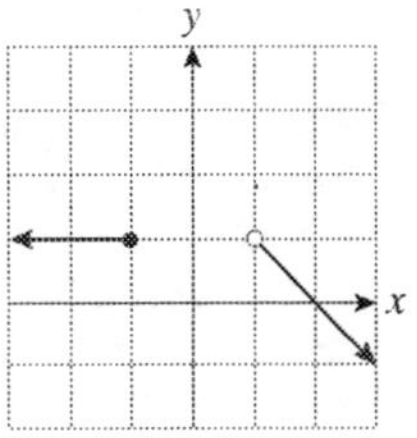

(F)
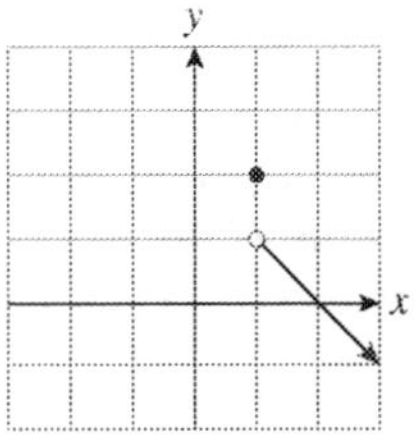

16. **(A)**
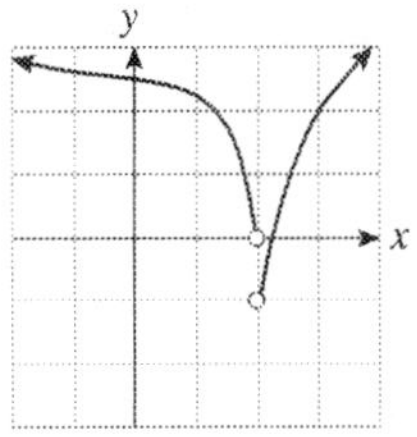

(B)
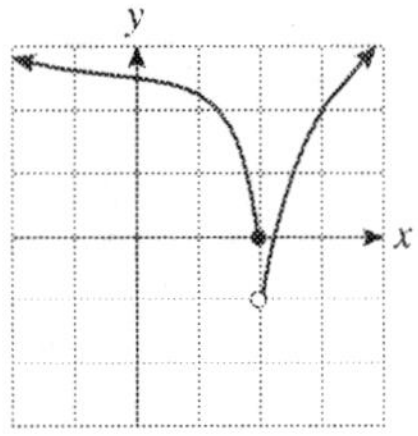

(C)
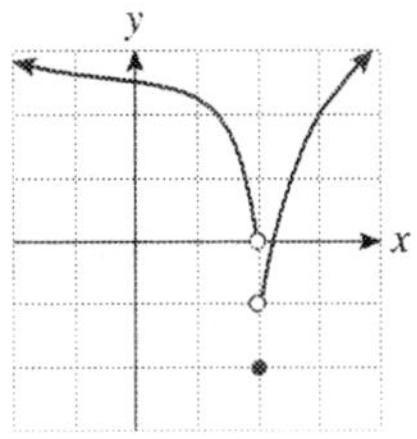

(D)
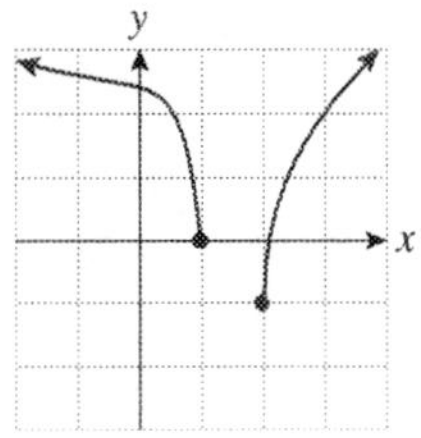

(E)

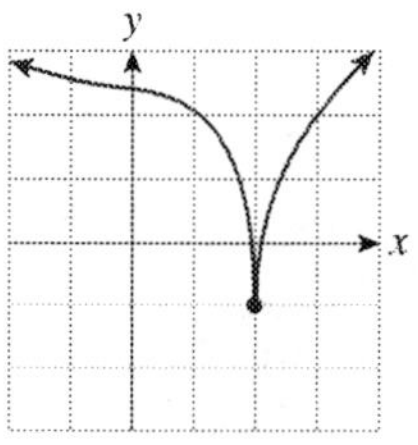

(F)

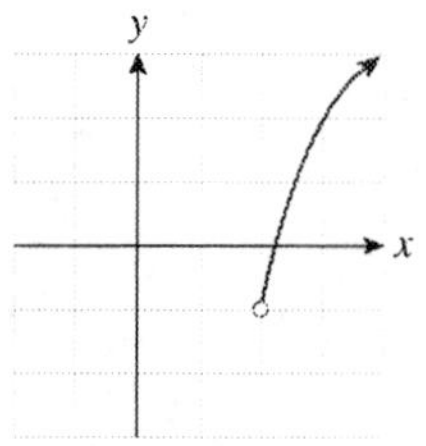

In Exercises 17–24, use a graph of f or some other method to determine what, if any, value to assign to f(a) to make f continuous at x = a. HINT [See Example 2.]

17. $f(x) = \dfrac{x^2 - 2x + 1}{x - 1}$; $a = 1$

18. $f(x) = \dfrac{x^2 + 3x + 2}{x + 1}$; $a = -1$

19. $f(x) = \dfrac{x}{3x^2 - x}$; $a = 0$

20. $f(x) = \dfrac{x^2 - 3x}{x + 4}$; $a = -4$

21. $f(x) = \dfrac{3}{3x^2 - x}$; $a = 0$

22. $f(x) = \dfrac{x - 1}{x^3 - 1}$; $a = 1$

23. $f(x) = \dfrac{1 - e^x}{x}$; $a = 0$

24. $f(x) = \dfrac{1 + e^x}{1 - e^x}$; $a = 0$

In Exercises 25–34, use a graph to determine whether the given function is continuous on its domain. If it is not continuous on its domain, list the points of discontinuity. HINT [See Example 1.]

25. $f(x) = |x|$

26. $f(x) = \dfrac{|x|}{x}$

27. $g(x) = \dfrac{1}{x^2 - 1}$

28. $g(x) = \dfrac{x - 1}{x + 2}$

29. $f(x) = \begin{cases} x + 2 & \text{if } x < 0 \\ 2x - 1 & \text{if } x \geq 0 \end{cases}$

30. $f(x) = \begin{cases} 1 - x & \text{if } x \leq 1 \\ x - 1 & \text{if } x > 1 \end{cases}$

31. $h(x) = \begin{cases} \dfrac{|x|}{x} & \text{if } x \neq 0 \\ 0 & \text{if } x = 0 \end{cases}$

32. $h(x) = \begin{cases} \dfrac{1}{x^2} & \text{if } x \neq 0 \\ 2 & \text{if } x = 0 \end{cases}$

33. $g(x) = \begin{cases} x + 2 & \text{if } x < 0 \\ 2x + 2 & \text{if } x \geq 0 \end{cases}$

34. $g(x) = \begin{cases} 1 - x & \text{if } x \leq 1 \\ x + 1 & \text{if } x > 1 \end{cases}$

COMMUNICATION AND REASONING EXERCISES

35. If a function is continuous on its domain, is it continuous at every real number? Explain.

36. True or false? The graph of a function that is continuous on its domain is a continuous curve with no breaks in it. Explain your answer.

37. True or false? The graph of a function that is continuous at every real number is a continuous curve with no breaks in it. Explain your answer.

38. True or false? If the graph of a function is a continuous curve with no breaks in it, then the function is continuous on its domain. Explain your answer.

39. ▼ Give a formula for a function that is continuous on its domain but whose graph consists of three distinct curves.

40. ▼ Give a formula for a function that is not continuous at $x = -1$ but is not discontinuous there either.

41. ▼ Draw the graph of a function that is discontinuous at every integer.

42. ▼ Draw the graph of a function that is continuous on its domain but whose graph has a break at every integer.

43. ▼ Describe a real-life scenario in the stock market that can be modeled by a discontinuous function.

44. ▼ Describe a real-life scenario in your room that can be modeled by a discontinuous function.

Practice Problems 10.2

Consider the function $f(x)$ defined by $f(x) = \begin{cases} 3x - 2 & \text{if } x < -1 \\ 4 - x^2 & \text{if } -1 \le x \le 3 \\ mx + 8 & \text{if } x > 3 \end{cases}$.

1. Calculate $\lim_{x \to -1^-} f(x)$.

2. Calculate $\lim_{x \to -1^+} f(x)$.

3. Calculate $\lim_{x \to 3^-} f(x)$.

4. Calculate $\lim_{x \to 3^+} f(x)$ (your result will involve m).

5. Determine the appropriate value of m so that $f(x)$ is continuous at $x = 3$ and sketch a graph of $f(x)$ on the provided grid (assume that gridlines each mark one unit).

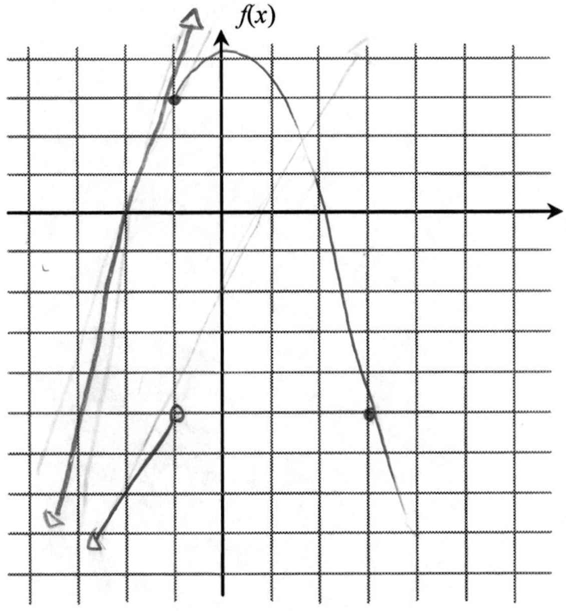

10.3 Limits and Continuity: Algebraic Viewpoint

Although numerical and graphical estimation of limits is effective, the estimates these methods yield may not be perfectly accurate. The algebraic method, when it can be used, will always yield an exact answer. Moreover, algebraic analysis of a function often enables us to take a function apart and see "what makes it tick."

Let's start with the function $f(x) = 2 + x$ and ask: What happens to $f(x)$ as x approaches 3? To answer this algebraically, notice that as x gets closer and closer to 3, the quantity $2 + x$ must get closer and closer to $2 + 3 = 5$. Hence,

$$\lim_{x \to 3} f(x) = \lim_{x \to 3}(2 + x) = 2 + 3 = 5$$

Q: *Is that all there is to the algebraic method? Just substitute $x = a$?*

A: Under certain circumstances: Notice that by substituting $x = 3$ we *evaluated the function at $x = 3$*. In other words, we relied on the fact that

$$\lim_{x \to 3} f(x) = f(3).$$

In Section 10.2 we said that a function satisfying this equation is *continuous* at $x = 3$.

Thus,

If we know that the function f is continuous at a point a, we can compute $\lim_{x \to a} f(x)$ by simply substituting $x = a$ into $f(x)$.

To use this fact, we need to know how to recognize continuous functions when we see them. Geometrically, they are easy to spot: A function is continuous at $x = a$ if its graph has no break at $x = a$. Algebraically, a large class of functions are known to be continuous on their domains—those, roughly speaking, that are *specified by a single formula*.

We can be more precise: A **closed-form function** is any function that can be obtained by combining constants, powers of x, exponential functions, radicals, logarithms, absolute values, trigonometric functions (and some other functions we do not encounter in this text) into a *single* mathematical formula by means of the usual arithmetic operations and composition of functions. (They can be as complicated as we like.)

Closed-Form Functions

A function is **written in closed form** if it is specified by combining constants, powers of x, exponential functions, radicals, logarithms, absolute values, trigonometric functions (and some other functions we do not encounter in this text) into a *single* mathematical formula by means of the usual arithmetic operations and composition of functions. A **closed-form function** is any function that can be written in closed form.

Quick Examples

1. $3x^2 - |x| + 1$, $\dfrac{\sqrt{x^2 - 1}}{6x - 1}$, $e^{-\frac{4x^2 - 1}{x}}$, and $\sqrt{\log_3(x^2 - 1)}$ are written in closed form, so they are all closed-form functions.

2. $f(x) = \begin{cases} -1 & \text{if } x \le -1 \\ x^2 + x & \text{if } -1 < x \le 1 \\ 2 - x & \text{if } 1 < x \le 2 \end{cases}$ is not written in closed-form because $f(x)$ is not expressed by a *single* mathematical formula.*

* It is possible to rewrite some piecewise-defined functions in closed form (using a single formula), but not this particular function, so $f(x)$ is not a closed-form function.

What is so special about closed-form functions is the following theorem.

Theorem 10.1 Continuity of Closed-Form Functions

Every closed-form function is continuous on its domain. Thus, if f is a closed-form function and $f(a)$ is defined, then $\lim_{x \to a} f(x)$ exists, and equals $f(a)$. (When a is an endpoint of the domain of f, we understand the limit to be the appropriate one-sided limit.)

Quick Example

$f(x) = 1/x$ is a closed-form function, and its natural domain consists of all real numbers except 0. Thus, f is continuous at every nonzero real number. That is,

$$\lim_{x \to a} \frac{1}{x} = \frac{1}{a}$$

provided $a \neq 0$.

Mathematics majors spend a great deal of time studying the proof of this theorem. We ask you to accept it without proof.

EXAMPLE 1 Limit of a Closed-Form Function

Evaluate the following limits algebraically:

a. $\lim_{x \to 1} \frac{x^3 - 8}{x - 2}$ **b.** $\lim_{x \to 2} \frac{x^3 - 8}{x - 2}$.

Solution

a. First, notice that $(x^3 - 8)/(x - 2)$ is a closed-form function because it is specified by a single algebraic formula. Also, $x = 1$ is in the domain of this function. Therefore the theorem applies, and

$$\lim_{x \to 1} \frac{x^3 - 8}{x - 2} = \frac{1^3 - 8}{1 - 2} = 7.$$

b. Although $(x^3 - 8)/(x - 2)$ is a closed-form function, $x = 2$ is not in its domain. Thus, the theorem does not apply and we cannot obtain the limit by substitution. However—and this is the key to finding such limits—*some preliminary algebraic simplification will allow us to obtain a closed-form function with $x = 2$ in its domain.* To do this, notice first that the numerator can be factored as

$$x^3 - 8 = (x - 2)(x^2 + 2x + 4).$$

Thus,

$$\frac{x^3 - 8}{x - 2} = \frac{(x - 2)(x^2 + 2x + 4)}{x - 2} = x^2 + 2x + 4.$$

Once we have canceled the offending $(x - 2)$ in the denominator, we are left with a closed-form function *with 2 in its domain*. Thus,

$$\lim_{x\to 2} \frac{x^3 - 8}{x - 2} = \lim_{x\to 2}(x^2 + 2x + 4)$$

$$= 2^2 + 2(2) + 4 = 12. \quad \text{Substitute } x = 2.$$

This confirms the answer we found numerically in Example 1 in Section 10.1.

➡ **Before we go on...** Notice that in Example 1(b) before simplification, the substitution $x = 2$ yields

$$\frac{x^3 - 8}{x - 2} = \frac{8 - 8}{2 - 2} = \frac{0}{0}.$$

Worse than the fact that 0/0 is undefined, it also conveys absolutely no information as to what the limit might be. (The limit turned out to be 12!) We therefore call the expression 0/0 an **indeterminate form**. Once simplified, the function became $x^2 + 2x + 4$, which, upon the substitution $x = 2$, yielded 12—no longer an indeterminate form. In general, we have the following rule of thumb:

If the substitution $x = a$ yields the indeterminate form 0/0, try simplifying by the method in Example 1.

We will say more about indeterminate forms in Example 2. ■

Q: *There is something suspicious about Example 1(b). If 2 was not in the domain before simplifying but was in the domain after simplifying, we must have changed the function, right?*

A: Correct. In fact, when we said that

$$\underbrace{\frac{x^3 - 8}{x - 2}}_{\text{Domain excludes 2}} = \underbrace{x^2 + 2x + 4}_{\text{Domain includes 2}}$$

we were lying a little bit. What we really meant is that these two expressions are equal *where both are defined*. The functions $(x^3 - 8)/(x - 2)$ and $x^2 + 2x + 4$ are different functions. The difference is that $x = 2$ is not in the domain of $(x^3 - 8)/(x - 2)$ and is in the domain of $x^2 + 2x + 4$. Since $\lim_{x\to 2} f(x)$ explicitly *ignores* any value that f may have at 2, this does not affect the limit. From the point of view of the limit at 2, these functions *are* equal. In general we have the following rule.

Functions with Equal Limits

If $f(x) = g(x)$ for all x except possibly $x = a$, then

$$\lim_{x\to a} f(x) = \lim_{x\to a} g(x).$$

Quick Example

$$\frac{x^2 - 1}{x - 1} = x + 1 \text{ for all } x \text{ except } x = 1.$$ Write $\frac{x^2 - 1}{x - 1}$ as $\frac{(x + 1)(x - 1)}{x - 1}$ and cancel the $(x - 1)$.

Therefore,

$$\lim_{x\to 1} \frac{x^2 - 1}{x - 1} = \lim_{x\to 1}(x + 1) = 1 + 1 = 2.$$

Q: *How do we find $\lim_{x \to a} f(x)$ when $x = a$ is not in the domain of the function f and we cannot simplify the given function to make a a point of the domain?*

A: In such a case, it might be necessary to analyze the function by some other method, such as numerically or graphically. However, if we do not obtain the indeterminate form 0/0 upon substitution, we can often say what the limit is, as the following example shows.

EXAMPLE 2 Limit of a Closed-Form Function at a Point Not in Its Domain: The Determinate Form *k*/0

Evaluate the following limits, if they exist:

a. $\lim_{x \to 1^+} \frac{x^2 - 4x + 1}{x - 1}$ **b.** $\lim_{x \to 1} \frac{x^2 - 4x + 1}{x - 1}$ **c.** $\lim_{x \to 1} \frac{x^2 - 4x + 1}{x^2 - 2x + 1}$

Solution

a. Although the function $f(x) = \frac{x^2 - 4x + 1}{x - 1}$ is a closed-form function, $x = 1$ is not in its domain. Notice that substituting $x = 1$ gives

$$\frac{x^2 - 4x + 1}{x - 1} = \frac{1^2 - 4 + 1}{1 - 1} = \frac{-2}{0}$$ The determinate form $\frac{k}{0}$

which, although not defined, conveys important information to us: As x gets closer and closer to 1, the numerator approaches -2 and the denominator gets closer and closer to 0. Now, if we divide a number close to -2 by a number close to zero, we get a number of large absolute value; for instance,

$$\frac{-2.1}{0.0001} = -21{,}000 \quad \text{and} \quad \frac{-2.1}{-0.0001} = 21{,}000$$

$$\frac{-2.01}{0.00001} = -201{,}000 \quad \text{and} \quad \frac{-2.01}{-0.00001} = 201{,}000.$$

(Compare Example 5 in Section 10.1.) In our limit for part (a), x is approaching 1 from the right, so the denominator $x - 1$ is positive (as x is to the right of 1). Thus we have the scenario illustrated previously on the left, and we can conclude that

$$\lim_{x \to 1^+} \frac{x^2 - 4x + 1}{x - 1} = -\infty.$$ Think of this as $\frac{-2}{0^+} = -\infty$.

b. This time, x could be approaching 1 from either side. We already have, from part (a)

$$\lim_{x \to 1^+} \frac{x^2 - 4x + 1}{x - 1} = -\infty.$$

The same reasoning we used in part (a) gives

$$\lim_{x \to 1^-} \frac{x^2 - 4x + 1}{x - 1} = +\infty$$ Think of this as $\frac{-2}{0^-} = +\infty$.

because now the denominator is negative and still approaching zero while the numerator still approaches -2 and therefore is also negative. (See the numerical calculations above on the right.) Because the left and right limits do not agree, we conclude that

$$\lim_{x \to 1} \frac{x^2 - 4x + 1}{x - 1} \text{ does not exist.}$$

c. First notice that the denominator factors:

$$\lim_{x\to 1}\frac{x^2-4x+1}{x^2-2x+1}=\lim_{x\to 1}\frac{x^2-4x+1}{(x-1)^2}.$$

As x approaches 1, the numerator approaches -2 as before, and the denominator approaches 0. However, this time, the denominator $(x-1)^2$, being a square, is ≥ 0, regardless of from which side x is approaching 1. Thus, the entire function is negative as x approaches 1, and

$$\lim_{x\to 1}\frac{x^2-4x+1}{(x-1)^2}=-\infty. \qquad \frac{-2}{0^+}=-\infty$$

Before we go on... In general, the determinate forms $\frac{k}{0^+}$ and $\frac{k}{0^-}$ will always yield $\pm\infty$, with the sign depending on the sign of the overall expression as $x \to a$. (When we write the form $\frac{k}{0}$ we always mean $k \neq 0$.) This and other determinate forms are discussed further after Example 4.

Figure 17 shows the graphs of $\frac{x^2-4x+1}{x-1}$ and $\frac{x^2-4x+1}{(x-1)^2}$ from Example 2. You should check that results we obtained above agree with a geometric analysis of these graphs near $x = 1$.

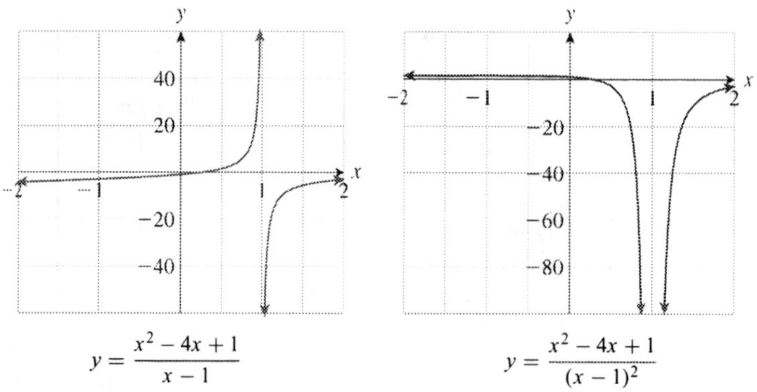

Figure 17

We can also use algebraic techniques to analyze functions that are not given in closed form.

EXAMPLE 3 Functions Not Written in Closed Form

For which values of x are the following piecewise defined functions continuous?

a. $f(x)=\begin{cases} x^2+2 & \text{if } x<1 \\ 2x-1 & \text{if } x\geq 1\end{cases}$ **b.** $g(x)=\begin{cases} x^2-x+1 & \text{if } x\leq 0 \\ 1-x & \text{if } 0<x\leq 1 \\ x-3 & \text{if } x>1\end{cases}$

Solution

a. The function $f(x)$ is given in closed form over the intervals $(-\infty, 1)$ and $[1, +\infty)$. At $x = 1$, $f(x)$ suddenly switches from one closed-form formula to another, so

$x = 1$ is the only place where there is a potential problem with continuity. To investigate the continuity of $f(x)$ at $x = 1$, let's calculate the limit there:

$$\lim_{x\to 1^-} f(x) = \lim_{x\to 1^-} (x^2 + 2) \qquad f(x) = x^2 + 2 \text{ for } x < 1.$$
$$= (1)^2 + 2 = 3 \qquad x^2 + 2 \text{ is closed-form.}$$
$$\lim_{x\to 1^+} f(x) = \lim_{x\to 1^+} (2x - 1) \qquad f(x) = 2x - 1 \text{ for } x > 1.$$
$$= 2(1) - 1 = 1. \qquad 2x - 1 \text{ is closed-form.}$$

Because the left and right limits are different, $\lim_{x\to 1} f(x)$ does not exist, and so $f(x)$ is discontinuous at $x = 1$.

b. The only potential points of discontinuity for $g(x)$ occur at $x = 0$ and $x = 1$:

$$\lim_{x\to 0^-} g(x) = \lim_{x\to 0^-} (x^2 - x + 1) = 1$$
$$\lim_{x\to 0^+} g(x) = \lim_{x\to 0^+} (1 - x) = 1.$$

Thus, $\lim_{x\to 0} g(x) = 1$. Further, $g(0) = 0^2 - 0 + 1 = 1$ from the formula, and so

$$\lim_{x\to 0} g(x) = g(0),$$

which shows that $g(x)$ is continuous at $x = 0$. At $x = 1$ we have

$$\lim_{x\to 1^-} g(x) = \lim_{x\to 1^-} (1 - x) = 0$$
$$\lim_{x\to 1^+} g(x) = \lim_{x\to 1^+} (x - 3) = -2$$

so that $\lim_{x\to 1} g(x)$ does not exist. Thus, $g(x)$ is discontinuous at $x = 1$. We conclude that $g(x)$ is continuous at every real number x except $x = 1$.

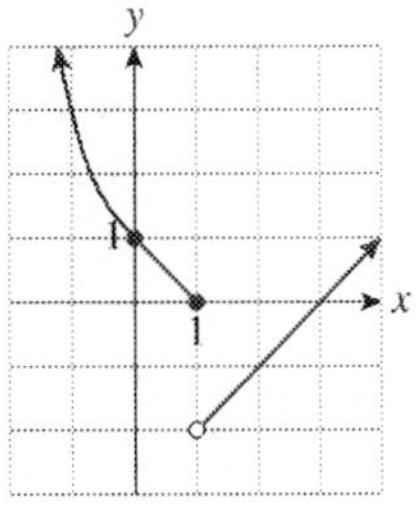

$y = g(x)$

Figure 18

Before we go on... Figure 18 shows the graph of g from Example 3(b). Notice how the discontinuity at $x = 1$ shows up as a break in the graph, whereas at $x = 0$ the two pieces "fit together" at the point (0, 1). ■

Limits at Infinity

Let's look once again at some limits similar to those in Examples 3 and 6 in Section 10.1.

EXAMPLE 4 Limits at Infinity

Compute the following limits, if they exist:

a. $\lim_{x\to +\infty} \frac{2x^2 - 4x}{x^2 - 1}$ **b.** $\lim_{x\to -\infty} \frac{2x^2 - 4x}{x^2 - 1}$

c. $\lim_{x\to +\infty} \frac{-x^3 - 4x}{2x^2 - 1}$ **d.** $\lim_{x\to +\infty} \frac{2x^2 - 4x}{5x^3 - 3x + 5}$

e. $\lim_{t\to +\infty} (e^{0.1t} - 20)$ **f.** $\lim_{t\to +\infty} \frac{80}{1 + 2.2(3.68)^{-t}}$

Solution a and **b.** While calculating the values for the tables used in Example 3 in Section 10.1, you might have noticed that the highest power of x in both the numerator and denominator dominated the calculations. For instance, when $x = 100{,}000$, the term $2x^2$ in the numerator has the value of 20,000,000,000, whereas the term $4x$ has the comparatively insignificant value of 400,000. Similarly, the term x^2 in the denominator overwhelms the term -1. In other words, for large values of x (or negative values with large magnitude),

$$\frac{2x^2-4x}{x^2-1} \approx \frac{2x^2}{x^2} = 2.$$ Use only the highest powers top and bottom.

Therefore,

$$\lim_{x\to\pm\infty}\frac{2x^2-4x}{x^2-1} = \lim_{x\to\pm\infty}\frac{2x^2}{x^2} = \lim_{x\to\pm\infty} 2 = 2.$$

The procedure of using only the highest powers of x to compute the limit is stated formally and justified after this example.

c. Applying the previous technique of looking only at highest powers gives

$$\lim_{x\to+\infty}\frac{-x^3-4x}{2x^2-1} = \lim_{x\to+\infty}\frac{-x^3}{2x^2}$$ Use only the highest powers top and bottom.

$$= \lim_{x\to+\infty}\frac{-x}{2}.$$ Simplify.

As x gets large, $-x/2$ gets large in magnitude but negative, so the limit is

$$\lim_{x\to+\infty}\frac{-x}{2} = -\infty.$$ $\frac{-\infty}{2} = -\infty$ (See below.)

d. $$\lim_{x\to+\infty}\frac{2x^2-4x}{5x^3-3x+5} = \lim_{x\to+\infty}\frac{2x^2}{5x^3}$$ Use only the highest powers top and bottom.

$$= \lim_{x\to+\infty}\frac{2}{5x}.$$

As x gets large, $2/(5x)$ gets close to zero, so the limit is

$$\lim_{x\to+\infty}\frac{2}{5x} = 0.$$ $\frac{2}{\infty} = 0$ (See below.)

e. Here we do not have a ratio of polynomials. However, we know that, as t becomes large and positive, so does $e^{0.1t}$, and hence also $e^{0.1t} - 20$. Thus,

$$\lim_{t\to+\infty}(e^{0.1t}-20) = +\infty$$ $e^{+\infty} = +\infty$ (See below.)

f. As $t \to +\infty$, the term $(3.68)^{-t} = \dfrac{1}{3.68^t}$ in the denominator, being 1 divided by a very large number, approaches zero. Hence the denominator $1 + 2.2(3.68)^{-t}$ approaches $1 + 2.2(0) = 1$ as $t \to +\infty$. Thus,

$$\lim_{t\to+\infty}\frac{80}{1+2.2(3.68)^{-t}} = \frac{80}{1+2.2(0)} = 80$$ $(3.68)^{-\infty} = 0$ (See below.)

Before we go on... Let's now look at the graph of the function $\dfrac{2x^2-4x}{x^2-1}$ in parts (a)and (b) of Example 4. We say that the graph of f has a **horizontal asymptote** at $y = 2$ because of the limits we have just calculated. This means that the graph approaches the horizontal line $y = 2$ far to the right or left (in this case, to both the right and left). Figure 19 shows the graph of f together with the line $y = 2$.

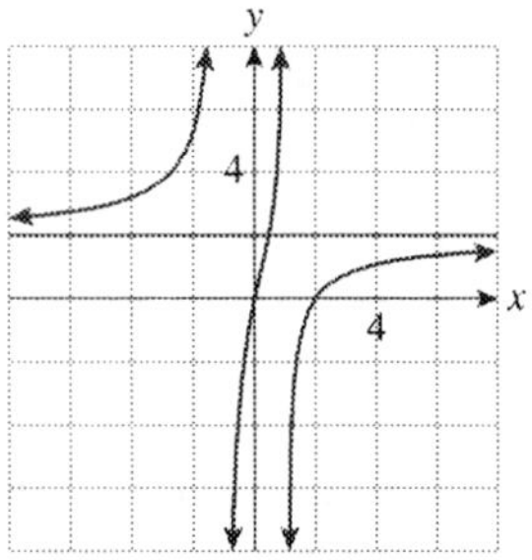

Figure 19

The graph reveals some additional interesting information: as $x \to 1^+$, $f(x) \to -\infty$, and as $x \to 1^-$, $f(x) \to +\infty$. Thus,

$$\lim_{x\to 1} f(x) \text{ does not exist.}$$

See if you can determine what happens as $x \to -1$.

If you graph the functions in parts (d) and (f) of Example 4, you will again see a horizontal asymptote. Do the limits in parts (c) and (e) show horizontal asymptotes? ■

It is worthwhile looking again at what we did in each of the limits in Example 4:

a and **b.** We saw that $\dfrac{2x^2 - 4x}{x^2 - 1} \approx \dfrac{2x^2}{x^2}$, and then we canceled the x^2. Notice that, before we cancel, letting x approach $\pm\infty$ in the numerator and denominator yields the ratio $\dfrac{\infty}{\infty}$, which, like $\dfrac{0}{0}$, is another *indeterminate form*, and indicates to us that further work is needed—in this case cancellation—before we can write down the limit.

c. We obtained $\dfrac{-x^3 - 4x}{2x^2 - 1} \approx \dfrac{-x^3}{2x^2}$, which results in another indeterminate form, $\dfrac{-\infty}{\infty}$, as $x \to +\infty$. Cancellation of the x^2 gave us $\dfrac{-x}{2}$, resulting in the *determinate* form $\dfrac{-\infty}{2} = -\infty$ (a very large number divided by 2 is again a very large number).

d. Here, $\dfrac{2x^2 - 4x}{5x^3 - 3x + 5} \approx \dfrac{2x^2}{5x^3} = \dfrac{2}{5x}$, and the cancellation step turns the indeterminate form $\dfrac{\infty}{\infty}$ into the determinate form $\dfrac{2}{\infty} = 0$ (dividing 2 by a very large number yields a very small number).

e. We reasoned that e raised to a large positive number is large and positive. Putting $t = +\infty$ gives us the determinate form $e^{+\infty} = +\infty$.

f. Here we reasoned that 3.68 raised to a large *negative* number is close to zero. Putting $t = -\infty$ gives us the determinate form $3.68^{-\infty} = 1/3.68^{+\infty} = 1/\infty = 0$ (see (d)).

In parts (a)–(d) of Example 4, $f(x)$ was a **rational function**: a quotient of polynomial functions. We calculated the limit of $f(x)$ at $\pm\infty$ by ignoring all powers of x in both the numerator and denominator except for the largest. Following is a theorem that justifies this procedure.

Theorem 10.2 Evaluating the Limit of a Rational Function at $\pm\infty$

If $f(x)$ has the form

$$f(x) = \frac{c_n x^n + c_{n-1}x^{n-1} + \cdots + c_1 x + c_0}{d_m x^m + d_{m-1}x^{m-1} + \cdots + d_1 x + d_0}$$

with the c_i and d_i constants ($c_n \neq 0$ and $d_m \neq 0$), then we can calculate the limit of $f(x)$ as $x \to \pm\infty$ by ignoring all powers of x except the highest in both the numerator and denominator. Thus,

$$\lim_{x\to\pm\infty} f(x) = \lim_{x\to\pm\infty} \frac{c_n x^n}{d_m x^m}.$$

Quick Examples

(See Example 4.)

1. $\lim_{x\to+\infty} \frac{2x^2-4x}{x^2-1} = \lim_{x\to+\infty} \frac{2x^2}{x^2} = \lim_{x\to+\infty} 2 = 2$

2. $\lim_{x\to+\infty} \frac{-x^3-4x}{2x^2-1} = \lim_{x\to+\infty} \frac{-x^3}{2x^2} = \lim_{x\to+\infty} \frac{-x}{2} = -\infty$

3. $\lim_{x\to+\infty} \frac{2x^2-4x}{5x^3-3x+5} = \lim_{x\to+\infty} \frac{2x^2}{5x^3} = \lim_{x\to+\infty} \frac{2}{5x} = 0$

Proof Our function $f(x)$ is a polynomial of degree n divided by a polynomial of degree m. If n happens to be larger than m, then dividing the top and bottom by the largest power x^n of x gives

$$f(x) = \frac{c_nx^n + c_{n-1}x^{n-1} + \cdots + c_1x + c_0}{d_mx^m + d_{m-1}x^{m-1} + \cdots + d_1x + d_0}$$

$$= \frac{c_nx^n/x^n + c_{n-1}x^{n-1}/x^n + \cdots + c_1x/x^n + c_0/x^n}{d_mx^m/x^n + d_{m-1}x^{m-1}/x^n + \cdots + d_1x/x^n + d_0/x^n}.$$

Canceling powers of x in each term and remembering that $n > m$ leaves us with

$$f(x) = \frac{c_n + c_{n-1}/x + \cdots + c_1/x^{n-1} + c_0/x^n}{d_m/x^{n-m} + d_{m-1}/x^{n-m+1} + \cdots + d_1/x^{n-1} + d_0/x^n}.$$

As $x \to \pm\infty$, all the terms shown in red approach 0, so we can ignore them in taking the limit. (The first term in the denominator happens to approach 0 as well, but we retain it for convenience.) Thus,

$$\lim_{x\to\pm\infty} f(x) = \lim_{x\to\pm\infty} \frac{c_n}{d_m/x^{n-m}} = \lim_{x\to\pm\infty} \frac{c_nx^n}{d_mx^m},$$

as required. The cases when n is smaller than m and $m = n$ are proved similarly by dividing top and bottom by the largest power of x in each case.

Some Determinate and Indeterminate Forms

The following table brings these ideas together with our observations in Example 2.

Some Determinate and Indeterminate Forms

$\frac{0}{0}$ and $\pm\frac{\infty}{\infty}$ are **indeterminate**; evaluating limits in which these arise requires simplification or further analysis.†

The following are **determinate** forms for any nonzero number k:

$\frac{k}{0^\pm} = \pm\infty$	$\frac{k}{\text{Small}} = \text{Big}^*$ (See Example 2.)
$k(\pm\infty) = \pm\infty$	$k \times \text{Big} = \text{Big}^*$
$k \pm \infty = \pm\infty$	$k \pm \text{Big} = \pm\text{Big}$

† Some other indeterminate forms are: $\pm\infty \cdot 0$, $\infty - \infty$, and 1^∞. (These are not discussed in this text, but see the Communication and Reasoning exercises for this section.)

$$\pm\frac{\infty}{k} = \pm\infty \qquad \frac{\text{Big}}{k} = \text{Big}^*$$

$$\pm\frac{k}{\infty} = 0 \qquad \frac{k}{\text{Big}} = \text{Small}$$

and, if $k > 1$, then

$$k^{+\infty} = +\infty \qquad k^{\text{Big positive}} = \text{Big}$$

$$k^{-\infty} = 0. \qquad k^{\text{Big negative}} = \text{Small}$$

*The sign gets switched in these forms if k is negative.

Quick Examples

1. $\lim_{x\to 0} \frac{60}{2x^2} = +\infty$ $\qquad \frac{k}{0^+} = +\infty$
2. $\lim_{x\to -1^-} \frac{2x-6}{x+1} = +\infty$ $\qquad \frac{-8}{0^-} = +\infty$
3. $\lim_{x\to -\infty} 3x - 5 = -\infty$ $\qquad 3(-\infty) - 5 = -\infty - 5 = -\infty$
4. $\lim_{x\to +\infty} \frac{2x}{60} = +\infty$ $\qquad \frac{2(\infty)}{60} = \infty$
5. $\lim_{x\to -\infty} \frac{60}{2x} = 0$ $\qquad \frac{60}{2(-\infty)} = 0$
6. $\lim_{x\to +\infty} \frac{60x}{2x} = 30$ $\qquad \frac{\infty}{\infty}$ is indeterminate but we can cancel.
7. $\lim_{x\to -\infty} \frac{60}{e^x - 1} = \frac{60}{0-1} = -60$ $\qquad e^{-\infty} = 0$

FAQs

Strategy for Evaluating Limits Algebraically

Q: *Is there a systematic way to evaluate a limit $\lim_{x\to a} f(x)$ algebraically?*

A: The following approach is often successful:

Case 1: a Is a Finite Number (Not $\pm\infty$)

1. Decide whether f is a closed-form function. If it is not, then find the left and right limits at the values of x where the function changes from one formula to another.
2. If f is a closed-form function, try substituting $x = a$ in the formula for $f(x)$. Then one of the following three things may happen:

   $f(a)$ is defined. Then $\lim_{x\to a} f(x) = f(a)$.

   $f(a)$ is not defined and has the indeterminate form 0/0. Try to simplify the expression for f to cancel one of the terms that gives 0.

   $f(a)$ is not defined and has one of the determinate forms listed above in the above table. Use the table to determine the limit as in the Quick Examples.

Case 2: $a = \pm\infty$

Remember that we can use the determinate forms $k^{+\infty} = \infty$ and $k^{-\infty} = 0$ if $k > 1$. Further, if the given function is a polynomial or ratio of polynomials, use the technique of Example 4: Focus only on the highest powers of x and then simplify to obtain either a number L, in which case the limit exists and equals L, or one of the determinate forms $\pm\infty/k = \pm\infty$ or $\pm k/\infty = 0$.

There is another technique for evaluating certain difficult limits, called *l'Hospital's rule,* but this uses derivatives, so we'll have to wait to discuss it until Section 11.1.

10.3 EXERCISES

▼ more advanced ◆ challenging

T indicates exercises that should be solved using technology

In Exercises 1–4, complete the given sentence.

1. The closed-form function $f(x) = \dfrac{1}{x-1}$ is continuous for all x except ______. HINT [See Quick Example on page 709.]

2. The closed-form function $f(x) = \dfrac{1}{x^2-1}$ is continuous for all x except ______. HINT [See Quick Example on page 709.]

3. The closed-form function $f(x) = \sqrt{x+1}$ has $x = 3$ in its domain. Therefore, $\lim_{x\to 3}\sqrt{x+1} =$ ___. HINT [See Example 1.]

4. The closed-form function $f(x) = \sqrt{x-1}$ has $x = 10$ in its domain. Therefore, $\lim_{x\to 10}\sqrt{x-1} =$ ___. HINT [See Example 1.]

In Exercises 5–20, determine whether the given limit leads to a determinate or indeterminate form. Evaluate the limit if it exists, or say why if not. HINT [See Example 2 and Quick Examples on page 717.]

5. $\lim\limits_{x\to 0} \dfrac{60}{x^4}$

6. $\lim\limits_{x\to 0} \dfrac{2x^2}{x^2}$

7. $\lim\limits_{x\to 0} \dfrac{x^3-1}{x^3}$

8. $\lim\limits_{x\to 0} \dfrac{-2}{x^2}$

9. $\lim\limits_{x\to -\infty} (-x^2+5)$

10. $\lim\limits_{x\to 0} \dfrac{2x^2+4}{x}$

11. $\lim\limits_{x\to +\infty} 4^{-x}$

12. $\lim\limits_{x\to +\infty} \dfrac{60+e^{-x}}{2-e^{-x}}$

13. $\lim\limits_{x\to 0} \dfrac{-x^3}{3x^3}$

14. $\lim\limits_{x\to -\infty} 3x^2+6$

15. $\lim\limits_{x\to -\infty} \dfrac{-x^3}{3x^6}$

16. $\lim\limits_{x\to +\infty} \dfrac{-x^6}{3x^3}$

17. $\lim\limits_{x\to -\infty} \dfrac{4}{-x+2}$

18. $\lim\limits_{x\to -\infty} e^x$

19. $\lim\limits_{x\to -\infty} \dfrac{60}{e^x-1}$

20. $\lim\limits_{x\to -\infty} \dfrac{2}{2x^2+3}$

Calculate the limits in Exercises 21–74 algebraically. If a limit does not exist, say why.

21. $\lim\limits_{x\to 0} (x+1)$ HINT [See Example 1(a).]

22. $\lim\limits_{x\to 0} (2x-4)$ HINT [See Example 1(a).]

23. $\lim\limits_{x\to 2} \dfrac{2+x}{x}$

24. $\lim\limits_{x\to -1} \dfrac{4x^2+1}{x}$

25. $\lim\limits_{x\to -1} \dfrac{x+1}{x}$

26. $\lim\limits_{x\to 4} (x+\sqrt{x})$

27. $\lim\limits_{x\to 8} (x-\sqrt[3]{x})$

28. $\lim\limits_{x\to 1} \dfrac{x-2}{x+1}$

29. $\lim\limits_{h\to 1} (h^2+2h+1)$

30. $\lim\limits_{h\to 0} (h^3-4)$

31. $\lim\limits_{h\to 3} 2$

32. $\lim\limits_{h\to 0} -5$

33. $\lim\limits_{h\to 0} \dfrac{h^2}{h+h^2}$ HINT [See Example 1(b).]

34. $\lim\limits_{h\to 0} \dfrac{h^2+h}{h^2+2h}$ HINT [See Example 1(b).]

35. $\lim\limits_{x\to 1} \dfrac{x^2-2x+1}{x^2-x}$

36. $\lim\limits_{x\to -1} \dfrac{x^2+3x+2}{x^2+x}$

37. $\lim\limits_{x\to 2} \dfrac{x^3-8}{x-2}$

38. $\lim\limits_{x\to -2} \dfrac{x^3+8}{x^2+3x+2}$

39. $\lim\limits_{x\to 0+} \dfrac{1}{x^2}$ HINT [See Example 2.]

40. $\lim\limits_{x\to 0^+} \dfrac{1}{x^2-x}$ HINT [See Example 2.]

41. $\lim\limits_{x\to -1} \dfrac{x^2+1}{x+1}$

42. $\lim\limits_{x\to -1^-} \dfrac{x^2+1}{x+1}$

43. $\lim\limits_{x\to -2^+} \dfrac{x^2+8}{x^2+3x+2}$

44. $\lim\limits_{x\to -1} \dfrac{x^2+3x}{x^2+x}$

45. $\lim_{x \to -2} \frac{x^2+8}{x^2+3x+2}$

46. $\lim_{x \to -1} \frac{x^2+3x}{x^2+2x+1}$

47. $\lim_{x \to 2} \frac{x^2+8}{x^2-4x+4}$

48. $\lim_{x \to -1} \frac{x^2+3x}{x^2+3x+2}$

49. ▼ $\lim_{x \to 2^+} \frac{x-2}{\sqrt{x-2}}$

50. ▼ $\lim_{x \to 3^-} \frac{\sqrt{3-x}}{3-x}$

51. ▼ $\lim_{x \to 9} \frac{\sqrt{x}-3}{x-9}$

52. ▼ $\lim_{x \to 4} \frac{x-4}{\sqrt{x}-2}$

53. $\lim_{x \to +\infty} \frac{3x^2+10x-1}{2x^2-5x}$ HINT [See Example 4.]

54. $\lim_{x \to +\infty} \frac{6x^2+5x+100}{3x^2-9}$ HINT [See Example 4.]

55. $\lim_{x \to +\infty} \frac{x^5-1{,}000x^4}{2x^5+10{,}000}$

56. $\lim_{x \to +\infty} \frac{x^6+3{,}000x^3+1{,}000{,}000}{2x^6+1{,}000x^3}$

57. $\lim_{x \to +\infty} \frac{10x^2+300x+1}{5x+2}$

58. $\lim_{x \to +\infty} \frac{2x^4+20x^3}{1{,}000x^3+6}$

59. $\lim_{x \to -\infty} \frac{3x^2+10x-1}{2x^2-5x}$

60. $\lim_{x \to -\infty} \frac{6x^2+5x+100}{3x^2-9}$

61. $\lim_{x \to -\infty} \frac{x^5-1{,}000x^4}{2x^5+10{,}000}$

62. $\lim_{x \to -\infty} \frac{x^6+3000x^3+1{,}000{,}000}{2x^6+1{,}000x^3}$

63. $\lim_{x \to -\infty} \frac{10x^2+300x+1}{5x+2}$

64. $\lim_{x \to -\infty} \frac{2x^4+20x^3}{1{,}000x^3+6}$

65. $\lim_{x \to -\infty} \frac{10x^2+300x+1}{5x^3+2}$

66. $\lim_{x \to -\infty} \frac{2x^4+20x^3}{1{,}000x^6+6}$

67. $\lim_{x \to +\infty} (4e^{-3x}+12)$

68. $\lim_{x \to +\infty} \frac{2}{5-5.3e^{-3x}}$

69. $\lim_{t \to +\infty} \frac{2}{5-5.3(3^{3t})}$

70. $\lim_{t \to +\infty} (4.1-2e^{3t})$

71. $\lim_{t \to +\infty} \frac{2^{3t}}{1+5.3e^{-t}}$

72. $\lim_{x \to -\infty} \frac{4.2}{2-3^{2x}}$

73. $\lim_{x \to -\infty} \frac{-3^{2x}}{2+e^x}$

74. $\lim_{x \to +\infty} \frac{2^{-3x}}{1+5.3e^{-x}}$

In each of Exercises 75–82, find all points of discontinuity of the given function. HINT [See Example 3.]

75. $f(x) = \begin{cases} x+2 & \text{if } x < 0 \\ 2x-1 & \text{if } x \ge 0 \end{cases}$

76. $g(x) = \begin{cases} 1-x & \text{if } x \le 1 \\ x-1 & \text{if } x > 1 \end{cases}$

77. $g(x) = \begin{cases} x+2 & \text{if } x < 0 \\ 2x+2 & \text{if } 0 \le x < 2 \\ x^2+2 & \text{if } x \ge 2 \end{cases}$

78. $f(x) = \begin{cases} 1-x & \text{if } x \le 1 \\ x+2 & \text{if } 1 < x < 3 \\ x^2-4 & \text{if } x \ge 3 \end{cases}$

79. ▼ $h(x) = \begin{cases} x+2 & \text{if } x < 0 \\ 0 & \text{if } x = 0 \\ 2x+2 & \text{if } x > 0 \end{cases}$

80. ▼ $h(x) = \begin{cases} 1-x & \text{if } x < 1 \\ 1 & \text{if } x = 1 \\ x+2 & \text{if } x > 1 \end{cases}$

81. ▼ $f(x) = \begin{cases} 1/x & \text{if } x < 0 \\ x & \text{if } 0 \le x \le 2 \\ 2^{x-1} & \text{if } x > 2 \end{cases}$

82. ▼ $f(x) = \begin{cases} x^3+2 & \text{if } x \le -1 \\ x^2 & \text{if } -1 < x < 0 \\ x & \text{if } x \ge 0 \end{cases}$

APPLICATIONS

83. ***Processor Speeds*** The processor speeds, in megahertz (MHz), of Intel processors during the period 1996–2010 can be approximated by the following function of time t in years since the start of 1990:[17]

$$v(t) = \begin{cases} 400t - 2{,}200 & \text{if } 6 \le t < 15 \\ 3{,}800 & \text{if } 15 \le t \le 20. \end{cases}$$

a. Compute $\lim_{t \to 15^-} v(t)$ and $\lim_{t \to 15^+} v(t)$ and interpret each answer. HINT [See Example 3.]

b. Is the function v continuous at $t = 15$? According to the model, was there any abrupt change in processor speeds during the period 1996–2010?

84. ***Processor Speeds*** The processor speeds, in megahertz (MHz), of Intel processors during the period 1970–2000 can be approximated by the following function of time t in years since the start of 1970:[18]

$$v(t) = \begin{cases} 3t & \text{if } 0 \le t < 20 \\ 174t - 3{,}420 & \text{if } 20 \le t \le 30. \end{cases}$$

[17] A rough model based on the fastest processors produced by Intel. Source for data: www.intel.com.

[18] *Ibid.*

a. Compute $\lim_{t\to 20^-} v(t)$ and $\lim_{t\to 20^+} v(t)$ and interpret each answer.

b. Is the function v continuous at $t = 20$? According to the model, was there any abrupt change in processor speeds during the period 1970–2000?

85. ***Movie Advertising*** Movie expenditures, in billions of dollars, on advertising in newspapers from 1995 to 2004 can be approximated by

$$f(t) = \begin{cases} 0.04t + 0.33 & \text{if } t \le 4 \\ -0.01t + 1.2 & \text{if } t > 4 \end{cases}$$

where t is time in years since 1995.[19]

a. Compute $\lim_{t\to 4^-} f(t)$ and $\lim_{t\to 4^+} f(t)$, and interpret each answer. HINT [See Example 3.]

b. Is the function f continuous at $t = 4$? What does the answer tell you about movie advertising expenditures?

86. ***Movie Advertising*** The percentage of movie advertising as a share of newspapers' total advertising revenue from 1995 to 2004 can be approximated by

$$p(t) = \begin{cases} -0.07t + 6.0 & \text{if } t \le 4 \\ 0.3t + 17.0 & \text{if } t > 4 \end{cases}$$

where t is time in years since 1995.[20]

a. Compute $\lim_{t\to 4^-} p(t)$ and $\lim_{t\to 4^+} p(t)$, and interpret each answer. HINT [See Example 3.]

b. Is the function p continuous at $t = 4$? What does the answer tell you about newspaper revenues?

87. ***Law Enforcement in the 1980s and 1990s*** The cost of fighting crime in the United States increased significantly during the period 1982–1999. Total spending on police and courts can be approximated, respectively, by[21]

$$P(t) = 1.745t + 29.84 \text{ billion dollars} \quad (2 \le t \le 19)$$
$$C(t) = 1.097t + 10.65 \text{ billion dollars} \quad (2 \le t \le 19),$$

where t is time in years since 1980. Compute $\lim_{t\to+\infty} \dfrac{P(t)}{C(t)}$ to two decimal places and interpret the result. HINT [See Example 4.]

88. ***Law Enforcement in the 1980s and 1990s*** Refer to Exercise 87. Total spending on police, courts, and prisons in the period 1982–1999 could be approximated, respectively, by[22]

$$P(t) = 1.745t + 29.84 \text{ billion dollars} \quad (2 \le t \le 19)$$
$$C(t) = 1.097t + 10.65 \text{ billion dollars} \quad (2 \le t \le 19)$$
$$J(t) = 1.919t + 12.36 \text{ billion dollars} \quad (2 \le t \le 19),$$

where t is time in years since 1980. Compute $\lim_{t\to+\infty} \dfrac{P(t)}{P(t) + C(t) + J(t)}$ to two decimal places and interpret the result. HINT [See Example 4.]

89. ***SAT Scores by Income*** The following bar graph shows U.S. math SAT scores as a function of household income:[23]

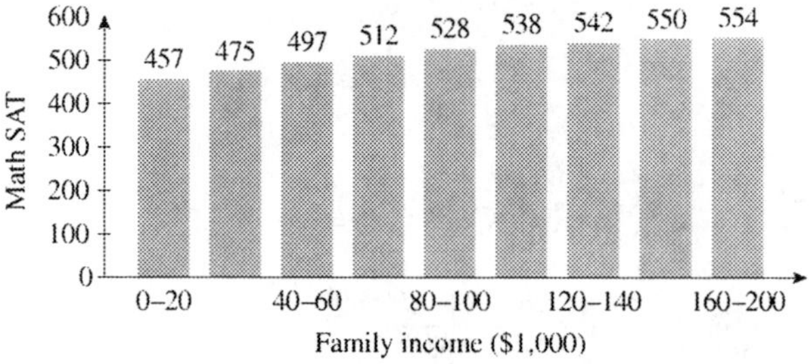

These data can be modeled by

$$S(x) = 573 - 33e^{-0.0131x},$$

where $S(x)$ is the average math SAT score of students whose household income is x thousand dollars per year. Calculate $\lim_{x\to+\infty} S(x)$ and interpret the answer.

90. ***SAT Scores by Income*** The following bar graph shows U.S. critical reading SAT scores as a function of household income:[24]

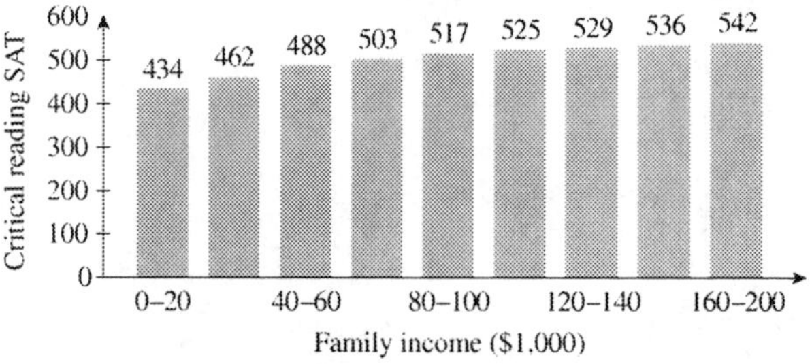

These data can be modeled by

$$S(x) = 550 - 136e^{-0.0151x},$$

where $S(x)$ is the average critical reading SAT score of students whose household income is x thousand dollars per year. Calculate $\lim_{x\to+\infty} S(x)$ and interpret the answer.

[19] Model by the authors. Source for data: Newspaper Association of America Business Analysis and Research/*New York Times*, May 16, 2005.

[20] *Ibid.*

[21] Spending is adjusted for inflation and shown in 1999 dollars. Models are based on a linear regression. Source for data: Bureau of Justice Statistics/*New York Times*, February 11, 2002, p. A14.

[22] *Ibid.*

[23] 2009 data. Source: College Board/*New York Times* http://economix.blogs.nytimes.com.

[24] *Ibid.*

Foreign Trade *Annual U.S. imports from China in the years 1996 through 2003 could be approximated by*

$$I(t) = t^2 + 3.5t + 50 \quad (1 \le t \le 9)$$

billion dollars, where t represents time in years since 1995. Annual U.S. exports to China in the same years could be approximated by

$$E(t) = 0.4t^2 - 1.6t + 14 \quad (0 \le t \le 10)$$

billion dollars.[25] *Exercises 91 and 92 are based on these models.*

91. Assuming that the trends shown in the above models continue indefinitely, calculate the limits

$$\lim_{t\to+\infty} I(t) \text{ and } \lim_{t\to+\infty} \frac{I(t)}{E(t)}$$

algebraically, interpret your answers, and comment on the results. HINT [See Example 4.]

92. Repeat Exercise 91, this time calculating

$$\lim_{t\to+\infty} E(t) \text{ and } \lim_{t\to+\infty} \frac{E(t)}{I(t)}$$ HINT [See Example 4.]

93. ***Acquisition of Language*** The percentage $p(t)$ of children who can speak in at least single words by the age of t months can be approximated by the equation[26]

$$p(t) = 100\left(\frac{1 - 12{,}200}{t^{4.48}}\right) \quad (t \ge 8.5).$$

Calculate $\lim_{t\to+\infty} p(t)$ and interpret the result. HINT [See Example 4.]

94. ***Acquisition of Language*** The percentage $q(t)$ of children who can speak in sentences of five or more words by the age of t months can be approximated by the equation[27]

$$q(t) = 100\left(1 - \frac{5.27 \times 10^{17}}{t^{12}}\right) \quad (t \ge 30).$$

If p is the function referred to in the preceding exercise, calculate $\lim_{t\to+\infty}[p(t) - q(t)]$ and interpret the result. HINT [See Example 4.]

COMMUNICATION AND REASONING EXERCISES

95. Describe the algebraic method of evaluating limits as discussed in this section and give at least one disadvantage of this method.

96. What is a closed-form function? What can we say about such functions?

97. Why was the following marked wrong? What is the correct answer?

$$\lim_{x\to 3} \frac{x^3 - 27}{x - 3} = \frac{0}{0} \text{ undefined} \qquad \text{✗ WRONG!}$$

98. Why was the following marked wrong? What is the correct answer?

$$\lim_{x\to 1^-} \frac{x - 1}{x^2 - 2x + 1} = \frac{0}{0} = 0 \qquad \text{✗ WRONG!}$$

99. ▼ Your friend Karin tells you that $f(x) = 1/(x-2)^2$ cannot be a closed-form function because it is not continuous at $x = 2$. Comment on her assertion.

100. ▼ Give an example of a function f specified by means of algebraic formulas such that the domain of f consists of all real numbers and f is not continuous at $x = 2$. Is f a closed-form function?

101. Give examples of two limits that lead to two different indeterminate forms, but where both limits exist.

102. Give examples of two limits: one that leads to a determinate form and another that leads to an indeterminate form, but where neither limit exists.

103. ▼ (Compare Exercise 59 in Section 10.1.) Which indeterminate form results from $\lim_{x\to+\infty} \frac{p(x)}{e^x}$ if $p(x)$ is a polynomial? Numerically or graphically estimate these limits for various polynomials $p(x)$. What does this suggest about limits that result in $\frac{p(\infty)}{e^\infty}$?

104. ▼ (Compare Exercise 60 in Section 10.1.) Which indeterminate form results from $\lim_{x\to-\infty} p(x)e^x$ if $p(x)$ is a polynomial? What does this suggest about the limits that result in $p(\infty)e^{-\infty}$?

105. ▼ What is wrong with the following statement? If $f(x)$ is specified algebraically and $f(a)$ is defined, then $\lim_{x\to a} f(x)$ exists and equals $f(a)$. How can it be corrected?

106. ▼ What is wrong with the following statement? If $f(x)$ is specified algebraically and $f(a)$ is not defined, then $\lim_{x\to a} f(x)$ does not exist.

107. ▼ Give the formula for a function that is continuous everywhere except at two points.

108. ▼ Give the formula for a function that is continuous everywhere except at three points.

109. ◆ ***The Indeterminate Form*** $\infty-\infty$ An indeterminate form not mentioned in Section 10.3 is $\infty-\infty$. Give examples of three limits that lead to this indeterminate form, and where the first limit exists and equals 5, where the second limit diverges to $+\infty$, and where the third exists and equals –5.

110. ◆ ***The Indeterminate Form*** 1^∞ An indeterminate form not mentioned in Section 10.3 is 1^∞. Give examples of three limits that lead to this indeterminate form, and where the first limit exists and equals 1, where the second limit exists and equals e, and where the third diverges to $+\infty$. HINT [For the third, consider modifying the second.]

---

[25] Based on quadratic regression using data from the U.S. Census Bureau Foreign Trade Division Web site www.census.gov/foreign-trade/sitc1/ as of December 2004.

[26] The model is the authors' and is based on data presented in the article *The Emergence of Intelligence* by William H. Calvin, *Scientific American*, October, 1994, pp. 101–107.

[27] *Ibid.*

10.4 Average Rate of Change

Calculus is the mathematics of change, inspired largely by observation of continuously changing quantities around us in the real world. As an example, the Consumer Price Index (CPI) C increased from 211 points in January 2009 to 220 points in January 2011.[28] As we saw in Chapter 1, the **change** in this index can be measured as the difference:

$$\Delta C = \text{Second value} - \text{First value} = 220 - 211 = 9 \text{ points.}$$

(The fact that the CPI increased is reflected in the positive sign of the change.) The kind of question we will concentrate on is *how fast* the CPI was changing. Because C increased by 9 points in 2 years, we say it averaged a $9/2 = 4.5$ point rise each year. (It actually rose 5 points the first year and 4 the second, giving an average rise of 4.5 points each year.)

Alternatively, we might want to measure this rate in points per month rather than points per year. Because C increased by 9 points in 24 months, it increased at an average rate of $9/24 = 0.375$ points per month.

In both cases, we obtained the average rate of change by dividing the change by the corresponding length of time:

$$\text{Average rate of change} = \frac{\text{Change in } C}{\text{Change in time}} = \frac{9}{2} = 4.50 \text{ points per year}$$

$$\text{Average rate of change} = \frac{\text{Change in } C}{\text{Change in time}} = \frac{9}{24} = 0.375 \text{ points per month.}$$

Average Rate of Change of a Function Numerically and Graphically

EXAMPLE 1 Standard and Poor's 500

The following table lists the approximate value of Standard and Poor's 500 stock market index (S&P) during the period 2005–2011[29] ($t = 5$ represents 2005):

t (year)	5	6	7	8	9	10	11
$S(t)$ (points)	1,200	1,300	1,400	1,400	900	1,150	1,300

a. What was the average rate of change in the S&P over the 2-year period 2005–2007 (the period $5 \le t \le 7$ or $[5, 7]$ in interval notation); over the 4-year period 2005–2009 (the period $5 \le t \le 9$ or $[5, 9]$); and over the period $[6, 11]$?

b. Graph the values shown in the table. How are the rates of change reflected in the graph?

[28]Figures are approximate. Source: Bureau of Labor Statistics www.bls.gov.

[29]The values are approximate values at the start of the given year. Source: http://finance.google.com.

Solution

a. During the 2-year period [5, 7], the S&P changed as follows:

Start of the period ($t = 5$):	$S(5) = 1{,}200$
End of the period ($t = 7$):	$S(7) = 1{,}400$
Change during the period [5, 7]:	$S(7) - S(5) = 200$

Thus, the S&P increased by 200 points in 2 years, giving an average rate of change of $200/2 = 100$ points per year. We can write the calculation this way:

$$\begin{aligned}\text{Average rate of change of } S &= \frac{\text{Change in } S}{\text{Change in } t}\\ &= \frac{\Delta S}{\Delta t}\\ &= \frac{S(7) - S(5)}{7 - 5}\\ &= \frac{1{,}400 - 1{,}200}{7 - 5} = \frac{200}{2} = 100 \text{ points per year.}\end{aligned}$$

Interpreting the result: During the period [5, 7] (that is, 2005–2007), the S&P increased at an average rate of 100 points per year.

Similarly, the average rate of change during the period [5, 9] was

$$\begin{aligned}\text{Average rate of change of } S &= \frac{\Delta S}{\Delta t} = \frac{S(9) - S(5)}{9 - 5} = \frac{900 - 1{,}200}{9 - 5}\\ &= \frac{-300}{4} = -75 \text{ points per year.}\end{aligned}$$

Interpreting the result: During the period [5, 9] (that is, 2005–2009), the S&P *decreased* at an average rate of 75 points per year.

Finally, during the period [6, 11], the average change was

$$\begin{aligned}\text{Average rate of change of } S &= \frac{\Delta S}{\Delta t} = \frac{S(11) - S(6)}{11 - 6} = \frac{1{,}300 - 1{,}300}{11 - 6}\\ &= \frac{0}{5} = 0 \text{ points per year.}\end{aligned}$$

Interpreting the result: During the period [6, 11] the average rate of change of the S&P was zero points per year (even though its value did fluctuate during that period).

b. In Chapter 1, we saw that the rate of change of a quantity that changes linearly with time is measured by the slope of its graph. However, the S&P index does not change linearly with time. Figure 20 shows the data plotted two different ways: (a) as a bar chart and (b) as a piecewise linear graph. Bar charts are more commonly used in the media, but Figure 20(b) on the right illustrates the changing index more clearly.

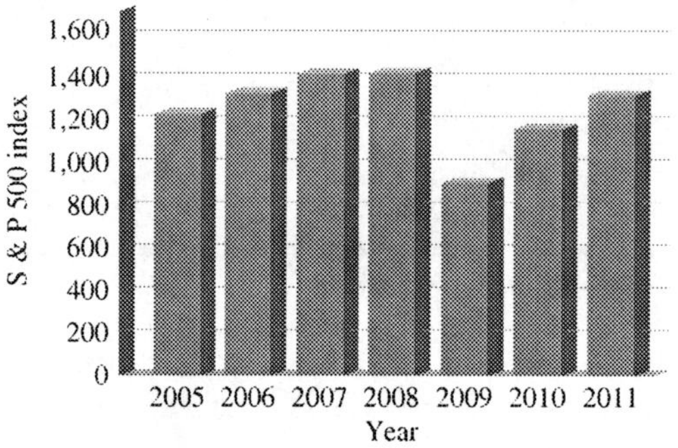

Figure 20(a)

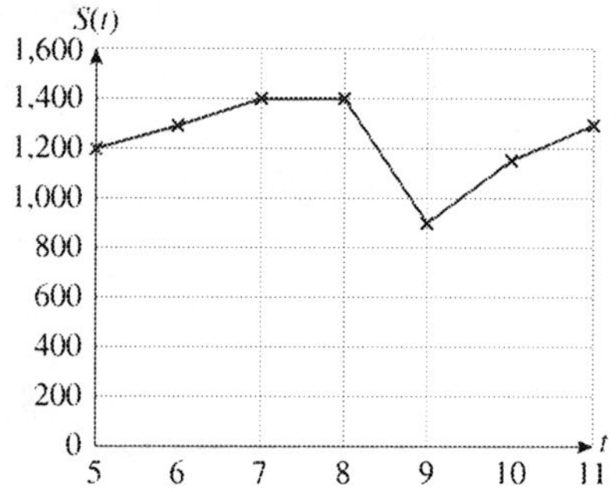

Figure 20(b)

We saw in part (a) that the average rate of change of S over the interval [5, 9] is the ratio

$$\text{Average rate of change of } S = \frac{\Delta S}{\Delta t} = \frac{S(9) - S(5)}{9 - 5} = -75 \text{ points per year.}$$

Notice that this rate of change is also the slope of the line through P and Q shown in Figure 21, and we can estimate this slope directly from the graph as shown.

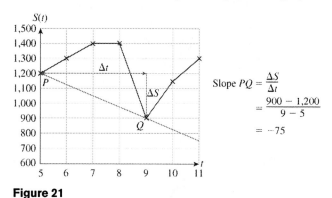

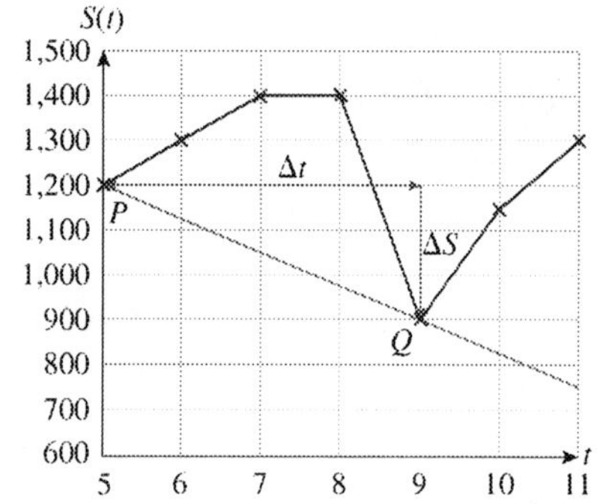

$$\text{Slope } PQ = \frac{\Delta S}{\Delta t} = \frac{900 - 1{,}200}{9 - 5} = -75$$

Figure 21

Average Rate of Change as Slope: The average rate of change of the S&P over the interval [5, 9] is the slope of the line passing through the points on the graph where $t = 5$ and $t = 9$.

Similarly, the average rates of change of the S&P over the intervals [5, 7] and [6, 11] are the slopes of the lines through pairs of corresponding points.

Here is the formal definition of the average rate of change of a function over an interval.

Change and Average Rate of Change of *f* over [*a*, *b*]: Difference Quotient

The **change** in $f(x)$ over the interval $[a, b]$ is

$$\begin{aligned}\text{Change in } f &= \Delta f \\ &= \text{Second value} - \text{First value} \\ &= f(b) - f(a).\end{aligned}$$

The **average rate of change** of $f(x)$ over the interval $[a, b]$ is

$$\text{Average rate of change of } f = \frac{\text{Change in } f}{\text{Change in } x}$$
$$= \frac{\Delta f}{\Delta x} = \frac{f(b) - f(a)}{b - a}$$
$$= \text{Slope of line through points } P \text{ and } Q$$
(see figure).

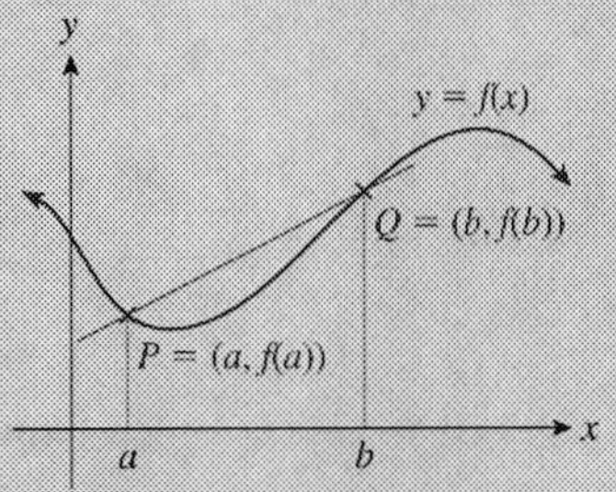

Average rate of change = Slope of PQ

We also call this average rate of change the **difference quotient** of f over the interval $[a, b]$. (It is the *quotient* of the *differences* $f(b) - f(a)$ and $b - a$.) A line through two points of a graph like P and Q is called a **secant line** of the graph.

Units

The units of the change Δf in f are the units of $f(x)$.
The units of the average rate of change of f are units of $f(x)$ per unit of x.*

* The average rate of change is a slope, and so it is measured in the same units as the slope: units of y (or $f(x)$) per unit of x.

Quick Example

If $f(3) = -1$ billion dollars, $f(5) = 0.5$ billion dollars, and x is measured in years, then the change and average rate of change of f over the interval $[3, 5]$ are given by

$$\text{Change in } f = f(5) - f(3) = 0.5 - (-1) = 1.5 \text{ billion dollars}$$
$$\text{Average rate of change} = \frac{f(5) - f(3)}{5 - 3} = \frac{0.5 - (-1)}{2}$$
$$= 0.75 \text{ billion dollars/year.}$$

Alternative Formula: Average Rate of Change of *f* over [*a*, *a* + *h*]

(Replace b in the formula for the average rate of change by $a + h$.) The average rate of change of f over the interval $[a, a + h]$ is

$$\text{Average rate of change of } f = \frac{f(a + h) - f(a)}{h}. \quad \text{Replace } b \text{ by } a + h.$$

In Example 1 we saw that the average rate of change of a quantity can be estimated directly from a graph. Here is an example that further illustrates the graphical approach.

EXAMPLE 2 Freon 22 Production

Figure 22 shows the number of tons $f(t)$ of ozone-layer-damaging Freon 22 (chlorodifluoromethane) produced annually in developing countries for the period 2000–2010 (t is time in years, and $t = 0$ represents 2000).[30]

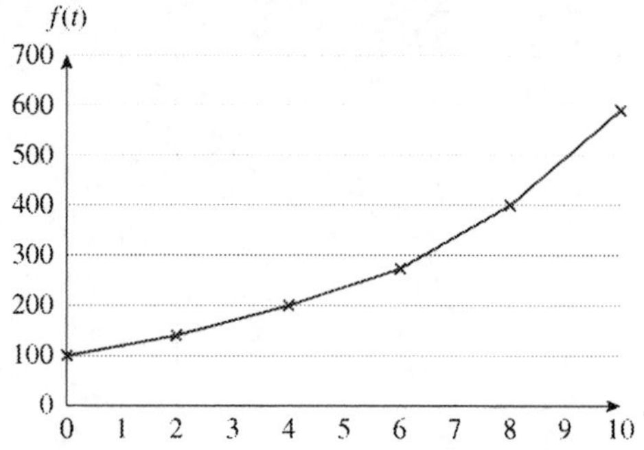

Figure 22

a. Use the graph to estimate the average rate of change of $f(t)$ with respect to t over the interval [4, 8] and interpret the result.

b. Over which 2-year period(s) was the average rate of change of Freon 22 production the greatest?

c. Multiple choice: For the period of time under consideration, Freon 22 production was

(A) increasing at a faster and faster rate.
(B) increasing at a slower and slower rate.
(C) decreasing at a faster and faster rate.
(D) decreasing at a slower and slower rate.

Solution

a. The average rate of change of f over the interval [4, 8] is given by the slope of the line through the points P and Q shown in Figure 23.

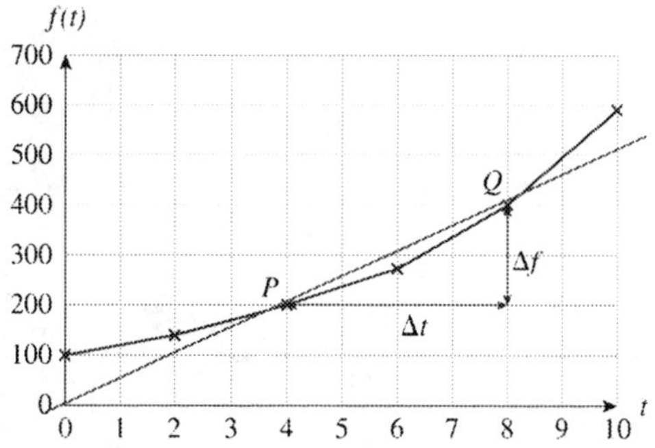

Figure 23

From the figure,

$$\text{Average rate of change of } f = \frac{\Delta f}{\Delta t} = \text{slope } PQ \approx \frac{400 - 200}{8 - 4} = \frac{200}{4} = 50.$$

Thus, the rate of change of f over the interval [4, 8] is approximately 50.

[30]Figures from 2007 on were projected. Source: *New York Times*, February 23, 2007, p. C1.

Q: *How do we interpret the result?*

A: A clue is given by the units of the average rate of change: units of f per unit of t. The units of f are tons of Freon 22 and the units of t are years. Thus, the average rate of change of f is measured in tons of Freon 22 per year, and we can now interpret the result as follows:

Interpreting the average rate of change: Annual production of Freon 22 was increasing at an average rate of 50 tons of Freon 22 per year from 2004 to 2008.

b. The rates of change of Freon 22 production over successive 2-year periods are given by the slopes of the individual line segments that make up the graph in Figure 22. Thus, the greatest average rate of change in a single 2-year period corresponds to the segment(s) with the largest slope. If you look at the figure, you will notice that the segment corresponding to [8, 10] is the steepest. Thus, the average rate of change of Freon 22 production was largest over the 2-year period from 2008 to 2010.

c. Looking again at the figure, notice that the graph rises as we go from left to right; that is, the value of the function (Freon 22 production) is increasing with increasing t. At the same time, the fact that the curve bends up (is concave up) with increasing t tells us that the successive slopes get steeper, and so the average rates of change increase as well (Choice (A)).

➡ **Before we go on...** Notice in Example 2 that we do not get exact answers from a graph; the best we can do is *estimate* the rates of change: Was the exact answer to part (a) closer to 49 or 51? Two people can reasonably disagree about results read from a graph, and you should bear this in mind when you check the answers to the exercises. ■

Perhaps the most sophisticated way to compute the average rate of change of a quantity is through the use of a mathematical formula or model for the quantity in question.

Average Rate of Change of a Function Using Algebraic Data

EXAMPLE 3 Average Rate of Change from a Formula

You are a commodities trader and you monitor the price of gold on the spot market very closely during an active morning. Suppose you find that the price of an ounce of gold can be approximated by the function

$$G(t) = 5t^2 - 85t + 1{,}762 \qquad (7.5 \le t \le 10.5),$$

where t is time in hours. (See Figure 24. $t = 8$ represents 8:00 am.)

Looking at the graph on the right, we can see that the price of gold was falling at the beginning of the time period, but by $t = 8.5$ the fall had slowed to a stop, whereupon the market turned around and the price began to rise more and more rapidly toward the end of the period. What was the average rate of change of the price of gold over the $1\frac{1}{2}$-hour period starting at 8:00 am (the interval [8, 9.5] on the t-axis)?

using Technology

See the Technology Guides at the end of the chapter for detailed instructions on how to calculate the average rate of change of the function in Example 3 using a TI-83/84 Plus or a spreadsheet. Here is an outline:

TI-83/84 Plus

`Y1=5X^2-85X+1762`

Home screen: `(Y1(9.5)-Y1(8))/(9.5-8)`

[More details on page 778.]

Spreadsheet

Headings t, $G(t)$, Rate of Change in A1–C1

t-values 8, 9.5 in A2–A3

`=5*A2^2-85*A2+1762` in B2, copied down to B3

`=(B3-B2)/(A3-A2)` in C2.

[More details on page 780.]

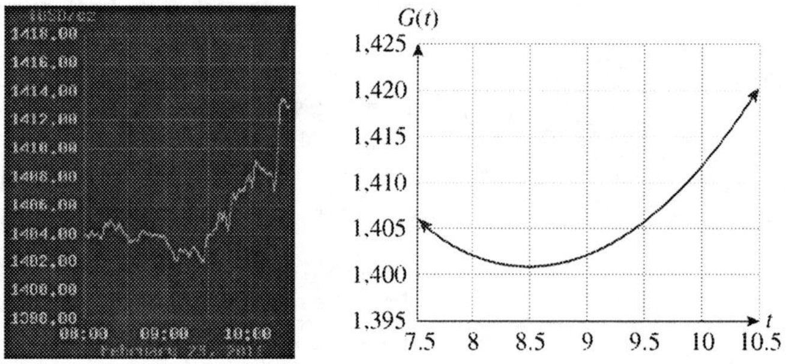

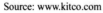

Source: www.kitco.com

$G(t) = 5t^2 - 85t + 1,762$

Figure 24

Solution We have

$$\text{Average rate of change of } G \text{ over } [8, 9.5] = \frac{\Delta G}{\Delta t} = \frac{G(9.5) - G(8)}{9.5 - 8}.$$

From the formula for $G(t)$, we find

$$G(9.5) = 5(9.5)^2 - 85(9.5) + 1,762 = 1,405.75$$
$$G(8) = 5(8)^2 - 85(8) + 1,762 = 1,402.$$

Thus, the average rate of change of G is given by

$$\frac{G(9.5) - G(8)}{9.5 - 8} = \frac{1,405.75 - 1,402}{1.5} = \frac{3.75}{1.5} = \$2.50 \text{ per hour.}$$

In other words, the price of gold increased at an average rate of \$2.50 per hour over the $1\frac{1}{2}$-hour period.

EXAMPLE 4 Rates of Change over Shorter Intervals

Continuing with Example 3, use technology to compute the average rate of change of

$$G(t) = 5t^2 - 85t + 1,762 \qquad (7.5 \le t \le 10.5)$$

over the intervals $[8, 8 + h]$, where $h = 1, 0.1, 0.01, 0.001$, and 0.0001. What do the answers tell you about the price of gold?

Solution

We use the "alternative" formula

$$\text{Average rate of change of } G \text{ over } [a, a + h] = \frac{G(a + h) - G(a)}{h}$$

so

$$\text{Average rate of change of } G \text{ over } [8, 8 + h] = \frac{G(8 + h) - G(8)}{h}.$$

using Technology

Example 4 is the kind of example where the use of technology can make a huge difference. See the Technology Guides at the end of the chapter to find out how to do the above computations almost effortlessly using a TI-83/84 Plus or a spreadsheet. Here is an outline:

TI-83/84 Plus

```
Y1=5X^2-85X+1762
```

Home screen:

```
(Y1(8+1)-Y1(8))/1
(Y1(8+0.1)-Y1(8))/0.1
(Y1(8+0.01)-Y1(8))/0.01
```

etc.

[More details on page 778.]

Spreadsheet

Headings *a*, *h*, *t*, *G*(*t*), Rate of Change in A1–E1

`8` in A2, `1` in B2,

`=A2` in C2, `=A2+B2` in C3

`=5*C2^2-85*C2+1762` in D2; copy down to D3

`=(D3-D2)/(C3-C2)` in E2

[More details on page 780.]

Let us calculate this average rate of change for some of the values of h listed:

$h = 1$: $G(8+h) = G(8+1) = G(9) = 5(9)^2 - 85(9) + 1,762 = 1,402$

$$G(8) = 5(8)^2 - 85(8) + 1,762 = 1,402$$

$$\text{Average rate of change of } G = \frac{G(9) - G(8)}{1} = \frac{1,402 - 1,402}{1} = 0$$

$h = 0.1$: $G(8+h) = G(8+0.1) = G(8.1) = 5(8.1)^2 - 85(8.1) + 1,762$

$$= 1,401.55$$

$$G(8) = 5(8)^2 - 85(8) + 1,762 = 1,402$$

$$\text{Average rate of change of } G = \frac{G(8.1) - G(8)}{0.1} = \frac{1,401.55 - 1,402}{0.1} = \frac{-0.45}{0.1}$$

$$= -4.5$$

$h = 0.01$: $G(8+h) = G(8+0.01) = G(8.01) = 5(8.01)^2 - 85(8.01) + 1,762$

$$= 1,401.9505$$

$$G(8) = 5(8)^2 - 85(8) + 1,762 = 1,402$$

$$\text{Average rate of change of } G = \frac{G(8.01) - G(8)}{0.01} = \frac{1,401.9505 - 1,402}{0.01} = \frac{-0.0495}{0.01}$$

$$= -4.95$$

Continuing in this way, we get the values in the following table:

h	1	0.1	0.01	0.001	0.0001
Ave. Rate of Change $\frac{G(8+h) - G(8)}{h}$	0	−4.5	−4.95	−4.995	−4.9995

Each value is an average rate of change of G. For example, the value corresponding to $h = 0.01$ is -4.95, which tells us:

Over the interval [8, 8.01] *the price of gold was decreasing at an average rate of* \$4.95 *per hour.*

In other words, during the first one hundredth of an hour (or 36 seconds) starting at $t = $ 8:00 am, the price of gold was decreasing at an average rate of \$4.95 per hour. Put another way, in those 36 seconds, the price of gold decreased at a rate that, if continued, would have produced a decrease of \$4.95 in the price of gold during the next hour. We will return to this example at the beginning of Section 10.5.

FAQs

Recognizing When and How to Compute the Average Rate of Change and How to Interpret the Answer

Q: *How do I know, by looking at the wording of a problem, that it is asking for an average rate of change?*

A: If a problem does not ask for an average rate of change directly, it might do so indirectly, as in "On average, how fast is quantity q increasing?"

Q: *If I know that a problem calls for computing an average rate of change, how should I compute it? By hand or using technology?*

A: All the computations can be done by hand, but when hand calculations are not called for, using technology might save time.

Q: *Lots of problems ask us to "interpret" the answer. How do I do that for questions involving average rates of change?*

A: The *units* of the average rate of change are often the key to interpreting the results:

The units of the average rate of change of $f(x)$ are units of $f(x)$ per unit of x.

Thus, for instance, if $f(x)$ is the cost, in dollars, of a trip of x miles in length, and the average rate of change of f is calculated to be 10, then the units of the average rate of change are dollars per mile, and so we can interpret the answer by saying that the cost of a trip rises an average of \$10 for each additional mile.

10.4 EXERCISES

▼ more advanced ◆ challenging

T indicates exercises that should be solved using technology

In Exercises 1–18, calculate the average rate of change of the given function over the given interval. Where appropriate, specify the units of measurement. HINT [See Example 1.]

1.

x	0	1	2	3
$f(x)$	3	5	2	−1

Interval: [1, 3]

2.

x	0	1	2	3
$f(x)$	−1	3	2	1

Interval: [0, 2]

3.

x	−3	−2	−1	0
$f(x)$	−2.1	0	−1.5	0

Interval: [−3, −1]

4.

x	−2	−1	0	1
$f(x)$	−1.5	−0.5	4	6.5

Interval: [−1, 1]

5.

t (months)	2	4	6
$R(t)$ (\$ millions)	20.2	24.3	20.1

Interval: [2, 6]

6.

x (kilos)	1	2	3
$C(x)$ (£)	2.20	3.30	4.00

Interval: [1, 3]

7.

p (\$)	5.00	5.50	6.00
$q(p)$ (items)	400	300	150

Interval: [5, 5.5]

8.

t (hours)	0	0.1	0.2
$D(t)$ (miles)	0	3	6

Interval: [0.1, 0.2]

9. Apple Computer Stock Price ($)

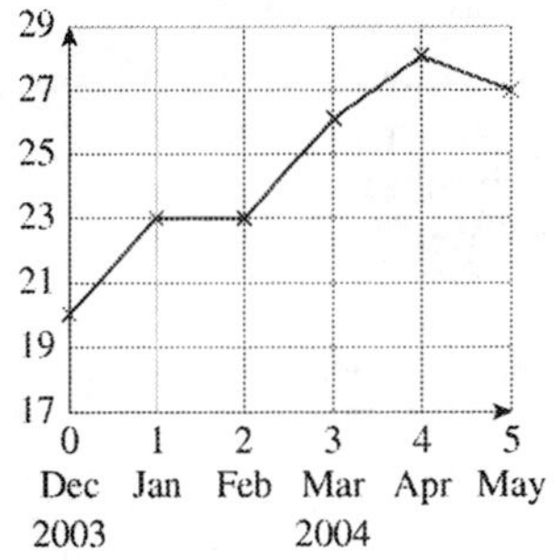

Interval: [2, 5]
HINT [See Example 2.]

10. Cisco Systems Stock Price ($)

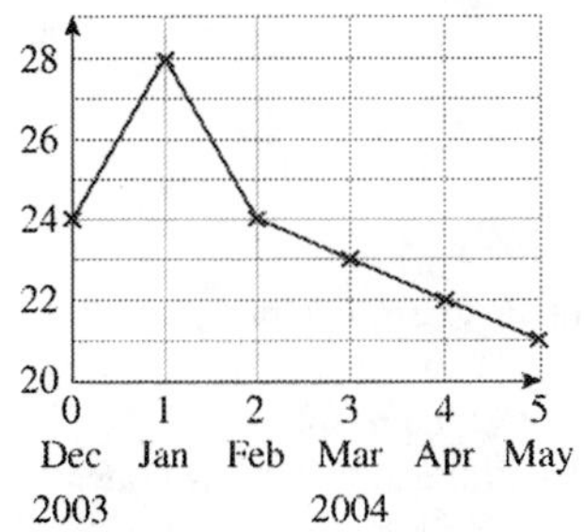

Interval: [1, 5]
HINT [See Example 2.]

11. Unemployment (%)

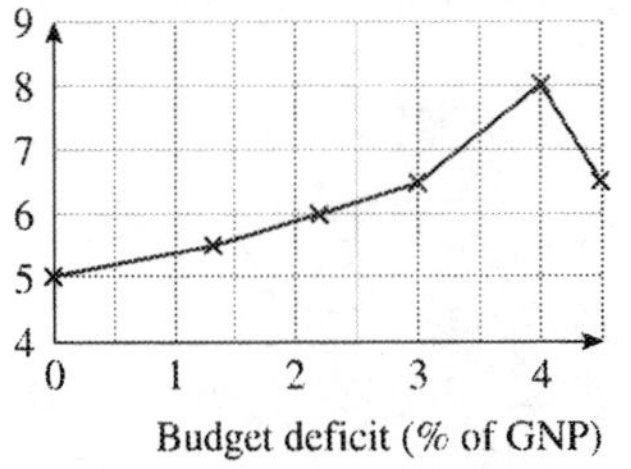

Interval: [0, 4]

12. Inflation (%)

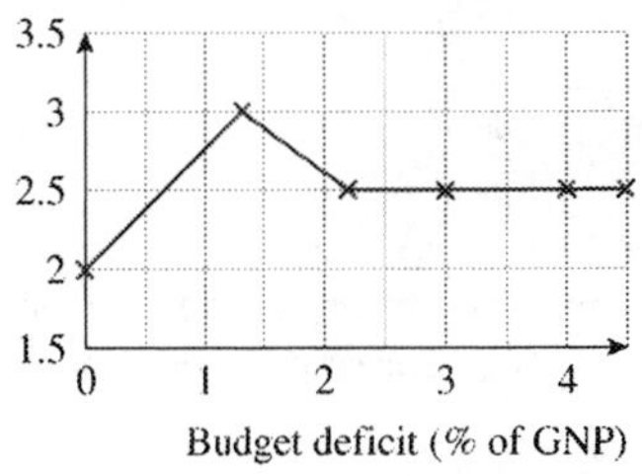

Interval: [0, 4]

13. $f(x) = x^2 - 3$; $[1, 3]$ HINT [See Example 3.]

14. $f(x) = 2x^2 + 4$; $[-1, 2]$ HINT [See Example 3.]

15. $f(x) = 2x + 4$; $[-2, 0]$

16. $f(x) = \dfrac{1}{x}$; $[1, 4]$

17. $f(x) = \dfrac{x^2}{2} + \dfrac{1}{x}$; $[2, 3]$ 18. $f(x) = 3x^2 - \dfrac{x}{2}$; $[3, 4]$

In Exercises 19–24, calculate the average rate of change of the given function f over the intervals $[a, a + h]$ where $h = 1, 0.1, 0.01, 0.001$, and 0.0001. (Technology is recommended for the cases $h = 0.01, 0.001$, and 0.0001.) HINT [See Example 4.]

19. $f(x) = 2x^2$; $a = 0$ 20. $f(x) = \dfrac{x^2}{2}$; $a = 1$

21. $f(x) = \dfrac{1}{x}$; $a = 2$ 22. $f(x) = \dfrac{2}{x}$; $a = 1$

23. $f(x) = x^2 + 2x$; $a = 3$ 24. $f(x) = 3x^2 - 2x$; $a = 0$

APPLICATIONS

25. ***World Military Expenditure*** The following table shows total military and arms trade expenditure in 2000, 2005, and 2010 ($t = 0$ represents 2000):[31]

Year t	0	5	10
Military Expenditure $C(t)$ ($ billion)	1,100	1,300	1,600

Compute and interpret the average rate of change of $C(t)$ **(a)** over the period 2005–2010 (that is, [5, 10]), and **(b)** over the period [0, 10]. Be sure to state the units of measurement. HINT [See Example 1.]

26. ***Education Expenditure*** The following table shows the percentage of the U.S. Discretionary Budget allocated to education in 2003, 2005, and 2009 ($t = 0$ represents 2000):[32]

Year t	3	5	9
Percentage $P(t)$	6.8	7	6.2

Compute and interpret the average rate of change of $P(t)$ **(a)** over the period 2003–2009 (that is, [3, 9]), and **(b)** over the period [5, 9]. Be sure to state the units of measurement. HINT [See Example 1.]

27. ***Oil Production in Mexico*** The following table shows approximate daily oil production by Pemex, Mexico's national oil company, for 2001–2009 ($t = 1$ represents the start of 2001):[33]

t (year since 2000)	1	2	3	4	5	6	7	8	9
$P(t)$ (million barrels)	3.1	3.3	3.4	3.4	3.4	3.3	3.2	3.1	3.0

[31] Source: www.globalissues.org/Geopolitics/ArmsTrade/Spending.asp.

[32] *Ibid.*

[33] Figures are approximate, and 2008–2009 figures are projections by the Department of Energy. Source: Energy Information Administration/Pemex (www.eia.doe.gov).

a. Compute the average rate of change of $P(t)$ over the period 2002–2007. Interpret the result. HINT [See Example 1.]

b. Which of the following is true? From 2001 to 2008, the one-year average rate of change of oil production by Pemex

(A) increased in value.
(B) decreased in value.
(C) never increased in value.
(D) never decreased in value.

HINT [See Example 2.]

28. ***Oil Imports from Mexico*** The following table shows U.S. daily oil imports from Mexico, for 2001–2009 ($t = 1$ represents the start of 2001):[34]

t (year since 2000)	1	2	3	4	5	6	7	8	9
$I(t)$ (million barrels)	1.4	1.35	1.5	1.55	1.6	1.5	1.5	1.5	1.2

a. Use the data in the table to compute the average rate of change of $I(t)$ over the period 2001–2006. Interpret the result.

b. Which of the following is true? From 2002 to 2006, the one-year average rate of change of oil imports from Mexico

(A) increased in value.
(B) decreased in value.
(C) never increased in value.
(D) never decreased in value.

29. ***Subprime Mortgages during the Housing Crisis*** The following graph shows the approximate percentage $P(t)$ of mortgages issued in the U.S. that were subprime (normally classified as risky):[35]

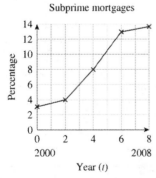

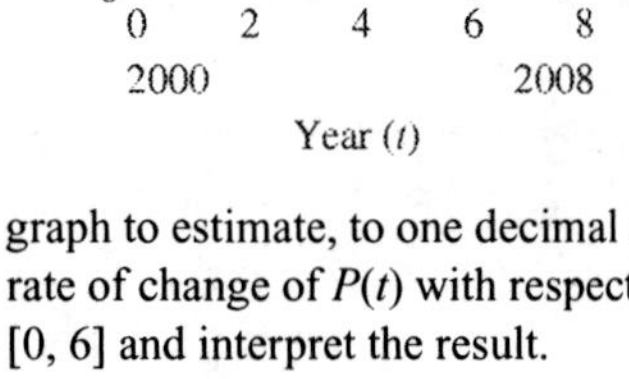

a. Use the graph to estimate, to one decimal place, the average rate of change of $P(t)$ with respect to t over the interval [0, 6] and interpret the result.

b. Over which 2-year period(s) was the average rate of change of $P(t)$ the greatest? HINT [See Example 2.]

30. ***Subprime Mortgage Debt during the Housing Crisis*** The following graph shows the approximate value $V(t)$ of subprime (normally classified as risky) mortgage debt outstanding in the United States:[36]

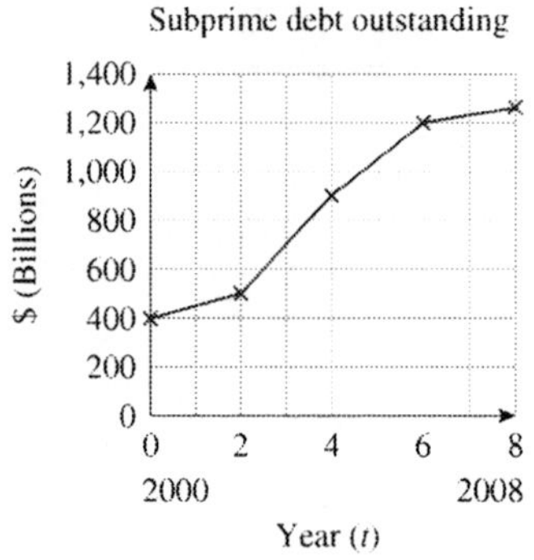

a. Use the graph to estimate, to one decimal place, the average rate of change of $V(t)$ with respect to t over the interval [2, 6] and interpret the result.

b. Over which 2-year period(s) was the average rate of change of $V(t)$ the least? HINT [See Example 2.]

31. ***Immigration to Ireland*** The following graph shows the approximate number (in thousands) of people who immigrated to Ireland during the period 2006–2010 (t is time in years since 2000):[37]

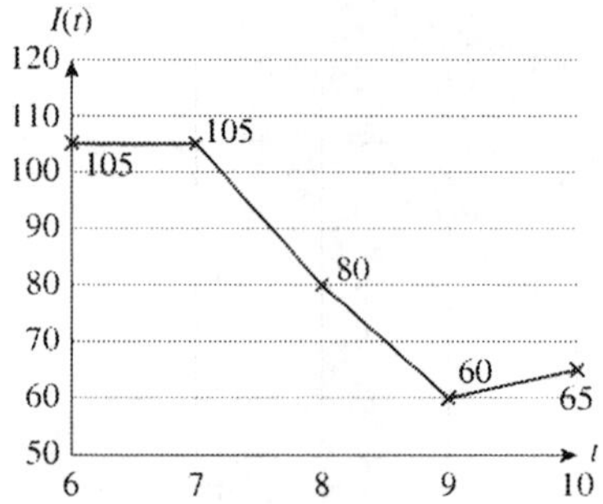

During which 2-year interval(s) was the magnitude of the average rate of change of $I(t)$ (**a**) greatest (**b**) least? Interpret your answers by referring to the rates of change.

32. ***Emigration from Ireland*** The following graph shows the approximate number (in thousands) of people who emigrated from Ireland during the period 2006–2010.[38]

[34] Figures are approximate, and 2008–2009 figures are projections by the Department of Energy. Source: Energy Information Administration/Pemex (www.eia.doe.gov).

[35] Sources: Mortgage Bankers Association, UBS.

[36] Source: Data 360 www.data360.org.

[37] Sources: Ireland Central Statistic Office/Data 360 www.data360.org.

[38] *Ibid.*

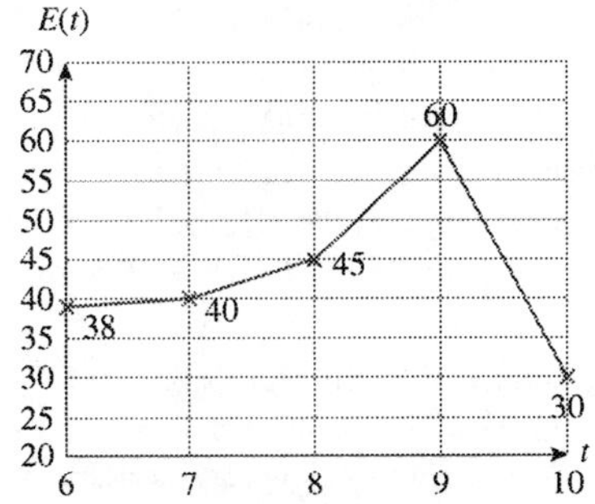

During which 2-year interval(s) was the magnitude of the average rate of change of $E(t)$ (**a**) greatest (**b**) least? Interpret your answers by referring to the rates of change.

33. ▼ ***Physics Research in the U.S.*** The following table shows the number of research articles in the journal *Physical Review* authored by U.S researchers during the period 1993–2003 ($t = 3$ represents 1993):[39]

t (year since 1990)	3	5	7	9	11	13
$N(t)$ (articles, thousands)	5.1	4.6	4.3	4.3	4.5	4.2

a. Find the interval(s) over which the average rate of change of N was the most negative. What was that rate of change? Interpret your answer.

b. The **percentage change of N over the interval $[a, b]$** is defined to be

$$\text{Percentage change of } N = \frac{\text{Change in } N}{\text{First value}} = \frac{N(b) - N(a)}{N(a)}.$$

Compute the percentage change of N over the interval $[3, 13]$ and also the average rate of change. Interpret the answers.

34. ▼ ***Physics Research in Europe*** The following table shows the number of research articles in the journal *Physical Review* authored by researchers in Europe during the period 1993–2003 ($t = 3$ represents 1993):[40]

t (year since 1990)	3	5	7	9	11	13
$N(t)$ (articles, thousands)	3.8	4.6	5.0	5.0	6.0	5.7

a. Find the interval(s) over which the average rate of change of N was the most positive. What was that rate of change? Interpret your answer.

b. The **percentage change of N over the interval $[a, b]$** is defined to be

$$\text{Percentage change of } N = \frac{\text{Change in } N}{\text{First value}} = \frac{N(b) - N(a)}{N(a)}.$$

Compute the percentage change of N over the interval $[7, 13]$ and also the average rate of change. Interpret the answers.

35. ***College Basketball: Men*** The following chart shows the number of NCAA men's college basketball teams in the United States during the period 2000–2010:[41]

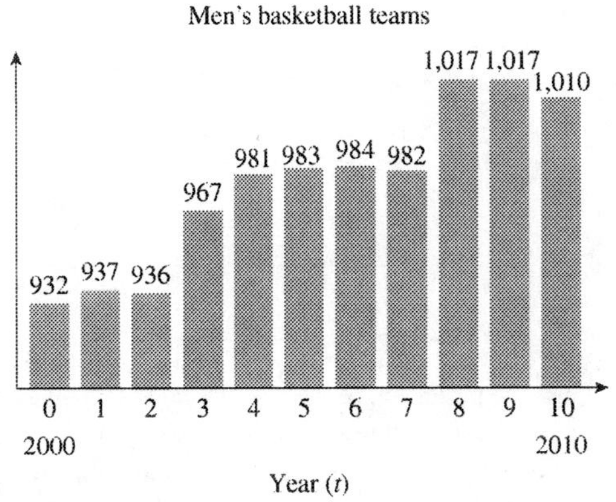

a. On average, how fast was the number of men's college basketball teams growing over the 4-year period beginning in 2002?

b. By inspecting the chart, determine whether the 3-year average rates of change increased or decreased beginning in 2005. HINT [See Example 2.]

36. ***College Basketball: Women*** The following chart shows the number of NCAA women's college basketball teams in the United States during the period 2000–2010:[42]

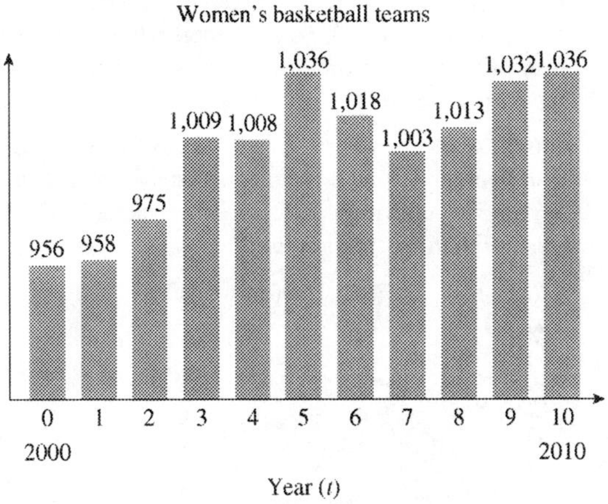

a. On average, how fast was the number of women's college basketball teams growing over the 4-year period beginning in 2004?

b. By inspecting the graph, find the 3-year period over which the average rate of change was largest.

[39]Source: The Americal Physical Society/*New York Times*, May 3, 2003, p. A1.

[40]*Ibid.*

[41]2010 figure is an estimate. Source: www.census.gov.

[42]*Ibid.*

37. ***Funding for the Arts*** State governments in the United States spend a total of between \$1 and \$2 per person on the arts and culture each year. The following chart shows the data for 2002–2010, together with the regression line:[43]

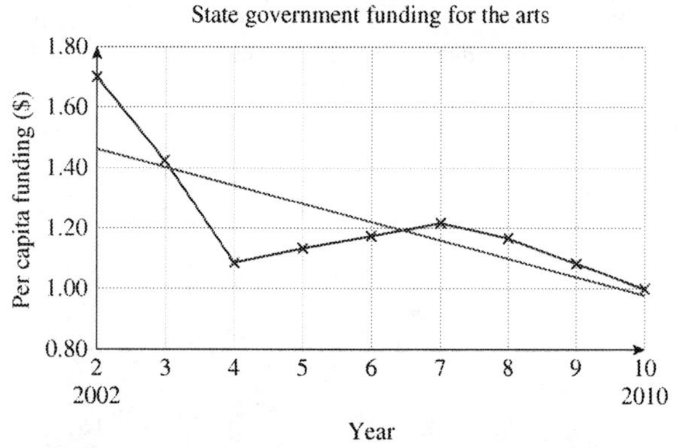

a. Over the period [2, 6] the average rate of change of state government funding for the arts was

(A) less than **(B)** greater than **(C)** approximately equal to

the rate predicted by the regression line.

b. Over the period [3, 10] the average rate of change of state government funding for the arts was

(A) less than **(B)** greater than **(C)** approximately equal to

the rate predicted by the regression line.

c. Over the period [4, 8] the average rate of change of state government funding for the arts was

(A) less than **(B)** greater than **(C)** approximately equal to

the rate predicted by the regression line.

d. Estimate, to two significant digits, the average rate of change of per capita state government funding for the arts over the period [2, 10]. (Be careful to state the units of measurement.) How does it compare to the slope of the regression line?

38. ***Funding for the Arts*** The U.S. federal government spends a total of between \$6 and \$7 per person on the arts and culture each year. The following chart shows the data for 2002–2010, together with the regression line:[44]

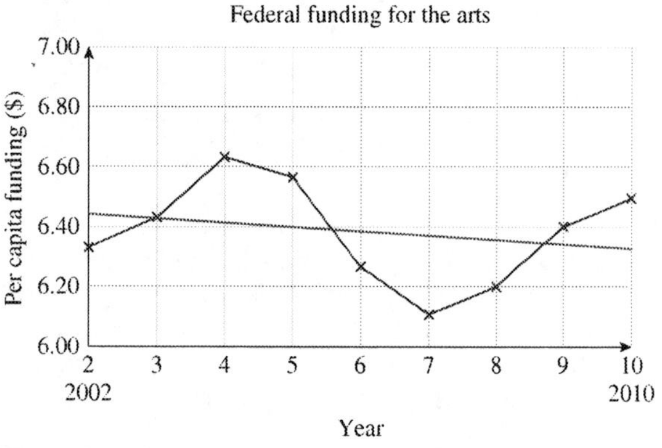

a. Over the period [4, 10] the average rate of change of federal government funding for the arts was

(A) less than **(B)** greater than **(C)** approximately equal to

the rate predicted by the regression line.

b. Over the period [2, 7] the average rate of change of federal government funding for the arts was

(A) less than **(B)** greater than **(C)** approximately equal to

the rate predicted by the regression line.

c. Over the period [3, 10] the average rate of change of federal government funding for the arts was

(A) less than **(B)** greater than **(C)** approximately equal to

the rate predicted by the regression line.

d. Estimate, to one significant digit, the average rate of change of per capita federal government funding for the arts over the period [2, 10]. (Be careful to state the units of measurement.) How does it compare to the slope of the regression line?

39. ▼ ***Market Volatility during the Dot-com Boom*** A volatility index generally measures the extent to which a market undergoes sudden changes in value. The volatility of the S&P 500 (as measured by one such index) was decreasing at an average rate of 0.2 points per year during 1991–1995, and was increasing at an average rate of about 0.3 points per year during 1995–1999. In 1995, the volatility of the S&P was 1.1.[45] Use this information to give a rough sketch of the volatility of the S&P 500 as a function of time, showing its values in 1991 and 1999.

40. ▼ ***Market Volatility during the Dot-com Boom*** The volatility (see the preceding exercise) of the NASDAQ had an average rate of change of 0 points per year during 1992–1995, and increased at an average rate of 0.2 points per year during 1995–1998. In 1995, the volatility of the NASDAQ was 1.1.[46] Use this information to give a rough sketch of the volatility of the NASDAQ as a function of time.

41. ***Market Index*** Joe Downs runs a small investment company from his basement. Every week he publishes a report on the success of his investments, including the progress of the "Joe Downs Index." At the end of one particularly memorable week, he reported that the index for that week had the value $I(t) = 1{,}000 + 1{,}500t - 800t^2 + 100t^3$ points, where t represents the number of business days into the week; t ranges from 0 at the beginning of the week to 5 at the end of the week. The graph of I is shown below.

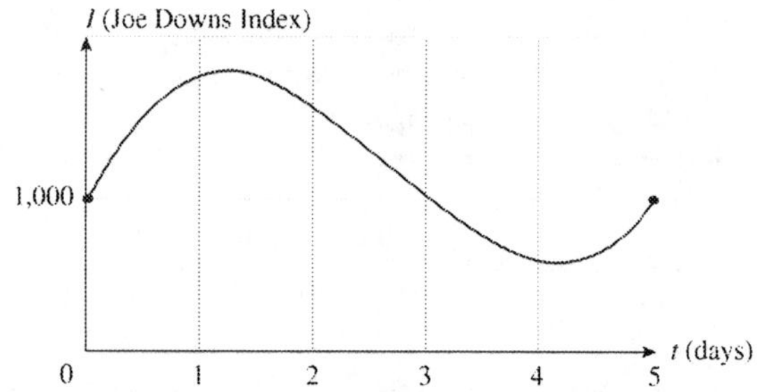

[43] Figures are in constant 2008 dollars, and the 2010 figure is the authors' estimate. Source: *Americans for the Arts* www.artsusa.org.

[44] *Ibid.*

[45] Source for data: Sanford C. Bernstein Company/*New York Times*, March 24, 2000, p. C1.

[46] *Ibid.*

On average, how fast, and in what direction, was the index changing over the first two business days (the interval [0, 2])? HINT [See Example 3.]

42. ***Market Index*** Refer to the Joe Downs Index in the preceding exercise. On average, how fast, and in which direction, was the index changing over the last three business days (the interval [2, 5])? HINT [See Example 3.]

43. ***Crude Oil Prices*** The price per barrel of crude oil in constant 2008 dollars can be approximated by

$$P(t) = 0.45t^2 - 12t + 105 \text{ dollars} \quad (0 \le t \le 28),$$

where t is time in years since the start of 1980.[47]

a. What, in constant 2008 dollars, was the average rate of change of the price of oil from the start of 1981 ($t = 1$) to the start of 2006 ($t = 26$)? HINT [See Example 3.]

b. Your answer to part (a) is quite small. Can you conclude that the price of oil hardly changed at all over the 25-year period 1981 to 2006? Explain.

44. ***Median Home Price*** The median home price in the U.S. over the period 2003–2011 can be approximated by

$$P(t) = -5t^2 + 75t - 30 \text{ thousand dollars} \quad (3 \le t \le 11),$$

where t is time in years since the start of 2000.[48]

a. What was the average rate of change of the median home price from the start of 2007 to the start of 2009? HINT [See Example 3.]

b. What, if anything, does your answer to part (a) say about the median home price in 2008? Explain.

45. ***SARS*** In the early stages of the deadly SARS (Severe Acute Respiratory Syndrome) epidemic in 2003, the number of reported cases could be approximated by

$$A(t) = 167(1.18)^t \quad (0 \le t \le 20)$$

t days after March 17, 2003 (the first day for which statistics were reported by the World Health Organization).

a. What was the average rate of change of $A(t)$ from March 17 to March 23? Interpret the result.

b. Which of the following is true? For the first 20 days of the epidemic, the number of reported cases
(A) increased at a faster and faster rate
(B) increased at a slower and slower rate
(C) decreased at a faster and faster rate
(D) decreased at a slower and slower rate HINT [See Example 2.]

46. ***SARS*** A few weeks into the deadly SARS (Severe Acute Respiratory Syndrome) epidemic in 2003, the number of reported cases could be approximated by

$$A(t) = 1{,}804(1.04)^t \quad (0 \le t \le 30)$$

t days after April 1, 2003.

a. What was the average rate of change of $A(t)$ from April 19 ($t = 18$) to April 29? Interpret the result.

b. Which of the following is true? During the 30-day period beginning April 1, the number of reported cases
(A) increased at a faster and faster rate
(B) increased at a slower and slower rate
(C) decreased at a faster and faster rate
(D) decreased at a slower and slower rate
HINT [See Example 2.]

47. ▼ ***Ecology*** Increasing numbers of manatees ("sea sirens") have been killed by boats off the Florida coast. The following graph shows the relationship between the number of boats registered in Florida and the number of manatees killed each year:

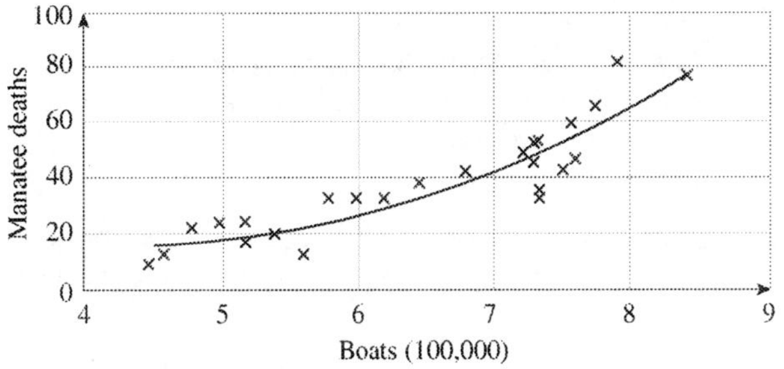

The regression curve shown is given by

$$f(x) = 3.55x^2 - 30.2x + 81 \text{ manatees} \quad (4.5 < x < 8.5),$$

where x is the number of boats (in hundreds of thousands) registered in Florida in a particular year, and $f(x)$ is the number of manatees killed by boats in Florida that year.[49]

a. Compute the average rate of change of f over the intervals [5, 6] and [7, 8].

b. What does the answer to part (a) tell you about the manatee deaths per boat?

48. ▼ ***Ecology*** Refer to Exercise 47.

a. Compute the average rate of change of f over the intervals [5, 7] and [6, 8].

b. Had we used a linear model instead of a quadratic one, how would the two answers in part (a) be related to each other?

49. ▼ ***SAT Scores by Income*** The math SAT score of a high school graduate can be approximated by

$$S(x) = 573 - 133(0.987)^x \text{ points on the math SAT test,}$$

where x is the household income of the student in thousands of dollars per year.[50]

a. Use technology to complete the following table, which shows the average rate of change of S over successive intervals of length 40. (Round all answers to two decimal places.) HINT [See Example 4.]

---

[47]Source for data: www.inflationdata.com.

[48]Source for data: www.zillow.com.

[49]Regression model is based on data from 1976 to 2000. Sources for data: Florida Department of Highway Safety & Motor Vehicles, Florida Marine Institute/*New York Times*, February 12, 2002, p. F4.

[50]The model is the authors'. Source for data: College Board/*New York Times* http://economix.blogs.nytimes.com.

Interval	[0, 40]	[40, 80]	[80, 120]	[120, 160]	[160, 200]
Average Rate of change of S					

b. Interpret your answer for the interval [40, 80], being sure to indicate the direction of change and the units of measurement.

c. Multiple choice: As her household income rises, a student's SAT score

(A) increases.

(B) decreases.

(C) increases, then decreases.

(D) decreases, then increases.

d. Multiple choice: As the household income increases, the effect on a student's SAT score is

(A) more pronounced.

(B) less pronounced.

50. ⬛ ▼ *SAT Scores by Income* Repeat Exercise 49 using the following model for the critical reading SAT score of a high school graduate:

$S(x) = 550 - 136(0.985)^x$ points on the critical reading SAT test,

where x is the household income of the student in thousands of dollars per year.[51]

COMMUNICATION AND REASONING EXERCISES

51. Describe three ways we have used to determine the average rate of change of f over an interval $[a, b]$. Which of the three ways is *least* precise? Explain.

52. If f is a linear function of x with slope m, what is its average rate of change over any interval $[a, b]$?

53. Is the average rate of change of a function over $[a, b]$ affected by the values of the function between a and b? Explain.

54. If the average rate of change of a function over $[a, b]$ is zero, this means that the function has not changed over $[a, b]$, right?

55. Sketch the graph of a function whose average rate of change over $[0, 3]$ is negative but whose average rate of change over $[1, 3]$ is positive.

56. Sketch the graph of a function whose average rate of change over $[0, 2]$ is positive but whose average rate of change over $[0, 1]$ is negative.

57. ▼ If the rate of change of quantity A is 2 units of quantity A per unit of quantity B, and the rate of change of quantity B is 3 units of quantity B per unit of quantity C, what is the rate of change of quantity A with respect to quantity C?

58. ▼ If the rate of change of quantity A is 2 units of quantity A per unit of quantity B, what is the rate of change of quantity B with respect to quantity A?

59. ▼ A certain function f has the property that its average rate of change over the interval $[1, 1+h]$ (for positive h) increases as h decreases. Which of the following graphs could be the graph of f?

(A)   **(B)**

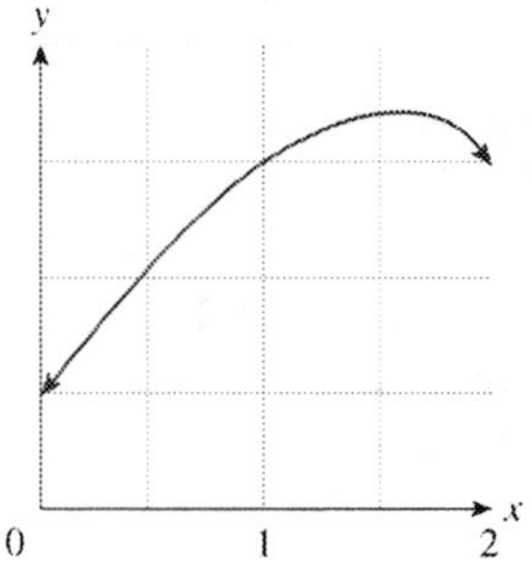

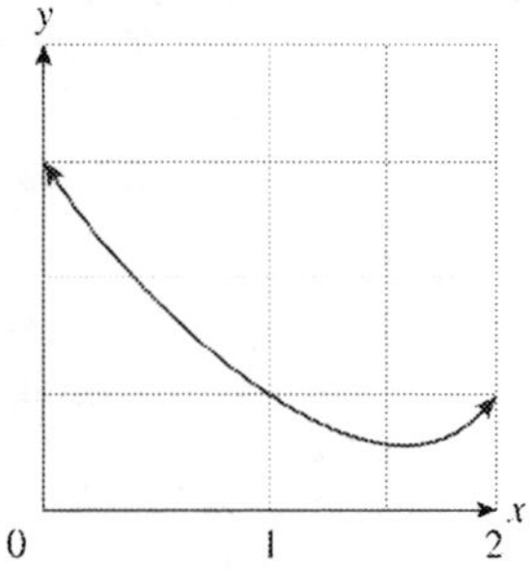

(C)

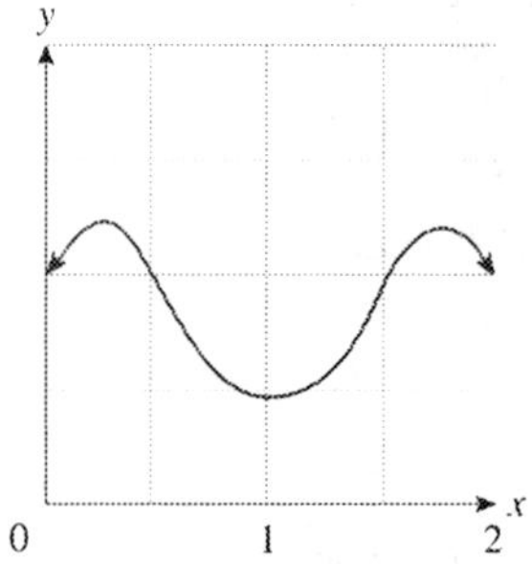

60. ▼ A certain function f has the property that its average rate of change over the interval $[1, 1 + h]$ (for positive h) decreases as h decreases. Which of the following graphs could be the graph of f?

(A)   **(B)**

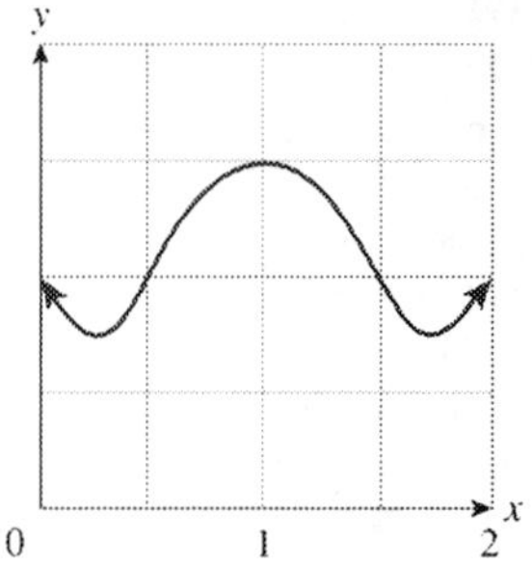

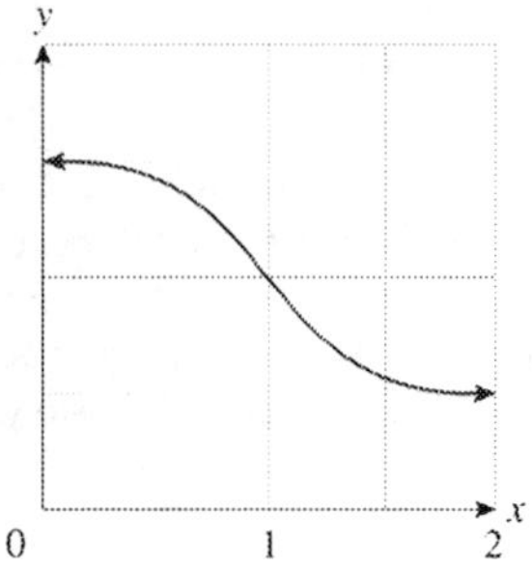

(C)

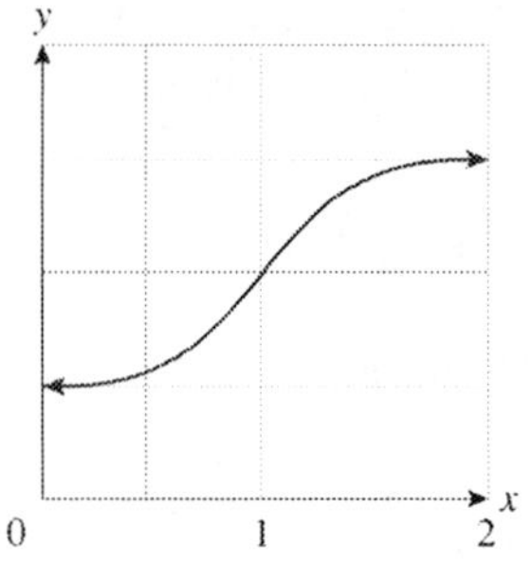

[51]The model is the authors'. Source for data: College Board/*New York Times* http://economix.blogs.nytimes.com.

61. Is it possible for a company's revenue to have a negative 3-year average rate of growth, but a positive average rate of growth in 2 of the 3 years? (If not, explain; if so, illustrate with an example.)

62. Is it possible for a company's revenue to have a larger 2-year average rate of change than either of the 1-year average rates of change? (If not, explain why with the aid of a graph; if so, illustrate with an example.)

63. ◆ The average rate of change of f over [1, 3] is

(A) always equal to **(B)** never equal to
(C) sometimes equal to

the average of its average rates of change over [1, 2] and [2, 3].

64. ◆ The average rate of change of f over [1, 4] is

(A) always equal to **(B)** never equal to
(C) sometimes equal to

the average of its average rates of change over [1, 2], [2, 3], and [3, 4].

Practice Problems 10.4, Part 1

1. To the right is the graph of a function $p(x)$. Gridlines each mark one unit.

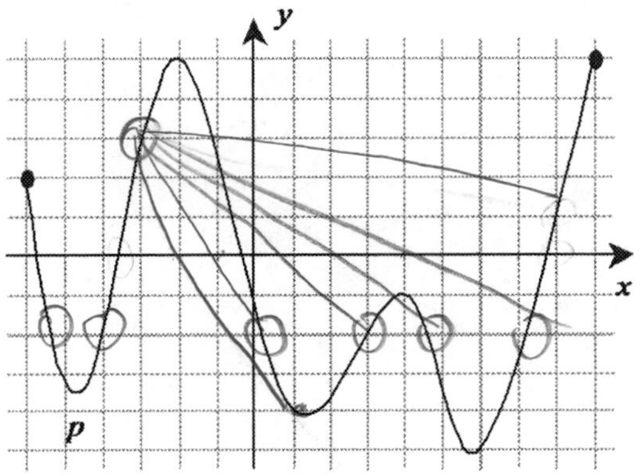

   a. Calculate the average rate of change of $p(x)$ from $x = -4$ to $x = 8$.

   b. Find all numbers t such that the average rate of change of $p(x)$ between $x = -4$ and $x = t$ is zero.

   c. Find the number b such that the average rate of change of $p(x)$ between $x = -3$ and $x = b$ is as small as possible (i.e., largest negative value). Explain your choice.

2. Weekly sales (in units of product) for a company are shown to the right.

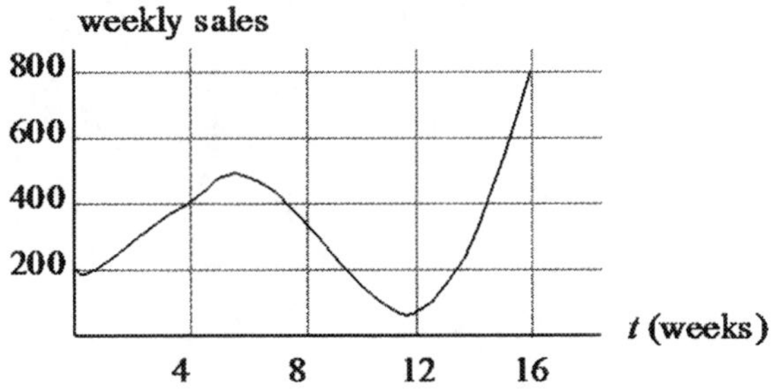

   a. During which of the following time intervals was the average rate of change of sales with respect to time larger?
      - $0 \le t \le 4$ or $0 \le t \le 8$
      - $0 \le t \le 8$ or $0 \le t \le 16$

   b. Estimate the average rate of change between $t = 0$ and $t = 16$. Interpret your answer in terms of sales. Include appropriate units in your response.

Practice Problems 10.4, Part 2

The distance a person can see depends on her elevation above level ground. Suppose that on a clear day, the function $v(x) = 1.2\sqrt{x}$ reasonably approximates viewing distance (in miles) at an elevation of x feet.

1. Fill in the chart, showing the average rate of change of $v(x)$ with respect to x over the indicated intervals. Round results to five decimal places.

Interval	$[95,100]$	$[99,100]$	$[99.99,100]$	$[100,100.01]$	$[100,101]$	$[100,105]$
$\frac{\Delta v}{\Delta x}$						

2. Simplify the difference quotient $\frac{v(100+h)-v(100)}{h}$. (Hint: Consider rationalizing the numerator.)

3. Fill in the chart (use your result from **2.**). Round results to five decimal places.

h	-5	-1	-0.01	0.01	1	5
$\frac{v(100+h)-v(100)}{h}$						

4. Calculate $\lim_{h\to 0} \frac{v(100+h)-v(100)}{h}$

10.5 Derivatives: Numerical and Graphical Viewpoints

In Example 4 of Section 10.4, we looked at the average rate of change of the function $G(t) = 5t^2 - 85t + 1,762$ approximating the price of gold on the spot market over smaller and smaller intervals of time. We obtained the following table showing the average rates of change of G over the intervals $[8, 8 + h]$ for successively smaller values of h:

h getting smaller; interval $[8, 8 + h]$ getting smaller →

h	1	0.1	0.01	0.001	0.0001
Ave. Rate of Change over $[8, 8 + h]$	0	−4.5	−4.95	−4.995	−4.9995

Rate of change approaching −$5 per hour →

The average rates of change of the price of gold over smaller and smaller periods of time, starting at the instant $t = 8$ (8:00 am), appear to be getting closer and closer to −$5 per hour. As we look at these shrinking periods of time, we are getting closer to looking at what happens at the *instant* $t = 8$. So it seems reasonable to say that the average rates of change are approaching the **instantaneous rate of change** at $t = 8$, which the table suggests is −$5 per hour. This is how fast the price of gold was changing *exactly* at 8:00 am.

At $t = 8$, the instantaneous rate of change of $G(t)$ is -5.

We express this fact mathematically by writing $G'(8) = -5$ (which we read as "G prime of 8 equals −5"). Thus

$G'(8) = -5$ *means that, at $t = 8$, the instantaneous rate of change of $G(t)$ is -5.*

The process of letting h get smaller and smaller is called taking the **limit** as h approaches 0 (as you recognize if you've done the sections on limits). As in the sections on limits, we write $h \to 0$ as shorthand for "h approaches 0." Thus, taking the limit of the average rates of change as $h \to 0$ gives us the instantaneous rate of change.

Q: *All these intervals [8, 8 + h] are intervals to the right of 8. What about small intervals to the left of 8, such as [7.9, 8]?*

A: We can compute the average rate of change of our function for such intervals by choosing h to be negative ($h = -0.1, -0.01$, etc.) and using the same difference quotient formula we used for positive h:

$$\text{Average rate of change of } G \text{ over } [8+h, 8] = \frac{G(8) - G(8+h)}{8 - (8+h)}$$

Here are the results we get using negative h:

h getting closer to 0; interval $[8+h, 8]$ getting smaller →

h	-1	-0.1	-0.01	-0.001	-0.0001
Ave. Rate of Change over [8 + h, 8]	-10	-5.5	-5.05	-5.005	-5.0005

Rate of change approaching −\$5 per hour →

Notice that the average rates of change are again getting closer and closer to −5 as h approaches 0, suggesting once again that the instantaneous rate of change is −\$5 per hour.

Instantaneous Rate of Change of $f(x)$ at $x = a$: Derivative

The **instantaneous rate of change** of $f(x)$ at $x = a$ is defined as

$$f'(a) = \lim_{h \to 0} \frac{f(a+h) - f(a)}{h}.$$

f prime of a equals the limit, as h approaches 0, of the ratio $\frac{f(a+h) - f(a)}{h}$.

The quantity $f'(a)$ is also called the **derivative of $f(x)$ at $x = a$.** Finding the derivative of f is called **differentiating f.**

Units

The units of $f'(a)$ are the same as the units of the average rate of change: units of f per unit of x.

Quick Examples

1. If $f(x) = 5x^2 - 85x + 1{,}762$, then the two tables above suggest that

$$f'(8) = \lim_{h \to 0} \frac{f(8+h) - f(8)}{h} = -5.$$

2. If $f(t)$ is the number of insects in your dorm room at time t hours, and you know that $f(3) = 5$ and $f'(3) = 8$, this means that, at time $t = 3$ hours, there are 5 insects in your room, and this number is growing at an instantaneous rate of 8 insects per hour.

IMPORTANT NOTES

1. Sections 10.1–10.3 discuss limits in some detail. If you have not (yet) covered those sections, you can trust to your intuition.
2. The formula for the derivative tells us that the instantaneous rate of change is the limit of the average rates of change $[f(a+h)-f(a)]/h$ over smaller and smaller intervals. Thus, the value of $f'(a)$ can be approximated by computing the average rate of change for smaller and smaller values of h, both positive and negative.
3. If a happens to be an endpoint of the domain of f, then $f'(a)$ does not exist, as then $[f(a+h)-f(a)]/h$ only has a one-sided limit as $h \to 0$, and so

   $\lim_{h \to 0} \dfrac{f(a+h)-f(a)}{h}$ does not exist.*

4. In this section we will only *approximate* derivatives. In Section 10.6 we will begin to see how we find the *exact* values of derivatives.
5. $f'(a)$ is a number we can calculate, or at least approximate, for various values of a, as we have done in the earlier example. Since $f'(a)$ depends on the value of a, we can think of f' as *a function of a*. (We return to this idea at the end of this section.) An old name for f' is "the function *derived from* f," which has been shortened to the *derivative* of f.
6. It is because f' is a function that we sometimes refer to $f'(a)$ as "the derivative of f *evaluated at* a," or the "derivative of $f(x)$ evaluated at $x = a$."

* One could define the derivative at an endpoint by instead using the associated one-sided limit; for instance, if a is a left endpoint of the domain of f, then one could define

$$f'(a) = \lim_{h \to 0^+} \frac{f(a+h)-f(a)}{h}$$

as we did in previous editions of this book. However, in this edition we have decided to follow the usual convention and say that the derivative at an endpoint does not exist.

It may happen that the average rates of change $[f(a+h)-f(a)]/h$ do not approach any fixed number at all as h approaches zero, or that they approach one number on the intervals using positive h, and another on those using negative h. If this happens, $\lim_{h\to 0}[f(a+h)-f(a)]/h$ does not exist, and we say that f is **not differentiable** at $x = a$, or **$f'(a)$ does not exist**. When the limit *does* exist, we say that f is **differentiable** at the point $x = a$, or **$f'(a)$ exists**. It is comforting to know that all polynomials and exponential functions are differentiable at *every* point. On the other hand, certain functions are not differentiable. Examples are $f(x) = |x|$ and $f(x) = x^{1/3}$, neither of which is differentiable at $x = 0$. (See Section 11.1.)

EXAMPLE 1 Instantaneous Rate of Change: Numerically and Graphically

The air temperature one spring morning, t hours after 7:00 am, was given by the function $f(t) = 50 + 0.1t^4$ degrees Fahrenheit ($0 \le t \le 4$).

a. How fast was the temperature rising at 9:00 am?

b. How is the instantaneous rate of change of temperature at 9:00 am reflected in the graph of temperature vs. time?

Solution

a. We are being asked to find the instantaneous rate of change of the temperature at $t = 2$, so we need to find $f'(2)$. To do this we examine the average rates of change

$$\frac{f(2+h)-f(2)}{h}$$ Average rate of change = difference quotient

for values of h approaching 0. Calculating the average rate of change over $[2, 2+h]$ for $h = 1$, 0.1, 0.01, 0.001, and 0.0001 we get the following values (rounded to four decimal places):*

* We can quickly compute these values using technology as in Example 4 in Section 10.4. (See the Technology Guides at the end of the chapter.)

h	1	0.1	0.01	0.001	0.0001
Average Rate of Change Over [2, 2 + h]	6.5	3.4481	3.2241	3.2024	3.2002

Here are the values we get using negative values of h:

h	−1	−0.1	−0.01	−0.001	−0.0001
Average Rate of Change Over [2 + h, 2]	1.5	2.9679	3.1761	3.1976	3.1998

The average rates of change are clearly approaching the number 3.2, so we can say that $f'(2) = 3.2$. Thus, at 9:00 in the morning, the temperature was rising at the rate of 3.2 degrees per hour.

b. We saw in Section 10.4 that the average rate of change of f over an interval is the slope of the secant line through the corresponding points on the graph of f. Figure 25 illustrates this for the intervals $[2, 2+h]$ with $h = 1$, 0.5, and 0.1.

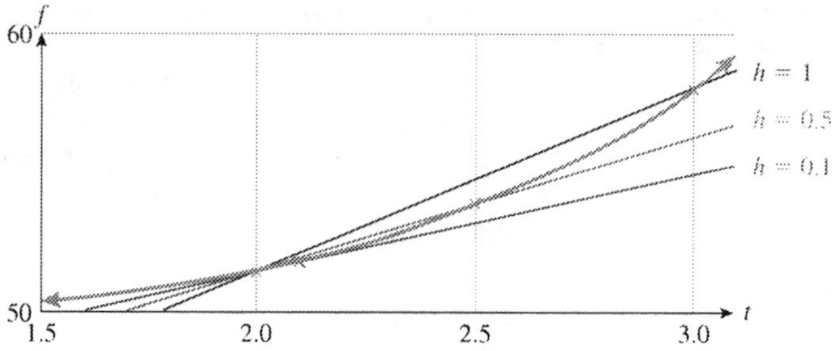

Figure 25

All three secant lines pass though the point $(2, f(2)) = (2, 51.6)$ on the graph of f. Each of them passes through a second point on the curve (the second point is different for each secant line) and this second point gets closer and closer to (2, 51.6) as h gets closer to 0. What seems to be happening is that the secant lines are getting closer and closer to a line that just touches the curve at (2, 51.6): the **tangent line** at (2, 51.6), shown in Figure 26.

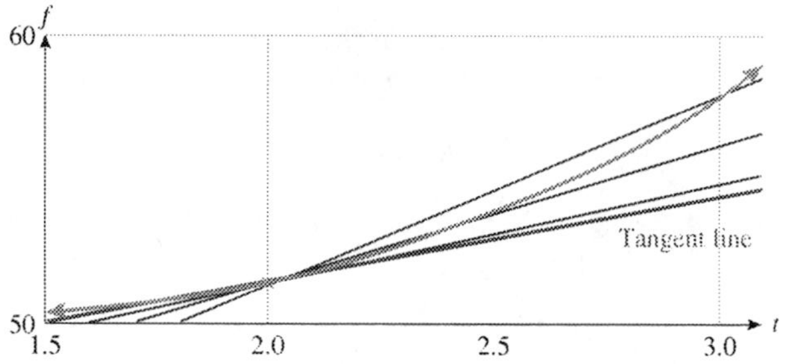

Figure 26

Q: *What is the slope of this tangent line?*

A: Because the slopes of the secant lines are getting closer and closer to 3.2, and because the secant lines are approaching the tangent line, the tangent line must have slope 3.2. In other words,

At the point on the graph where $x = 2$, the slope of the tangent line is $f'(2)$.

Q: *What is the difference between $f(2)$ and $f'(2)$?*

A: An important question. Briefly, $f(2)$ is the *value of f* when $t = 2$, while $f'(2)$ is the *rate at which f is changing* when $t = 2$. Here,

$$f(2) = 50 + 0.1(2)^4 = 51.6 \text{ degrees.}$$

Thus, at 9:00 am ($t = 2$), the temperature was 51.6 degrees. On the other hand,

$$f'(2) = 3.2 \text{ degrees per hour.}$$ Units of slope are units of f per unit of t.

This means that, at 9:00 am ($t = 2$), the temperature was increasing at a rate of 3.2 degrees per hour.

Because we have been talking about tangent lines, we should say more about what they *are*. A tangent line to a *circle* is a line that touches the circle in just one point. A tangent line gives the circle "a glancing blow," as shown in Figure 27.

For a smooth curve other than a circle, a tangent line may touch the curve at more than one point, or pass through it (Figure 28).

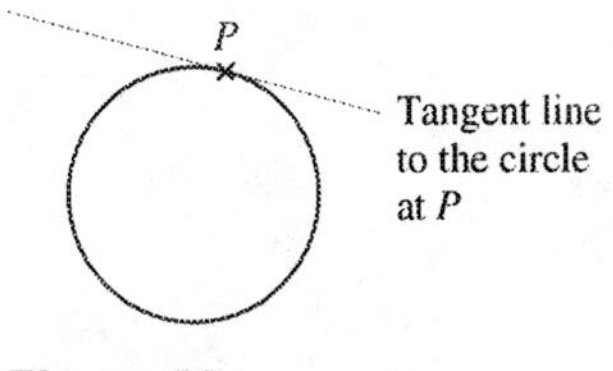

Figure 27

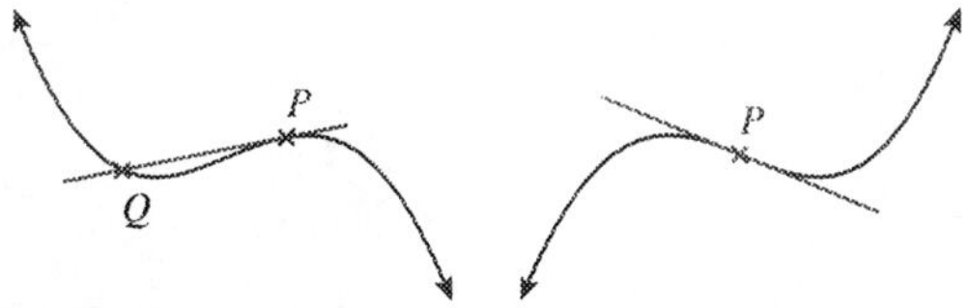

Tangent line at P intersects graph at Q

Tangent line at P passes through curve at P

Figure 28

However, all tangent lines have the following interesting property in common: If we focus on a small portion of the curve very close to the point P—in other words, if we "zoom in" to the graph near the point P—the curve will appear almost straight, and almost indistinguishable from the tangent line (Figure 29).

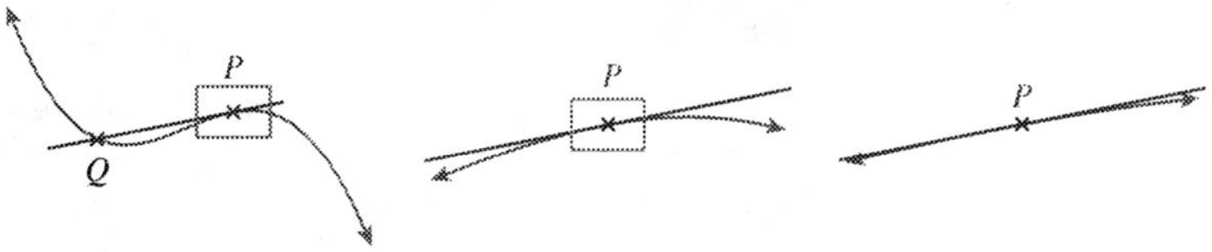

Original curve

Zoomed-in once

Zoomed-in twice

Figure 29

You can check this property by zooming in on the curve shown in Figures 25 and 26 in the previous example near the point where $x = 2$.

Secant and Tangent Lines

The *slope of the secant line* through the points on the graph of f where $x = a$ and $x = a + h$ is given by the average rate of change, or difference quotient,

$$m_{\text{sec}} = \text{slope of secant} = \text{average rate of change} = \frac{f(a+h) - f(a)}{h}.$$

The *slope of the tangent line* through the point on the graph of f where $x = a$ is given by the instantaneous rate of change, or derivative

$$m_{\tan} = \text{slope of tangent} = \text{instantaneous rate of change} = \text{derivative}$$
$$= f'(a) = \lim_{h \to 0} \frac{f(a+h) - f(a)}{h},$$

assuming the limit exists.

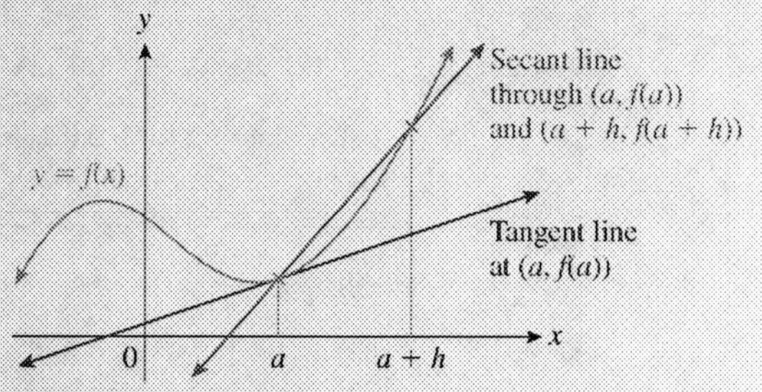

Quick Example

In the following graph, the tangent line at the point where $x = 2$ has slope 3. Therefore, the derivative at $x = 2$ is 3. That is, $f'(2) = 3$.

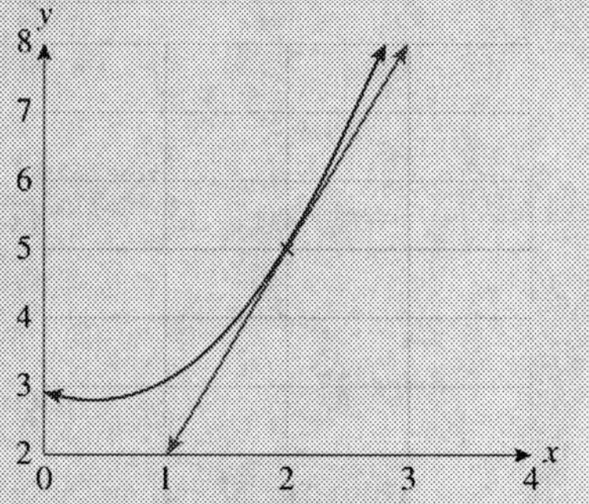

Note It might happen that the tangent line is vertical at some point or does not exist at all. These are the cases in which f is not differentiable at the given point. (See Section 10.6.) ■

We can now give a more precise definition of what we mean by the tangent line to a point P on the graph of f at a given point: The **tangent line** to the graph of f at the point $P(a, f(a))$ is the straight line passing through P with slope $f'(a)$.

Quick Approximation of the Derivative

Q: *Do we always need to make tables of difference quotients as above in order to calculate an approximate value for the derivative? That seems like a large amount of work just to get an approximation.*

A: We can usually *approximate* the value of the derivative by using a single, small value of h. In the example above, the value $h = 0.0001$ would have given a pretty good approximation. The problems with using a fixed value of h are that (1) we do not get an *exact* answer, only an *approximation* of the derivative, and (2) how good an approximation it is depends on the function we're differentiating.* However, with most of the functions we'll be considering, setting $h = 0.0001$ does give us a good approximation.

* In fact, no matter how small the value we decide to use for h, it is possible to craft a function f for which the difference quotient at a is not even close to $f'(a)$.

Calculating a Quick Approximation of the Derivative

We can calculate an approximate value of $f'(a)$ by using the formula

$$f'(a) \approx \frac{f(a+h) - f(a)}{h} \qquad \text{Rate of change over } [a,\ a+h]$$

with a small value of h. The value $h = 0.0001$ works for most examples we encounter (students of numerical methods study the question of exactly how accurate this approximation is).

Alternative Formula: The Balanced Difference Quotient

The following alternative formula, which measures the rate of change of f over the interval $[a-h, a+h]$, often gives a more accurate result, and is the one used in many calculators:

$$f'(a) \approx \frac{f(a+h) - f(a-h)}{2h}. \qquad \text{Rate of change over } [a-h,\ a+h]$$

Note For the quick approximations to be valid, the function f must be differentiable; that is, $f'(a)$ must exist. ■

EXAMPLE 2 Quick Approximation of the Derivative

a. Calculate an approximate value of $f'(1.5)$ if $f(x) = x^2 - 4x$.

b. Find the equation of the tangent line at the point on the graph where $x = 1.5$.

Solution

a. We shall compute both the ordinary difference quotient and the balanced difference quotient.

Ordinary Difference Quotient: Using $h = 0.0001$, the ordinary difference quotient is:

$$f'(1.5) \approx \frac{f(1.5 + 0.0001) - f(1.5)}{0.0001} \qquad \text{Ordinary difference quotient}$$

$$= \frac{f(1.5001) - f(1.5)}{0.0001}$$

$$= \frac{(1.5001^2 - 4 \times 1.5001) - (1.5^2 - 4 \times 1.5)}{0.0001} = -0.9999.$$

This answer is accurate to 0.0001; in fact, $f'(1.5) = -1$.

Graphically, we can picture this approximation as follows: Zoom in on the curve using the window $1.5 \le x \le 1.5001$ and measure the slope of the secant line joining both ends of the curve segment. Figure 30 shows close-up views of the curve and tangent line near the point P in which we are interested, the third view being the zoomed-in view used for this approximation.

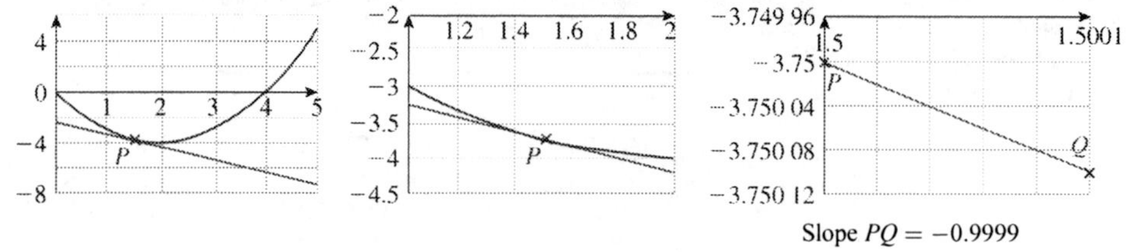

Figure 30

Notice that in the third window the tangent line and curve are indistinguishable. Also, the point P in which we are interested is on the left edge of the window.

Balanced Difference Quotient: For the balanced difference quotient, we get

$$f'(1.5) \approx \frac{f(1.5+0.0001)-f(1.5-0.0001)}{2(0.0001)} \qquad \text{Balanced difference quotient}$$

$$= \frac{f(1.5001)-f(1.4999)}{0.0002}$$

$$= \frac{(1.5001^2 - 4\times 1.5001)-(1.4999^2-4\times 1.4999)}{0.0002} = -1.$$

This balanced difference quotient gives the exact answer in this case!* Graphically, it is as though we have zoomed in using a window that puts the point P in the *center* of the screen (Figure 31) rather than at the left edge.

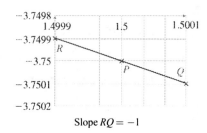

* The balanced difference quotient always gives the exact derivative for a quadratic function.

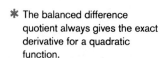

using Technology

See the Technology Guides at the end of the chapter to find out how to calculate the quick approximations to the derivative in Example 2 using a TI-83/84 Plus or a spreadsheet. Here is an outline:

TI-83/84 Plus

`Y1=X^2-4*X`

Home screen:

`(Y1(1.5001)-Y1(1.5))/0.0001`

`(Y1(1.5001)-Y1(1.4999))/0.0002`

[More details on page 779.]

Spreadsheet

Headings a, h, x, f(x), Diff Quotient, Balanced Diff Quotient in A1–F1

`1.5` in A2, `0.0001` in B2,

`=A2-B2` in C2, `=A2` in C3, `=A2+B2` in C4

`=C2^2-4*C2` in D2; copy down to D4

`=(D3-D2)/(C3-C2)` in E2

`=(D4-D2)/(C4-C2)` in E3

[More details on page 781.]

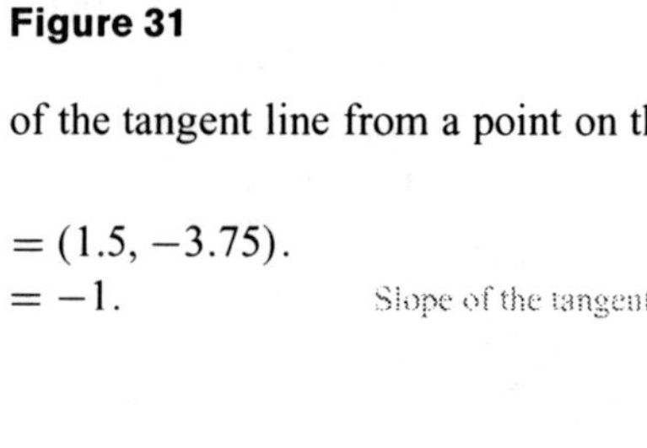

Figure 31

b. We find the equation of the tangent line from a point on the line and its slope, as we did in Chapter 1:

- ***Point*** $(1.5, f(1.5)) = (1.5, -3.75)$.
- ***Slope*** $m = f'(1.5) = -1$. Slope of the tangent line = derivative.

The equation is

$$y = mx + b,$$

where $m = -1$ and $b = y_1 - mx_1 = -3.75 - (-1)(1.5) = -2.25$. Thus, the equation of the tangent line is

$$y = -x - 2.25.$$

Q: *Why can't we simply put $h = 0.000\,000\,000\,000\,000\,000\,01$ for an incredibly accurate approximation to the instantaneous rate of change and be done with it?*

A: This approach would certainly work if you were patient enough to do the (thankless) calculation by hand! However, doing it with the help of technology–even an ordinary calculator–will cause problems: The issue is that calculators and spreadsheets represent numbers with a maximum number of significant digits (15 in the case of Excel). As the value of h gets smaller, the value of $f(a+h)$ gets closer and closer to the value of $f(a)$. For example, if $f(x) = 50 + 0.1x^4$, Excel might compute

$$\begin{aligned} &f(2 + 0.000\,000\,000\,000\,000\,1) - f(2) \\ &\quad = 51.600\,000\,000\,000\,000\,3 - 51.6 \qquad \text{Rounded to 15 digits} \\ &\quad = 0.000\,000\,000\,000\,000\,3 \end{aligned}$$

and the corresponding difference quotient would be 3, not 3.2 as it should be. If h gets even smaller, Excel will not be able to distinguish between $f(a+h)$ and $f(a)$ at all, in which case it will compute 0 for the rate of change. This loss in accuracy when subtracting two very close numbers is called **subtractive error**.

Thus, there is a trade-off in lowering the value of h: Smaller values of h yield *mathematically* more accurate approximations of the derivative, but if h gets too small, subtractive error becomes a problem and decreases the accuracy of computations that use technology.

Leibniz *d* Notation

We introduced the notation $f'(x)$ for the derivative of f at x, but there is another interesting notation. We have written the average rate of change as

$$\text{Average rate of change} = \frac{\Delta f}{\Delta x}. \qquad \frac{\text{Change in } f}{\text{Change in } x}$$

As we use smaller and smaller values for Δx, we approach the instantaneous rate of change, or derivative, for which we also have the notation df/dx, due to Leibniz:

$$\text{Instantaneous rate of change} = \lim_{\Delta x \to 0} \frac{\Delta f}{\Delta x} = \frac{df}{dx}.$$

That is, df/dx is just another notation for $f'(x)$. Do not think of df/dx as an actual quotient of two numbers: Remember that we only use an actual quotient $\Delta f/\Delta x$ to *approximate* the value of df/dx.

In Example 3, we apply the quick approximation method of estimating the derivative.

EXAMPLE 3 Velocity

My friend Eric, an enthusiastic baseball player, claims he can "probably" throw a ball upward at a speed of 100 feet per second (ft/s).* Our physicist friends tell us that its height s (in feet) t seconds later would be $s = 100t - 16t^2$. Find its average velocity over the interval [2, 3] and its instantaneous velocity exactly 2 seconds after Eric throws it.

* Eric's claim is difficult to believe; 100 ft/s corresponds to around 68 mph, and professional pitchers can throw *forward* at about 100 mph.

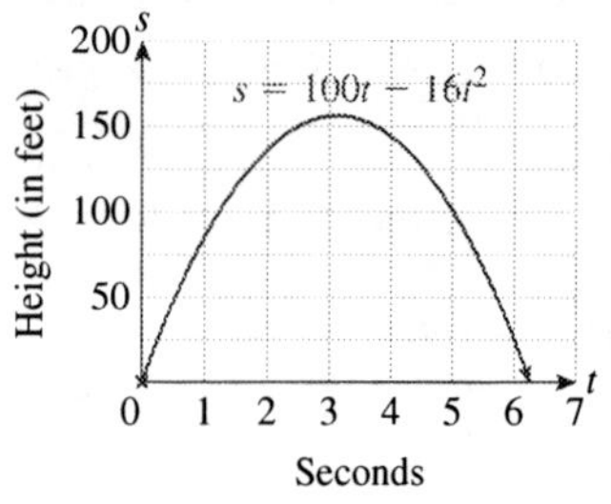

Figure 32

Solution The graph of the ball's height as a function of time is shown in Figure 32. Asking for the velocity is really asking for the rate of change of height with respect to time. (Why?) Consider average velocity first. To compute the **average velocity** of the ball from time 2 to time 3, we first compute the change in height:

$$\Delta s = s(3) - s(2) = 156 - 136 = 20 \text{ ft}.$$

Since it rises 20 feet in $\Delta t = 1$ second, we use the defining formula *speed = distance/time* to get the average velocity:

$$\text{Average velocity} = \frac{\Delta s}{\Delta t} = \frac{20}{1} = 20 \text{ ft/sec}.$$

from time $t = 2$ to $t = 3$. This is just the difference quotient, so

The average velocity is the average rate of change of height.

To get the **instantaneous velocity** at $t = 2$, we find the instantaneous rate of change of height. In other words, we need to calculate the derivative ds/dt at $t = 2$. Using the balanced quick approximation described earlier, we get

$$\begin{aligned}\frac{ds}{dt} &\approx \frac{s(2+0.0001) - s(2-0.0001)}{2(0.0001)}\\ &= \frac{s(2.0001) - s(1.9999)}{0.0002}\\ &= \frac{100(2.0001) - 16(2.0001)^2 - (100(1.9999) - 16(1.9999)^2)}{0.0002}\\ &= 36 \text{ ft/sec}.\end{aligned}$$

In fact, this happens to be the exact answer; the instantaneous velocity at $t = 2$ is exactly 36 ft/sec. (Try an even smaller value of h to persuade yourself.)

➡ **Before we go on...** If we repeat the calculation in Example 3 at time $t = 5$, we get

$$\frac{ds}{dt} = -60 \text{ ft/sec}.$$

The negative sign tells us that the ball is *falling* at a rate of 60 feet per second at time $t = 5$. (How does the fact that it is falling at $t = 5$ show up on the graph?) ■

The preceding example gives another interpretation of the derivative.

Average and Instantaneous Velocity

For an object moving in a straight line with position $s(t)$ at time t, the **average velocity** from time t to time $t + h$ is the average rate of change of position with respect to time:

$$v_{ave} = \frac{s(t+h) - s(t)}{h} = \frac{\Delta s}{\Delta t}.$$

Average velocity = Average rate of change of position

The **instantaneous velocity** at time t is

$$v = \lim_{h \to 0} \frac{s(t+h) - s(t)}{h} = \frac{ds}{dt}.$$

Instantaneous velocity = Instantaneous rate of change of position

In other words, *instantaneous velocity is the derivative of position with respect to time.*

Here is one last comment on Leibniz notation. In Example 3, we could have written the velocity either as s' or as ds/dt, as we chose to do. To write the answer to the question, that the velocity at $t = 2$ sec was 36 ft/sec, we can write either

$$s'(2) = 36$$

or

$$\left.\frac{ds}{dt}\right|_{t=2} = 36.$$

The notation "$|_{t=2}$" is read "evaluated at $t = 2$." Similarly, if $y = f(x)$, we can write the instantaneous rate of change of f at $x = 5$ in either functional notation as

$$f'(5) \qquad \text{The derivative of } f \text{, evaluated at } x = 5$$

or in Leibniz notation as

$$\left.\frac{dy}{dx}\right|_{x=5}. \qquad \text{The derivative of } y \text{, evaluated at } x = 5$$

The latter notation is obviously more cumbersome than the functional notation $f'(5)$, but the notation dy/dx has compensating advantages. You should practice using both notations.

The Derivative Function

The derivative $f'(x)$ is a number we can calculate, or at least approximate, for various values of x. Because $f'(x)$ depends on the value of x, we may think of f' as a function of x. This function is the **derivative function**.

Derivative Function

If f is a function, its **derivative function** f' is the function whose value $f'(x)$ is the derivative of f at x. Its domain is the set of all x at which f is differentiable. Equivalently, f' associates to each x the slope of the tangent to the graph of the function f at x, or the rate of change of f at x. The formula for the derivative function is

$$f'(x) = \lim_{h\to 0} \frac{f(x+h) - f(x)}{h}. \qquad \text{Derivative function}$$

Quick Examples

1. Let $f(x) = 3x - 1$. The graph of f is a straight line that has slope 3 everywhere. In other words, $f'(x) = 3$ for every choice of x; that is, f' is a constant function.

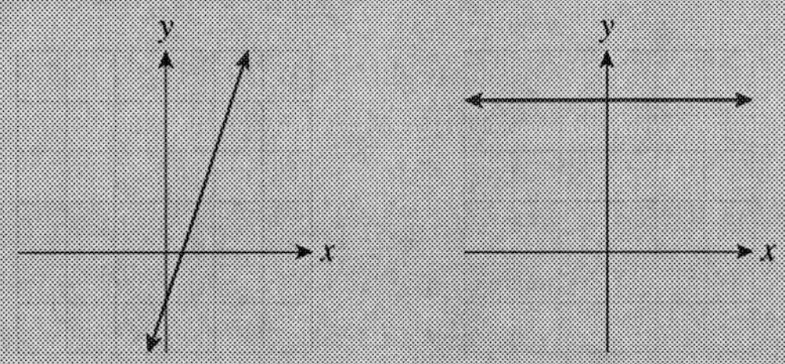

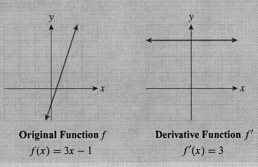

Original Function f
$f(x) = 3x - 1$

Derivative Function f'
$f'(x) = 3$

2. Given the graph of a function f, we can get a rough sketch of the graph of f' by estimating the slope of the tangent to the graph of f at several points, as illustrated below.*

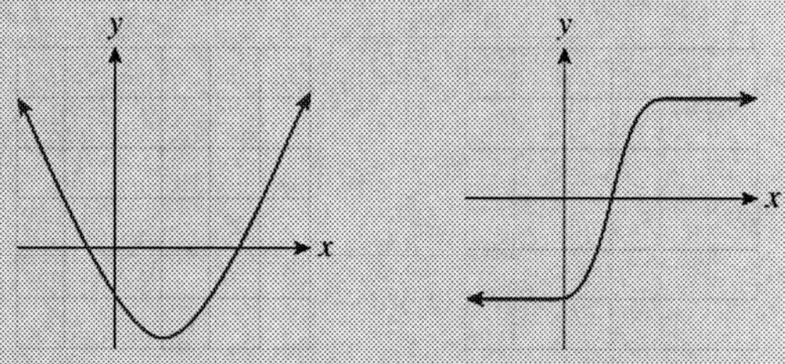

Original Function f $y = f(x)$ **Derivative Function f'** $y = f'(x)$

For x between -2 and 0, the graph of f is linear with slope -2. As x increases from 0 to 2, the slope increases from -2 to 2. For x larger than 2, the graph of f is linear with slope 2. (Notice that, when $x = 1$, the graph of f has a horizontal tangent, so $f'(1) = 0$.)

3. Look again at the graph on the left in Quick Example 2. When $x < 1$ the derivative $f'(x)$ is negative, so the graph has negative slope and f is **decreasing**; its values are going down as x increases. When $x > 1$ the derivative $f'(x)$ is positive, so the graph has positive slope and f is **increasing**; its values are going up as x increases.

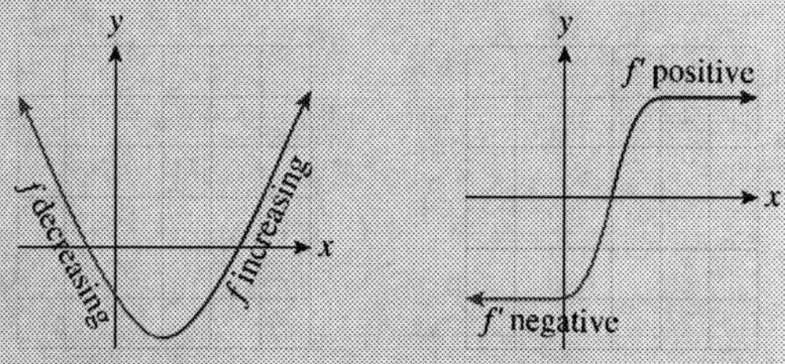

f decreasing for $x < 1$ f' negative for $x < 1$
f increasing for $x > 1$ f' positive for $x > 1$

* This method is discussed in detail on the Website at Online Text → Sketching the Graph of the Derivative.

The following example shows how we can use technology to graph the (approximate) derivative of a function, where it exists.

EXAMPLE 4 Graphing the Derivative with Technology

Use technology to graph the derivative of $f(x) = -2x^2 + 6x + 5$ for values of x starting at -5.

Solution The TI-83/84 Plus has a built-in function that approximates the derivative, and we can use it to graph the derivative of a function. In a spreadsheet, we need to create the approximation using one of the quick approximation formulas and we can then graph a table of its values. See the technology note in the margin on the next page to find out how to graph the derivative (Figure 33) using the Website graphing utility, the TI-83/84 Plus, and a spreadsheet.

using Technology

See the Technology Guides at the end of the chapter to find out how to obtain a table of values of and graph the derivative in Example 4 using a TI-83/84 Plus or a spreadsheet. Here is an outline:

TI-83/84 Plus

```
Y1=-2X^2+6X+5
Y2=nDeriv(Y1,X,X)
```

[More details on page 779.]

Spreadsheet

Value of *h* in E2

Values of *x* from A2 down increasing by *h*

`-2*A2^2+6*A2+5` from B2 down

`=(B3-B2)/$E$2` from C2 down

Insert scatter chart using columns A and C [More details on page 781.]

Website

www.WanerMath.com

Web grapher:

Online Utilities→ Function Evaluator and Grapher

Enter `deriv(-2*x^2+6*x+5)` for y_1. Alternatively, enter `-2*x^2+6*x+5` for y_1 and `deriv(y1)` for y_2.

Excel grapher:

Student Home→Online Utilities→Excel First and Second Derivative Graphing Utility

Function: `-2*x^2+6*x+5`

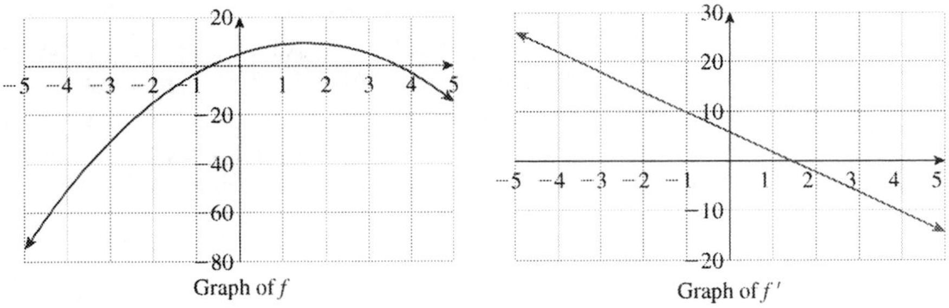

Figure 33

We said that f' records the slope of (the tangent line to) the function f at each point. Notice that the graph of f' confirms that the slope of the graph of f is decreasing as x increases from -5 to 5. Note also that the graph of f reaches a high point at $x = 1.5$ (the vertex of the parabola). At that point, the slope of the tangent is zero; that is, $f'(1.5) = 0$, as we see in the graph of f'.

EXAMPLE 5 An Application: Broadband Penetration

Wired broadband penetration in the United States can be modeled by

$$P(t) = \frac{29.842}{1 + 12.502(1.642)^{-t}} \qquad (0 \le t \le 12),$$

where t is time in years since 2000.[52] Graph both P and its derivative, and determine when broadband penetration was growing most rapidly.

Solution Using one of the methods in Example 4, we obtain the graphs shown in Figure 34.

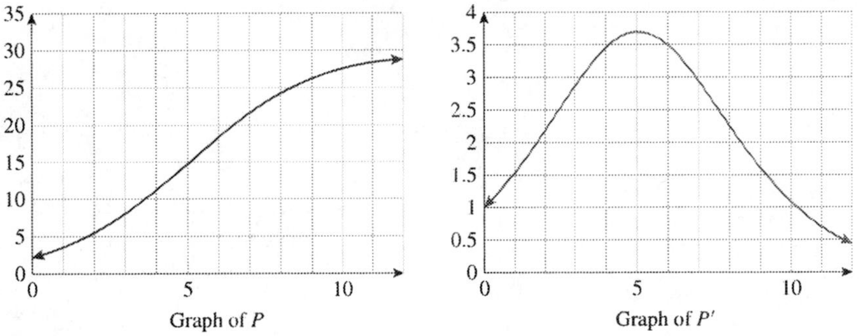

Figure 34

[52]Broadband penetration is the number of broadband installations divided by the total population. Source for data: Organisation for Economic Co-operation and Development (OECD) Directorate for Science, Technology, and Industry, table of Historical Penetration Rates, June 2010, downloaded April 2011 from www.oecd.org/sti/ict/broadband.

From the graph on the right, we see that P' reaches a peak somewhere near $t = 5$ (the beginning of 2005). Recalling that P' measures the *slope* of the graph of P, we can conclude that the graph of P is steepest near $t = 5$, indicating that, according to the model, broadband penetration was growing most rapidly at the start of 2005. Notice that this is not so easy to see directly on the graph of P.

To determine the point of maximum growth more accurately, we can zoom in on the graph of P' using the range $4.5 \le t \le 5.5$ (Figure 35).

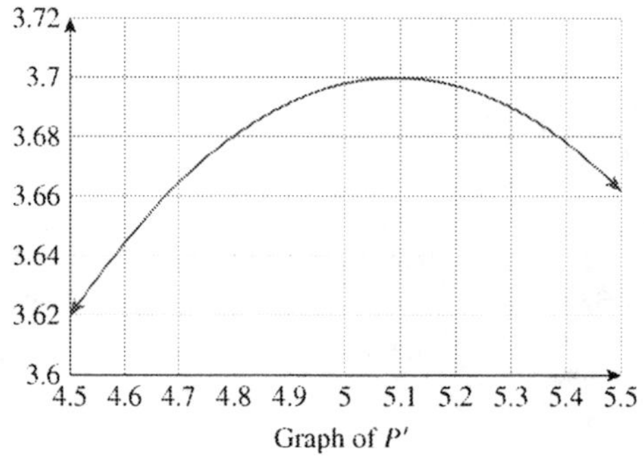

Figure 35

We can now see that P' reaches its highest point around $t = 5.1$, so we conclude that broadband penetration was growing most rapidly in early 2005.

➡ **Before we go on...** Besides helping us to determine the point of maximum growth, the graph of P' in Example 5 gives us a great deal of additional information. As just one example, in Figure 35 we can see that the maximum value of P' is about 3.7, indicating that broadband penetration grew at a fastest rate of about 3.7 percentage points per year. ■

FAQs

Recognizing When and How to Compute the Instantaneous Rate of Change

Q: *How do I know, by looking at the wording of a problem, that it is asking for an instantaneous rate of change?*

A: If a problem does not ask for an instantaneous rate of change directly, it might do so indirectly, as in "How fast is quantity q increasing?" or "Find the rate of increase of q."

Q: *If I know that a problem calls for estimating an instantaneous rate of change, how should I estimate it: with a table showing smaller and smaller values of h, or by using a quick approximation?*

A: For most practical purposes, a quick approximation is accurate enough. Use a table showing smaller and smaller values of h when you would like to check the accuracy.

Q: *Which should I use in computing a quick approximation: the balanced difference quotient or the ordinary difference quotient?*

A: In general, the balanced difference quotient gives a more accurate answer.

WW Website
www.WanerMath.com
At the Website you can find the following optional interactive online sections:
- **Continuity and Differentiability**
- **Sketching the Graph of the Derivative**

You can find these sections by following
Everything → Chapter 10 (Online Sections)

10.5 EXERCISES

▼ more advanced ◆ challenging

T indicates exercises that should be solved using technology

In Exercises 1–4, estimate the derivative from the table of average rates of change. HINT **[See discussion at the beginning of the section.]**

1.

h	1	0.1	0.01	0.001	0.0001
Average Rate of Change of f Over $[5, 5+h]$	12	6.4	6.04	6.004	6.0004
h	−1	−0.1	−0.01	−0.001	−0.0001
Average Rate of Change of f Over $[5+h, 5]$	3	5.6	5.96	5.996	5.9996

Estimate $f'(5)$.

2.

h	1	0.1	0.01	0.001	0.0001
Average Rate of Change of g Over $[7, 7+h]$	4	4.8	4.98	4.998	4.9998
h	−1	−0.1	−0.01	−0.001	−0.0001
Average Rate of Change of g Over $[7+h, 7]$	5	5.3	5.03	5.003	5.0003

Estimate $g'(7)$.

3.

h	1	0.1	0.01	0.001	0.0001
Average Rate of Change of r Over $[-6, -6+h]$	−5.4	−5.498	−5.4998	−5.499982	−5.49999822
h	−1	−0.1	−0.01	−0.001	−0.0001
Average Rate of Change of r Over $[-6+h, -6]$	−7.52	−6.13	−5.5014	−5.5000144	−5.500001444

Estimate $r'(-6)$.

4.

h	1	0.1	0.01	0.001	0.0001
Average Rate of Change of s Over $[0, h]$	−2.52	−1.13	−0.6014	−0.6000144	−0.600001444
h	−1	−0.1	−0.01	−0.001	−0.0001
Average Rate of Change of s Over $[h, 0]$	−0.4	−0.598	−0.5998	−0.599982	−0.59999822

Estimate $s'(0)$.

Consider the functions in Exercises 5–8 as representing the value of an ounce of palladium in U.S. dollars as a function of the time t in days.[53] *Find the average rates of change of $R(t)$ over the time intervals $[t, t+h]$, where t is as indicated and $h = 1, 0.1$, and 0.01 days. Hence, estimate the instantaneous rate of change of R at time t, specifying the units of measurement. (Use smaller values of h to check your estimates.)* HINT **[See Example 1.]**

5. $R(t) = 60 + 50t - t^2; t = 5$

6. $R(t) = 60t - 2t^2; t = 3$

7. $R(t) = 270 + 20t^3; t = 1$

8. $R(t) = 200 + 50t - t^3; t = 2$

Each of the functions in Exercises 9–12 gives the cost to manufacture x items. Find the average cost per unit of manufacturing h more items (i.e., the average rate of change of the total cost) at a production level of x, where x is as indicated and $h = 10$ and 1. Hence, estimate the instantaneous rate of change of the total cost at the given production level x, specifying the units of measurement. (Use smaller values of h to check your estimates.) HINT **[See Example 1.]**

9. $C(x) = 10{,}000 + 5x - \dfrac{x^2}{10{,}000}; x = 1{,}000$

10. $C(x) = 20{,}000 + 7x - \dfrac{x^2}{20{,}000}; x = 10{,}000$

11. $C(x) = 15{,}000 + 100x + \dfrac{1{,}000}{x}; \ x = 100$

12. $C(x) = 20{,}000 + 50x + \dfrac{10{,}000}{x}; x = 100$

In Exercises 13–16, the graph of a function is shown together with the tangent line at a point P. Estimate the derivative of f at the corresponding x value. HINT **[See Quick Example page 742.]**

13.

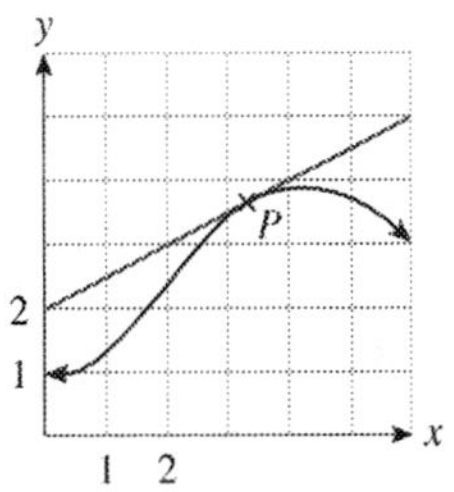

14.

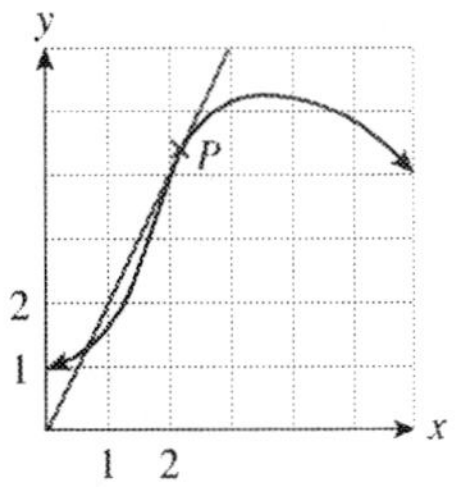

15.

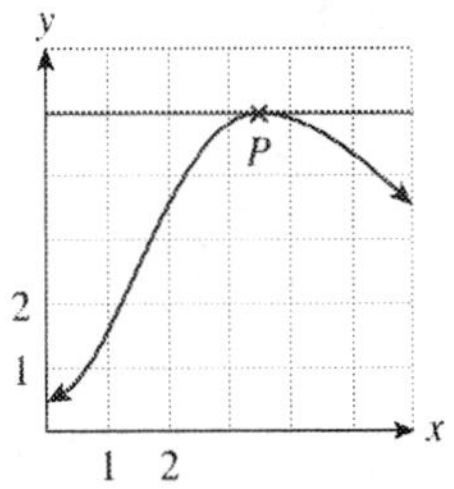

16.

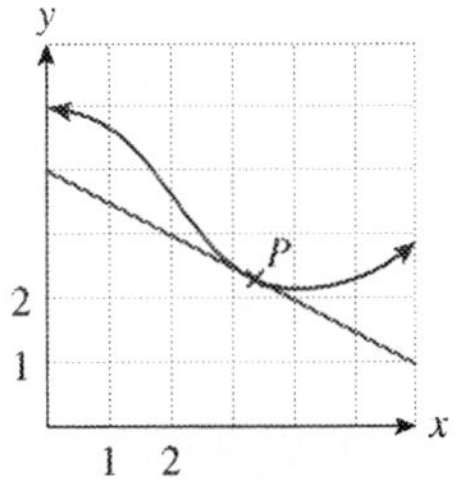

[53] Palladium was trading at around $290 in August 2008.

*In each of the graphs given in Exercises 17–22, say at which labeled point the slope of the tangent is **(a)** greatest and **(b)** least (in the sense that* -7 *is less than* 1*).* HINT [See Quick Example page 742.]

17.

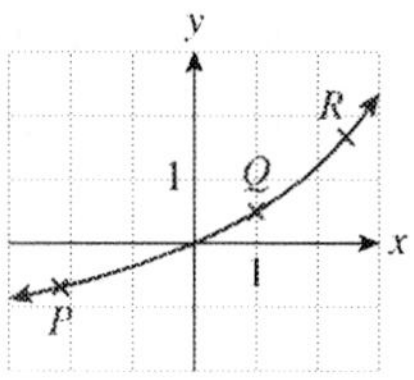

18.

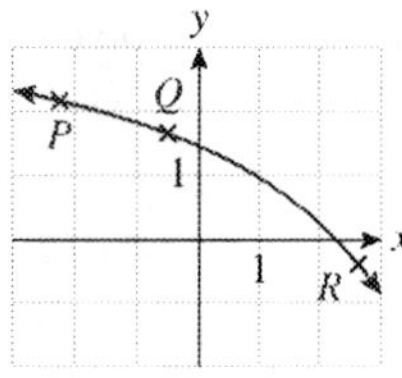

19.

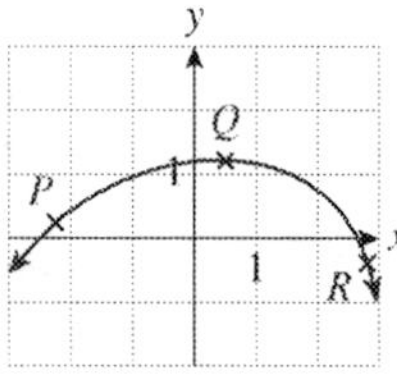

20.

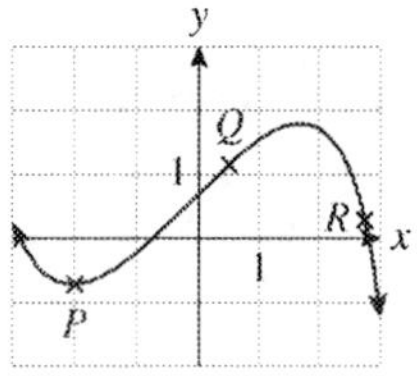

21.

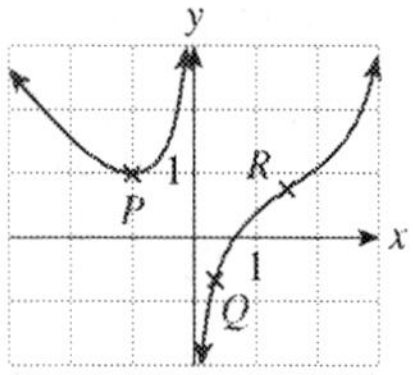

22.

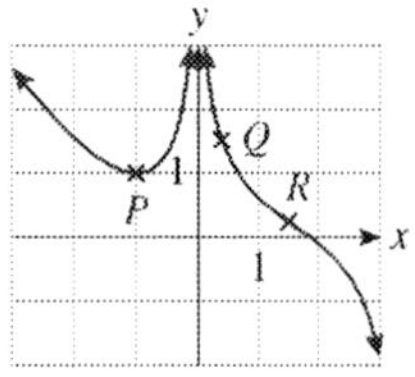

In each of Exercises 23–26, three slopes are given. For each slope, determine at which of the labeled points on the graph the tangent line has that slope.

23. a. 0 **b.** 4 **c.** -1

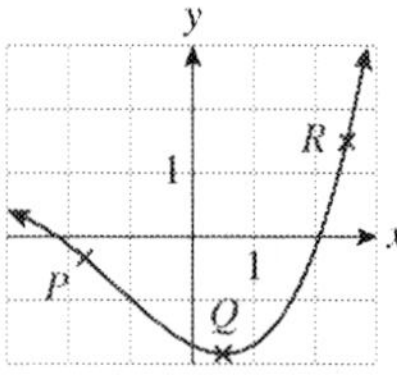

24. a. 0 **b.** 1 **c.** -1

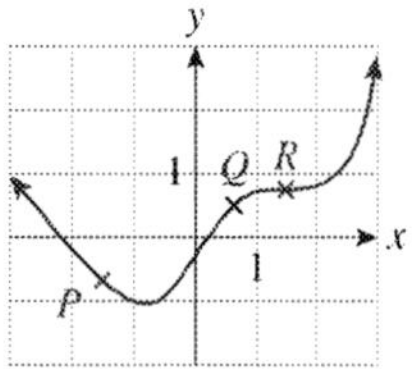

25. a. 0 **b.** 3 **c.** -3

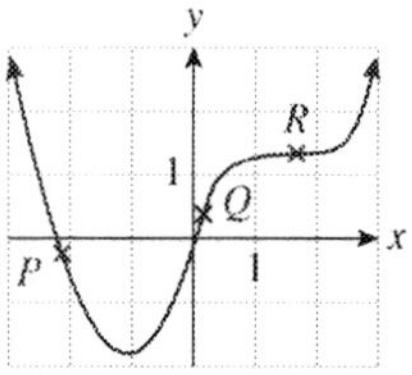

26. a. 0 **b.** 3 **c.** 1

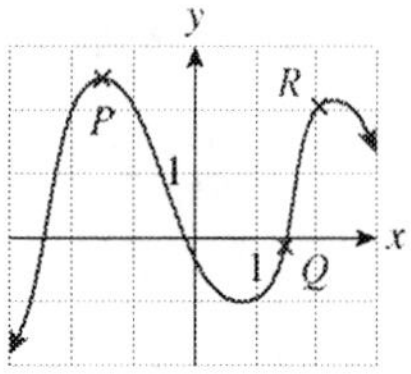

*In each of Exercises 27–30, find the approximate coordinates of all points (if any) where the slope of the tangent is: **(a)** 0, **(b)** 1, **(c)* -1. HINT [See Quick Example page 742.]

27.

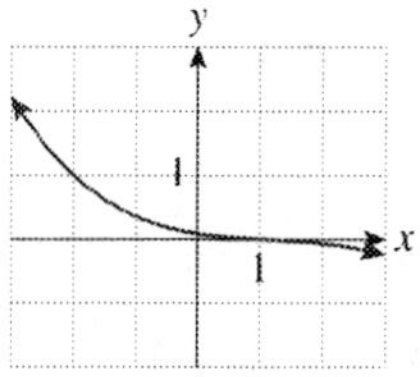

28.

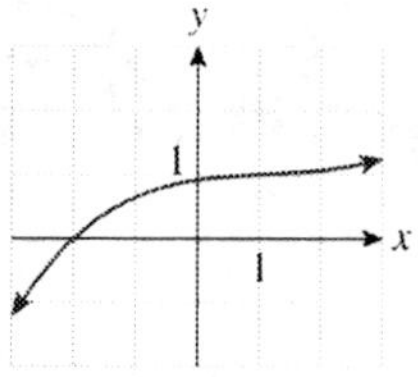

29.

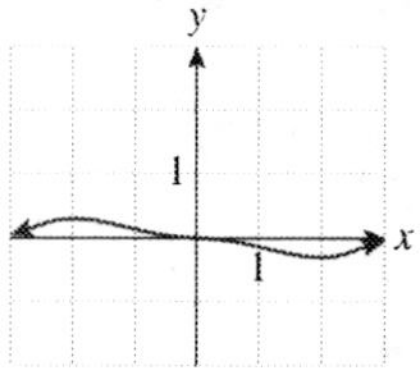

30.

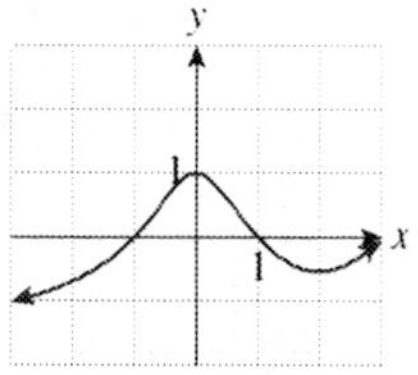

31. Complete the following: The tangent to the graph of the function f at the point where $x = a$ is the line passing through the point ____ with slope ____ .

32. Complete the following: The difference quotient for f at the point where $x = a$ gives the slope of the ____ line that passes through _____ .

33. Which is correct? The derivative function assigns to each value x

(A) the average rate of change of f at x.
(B) the slope of the tangent to the graph of f at $(x, f(x))$.
(C) the rate at which f is changing over the interval $[x, x + h]$ for $h = 0.0001$.
(D) the balanced difference quotient $[f(x + h) - f(x - h)]/(2h)$ for $h \approx 0.0001$.

34. Which is correct? The derivative function $f'(x)$ tells us

(A) the slope of the tangent line at each of the points $(x, f(x))$.
(B) the approximate slope of the tangent line at each of the points $(x, f(x))$.
(C) the slope of the secant line through $(x, f(x))$ and $(x + h, f(x + h))$ for $h = 0.0001$.
(D) the slope of a certain secant line through each of the points $(x, f(x))$.

35. Let f have the graph shown.

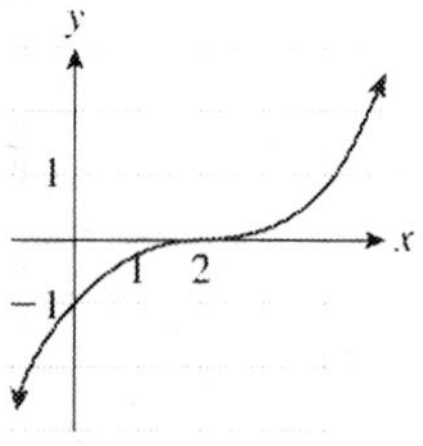

a. The average rate of change of f over the interval $[2, 4]$ is
(A) greater than $f'(2)$. **(B)** less than $f'(2)$.
(C) approximately equal to $f'(2)$.

b. The average rate of change of f over the interval $[-1, 1]$ is
(A) greater than $f'(0)$. **(B)** less than $f'(0)$.
(C) approximately equal to $f'(0)$.

c. Over the interval [0, 2], the instantaneous rate of change of *f* is
(A) increasing. **(B)** decreasing. **(C)** neither.

d. Over the interval [0, 4], the instantaneous rate of change of *f* is
(A) increasing, then decreasing.
(B) decreasing, then increasing.
(C) always increasing.
(D) always decreasing.

e. When $x = 4$, $f(x)$ is
(A) approximately 0, and increasing at a rate of about 0.7 units per unit of *x*.
(B) approximately 0, and decreasing at a rate of about 0.7 units per unit of *x*.
(C) approximately 0.7, and increasing at a rate of about 1 unit per unit of *x*.
(D) approximately 0.7, and increasing at a rate of about 3 units per unit of *x*.

36. A function *f* has the following graph.

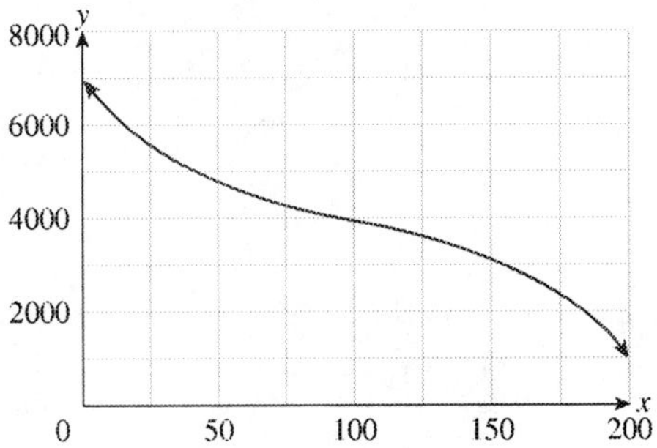

a. The average rate of change of *f* over [0, 200] is
(A) greater than
(B) less than
(C) approximately equal to
the instantaneous rate of change at $x = 100$.

b. The average rate of change of *f* over [0, 200] is
(A) greater than
(B) less than
(C) approximately equal to
the instantaneous rate of change at $x = 150$.

c. Over the interval [0, 50] the instantaneous rate of change of *f* is
(A) increasing, then decreasing.
(B) decreasing, then increasing.
(C) always increasing.
(D) always decreasing.

d. On the interval [0, 200], the instantaneous rate of change of *f* is
(A) always positive. **(B)** always negative.
(C) negative, positive, and then negative.

e. $f'(100)$ is
(A) greater than $f'(25)$. **(B)** less than $f'(25)$.
(C) approximately equal to $f'(25)$.

In Exercises 37–40, use a quick approximation to estimate the derivative of the given function at the indicated point. HINT [See Example 2(a).]

37. $f(x) = 1 - 2x;\ x = 2$

38. $f(x) = \frac{x}{3} - 1;\ x = -3$

39. $f(x) = \frac{x^2}{4} - \frac{x^3}{3};\ x = -1$

40. $f(x) = \frac{x^2}{2} + \frac{x}{4};\ x = 2$

In Exercises 41–48, estimate the indicated derivative by any method. HINT [See Example 2.]

41. $g(t) = \frac{1}{t^5}$; estimate $g'(1)$

42. $s(t) = \frac{1}{t^3}$; estimate $s'(-2)$

43. $y = 4x^2$; estimate $\left.\frac{dy}{dx}\right|_{x=2}$

44. $y = 1 - x^2$; estimate $\left.\frac{dy}{dx}\right|_{x=-1}$

45. $s = 4t + t^2$; estimate $\left.\frac{ds}{dt}\right|_{t=-2}$

46. $s = t - t^2$; estimate $\left.\frac{ds}{dt}\right|_{t=2}$

47. $R = \frac{1}{p}$; estimate $\left.\frac{dR}{dp}\right|_{p=20}$

48. $R = \sqrt{p}$; estimate $\left.\frac{dR}{dp}\right|_{p=400}$

In Exercises 49–54, ***(a)*** *use any method to estimate the slope of the tangent to the graph of the given function at the point with the given x-coordinate, and* ***(b)*** *find an equation of the tangent line in part (a). In each case, sketch the curve together with the appropriate tangent line.* HINT [See Example 2(b).]

49. $f(x) = x^3;\ x = -1$

50. $f(x) = x^2;\ x = 0$

51. $f(x) = x + \frac{1}{x};\ x = 2$

52. $f(x) = \frac{1}{x^2};\ x = 1$

53. $f(x) = \sqrt{x};\ x = 4$

54. $f(x) = 2x + 4;\ x = -1$

In each of Exercises 55–58, estimate the given quantity.

55. $f(x) = e^x$; estimate $f'(0)$

56. $f(x) = 2e^x$; estimate $f'(1)$

57. $f(x) = \ln x$; estimate $f'(1)$

58. $f(x) = \ln x$; estimate $f'(2)$

In Exercises 59–64, match the graph of f to the graph of f′ (the graphs of f′ are shown after Exercise 64).

59.

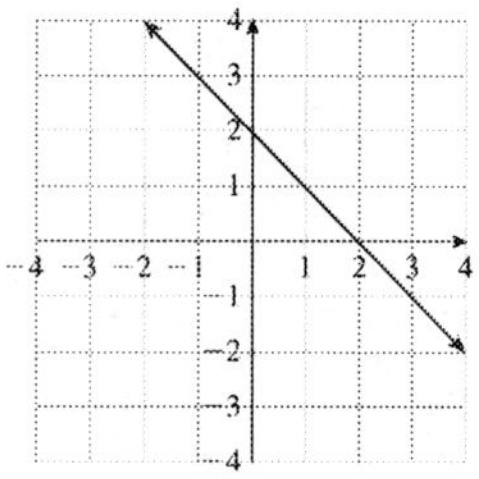

60.

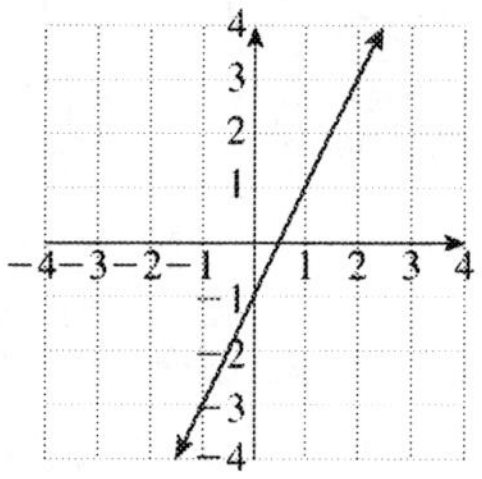

61.

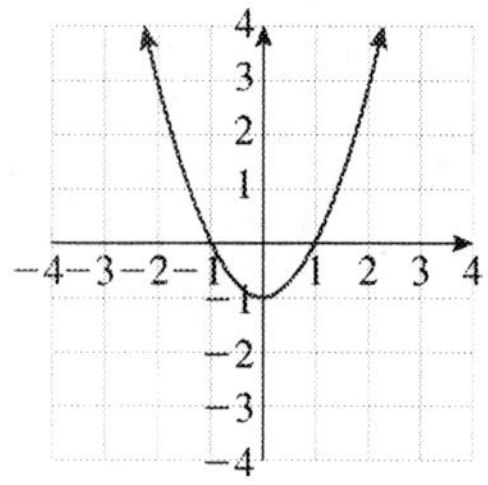

62.

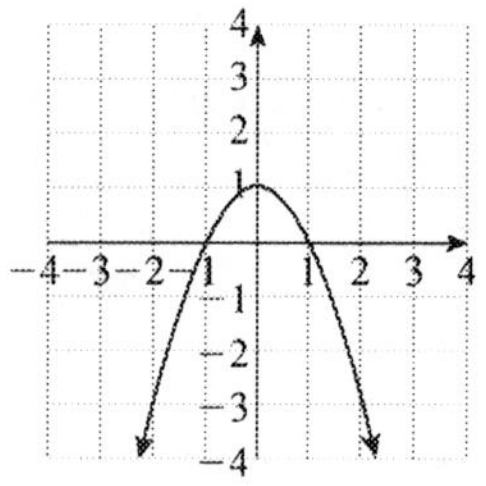

63.

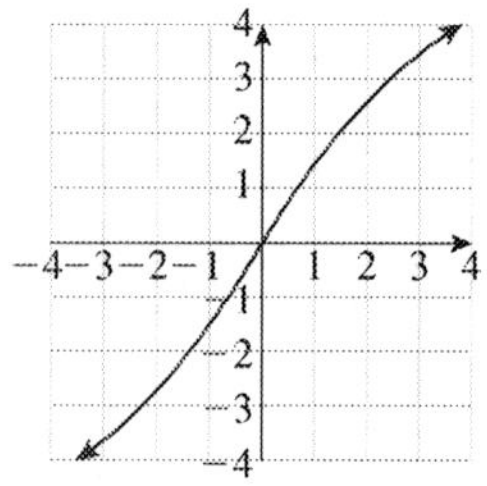

64.

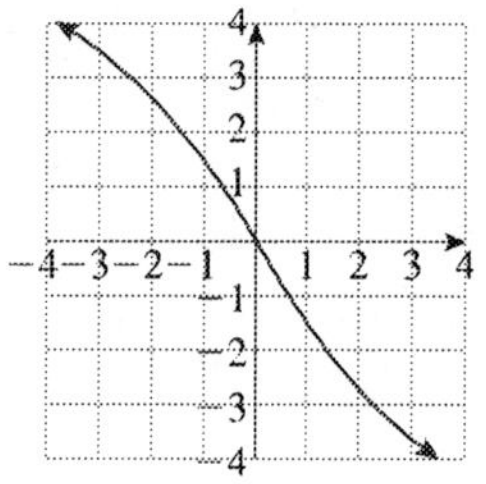

Graphs of derivatives for Exercises 59–64:

(A)

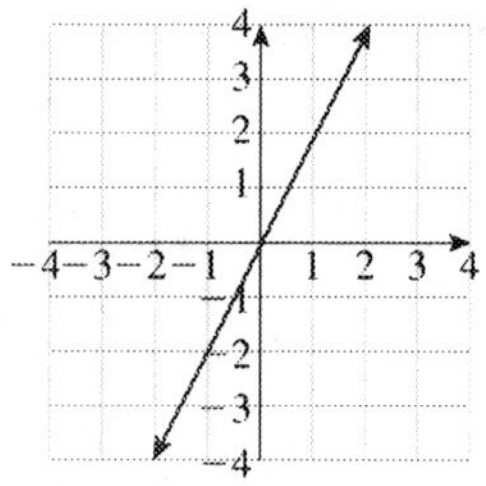

(B)

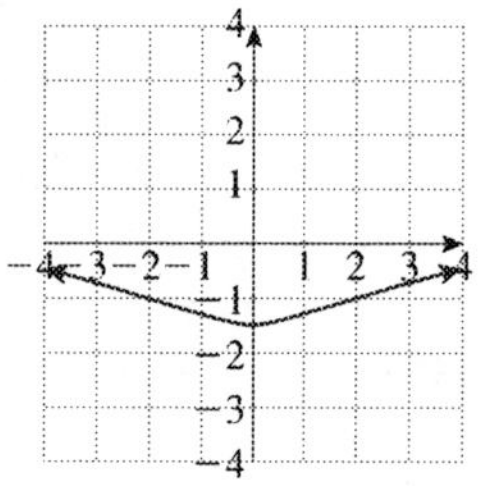

(C)

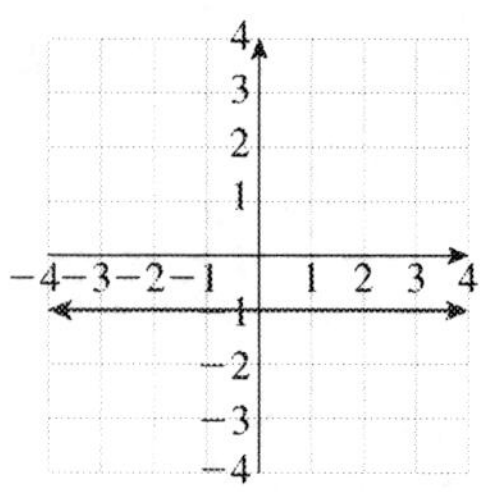

(D)

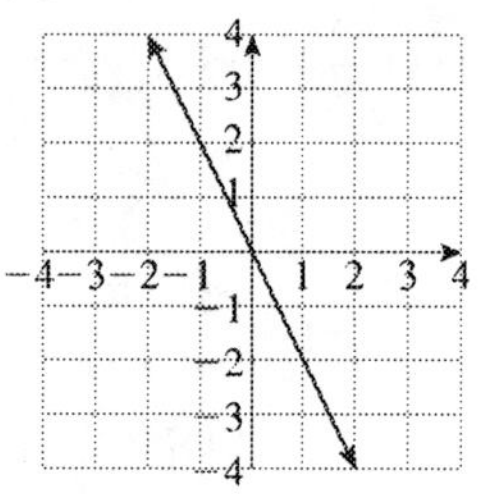

(E)

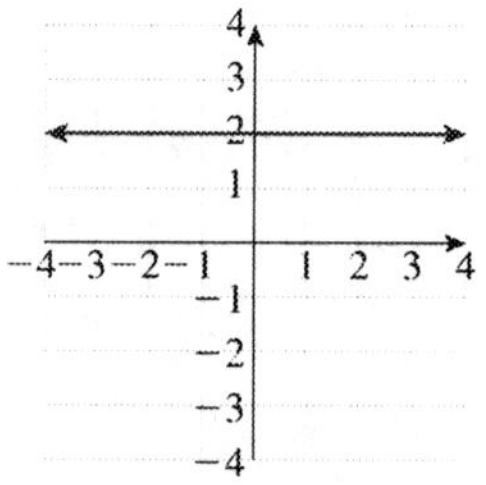

(F)

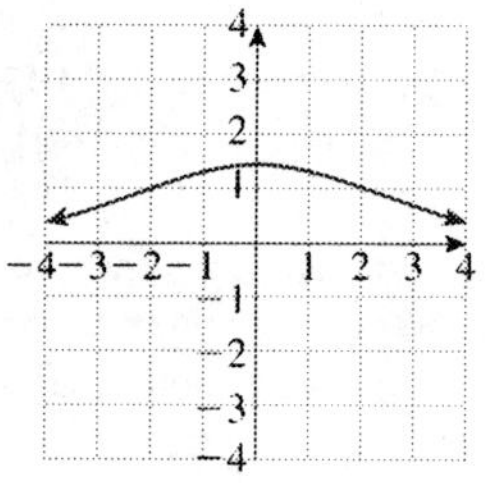

In Exercises 65–68, the graph of a function is given. For which x in the range shown is the function increasing? For which x is the function decreasing? HINT **[See Quick Example 3 page 748.]**

65.

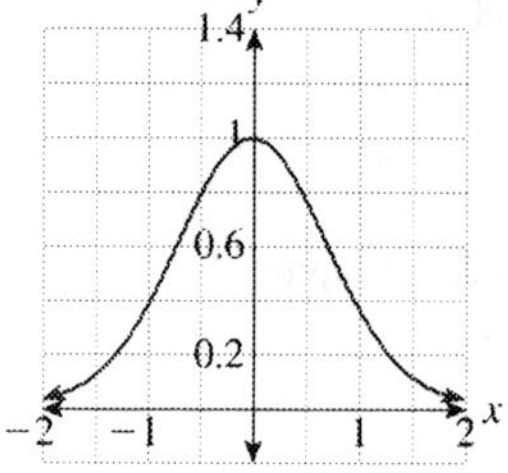

66.

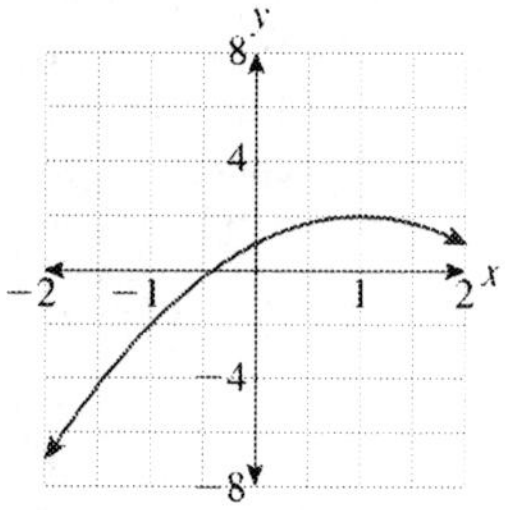

67.

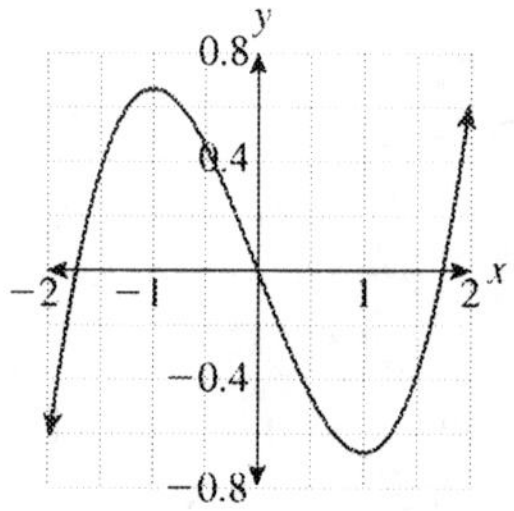

68.

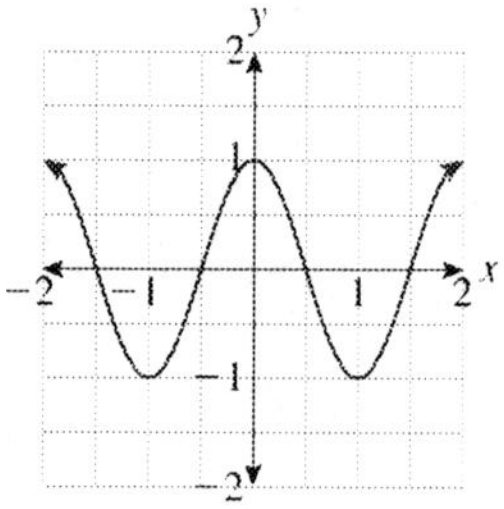

In Exercises 69–72, the graph of the derivative of a function is given. For which x is the (original) function increasing? For which x is the (original) function decreasing? HINT **[See Quick Example 3 page 748.]**

69.

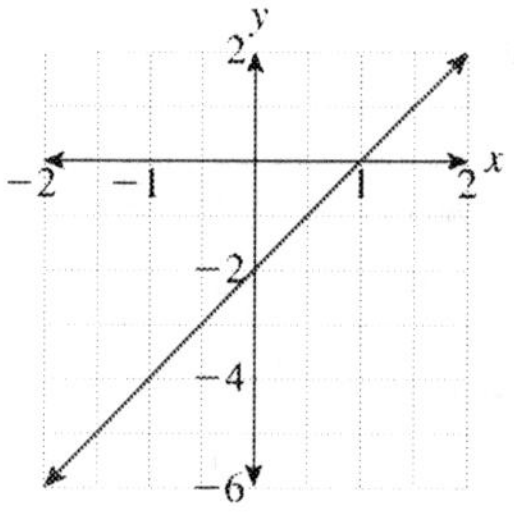

70.

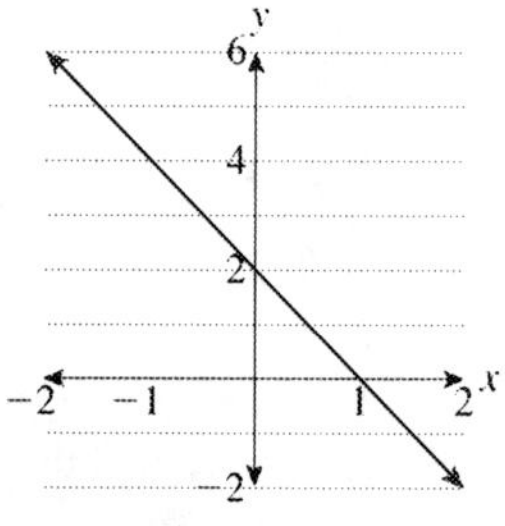

71.

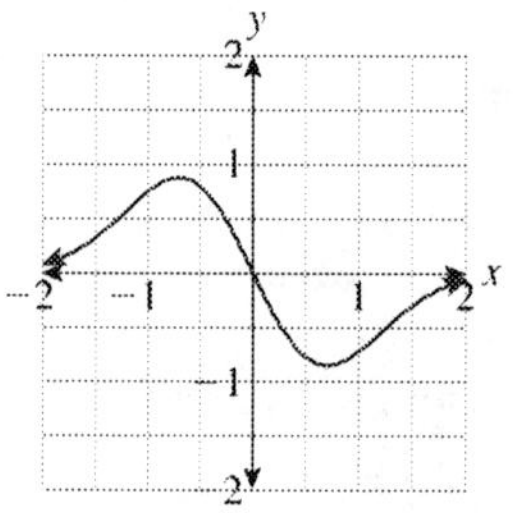

72.

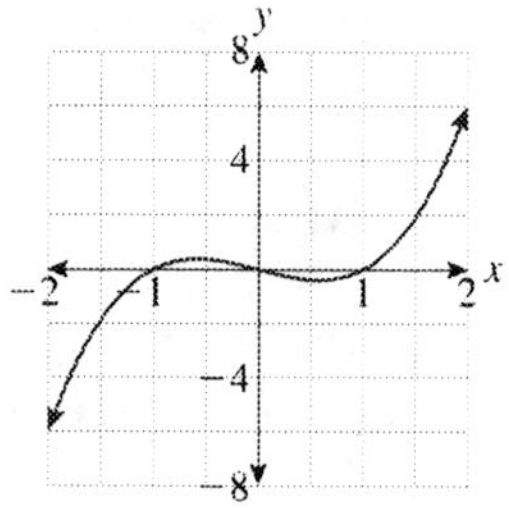

In Exercises 73 and 74, use technology to graph the derivative of the given function for the given range of values of x. Then use your graph to estimate all values of x (if any) where the tangent line to the graph of the given function is horizontal. Round answers to one decimal place. HINT [See Example 4.]

73. $f(x) = x^4 + 2x^3 - 1; \quad -2 \le x \le 1$

74. $f(x) = -x^3 - 3x^2 - 1; \quad -3 \le x \le 1$

In Exercises 75 and 76, use the method of Example 4 to list approximate values of f′(x) for x in the given range. Graph f(x) together with f′(x) for x in the given range.

75. $f(x) = \dfrac{x+2}{x-3}; \quad 4 \le x \le 5$

76. $f(x) = \dfrac{10x}{x-2}; \quad 2.5 \le x \le 3$

APPLICATIONS

77. *Demand* Suppose the demand for a new brand of sneakers is given by

$$q = \frac{5{,}000{,}000}{p}$$

where p is the price per pair of sneakers, in dollars, and q is the number of pairs of sneakers that can be sold at price p. Find $q(100)$ and estimate $q'(100)$. Interpret your answers. HINT [See Example 1.]

78. *Demand* Suppose the demand for an old brand of TV is given by

$$q = \frac{100{,}000}{p+10}$$

where p is the price per TV set, in dollars, and q is the number of TV sets that can be sold at price p. Find $q(190)$ and estimate $q'(190)$. Interpret your answers. HINT [See Example 1.]

79. *Oil Imports from Mexico* The following graph shows approximate daily oil imports to the U.S. from Mexico.[54] Also shown is the tangent line at the point corresponding to year 2005.

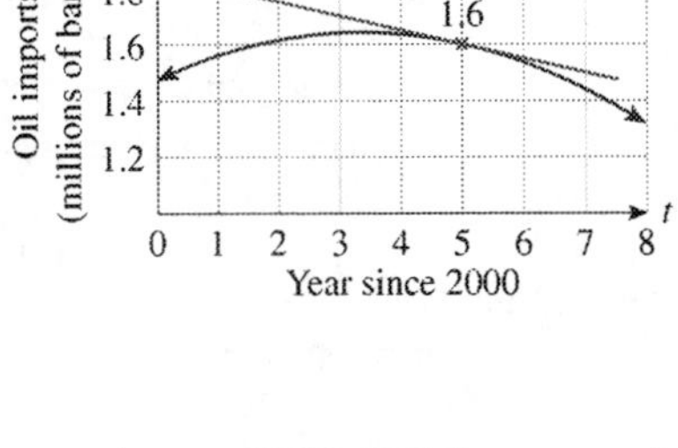

a. Estimate the slope of the tangent line shown on the graph. What does the graph tell you about oil imports from Mexico in 2005? HINT [Identify two points on the tangent line. Then see Quick Example page 742.]

b. According to the graph, is the rate of change of oil imports from Mexico increasing, decreasing, or increasing then decreasing? Why?

80. *Oil Production in Mexico* The following graph shows approximate daily oil production by Pemex, Mexico's national oil company.[55] Also shown is the tangent line at the point corresponding to year 2003.

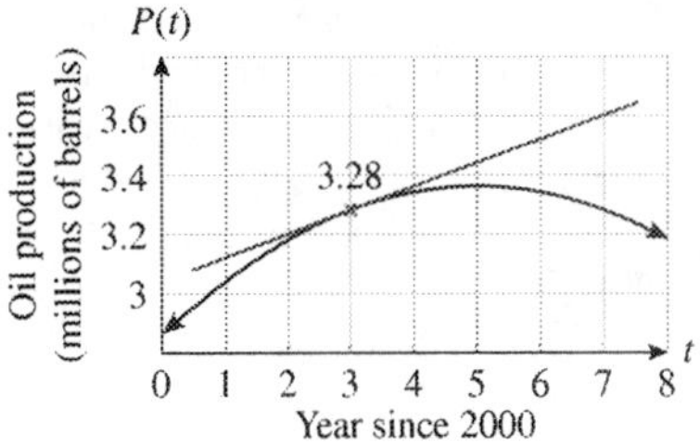

a. Estimate the slope of the tangent line shown on the graph. What does the graph tell you about oil production by Pemex in 2003? HINT [Identify two points on the tangent line. Then see Quick Example page 742.]

b. According to the graph, is the rate of change of oil production by Pemex increasing or decreasing over the range [0, 4]? Why?

81. ▼ ***Prison Population*** The following curve is a model of the total U.S. prison population as a function of time in years ($t = 0$ represents 2000).[56]

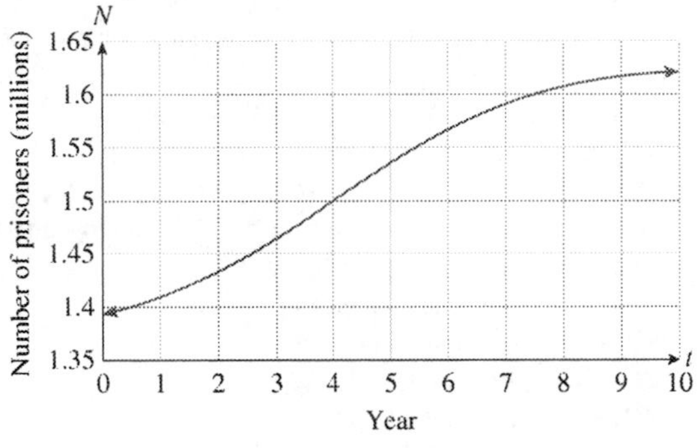

a. Which is correct? Over the period [5, 10] the instantaneous rate of change of N is
(A) increasing. **(B)** decreasing.

b. Which is correct? The instantaneous rate of change of prison population at $t = 4$ was
(A) less than **(B)** greater than
(C) approximately equal to
the average rate of change over the interval [0, 10].

[54]Figures are approximate, and 2008–2009 figures are projections by the Department of Energy. Source: Energy Information Administration/Pemex (www.eia.doe.gov).

[55]*Ibid.*

[56]Source: Bureau of Justice Statistics http://bjs.ojp.usdoj.gov.

c. Which is correct? Over the period [0, 10] the instantaneous rate of change of N is
(A) increasing, then decreasing.
(B) decreasing, then increasing.
(C) always increasing.
(D) always decreasing.

d. According to the model, the U.S. prison population was increasing fastest around what year?

e. Roughly estimate the instantaneous rate of change of N at $t = 4$ by using a balanced difference quotient with $h = 1.5$. Interpret the result.

82. ▼ ***Demand for Freon 12*** The demand for chlorofluorocarbon-12 (CFC-12)—the ozone-depleting refrigerant commonly known as Freon 12[57]—has been declining significantly in response to regulation and concern about the ozone layer. The graph below represents a model for the projected demand for CFC-12 as a function of time in years ($t = 0$ represents 1990).[58]

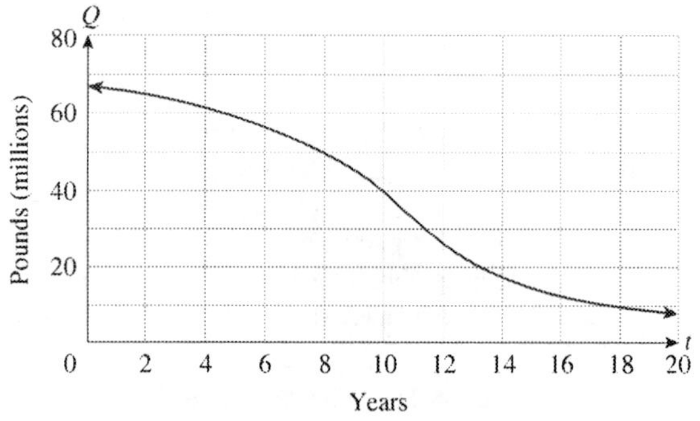

a. Which is correct? Over the period [12, 20] the instantaneous rate of change of Q is
(A) increasing. **(B)** decreasing.

b. Which is correct? The instantaneous rate of change of demand for Freon 12 at $t = 10$ was
(A) less than **(B)** greater than
(C) approximately equal to
the average rate of change over the interval [0, 20].

c. Which is correct? Over the period [0, 20] the instantaneous rate of change of Q is
(A) increasing, then decreasing.
(B) decreasing, then increasing.
(C) always increasing.
(D) always decreasing.

d. According to the model, the demand for Freon 12 was decreasing most rapidly around what year?

e. Roughly estimate the instantaneous rate of change of Q at $t = 13$ by using a balanced difference quotient with $h = 5$. Interpret the result.

[57]The name given to it by DuPont. Freon 12 (dichlorodifluoromethane) is distinct from Freon 22 (chlorodifluoromethane, also registered by DuPont; see p. 232).

[58]Source for data: The Automobile Consulting Group (*New York Times*, December 26, 1993, p. F23). The exact figures were not given, and the chart is a reasonable facsimile of the chart that appeared in *New York Times*.

83. ***Velocity*** If a stone is dropped from a height of 400 feet, its height after t seconds is given by $s = 400 - 16t^2$.

a. Find its average velocity over the period [2, 4].

b. Estimate its instantaneous velocity at time $t = 4$. HINT [See Example 3.]

84. ***Velocity*** If a stone is thrown down at 120 ft/s from a height of 1,000 feet, its height after t seconds is given by $s = 1{,}000 - 120t - 16t^2$.

a. Find its average velocity over the period [1, 3].

b. Estimate its instantaneous velocity at time $t = 3$. HINT [See Example 3.]

85. ***Crude Oil Prices*** The price per barrel of crude oil in constant 2008 dollars can be approximated by

$$P(t) = 0.45t^2 - 12t + 105 \text{ dollars} \quad (0 \le t \le 28),$$

where t is time in years since the start of 1980.[59]

a. Compute the average rate of change of $P(t)$ over the interval [0, 28], and interpret your answer. HINT [See Section 10.4 Example 3.]

b. Estimate the instantaneous rate of change of $P(t)$ at $t = 0$, and interpret your answer. HINT [See Example 2(a).]

c. The answers to part (a) and part (b) have opposite signs. What does this indicate about the price of oil?

86. ***Median Home Prices*** The median home price in the U.S. over the period 2003–2011 can be approximated by

$$P(t) = -5t^2 + 75t - 30 \text{ thousand dollars} \quad (3 \le t \le 11),$$

where t is time in years since the start of 2000.[60]

a. Compute the average rate of change of $P(t)$ over the interval [5, 9], and interpret your answer. HINT [See Section 10.4 Example 3.]

b. Estimate the instantaneous rate of change of $P(t)$ at $t = 5$, and interpret your answer. HINT [See Example 2(a).]

c. The answer to part (b) has larger absolute value than the answer to part (a). What does this indicate about the median home price?

87. ***SARS*** In the early stages of the deadly SARS (Severe Acute Respiratory Syndrome) epidemic in 2003, the number of reported cases could be approximated by

$$A(t) = 167(1.18)^t \quad (0 \le t \le 20)$$

t days after March 17, 2003 (the first day in which statistics were reported by the World Health Organization).

a. What, approximately, was the instantaneous rate of change of $A(t)$ on March 27 ($t = 10$)? Interpret the result.

b. Which of the following is true? For the first 20 days of the epidemic, the instantaneous rate of change of the number of cases
(A) increased. **(B)** decreased.
(C) increased and then decreased.
(D) decreased and then increased.

[59]Source for data: www.inflationdata.com.

[60]Source for data: www.zillow.com.

88. ***SARS*** A few weeks into the deadly SARS (Severe Acute Respiratory Syndrome) epidemic in 2003, the number of reported cases could be approximated by

$$A(t) = 1{,}804(1.04)^t \quad (0 \le t \le 30)$$

t days after April 1, 2003.

a. What, approximately, was the instantaneous rate of change of $A(t)$ on April 21 ($t = 20$)? Interpret the result.

b. Which of the following is true? During April, the instantaneous rate of change of the number of cases

(A) increased. **(B)** decreased.

(C) increased and then decreased.

(D) decreased and then increased.

89. ***Sales*** Weekly sales of a new brand of sneakers are given by

$$S(t) = 200 - 150e^{-t/10}$$

pairs sold per week, where t is the number of weeks since the introduction of the brand. Estimate $S(5)$ and $\left.\frac{dS}{dt}\right|_{t=5}$ and interpret your answers.

90. ***Sales*** Weekly sales of an old brand of TV are given by

$$S(t) = 100e^{-t/5}$$

sets per week, where t is the number of weeks after the introduction of a competing brand. Estimate $S(5)$ and $\left.\frac{dS}{dt}\right|_{t=5}$ and interpret your answers.

91. ***Early Internet Services*** On January 1, 1996, America Online was the biggest online service provider, with 4.5 million subscribers, and was adding new subscribers at a rate of 60,000 per week.[61] If $A(t)$ is the number of America Online subscribers t weeks after January 1, 1996, what do the given data tell you about values of the function A and its derivative? HINT [See Quick Example 2 on page 738.]

92. ***Early Internet Services*** On January 1, 1996, Prodigy was the third-biggest online service provider, with 1.6 million subscribers, but was losing subscribers.[62] If $P(t)$ is the number of Prodigy subscribers t weeks after January 1, 1996, what do the given data tell you about values of the function P and its derivative? HINT [See Quick Example 2 on page 738.]

93. ▼ ***Learning to Speak*** Let $p(t)$ represent the percentage of children who are able to speak at the age of t months.

a. It is found that $p(10) = 60$ and $\left.\frac{dp}{dt}\right|_{t=10} = 18.2$. What does this mean?[63] HINT [See Quick Example 2 on page 738.]

b. As t increases, what happens to p and $\frac{dp}{dt}$?

94. ▼ ***Learning to Read*** Let $p(t)$ represent the percentage of children in your class who learned to read at the age of t years.

a. Assuming that everyone in your class could read by the age of 7, what does this tell you about $p(7)$ and $\left.\frac{dp}{dt}\right|_{t=7}$? HINT [See Quick Example 2 on page 738.]

b. Assuming that 25.0% of the people in your class could read by the age of 5, and that 25.3% of them could read by the age of 5 years and one month, estimate $\left.\frac{dp}{dt}\right|_{t=5}$. Remember to give its units.

95. ***Subprime Mortgages during the Housing Crisis*** (Compare Exercise 29 of Section 10.4.) The percentage of mortgages issued in the United States during the period 2000–2009 that were subprime (normally classified as risky) can be approximated by

$$A(t) = \frac{15}{1 + 8.6(1.8)^{-t}} \quad (0 \le t \le 9),$$

where t is the number of years since the start of 2000.[64]

a. Estimate $A(6)$ and $A'(6)$. (Round answers to two significant digits.) What do the answers tell you about subprime mortgages?

b. Graph the extrapolated function and its derivative for $0 \le t \le 16$ and use your graphs to describe how the derivative behaves as t becomes large. (Express this behavior in terms of limits if you have studied the sections on limits.) What does this tell you about subprime mortgages? HINT [See Example 5.]

96. ***Subprime Mortgage Debt during the Housing Crisis*** (Compare Exercise 30 of Section 10.4.) The value of subprime (normally classified as risky) mortgage debt outstanding in the U.S. during the period 2000–2009 can be approximated by

$$A(t) = \frac{1{,}350}{1 + 4.2(1.7)^{-t}} \text{ billion dollars} \quad (0 \le t \le 9),$$

where t is the number of years since the start of 2000.[65]

a. Estimate $A(7)$ and $A'(7)$. (Round answers to three significant digits.) What do the answers tell you about subprime mortgages?

b. Graph the function and its derivative and use your graphs to estimate when, to the nearest year, $A'(t)$ is greatest. What does this tell you about subprime mortgages? HINT [See Example 5.]

97. ▼ ***Embryo Development*** The oxygen consumption of a turkey embryo increases from the time the egg is laid through the time the turkey chick hatches. In a brush turkey, the oxygen consumption (in milliliters per hour) can be approximated by

$$c(t) = -0.0012t^3 + 0.12t^2 - 1.83t + 3.97 \quad (20 \le t \le 50),$$

[61]Source: Information and Interactive Services Report/*New York Times*, January 2, 1996, p. C14.

[62]*Ibid.*

[63]Based on data presented in the article *The Emergence of Intelligence* by William H. Calvin, *Scientific American*, October, 1994, pp. 101–107.

[64]Sources: Mortgage Bankers Association, UBS.

[65]Source: Data 360 www.data360.org.

where t is the time (in days) since the egg was laid.[66] (An egg will typically hatch at around $t = 50$.) Use technology to graph $c'(t)$ and use your graph to answer the following questions. HINT [See Example 5.]

a. Over the interval [20, 32] the derivative c' is
(A) increasing, then decreasing.
(B) decreasing, then increasing.
(C) decreasing. **(D)** increasing.

b. When, to the nearest day, is the oxygen consumption increasing at the fastest rate?

c. When, to the nearest day, is the oxygen consumption increasing at the slowest rate?

98. *Embryo Development* The oxygen consumption of a bird embryo increases from the time the egg is laid through the time the chick hatches. In a typical galliform bird, the oxygen consumption (in milliliters per hour) can be approximated by

$$c(t) = -0.0027t^3 + 0.14t^2 - 0.89t + 0.15 \quad (8 \le t \le 30),$$

where t is the time (in days) since the egg was laid.[67] (An egg will typically hatch at around $t = 28$.) Use technology to graph $c'(t)$ and use your graph to answer the following questions. HINT [See Example 5.]

a. Over the interval [8, 30] the derivative c' is
(A) increasing, then decreasing.
(B) decreasing, then increasing.
(C) decreasing. **(D)** increasing.

b. When, to the nearest day, is the oxygen consumption increasing the fastest?

c. When, to the nearest day, is the oxygen consumption increasing at the slowest rate?

The next two exercises are applications of Einstein's Special Theory of Relativity and relate to objects that are moving extremely fast. In science fiction terminology, a speed of warp 1 is the speed of light—about 3×10^8 meters per second. (Thus, for instance, a speed of warp 0.8 corresponds to 80% of the speed of light—about 2.4×10^8 meters per second.)

99. ◆ ***Lorentz Contraction*** According to Einstein's Special Theory of Relativity, a moving object appears to get shorter to a stationary observer as its speed approaches the speed of light. If a spaceship that has a length of 100 meters at rest travels at a speed of warp p, its length in meters, as measured by a stationary observer, is given by

$$L(p) = 100\sqrt{1 - p^2}$$

with domain [0, 1). Estimate $L(0.95)$ and $L'(0.95)$. What do these figures tell you?

[66] The model approximates graphical data published in the article *The Brush Turkey* by Roger S. Seymour, *Scientific American*, December, 1991, pp. 108–114.

[67] *Ibid.*

100. ◆ ***Time Dilation*** Another prediction of Einstein's Special Theory of Relativity is that, to a stationary observer, clocks (as well as all biological processes) in a moving object appear to go more and more slowly as the speed of the object approaches that of light. If a spaceship travels at a speed of warp p, the time it takes for an onboard clock to register one second, as measured by a stationary observer, will be given by

$$T(p) = \frac{1}{\sqrt{1 - p^2}} \text{ seconds}$$

with domain [0, 1). Estimate $T(0.95)$ and $T'(0.95)$. What do these figures tell you?

COMMUNICATION AND REASONING EXERCISES

101. Explain why we cannot put $h = 0$ in the approximation

$$f'(x) \approx \frac{f(x+h) - f(x)}{h}$$

for the derivative of f.

102. The balanced difference quotient

$$f'(a) \approx \frac{f(a + 0.0001) - f(a - 0.0001)}{0.0002}$$

is the average rate of change of f on what interval?

103. Let $H(t)$ represent the number of Handbook members in millions t years after its inception in 2020. It is found that $H(10) = 50$ and $H'(10) = -6$. This means that, in 2030 (Multiple Choice):

(A) There were 6 million members and this number was decreasing at a rate of 50 million per year.
(B) There were –6 million members and this number was increasing at a rate of 50 million per year.
(C) Membership had dropped by 6 million since the previous year, but was now increasing at a rate of 50 million per year.
(D) There were 50 million members and this number was decreasing at a rate of 6 million per year.
(E) There were 50 million members and membership had dropped by 6 million since the previous year.

104. Let $F(t)$ represent the net earnings of Footbook Inc. in millions of dollars t years after its inception in 3020. It is found that $F(100) = -10$ and $F'(100) = 60$. This means that, in 3120 (Multiple Choice):

(A) Footbook lost $10 million but its net earnings were increasing at a rate of $60 million per year.
(B) Footbook earned $60 million but its earnings were decreasing at a rate of $10 million per year.
(C) Footbook's net earnings had increased by $60 million since the year before, but it still lost $10 million.

(D) Footbook earned \$10 million but its net earnings were decreasing at a rate of \$60 million per year.

(E) Footbook's net earnings had decreased by \$10 million since the year before, but it still earned \$60 million.

105. It is now eight months since the Garden City lacrosse team won the national championship, and sales of team paraphernalia, while still increasing, have been leveling off. What does this tell you about the derivative of the sales curve?

106. Having been soundly defeated in the national lacrosse championships, Brakpan High has been faced with decreasing sales of its team paraphernalia. However, sales, while still decreasing, appear to be bottoming out. What does this tell you about the derivative of the sales curve?

107. ▼ Company A's profits are given by $P(0) = \$1$ million and $P'(0) = -\$1$ million/month. Company B's profits are given by $P(0) = -\$1$ million and $P'(0) = \$1$ million/month. In which company would you rather invest? Why?

108. ▼ Company C's profits are given by $P(0) = \$1$ million and $P'(0) = \$0.5$ million/month. Company D's profits are given by $P(0) = \$0.5$ million and $P'(0) = \$1$ million/month. In which company would you rather invest? Why?

109. ▼ During the one-month period starting last January 1, your company's profits increased at an average rate of change of \$4 million per month. On January 1, profits were increasing at an instantaneous rate of \$5 million per month. Which of the following graphs could represent your company's profits? Why?

(A)

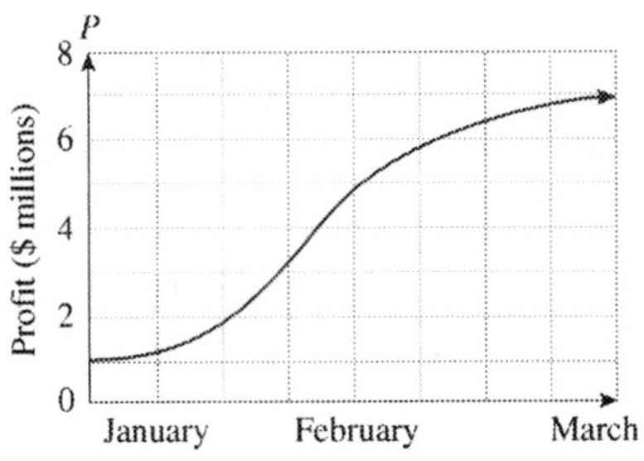

(B)

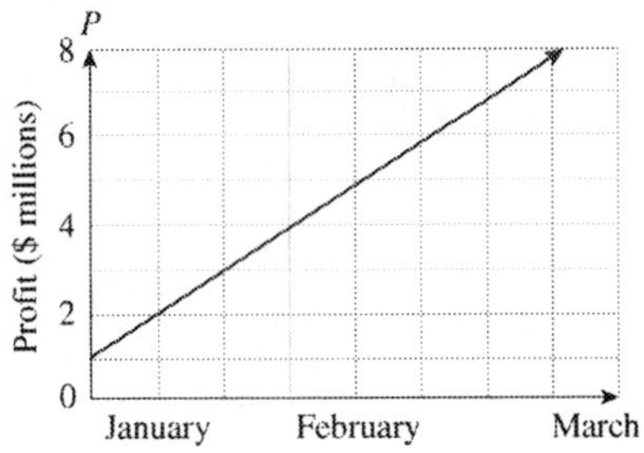

(C)

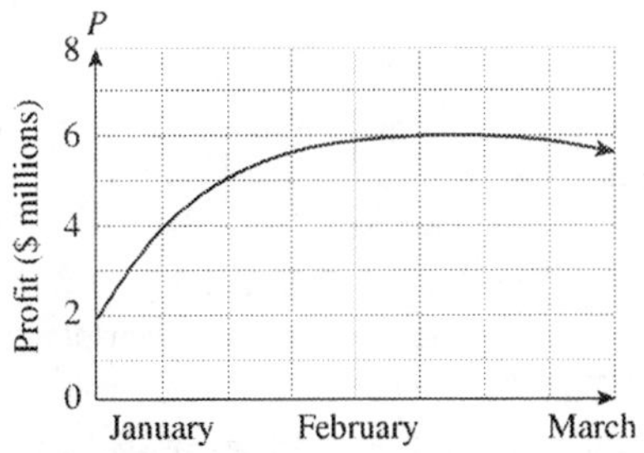

110. ▼ During the one-month period starting last January 1, your company's sales increased at an average rate of change of \$3,000 per month. On January 1, sales were changing at an instantaneous rate of –\$1,000 per month. Which of the following graphs could represent your company's sales? Why?

(A)

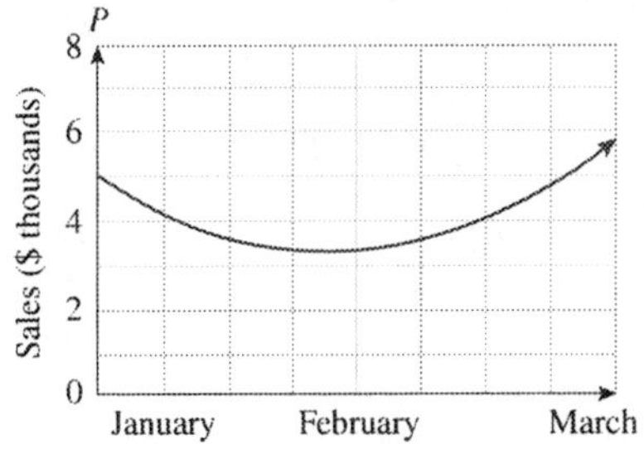

(B)

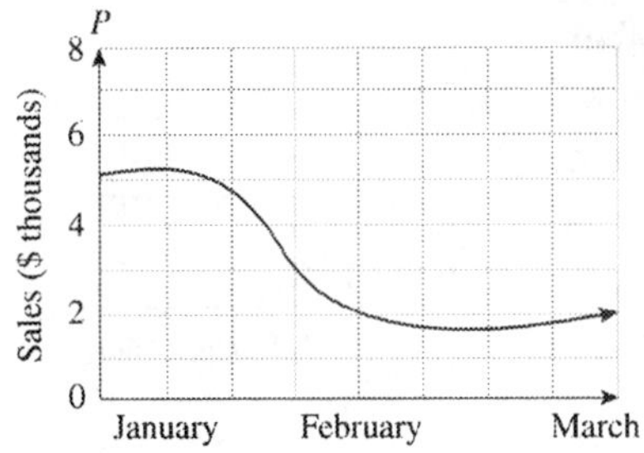

(C)

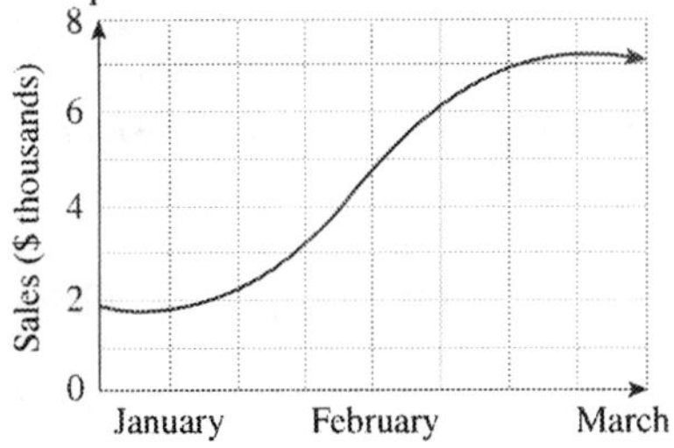

111. ▼ If the derivative of *f* is zero at a point, what do you know about the graph of *f* near that point?

112. ▼ Sketch the graph of a function whose derivative never exceeds 1.

113. ▼ Sketch the graph of a function whose derivative exceeds 1 at every point.

114. ▼ Sketch the graph of a function whose derivative is exactly 1 at every point.

115. ▼ Use the difference quotient to explain the fact that if *f* is a linear function, then the average rate of change over any interval equals the instantaneous rate of change at any point.

116. ▼ Give a numerical explanation of the fact that if *f* is a linear function, then the average rate of change over any interval equals the instantaneous rate of change at any point.

117. ◆ Consider the following values of the function *f* from Exercise 1.

h	0.1	0.01	0.001	0.0001
Average Rate of Change of f over $[5, 5+h]$	6.4	6.04	6.004	6.0004
h	−0.1	−0.01	−0.001	−0.0001
Average Rate of Change of f over $[5+h, 5]$	5.6	5.96	5.996	5.9996

Does the table suggests that the instantaneous rate of change of *f* is

(A) increasing **(B)** decreasing

as x increases toward 5?

118. ◆ Consider the following values of the function g from Exercise 2.

h	0.1	0.01	0.001	0.0001
Average Rate of Change of g over $[7, 7+h]$	4.8	4.98	4.998	4.9998
h	−0.1	−0.01	−0.001	−0.0001
Average Rate of Change of g over $[7+h, 7]$	5.3	5.03	5.003	5.0003

Does the table suggest that the instantaneous rate of change of g is

(A) increasing **(B)** decreasing

as x increases toward 7?

119. ▼ Sketch the graph of a function whose derivative is never zero but decreases as x increases.

120. ▼ Sketch the graph of a function whose derivative is never negative but is zero at exactly two points.

121. ◆ Here is the graph of the derivative f' of a function *f*. Give a rough sketch of the graph of *f*, given that $f(0) = 0$.

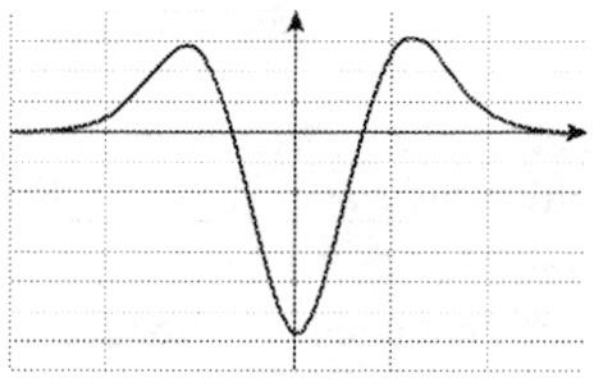

122. ◆ Here is the graph of the derivative f' of a function *f*. Give a rough sketch of the graph of *f*, given that $f(0) = 0$.

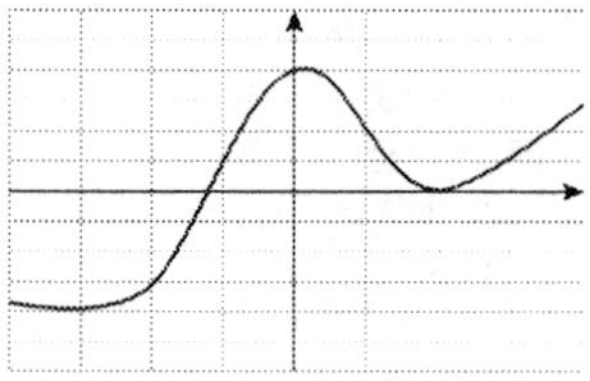

123. ◆ Professor Talker of the physics department drove a 60-mile stretch of road in exactly one hour. The speed limit along that stretch was 55 miles per hour. Which of the following must be correct?

(A) He exceeded the speed limit at no point of the journey.
(B) He exceeded the speed limit at some point of the journey.
(C) He exceeded the speed limit throughout the journey.
(D) He traveled slower than the speed limit at some point of the journey.

124. ◆ Professor Silent, another physics professor, drove a 50-mile stretch of road in exactly one hour. The speed limit along that stretch was 55 miles per hour. Which of the following must be correct?

(A) She exceeded the speed limit at no point of the journey.
(B) She exceeded the speed limit at some point of the journey.
(C) She traveled slower than the speed limit throughout the journey.
(D) She traveled slower than the speed limit at some point of the journey.

125. ◆ Draw the graph of a function *f* with the property that the balanced difference quotient gives a more accurate approximation of $f'(1)$ than the ordinary difference quotient.

126. ◆ Draw the graph of a function *f* with the property that the balanced difference quotient gives a less accurate approximation of $f'(1)$ than the ordinary difference quotient.

Practice Problems 10.5, Part 1

1. Suppose that $P(t) = 30e^{-2t}$. Fill in the table below and use your results to give a reasonable estimate for $P'(5)$. Give all estimates correct to five decimal places.

Interval	$[4.99,5]$	$[4.999,5]$	$[4.9999,5]$	$[5,5.0001]$	$[5,5.001]$	$[5,5.01]$
Average Rate of Change $\left(\frac{\Delta P}{\Delta t}\right)$						

$P'(5) \approx$ ____________________

2. The size, *S*, of a malignant tumor is given by $S = 3(1.25)^t$ cubic millimeters, where t is the number of months since the tumor was discovered. Give appropriate units with your answers to the following questions. Round results to four decimal places.

a. What is the total change in the size (ΔS) of the tumor during the first four months since discovery?

b. What is the average rate of change in the size $\left(\frac{\Delta S}{\Delta t}\right)$ of the tumor during the first four months since discovery?

c. Fill in the table and use the results to estimate the (instantaneous) rate at which the tumor is growing when $t = 4$ months(i.e., to estimate $\left.\frac{dS}{dt}\right|_{t=4}$). Round all results to four decimal places.

Interval	$[3.99,4]$	$[3.999,4]$	$[3.9999,4]$	$[4,4.0001]$	$[4,4.001]$	$[4,4.01]$
$\frac{\Delta S}{\Delta t}$						

$\left.\frac{dS}{dt}\right|_{t=4} \approx$ ____________________

Practice Problems 10.5, Part 2

1. An equation for the line tangent to the graph of a function $g(x)$ at the point where $x = 6$ is $y = 3x - 9$. Given this, calculate $g(6)$ and $g'(6)$.

2. Suppose that $c(t) = 18te^{-0.1t}$. Which is larger: $c'(4)$ or $c'(8)$? Use either numerical or graphical evidence to support your claim.

3. Suppose that a car is being driven along a straight stretch of roadway. For each of the following scenarios, make a sketch of a graph of distance the car has traveled as a function of time traveling along the stretch of roadway.

a. The car is traveling at a constant speed.

b. The car is traveling at an increasing speed.

c. The car is initially traveling at a high speed, but its speed is gradually decreasing.

Practice Problems 10.5, Part 3

1. Like many other businesses, Maria's Morning Muffinhut has experienced a downturn in sales during the last several months. The graph below describes the sales of blueberry muffins over the course of a twelve-month period. Here, x measures months, with $x = 0$ corresponding to January 1st, 2012, and $f(x)$ measures the number of muffins sold, in thousands.

   a. Estimate the (instantaneous) rate of change in blueberry muffin sales at the beginning of May. Label your response appropriately.

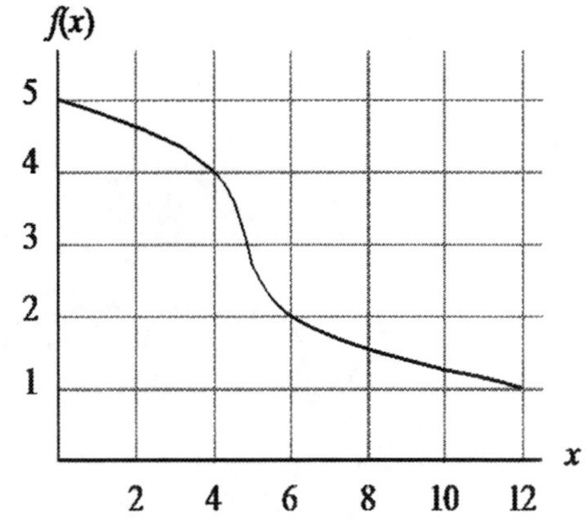

   b. Every two months, Maria calculates the average rate of change of muffin sales over the just-completed two month period. Determine the two-month period of time where blueberry muffin sales had the largest average rate of decrease.

   c. Are there specific points in time when the instantaneous rate of change in blueberry muffin sales matches the average rate of change in sales over the course of 2012? If so, then give the approximate date(s). If not, then explain why.

2. Let $R(x)$ be the elevation of the Red River, in feet, x miles from its source.

   a. Is $R'(x)$ positive or negative? Explain.

   b. What are the units of $R'(x)$?

Practice Problems 10.5, Part 4

To the right is the graph of a function $f(x)$. Fill in the provided table with your best estimates and sketch a graph of the corresponding derivative function, $f'(x)$. Be cautious of points of non-differentiability. You can assume that gridlines each mark one unit.

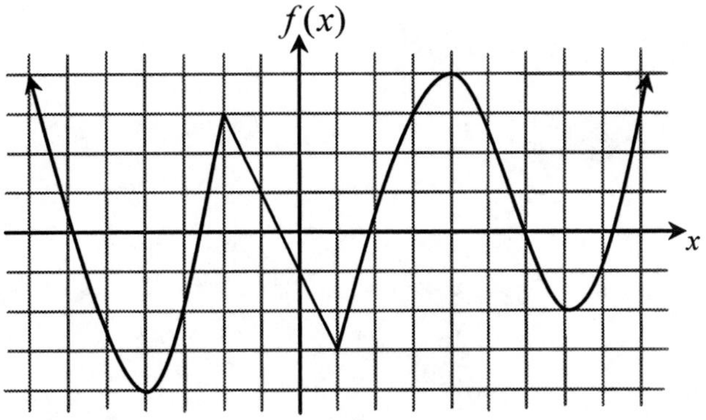

x	–5	–3	–1	1	3	5	7
$f'(x)$							

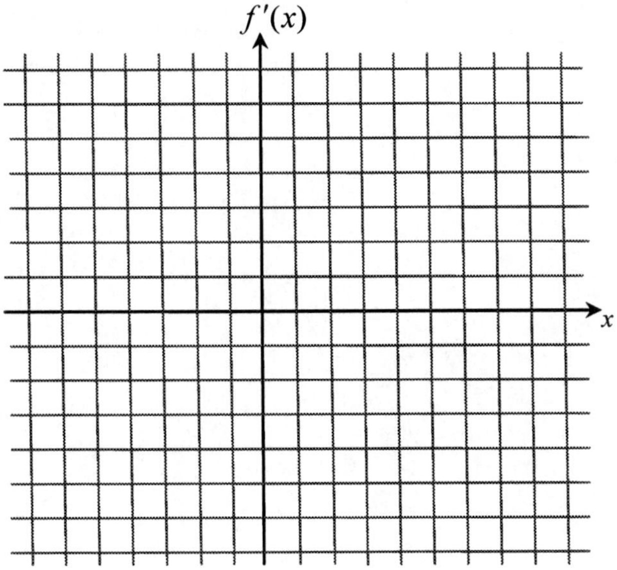

Practice Problems 10.5, Part 5

1. Let $f(t)$ be the number of centimeters of rainfall that has fallen, where t is the time in hours after midnight. Give meaningful interpretations of the following in terms of rainfall, including appropriate labels in your responses.
   a. $f(14) = 5.9$

   b. $f'(7) = 0.8$

2. Suppose that $C(t)$ denotes the number of milligrams of caffeine you have ingested after t hours of studying for a calculus exam. Give meaningful interpretations of the following in terms of caffeine and study time, including appropriate labels in your responses.
   a. $C(3) = 625$

   b. $\dfrac{C(4) - C(1)}{4 - 1} = 72$

   c. $C'(3) = 56$

10.6 Derivatives: Algebraic Viewpoint

In Section 10.5 we saw how to estimate the derivative of a function using numerical and graphical approaches. In this section we use an algebraic approach that will give us the *exact value* of the derivative, rather than just an approximation, when the function is specified algebraically.

This algebraic approach is quite straightforward: Instead of subtracting numbers to estimate the average rate of change over smaller and smaller intervals, we subtract algebraic expressions. Our starting point is the definition of the derivative in terms of the difference quotient:

$$f'(a) = \lim_{h\to 0} \frac{f(a+h) - f(a)}{h}.$$

EXAMPLE 1 Calculating the Derivative at a Point Algebraically

Let $f(x) = x^2$. Use the definition of the derivative to compute $f'(3)$ algebraically.

Solution Substituting $a = 3$ into the definition of the derivative, we get:

$$
\begin{aligned}
f'(3) &= \lim_{h\to 0} \frac{f(3+h) - f(3)}{h} && \text{Formula for the derivative} \\
&= \lim_{h\to 0} \frac{\overbrace{(3+h)^2}^{f(3+h)} - \overbrace{3^2}^{f(3)}}{h} && \text{Substitute for } f(3) \text{ and } f(3+h). \\
&= \lim_{h\to 0} \frac{(9 + 6h + h^2) - 9}{h} && \text{Expand } (3+h)^2. \\
&= \lim_{h\to 0} \frac{6h + h^2}{h} && \text{Cancel the 9.} \\
&= \lim_{h\to 0} \frac{h(6+h)}{h} && \text{Factor out } h. \\
&= \lim_{h\to 0} (6+h). && \text{Cancel the } h.
\end{aligned}
$$

Now we let h approach 0. As h gets closer and closer to 0, the sum $6 + h$ clearly gets closer and closer to $6 + 0 = 6$. Thus,

$$f'(3) = \lim_{h\to 0} (6+h) = 6. \qquad \text{As } h \to 0,\ (6+h) \to 6$$

(Calculations of limits like this are discussed and justified more fully in Sections 10.2 and 10.3.)

➡ **Before we go on...** We did the following calculation in Example 1: If $f(x) = x^2$, then $f'(3) = 6$. In other words, the tangent to the graph of $y = x^2$ at the point (3, 9) has slope 6 (Figure 36). ■

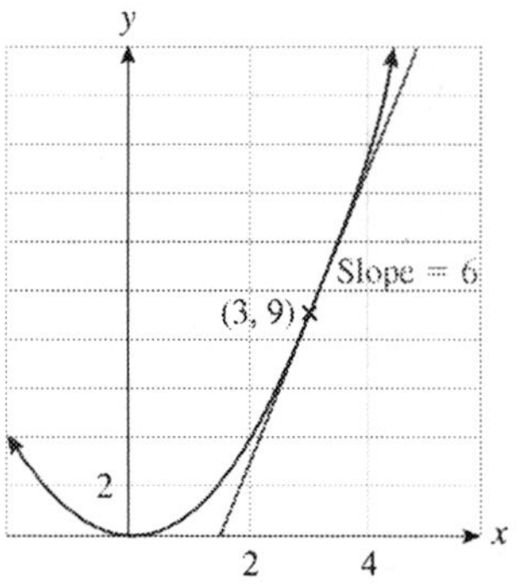

Figure 36

There is nothing very special about $a = 3$ in Example 1. Let's try to compute $f'(x)$ for general x.

EXAMPLE 2 Calculating the Derivative Function Algebraically

Let $f(x) = x^2$.

a. Use the definition of the derivative to compute $f'(x)$ algebraically.

b. Use the answer to evaluate $f'(3)$.

Solution

a. Once again, our starting point is the definition of the derivative in terms of the difference quotient:

$$f'(x) = \lim_{h \to 0} \frac{f(x+h) - f(x)}{h}$$ Formula for the derivative

$$= \lim_{h \to 0} \frac{\overbrace{(x+h)^2}^{f(x+h)} - \overbrace{x^2}^{f(x)}}{h}$$ Substitute for $f(x)$ and $f(x+h)$.

$$= \lim_{h \to 0} \frac{(x^2 + 2xh + h^2) - x^2}{h}$$ Expand $(x+h)^2$.

$$= \lim_{h \to 0} \frac{2xh + h^2}{h}$$ Cancel the x^2.

$$= \lim_{h \to 0} \frac{h(2x+h)}{h}$$ Factor out h.

$$= \lim_{h \to 0} (2x + h).$$ Cancel the h.

Now we let h approach 0. As h gets closer and closer to 0, the sum $2x + h$ clearly gets closer and closer to $2x + 0 = 2x$. Thus,

$$f'(x) = \lim_{h \to 0} (2x + h) = 2x.$$

This is the derivative function.

b. Now that we have a *formula* for the derivative of *f*, we can obtain $f'(a)$ for any value of a we choose by simply evaluating f' there. For instance,

$$f'(3) = 2(3) = 6$$

as we saw in Example 1.

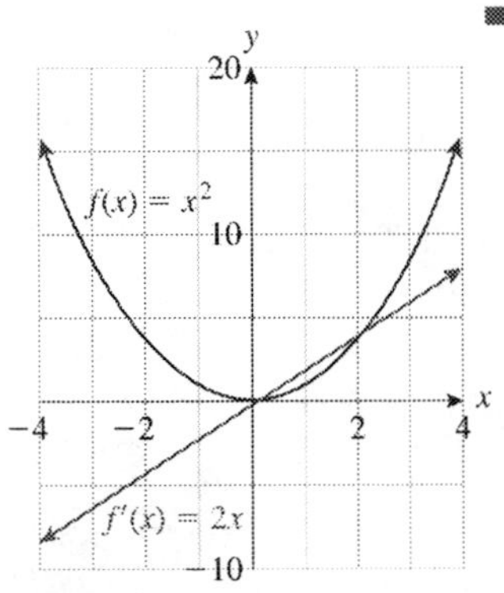

Figure 37

Before we go on... The graphs of $f(x) = x^2$ and $f'(x) = 2x$ from Example 2 are familiar. Their graphs are shown in Figure 37.

When $x < 0$, the parabola slopes downward, which is reflected in the fact that the derivative $2x$ is negative there. When $x > 0$, the parabola slopes upward, which is reflected in the fact that the derivative is positive there. The parabola has a horizontal tangent line at $x = 0$, reflected in the fact that $2x = 0$ there. ■

EXAMPLE 3 More Computations of Derivative Functions

Compute the derivative $f'(x)$ for each of the following functions:

a. $f(x) = x^3$ **b.** $f(x) = 2x^2 - x$ **c.** $f(x) = \frac{1}{x}$

Solution

a. $f'(x) = \lim_{h\to 0} \frac{f(x+h) - f(x)}{h}$ — Derivative formula

$= \lim_{h\to 0} \frac{\overbrace{(x+h)^3}^{f(x+h)} - \overbrace{x^3}^{f(x)}}{h}$ — Substitute for $f(x)$ and $f(x+h)$.

$= \lim_{h\to 0} \frac{(x^3 + 3x^2h + 3xh^2 + h^3) - x^3}{h}$ — Expand $(x+h)^3$.

$= \lim_{h\to 0} \frac{3x^2h + 3xh^2 + h^3}{h}$ — Cancel the x^3.

$= \lim_{h\to 0} \frac{h(3x^2 + 3xh + h^2)}{h}$ — Factor out h.

$= \lim_{h\to 0} (3x^2 + 3xh + h^2)$ — Cancel the h.

$= 3x^2.$ — Let h approach 0.

b. $f'(x) = \lim_{h\to 0} \frac{f(x+h) - f(x)}{h}$ — Derivative formula

$= \lim_{h\to 0} \frac{\overbrace{(2(x+h)^2 - (x+h))}^{f(x+h)} - \overbrace{(2x^2 - x)}^{f(x)}}{h}$ — Substitute for $f(x)$ and $f(x+h)$.

$= \lim_{h\to 0} \frac{(2x^2 + 4xh + 2h^2 - x - h) - (2x^2 - x)}{h}$ — Expand.

$= \lim_{h\to 0} \frac{4xh + 2h^2 - h}{h}$ — Cancel the $2x^2$ and x.

$= \lim_{h\to 0} \frac{h(4x + 2h - 1)}{h}$ — Factor out h.

$= \lim_{h\to 0} (4x + 2h - 1)$ — Cancel the h

$= 4x - 1.$ — Let h approach 0.

c. $f'(x) = \lim_{h\to 0} \frac{f(x+h) - f(x)}{h}$ — Derivative formula

$= \lim_{h\to 0} \frac{\left[\overbrace{\frac{1}{x+h}}^{f(x+h)} - \overbrace{\frac{1}{x}}^{f(x)}\right]}{h}$ — Substitute for $f(x)$ and $f(x+h)$.

$= \lim_{h\to 0} \frac{\left[\frac{x - (x+h)}{(x+h)x}\right]}{h}$ — Subtract the fractions.

$= \lim_{h\to 0} \frac{1}{h}\left[\frac{x - (x+h)}{(x+h)x}\right]$ — Dividing by h = Multiplying by $1/h$.

$$= \lim_{h\to 0}\left[\frac{-h}{h(x+h)x}\right] \qquad \text{Simplify.}$$

$$= \lim_{h\to 0}\left[\frac{-1}{(x+h)x}\right] \qquad \text{Cancel the } h.$$

$$= \frac{-1}{x^2} \qquad \text{Let } h \text{ approach } 0.$$

In Example 4, we redo Example 3 of Section 10.5, this time getting an exact, rather than approximate, answer.

EXAMPLE 4 Velocity

My friend Eric, an enthusiastic baseball player, claims he can "probably" throw a ball upward at a speed of 100 feet per second (ft/sec). Our physicist friends tell us that its height s (in feet) t seconds later would be $s(t) = 100t - 16t^2$. Find the ball's instantaneous velocity function and its velocity exactly 2 seconds after Eric throws it.

Solution The instantaneous velocity function is the derivative ds/dt, which we calculate as follows:

$$\frac{ds}{dt} = \lim_{h\to 0}\frac{s(t+h)-s(t)}{h}.$$

Let us compute $s(t+h)$ and $s(t)$ separately:

$$\begin{aligned} s(t) &= 100t - 16t^2 \\ s(t+h) &= 100(t+h) - 16(t+h)^2 \\ &= 100t + 100h - 16(t^2 + 2th + h^2) \\ &= 100t + 100h - 16t^2 - 32th - 16h^2. \end{aligned}$$

Therefore,

$$\begin{aligned} \frac{ds}{dt} &= \lim_{h\to 0}\frac{s(t+h)-s(t)}{h} \\ &= \lim_{h\to 0}\frac{100t + 100h - 16t^2 - 32th - 16h^2 - (100t - 16t^2)}{h} \\ &= \lim_{h\to 0}\frac{100h - 32th - 16h^2}{h} \\ &= \lim_{h\to 0}\frac{h(100 - 32t - 16h)}{h} \\ &= \lim_{h\to 0}(100 - 32t - 16h) \\ &= 100 - 32t \text{ ft/sec.} \end{aligned}$$

Thus, the velocity exactly 2 seconds after Eric throws it is

$$\left.\frac{ds}{dt}\right|_{t=2} = 100 - 32(2) = 36 \text{ ft/sec.}$$

This verifies the accuracy of the approximation we made in Section 10.5.

➡ **Before we go on...** From the derivative function in Example 4, we can now describe the behavior of the velocity of the ball: Immediately on release ($t = 0$) the ball is traveling at 100 feet per second upward. The ball then slows down; precisely, it loses 32 feet per second of speed every second. When, exactly, does the velocity become zero and what happens after that? ■

Q: *Do we always have to calculate the limit of the difference quotient to find a formula for the derivative function?*

A: As it turns out, no. In Section 11.1 we will start to look at shortcuts for finding derivatives that allow us to bypass the definition of the derivative in many cases.

A Function Not Differentiable at a Point

Recall from Section 10.5 that a function is **differentiable** at a point a if $f'(a)$ exists; that is, if the difference quotient $[f(a+h) - f(a)]/h$ approaches a fixed value as h approaches 0. In Section 10.5, we mentioned that the function $f(x) = |x|$ is not differentiable at $x = 0$. In Example 5, we find out why.

EXAMPLE 5 A Function Not Differentiable at 0

Numerically, graphically, and algebraically investigate the differentiability of the function $f(x) = |x|$ at the points **(a)** $x = 1$ and **(b)** $x = 0$.

Solution

a. We compute

$$f'(1) = \lim_{h\to 0} \frac{f(1+h) - f(1)}{h} = \lim_{h\to 0} \frac{|1+h| - 1}{h}.$$

Numerically, we can make tables of the values of the average rate of change $(|1+h| - 1)/h$ for h positive or negative and approaching 0:

h	1	0.1	0.01	0.001	0.0001
Average Rate of Change Over [1, 1 + *h*]	1	1	1	1	1

h	−1	−0.1	−0.01	−0.001	−0.0001
Average Rate of Change Over [1 + *h*, 1]	1	1	1	1	1

From these tables it appears that $f'(1)$ is equal to 1. We can verify that algebraically: For h that is sufficiently small, $1 + h$ is positive (even if h is negative) and so

$$\begin{aligned} f'(1) &= \lim_{h\to 0} \frac{1+h-1}{h} \\ &= \lim_{h\to 0} \frac{h}{h} && \text{Cancel the 1s.} \\ &= \lim_{h\to 0} 1 && \text{Cancel the } h. \\ &= 1. \end{aligned}$$

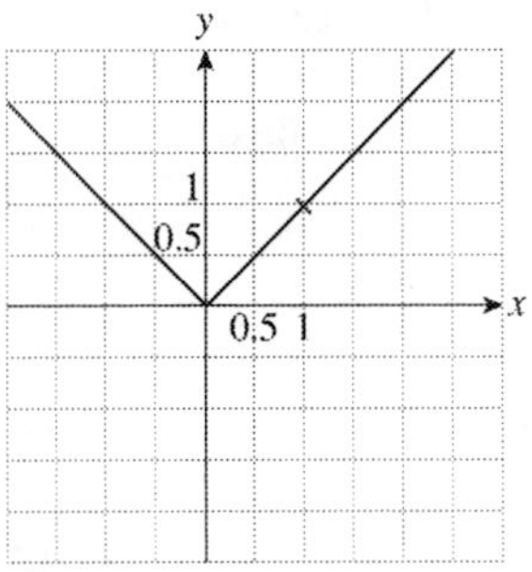

Figure 38

Graphically, we are seeing the fact that the tangent line at the point (1, 1) has slope 1 because the graph is a straight line with slope 1 near that point (Figure 38).

b. $$f'(0) = \lim_{h\to 0} \frac{f(0+h) - f(0)}{h}$$
$$= \lim_{h\to 0} \frac{|0+h| - 0}{h}$$
$$= \lim_{h\to 0} \frac{|h|}{h}$$

If we make tables of values in this case we get the following:

h	1	0.1	0.01	0.001	0.0001
Average Rate of Change over [0, 0 + *h*]	1	1	1	1	1

h	−1	−0.1	−0.01	−0.001	−0.0001
Average Rate of Change over [0 + *h*, 0]	−1	−1	−1	−1	−1

For the limit and hence the derivative $f'(0)$ to exist, the average rates of change should approach the same number for both positive and negative h. Because they do not, f is not differentiable at $x = 0$. We can verify this conclusion algebraically: If h is positive, then $|h| = h$, and so the ratio $|h|/h$ is 1, regardless of how small h is. Thus, according to the values of the difference quotients with $h > 0$, the limit should be 1. On the other hand if h is negative, then $|h| = -h$ (positive) and so $|h|/h = -1$, meaning that the limit should be -1. Because the limit cannot be both -1 and 1 (it must be a single number for the derivative to exist), we conclude that $f'(0)$ does not exist.

To see what is happening graphically, take a look at Figure 39, which shows zoomed-in views of the graph of f near $x = 0$.

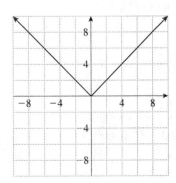

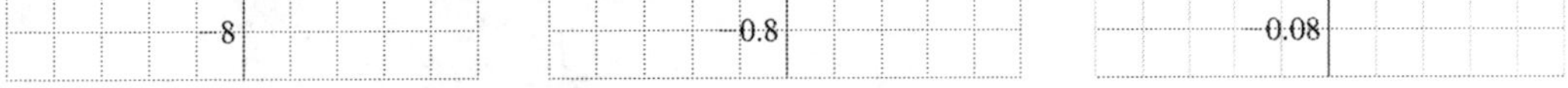

Figure 39

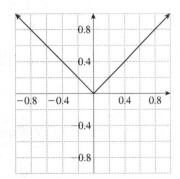

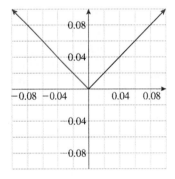

No matter what scale we use to view the graph, it has a sharp corner at $x = 0$ and hence has no tangent line there. Since there is no tangent line at $x = 0$, the function is not differentiable there.

➡ **Before we go on...** Notice that $|x| = \begin{cases} -x & \text{if } x < 0 \\ x & \text{if } x \ge 0 \end{cases}$ is an example of a piecewise-linear function whose graph comes to a point at $x = 0$. In general, if $f(x)$ is any piecewise linear function whose graph comes to a point at $x = a$, it will be nondifferentiable at $x = a$ for the same reason that $|x|$ fails to be differentiable at $x = 0$.

If we repeat the computation in Example 5(a) using any nonzero value for a in place of 1, we see that f is differentiable there as well. If a is positive, we find that $f'(a) = 1$ and, if a is negative, $f'(a) = -1$. In other words, the derivative function is

$$f'(x) = \begin{cases} -1 & \text{if } x < 0 \\ 1 & \text{if } x > 0 \end{cases}.$$

Immediately to the left of $x = 0$, we see that $f'(x) = -1$, immediately to the right, $f'(x) = 1$; and when $x = 0$, $f'(x)$ is not defined. ■

Q: *So does that mean there is no single formula for the derivative of $|x|$?*

A: Actually, there is a convenient formula. Consider the ratio $\frac{|x|}{x}$. If x is positive, then $|x| = x$, so $\frac{|x|}{x} = \frac{x}{x} = 1$. On the other hand, if x is negative, then $|x| = -x$, so $\frac{|x|}{x} = \frac{-x}{x} = -1$. In other words,

$$\frac{|x|}{x} = \begin{cases} -1 & \text{if } x < 0 \\ 1 & \text{if } x > 0 \end{cases},$$

which is exactly the formula we obtained for $f'(x)$. We have therefore obtained a convenient closed-form formula for the derivative of |x|!

Derivative of |x|

If $f(x) = |x|$, then $f'(x) = \frac{|x|}{x}$.

Note that $|x|/x$ is not defined if $x = 0$, reflecting the fact that $f'(x)$ does not exist when $x = 0$.

We will use the above formula extensively in the next chapter.

FAQ

Computing Derivatives Algebraically

Q: *The algebraic computation of $f'(x)$ seems to require a number of steps. How do I remember what to do, and when?*

A: If you examine the computations in the examples above, you will find the following pattern:

1. Write out the formula for $f'(x)$, as the limit of the difference quotient, then substitute $f(x+h)$ and $f(x)$.
2. Expand and simplify the *numerator* of the expression, but not the denominator.
3. After simplifying the numerator, factor out an h to cancel with the h in the denominator. If h does not factor out of the numerator, you might have made an error. (A frequent error is a wrong sign.)
4. After canceling the h, you should be able to see what the limit is by letting $h \to 0$.

10.6 EXERCISES

▼ more advanced ◆ challenging

T indicates exercises that should be solved using technology

In Exercises 1–14, compute $f'(a)$ algebraically for the given value of a. HINT [See Example 1.]

1. $f(x) = x^2 + 1; a = 2$
2. $f(x) = x^2 - 3; a = 1$
3. $f(x) = 3x - 4; a = -1$
4. $f(x) = -2x + 4; a = -1$
5. $f(x) = 3x^2 + x; a = 1$
6. $f(x) = 2x^2 + x; a = -2$
7. $f(x) = 2x - x^2; a = -1$
8. $f(x) = -x - x^2; a = 0$
9. $f(x) = x^3 + 2x; a = 2$
10. $f(x) = x - 2x^3; a = 1$
11. $f(x) = \frac{-1}{x}; a = 1$ HINT [See Example 3.]
12. $f(x) = \frac{2}{x}; a = 5$ HINT [See Example 3.]
13. ▼ $f(x) = mx + b; a = 43$
14. ▼ $f(x) = \frac{x}{k} - b\ (k \neq 0); a = 12$

In Exercises 15–28, compute the derivative function $f'(x)$ algebraically. (Notice that the functions are the same as those in Exercises 1–14.) HINT [See Examples 2 and 3.]

15. $f(x) = x^2 + 1$
16. $f(x) = x^2 - 3$
17. $f(x) = 3x - 4$
18. $f(x) = -2x + 4$
19. $f(x) = 3x^2 + x$
20. $f(x) = 2x^2 + x$
21. $f(x) = 2x - x^2$
22. $f(x) = -x - x^2$
23. $f(x) = x^3 + 2x$
24. $f(x) = x - 2x^3$
25. ▼ $f(x) = \frac{-1}{x}$
26. ▼ $f(x) = \frac{2}{x}$
27. ▼ $f(x) = mx + b$
28. ▼ $f(x) = \frac{x}{k} - b\ (k \neq 0)$

In Exercises 29–38, compute the indicated derivative.

29. $R(t) = -0.3t^2; R'(2)$
30. $S(t) = 1.4t^2; S'(-1)$
31. $U(t) = 5.1t^2 + 5.1; U'(3)$
32. $U(t) = -1.3t^2 + 1.1; U'(4)$
33. $U(t) = -1.3t^2 - 4.5t; U'(1)$
34. $U(t) = 5.1t^2 - 1.1t; U'(1)$
35. $L(r) = 4.25r - 5.01; L'(1.2)$
36. $L(r) = -1.02r + 5.7; L'(3.1)$
37. ▼ $q(p) = \frac{2.4}{p} + 3.1; q'(2)$
38. ▼ $q(p) = \frac{1}{0.5p} - 3.1; q'(2)$

In Exercises 39–44, find the equation of the tangent to the graph at the indicated point. HINT [Compute the derivative algebraically; then see Example 2(b) in Section 10.5.]

39. ▼ $f(x) = x^2 - 3; a = 2$
40. ▼ $f(x) = x^2 + 1; a = 2$
41. ▼ $f(x) = -2x - 4; a = 3$
42. ▼ $f(x) = 3x + 1; a = 1$
43. ▼ $f(x) = x^2 - x; a = -1$
44. ▼ $f(x) = x^2 + x; a = -1$

APPLICATIONS

45. ***Velocity*** If a stone is dropped from a height of 400 feet, its height after t seconds is given by $s = 400 - 16t^2$. Find its instantaneous velocity function and its velocity at time $t = 4$. HINT [See Example 4.]

46. ***Velocity*** If a stone is thrown down at 120 feet per second from a height of 1,000 feet, its height after t seconds is given by $s = 1{,}000 - 120t - 16t^2$. Find its instantaneous velocity function and its velocity at time $t = 3$. HINT [See Example 4.]

47. ***Oil Imports from Mexico*** Daily oil imports to the United States from Mexico can be approximated by

$$I(t) = -0.015t^2 + 0.1t + 1.4 \text{ million barrels} \quad (0 \le t \le 8),$$

where t is time in years since the start of 2000.[68] Find the derivative function $\frac{dI}{dt}$. At what rate were oil imports changing at the start of 2007 ($t = 7$)? HINT [See Example 4.]

48. ***Oil Production in Mexico*** Daily oil production by Pemex, Mexico's national oil company, can be approximated by

$$P(t) = -0.022t^2 + 0.2t + 2.9 \text{ million barrels} \quad (1 \le t \le 9),$$

where t is time in years since the start of 2000.[69] Find the derivative function $\frac{dP}{dt}$. At what rate was oil production changing at the start of 2004 ($t = 4$)? HINT [See Example 4.]

49. ***Bottled Water Sales*** The following chart shows the amount of bottled water sold in the United States for the period 2000–2010:[70]

[68] Source for data: Energy Information Administration/Pemex (www.eia.doe.gov).

[69] *Ibid.*

[70] The 2010 figure is an estimate. Source: Beverage Marketing Corporation/ www.bottledwater.org.

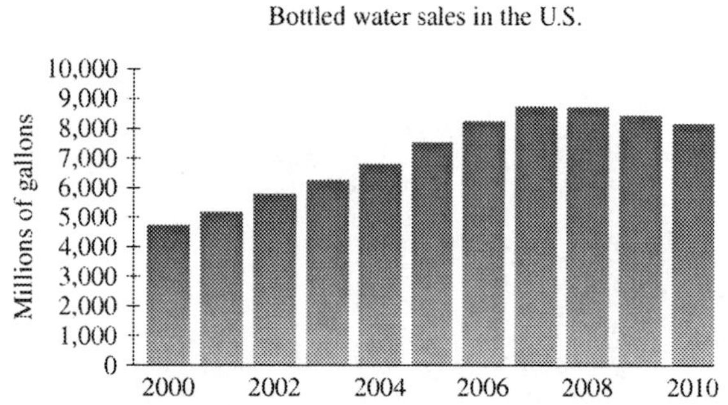

The function

$$R(t) = -45t^2 + 900t + 4{,}200 \text{ million gallons} \quad (0 \le t \le 10)$$

gives a good approximation, where t is time in years since 2000. Find the derivative function $R'(t)$. According to the model, how fast were annual sales of bottled water changing in 2005?

50. ***Bottled Water Sales*** The following chart shows annual per capita sales of bottled water in the United States for the period 2000–2010:[71]

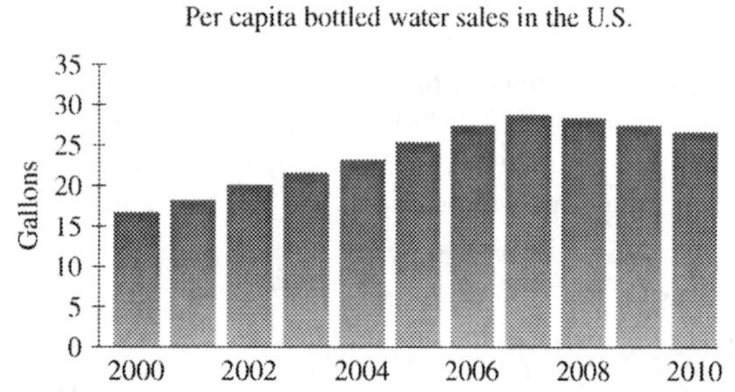

The function

$$R(t) = -0.18t^2 + 3t + 15 \text{ gallons} \qquad (0 \le t \le 10)$$

gives a good approximation, where t is time in years since 2000. Find the derivative function $R'(t)$. According to the model, how fast were per capita sales of bottled water changing in 2009?

51. ▼ ***Ecology*** Increasing numbers of manatees ("sea sirens") have been killed by boats off the Florida coast. The following graph shows the relationship between the number of boats registered in Florida and the number of manatees killed each year.

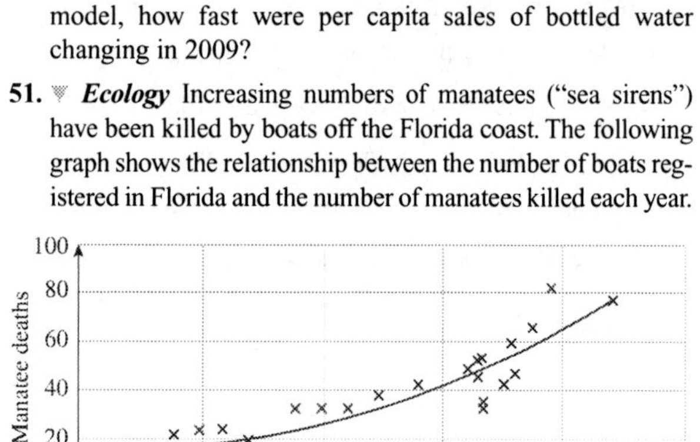

The regression curve shown is given by

$$f(x) = 3.55x^2 - 30.2x + 81 \text{ manatee deaths} \quad (4.5 \le x \le 8.5),$$

where x is the number of boats (hundreds of thousands) registered in Florida in a particular year and $f(x)$ is the number of manatees killed by boats in Florida that year.[72] Compute and interpret $f'(8)$.

52. ▼ ***SAT Scores by Income*** The following graph shows U.S. math SAT scores as a function of parents' income level.[73]

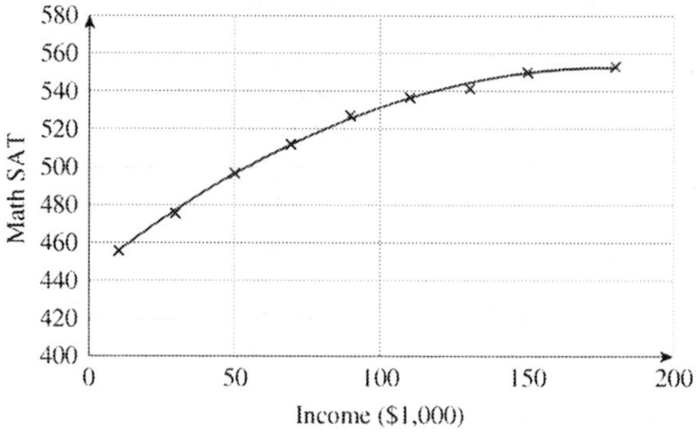

The regression curve shown is given by

$$f(x) = -0.0034x^2 + 1.2x + 444 \qquad (10 \le x \le 180),$$

where $f(x)$ is the average math SAT score of a student whose parents earn x thousand dollars per year. Compute and interpret $f'(30)$.

53. ▼ ***Television Advertising*** The cost, in thousands of dollars, of a 30-second television ad during the Super Bowl in the years 1970 to 2010 can be approximated by the following piecewise linear function ($t = 0$ represents 1970):[74]

$$C(t) = \begin{cases} 31.1t + 78 & \text{if } 0 \le t < 20 \\ 90t - 1{,}100 & \text{if } 20 \le t \le 40 \end{cases}.$$

a. Is C a continuous function of t? Why? HINT **[See Example 4 of Section 10.3.]**

b. Is C a differentiable function of t? Compute $\lim_{t \to 20^-} C'(t)$ and $\lim_{t \to 20^+} C'(t)$ and interpret the results. HINT **[See *Before we go on...* after Example 5.]**

54. ▼ ***Television Advertising*** (Compare Exercise 53.) The cost, in thousands of dollars, of a 30-second television ad during the Super Bowl in the years 1980 to 2010 can be approximated by the following piecewise linear function ($t = 0$ represents 1980):[75]

$$C(t) = \begin{cases} 43.9t + 222 & \text{if } 0 \le t \le 20 \\ 140t - 1{,}700 & \text{if } 20 < t \le 30 \end{cases}.$$

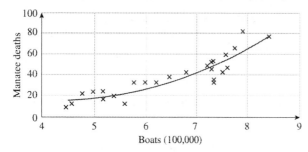

[71] The 2010 figure is an estimate. Source: Beverage Marketing Corporation/www.bottledwater.org.

[72] Regression model is based on data from 1976 to 2000. Sources for data: Florida Department of Highway Safety & Motor Vehicles, Florida Marine Institute/*New York Times*, February 12, 2002, p. F4.

[73] Regression model is based on 2009 data. Source: College Board/*New York Times* http://economix.blogs.nytimes.com.

[74] Source: http://en.wikipedia.org/wiki/Super_Bowl_advertising.

[75] *Ibid.*

a. Is C a continuous function of t? Why? HINT [See Example 4 of Section 10.3.]

b. Is C a differentiable function of t? Compute $\lim_{t\to 20^-} C'(t)$ and $\lim_{t\to 20^+} C'(t)$ and interpret the results. HINT [See *Before we go on...* after Example 5.]

COMMUNICATION AND REASONING EXERCISES

55. Of the three methods (numerical, graphical, algebraic) we can use to estimate the derivative of a function at a given value of x, which is always the most accurate? Explain.

56. Explain why we cannot put $h = 0$ in the formula

$$f'(a) = \lim_{h\to 0} \frac{f(a+h) - f(a)}{h}$$

for the derivative of f.

57. You just got your derivatives test back and you can't understand why that teacher of yours deducted so many points for what you thought was your best work:

$$\lim_{h\to 0} \frac{f(x+h) - f(x)}{h}$$
$$= \lim_{h\to 0} \frac{f(x) + h - f(x)}{h}$$
$$= \lim_{h\to 0} \frac{h}{h} \qquad \text{Canceled the } f(x)$$
$$= 1. \qquad \text{✗ WRONG } -10$$

What was wrong with your answer?

58. Your friend just got his derivatives test back and can't understand why that teacher of his deducted so many points for the following:

$$\lim_{h\to 0} \frac{f(x+h) - f(x)}{h}$$
$$= \lim_{h\to 0} \frac{f(x) + f(h) - f(x)}{h}$$
$$= \lim_{h\to 0} \frac{f(h)}{h} \qquad \text{Canceled the } f(x)$$
$$= \lim_{h\to 0} \frac{f(\not{h})}{\not{h}} \qquad \text{Now cancel the } h.$$
$$= f. \qquad \text{✗ WRONG } -50$$

What was wrong with his answer?

59. Your other friend just got her derivatives test back and can't understand why that teacher of hers took off so many points for the following:

$$\lim_{h\to 0} \frac{f(x+h) - f(x)}{h}$$
$$= \lim_{h\to 0} \frac{f(x+\not{h}) - f(x)}{\not{h}} \qquad \text{Now cancel the } h.$$
$$= \lim_{h\to 0} f(x) - f(x) \qquad \text{Cancel the } f(x)$$
$$= 0. \qquad \text{✗ WRONG } -15$$

What was wrong with her answer?

60. Your third friend just got her derivatives test back and can't understand why that teacher of hers took off so many points for the following:

$$\lim_{h\to 0} \frac{f(x+h) - f(x)}{h}$$
$$= \lim_{h\to 0} \frac{f(x) + h - f(x)}{h}$$
$$= \lim_{h\to 0} \frac{f(x) + \not{h} - f(x)}{\not{h}} \qquad \text{Now cancel the } h.$$
$$= \lim_{h\to 0} f(x) - f(x) \qquad \text{Cancel the } f(x)$$
$$= 0. \qquad \text{✗ WRONG } -25$$

What was wrong with her answer?

61. Your friend Muffy claims that, because the balanced difference quotient is more accurate, it would be better to use that instead of the usual difference quotient when computing the derivative algebraically. Comment on this advice.

62. Use the balanced difference quotient formula,

$$f'(a) = \lim_{h\to 0} \frac{f(a+h) - f(a-h)}{2h},$$

to compute $f'(3)$ when $f(x) = x^2$. What do you find?

63. ▼ A certain function f has the property that $f'(a)$ does not exist. How is that reflected in the attempt to compute $f'(a)$ algebraically?

64. ▼ One cannot put $h = 0$ in the formula

$$f'(a) = \lim_{h\to 0} \frac{f(a+h) - f(a)}{h}$$

for the derivative of f. (See Exercise 56.) However, in the last step of each of the computations in the text, we are effectively setting $h = 0$ when taking the limit. What is going on here?

Practice Problems 10.6, Part 1

A ball is tossed straight up into the air from a bridge, and its height above the ground t seconds after it is thrown is $f(t) = -16t^2 + 132t + 76$ feet.

1. How high above the ground is the bridge?

2. Write a function $A(b)$ that gives the average velocity of the ball from $t = 0$ to $t = b$ seconds. Use that function to calculate the average velocity of the ball the first three seconds it is in the air, and label your result appropriately.

3. **Using an appropriate limit**, calculate $\left.\dfrac{df}{dt}\right|_{t=2}$. Indicate what this quantity represents, including an appropriate label in your response.

Practice Problems 10.6, Part 2

It is estimated that x weeks from now, the total number of rats that have been caught in traps set around a large industrial area will be $R(x) = 160x - 4x^2$, where $0 \le x \le 20$.

1. Using an appropriate limit, calculate $R'(x)$.

2. Find a point in time where the (instantaneous) rate per week at which rats are being caught matches the average rate per week that rats are being caught over the entire 20-week period.

CHAPTER 10 REVIEW

KEY CONCEPTS

Website www.WanerMath.com
Go to the Website at www.WanerMath.com to find a comprehensive and interactive Web-based summary of Chapter 10.

10.1 Limits: Numerical and Graphical Viewpoints

$\lim_{x\to a} f(x) = L$ means that $f(x)$ approaches L as x approaches a *p. 690*
What it means for a limit to exist *p. 691*
Limits at infinity *p. 693*
Estimating limits graphically *p. 693*
Interpreting limits in real-world situations *p. 696*

10.2 Limits and Continuity

f is continuous at a if $\lim_{x\to a} f(x)$ exists and $\lim_{x\to a} f(x) = f(a)$ *p. 702*
Discontinuous, continuous on domain *p. 702*
Determining whether a given function is continuous *p. 703*

10.3 Limits and Continuity: Algebraic Viewpoint

Closed-form function *p. 708*
Limits of closed form functions *p. 709*
Simplifying to obtain limits *p. 709*
The indeterminate form 0/0 *p. 710*
The determinate form *k*/0 *p. 711*
Limits of piecewise-defined functions *p. 712*
Limits at infinity *p. 713*
Determinate and indeterminate forms *p. 716*

10.4 Average Rate of Change

Average rate of change of $f(x)$ over $[a, b]$: $\dfrac{\Delta f}{\Delta x} = \dfrac{f(b) - f(a)}{b - a}$ *p. 724*
Average rate of change as slope of the secant line *p. 725*
Computing the average rate of change from a graph *p. 726*
Computing the average rate of change from a formula *p. 727*
Computing the average rate of change over short intervals $[a, a + h]$ *p. 728*

10.5 Derivatives: Numerical and Graphical Viewpoints

Instantaneous rate of change of $f(x)$ (derivative of f at a);
$f'(a) = \lim_{h\to 0} \dfrac{f(a+h) - f(a)}{h}$ *p. 738*
The derivative as slope of the tangent line *p. 742*
Quick approximation of the derivative *p. 743*
$\dfrac{d}{dx}$ Notation *p. 745*
The derivative as velocity *p. 745*
Average and instantaneous velocity *p. 746*
The derivative function *p. 747*
Graphing the derivative function with technology *p. 748*

10.6 Derivatives: Algebraic Viewpoint

Derivative at the point $x = a$:
$f'(a) = \lim_{h\to 0} \dfrac{f(a+h) - f(a)}{h}$ *p. 761*
Derivative function:
$f'(x) = \lim_{h\to 0} \dfrac{f(x+h) - f(x)}{h}$ *p. 762*
Examples of the computation of $f'(x)$ *p. 763*
$f(x) = |x|$ is not differentiable at $x = 0$ *p. 765*

REVIEW EXERCISES

T indicates exercises that must be solved using technology

Numerically *estimate whether the limits in Exercises 1–4 exist. If a limit does exist, give its approximate value.*

1. $\lim_{x\to 3} \dfrac{x^2 - x - 6}{x - 3}$ **2.** $\lim_{x\to 3} \dfrac{x^2 - 2x - 6}{x - 3}$

3. $\lim_{x\to -1} \dfrac{|x+1|}{x^2 - x - 2}$ **4.** $\lim_{x\to -1} \dfrac{|x+1|}{x^2 + x - 2}$

In Exercises 5 and 6, the graph of a function f is shown. Graphically determine whether the given limits exist. If a limit does exist, give its approximate value.

5.

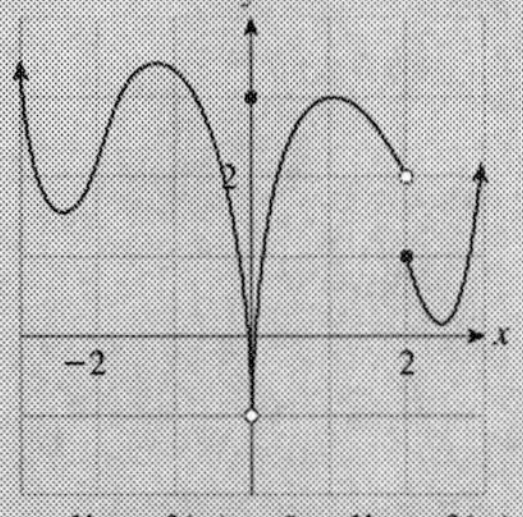

a. $\lim_{x\to 0} f(x)$ **b.** $\lim_{x\to 1} f(x)$
c. $\lim_{x\to 2} f(x)$

6.

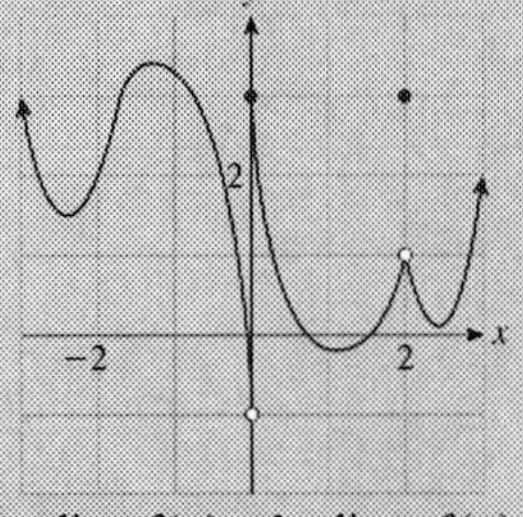

a. $\lim_{x\to 0} f(x)$ **b.** $\lim_{x\to -2} f(x)$
c. $\lim_{x\to 2} f(x)$

Calculate the limits in Exercises 7–30 algebraically. If a limit does not exist, say why.

7. $\lim_{x\to -2} \dfrac{x^2}{x - 3}$ **8.** $\lim_{x\to 3} \dfrac{x^2 - 9}{2x - 6}$

9. $\lim_{x\to -2} \dfrac{x^2 - 4}{x^3 + 2x^2}$ **10.** $\lim_{x\to -1} \dfrac{x^2 - 9}{2x - 6}$

11. $\lim_{x\to 0} \dfrac{x}{2x^2 - x}$ **12.** $\lim_{x\to 1} \dfrac{x^2 - 9}{x - 1}$

13. $\lim_{x\to -1} \dfrac{x^2 + 3x}{x^2 - x - 2}$ **14.** $\lim_{x\to -1^+} \dfrac{x^2 + 1}{x^2 + 3x + 2}$

15. $\lim_{x\to 8} \dfrac{x^2 - 6x - 16}{x^2 - 9x + 8}$ **16.** $\lim_{x\to 4} \dfrac{x^2 + 3x}{x^2 - 8x + 16}$

17. $\lim_{x\to 4} \dfrac{x^2 + 8}{x^2 - 2x - 8}$ **18.** $\lim_{x\to 6} \dfrac{x^2 - 5x - 6}{x^2 - 36}$

19. $\lim_{x\to 1/2} \dfrac{x^2 + 8}{4x^2 - 4x + 1}$ **20.** $\lim_{x\to 1/2} \dfrac{x^2 + 3x}{2x^2 + 3x - 1}$

21. $\lim_{x\to +\infty} \dfrac{10x^2 + 300x + 1}{5x^3 + 2}$ **22.** $\lim_{x\to +\infty} \dfrac{2x^4 + 20x^3}{1{,}000x^6 + 6}$

23. $\lim_{x\to -\infty} \dfrac{x^2 - x - 6}{x - 3}$ **24.** $\lim_{x\to +\infty} \dfrac{x^2 - x - 6}{4x^2 - 3}$

25. $\lim_{t \to +\infty} \dfrac{-5}{5 + 5.3(3^{2t})}$

26. $\lim_{t \to +\infty} \left(3 + \dfrac{2}{e^{4t}}\right)$

27. $\lim_{x \to +\infty} \dfrac{2}{5 + 4e^{-3x}}$

28. $\lim_{x \to +\infty} (4e^{3x} + 12)$

29. $\lim_{t \to +\infty} \dfrac{1 + 2^{-3t}}{1 + 5.3e^{-t}}$

30. $\lim_{x \to -\infty} \dfrac{8 + 0.5^x}{2 - 3^{2x}}$

In Exercises 31–34, find the average rate of change of the given function over the interval $[a, a + h]$ for $h = 1, 0.01,$ and 0.001. (Round answers to four decimal places.) Then estimate the slope of the tangent line to the graph of the function at a.

31. $f(x) = \frac{1}{x+1}$; $a = 0$

32. $f(x) = x^x$; $a = 2$

33. $f(x) = e^{2x}$; $a = 0$

34. $f(x) = \ln(2x)$; $a = 1$

*In Exercises 35–38, you are given the graph of a function with four points marked. Determine at which (if any) of these points the derivative of the function is: **(a)** −1, **(b)** 0, **(c)** 1, and **(d)** 2.*

35.

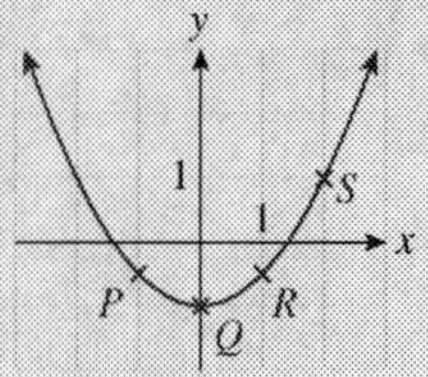

36.

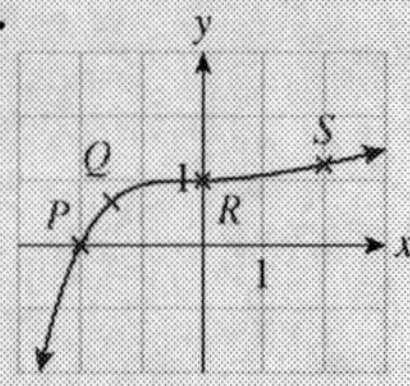

37.

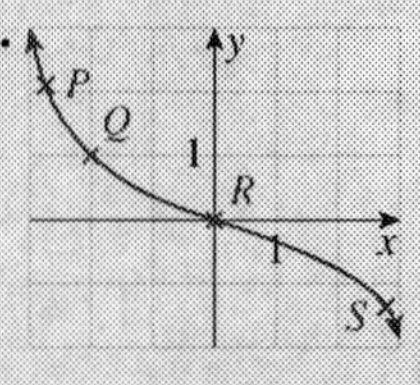

38.

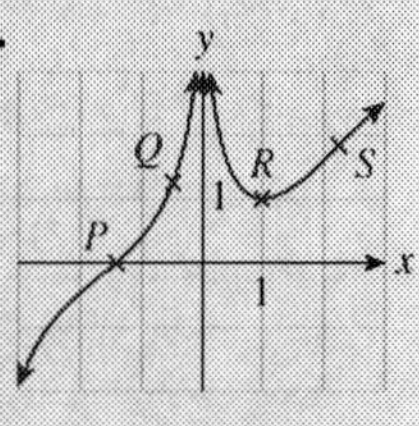

39. Let f have the graph shown.

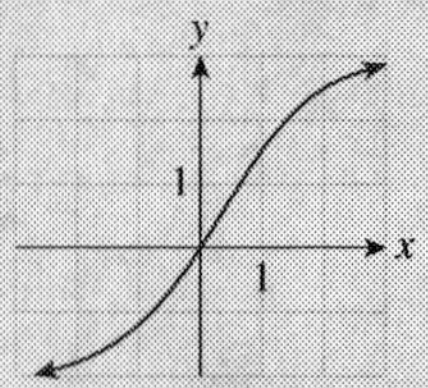

Select the correct answer.

a. The average rate of change of f over the interval [0, 2] is
(A) greater than $f'(0)$. **(B)** less than $f'(0)$.
(C) approximately equal to $f'(0)$.

b. The average rate of change of f over the interval $[-1, 1]$ is
(A) greater than $f'(0)$. **(B)** less than $f'(0)$.
(C) approximately equal to $f'(0)$.

c. Over the interval [0, 2], the instantaneous rate of change of f is
(A) increasing. **(B)** decreasing.
(C) neither increasing nor decreasing.

d. Over the interval $[-2, 2]$, the instantaneous rate of change of f is
(A) increasing, then decreasing.
(B) decreasing, then increasing.
(C) approximately constant.

e. When $x = 2$, $f(x)$ is
(A) approximately 1 and increasing at a rate of about 2.5 units per unit of x.
(B) approximately 1.2 and increasing at a rate of about 1 unit per unit of x.
(C) approximately 2.5 and increasing at a rate of about 0.5 units per unit of x.
(D) approximately 2.5 and increasing at a rate of about 2.5 units per unit of x.

40. Let f have the graph shown.

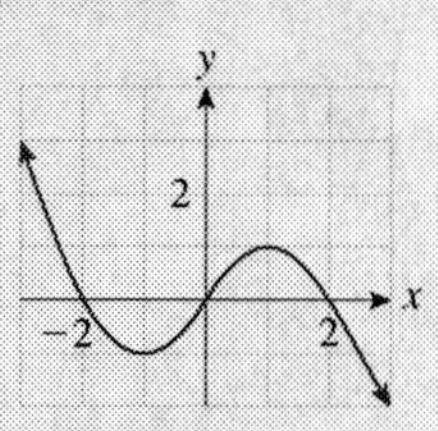

Select the correct answer.

a. The average rate of change of f over the interval [0, 1] is
(A) greater than $f'(0)$. **(B)** less than $f'(0)$.
(C) approximately equal to $f'(0)$.

b. The average rate of change of f over the interval [0, 2] is
(A) greater than $f'(1)$. **(B)** less than $f'(1)$.
(C) approximately equal to $f'(1)$.

c. Over the interval $[-2, 0]$, the instantaneous rate of change of f is
(A) increasing. **(B)** decreasing.
(C) neither increasing nor decreasing.

d. Over the interval $[-2, 2]$, the instantaneous rate of change of f is
(A) increasing, then decreasing.
(B) decreasing, then increasing.
(C) approximately constant.

e. When $x = 0$, $f(x)$ is
(A) approximately 0 and increasing at a rate of about 1.5 units per unit of x.
(B) approximately 0 and decreasing at a rate of about 1.5 units per unit of x.
(C) approximately 1.5 and neither increasing nor decreasing.
(D) approximately 0 and neither increasing nor decreasing.

In Exercises 41–44, use the definition of the derivative to calculate the derivative of each of the given functions algebraically.

41. $f(x) = x^2 + x$

42. $f(x) = 3x^2 - x + 1$

43. $f(x) = 1 - \dfrac{2}{x}$

44. $f(x) = \dfrac{1}{x} + 1$

T *In Exercises 45–48, use technology to graph the derivative of the given function. In each case, choose a range of x-values and y-values that shows the interesting features of the graph.*

45. $f(x) = 10x^5 + \dfrac{1}{2}x^4 - x + 2$

46. $f(x) = \frac{10}{x^5} + \frac{1}{2x^4} - \frac{1}{x} + 2$

47. $f(x) = 3x^3 + 3\sqrt[3]{x}$

48. $f(x) = \frac{2}{x^{2.1}} - \frac{x^{0.1}}{2}$

APPLICATIONS: OHaganBooks.com

49. ***Stock Investments*** OHaganBooks.com CEO John O'Hagan has terrible luck with stocks. The following graph shows the value of Fly-By-Night Airlines stock that he bought acting on a "hot tip" from Marjory Duffin (CEO of Duffin House publishers and a close business associate):

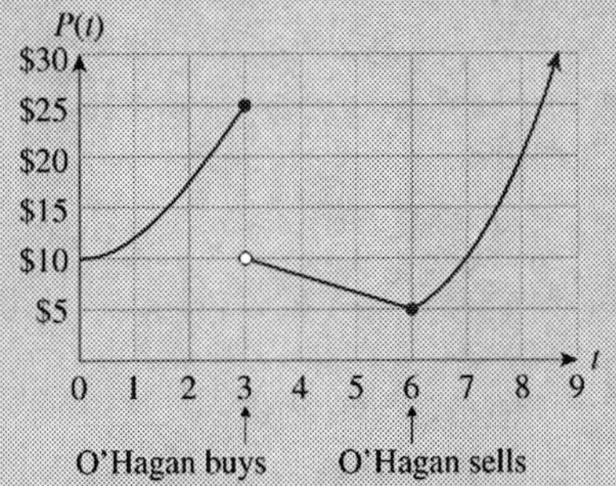

a. Compute $P(3)$, $\lim_{t\to 3^-} P(t)$ and $\lim_{t\to 3^+} P(t)$. Does $\lim_{t\to 3} P(t)$ exist? Interpret your answers in terms of Fly-By-Night stock.

b. Is P continuous at $t = 6$? Is P differentiable at $t = 6$? Interpret your answers in terms of Fly-By-Night stock.

50. ***Stock Investments*** John O'Hagan's golf partner Juan Robles seems to have had better luck with his investment in Gapple Gomputer Inc. stocks as shown in the following graph:

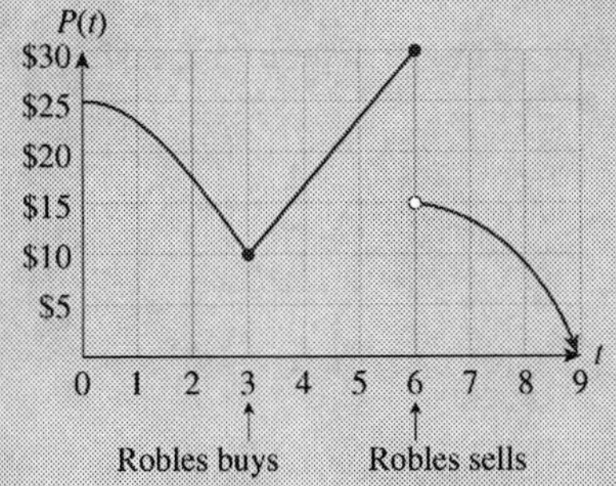

a. Compute $P(6)$, $\lim_{t\to 6^-} P(t)$ and $\lim_{t\to 6^+} P(t)$. Does $\lim_{t\to 6} P(t)$ exist? Interpret your answers in terms of Gapple stock.

b. Is P continuous at $t = 3$? Is P differentiable at $t = 3$? Interpret your answers in terms of Gapple stock.

51. ***Real Estate*** Marjory Duffin has persuaded John O'Hagan to consider investing a portion of OHaganBooks.com profits in real estate, now that the real estate market seems to have bottomed out. A real estate broker friend of hers emailed her the following (somewhat optimistic) graph from brokersadvocacy.com:[76]

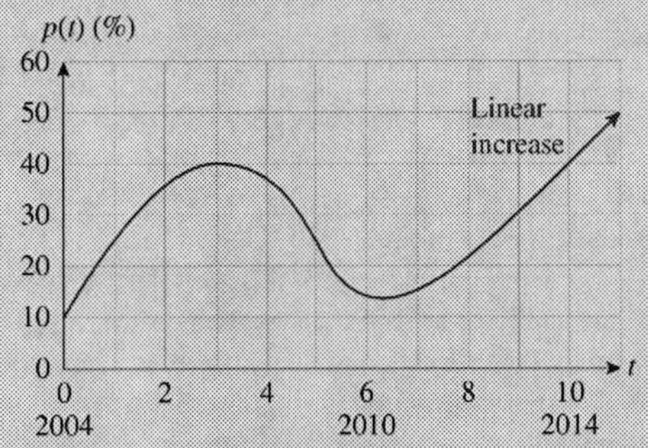

Here, $p(t)$ is the home price percentage over the 2003 level.

a. Assuming the trend shown in the graph were to continue indefinitely, estimate $\lim_{t\to 3} p(t)$ and $\lim_{t\to +\infty} p(t)$ and interpret the results.

b. Estimate $\lim_{t\to +\infty} p'(t)$ and interpret the result.

52. ***Advertising Costs*** OHaganBooks.com has (on further advice from Marjory Duffin) mounted an aggressive online marketing strategy. The following graph shows the weekly cost of this campaign for the six-week period since the start of July (t is time in weeks):

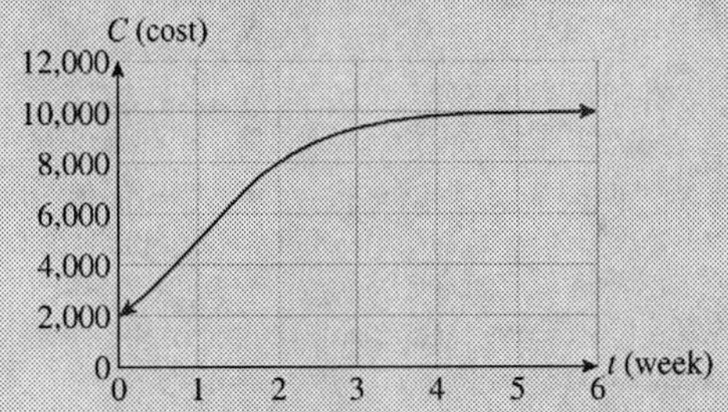

a. Assuming the trend shown in the graph were to continue indefinitely, estimate $\lim_{t\to 2} C(t)$ and $\lim_{t\to +\infty} C(t)$ and interpret the results.

b. Estimate $\lim_{t\to +\infty} C'(t)$ and interpret the result.

53. ***Sales*** Since the start of July, OHaganBooks.com has seen its weekly sales increase, as shown in the following table:

Week	1	2	3	4	5	6
Sales (books)	6,500	7,000	7,200	7,800	8,500	9,000

a. What was the average rate of increase of weekly sales over this entire period?

b. During which 1-week interval(s) did the rate of increase of sales exceed the average rate?

c. During which 2-week interval(s) did the weekly sales rise at the highest average rate, and what was that average rate?

[76] Authors' note: As of August 2012, brokersadvocacy.com is unregistered.

54. ***Rising Sea Level*** Marjory Duffin recently purchased a beachfront condominium in New York and is now in a panic, having just seen some disturbing figures about rising sea levels (sea levels as measured in New York relative to the 1900 level).[77]

Year since 1900	0	25	50	75	100	125
Sea Level (mm)	0	60	140	240	310	390

a. What was the average rate of increase of the sea level over this entire period?
b. During which 25-year interval(s) did the rate of increase of the sea level exceed the average rate?
c. Marjory Duffin's condominium is about 2 meters above sea level. Using the average rate of change from part (a), estimate how long she has before the sea rises to her condominium.

55. ***Real Estate*** The following graph (see Exercise 51) shows the home price index chart emailed to Marjory Duffin by a real estate broker:

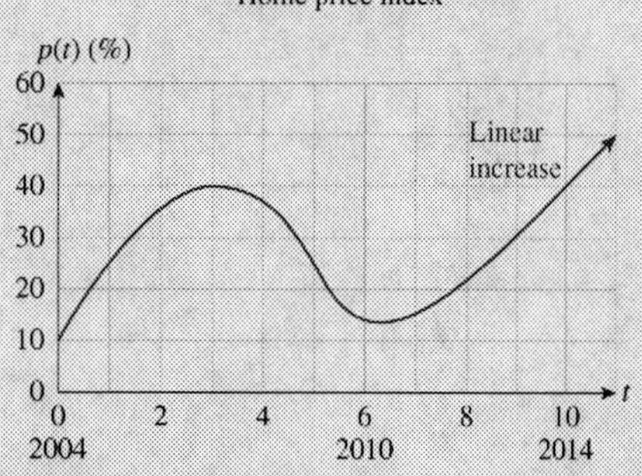

Use the graph to answer the following questions:
a. What was the average rate of change of the index over the 10-year period beginning 2004?
b. What was the average rate of change of the index over the period [3, 10]?
c. Which of the following is correct? Over the period [4, 6],
(A) The rate of change of the index increased.
(B) The rate of change of the index increased and then decreased.
(C) The rate of change of the index decreased.
(D) The rate of change of the index decreased and then increased.

56. ***Advertising Costs*** The following graph (see Exercise 52) shows the weekly cost of OHaganBooks.com's online ad campaign for the 6-week period since the start of July (t is time in weeks).

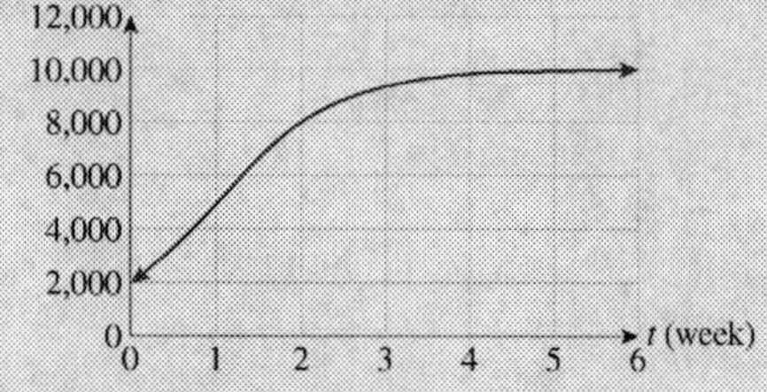

Use the graph to answer the following questions:
a. What was the average rate of change of cost over the entire six-week period?
b. What was the average rate of change of cost over the period [2, 6]?
c. Which of the following is correct? Over the period [2, 6],
(A) The rate of change of cost increased and the cost increased.
(B) The rate of change of cost decreased and the cost increased.
(C) The rate of change of cost increased and the cost decreased.
(D) The rate of change of cost decreased and the cost decreased.

57. ***Sales*** OHaganBooks.com fits the curve

$$w(t) = 36t^2 + 250t + 6{,}240 \quad (0 \le t \le 6)$$

to its weekly sales figures from Exercise 53, as shown in the following graph:

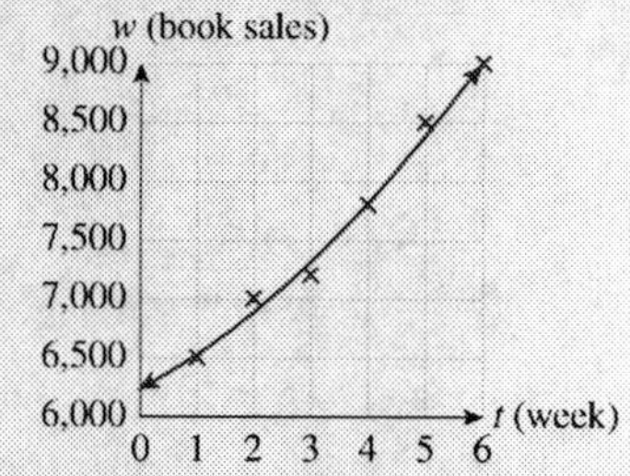

a. Compute the derivative function $w'(t)$.
b. According to the model, what was the rate of increase of sales at the beginning of the second week ($t = 1$)?
c. If we extrapolate the model, what would be the rate of increase of weekly sales at the beginning of the 8th week ($t = 7$)?

58. ***Sea Levels*** Marjory Duffin fit the curve

$$s(t) = 0.002t^2 + 3t - 6.4 \quad (0 \le t \le 125)$$

to her sea level figures from Exercise 54, as shown in the following graph:

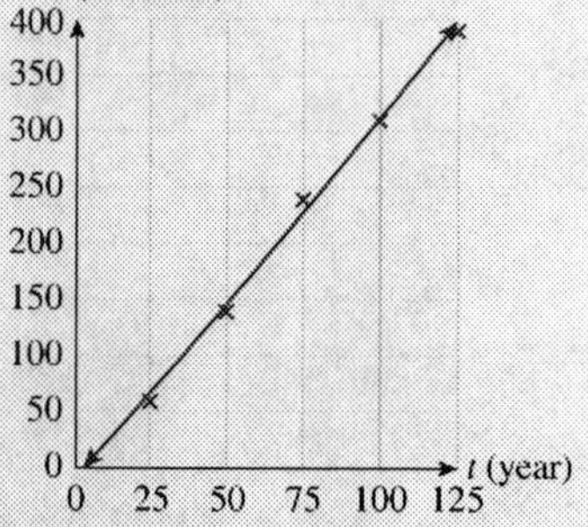

a. Compute the derivative function $s'(t)$.
b. According to the model, what was the rate of increase of the sea level in 2000 ($t = 100$)?
c. If we extrapolate the model, what would be the rate of increase of the sea level in 2100 ($t = 200$)?

[77] The 2025 level is a projection. Source: New England Integrated Science & Assessment (www.neisa.unh.edu/Climate/index.html).

Norbert Schaefer/CORBIS

Reducing Sulfur Emissions

The Environmental Protection Agency (EPA) wishes to formulate a policy that will encourage utilities to reduce sulfur emissions. Its goal is to reduce annual emissions of sulfur dioxide by a total of 10 million tons from the current level of 25 million tons by imposing a fixed charge for every ton of sulfur released into the environment per year. As a consultant to the EPA, you must determine the amount to be charged per ton of sulfur emissions.

You would like first to know the cost to the utility industry of reducing sulfur emissions. In other words, you would like to have a cost function of the form

$$C(q) = \text{Cost of removing } q \text{ tons of sulfur dioxide.}$$

Unfortunately, you do not have such a function handy. You do, however, have the following data, which show the *marginal* cost (that is, the *rate of change* of cost) to the utility industry of reducing sulfur emissions at several levels of reduction.[78]

Reduction (tons) q	8,000,000	10,000,000	12,000,000
Marginal Cost ($ per ton) $C'(q)$	270	360	779

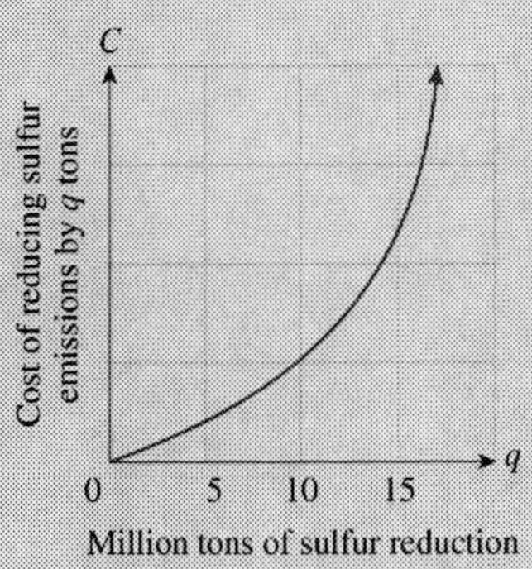

Figure 40

The table tells you that $C'(8{,}000{,}000) = \$270$ per ton, $C'(10{,}000{,}000) = \$360$ per ton, and $C'(12{,}000{,}000) = \$779$ per ton. Recalling that $C'(q)$ is the slope of the tangent to the graph of the cost function, you can see from the table that this slope is positive and increasing as q increases, so the graph of the cost function has the general shape shown in Figure 40.

Notice that the slope (additional cost) is increasing as you move to the right, so the utility industry has no cost incentive to reduce emissions further, as it costs the industry significantly more per ton for each additional ton of sulfur it removes. What you would like—if the goal of reducing total emissions by 10 million tons is to be reached—is that, somehow, the imposition of a fixed charge for every ton of sulfur dioxide released will *alter* the form of the cost curve so that it has the general shape shown in Figure 41. In this ideal curve, the cost D to utilities is lowest at a reduction level of 10 million tons, so if the utilities act to minimize cost, they can be expected to reduce emissions by 10 million tons, which is exactly the EPA goal! From the graph, you can see that the tangent line to the curve at the point where $q = 10$ million tons is horizontal, and thus has zero slope: $D'(10{,}000{,}000) = \$0$ per ton. Further, the slope $D'(q)$ is negative for values of q to the left of 10 million tons and positive for values to the right.

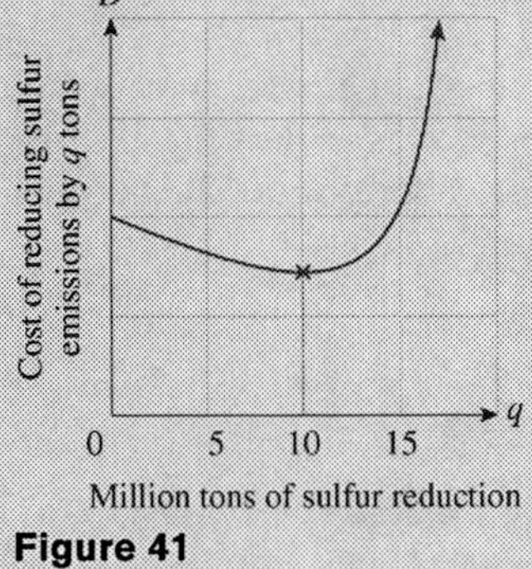

Figure 41

So, how much should the EPA charge per ton of sulfur released into the environment? Suppose the EPA charges $\$k$ per ton, so that

$$\text{Emission charge to utilities} = k \times \text{Sulfur emissions.}$$

It is your job to calculate k. Because you are working with q as the independent variable, you decide that it would be best to formulate the emission charge as a function of q. However, q represents the amount by which sulfur emissions have been reduced from the original 25 million tons; that is, the amount by which sulfur emissions are *lower than* the original 25 million tons:

$$q = 25{,}000{,}000 - \text{Sulfur emissions.}$$

[78] These figures were produced in a computerized study of reducing sulfur emissions from the 1980 level by the given amounts. Source: Congress of the United States, Congressional Budget Office, *Curbing Acid Rain: Cost, Budget and Coal Market Effects* (Washington, DC: Government Printing Office, 1986): xx, xxii, 23, 80.

Thus, the total annual emission charge to the utilities is

$$k \times \text{Sulfur emissions} = k(25{,}000{,}000 - q) = 25{,}000{,}000k - kq.$$

This results in a total cost to the utilities of

$$\text{Total cost} = \text{Cost of reducing emissions} + \text{Emission charge}$$
$$D(q) = C(q) + 25{,}000{,}000k - kq.$$

You now recall from calculus that the derivative of a sum of two functions is the sum of their derivatives (you will see why in Section 11.1*), so the derivative of D is given by

* This statement makes intuitive sense: For instance, if C is changing at a rate of 3 units per second and D is changing at a rate of 2 units per second, then their sum is changing at a rate of $3 + 2 = 5$ units per second.

$$D'(q) = \text{Derivative of } C + \text{Derivative of } (25{,}000{,}000k - kq).$$

The function $y = 25{,}000{,}000k - kq$ is a linear function of q with slope $-k$ and intercept 25,000,000k. Thus its derivative is just its slope: $-k$. Therefore:

$$D'(q) = C'(q) - k.$$

Remember that you want

$$D'(10{,}000{,}000) = 0.$$

Thus,

$$C'(10{,}000{,}000) - k = 0.$$

Referring to the table, you see that

$$360 - k = 0$$

or

$$k = \$360 \text{ per ton.}$$

In other words, all you need to do is set the emission charge at $k = \$360$ per ton of sulfur emitted. Further, to ensure that the resulting curve will have the general shape shown in Figure 40, you would like to have $D'(q)$ negative for $q < 10{,}000{,}000$ and positive for $q > 10{,}000{,}000$. To check this, write

$$D'(q) = C'(q) - k$$
$$= C'(q) - 360$$

and refer to the table to obtain

$$D'(8{,}000{,}000) = 270 - 360 = -90 < 0 \checkmark$$

and

$$D'(12{,}000{,}000) = 779 - 360 = 419 > 0 \checkmark$$

Thus, based on the given data, the resulting curve will have the shape you require. You therefore inform the EPA that an annual emissions charge of \$360 per ton of sulfur released into the environment will create the desired incentive: to reduce sulfur emissions by 10 million tons per year.

One week later, you are informed that this charge would be unrealistic because the utilities cannot possibly afford such a cost. You are asked whether there is an alternative plan that accomplishes the 10-million-ton reduction goal and yet is cheaper to the utilities by \$5 billion per year. You then look at your expression for the emission charge

$$25{,}000{,}000k - kq$$

and notice that, if you decrease this amount by \$5 billion, the derivative will not change at all because it will still have the same slope (only the intercept is affected). Thus, you propose the following revised formula for the emission charge:

$$\begin{aligned} &25{,}000{,}000k - kq - 5{,}000{,}000{,}000 \\ &= 25{,}000{,}000(360) - 360q - 5{,}000{,}000{,}000 \\ &= 4{,}000{,}000{,}000 - 360q. \end{aligned}$$

At the expected reduction level of 10 million tons, the total amount paid by the utilities will then be

$$4{,}000{,}000{,}000 - 360(10{,}000{,}000) = \$400{,}000{,}000.$$

Thus, your revised proposal is the following: Impose an annual emissions charge of \$360 per ton of sulfur released into the environment and hand back \$5 billion in the form of subsidies. The effect of this policy will be to cause the utilities industry to reduce sulfur emissions by 10 million tons per year and will result in \$400 million in annual revenues to the government.

Notice that this policy also provides an incentive for the utilities to search for cheaper ways to reduce emissions. For instance, if they lowered costs to the point where they could achieve a reduction level of 12 million tons, they would have a total emission charge of

$$4{,}000{,}000{,}000 - 360(12{,}000{,}000) = -\$320{,}000{,}000.$$

The fact that this is negative means that the government would be paying the utilities industry \$320 million more in annual subsidies than the industry is paying in per ton emission charges.

EXERCISES

1. Excluding subsidies, what should the annual emission charge be if the goal is to reduce sulfur emissions by 8 million tons?
2. Excluding subsidies, what should the annual emission charge be if the goal is to reduce sulfur emissions by 12 million tons?
3. What is the *marginal emission charge* (derivative of emission charge) in your revised proposal (as stated before the exercise set)? What is the relationship between the marginal cost of reducing sulfur emissions before emissions charges are implemented and the marginal emission charge, at the optimal reduction under your revised proposal?
4. We said that the revised policy provided an incentive for utilities to find cheaper ways to reduce emissions. How would $C(q)$ have to change to make 12 million tons the optimum reduction?
5. What change in $C(q)$ would make 8 million tons the optimum reduction?
6. If the scenario in Exercise 5 took place, what would the EPA have to do in order to make 10 million tons the optimal reduction once again?
7. Due to intense lobbying by the utility industry, you are asked to revise the proposed policy so that the utility industry will pay no charge if sulfur emissions are reduced by the desired 10 million tons. How can you accomplish this?
8. Suppose that instead of imposing a fixed charge per ton of emission, you decide to use a sliding scale, so that the total charge to the industry for annual emissions of x tons will be $\$kx^2$ for some k. What must k be to again make 10 million tons the optimum reduction? HINT [The derivative of kx^2 is $2kx$.]

TI-83/84 Plus Technology Guide

Section 10.1

Example 1 (page 689) Use a table to estimate the following limits.

a. $\lim_{x \to 2} \frac{x^3 - 8}{x - 2}$ **b.** $\lim_{x \to 0} \frac{e^{2x} - 1}{x}$

Solution with Technology

On the TI-83/84 Plus, use the table feature to automate these computations as follows:

1. Define `Y1=(X^3-8)/(X-2)` for part (a) or `Y1=(e^(2X)-1)/X` for part (b).
2. Press 2ND TABLE to list its values for the given values of x. (If the calculator does not allow you to enter values of x, press 2ND TBLSET and set `Indpnt` to `Ask`).

   Here is the table showing some of the values for part (a):

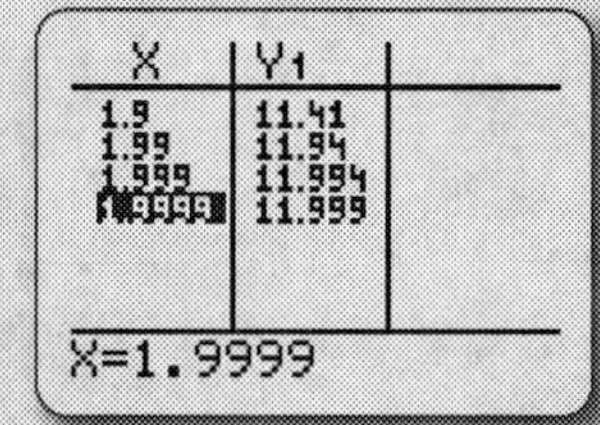

3. For part (b) use `Y1=(e^(2X)-1)/X` and use values of x approaching 0 from either side.

Section 10.4

Example 3 (page 727) The price of an ounce of gold can be approximated by the function

$$G(t) = 5t^2 - 85t + 1{,}762 \quad (7.5 \le t \le 10.5)$$

where t is time in hours. ($t = 8$ represents 8:00 am.) What was the average rate of change of the price of gold over the $1\frac{1}{2}$-hour period starting at 8:00 am (the interval [8, 9.5] on the t-axis)?

Solution with Technology

On the TI-83/84 Plus:

1. Enter the function G as `Y1` (using X for t):

   `Y1=5X²-85X+1762`

2. Now find the average rate of change over [8, 9.5] by evaluating the following on the home screen:

   `(Y1(9.5)-Y1(8))/(9.5-8)`

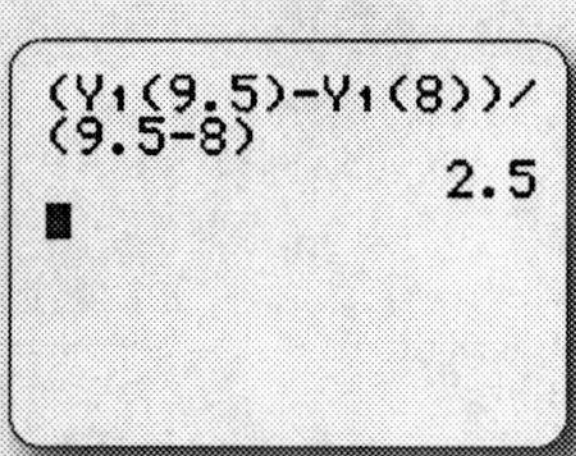

As shown on the screen, the average rate is of change is 2.5.

Example 4 (page 728) Continuing with Example 3, use technology to compute the average rate of change of

$$G(t) = 5t^2 - 85t + 1{,}762 \qquad (7.5 \le t \le 10.5)$$

over the intervals $[8, 8 + h]$, where $h = 1$, 0.1, 0.01, 0.001, and 0.0001.

Solution with Technology

1. As in Example 4, enter the function G as `Y1` (using X for t):

   `Y1=5X²-85X+1762`

2. Now find the average rate of change for $h = 1$ by evaluating, on the home screen,

   `(Y1(8+1)-Y1(8))/1,`

   which gives 0.

3. To evaluate for $h = 0.1$, recall the expression using 2ND ENTER and then change the 1, both places it occurs, to 0.1, getting

   `(Y1(8+0.1)-Y1(8))/0.1,`

   which gives −4.95.

4. Continuing, we can evaluate the average rate of change for all the desired values of h:

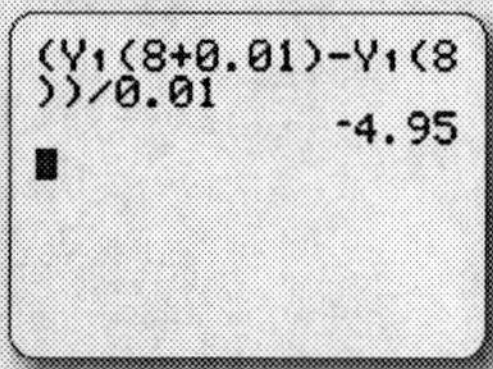

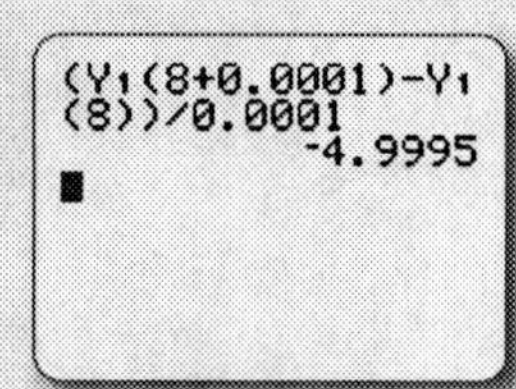

Section 10.5

Example 2 (page 743) Calculate an approximate value of $f'(1.5)$ if $f(x) = x^2 - 4x$, and then find the equation of the tangent line at the point on the graph where $x = 1.5$.

Solution with Technology

1. In the TI-83/84 Plus, enter the function f as `Y1`

   `Y1=X^2-4*X`

2. Go to the home screen to compute the approximations:

   `(Y1(1.5001)-Y1(1.5))/0.0001` — Usual difference quotient

   `(Y1(1.5001)-Y1(1.4999))/0.0002` — Balanced difference quotient

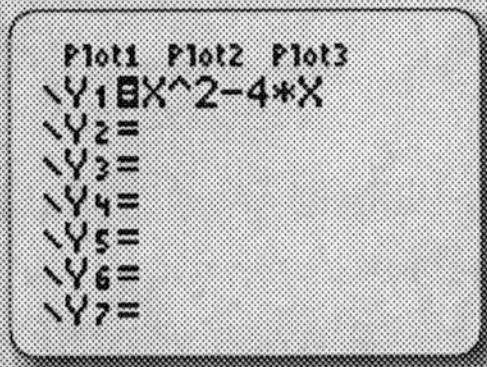

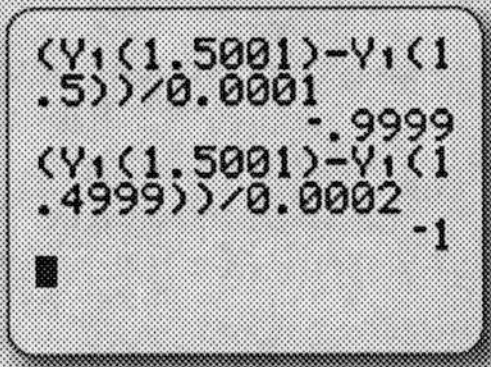

From the display on the right, we find that the difference quotient quick approximation is -0.9999 and the balanced difference quotient quick approximation is -1, which is in fact the exact value of $f'(1.5)$. See the discussion in the text for the calculation of the equation of the tangent line.

Example 4 (page 748) Use technology to graph the derivative of $f(x) = -2x^2 + 6x + 5$ for values of x in starting at -5.

Solution with Technology

On the TI-83/84 Plus, the easiest way to obtain quick approximations of the derivative of a given function is to use the built-in `nDeriv` function, which calculates balanced difference quotients.

1. On the `Y=` screen, first enter the function:

   `Y1=-2X^2+6X+5`

2. Then set

   `Y2=nDeriv(Y1,X,X)` — For `nDeriv` press [MATH] [8]

   which is the TI-83/84 Plus's approximation of $f'(x)$ (see figure on the left below). Alternatively, we can enter the balanced difference quotient directly:

   `Y2=(Y1(X+0.001)-Y1(X-0.001))/0.002`

   (The TI-83/84 Plus uses $h = 0.001$ by default in the balanced difference quotient when calculating `nDeriv`, but this can be changed by giving a value of h as a fourth argument, like `nDeriv(Y1,X,X,0.0001)`.) To see a table of approximate values of the derivative, we press 2ND TABLE and choose a collection of values for x (shown on the right below):

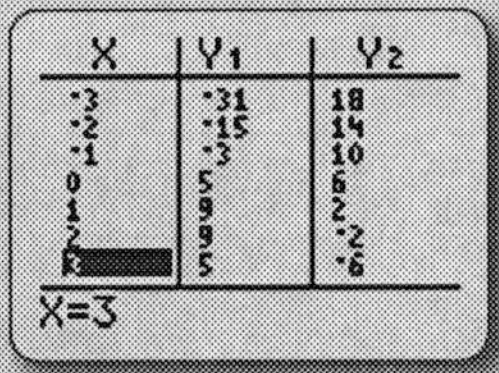

Here, `Y1` shows the value of f and `Y2` shows the values of f'.

To graph the function or its derivative, we can graph `Y1` or `Y2` in a window showing the given domain $[-5, 5]$:

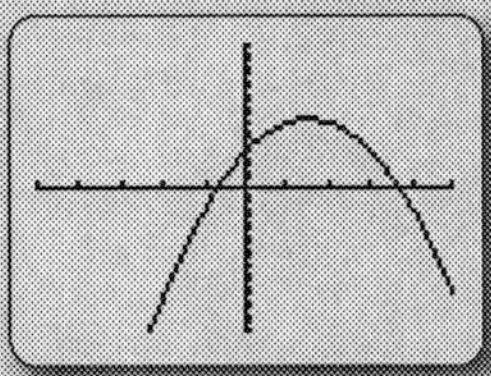

Graph of f

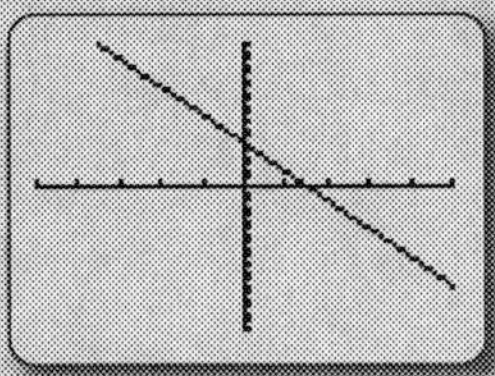

Graph of f'

SPREADSHEET Technology Guide

Section 10.1

Example 1 (page 689) Use a table to estimate the following limits.

a. $\lim_{x \to 2} \frac{x^3 - 8}{x - 2}$ **b.** $\lim_{x \to 0} \frac{e^{2x} - 1}{x}$

Solution with Technology

1. Set up your spreadsheet to duplicate the table in part (a) as follows:

	A	B	C	D
1	x	f(x)	x	f(x)
2	1.9	=(A2^3-8)/(A2-2)	2.1	
3	1.99		2.01	
4	1.999		2.001	
5	1.9999		2.0001	

↓

	A	B	C	D
1	x	f(x)	x	f(x)
2	1.9	11.41	2.1	12.61
3	1.99	11.9401	2.01	12.0601
4	1.999	11.994001	2.001	12.006001
5	1.9999	11.99940001	2.0001	12.00060001

(The formula in cell B2 is copied to columns B and D as indicated by the shading.) The values of $f(x)$ will be calculated in columns B and D.

2. For part (b), use the formula `=(EXP(2*A2)-1)/A2` in cell B2 and, in columns A and C, use values of x approaching 0 from either side.

Section 10.4

Example 3 (page 727) The price of an ounce of gold can be approximated by the function

$$G(t) = 5t^2 + 85t + 1{,}762 \quad (7.5 \le t \le 10.5)$$

where t is time in hours. ($t = 8$ represents 8:00 am.) What was the average rate of change of the price of gold over the $1\frac{1}{2}$-hour period starting at 8:00 am (the interval [8, 9.5] on the t-axis)?

Solution with Technology

To use a spreadsheet to compute the average rate of change of G:

1. Start with two columns, one for values of t and one for values of $G(t)$, which you enter using the formula for G:

```
=5*A2^2-85*A2+1762
```

	A	B
1	t	G(t)
2	8	=5*A2^2-85*A2+1762
3	9.5	

2. Next, calculate the average rate of change as shown here:

	A	B	C	D
1	t	G(t)		
2	8	1402	Rate of change over [8, 9.5]:	
3	9.5	1405.75	=(B3-B2)/(A3-A2)	

↓

	A	B	C	D
1	t	G(t)		
2	8	1402	Rate of change over [8, 9.5]:	
3	9.5	1405.75	2.5	

In Example 4, we describe another, more versatile Excel template for computing rates of change.

Example 4 (page 728) Continuing with Example 3, use technology to compute the average rate of change of

$$G(t) = 5t^2 + 85t + 1{,}762 \qquad (7.5 \le t \le 10.5)$$

over the intervals $[8, 8 + h]$, where $h = 1$, 0.1, 0.01, 0.001, and 0.0001.

Solution with Technology

The template we can use to compute the rates of change is an extension of what we used in Example 3:

	A	B	C	D	E
1	a	h	t	G(t)	Rate of Change
2	8	0.001	=A2	=5*C2^2-85*C2+1762	=(D3-D2)/(C3-C2)
3			=A2+B2		

↓

	A	B	C	D	E
1	a	h	t	G(t)	Rate of Change
2	8	0.001	8	1402	-4.995
3			8.001	1401.99501	

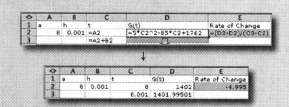

1. Column C contains the values $t = a$ and $t = a + h$ we are using for the independent variable.
2. The formula in cell E2 is the average-rate-of-change formula $\Delta G/\Delta t$. Entering the different values $h = 1$, 0.1, 0.01, 0.001, and 0.0001 in cell B2 gives the results shown in Example 4.

Section 10.5

Example 2 (page 743) Calculate an approximate value of $f'(1.5)$ if $f(x) = x^2 - 4x$, and then find the equation of the tangent line at the point on the graph where $x = 1.5$.

Solution with Technology

You can compute both the difference quotient and the balanced difference quotient approximations in a spreadsheet using the following extension of the worksheet in Example 4 in Section 10.4:

	A	B	C	D	E	F
1	a	h	x	f(x)	Diff Quotients	Balanced Diff Quotient
2	1.5	0.0001	=A2-B2	=C2^2-4*C2	=(D3-D2)/(C3-C2)	=(D4-D2)/(C4-C2)
3			=A2			
4			=A2+B2			

Notice that we get two difference quotients in column E. The first uses $h = -0.0001$ while the second uses $h = 0.0001$ and is the one we use for our quick approximation. The balanced quotient is their average (column F). The results are as follows.

	A	B	C	D	E	F
1	a	h	x	f(x)	Diff Quotients	Balanced Diff Quotient
2	1.5	0.0001	1.4999	-3.7499	-1.0001	-1
3			1.5	-3.75	-0.9999	
4			1.5001	-3.7501		

From the results shown above, we find that the difference quotient quick approximation is -0.9999 and that the balanced difference quotient quick approximation is -1, which is in fact the exact value of $f'(1.5)$. See the discussion in the text for the calculation of the equation of the tangent line.

Example 4 (page 748) Use technology to graph the derivative of $f(x) = -2x^2 + 6x + 5$ for values of x starting at -5.

Solution with Technology

1. Start with a table of values for the function f:

	A	B	C	D	E
1	x	f(x)		Xmin	-5
2	=$E$1	=-2*A2^2+6*A2+5		h	0.1
3	=A2+$E$2				
4					
5					
101					
102					

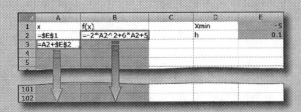

2. Next, compute approximate derivatives in Column C:

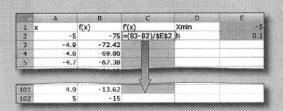

	A	B	C	D	E
1	x	f(x)	f'(x)	Xmin	-5
2	-5	-75	=(B3-B2)/$E$2	h	0.1
3	-4.9	-72.42			
4	-4.8	-69.88			
5	-4.7	-67.38			
101	4.9	-13.62			
102	5	-15			

	A	B	C	D	E
1	x	f(x)	f'(x)	Xmin	-5
2	-5	-75	25.8	h	0.1
3	-4.9	-72.42	25.4		
4	-4.8	-69.88	25		
5	-4.7	-67.38	24.6		
101	4.9	-13.62	-13.8		
102	5	-15			

You cannot paste the difference quotient formula into cell C102. (Why?) Notice that this worksheet uses the ordinary difference quotients, $[f(x+h) - f(x)]/h$. If you prefer, you can use balanced difference quotients $[f(x+h) - f(x-h)]/(2h)$, in which case cells C2 and C102 would both have to be left blank.

We now graph the function and the derivative on different graphs as follows:

1. First, graph the function f in the usual way, using Columns A and B.
2. Make a copy of this graph and click on it once. Columns A and B should be outlined, indicating that these are the columns used in the graph.
3. By dragging from the center of the bottom edge of the box, move the Column B box over to Column C as shown:

	A	B	C
96	4.4	-7.32	-11.8
97	4.5	-8.5	-12.2
98	4.6	-9.72	-12.6
99	4.7	-10.98	-13
100	4.8	-12.28	-13.4
101	4.9	-13.62	-13.8
102	5	-15	

↓

	A	B	C
96	4.4	-7.32	-11.8
97	4.5	-8.5	-12.2
98	4.6	-9.72	-12.6
99	4.7	-10.98	-13
100	4.8	-12.28	-13.4
101	4.9	-13.62	-13.8
102	5	-15	

The graph will then show the derivative (Columns A and C):

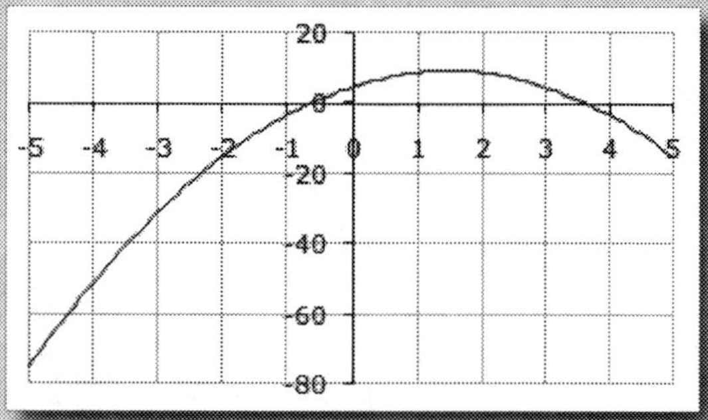

Graph of f

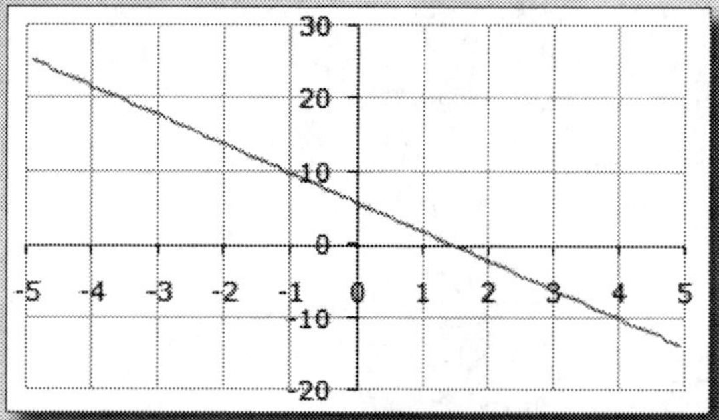

Graph of f'

CHAPTER 10 QUIZ

1. The amount of commission earned by an online brokerage firm in a month, C (in hundreds of dollars), is a function of online advertising expenditure, a, (in hundreds of dollars), so we write $C = f(a)$.
   a. What does the statement $f'(12) = 1.4$ mean in terms of advertising and commission?

   b. What does the statement $f'(12) = 0.6$ mean in terms of advertising and commission?

   c. Suppose that the company plans to spend about \$1200 on advertising. If $f'(12) = 1.4$, then should the company spend more or less on advertising? What if $f'(12) = 0.6$? Explain your conclusions.

2. Give an example of a closed-form function $f(x)$ that is continuous on its domain but has at least one point where it is not differentiable. Identify the value(s) of x where $f(x)$ fails to be differentiable.

3. Robert, one of the bright-eyed freshmen at Vile State University, was subjected to an initiation ritual prior to being allowed formal admittance to the campus math club. He was blindfolded, bound hand and foot, and dangled by a makeshift crane above a large tank of ice-cold water. The initiation procedure itself was very simple, as he was repeatedly dunked into the tank of water until he had successfully recited the first 100 digits in the decimal expansion of the number *e*. At first, he was lowered (feet first) into the tank at a fairly rapid but constant rate until completely submerged, held under water for one minute, and then raised out of the tank at a similarly rapid constant rate. He was allowed to dangle above the tank for one minute, all the while rattling off numbers. This process was repeated for two more dunkings, except in each of those he was only lowered into the water until he was submerged to the chest. With each subsequent dunking the rate at which he was lowered and raised slowed. Given this, sketch a plausible graph that shows the depth of the water in the tank as a function of time while this initiation procedure was taking place. Provide scale on your horizontal axis.

4. Suppose that $f(x)$ is some function such that $f'(4) = \lim_{h \to 0} \dfrac{\frac{3}{13+h} - \frac{3}{13}}{h}$. Propose two distinct possibilities for $f(x)$ (i.e., $f(x) = ?????????$).

5. The graph to the right shows the number of dandelions, $d = f(x)$, in Don's yard over the course of several weeks this summer. Here, x represents the number of weeks since the beginning of May.

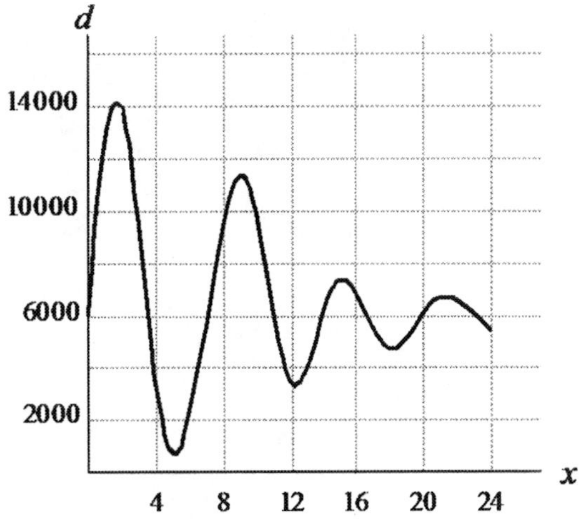

a. Estimate $f'(16)$ and interpret your result in terms of dandelions. Include units in your response.

b. Find the average rate of change in d between $x = 8$ and $x = 20$. Label your answer appropriately.

c. Arrange the following quantities in ascending order:

$$f(4), f'(10), f'(12), \frac{f(14) - f(2)}{14 - 2}$$

6. To the right is the graph of some function $f(x)$.

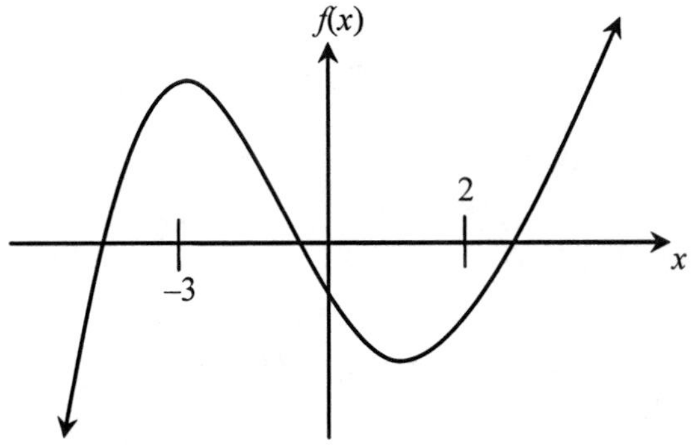

a. Suppose that I claim $f'(x) = x^2 + x$. Do you support my claim? Why or why not?

b. Suppose I also claim that the average rate of change of $f(x)$ between $x = -3$ and $x = 2$ is 4. Is that claim plausible? Why or why not?

7. To the right is the graph of a function $f(x)$. Fill in the provided table with your best estimates and sketch a graph of the corresponding derivative function, $f'(x)$. Be cautious of points of non-differentiability. You can assume that gridlines each mark one unit.

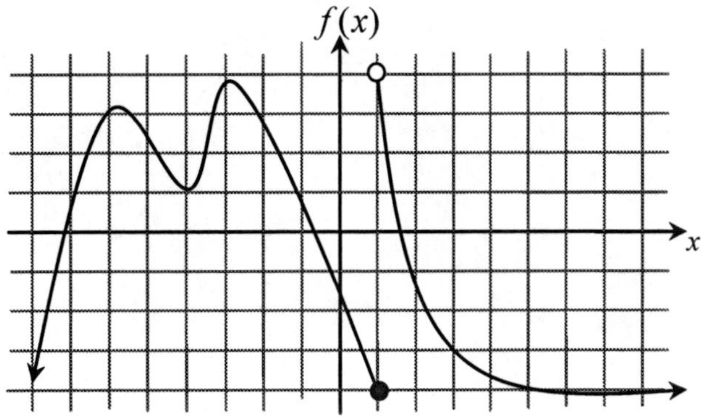

x	–6	–4	–2	0	2	4	6
$f'(x)$							

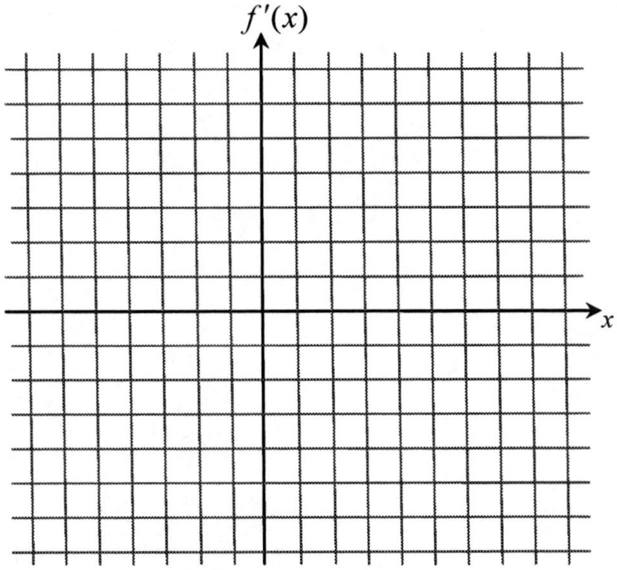

8. Consider $\lim_{x \to 0} \frac{e^x - 1}{x}$. Determine whether or not the limit exists. If the limit exists, then propose a value for the limit. Support your conclusion with appropriate graphical **and** numerical evidence (use the table and space provided).

x	-0.01	-0.001	-0.0001	0.0001	0.001	0.01
$\frac{e^x - 1}{x}$						

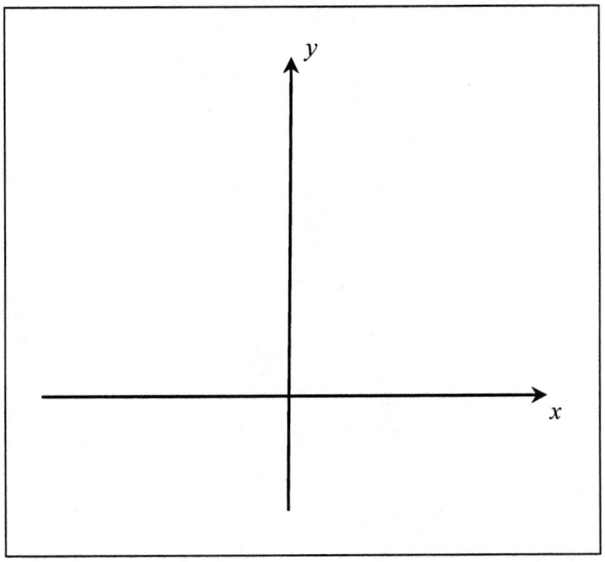

Proposal:

9. Sketch the graph of a function $f(x)$ that satisfies **all** of the following conditions. Label important points on your graph. (There are many possible graphs here.)

- $f(x)$ is defined for all values of x
- $\lim_{x \to -3} f(x)$ exists; however, $f(x)$ is not continuous at $x = -3$
- $f(x)$ is not differentiable at $x = 2$
- The average rate of change of $f(x)$ on the interval $[0,2]$ is 4
- $\lim_{x \to \infty} f(x) = 1$

11

Techniques of Differentiation with Applications

Website
www.WanerMath.com
At the Website you will find:

- Section-by-section tutorials, including game tutorials with randomized quizzes
- A detailed chapter summary
- A true/false quiz
- Additional review exercises
- Graphers, Excel tutorials, and other resources
- The following extra topic:

    Linear Approximation and Error Estimation

Case Study Projecting Market Growth

You are on the board of directors at Fullcourt Academic Press. The sales director of the high school division has just burst into your office with a proposal for an expansion strategy based on the assumption that the number of graduates from private high schools in the U.S. will grow at a rate of at least 4,000 per year through the year 2015. Because the figures actually appear to be leveling off, you are suspicious about this estimate. You would like to devise a model that predicts this trend before tomorrow's scheduled board meeting. **How do you go about doing this?**

Yuri Arcurs/Shutterstock

Introduction

In Chapter 10 we studied the concept of the derivative of a function, and we saw some of the applications for which derivatives are useful. However, computing the derivative of a function algebraically seemed to be a time-consuming process, forcing us to restrict attention to fairly simply functions.

In this chapter we develop shortcut techniques that will allow us to write down the derivative of a function directly without having to calculate any limit. These techniques will also enable us to differentiate any closed-form function—that is, any function, no matter how complicated, that can be specified by a formula involving powers, radicals, absolute values, exponents, and logarithms. (In Chapter 16 we will discuss how to add trigonometric functions to this list.) We also show how to find the derivatives of functions that are only specified *implicitly*—that is, functions for which we are not given an explicit formula for y in terms of x but only an equation relating x and y.

algebra Review

For this chapter, you should be familiar with the algebra reviewed in **Chapter 0, Sections 3 and 4.**

11.1 Derivatives of Powers, Sums, and Constant Multiples

Up to this point we have approximated derivatives using difference quotients, and we have done exact calculations using the definition of the derivative as the limit of a difference quotient. In general, we would prefer to have an exact calculation, and it is also very useful to have a formula for the derivative function when we can find one. However, the calculation of a derivative as a limit is often tedious, so it would be nice to have a quicker method. We discuss the first of the shortcut rules in this section. By the end of this chapter, we will be able to find fairly quickly the derivative of almost any function we can write.

Shortcut Formula: The Power Rule

If you look at Examples 2 and 3 in Section 10.6, you may notice a pattern:

$$f(x) = x^2 \quad \Rightarrow \quad f'(x) = 2x$$
$$f(x) = x^3 \quad \Rightarrow \quad f'(x) = 3x^2.$$

This pattern generalizes to any power of x:

Theorem 11.1 The Power Rule

If n is any constant and $f(x) = x^n$, then

$$f'(x) = nx^{n-1}.$$

Quick Examples

1. If $f(x) = x^2$, then $f'(x) = 2x^1 = 2x$.
2. If $f(x) = x^3$, then $f'(x) = 3x^2$.
3. If $f(x) = x$, rewrite as $f(x) = x^1$, so $f'(x) = 1x^0 = 1$.
4. If $f(x) = 1$, rewrite as $f(x) = x^0$, so $f'(x) = 0x^{-1} = 0$.

Website
www.WanerMath.com
At the Website you can find a proof of the power rule by following:
Everything
→ Chapter 11
→ Proof of the Power Rule

The proof of the power rule involves first studying the case when n is a positive integer, and then studying the cases of other types of exponents (negative integer, rational number, irrational number). You can find a proof at the Website.

EXAMPLE 1 Using the Power Rule for Negative and Fractional Exponents

Calculate the derivatives of the following:

a. $f(x) = \frac{1}{x}$ **b.** $f(x) = \frac{1}{x^2}$ **c.** $f(x) = \sqrt{x}$

Solution

a. Rewrite* as $f(x) = x^{-1}$. Then $f'(x) = (-1)x^{-2} = -\frac{1}{x^2}$.

b. Rewrite as $f(x) = x^{-2}$. Then $f'(x) = (-2)x^{-3} = -\frac{2}{x^3}$.

c. Rewrite as $f(x) = x^{0.5}$. Then $f'(x) = 0.5x^{-0.5} = \frac{0.5}{x^{0.5}}$. Alternatively, rewrite $f(x)$ as $x^{1/2}$, so that $f'(x) = \frac{1}{2}x^{-1/2} = \frac{1}{2x^{1/2}} = \frac{1}{2\sqrt{x}}$.

* See Section 0.2 in the Precalculus Review to brush up on negative and fractional exponents. Pay particular attention to rational, radical, and exponent forms.

By rewriting the given functions in Example 1 before taking derivatives, we converted them from **rational** or **radical form** (as in, say, $\frac{1}{x^2}$ and $\sqrt{x}$) to **exponent form** (as in x^{-2} and $x^{0.5}$; see the Precalculus Review, Section 0.2) to enable us to use the power rule. (See the Caution below.)

Caution

We cannot apply the power rule to terms in the denominators or under square roots. For example:

1. The derivative of $\frac{1}{x^2}$ is **NOT** $\frac{1}{2x}$; it is $-\frac{2}{x^3}$. See Example 1(b).
2. The derivative of $\sqrt{x^3}$ is **NOT** $\sqrt{3x^2}$; it is $1.5x^{0.5}$. Rewrite $\sqrt{x^3}$ as $x^{3/2}$ or $x^{1.5}$ and apply the power rule.

Some of the derivatives in Example 1 are very useful to remember, so we summarize them in Table 1. We suggest that you add to this table as you learn more derivatives. It is *extremely* helpful to remember the derivatives of common functions such as $1/x$ and $\sqrt{x}$, even though they can be obtained by using the power rule as in the above example.

Table 1 Table of Derivative Formulas

$f(x)$	$f'(x)$
1	0
x	1
x^2	$2x$
x^3	$3x^2$
x^n	nx^{n-1}
$\frac{1}{x}$	$-\frac{1}{x^2}$
$\frac{1}{x^2}$	$-\frac{2}{x^3}$
$\sqrt{x}$	$\frac{1}{2\sqrt{x}}$

Another Notation: Differential Notation

Here is a useful notation based on the "d-notation" we discussed in Section 10.5. **Differential notation** is based on an abbreviation for the phrase "the derivative with respect to x." For example, we learned that if $f(x) = x^3$, then $f'(x) = 3x^2$. When we say "$f'(x) = 3x^2$," we mean the following:

The derivative of x^3 with respect to x equals $3x^2$.

You may wonder why we sneaked in the words "with respect to x." All this means is that the variable of the function is x, and not any other variable.* Because we use the phrase "the derivative with respect to x" often, we use the following abbreviation.

* This may seem odd in the case of $f(x) = x^3$ because there are no other variables to worry about. But in expressions like st^3 that involve variables other than x, it is necessary to specify just what the variable of the function is. This is the same reason that we write "$f(x) = x^3$" rather than just "$f = x^3$."

Differential Notation; Differentiation

$\frac{d}{dx}$ means "the derivative with respect to x."

Thus, $\frac{d}{dx}[f(x)]$ is the same thing as $f'(x)$, the derivative of $f(x)$ with respect to x. If y is a function of x, then the derivative of y with respect to x is

$$\frac{d}{dx}(y) \quad \text{or, more compactly,} \quad \frac{dy}{dx}.$$

To **differentiate** a function $f(x)$ with respect to x means to take its derivative with respect to x.

Quick Examples

In Words	Formula
1. The derivative with respect to x of x^3 is $3x^2$.	$\frac{d}{dx}(x^3) = 3x^2$
2. The derivative with respect to t of $\frac{1}{t}$ is $-\frac{1}{t^2}$.	$\frac{d}{dt}\left(\frac{1}{t}\right) = -\frac{1}{t^2}$
3. If $y = x^4$, then $\frac{dy}{dx} = 4x^3$.	
4. If $u = \frac{1}{t^2}$, then $\frac{du}{dt} = -\frac{2}{t^3}$.	

Notes

1. $\frac{dy}{dx}$ is Leibniz's notation for the derivative we discussed in Section 10.5. (See the discussion before Example 3 there.)
2. Leibniz notation illustrates units nicely: Units of $\frac{dy}{dx}$ are units of y per unit of x.
3. We can (and often do!) use different kind of brackets or parentheses in Liebniz notation; for instance, $\frac{d}{dx}[x^3]$, $\frac{d}{dx}(x^3)$, and $\frac{d}{dx}\{x^3\}$ all mean the same thing (and equal $3x^2$). ■

The Rules for Sums and Constant Multiples

We can now find the derivatives of more complicated functions, such as polynomials, using the following rules. If f and g are functions and if c is a constant, we saw in Section 1.2 how to obtain the **sum, $f + g$, difference, $f - g$,** and **constant multiple, cf.**

Theorem 11.2 Derivatives of Sums, Differences, and Constant Multiples

If f and g are any two differentiable functions, and if c is any constant, then the sum, $f+g$, the difference, $f-g$, and the constant multiple, cf, are differentiable, and

$$[f \pm g]'(x) = f'(x) \pm g'(x) \qquad \text{Sum Rule}$$

$$[cf]'(x) = cf'(x). \qquad \text{Constant Multiple Rule}$$

In Words:

- The derivative of a sum is the sum of the derivatives, and the derivative of a difference is the difference of the derivatives.
- The derivative of c times a function is c times the derivative of the function.

Differential Notation:

$$\frac{d}{dx}[f(x) \pm g(x)] = \frac{d}{dx}f(x) \pm \frac{d}{dx}g(x)$$

$$\frac{d}{dx}[cf(x)] = c\frac{d}{dx}f(x)$$

Quick Examples

1. $\frac{d}{dx}(x^2 - x^4) = \frac{d}{dx}(x^2) - \frac{d}{dx}(x^4) = 2x - 4x^3$
2. $\frac{d}{dx}(7x^3) = 7\frac{d}{dx}(x^3) = 7(3x^2) = 21x^2$

   In other words, we multiply the coefficient (7) by the exponent (3), and then decrease the exponent by 1.
3. $\frac{d}{dx}(12x) = 12\frac{d}{dx}(x) = 12(1) = 12$

   In other words, the derivative of a constant times x is that constant.
4. $\frac{d}{dx}(-x^{0.5}) = \frac{d}{dx}[(-1)x^{0.5}] = (-1)\frac{d}{dx}(x^{0.5}) = (-1)(0.5)x^{-0.5}$
   $= -0.5x^{-0.5}$
5. $\frac{d}{dx}(12) = \frac{d}{dx}[12(1)] = 12\frac{d}{dx}(1) = 12(0) = 0.$

   In other words, the derivative of a constant is zero.
6. If my company earns twice as much (annual) revenue as yours and the derivative of your revenue function is the curve on the left, then the derivative of my revenue function is the curve on the right.

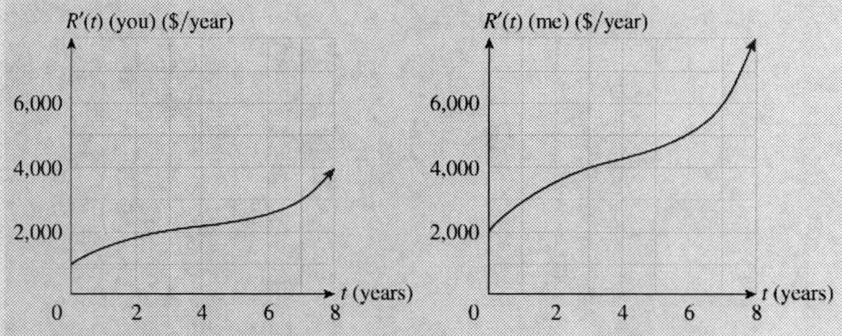

7. Suppose that a company's revenue R and cost C are changing with time. Then so is the profit, $P(t) = R(t) - C(t)$, and the rate of change of the profit is

$$P'(t) = R'(t) - C'(t).$$

In words: *The derivative of the profit is the derivative of revenue minus the derivative of cost.*

Proof of the Sum Rule

By the definition of the derivative of a function,

$$\frac{d}{dx}[f(x)+g(x)] = \lim_{h\to 0}\frac{[f(x+h)+g(x+h)]-[f(x)+g(x)]}{h}$$

$$= \lim_{h\to 0}\frac{[f(x+h)-f(x)]+[g(x+h)-g(x)]}{h}$$

$$= \lim_{h\to 0}\left[\frac{f(x+h)-f(x)}{h}+\frac{g(x+h)-g(x)}{h}\right]$$

$$= \lim_{h\to 0}\frac{f(x+h)-f(x)}{h}+\lim_{h\to 0}\frac{g(x+h)-g(x)}{h}$$

$$= \frac{d}{dx}[f(x)]+\frac{d}{dx}[g(x)].$$

The next-to-last step uses a property of limits: The limit of a sum is the sum of the limits. Think about why this should be true. The last step uses the definition of the derivative again (and the fact that the functions are differentiable).

The proof of the rule for constant multiples is similar.

EXAMPLE 2 Combining the Sum and Constant Multiple Rules, and Dealing with x in the Denominator

Find the derivatives of the following:

a. $f(x) = 3x^2 + 2x - 4$

b. $f(x) = \dfrac{2x}{3} - \dfrac{6}{x} + \dfrac{2}{3x^{0.2}} - \dfrac{x^4}{2}$

c. $f(x) = \dfrac{|x|}{4} + \dfrac{1}{2\sqrt{x}}$

Solution

a. $\frac{d}{dx}(3x^2 + 2x - 4) = \frac{d}{dx}(3x^2) + \frac{d}{dx}(2x - 4)$ Rule for sums

$= \frac{d}{dx}(3x^2) + \frac{d}{dx}(2x) - \frac{d}{dx}(4)$ Rule for differences

$= 3(2x) + 2(1) - 0$ See Quick Example 2.

$= 6x + 2$

b. Notice that f has x and powers of x in the denominator. We deal with these terms the same way we did in Example 1, by rewriting them in exponent form (that is, in the form constant × power of x; see Section 0.2 in the Precalculus Review):

$$f(x) = \frac{2x}{3} - \frac{6}{x} + \frac{2}{3x^{0.2}} - \frac{x^4}{2} \qquad \text{Rational form}$$

$$= \frac{2}{3}x - 6x^{-1} + \frac{2}{3}x^{-0.2} - \frac{1}{2}x^4. \qquad \text{Exponent form}$$

We are now ready to take the derivative:

$$f'(x) = \frac{2}{3}(1) - 6(-1)x^{-2} + \frac{2}{3}(-0.2)x^{-1.2} - \frac{1}{2}(4x^3)$$

$$= \frac{2}{3} + 6x^{-2} - \frac{0.4}{3}x^{-1.2} - 2x^3 \qquad \text{Exponent form}$$

$$= \frac{2}{3} + \frac{6}{x^2} - \frac{0.4}{3x^{1.2}} - 2x^3. \qquad \text{Rational form}$$

c. Rewrite $f(x)$ using exponent form as follows:

$$f(x) = \frac{|x|}{4} + \frac{1}{2\sqrt{x}} \qquad \text{Rational form}$$

$$= \frac{1}{4}|x| + \frac{1}{2}x^{-1/2}. \qquad \text{Exponent form}$$

Now recall from the end of Section 10.6 that the derivative of $|x|$ is $\frac{|x|}{x}$. Thus,

$$f'(x) = \frac{1}{4}\frac{|x|}{x} + \frac{1}{2}\left(\frac{-1}{2}x^{-3/2}\right)$$

$$= \frac{|x|}{4x} - \frac{1}{4}x^{-3/2} \qquad \text{Simplify}$$

$$= \frac{|x|}{4x} - \frac{1}{4x^{3/2}}. \qquad \text{Rational form}$$

Notice that in Example 2(a) we had three terms in the expression for $f(x)$, not just two. By applying the rule for sums and differences twice, we saw that the derivative of a sum or difference of three terms is the sum or difference of the derivatives of the terms. (One of those terms had zero derivative, so the final answer had only two terms.) In fact, the derivative of a sum or difference of any number of terms is the sum or difference of the derivatives of the terms. Put another way, to take the derivative of a sum or difference of any number of terms, we take derivatives term by term.

Note Nothing forces us to use only x as the independent variable when taking derivatives (although it is traditional to give x preference). For instance, part (a) in Example 2 can be rewritten as

$$\frac{d}{dt}(3t^2 + 2t - 4) = 6t + 2$$

$\frac{d}{dt}$ means "derivative with respect to t."

or

$$\frac{d}{du}(3u^2 + 2u - 4) = 6u + 2.$$

$\frac{d}{du}$ means "derivative with respect to u." ■

In the previous examples, we saw instances of the following important facts. (Think about these graphically to see why they must be true.)

The Derivative of a Constant Times *x* and the Derivative of a Constant

If c is any constant, then:

Rule	Quick Examples	
$\frac{d}{dx}(cx) = c$	$\frac{d}{dx}(6x) = 6$	$\frac{d}{dx}(-x) = -1$
$\frac{d}{dx}(c) = 0$	$\frac{d}{dx}(5) = 0$	$\frac{d}{dx}(\pi) = 0$

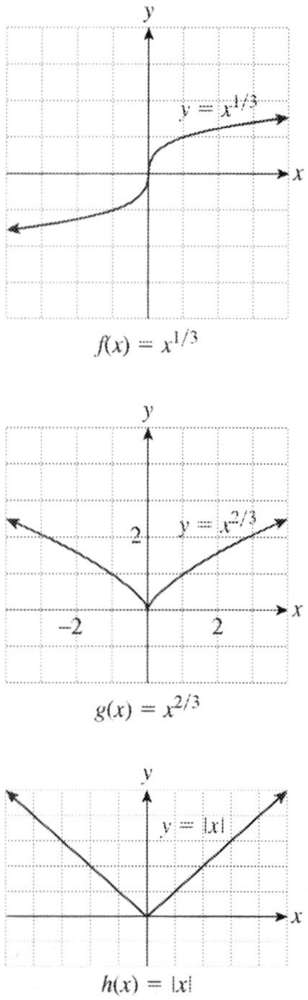

Figure 1

In Section 10.5 we pointed out that the derivative of a function cannot exist at an endpoint of its domain, as the defining limit does not exist there (see the "Important Notes" after the definition of instantaneous rate of change). Thus, for instance, $f(x) = \sqrt{x}$ and $g(x) = x^{1/4}$ are not differentiable at the endpoint $x = 0$ of their domains. In Example 5 of Section 10.6 we saw that $h(x) = |x|$ also fails to be differentiable at $x = 0$, even though $x = 0$ is not an endpoint of its domain (the domain of h is the set of all real numbers). In the next example we see how to spot the non-differentiability at a point of this and other functions simply by looking at the formulas for their derivatives.

EXAMPLE 3 Functions Not Differentiable at a Point

Find the natural domains of the derivatives of $f(x) = x^{1/3}$, $g(x) = x^{2/3}$, and $h(x) = |x|$.

Solution Let's look at the derivatives of the three functions given:

$$f(x) = x^{1/3}, \text{ so } f'(x) = \frac{1}{3}x^{-2/3} = \frac{1}{3x^{2/3}}.$$

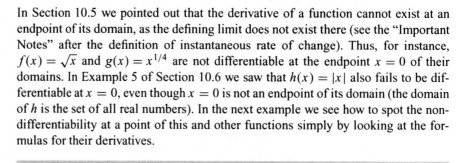

$$g(x) = x^{2/3}, \text{ so } g'(x) = \frac{2}{3}x^{-1/3} = \frac{2}{3x^{1/3}}.$$

$$h(x) = |x|, \text{ so } h'(x) = \frac{|x|}{x}.$$

The derivatives of all three functions are defined only for nonzero values of x, and their natural domains consist of all real numbers except 0. Thus, the derivatives f', g', and h' do not exist at $x = 0$. In other words, these functions are not differentiable at $x = 0$. If we look at Figure 1 we notice why these functions fail to be differentiable at $x = 0$: The graph of f has a vertical tangent line at 0. Because a vertical line

using Technology

If you try to graph the function $f(x) = x^{2/3}$ using the format

```
X^(2/3)
```

you may get only the right-hand portion of the graph of g in Figure 1 because graphing utilities are (often) not programmed to raise negative numbers to fractional exponents. (However, many will handle `X^(1/3)` correctly, as a special case they recognize.) To avoid this difficulty, you can take advantage of the identity

$$x^{2/3} = (x^2)^{1/3}$$

so that it is always a nonnegative number that is being raised to a fractional exponent. Thus, use the format

```
(X^2)^(1/3)
```

to obtain both portions of the graph.

has undefined slope, the derivative is undefined at that point. The graphs of g and h come to a sharp point at 0, where it is not meaningful to speak about the slope of the tangent line; therefore, the derivatives of g and h are not defined there. (In the case of g, where the sharp point is called a *cusp,* a vertical tangent line would seem appropriate, but as in the case of f, its slope is undefined.)

You can also detect this nondifferentiability by computing some difference quotients numerically, as we did for h in Section 10.6.

APPLICATION

EXAMPLE 4 Gold Price

You are a commodities trader and you monitor the price of gold on the spot market very closely during an active morning. Suppose you find that the price of an ounce of gold can be approximated by the function

$$G(t) = 5t^2 - 85t + 1{,}762 \quad (7.5 \le t \le 10.5),$$

where t is time in hours. (See Figure 2. $t = 8$ represents 8:00 am.)

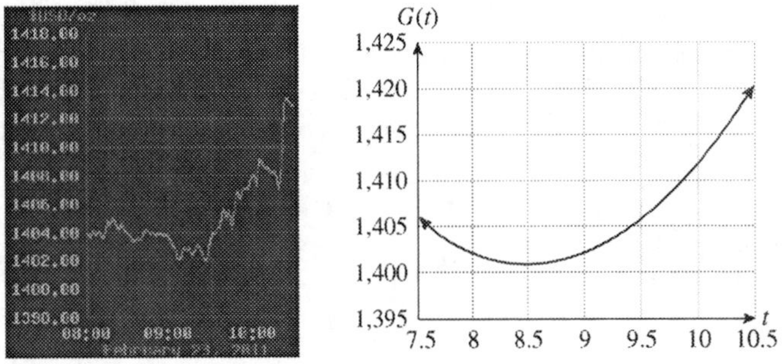

Source: www.kitco.com

$G(t) = 5t^2 - 85t + 1{,}762$

Figure 2

a. According to the model, how fast was the price of gold changing at 8:00 am?

b. According to the model, the price of gold

(A) increased at a faster and faster rate
(B) increased at a slower and slower rate
(C) decreased at a faster and faster rate
(D) decreased at a slower and slower rate

between 7:30 and 8:30 am.

Solution

a. Differentiating the given function with respect to t gives

$$G'(t) = 10t - 85.$$

Because 8:00 am corresponds to $t = 8$, we obtain

$$G'(8) = 10(8) - 85 = -5.$$

The units of the derivative are dollars per hour, so we conclude that, at 8:00 am, the price of gold was dropping at a rate of \$5 per hour.

b. From the graph, we can see that, between 7:30 and 8:30 am (the interval [7.5, 8.5]), the price of gold was decreasing. Also from the graph, we see that the slope of the tangent becomes less and less negative as t increases, so the price of gold is decreasing at a slower and slower rate (choice (D)).

We can also see this algebraically from the derivative, $G'(t) = 10t - 85$: For values of t less than 8.5, $G'(t)$ is negative; that is, the rate of change of G is negative, so the price of gold is decreasing. Further, as t increases, $G'(t)$ becomes less and less negative, so the price of gold is decreasing at a slower and slower rate, confirming that choice (D) is the correct one.

An Application to Limits: L'Hospital's Rule

The limits that caused us some trouble in Sections 10.1–10.3 are those of the form $\lim_{x\to a} f(x)$ in which substituting $x = a$ gave us an indeterminate form, such as

$$\lim_{x\to 2} \frac{x^3-8}{x-2} \qquad \text{Substituting } x = 2 \text{ yields } \tfrac{0}{0}.$$

$$\lim_{x\to +\infty} \frac{2x-4}{x-1}. \qquad \text{Substituting } x = +\infty \text{ yields } \tfrac{\infty}{\infty}.$$

L'Hospital's rule* gives us an alternate way of computing limits such as these without the need to do any preliminary simplification. It also allows us to compute some limits for which algebraic simplification does not work.

* Guillaume François Antoine, Marquis de l'Hospital (1661–1704) wrote the first textbook on calculus, *Analyse des infiniment petits pour l'intelligence des lignes courbes,* in 1692. The rule now known as l'Hospital's rule appeared first in this book.

Theorem 11.3 L'Hospital's Rule

If f and g are two differentiable functions such that substituting $x = a$ in the expression $\dfrac{f(x)}{g(x)}$ gives the indeterminate form $\dfrac{0}{0}$ or $\dfrac{\infty}{\infty}$, then

$$\lim_{x\to a} \frac{f(x)}{g(x)} = \lim_{x\to a} \frac{f'(x)}{g'(x)}.$$

That is, we can replace $f(x)$ and $g(x)$ with their *derivatives* and try again to take the limit.

Quick Examples

1. Substituting $x = 2$ in $\dfrac{x^3-8}{x-2}$ yields $\dfrac{0}{0}$. Therefore, l'Hospital's rule applies and

$$\lim_{x\to 2} \frac{x^3-8}{x-2} = \lim_{x\to 2} \frac{3x^2}{1} = \frac{3(2)^2}{1} = 12.$$

2. Substituting $x = +\infty$ in $\dfrac{2x-4}{x-1}$ yields $\dfrac{\infty}{\infty}$. Therefore, l'Hospital's rule applies and

$$\lim_{x\to +\infty} \frac{2x-4}{x-1} = \lim_{x\to +\infty} \frac{2}{1} = 2.$$

The proof of l'Hospital's rule is beyond the scope of this text.†

† A proof of l'Hospital's rule can be found in most advanced calculus textbooks.

EXAMPLE 5 Applying L'Hospital's Rule

Check whether l'Hospital's rule applies to each of the following limits. If it does, use it to evaluate the limit. Otherwise, use some other method to evaluate the limit.

a. $\lim_{x \to 1} \frac{x^2 - 2x + 1}{4x^3 - 3x^2 - 6x + 5}$

b. $\lim_{x \to +\infty} \frac{2x^2 - 4x}{5x^3 - 3x + 5}$

c. $\lim_{x \to 1} \frac{x - 1}{x^3 - 3x^2 + 3x - 1}$

d. $\lim_{x \to 1} \frac{x}{x^3 - 3x^2 + 3x - 1}$

Solution

a. Setting $x = 1$ yields

$$\frac{1 - 2 + 1}{4 - 3 - 6 + 5} = \frac{0}{0}.$$

Therefore, l'Hospital's rule applies and

$$\lim_{x \to 1} \frac{x^2 - 2x + 1}{4x^3 - 3x^2 - 6x + 5} = \lim_{x \to 1} \frac{2x - 2}{12x^2 - 6x - 6}.$$

We are left with a closed-form function. However, we cannot substitute $x = 1$ to find the limit because the function $(2x - 2)/(12x^2 - 6x - 6)$ is still not defined at $x = 1$. In fact, if we set $x = 1$, we again get $0/0$. Thus, l'Hospital's rule applies again, and

$$\lim_{x \to 1} \frac{2x - 2}{12x^2 - 6x - 6} = \lim_{x \to 1} \frac{2}{24x - 6}.$$

Once again we have a closed-form function, but this time it is defined when $x = 1$, giving

$$\frac{2}{24 - 6} = \frac{1}{9}.$$

Thus,

$$\lim_{x \to 1} \frac{x^2 - 2x + 1}{4x^3 - 3x^2 - 6x + 5} = \frac{1}{9}.$$

b. Setting $x = +\infty$ yields $\frac{\infty}{\infty}$, so

$$\lim_{x \to +\infty} \frac{2x^2 - 4x}{5x^3 - 3x + 5} = \lim_{x \to +\infty} \frac{4x - 4}{15x^2 - 3}.$$

Setting $x = +\infty$ again yields $\frac{\infty}{\infty}$, so we can apply the rule again to obtain

$$\lim_{x \to +\infty} \frac{4x - 4}{15x^2 - 3} = \lim_{x \to +\infty} \frac{4}{30x}.$$

Note that we cannot apply l'Hospital's rule a third time because setting $x = +\infty$ yields the *determinate* form $4/\infty = 0$ (see the discussion at the end of Section 10.3). Thus, the limit is 0.

c. Setting $x = 1$ yields $0/0$ so, by l'Hospital's rule,

$$\lim_{x \to 1} \frac{x - 1}{x^3 - 3x^2 + 3x - 1} = \lim_{x \to 1} \frac{1}{3x^2 - 6x + 3}.$$

We are left with a closed-form function that is still not defined at $x = 1$. Further, l'Hospital's rule no longer applies because putting $x = 1$ yields the determinate form 1/0. To investigate this limit, we refer to the discussion at the end of Section 10.3 and find

$$\lim_{x\to 1}\frac{1}{3x^2-6x+3}=\lim_{x\to 1}\frac{1}{3(x-1)^2}=+\infty. \qquad \frac{1}{0^+}=+\infty$$

d. Setting $x = 1$ in the expression yields the determinate form 1/0, so l'Hospital's rule does not apply here. Using the methods of Section 10.3 again, we find that the limit does not exist.

FAQs

Using the Rules and Recognizing when a Function Is Not Differentiable

Q: I would *like* to say that the derivative of $5x^2 - 8x + 4$ is just $10x - 8$ without having to go through all that stuff about derivatives of sums and constant multiples. Can I simply forget about all the rules and write down the answer?

A: We developed the rules for sums and constant multiples precisely for that reason: so that we could simply write down a derivative without having to think about it too hard. So, you are perfectly justified in simply writing down the derivative without going through the rules, but bear in mind that what you are really doing is applying the power rule, the rule for sums, and the rule for multiples over and over.

Q: Is there a way of telling from its formula whether a function f is not differentiable at a point?

A: Here are some indicators to look for in the formula for f:

- The absolute value of some expression; f may not be differentiable at points where that expression is zero.

  Example: $f(x) = 3x^2 - |x - 4|$ is not differentiable at $x = 4$.

- A fractional power smaller than 1 of some expression; f may not be differentiable at points where that expression is zero.

  Example: $f(x) = (x^2 - 16)^{2/3}$ is not differentiable at $x = \pm 4$.

11.1 EXERCISES

▼ more advanced ◆ challenging

T indicates exercises that should be solved using technology

*In Exercises 1–10, use the shortcut rules to **mentally** calculate the derivative of the given function.* HINT [See Examples 1 and 2.]

1. $f(x) = x^5$

2. $f(x) = x^4$

3. $f(x) = 2x^{-2}$

4. $f(x) = 3x^{-1}$

5. $f(x) = -x^{0.25}$

6. $f(x) = -x^{-0.5}$

7. $f(x) = 2x^4 + 3x^3 - 1$

8. $f(x) = -x^3 - 3x^2 - 1$

9. $f(x) = -x + \frac{1}{x} + 1$

10. $f(x) = \frac{1}{x} + \frac{1}{x^2}$

In Exercises 11–16, obtain the derivative dy/dx and state the rules that you use. HINT [See Example 2.]

11. $y = 10$

12. $y = x^3$

13. $y = x^2 + x$

14. $y = x - 5$

15. $y = 4x^3 + 2x - 1$

16. $y = 4x^{-1} - 2x - 10$

In Exercises 17–40, find the derivative of each function. HINT [See Examples 1 and 2.]

17. $f(x) = x^2 - 3x + 5$

18. $f(x) = 3x^3 - 2x^2 + x$

19. $f(x) = x + x^{0.5}$

20. $f(x) = x^{0.5} + 2x^{-0.5}$

21. $g(x) = x^{-2} - 3x^{-1} - 2$

22. $g(x) = 2x^{-1} + 4x^{-2}$

23. $g(x) = \frac{1}{x} - \frac{1}{x^2}$

24. $g(x) = \frac{1}{x^2} + \frac{1}{x^3}$

25. $h(x) = \frac{2}{x^{0.4}}$

26. $h(x) = -\frac{1}{2x^{0.2}}$

27. $h(x) = \frac{1}{x^2} + \frac{2}{x^3}$

28. $h(x) = \frac{2}{x} - \frac{2}{x^3} + \frac{1}{x^4}$

29. $r(x) = \frac{2}{3x} - \frac{1}{2x^{0.1}}$

30. $r(x) = \frac{4}{3x^2} + \frac{1}{x^{3.2}}$

31. $r(x) = \frac{2x}{3} - \frac{x^{0.1}}{2} + \frac{4}{3x^{1.1}} - 2$

32. $r(x) = \frac{4x^2}{3} + \frac{x^{3.2}}{6} - \frac{2}{3x^2} + 4$

33. $t(x) = |x| + \frac{1}{x}$

34. $t(x) = 3|x| - \sqrt{x}$

35. $s(x) = \sqrt{x} + \frac{1}{\sqrt{x}}$

36. $s(x) = x + \frac{7}{\sqrt{x}}$

HINT [For Exercises 37–38, first expand the given function.]

37. ▼ $s(x) = x\left(x^2 - \frac{1}{x}\right)$

38. ▼ $s(x) = x^{-1}\left(x - \frac{2}{x}\right)$

HINT [For Exercises 39–40, first rewrite the given function.]

39. ▼ $t(x) = \frac{x^2 - 2x^3}{x}$

40. ▼ $t(x) = \frac{2x + x^2}{x}$

In Exercises 41–46, evaluate the given expression.

41. $\frac{d}{dx}(2x^{1.3} - x^{-1.2})$

42. $\frac{d}{dx}(2x^{4.3} + x^{0.6})$

43. ▼ $\frac{d}{dx}[1.2(x - |x|)]$

44. ▼ $\frac{d}{dx}[4(x^2 + 3|x|)]$

45. ▼ $\frac{d}{dt}(at^3 - 4at)$; (a constant)

46. ▼ $\frac{d}{dt}(at^2 + bt + c)$; ($a$, b, c constant)

In Exercises 47–52, find the indicated derivative.

47. $y = \frac{x^{10.3}}{2} + 99x^{-1}$; $\frac{dy}{dx}$

48. $y = \frac{x^{1.2}}{3} - \frac{x^{0.9}}{2}$; $\frac{dy}{dx}$

49. $s = 2.3 + \frac{2.1}{t^{1.1}} - \frac{t^{0.6}}{2}$; $\frac{ds}{dt}$

50. $s = \frac{2}{t^{1.1}} + t^{-1.2}$; $\frac{ds}{dt}$

51. ▼ $V = \frac{4}{3}\pi r^3$; $\frac{dV}{dr}$

52. ▼ $A = 4\pi r^2$; $\frac{dA}{dr}$

In Exercises 53–58, find the slope of the tangent to the graph of the given function at the indicated point. HINT [Recall that the slope of the tangent to the graph of f at $x = a$ is $f'(a)$.]

53. $f(x) = x^3$; $(-1, -1)$

54. $g(x) = x^4$; $(-2, 16)$

55. $f(x) = 1 - 2x$; $(2, -3)$

56. $f(x) = \frac{x}{3} - 1$; $(-3, -2)$

57. $g(t) = \frac{1}{t^5}$; $(1, 1)$

58. $s(t) = \frac{1}{t^3}$; $\left(-2, -\frac{1}{8}\right)$

In Exercises 59–64, find the equation of the tangent line to the graph of the given function at the point with the indicated x-coordinate. In each case, sketch the curve together with the appropriate tangent line.

59. ▼ $f(x) = x^3$; $x = -1$

60. ▼ $f(x) = x^2$; $x = 0$

61. ▼ $f(x) = x + \frac{1}{x}$; $x = 2$

62. ▼ $f(x) = \frac{1}{x^2}$; $x = 1$

63. ▼ $f(x) = \sqrt{x}$; $x = 4$

64. ▼ $f(x) = 2x + 4$; $x = -1$

In Exercises 65–70, find all values of x (if any) where the tangent line to the graph of the given equation is horizontal. HINT [The tangent line is horizontal when its slope is zero.]

65. ▼ $y = 2x^2 + 3x - 1$

66. ▼ $y = -3x^2 - x$

67. ▼ $y = 2x + 8$

68. ▼ $y = -x + 1$

69. ▼ $y = x + \frac{1}{x}$

70. ▼ $y = x - \sqrt{x}$

71. ◆ Write out the proof that $\frac{d}{dx}(x^4) = 4x^3$.

72. ◆ Write out the proof that $\frac{d}{dx}(x^5) = 5x^4$.

In Exercises 73–76, determine whether f is differentiable at the given point. If f′(a) exists, give its value. HINT [See Example 3.]

73. $f(x) = x - x^{1/3}$ **a.** $a = 1$ **b.** $a = 0$

74. $f(x) = 2x + x^{4/3}$ **a.** $a = 8$ **b.** $a = 0$

75. $f(x) = x^{5/4} - 1$ **a.** $a = 16$ **b.** $a = 0$

76. $f(x) = x^{1/5} + 5$ **a.** $a = 1$ **b.** $a = 0$

In Exercises 77–88 say whether l'Hospital's rule applies. If is does, use it to evaluate the given limit. If not, use some other method.

77. $\lim_{x\to 1} \frac{x^2 - 2x + 1}{x^2 - x}$

78. $\lim_{x\to -1} \frac{x^2 + 3x + 2}{x^2 + x}$

79. $\lim_{x\to 2} \frac{x^3 - 8}{x - 2}$

80. $\lim_{x\to 0} \frac{x^3 + 8}{x^2 + 3x + 2}$

81. $\lim_{x\to 1} \frac{x^2 + 3x + 2}{x^2 + x}$

82. $\lim_{x\to -2} \frac{x^3 + 8}{x^2 + 3x + 2}$

83. $\lim_{x\to -\infty} \frac{3x^2 + 10x - 1}{2x^2 - 5x}$

84. $\lim_{x\to -\infty} \frac{6x^2 + 5x + 100}{3x^2 - 9}$

85. $\lim_{x\to -\infty} \frac{10x^2 + 300x + 1}{5x + 2}$

86. $\lim_{x\to -\infty} \frac{2x^4 + 20x^3}{1{,}000x^3 + 6}$

87. $\lim_{x \to -\infty} \frac{x^3 - 100}{2x^2 + 500}$

88. $\lim_{x \to -\infty} \frac{x^2 + 30x}{2x^6 + 10x}$

APPLICATIONS

89. ***Crude Oil Prices*** The price per barrel of crude oil in constant 2008 dollars can be approximated by

$$P(t) = 0.45t^2 - 12t + 105 \text{ dollars} \quad (0 \le t \le 28),$$

where t is time in years since the start of 1980.[1] Find $P'(t)$ and $P'(20)$. What does the answer tell you about the price of crude oil? HINT [See Example 2.]

90. ***Median Home Prices*** The median home price in the United States over the period 2003–2011 can be approximated by

$$P(t) = -5t^2 + 75t - 30 \text{ thousand dollars} \quad (3 \le t \le 11),$$

where t is time in years since the start of 2000.[2] Find $P'(t)$ and $P'(6)$. What does the answer tell you about home prices? HINT [See Example 2.]

91. ***Food versus Education*** The following equation shows the approximate relationship between the percentage y of total personal consumption spent on food and the corresponding percentage x spent on education.[3]

$$y = \frac{35}{x^{0.35}} \text{ percentage points} \quad (6.5 \le x \le 17.5).$$

According to the model, spending on food is decreasing at a rate of _____ percentage points per one percentage point increase in spending on education when 10% of total consumption is spent on education. (Answer should be rounded to two significant digits.) HINT [See Example 2(b).]

92. ***Food versus Recreation*** The following equation shows the approximate relationship between the percentage y of total personal consumption spent on food and the corresponding percentage x spent on recreation.[4]

$$y = \frac{33}{x^{0.63}} \text{ percentage points} \quad (6.5 \le x \le 17.5).$$

According to the model, spending on food is decreasing at a rate of _____ percentage points per one percentage point increase in spending on recreation when 3% of total consumption is spent on recreation. (Answer should be rounded to two significant digits.) HINT [See Example 2(b).]

93. ***Velocity*** If a stone is dropped from a height of 400 feet, its height s after t seconds is given by $s(t) = 400 - 16t^2$, with s in feet.

a. Compute $s'(t)$ and hence find its velocity at times $t = 0, 1, 2, 3$, and 4 seconds.

b. When does it reach the ground, and how fast is it traveling when it hits the ground? HINT [It reaches the ground when $s(t) = 0$.]

94. ***Velocity*** If a stone is thrown down at 120 ft/s from a height of 1,000 feet, its height s after t seconds is given by $s(t) = 1{,}000 - 120t - 16t^2$, with s in feet.

a. Compute $s'(t)$ and hence find its velocity at times $t = 0$, 1, 2, 3, and 4 seconds.

b. When does it reach the ground, and how fast is it traveling when it hits the ground? HINT [It reaches the ground when $s(t) = 0$.]

95. ***GE Net Income 2005–2009*** The annual net income of General Electric for the period 2005–2009 could be approximated by[5]

$$P(t) = -2.0t^2 + 6.6t + 16 \text{ billion dollars} \quad (0 \le t \le 4),$$

where t is time in years since 2005.

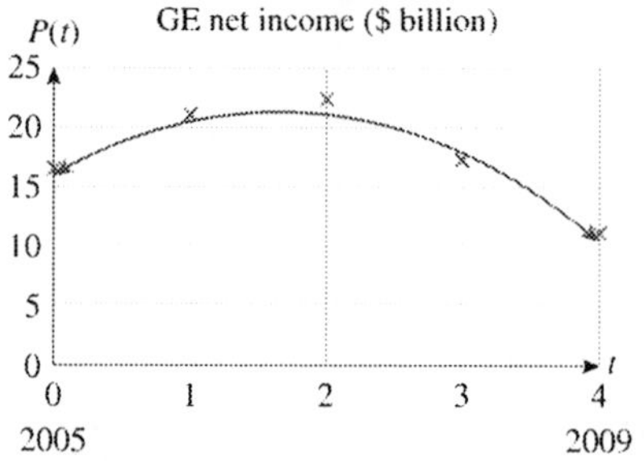

a. Compute $P'(t)$. How fast was GE's annual net income changing in 2008? (Be careful to give correct units of measurement.)

b. According to the model, GE's annual net income

(A) increased at a faster and faster rate

(B) increased at a slower and slower rate

(C) decreased at a faster and faster rate

(D) decreased at a slower and slower rate

during the first year and a half shown (the interval [0, 1.5]). Justify your answer in two ways: geometrically, reasoning entirely from the graph; and algebraically, reasoning from the derivative of P. HINT [See Example 4.]

96. ***GE Net Income 2007–2011*** The annual net income of General Electric for the period 2007–2011 could be approximated by[6]

$$P(t) = 3t^2 - 24t + 59 \text{ billion dollars} \quad (2 \le t \le 6),$$

where t is time in years since 2005.

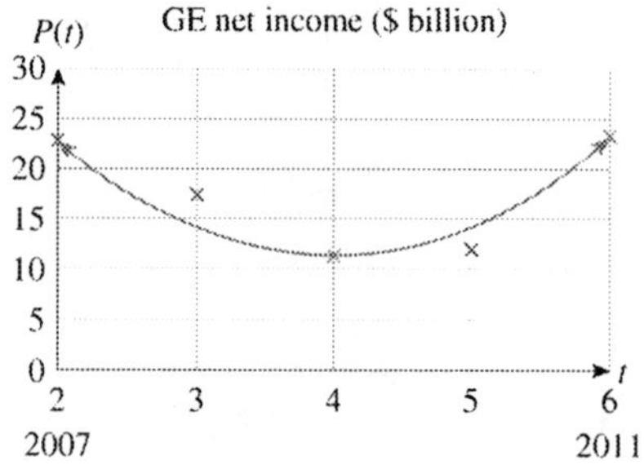

[1] Source for data: www.inflationdata.com.

[2] Source for data: www.zillow.com.

[3] Model based on historical and projected data from 1908–2010. Sources: Historical data, Bureau of Economic Analysis; projected data, Bureau of Labor Statistics/*New York Times*, December 1, 2003, p. C2.

[4] *Ibid.*

[5] Source for data: www.wikinvest.com.

[6] 2011 value estimated. Source: *Ibid.*

a. Compute $P'(t)$. How fast was GE's annual net income changing in 2010? (Be careful to give correct units of measurement.)

b. According to the model, GE's annual net income

(A) increased at a faster and faster rate
(B) increased at a slower and slower rate
(C) decreased at a faster and faster rate
(D) decreased at a slower and slower rate

during the first two years shown (the interval [2, 4]). Justify your answer in two ways: geometrically, reasoning entirely from the graph; and algebraically, reasoning from the derivative of P. HINT [See Example 4.]

97. ***Ecology*** Increasing numbers of manatees ("sea sirens") have been killed by boats off the Florida coast. The following graph shows the relationship between the number of boats registered in Florida and the number of manatees killed each year.

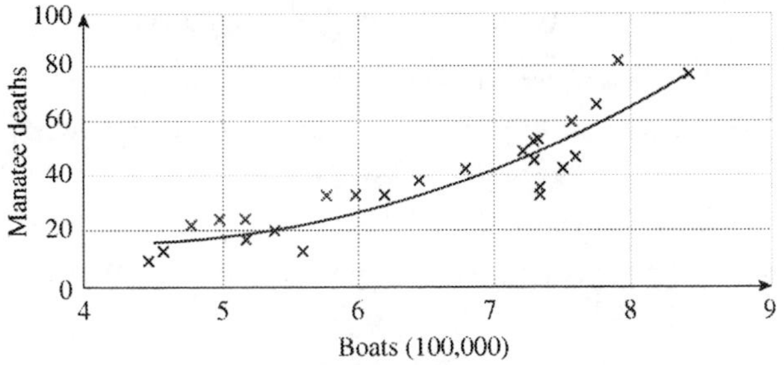

The regression curve shown is given by

$$f(x) = 3.55x^2 - 30.2x + 81 \quad (4.5 \le x \le 8.5),$$

where x is the number of boats (hundreds of thousands) registered in Florida in a particular year and $f(x)$ is the number of manatees killed by boats in Florida that year.[7]

a. Find $f'(x)$, and use your formula to compute $f'(8)$, stating its units of measurement. What does the answer say about manatee deaths?

b. Is $f'(x)$ increasing or decreasing with increasing x? Interpret the answer. HINT [See Example 4.]

98. ***SAT Scores by Income*** The following graph shows U.S. math SAT scores as a function of parents' income level.[8]

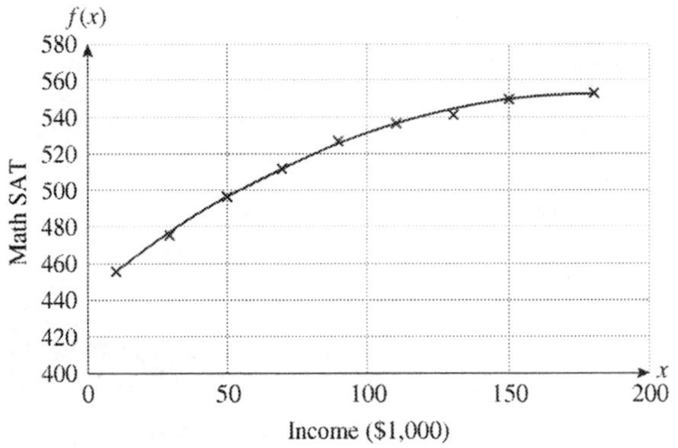

The regression curve shown is given by

$$f(x) = -0.0034x^2 + 1.2x + 444 \quad (10 \le x \le 180),$$

where $f(x)$ is the average math SAT score of a student whose parents earn x thousand dollars per year.

a. Find $f'(x)$, and use your formula to compute $f'(100)$, stating its units of measurement. What does the answer say about math SAT scores?

b. Does $f'(x)$ increase or decrease with increasing x? What does your answer say about math SAT scores? HINT [See Example 4.]

99. ***Market Share: Smart Phones*** The following graph shows the approximate market shares, in percentage points, of Apple's *iPhone* and Google's *Android*-based smart phones from January 2009 to May 2010 (t is time in months, and $t = 0$ represents January, 2009):[9]

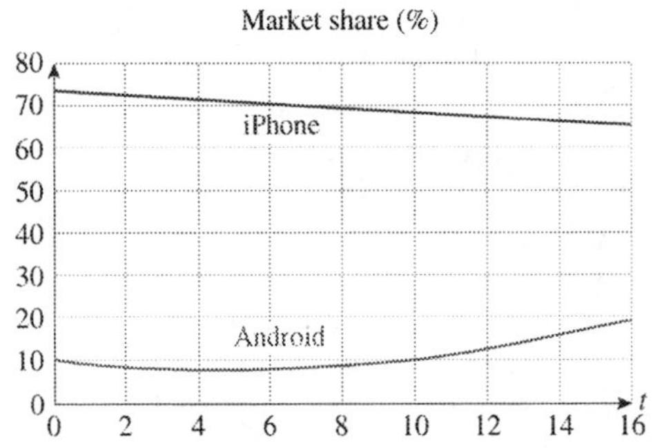

Let $I(t)$ be the iPhone market share at time t, and let $A(t)$ be the Android market share at time t.

a. What does the function $I - A$ measure? What does its derivative $(I - A)'$ measure?

b. The graph suggests that, on the interval [6, 16], $I - A$ is

(A) increasing.
(B) decreasing.
(C) increasing, then decreasing.
(D) decreasing, then increasing.

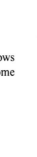

[7]Regression model is based on data from 1976 to 2000. Sources for data: Florida Department of Highway Safety & Motor Vehicles, Florida Marine Institute/*New York Times*, February 12, 2002, p. F4.

[8]Regression model is based on 2009 data. Source: College Board/*New York Times* http://economix.blogs.nytimes.com.

[9]Source for data: Quantcast www.quantcast.com.

c. The two market shares are approximated by
iPhone: $I(t) = -0.5t + 73$
Android: $A(t) = 0.1t^2 - t + 10$.

Compute $(I - A)'$, stating its units of measurement. On the interval [0, 16], $(I - A)'$ is

(A) positive.
(B) negative.
(C) positive, then negative.
(D) negative, then positive.

How is this behavior reflected in the graph, and what does it mean about the market shares of iPhone and Android?

d. Compute $(I - A)'(4)$. Interpret your answer.

100. *Market Share: Smart Phones* The following graph shows the approximate market shares, in percentage points, of Research In Motion's *BlackBerry* smartphones and Google's *Android*-based smartphones from July 2009 to May 2010 (t is time in months, and $t = 0$ represents January 2009):[10]

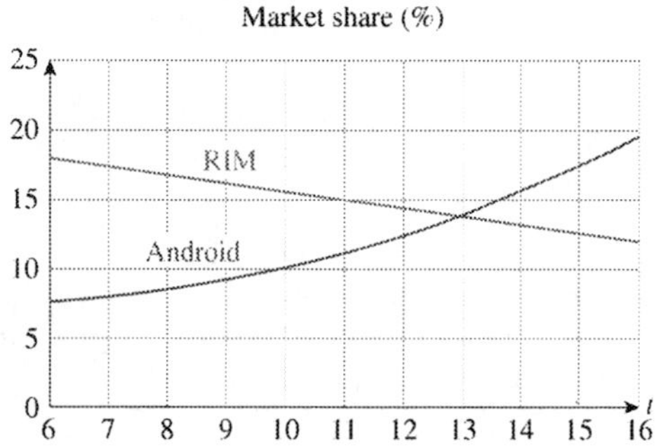

Let $B(t)$ be the BlackBerry market share at time t, and let $A(t)$ be the Android market share at time t.

a. What does the function $B - A$ measure? What does its derivative $(B - A)'$ measure?

b. The graph suggests that, on the interval [6, 16], $B - A$ is

(A) increasing.
(B) decreasing.
(C) increasing, then decreasing.
(D) decreasing, then increasing.

c. The two market shares are approximated by

BlackBerry: $B(t) = -0.6t + 21.6$
Android: $A(t) = 0.1t^2 - t + 10$.

Compute $(B - A)'$, stating its units of measurement. On the interval [6, 16], $(B - A)'$ is

(A) positive.
(B) negative.
(C) positive, then negative.
(D) negative, then positive.

How is this reflected in the graph, and what does it mean about the market shares of BlackBerry and Android?

d. Compute $(B - A)'(10)$. Interpret your answer.

[10]Source for data: Quantcast www.quantcast.com.

COMMUNICATION AND REASONING EXERCISES

101. What instructions would you give to a fellow student who wanted to accurately graph the tangent line to the curve $y = 3x^2$ at the point $(-1, 3)$?

102. What instructions would you give to a fellow student who wanted to accurately graph a line at right angles to the curve $y = 4/x$ at the point where $x = 0.5$?

103. Consider $f(x) = x^2$ and $g(x) = 2x^2$. How do the slopes of the tangent lines of f and g at the same x compare?

104. Consider $f(x) = x^3$ and $g(x) = x^3 + 3$. How do the slopes of the tangent lines of f and g compare?

105. Suppose $g(x) = -f(x)$. How do the derivatives of f and g compare?

106. Suppose $g(x) = f(x) - 50$. How do the derivatives of f and g compare?

107. Following is an excerpt from your best friend's graded homework:

$$3x^4 + 11x^5 = 12x^3 + 55x^4. \quad ✗\ \textit{WRONG} \quad -8$$

Why was it marked wrong? How would you correct it?

108. Following is an excerpt from your own graded homework:

$$x^n = nx^{n-1}. \quad ✗\ \textit{WRONG} \quad -10$$

Why was it marked wrong? How would you correct it?

109. Following is another excerpt from your best friend's graded homework:

$$y = \frac{1}{2x} = 2x^{-1}, \text{ so } \frac{dy}{dx} = -2x^{-2}. \quad ✗\ \textit{WRONG} \quad -5$$

Why was it marked wrong? How would you correct it?

110. Following is an excerpt from your second best friend's graded homework:

$$f(x) = \frac{3}{4x^2};\ f'(x) = \frac{3}{8x}. \quad ✗\ \textit{WRONG} \quad -10$$

Why was it marked wrong? How would you correct it?

111. Following is an excerpt from your worst enemy's graded homework:

$$f(x) = 4x^2;\ f'(x) = (0)(2x) = 0. \quad ✗\ \textit{WRONG} \quad -6$$

Why was it marked wrong? How would you correct it?

112. Following is an excerpt from your second worst enemy's graded homework:

$$f(x) = \frac{3}{4x};\ f'(x) = \frac{0}{4} = 0. \quad ✗\ \textit{WRONG} \quad -10$$

Why was it marked wrong? How would you correct it?

113. One of the questions in your last calculus test was "**Question 1(a)** Give the definition of the derivative of a function f." Following is your answer and the grade you received:

$$nx^{n-1}. \quad ✗\ \textit{WRONG} \quad -10$$

Why was it marked wrong? What is the correct answer?

114. ▼ How would you respond to an acquaintance who says, "I finally understand what the derivative is: It is nx^{n-1}! Why weren't we taught that in the first place instead of the difficult way using limits?"

115. ▼ Sketch the graph of a function whose derivative is undefined at exactly two points but that has a tangent line at all but one point.

116. ▼ Sketch the graph of a function that has a tangent line at each of its points, but whose derivative is undefined at exactly two points.

Practice Problems 11.1, Part 1

1. Let $f(x) = 2^x$. Use graphs or numerical evidence to explain why $f'(x) \neq x2^{x-1}$.

2. A ball is thrown straight up into the air from the top of a building, and its height above the ground t seconds after it is thrown is $f(t) = -16t^2 + 88t + 240$ feet.

a. Determine the velocity of the ball at the moment it hits the ground.

b. Determine all points in time after the ball is tossed that it has a **speed** of exactly 60 feet per second (speed is the magnitude of velocity).

Practice Problems 11.1, Part 2

1. The monthly earnings of a company that offers access to customizable personal internet radio stations to subscribers of the service has been steadily increasing over the last several months, as described by the model $m(t) = 50 + 2t + 4t^{3/2}$, where t measures months, with $t = 0$ corresponding to the start of 2011, and $m(t)$ gives the corresponding monthly earnings, in thousands of dollars.

a. Calculate the rate at which monthly earnings were changing as of the start of 2012, rounded and labeled accordingly.

b. Determine the first full month when earnings were growing at a rate of at least \$24,000 per month.

2. Let $g(x) = |x^2 - 4|$. Find a piecewise-defined formula for $g'(x)$. (Hint: It might be helpful to write $g(x)$ as a piecewise-defined function, or you may find a graph useful.)

11.2 A First Application: Marginal Analysis

In Chapter 1, we considered linear *cost functions* of the form $C(x) = mx + b$, where C is the total cost, x is the number of items, and m and b are constants. The slope m is the *marginal cost.* It measures the *cost of one more item.* Notice that the derivative of $C(x) = mx + b$ is $C'(x) = m$. In other words, for a linear cost function, *the marginal cost is the derivative of the cost function.*

In general, we make the following definition.

Marginal Cost

Recall from Section 1.2 that a **cost function** C specifies the total cost as a function of the number of items x, so that $C(x)$ is the total cost of x items. The **marginal cost function** is the derivative C' of the cost function C. Thus, $C'(x)$ measures the rate of change of cost with respect to x.

Units

The units of marginal cost are units of cost (dollars, say) per item.

Interpretation

*We interpret $C'(x)$ as the approximate cost of one more item.**

* See Example 1.

Quick Example

If $C(x) = 400x + 1{,}000$ dollars, then the marginal cost function is $C'(x) = \$400$ per item (a constant).

EXAMPLE 1 Marginal Cost

Suppose that the cost in dollars to manufacture portable music players is given by

$$C(x) = 150{,}000 + 20x - 0.0001x^2$$

where x is the number of music players manufactured.† Find the marginal cost function C' and use it to estimate the cost of manufacturing the 50,001st music player.

† The term $0.0001x^2$ may reflect a cost saving for high levels of production, such as a bulk discount in the cost of electronic components.

Solution Since

$$C(x) = 150{,}000 + 20x - 0.0001x^2$$

the marginal cost function is

$$C'(x) = 20 - 0.0002x.$$

The units of $C'(x)$ are units of C (dollars) per unit of x (music players). Thus, $C'(x)$ is measured in dollars per music player.

The cost of the 50,001st music player is the amount by which the total cost would rise if we increased production from 50,000 music players to 50,001. Thus, we need to know the rate at which the total cost rises as we increase production. This rate of change is measured by the derivative, or marginal cost, which we just computed. At $x = 50{,}000$, we get

$$C'(50{,}000) = 20 - 0.0002(50{,}000) = \$10 \text{ per music player.}$$

In other words, we estimate that the 50,001st music player will cost approximately $10.

Before we go on... In Example 1, the marginal cost is really only an *approximation* to the cost of the 50,001st music player:

$$\begin{aligned} C'(50{,}000) &\approx \frac{C(50{,}001) - C(50{,}000)}{1} && \text{Set } h = 1 \text{ in the definition of the derivative.} \\ &= C(50{,}001) - C(50{,}000) \\ &= \text{cost of the 50,001st music player} \end{aligned}$$

The exact cost of the 50,001st music player is

$$\begin{aligned} C(50{,}001) - C(50{,}000) &= [150{,}000 + 20(50{,}001) - 0.0001(50{,}001)^2] \\ &\quad - [150{,}000 + 20(50{,}000) - 0.0001(50{,}000)^2] \\ &= \$9.9999 \end{aligned}$$

So, the marginal cost is a good approximation to the actual cost.

Graphically, we are using the tangent line to approximate the cost function near a production level of 50,000. Figure 3 shows the graph of the cost function together with the tangent line at $x = 50{,}000$. Notice that the tangent line is essentially indistinguishable from the graph of the function for some distance on either side of 50,000.

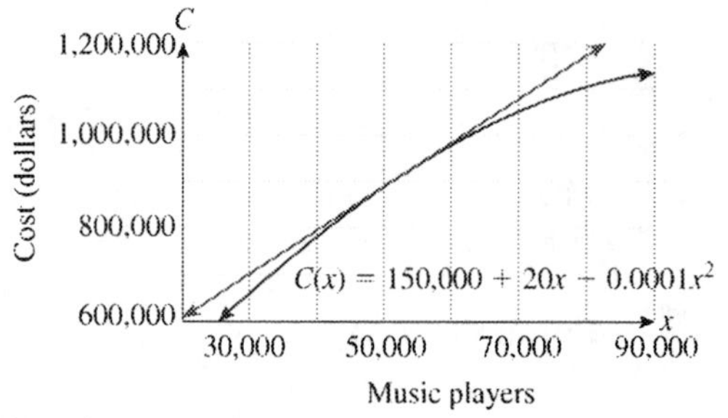

Figure 3

Notes

1. In general, the difference quotient $[C(x+h) - C(x)]/h$ gives the **average cost per item** to produce h more items at a current production level of x items. (Why?)
2. Notice that $C'(x)$ is much easier to calculate than $[C(x+h) - C(x)]/h$. (Try it.) ■

We can extend the idea of marginal cost to include other functions we discussed in Section 1.2, like revenue and profit:

Marginal Revenue and Profit

Recall that a **revenue** or **profit function** specifies the total revenue R or profit P as a function of the number of items x. The derivatives, R' and P', of these functions are called the **marginal revenue** and **marginal profit** functions. They measure the rate of change of revenue and profit with respect to the number of items.

Units

The units of marginal revenue and profit are the same as those of marginal cost: dollars (or euros, pesos, etc.) per item.

Interpretation

We interpret $R'(x)$ and $P'(x)$ as the approximate revenue and profit from the sale of one more item.

EXAMPLE 2 Marginal Revenue and Profit

You operate an *iPod* refurbishing service (a typical refurbished iPod might have a custom color case with blinking lights and a personalized logo). The cost to refurbish x iPods in a month is calculated to be

$$C(x) = 0.25x^2 + 40x + 1{,}000 \text{ dollars.}$$

You charge customers \$80 per iPod for the work.

a. Calculate the marginal revenue and profit functions. Interpret the results.

b. Compute the revenue and profit, and also the marginal revenue and profit, if you have refurbished 20 units this month. Interpret the results.

c. For which value of x is the marginal profit zero? Interpret your answer.

Solution

a. We first calculate the revenue and profit functions:

$$R(x) = 80x \qquad \text{Revenue = Price × Quantity}$$

$$P(x) = R(x) - C(x) \qquad \text{Profit = Revenue − Cost}$$

$$= 80x - (0.25x^2 + 40x + 1{,}000)$$

$$P(x) = -0.25x^2 + 40x - 1{,}000.$$

The marginal revenue and profit functions are then the derivatives:

$$\text{Marginal revenue} = R'(x) = 80$$

$$\text{Marginal profit} = P'(x) = -0.5x + 40.$$

Interpretation: $R'(x)$ gives the approximate revenue from the refurbishing of one more item, and $P'(x)$ gives the approximate profit from the refurbishing of one more item. Thus, if x iPods have been refurbished in a month, you will earn a revenue of \$80 and make a profit of approximately $\$(-0.5x + 40)$ if you refurbish one more that month.

Notice that the marginal revenue is a constant, so you earn the same revenue ($80) for each iPod you refurbish. However, the marginal profit, $\$(-0.5x + 40)$, decreases as x increases, so your additional profit is about 50¢ less for each additional iPod you refurbish.

b. From part (a), the revenue, profit, marginal revenue, and marginal profit functions are

$$R(x) = 80x$$
$$P(x) = -0.25x^2 + 40x - 1{,}000$$
$$R'(x) = 80$$
$$P'(x) = -0.5x + 40$$

Because you have refurbished $x = 20$ iPods this month, $x = 20$, so

$R(20) = 80(20) = \$1{,}600$	Total revenue from 20 iPods
$P(20) = -0.25(20)^2 + 40(20) - 1{,}000 = -\$300$	Total profit from 20 iPods
$R'(20) = \$80$ per unit	Approximate revenue from the 21st iPod
$P'(20) = -0.5(20) + 40 = \$30$ per unit	Approximate profit from the 21st iPod

Interpretation: If you refurbish 20 iPods in a month, you will earn a total revenue of \$160 and a profit of –\$300 (indicating a loss of \$300). Refurbishing one more iPod that month will earn you an additional revenue of \$80 and an additional profit of about \$30.

c. The marginal profit is zero when $P'(x) = 0$:

$$-0.5x + 40 = 0$$
$$x = \frac{40}{0.5} = 80 \text{ iPods}$$

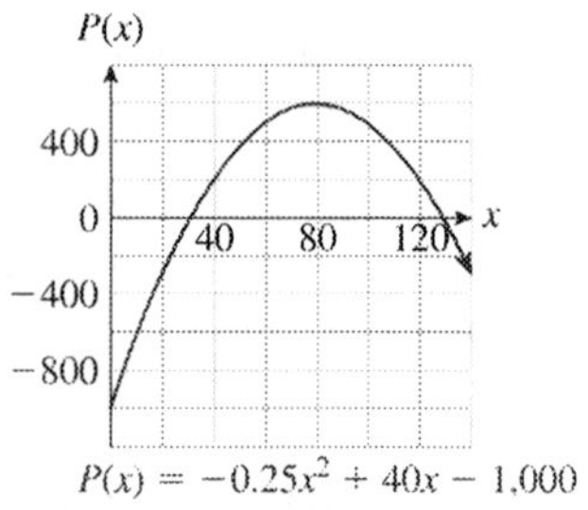

Figure 4

Thus, if you refurbish 80 iPods in a month, refurbishing one more will get you (approximately) zero additional profit. To understand this further, let us take a look at the graph of the profit function, shown in Figure 4. Notice that the graph is a parabola (the profit function is quadratic) with vertex at the point $x = 80$, where $P'(x) = 0$, so the profit is a maximum at this value of x.

➡ **Before we go on...** In general, setting $P'(x) = 0$ and solving for x will always give the exact values of x for which the profit peaks as in Figure 4, assuming there is such a value. We recommend that you graph the profit function to check whether the profit is indeed a maximum at such a point. ■

EXAMPLE 3 Marginal Product

A consultant determines that *Precision Manufacturers'* annual profit (in dollars) is given by

$$P(n) = -200{,}000 + 400{,}000n - 4{,}600n^2 - 10n^3 \qquad (10 \le n \le 50),$$

where n is the number of assembly-line workers it employs.

a. Compute $P'(n)$. $P'(n)$ is called the **marginal product** at the employment level of n assembly-line workers. What are its units?

b. Calculate $P(20)$ and $P'(20)$, and interpret the results.

c. Precision Manufacturers currently employs 20 assembly-line workers and is considering laying off some of them. What advice would you give the company's management?

Solution

a. Taking the derivative gives

$$P'(n) = 400{,}000 - 9{,}200n - 30n^2.$$

The units of $P'(n)$ are profit (in dollars) per worker.

b. Substituting into the formula for $P(n)$, we get

$$P(20) = -200{,}000 + 400{,}000(20) - 4{,}600(20)^2 - 10(20)^3 = \$5{,}880{,}000.$$

Thus, Precision Manufacturers will make an annual profit of \$5,880,000 if it employs 20 assembly-line workers. On the other hand,

$$P'(20) = 400{,}000 - 9{,}200(20) - 30(20)^2 = \$204{,}000/\text{worker}.$$

Thus, at an employment level of 20 assembly-line workers, annual profit is increasing at a rate of \$204,000 per additional worker. In other words, if the company were to employ one more assembly-line worker, its annual profit would increase by approximately \$204,000.

c. Because the marginal product is positive, profits will increase if the company increases the number of workers and will decrease if it decreases the number of workers, so your advice would be to hire additional assembly-line workers. Downsizing the assembly-line workforce would reduce its annual profits.

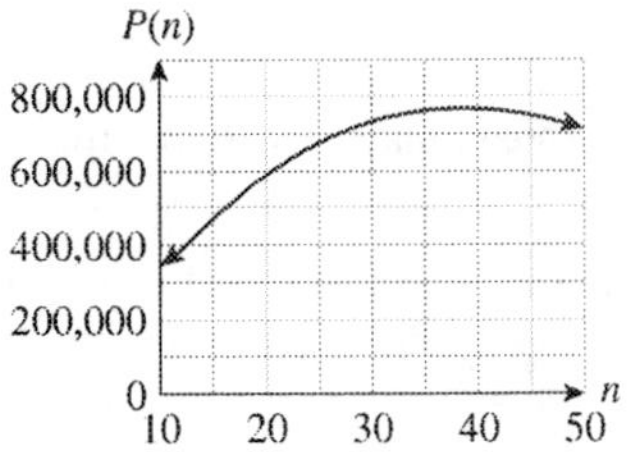

Figure 5

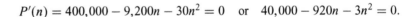

Before we go on... In Example 3, it would be interesting for Precision Manufacturers to ascertain how many additional assembly-line workers it should hire to obtain the *maximum* annual profit. Taking our cue from Example 2, we suspect that such a value of n would correspond to a point where $P'(n) = 0$. Figure 5 shows the graph of P, and on it we see that the highest point of the graph is indeed a point where the tangent line is horizontal; that is, $P'(n) = 0$, and occurs somewhere between $n = 35$ and 40. To compute this value of n more accurately, set $P'(n) = 0$ and solve for n:

$$P'(n) = 400{,}000 - 9{,}200n - 30n^2 = 0 \quad \text{or} \quad 40{,}000 - 920n - 3n^2 = 0.$$

We can now obtain n using the quadratic formula:

$$n = \frac{-b \pm \sqrt{b^2 - 4ac}}{2a} = \frac{920 \pm \sqrt{920^2 - 4(-3)(40{,}000)}}{2(-3)}$$

$$= \frac{920 \pm \sqrt{1{,}326{,}400}}{-6} \approx -345.3 \text{ or } 38.6.$$

The only meaningful solution is the positive one, $n \approx 38.6$ workers, and we conclude that the company should employ between 38 and 39 assembly-line workers for a maximum profit. To see which gives the larger profit, 38 or 39, we check:

$$P(38) = \$7{,}808{,}880$$

while

$$P(39) = \$7{,}810{,}210.$$

This tells us that the company should employ 39 assembly-line workers for a maximum profit. Thus, instead of laying off any of its 20 assembly-line workers, the company should hire 19 additional assembly-line workers for a total of 39. ■

Average Cost

EXAMPLE 4 Average Cost

Suppose the cost in dollars to manufacture portable music players is given by

$$C(x) = 150{,}000 + 20x - 0.0001x^2$$

where x is the number of music players manufactured. (This is the cost equation we saw in Example 1.)

a. Find the average cost per music player if 50,000 music players are manufactured.

b. Find a formula for the average cost per music player if x music players are manufactured. This function of x is called the **average cost function, $\bar{C}(x)$**.

Solution

a. The total cost of manufacturing 50,000 music players is given by

$$\begin{aligned} C(50{,}000) &= 150{,}000 + 20(50{,}000) - 0.0001(50{,}000)^2 \\ &= \$900{,}000. \end{aligned}$$

Because 50,000 music players cost a total of \$900,000 to manufacture, the average cost of manufacturing one music player is this total cost divided by 50,000:

$$\bar{C}(50{,}000) = \frac{900{,}000}{50{,}000} = \$18.00 \text{ per music player.}$$

Thus, if 50,000 music players are manufactured, each music player costs the manufacturer an average of \$18.00 to manufacture.

b. If we replace 50,000 by x, we get the general formula for the average cost of manufacturing x music players:

$$\begin{aligned} \bar{C}(x) &= \frac{C(x)}{x} \\ &= \frac{1}{x}(150{,}000 + 20x - 0.0001x^2) \\ &= \frac{150{,}000}{x} + 20 - 0.0001x. \end{aligned}$$ Average cost function

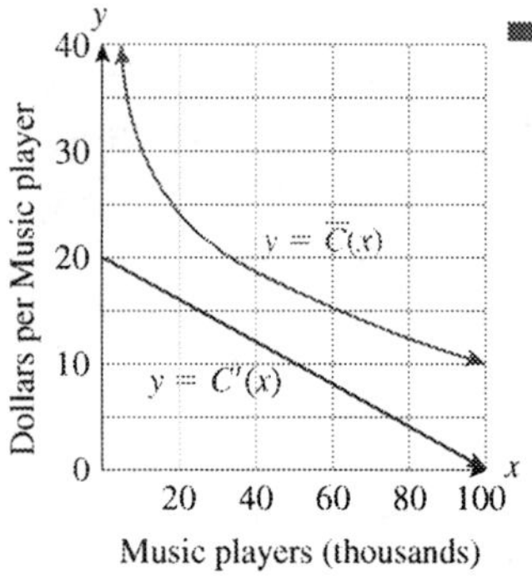

Figure 6

Before we go on... Average cost and marginal cost convey different but related information. The average cost $\bar{C}(50{,}000) = \$18$ that we calculated in Example 4 is the cost per item of manufacturing the first 50,000 music players, whereas the marginal cost $C'(50{,}000) = \$10$ that we calculated in Example 1 gives the (approximate) cost of manufacturing the *next* music player. Thus, according to our calculations, the first 50,000 music players cost an average of \$18 to manufacture, but it costs only about \$10 to manufacture the next one. Note that the marginal cost at a production level of 50,000 music players is lower than the average cost. This means that the average cost to manufacture CDs is going down with increasing volume. (Think about why.)

Figure 6 shows the graphs of average and marginal cost. Notice how the decreasing marginal cost seems to pull the average cost down with it. ■

To summarize:

Average Cost

Given a cost function C, the **average cost** of the first x items is given by

$$\bar{C}(x) = \frac{C(x)}{x}.$$

The average cost is distinct from the **marginal cost** $C'(x)$, which tells us the approximate cost of the *next* item.

Quick Example

For the cost function $C(x) = 20x + 100$ dollars

Marginal Cost $= C'(x) = \$20$ per additional item.

Average Cost $= \bar{C}(x) = \frac{C(x)}{x} = \frac{20x + 100}{x} = \$(20 + 100/x)$ per item.

11.2 EXERCISES

▼ more advanced ◆ challenging

T indicates exercises that should be solved using technology

In Exercises 1–4, for each cost function, find the marginal cost at the given production level x, and state the units of measurement. (All costs are in dollars.) HINT [See Example 1.]

1. $C(x) = 10{,}000 + 5x - 0.0001x^2;\ x = 1{,}000$

2. $C(x) = 20{,}000 + 7x - 0.00005x^2;\ x = 10{,}000$

3. $C(x) = 15{,}000 + 100x + \frac{1{,}000}{x};\ x = 100$

4. $C(x) = 20{,}000 + 50x + \frac{10{,}000}{x};\ x = 100$

In Exercises 5 and 6, find the marginal cost, marginal revenue, and marginal profit functions, and find all values of x for which the marginal profit is zero. Interpret your answer. HINT [See Example 2.]

5. $C(x) = 4x;\quad R(x) = 8x - 0.001x^2$

6. $C(x) = 5x^2;\quad R(x) = x^3 + 7x + 10$

7. ▼ A certain cost function has the following graph:

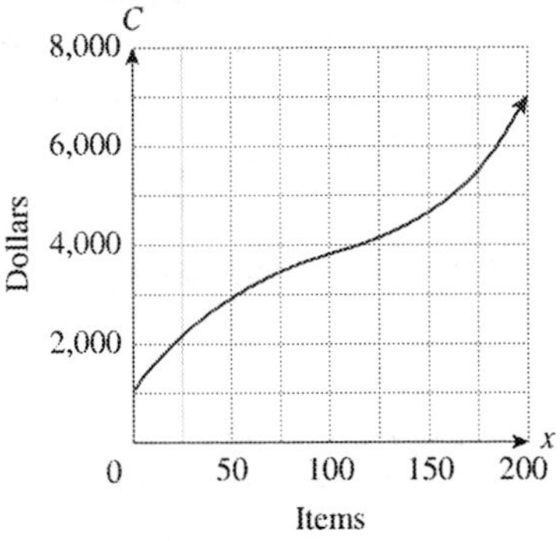

a. The associated marginal cost is

(A) increasing, then decreasing.
(B) decreasing, then increasing.
(C) always increasing.
(D) always decreasing.

b. The marginal cost is least at approximately

(A) $x = 0$. **(B)** $x = 50$. **(C)** $x = 100$. **(D)** $x = 150$.

c. The cost of 50 items is

(A) approximately \$20, and increasing at a rate of about \$3,000 per item.
(B) approximately \$0.50, and increasing at a rate of about \$3,000 per item.
(C) approximately \$3,000, and increasing at a rate of about \$20 per item.
(D) approximately \$3,000, and increasing at a rate of about \$0.50 per item.

8. ▼ A certain cost function has the following graph:

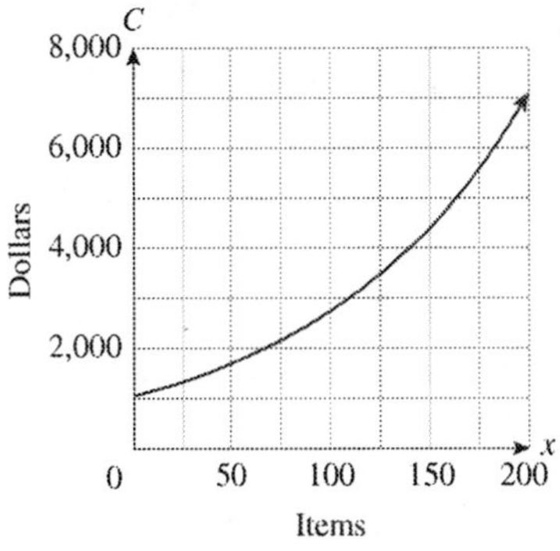

a. The associated marginal cost is

(A) increasing, then decreasing.
(B) decreasing, then increasing.
(C) always increasing.
(D) always decreasing.

b. When $x = 100$, the marginal cost is

(A) greater than the average cost.
(B) less than the average cost.
(C) approximately equal to the average cost.

c. The cost of 150 items is

(A) approximately \$4,400, and increasing at a rate of about \$40 per item.
(B) approximately \$40, and increasing at a rate of about \$4,400 per item.
(C) approximately \$4,400, and increasing at a rate of about \$1 per item.
(D) approximately \$1, and increasing at a rate of about \$4,400 per item.

APPLICATIONS

9. ***Advertising Costs*** The cost, in thousands of dollars, of airing x television commercials during a Super Bowl game is given by[11]

$$C(x) = 150 + 2{,}500x - 0.02x^2.$$

a. Find the marginal cost function and use it to estimate how fast the cost is increasing when $x = 4$. Compare this with the exact cost of airing the fifth commercial. HINT [See Example 1.]

b. Find the average cost function $\bar{C}$, and evaluate $\bar{C}(4)$. What does the answer tell you? HINT [See Example 4.]

10. ***Marginal Cost and Average Cost*** The cost of producing x teddy bears per day at the *Cuddly Companion Co.* is calculated by the company's marketing staff to be given by the formula

$$C(x) = 100 + 40x - 0.001x^2.$$

a. Find the marginal cost function and use it to estimate how fast the cost is going up at a production level of 100 teddy bears. Compare this with the exact cost of producing the 101st teddy bear. HINT [See Example 1.]

b. Find the average cost function $\bar{C}$, and evaluate $\bar{C}(100)$. What does the answer tell you? HINT [See Example 4.]

11. ***Marginal Revenue and Profit*** Your college newspaper, *The Collegiate Investigator*, sells for 90¢ per copy. The cost of producing x copies of an edition is given by

$$C(x) = 70 + 0.10x + 0.001x^2 \text{ dollars.}$$

a. Calculate the marginal revenue and profit functions. HINT [See Example 2.]

b. Compute the revenue and profit, and also the marginal revenue and profit, if you have produced and sold 500 copies of the latest edition. Interpret the results.

c. For which value of x is the marginal profit zero? Interpret your answer.

12. ***Marginal Revenue and Profit*** The Audubon Society at Enormous State University (ESU) is planning its annual fund-raising "Eatathon." The society will charge students \$1.10 per serving of pasta. The society estimates that the total cost of producing x servings of pasta at the event will be

$$C(x) = 350 + 0.10x + 0.002x^2 \text{ dollars.}$$

a. Calculate the marginal revenue and profit functions. HINT [See Example 2.]

b. Compute the revenue and profit, and also the marginal revenue and profit, if you have produced and sold 200 servings of pasta. Interpret the results.

c. For which value of x is the marginal profit zero? Interpret your answer.

13. ***Marginal Profit*** Suppose $P(x)$ represents the profit in dollars on the sale of x DVDs. If $P(1{,}000) = 3{,}000$ and $P'(1{,}000) = -3$, what do these values tell you about the profit?

14. ***Marginal Loss*** An automobile retailer calculates that its loss in dollars on the sale of *Type M* cars is given by $L(50) = 5{,}000$ and $L'(50) = -200$, where $L(x)$ represents the loss on the sale of x Type M cars. What do these values tell you about losses?

15. ***Marginal Profit*** Your monthly profit (in dollars) from selling magazines is given by

$$P = 5x + \sqrt{x}$$

where x is the number of magazines you sell in a month. If you are currently selling 50 magazines per month, find your profit and your marginal profit. Interpret your answers.

16. ***Marginal Profit*** Your monthly profit (in dollars) from your newspaper route is given by

$$P = 2n - \sqrt{n}$$

where n is the number of subscribers on your route. If you currently have 100 subscribers, find your profit and your marginal profit. Interpret your answers.

17. ▼ ***Marginal Revenue: Pricing Tuna*** Assume that the demand equation for tuna in a small coastal town is given by

$$p = \frac{20{,}000}{q^{1.5}} \qquad (200 \le q \le 800),$$

where p is the price (in dollars) per pound of tuna, and q is the number of pounds of tuna that can be sold at the price p in one month.[12]

[11] The cost of a 30-second ad during the 2010 Super Bowl game was about \$2.5 million. This explains the coefficient of x in the cost function. Source: http://en.wikipedia.org/wiki/Super_Bowl_advertising.

[12] Notice that here we have specified p as a function of q, and not the other way around as we did in Section 1.2. Economists frequently specify demand curves this way.

a. Calculate the price that the town's fishery should charge for tuna in order to produce a demand of 400 pounds of tuna per month.

b. Calculate the monthly revenue R as a function of the number of pounds of tuna q.

c. Calculate the revenue and marginal revenue (derivative of the revenue with respect to q) at a demand level of 400 pounds per month, and interpret the results.

d. If the town fishery's monthly tuna catch amounted to 400 pounds of tuna, and the price is at the level in part (a), would you recommend that the fishery raise or lower the price of tuna in order to increase its revenue?

18. ▼ ***Marginal Revenue: Pricing Tuna*** Repeat Exercise 17, assuming a demand equation of

$$p = \frac{60}{q^{0.5}} \qquad (200 \le q \le 800).$$

19. ***Marginal Product*** A car wash firm calculates that its daily profit (in dollars) depends on the number n of workers it employs according to the formula

$$P = 400n - 0.5n^2.$$

Calculate the marginal product at an employment level of 50 workers, and interpret the result. HINT [See Example 3.]

20. ***Marginal Product*** Repeat the preceding exercise using the formula

$$P = -100n + 25n^2 - 0.005n^4.$$

HINT [See Example 3.]

21. ***Average and Marginal Cost*** The daily cost to manufacture generic trinkets for gullible tourists is given by the cost function

$$C(x) = -0.001x^2 + 0.3x + 500 \text{ dollars}$$

where x is the number of trinkets.

a. As x increases, the marginal cost
(A) increases. **(B)** decreases. **(C)** increases, then decreases. **(D)** decreases, then increases.

b. As x increases, the average cost
(A) increases. **(B)** decreases. **(C)** increases, then decreases. **(D)** decreases, then increases.

c. The marginal cost is
(A) greater than **(B)** equal to **(C)** less than
the average cost when $x = 100$. HINT [See Example 4.]

22. ***Average and Marginal Cost*** Repeat Exercise 21, using the following cost function for imitation oil paintings (x is the number of "oil paintings" manufactured):

$$C(x) = 0.1x^2 - 3.5x + 500 \text{ dollars.}$$

HINT [See Example 4.]

23. ***Advertising Cost*** Your company is planning to air a number of television commercials during the ABC Television Network's presentation of the Academy Awards. ABC is charging your company \$1.6 million per 30-second spot.[13] Additional fixed costs (development and personnel costs) amount to \$500,000, and the network has agreed to provide a discount of $\$10{,}000\sqrt{x}$ for x television spots.

a. Write down the cost function C, marginal cost function C', and average cost function $\bar{C}$.

b. Compute $C'(3)$ and $\bar{C}(3)$. (Round all answers to three significant digits.) Use these two answers to say whether the average cost is increasing or decreasing as x increases.

24. ***Housing Costs*** The cost C of building a house is related to the number k of carpenters used and the number x of electricians used by the formula[14]

$$C = 15{,}000 + 50k^2 + 60x^2.$$

a. Assuming that 10 carpenters are currently being used, find the cost function C, marginal cost function C', and average cost function $\bar{C}$, all as functions of x.

b. Use the functions you obtained in part (a) to compute $C'(15)$ and $\bar{C}(15)$. Use these two answers to say whether the average cost is increasing or decreasing as the number of electricians increases.

25. ▼ ***Emission Control*** The cost of controlling emissions at a firm rises rapidly as the amount of emissions reduced increases. Here is a possible model:

$$C(q) = 4{,}000 + 100q^2$$

where q is the reduction in emissions (in pounds of pollutant per day) and C is the daily cost (in dollars) of this reduction.

a. If a firm is currently reducing its emissions by 10 pounds each day, what is the marginal cost of reducing emissions further?

b. Government clean-air subsidies to the firm are based on the formula

$$S(q) = 500q$$

where q is again the reduction in emissions (in pounds per day) and S is the subsidy (in dollars). At what reduction level does the marginal cost surpass the marginal subsidy?

c. Calculate the net cost function, $N(q) = C(q) - S(q)$, given the cost function and subsidy above, and find the value of q that gives the lowest net cost. What is this lowest net cost? Compare your answer to that for part (b) and comment on what you find.

26. ▼ ***Taxation Schemes*** In order to raise revenues during the recent recession, the governor of your state proposed the following taxation formula:

$$T(i) = 0.001i^{0.5},$$

[13]ABC charged an average of \$1.6 million for a 30-second spot during the 2005 Academy Awards presentation. Source: CNN/Reuters, www.cnn.com, February 9, 2005.

[14]Based on an exercise in *Introduction to Mathematical Economics* by A. L. Ostrosky, Jr., and J. V. Koch (Waveland Press, Prospect Heights, Illinois, 1979).

where i represents total annual income earned by an individual in dollars and $T(i)$ is the income tax rate as a percentage of total annual income. (Thus, for example, an income of \$50,000 per year would be taxed at about 22%, while an income of double that amount would be taxed at about 32%.)[15]

a. Calculate the after-tax (net) income $N(i)$ an individual can expect to earn as a function of income i.

b. Calculate an individual's marginal after-tax income at income levels of \$100,000 and \$500,000.

c. At what income does an individual's marginal after-tax income become negative? What is the after-tax income at that level, and what happens at higher income levels?

d. What do you suspect is the most anyone can earn after taxes? (See NOTE at the bottom of this page.)

27. ▼ ***Fuel Economy*** Your Porsche's gas mileage (in miles per gallon) is given as a function $M(x)$ of speed x in miles per hour. It is found that

$$M'(x) = \frac{3{,}600x^{-2} - 1}{(3{,}600x^{-1} + x)^2}.$$

Estimate $M'(10)$, $M'(60)$, and $M'(70)$. What do the answers tell you about your car?

28. ▼ ***Marginal Revenue*** The estimated marginal revenue for sales of ESU soccer team T-shirts is given by

$$R'(p) = \frac{(8 - 2p)e^{-p^2+8p}}{10{,}000{,}000}$$

where p is the price (in dollars) that the soccer players charge for each shirt. Estimate $R'(3)$, $R'(4)$, and $R'(5)$. What do the answers tell you?

29. ◆ ***Marginal Cost*** *(from the GRE Economics Test)* In a multiplant firm in which the different plants have different and continuous cost schedules, if costs of production for a given output level are to be minimized, which of the following is essential?

(A) Marginal costs must equal marginal revenue.
(B) Average variable costs must be the same in all plants.
(C) Marginal costs must be the same in all plants.
(D) Total costs must be the same in all plants.
(E) Output per worker per hour must be the same in all plants.

30. ◆ ***Study Time*** *(from the GRE economics test)* A student has a fixed number of hours to devote to study and is certain of the relationship between hours of study and the final grade for each course. Grades are given on a numerical scale (0 to 100), and each course is counted equally in computing the grade average. In order to maximize his or her grade average, the student should allocate these hours to different courses so that

(A) the grade in each course is the same.
(B) the marginal product of an hour's study (in terms of final grade) in each course is zero.
(C) the marginal product of an hour's study (in terms of final grade) in each course is equal, although not necessarily equal to zero.
(D) the average product of an hour's study (in terms of final grade) in each course is equal.
(E) the number of hours spent in study for each course is equal.

31. ◆ ***Marginal Product*** *(from the GRE Economics Test)* Assume that the marginal product of an additional senior professor is 50% higher than the marginal product of an additional junior professor and that junior professors are paid one half the amount that senior professors receive. With a fixed overall budget, a university that wishes to maximize its quantity of output from professors should do which of the following?

(A) Hire equal numbers of senior professors and junior professors.
(B) Hire more senior professors and junior professors.
(C) Hire more senior professors and discharge junior professors.
(D) Discharge senior professors and hire more junior professors.
(E) Discharge all senior professors and half of the junior professors.

32. ◆ ***Marginal Product (based on a question from the GRE Economics Test)*** Assume that the marginal product of an additional senior professor is twice the marginal product of an additional junior professor and that junior professors are paid two thirds the amount that senior professors receive. With a fixed overall budget, a university that wishes to maximize its quantity of output from professors should do which of the following?

(A) Hire equal numbers of senior professors and junior professors.
(B) Hire more senior professors and junior professors.
(C) Hire more senior professors and discharge junior professors.
(D) Discharge senior professors and hire more junior professors.
(E) Discharge all senior professors and half of the junior professors.

COMMUNICATION AND REASONING EXERCISES

33. The marginal cost of producing the 1,001st item is

(A) equal to
(B) approximately equal to
(C) always slightly greater than
(D) always slightly less than

the actual cost of producing the 1,001st item.

34. For the cost function $C(x) = mx + b$, the marginal cost of producing the 1,001st item is,

(A) equal to
(B) approximately equal to
(C) always slightly greater than
(D) always slightly less than

the actual cost of producing the 1,001st item.

[15]This model has the following interesting feature: An income of \$1 million per year would be taxed at 100%, leaving the individual penniless!

35. What is a cost function? Carefully explain the difference between *average cost* and *marginal cost* in terms of **(a)** their mathematical definition, **(b)** graphs, and **(c)** interpretation.

36. The cost function for your grand piano manufacturing plant has the property that $\bar{C}(1{,}000) = \$3{,}000$ per unit and $C'(1{,}000) = \$2{,}500$ per unit. Will the average cost increase or decrease if your company manufactures a slightly larger number of pianos? Explain your reasoning.

37. Give an example of a cost function for which the marginal cost function is the same as the average cost function.

38. Give an example of a cost function for which the marginal cost function is always less than the average cost function.

39. If the average cost to manufacture one grand piano increases as the production level increases, which is greater, the marginal cost or the average cost?

40. If your analysis of a manufacturing company yielded positive marginal profit but negative profit at the company's current production levels, what would you advise the company to do?

41. ▼ If the marginal cost is decreasing, is the average cost necessarily decreasing? Explain.

42. ▼ If the average cost is decreasing, is the marginal cost necessarily decreasing? Explain.

43. ◆ If a company's marginal average cost is zero at the current production level, positive for a slightly higher production level, and negative for a slightly lower production level, what should you advise the company to do?

44. ◆ The **acceleration** of cost is defined as the derivative of the marginal cost function: that is, the derivative of the derivative—or *second derivative*—of the cost function. What are the units of acceleration of cost, and how does one interpret this measure?

Practice Problems 11.2, Part 1

The graph to the right shows cost and revenue as functions of number of units of a product produced and sold. You need to decide which graph is the cost function and which graph is the revenue function.

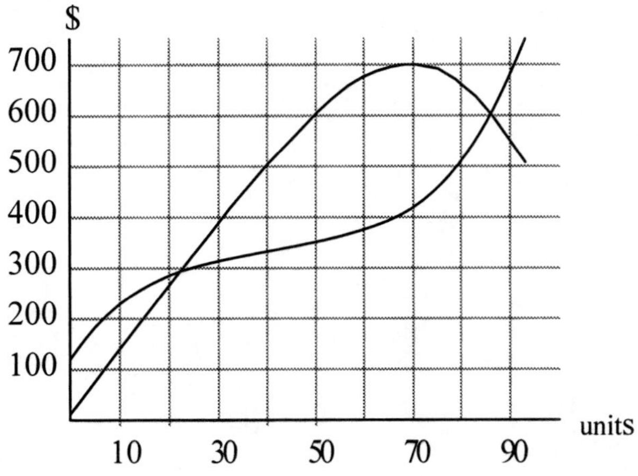

1. Estimate marginal cost and marginal revenue at 40 units. Label appropriately.

2. Estimate the number of units produced and sold where marginal cost and marginal revenue are equal.

3. Estimate the number of units that should be produced and sold in order to generate maximum possible profit.

4. Is profit increasing or decreasing at 40 units produced and sold? Explain your conclusion using marginal cost and marginal revenue.

5. Estimate a production level where average cost and marginal cost are equal.

Practice Problems 11.2, Part 2

1. The manager of a small furniture manufacturing company has agreed to deliver an order of up to 600 chairs to a customer. If the size of the order is 400 chairs or less, the price per chair will be \$60. If more than 400 chairs are ordered, then the price per chair will be discounted by \$0.20 for each chair **over** 400 ordered (the discounted price applies to the entire order). Let $R(x)$ denote the revenue from an order of x chairs.
   a. Calculate $R(320)$ and $R'(320)$. Label each appropriately.

   b. Calculate $R(450)$ and $R'(450)$. Label each appropriately.

2. Lucinda sells packets of old Math 146 exams (and solutions!) to willing purchasers. Her profit per semester from selling x packets is given by $P(x) = 5x + \sqrt{x}$ dollars.
   a. How many packets has she sold if her marginal profit is \$5.05 per packet?

   b. Suppose that it costs Lucinda, on average, \$1.625 per packet for photocopying if she photocopies 64 packets. If she sells each packet for \$$p$, then determine the value of p.

Practice Problems 11.2, Part 3

A state operates a weekly lottery where the jackpot starts at $100,000 and grows each week until a winning ticket is purchased. The state reclaims some of the lottery winnings by way of a tax on those winnings. If w is the size of the winning jackpot (in dollars), then the corresponding tax is $T(w) = 0.02w^{1.2}$ dollars.

1. Suppose that one week the jackpot is $2,000,000. If a winning ticket is sold, then what are the net winnings, to the nearest dollar?

2. Given a jackpot of $2,000,000, calculate the marginal after-tax winnings. Label appropriately.

3. Is there a jackpot size where the marginal after-tax winnings changes from positive to negative? If so, find that jackpot size (to the nearest dollar) and explain what is significant (in terms of winnings) about that jackpot size. If no such jackpot size exists, then explain why.

11.3 The Product and Quotient Rules

We know how to find the derivatives of functions that are sums of powers, such as polynomials. In general, if a function is a sum or difference of functions whose derivatives we know, then we know how to find its derivative. But what about *products and quotients* of functions whose derivatives we know? For instance, how do we calculate the derivative of something like $x^2/(x+1)$? The derivative of $x^2/(x+1)$ is not, as one might suspect, $2x/1 = 2x$. That calculation is based on an assumption that the derivative of a quotient is the quotient of the derivatives. But it is easy to see that this assumption is false: For instance, the derivative of $1/x$ is not $0/1 = 0$, but $-1/x^2$. Similarly, the derivative of a product is not the product of the derivatives: For instance, the derivative of $x = 1 \cdot x$ is not $0 \cdot 1 = 0$, but 1.

To identify the correct method of computing the derivatives of products and quotients, let's look at a simple example. We know that the daily revenue resulting from the sale of q items per day at a price of p dollars per item is given by the product, $R = pq$ dollars. Suppose you are currently selling wall posters on campus. At this time your daily sales are 50 posters, and sales are increasing at a rate of 4 per day. Furthermore, you are currently charging \$10 per poster, and you are also raising the price at a rate of \$2 per day. Let's use this information to estimate how fast your daily revenue is increasing. In other words, let us estimate the rate of change, dR/dt, of the revenue R.

There are two contributions to the rate of change of daily revenue: the increase in daily sales and the increase in the unit price. We have

$$\frac{dR}{dt} \text{ due to increasing price:} \quad \$2 \text{ per day} \times 50 \text{ posters} = \$100 \text{ per day}$$

$$\frac{dR}{dt} \text{ due to increasing sales:} \quad \$10 \text{ per poster} \times 4 \text{ posters per day} = \$40 \text{ per day.}$$

Thus, we estimate the daily revenue to be increasing at a rate of \$100 + \$40 = \$140 per day. Let us translate what we have said into symbols:

$$\frac{dR}{dt} \text{ due to increasing price: } \quad \frac{dp}{dt} \times q$$

$$\frac{dR}{dt} \text{ due to increasing sales: } \quad p \times \frac{dq}{dt}.$$

Thus, the rate of change of revenue is given by

$$\frac{dR}{dt} = \frac{dp}{dt}q + p\frac{dq}{dt}.$$

Because $R = pq$, we have discovered the following rule for differentiating a product:

$$\frac{d}{dt}(pq) = \frac{dp}{dt}q + p\frac{dq}{dt}.$$

The derivative of a product is the derivative of the first times the second, plus the first times the derivative of the second.

This rule and a similar rule for differentiating quotients are given next, and also a discussion of how these results are proved rigorously.

Product Rule

If f and g are differentiable functions of x, then so is their product fg, and

$$\frac{d}{dx}[f(x)g(x)] = f'(x)g(x) + f(x)g'(x).$$

Product Rule in Words

The derivative of a product is the derivative of the first times the second, plus the first times the derivative of the second.

Quick Example

Let $f(x) = x^2$ and $g(x) = 3x - 1$. Because f and g are both differentiable functions of x, so is their product fg, and its derivative is

$$\frac{d}{dx}[x^2(3x - 1)] = \underset{\text{Derivative of first}}{2x} \cdot \underset{\text{Second}}{(3x - 1)} + \underset{\text{First}}{x^2} \cdot \underset{\text{Derivative of second}}{(3)}.$$

Quotient Rule

If f and g are differentiable functions of x, then so is their quotient f/g, and

$$\frac{d}{dx}\left(\frac{f(x)}{g(x)}\right) = \frac{f'(x)g(x) - f(x)g'(x)}{[g(x)]^2}.$$

provided $g(x) \neq 0$.*

Quotient Rule in Words

The derivative of a quotient is the derivative of the top times the bottom, minus the top times the derivative of the bottom, all over the bottom squared.

* If $g(x)$ is zero, then the quotient $f(x)/g(x)$ is not defined in the first place.

Quick Example

Let $f(x) = x^3$ and $g(x) = x^2 - 1$. Because f and g are both differentiable functions of x, so is their quotient f/g, and its derivative is

$$\frac{d}{dx}\left(\frac{x^3}{x^2-1}\right) = \frac{\overset{\text{Derivative of top}}{3x^2}\,\overset{\text{Bottom}}{(x^2-1)} - \overset{\text{Top}}{x^3} \cdot \overset{\text{Derivative of bottom}}{2x}}{\underset{\text{Bottom squared}}{(x^2-1)^2}},$$

provided $x \neq 1$ or -1.

Notes

1. Don't try to remember the rules by the symbols we have used, but remember them in words. (The slogans are easy to remember, even if the terms are not precise.)
2. One more time: *The derivative of a product is* NOT *the product of the derivatives, and the derivative of a quotient is* NOT *the quotient of the derivatives.* To find the derivative of a product, you must use the product rule, and to find the derivative of a quotient, you must use the quotient rule.* ■

* Leibniz made this mistake at first, too, so you would be in good company if you forgot to use the product or quotient rule.

Q: *Wait a minute! The expression $2x^3$ is a product, and we already know that its derivative is $6x^2$. Where did we use the product rule?*

A: To differentiate functions such as $2x^3$, we have used the rule from Section 11.1:

The derivative of c times a function is c times the derivative of the function.

However, the product rule gives us the same result:

$$\frac{d}{dx}(2x^3) = \overset{\text{Derivative of first}}{(0)}\,\overset{\text{Second}}{(x^3)} + \overset{\text{First}}{(2)}\,\overset{\text{Derivative of second}}{(3x^2)} = 6x^2 \qquad \text{Product rule}$$

$$\frac{d}{dx}(2x^3) = (2)(3x^2) = 6x^2 \qquad \text{Derivative of a constant times a function}$$

We do not recommend that you use the product rule to differentiate functions such as $2x^3$; continue to use the simpler rule when one of the factors is a constant.

Derivation of the Product Rule

Before we look at more examples of using the product and quotient rules, let's see why the product rule is true. To calculate the derivative of the product $f(x)g(x)$ of two differentiable functions, we go back to the definition of the derivative:

$$\frac{d}{dx}[f(x)g(x)] = \lim_{h\to 0} \frac{f(x+h)g(x+h) - f(x)g(x)}{h}.$$

We now rewrite this expression so that we can evaluate the limit: Notice that the numerator reflects a simultaneous change in f [from $f(x)$ to $f(x+h)$] and g [from

$g(x)$ to $g(x+h)$]. To separate the two effects, we add and subtract a quantity in the numerator that reflects a change in only one of the functions:

$$\frac{d}{dx}[f(x)g(x)] = \lim_{h\to 0} \frac{f(x+h)g(x+h) - f(x)g(x)}{h}$$

$$= \lim_{h\to 0} \frac{f(x+h)g(x+h) - f(x)g(x+h) + f(x)g(x+h) - f(x)g(x)}{h}$$ We subtracted and added the quantity* $f(x)g(x+h)$.

$$= \lim_{h\to 0} \frac{[f(x+h) - f(x)]\,g(x+h) + f(x)[g(x+h) - g(x)]}{h}$$ Common factors

$$= \lim_{h\to 0} \left(\frac{f(x+h)-f(x)}{h}\right) g(x+h) + \lim_{h\to 0} f(x)\left(\frac{g(x+h)-g(x)}{h}\right)$$ Limit of sum

$$= \lim_{h\to 0} \left(\frac{f(x+h)-f(x)}{h}\right) \lim_{h\to 0} g(x+h) + \lim_{h\to 0} f(x) \lim_{h\to 0}\left(\frac{g(x+h)-g(x)}{h}\right)$$ Limit of product

Now we already know the following four limits:

$$\lim_{h\to 0} \frac{f(x+h)-f(x)}{h} = f'(x)$$ Definition of derivative of f; f is differentiable.

$$\lim_{h\to 0} \frac{g(x+h)-g(x)}{h} = g'(x)$$ Definition of derivative of g; g is differentiable.

$$\lim_{h\to 0} g(x+h) = g(x)$$ If g is differentiable, it must be continuous.†

$$\lim_{h\to 0} f(x) = f(x)$$ Limit of a constant

Putting these limits into the one we're calculating, we get

$$\frac{d}{dx}[f(x)g(x)] = f'(x)g(x) + f(x)g'(x)$$

which is the product rule.

* Adding an appropriate form of zero is an age-old mathematical ploy.

† For a proof of the fact that, if g is differentiable, it must be continuous, go to the Website and follow the path

Everything
→ Chapter 11
→ Continuity and Differentiability

EXAMPLE 1 Using the Product Rule

Compute the following derivatives.

a. $\frac{d}{dx}[(x^{3.2}+1)(1-x)]$ Simplify the answer.

b. $\frac{d}{dx}[(x+1)(x^2+1)(x^3+1)]$ Do not expand the answer.

c. $\frac{d}{dx}\left[\frac{x|x|}{2}\right]$

Website
www.WanerMath.com
The quotient rule can be proved in a very similar way. Go to the Website and follow the path

Everything
→ Chapter 11
→ Proof of Quotient Rule

Solution

a. We can do the calculation in two ways.

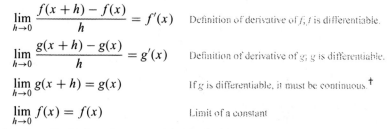

Using the Product Rule:

$$\frac{d}{dx}[(x^{3.2}+1)(1-x)] = \underbrace{(3.2x^{2.2})}_{\text{Derivative of first}}\underbrace{(1-x)}_{\text{Second}} + \underbrace{(x^{3.2}+1)}_{\text{First}}\underbrace{(-1)}_{\text{Derivative of second}}$$

$$= 3.2x^{2.2} - 3.2x^{3.2} - x^{3.2} - 1$$ Expand the answer.

$$= -4.2x^{3.2} + 3.2x^{2.2} - 1$$

Not Using the Product Rule: First, expand the given expression.

$$(x^{3.2}+1)(1-x) = -x^{4.2}+x^{3.2}-x+1$$

Thus,

$$\frac{d}{dx}[(x^{3.2}+1)(1-x)] = \frac{d}{dx}(-x^{4.2}+x^{3.2}-x+1)$$
$$= -4.2x^{3.2}+3.2x^{2.2}-1$$

In this example the product rule saves us little or no work, but in later sections we shall see examples that can be done in no other way. Learn how to use the product rule now!

b. Here we have a product of *three* functions, not just two. We can find the derivative by using the product rule twice:

$$\frac{d}{dx}[(x+1)(x^2+1)(x^3+1)]$$
$$= \frac{d}{dx}(x+1)\cdot[(x^2+1)(x^3+1)] + (x+1)\cdot\frac{d}{dx}[(x^2+1)(x^3+1)]$$
$$= (1)(x^2+1)(x^3+1) + (x+1)[(2x)(x^3+1)+(x^2+1)(3x^2)]$$
$$= (1)(x^2+1)(x^3+1) + (x+1)(2x)(x^3+1) + (x+1)(x^2+1)(3x^2)$$

We can see here a more general product rule:

$$(fgh)' = f'gh + fg'h + fgh'$$

Notice that every factor has a chance to contribute to the rate of change of the product. There are similar formulas for products of four or more functions.

c. First write $\frac{x|x|}{2}$ as $\frac{1}{2}x|x|$.

$$\frac{d}{dx}\left[\frac{1}{2}x|x|\right] = \frac{1}{2}\frac{d}{dx}[x|x|]$$ Constant multiple rule

$$= \frac{1}{2}\left((1)\cdot|x| + x\cdot\frac{|x|}{x}\right)$$ Recall that $\frac{d}{dx}|x| = \frac{|x|}{x}$.

$$= \frac{1}{2}(|x|+|x|)$$ Cancel the x.

$$= \frac{1}{2}(2|x|) = |x|$$ See the note.*

* Notice that we have found a function whose derivative is $|x|$; namely $x|x|/2$. Notice also that the derivation we gave assumes that $x \neq 0$ because we divided by x in the third step. However, one can verify, using the definition of the derivative as a limit, that $x|x|/2$ is differentiable at $x = 0$ as well, and that its derivative at $x = 0$ is 0, implying that the formula $\frac{d}{dx}(x|x|/2) = |x|$ is valid for all values of x, including 0.

EXAMPLE 2 Using the Quotient Rule

Compute the derivatives **a.** $\frac{d}{dx}\left[\frac{1-3.2x^{-0.1}}{x+1}\right]$ **b.** $\frac{d}{dx}\left[\frac{(x+1)(x+2)}{x-1}\right]$

Solution

Derivative of top ↓ Bottom ↓ Top ↓ Derivative of bottom ↓

a. $$\frac{d}{dx}\left[\frac{1-3.2x^{-0.1}}{x+1}\right] = \frac{(0.32x^{-1.1})(x+1)-(1-3.2x^{-0.1})(1)}{(x+1)^2}$$

↑ Bottom squared

$$= \frac{0.32x^{-0.1} + 0.32x^{-1.1} - 1 + 3.2x^{-0.1}}{(x+1)^2} \qquad \text{Expand the numerator.}$$

$$= \frac{3.52x^{-0.1} + 0.32x^{-1.1} - 1}{(x+1)^2}$$

b. Here we have both a product and a quotient. Which rule do we use, the product or the quotient rule? Here is a way to decide. Think about how we would calculate, step by step, the value of $(x+1)(x+2)/(x-1)$ for a specific value of x—say $x = 11$. Here is how we would probably do it:

1. Calculate $(x+1)(x+2) = (11+1)(11+2) = 156$.
2. Calculate $x - 1 = 11 - 1 = 10$.
3. Divide 156 by 10 to get 15.6.

Now ask: *What was the last operation we performed?* The last operation we performed was division, so we can regard the whole expression as a *quotient*—that is, as $(x+1)(x+2)$ *divided by* $(x-1)$. Therefore, we should use the quotient rule.

The first thing the quotient rule tells us to do is to take the derivative of the numerator. Now, the numerator is a product, so we must use the product rule to take its derivative. Here is the calculation:

$$\frac{d}{dx}\left[\frac{(x+1)(x+2)}{x-1}\right] = \frac{\overbrace{[(1)(x+2)+(x+1)(1)]}^{\text{Derivative of top}}\overbrace{(x-1)}^{\text{Bottom}} - \overbrace{[(x+1)(x+2)]}^{\text{Top}}\overbrace{(1)}^{\text{Derivative of bottom}}}{\underbrace{(x-1)^2}_{\text{Bottom squared}}}$$

$$= \frac{(2x+3)(x-1) - (x+1)(x+2)}{(x-1)^2}$$

$$= \frac{x^2 - 2x - 5}{(x-1)^2}$$

What is important is to determine the *order of operations* and, in particular, to determine the last operation to be performed. Pretending to do an actual calculation reminds us of the order of operations; we call this technique the **calculation thought experiment**.

➡ **Before we go on...** We used the quotient rule in Example 2 because the function was a quotient; we used the product rule to calculate the derivative of the numerator because the numerator was a product. Get used to this: Differentiation rules usually must be used in combination.

Here is another way we could have done this problem: Our calculation thought experiment could have taken the following form.

1. Calculate $(x+1)/(x-1) = (11+1)/(11-1) = 1.2$.
2. Calculate $x + 2 = 11 + 2 = 13$.
3. Multiply 1.2 by 13 to get 15.6.

We would have then regarded the expression as a *product*—the product of the factors $(x+1)/(x-1)$ and $(x+2)$—and used the product rule instead. We can't escape the quotient rule, however: We need to use it to take the derivative of the first factor, $(x+1)/(x-1)$. Try this approach for practice and check that you get the same answer. ■

Calculation Thought Experiment

The **calculation thought experiment** is a technique to determine whether to treat an algebraic expression as a product, quotient, sum, or difference. Given an expression, consider the steps you would use in computing its value. If the last operation is multiplication, treat the expression as a product; if the last operation is division, treat the expression as a quotient; and so on.

Quick Examples

1. $(3x^2-4)(2x+1)$ can be computed by first calculating the expressions in parentheses and then multiplying. Because the last step is multiplication, we can treat the expression as a product.
2. $\dfrac{2x-1}{x}$ can be computed by first calculating the numerator and denominator and then dividing one by the other. Because the last step is division, we can treat the expression as a quotient.
3. $x^2+(4x-1)(x+2)$ can be computed by first calculating x^2, then calculating the product $(4x-1)(x+2)$, and finally adding the two answers. Thus, we can treat the expression as a sum.
4. $(3x^2-1)^5$ can be computed by first calculating the expression in parentheses and then raising the answer to the fifth power. Thus, we can treat the expression as a power. (We shall see how to differentiate powers of expressions in Section 11.4.)
5. The expression $(x+1)(x+2)/(x-1)$ can be treated as either a quotient or a product: We can write it as a quotient: $\dfrac{(x+1)(x+2)}{x-1}$ or as a product: $(x+1)\left(\dfrac{x+2}{x-1}\right)$. (See Example 2(b).)

EXAMPLE 3 Using the Calculation Thought Experiment

Find $\dfrac{d}{dx}\left[6x^2+5\left(\dfrac{x}{x-1}\right)\right]$.

Solution The calculation thought experiment tells us that the expression we are asked to differentiate can be treated as a *sum*. Because the derivative of a sum is the sum of the derivatives, we get

$$\frac{d}{dx}\left[6x^2+5\left(\frac{x}{x-1}\right)\right]=\frac{d}{dx}(6x^2)+\frac{d}{dx}\left[5\left(\frac{x}{x-1}\right)\right].$$

In other words, we must take the derivatives of $6x^2$ and $5\left(\frac{x}{x-1}\right)$ separately and then add the answers. The derivative of $6x^2$ is $12x$. There are two ways of taking the derivative of $5\left(\frac{x}{x-1}\right)$: We could either first multiply the expression $\left(\frac{x}{x-1}\right)$ by 5 to get $\left(\frac{5x}{x-1}\right)$ and then take its derivative using the quotient rule, or we could pull the 5 out, as we do next.

$$\frac{d}{dx}\left[6x^2 + 5\left(\frac{x}{x-1}\right)\right] = \frac{d}{dx}(6x^2) + \frac{d}{dx}\left[5\left(\frac{x}{x-1}\right)\right] \qquad \text{Derivative of sum}$$

$$= 12x + 5\frac{d}{dx}\left(\frac{x}{x-1}\right) \qquad \text{Constant} \times \text{Function}$$

$$= 12x + 5\left(\frac{(1)(x-1) - (x)(1)}{(x-1)^2}\right) \qquad \text{Quotient rule}$$

$$= 12x + 5\left(\frac{-1}{(x-1)^2}\right)$$

$$= 12x - \frac{5}{(x-1)^2}$$

APPLICATIONS

In the next example, we return to a scenario similar to the one discussed at the start of this section.

EXAMPLE 4 Applying the Product and Quotient Rules: Revenue and Average Cost

Sales of your newly launched miniature wall posters for college dorms, *iMiniPosters,* are really taking off. (Those old-fashioned large wall posters no longer fit in today's "downsized" college dorm rooms.) Monthly sales to students at the start of this year were 1,500 iMiniPosters, and since that time, sales have been increasing by 300 posters each month, even though the price you charge has also been going up.

a. The price you charge for iMiniPosters is given by

$$p(t) = 10 + 0.05t^2 \text{ dollars per poster,}$$

where t is time in months since the start of January of this year. Find a formula for the monthly revenue, and then compute its rate of change at the beginning of March.

b. The number of students who purchase iMiniPosters in a month is given by

$$n(t) = 800 + 0.2t,$$

where t is as in part (a). Find a formula for the average number of posters each student buys, and hence estimate the rate at which this number was growing at the beginning of March.

Solution

a. To compute monthly revenue as a function of time t, we use

$$R(t) = p(t)q(t). \qquad \text{Revenue} = \text{Price} \times \text{Quantity}$$

We already have a formula for $p(t)$. The function $q(t)$ measures sales, which were 1,500 posters/month at time $t = 0$, and were rising by 300 per month:

$$q(t) = 1{,}500 + 300t.$$

Therefore, the formula for revenue is

$$R(t) = p(t)q(t)$$
$$R(t) = (10 + 0.05t^2)(1{,}500 + 300t).$$

Rather than expand this expression, we shall leave it as a product so that we can use the product rule in computing its rate of change:

$$\begin{aligned} R'(t) &= p'(t)q(t) + p(t)q'(t) \\ &= [0.10t][1{,}500 + 300t] + [10 + 0.05t^2][300]. \end{aligned}$$

Because the beginning of March corresponds to $t = 2$, we have

$$\begin{aligned} R'(2) &= [0.10(2)][1{,}500 + 300(2)] + [10 + 0.05(2)^2][300] \\ &= (0.2)(2{,}100) + (10.2)(300) = \$3{,}480 \text{ per month.} \end{aligned}$$

Therefore, your monthly revenue was increasing at a rate of \$3,480 per month at the beginning of March.

b. The average number of posters sold to each student is

$$k(t) = \frac{\text{Number of posters}}{\text{Number of students}} = \frac{q(t)}{n(t)} = \frac{1{,}500 + 300t}{800 + 0.2t}.$$

The rate of change of $k(t)$ is computed with the quotient rule:

$$\begin{aligned} k'(t) &= \frac{q'(t)n(t) - q(t)n'(t)}{n(t)^2} \\ &= \frac{(300)(800 + 0.2t) - (1{,}500 + 300t)(0.2)}{(800 + 0.2t)^2} \end{aligned}$$

so that

$$\begin{aligned} k'(2) &= \frac{(300)[800 + 0.2(2)] - [1{,}500 + 300(2)](0.2)}{[800 + 0.2(2)]^2} \\ &= \frac{(300)(800.4) - (2{,}100)(0.2)}{800.4^2} \approx 0.37 \text{ posters/student per month.} \end{aligned}$$

Therefore, the average number of posters sold to each student was increasing at a rate of about 0.37 posters/student per month.

11.3 EXERCISES

▼ more advanced ◆ challenging

T indicates exercises that should be solved using technology

In Exercises 1–12:

a. *Calculate the derivative of the given function without using either the product or quotient rule.*

b. *Use the product or quotient rule to find the derivative. Check that you obtain the same answer.* HINT [See Quick Examples on pages 810–811.]

1. $f(x) = 3x$ **2.** $f(x) = 2x^2$

3. $g(x) = x \cdot x^2$ **4.** $g(x) = x \cdot x$

5. $h(x) = x(x + 3)$ **6.** $h(x) = x(1 + 2x)$

7. $r(x) = 100x^{2.1}$ **8.** $r(x) = 0.2x^{-1}$ **9.** $s(x) = \frac{2}{x}$

10. $t(x) = \frac{x}{3}$ **11.** $u(x) = \frac{x^2}{3}$ **12.** $s(x) = \frac{3}{x^2}$

Calculate $\frac{dy}{dx}$ *in Exercises 13–28. Simplify your answer.* HINT [See Examples 1 and 2.]

13. $y = 3x(4x^2-1)$

14. $y = 3x^2(2x+1)$

15. $y = x^3(1-x^2)$

16. $y = x^5(1-x)$

17. $y = (2x+3)^2$

18. $y = (4x-1)^2$

19. $y = \frac{4x}{5x-2}$

20. $y = \frac{3x}{-3x+2}$

21. $y = \frac{2x+4}{3x-1}$

22. $y = \frac{3x-9}{2x+4}$

23. $y = \frac{|x|}{x}$

24. $y = \frac{x}{|x|}$

25. $y = \frac{|x|}{x^2}$

26. $y = \frac{x^2}{|x|}$

27. $y = x\sqrt{x}$

28. $y = x^2\sqrt{x}$

Calculate $\frac{dy}{dx}$ *in Exercises 29–56. You need not expand your answers.* HINT [See Examples 1 and 2.]

29. $y = (x+1)(x^2-1)$

30. $y = (4x^2+x)(x-x^2)$

31. $y = (2x^{0.5}+4x-5)(x-x^{-1})$

32. $y = (x^{0.7}-4x-5)(x^{-1}+x^{-2})$

33. $y = (2x^2-4x+1)^2$

34. $y = (2x^{0.5}-x^2)^2$

35. $y = \left(\frac{x}{3.2}+\frac{3.2}{x}\right)(x^2+1)$

36. $y = \left(\frac{x^{2.1}}{7}+\frac{2}{x^{2.1}}\right)(7x-1)$

37. $y = x^2(2x+3)(7x+2)$ HINT [See Example 1(b).]

38. $y = x(x^2-3)(2x^2+1)$ HINT [See Example 1(b).]

39. $y = (5.3x-1)(1-x^{2.1})(x^{-2.3}-3.4)$

40. $y = (1.1x+4)(x^{2.1}-x)(3.4-x^{-2.1})$

41. ▼ $y = (\sqrt{x}+1)\left(\sqrt{x}+\frac{1}{x^2}\right)$

42. ▼ $y = (4x^2-\sqrt{x})\left(\sqrt{x}-\frac{2}{x^2}\right)$

43. $y = \frac{2x^2+4x+1}{3x-1}$

44. $y = \frac{3x^2-9x+11}{2x+4}$

45. $y = \frac{x^2-4x+1}{x^2+x+1}$

46. $y = \frac{x^2+9x-1}{x^2+2x-1}$

47. $y = \frac{x^{0.23}-5.7x}{1-x^{-2.9}}$

48. $y = \frac{8.43x^{-0.1}-0.5x^{-1}}{3.2+x^{2.9}}$

49. ▼ $y = \frac{\sqrt{x}+1}{\sqrt{x}-1}$

50. ▼ $y = \frac{\sqrt{x}-1}{\sqrt{x}+1}$

51. ▼ $y = \frac{\left(\frac{1}{x}+\frac{1}{x^2}\right)}{x+x^2}$

52. ▼ $y = \frac{\left(1-\frac{1}{x^2}\right)}{x^2-1}$

53. $y = \frac{(x+3)(x+1)}{3x-1}$ HINT [See Example 2(b).]

54. $y = \frac{x}{(x-5)(x-4)}$ HINT [See Example 2(b).]

55. $y = \frac{(x+3)(x+1)(x+2)}{3x-1}$

56. $y = \frac{3x-1}{(x-5)(x-4)(x-1)}$

In Exercises 57–62, compute the indicated derivatives.

57. $\frac{d}{dx}[(x^2+x)(x^2-x)]$

58. $\frac{d}{dx}[(x^2+x^3)(x+1)]$

59. $\frac{d}{dx}[(x^3+2x)(x^2-x)]\Big|_{x=2}$

60. $\frac{d}{dx}[(x^2+x)(x^2-x)]\Big|_{x=1}$

61. $\frac{d}{dt}[(t^2-t^{0.5})(t^{0.5}+t^{-0.5})]\Big|_{t=1}$

62. $\frac{d}{dt}[(t^2+t^{0.5})(t^{0.5}-t^{-0.5})]\Big|_{t=1}$

In Exercises 63–70, use the calculation thought experiment to say whether the expression is written as a sum, difference, scalar multiple, product, or quotient. Then use the appropriate rules to find its derivative. HINT [See Quick Examples on page 815 and Example 3.]

63. $y = x^4-(x^2+120)(4x-1)$

64. $y = x^4-\frac{x^2+120}{4x-1}$

65. $y = x+1+2\left(\frac{x}{x+1}\right)$

66. $y = (x+2)-4(x^2-x)\left(x+\frac{1}{x}\right)$

(Do not simplify the answer.)

67. $y = (x+2)\left(\frac{x}{x+1}\right)$ (Do not simplify the answer.)

68. $y = \frac{(x+2)x}{x+1}$ (Do not simplify the answer.)

69. $y = (x+1)(x-2)-2\left(\frac{x}{x+1}\right)$

70. $y = \frac{x+2}{x+1}+(x+1)(x-2)$

In Exercises 71–76, find the equation of the line tangent to the graph of the given function at the point with the indicated x-coordinate.

71. $f(x) = (x^2+1)(x^3+x);\ x=1$

72. $f(x) = (x^{0.5}+1)(x^2+x);\ x=1$

73. $f(x) = \dfrac{x+1}{x+2}; x = 0$

74. $f(x) = \dfrac{\sqrt{x}+1}{\sqrt{x}+2}; x = 4$

75. $f(x) = \dfrac{x^2+1}{x}; x = -1$

76. $f(x) = \dfrac{x}{x^2+1}; x = 1$

APPLICATIONS

77. ***Revenue*** The monthly sales of *Sunny Electronics'* new sound system are given by $q(t) = 2{,}000t - 100t^2$ units per month, t months after its introduction. The price Sunny charges is $p(t) = 1{,}000 - t^2$ dollars per sound system, t months after introduction. Find the rate of change of monthly sales, the rate of change of the price, and the rate of change of monthly revenue 5 months after the introduction of the sound system. Interpret your answers. HINT [See Example 4(a).]

78. ***Revenue*** The monthly sales of *Sunny Electronics'* new *iSun* walkman is given by $q(t) = 2{,}000t - 100t^2$ units per month, t months after its introduction. The price Sunny charges is $p(t) = 100 - t^2$ dollars per iSun, t months after introduction. Find the rate of change of monthly sales, the rate of change of the price, and the rate of change of monthly revenue 6 months after the introduction of the iSun. Interpret your answers. HINT [See Example 4(a).]

79. ***Saudi Oil Revenues*** The price of crude oil during the period 2000–2010 can be approximated by

$$P(t) = 6t + 18 \text{ dollars per barrel} \quad (0 \le t \le 10)$$

in year t, where $t = 0$ represents 2000. Saudi Arabia's crude oil production over the same period can be approximated by[16]

$$Q(t) = -0.036t^2 + 0.62t + 8 \text{ million barrels per day.} \quad (0 \le t \le 10).$$

Use these models to estimate Saudi Arabia's daily oil revenue and also its rate of change in 2008. (Round your answers to the nearest \$1 million.)

80. ***Russian Oil Revenues*** The price of crude oil during the period 2000–2010 can be approximated by

$$P(t) = 6t + 18 \text{ dollars per barrels} \quad (0 \le t \le 10)$$

in year t, where $t = 0$ represents 2000. Russia's crude oil production over the same period can be approximated by[17]

$$Q(t) = -0.08t^2 + 1.2t + 5.5 \text{ million barrels per day} \quad (0 \le t \le 10).$$

Use these models to estimate Russia's daily oil revenue and also its rate of change in 2005. (Round your answers to the nearest \$1 million.)

81. ***Revenue*** Dorothy Wagner is currently selling 20 "I ♥ Calculus" T-shirts per day, but sales are dropping at a rate of 3 per day. She is currently charging \$7 per T-shirt, but to compensate for dwindling sales, she is increasing the unit price by \$1 per day. How fast, and in what direction, is her daily revenue currently changing?

[16] Sources for data: Oil price: InflationData.com www.inflationdata.com, Production: Energy Bulletin www.energybulletin.net.

[17] *Ibid.*

82. ***Pricing Policy*** Let us turn Exercise 81 around a little: Dorothy Wagner is currently selling 20 "I ♥ Calculus" T-shirts per day, but sales are dropping at a rate of 3 per day. She is currently charging \$7 per T-shirt, and she wishes to increase her daily revenue by \$10 per day. At what rate should she increase the unit price to accomplish this (assuming that the price increase does not affect sales)?

83. ***Bus Travel*** *Thoroughbred Bus Company* finds that its monthly costs for one particular year were given by $C(t) = 10{,}000 + t^2$ dollars after t months. After t months the company had $P(t) = 1{,}000 + t^2$ passengers per month. How fast is its cost per passenger changing after 6 months? HINT [See Example 4(b).]

84. ***Bus Travel*** *Thoroughbred Bus Company* finds that its monthly costs for one particular year were given by $C(t) = 100 + t^2$ dollars after t months. After t months, the company had $P(t) = 1{,}000 + t^2$ passengers per month. How fast is its cost per passenger changing after 6 months? HINT [See Example 4(b).]

85. ***Fuel Economy*** Your muscle car's gas mileage (in miles per gallon) is given as a function $M(x)$ of speed x in mph, where

$$M(x) = \frac{3{,}000}{x + 3{,}600x^{-1}}.$$

Calculate $M'(x)$, and then $M'(10)$, $M'(60)$, and $M'(70)$. What do the answers tell you about your car?

86. ***Fuel Economy*** Your used Chevy's gas mileage (in miles per gallon) is given as a function $M(x)$ of speed x in mph, where

$$M(x) = \frac{4{,}000}{x + 3{,}025x^{-1}}.$$

Calculate $M'(x)$ and hence determine *the sign* of each of the following: $M'(40)$, $M'(55)$, and $M'(60)$. Interpret your results.

87. ***Oil Imports from Mexico*** Daily oil production in Mexico and daily U.S. oil imports from Mexico during 2005–2009 could be approximated by

$$P(t) = 3.9 - 0.10t \text{ million barrels} \quad (5 \le t \le 9)$$

$$I(t) = 2.1 - 0.11t \text{ million barrels} \quad (5 \le t \le 9),$$

where t is time in years since the start of 2000.[18]

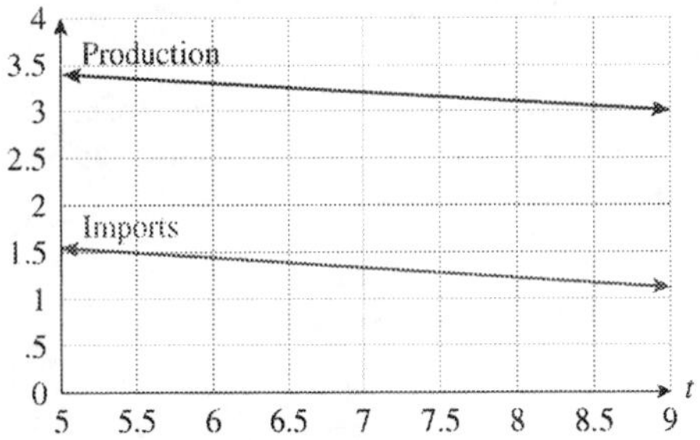

a. What are represented by the functions $P(t) - I(t)$ and $I(t)/P(t)$?

[18] Source for data: Energy Information Administration (www.eia.doe.gov)/Pemex.

b. Compute $\left. \dfrac{d}{dt}\left[\dfrac{I(t)}{P(t)} \right] \right|_{t=8}$ to two significant digits. What does the answer tell you about oil imports from Mexico?

88. ▼ *Oil Imports from Mexico* Daily oil production in Mexico and daily U.S. oil imports from Mexico during 2000–2004 could be approximated by

$$P(t) = 3.0 + 0.13t \text{ million barrels} \quad (0 \le t \le 4)$$

$$I(t) = 1.4 + 0.06t \text{ million barrels} \quad (0 \le t \le 4),$$

where t is time in years since the start of 2000.[19]

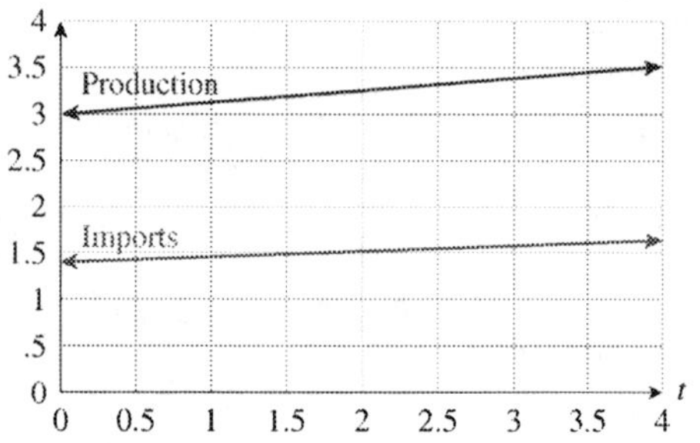

a. What are represented by the functions $P(t) - I(t)$ and $I(t)/P(t)$?

b. Compute $\left. \dfrac{d}{dt}\left[\dfrac{I(t)}{P(t)} \right] \right|_{t=3}$ to two significant digits. What does the answer tell you about oil imports from Mexico?

89. ▼ *Military Spending* The annual cost per active-duty armed service member in the United States increased from $80,000 in 1995 to a projected $120,000 in 2007. In 1995, there were 1.5 million armed service personnel, and this number was projected to decrease to 1.4 million in 2003.[20] Use linear models for annual cost and personnel to estimate, to the nearest $10 million, the rate of change of total military personnel costs in 2002.

90. ▼ *Military Spending in the 1990s* The annual cost per active-duty armed service member in the United States increased from $80,000 in 1995 to $90,000 in 2000. In 1990, there were 2 million armed service personnel and this number decreased to 1.5 million in 2000.[21] Use linear models for annual cost and personnel to estimate, to the nearest $10 million, the rate of change of total military personnel costs in 1995.

91. ▼ *Biology—Reproduction* The Verhulst model for population growth specifies the reproductive rate of an organism as a function of the total population according to the following formula:

$$R(p) = \frac{r}{1 + kp}$$

where p is the total population in thousands of organisms, r and k are constants that depend on the particular circumstances and the organism being studied, and $R(p)$ is the reproduction rate in thousands of organisms per hour.[22] If $k = 0.125$ and $r = 45$, find $R'(p)$ and then $R'(4)$. Interpret the result.

92. ▼ *Biology—Reproduction* Another model, the predator satiation model for population growth, specifies that the reproductive rate of an organism as a function of the total population varies according to the following formula:

$$R(p) = \frac{rp}{1 + kp}$$

where p is the total population in thousands of organisms, r and k are constants that depend on the particular circumstances and the organism being studied, and $R(p)$ is the reproduction rate in new organisms per hour.[23] Given that $k = 0.2$ and $r = 0.08$, find $R'(p)$ and $R'(2)$. Interpret the result.

93. ▼ *Embryo Development* Bird embryos consume oxygen from the time the egg is laid through the time the chick hatches. For a typical galliform bird egg, the oxygen consumption (in milliliters) t days after the egg was laid can be approximated by[24]

$$C(t) = -0.016t^4 + 1.1t^3 - 11t^2 + 3.6t \quad (15 \le t \le 30).$$

(An egg will usually hatch at around $t = 28$.) Suppose that at time $t = 0$ you have a collection of 30 newly laid eggs and that the number of eggs decreases linearly to zero at time $t = 30$ days. How fast is the total oxygen consumption of your collection of embryos changing after 25 days? (Round your answers to two significant digits.) Comment on the result. HINT [Total oxygen consumption = Oxygen consumption per egg × Number of eggs.]

94. ▼ *Embryo Development* Turkey embryos consume oxygen from the time the egg is laid through the time the chick hatches. For a brush turkey, the oxygen consumption (in milliliters) t days after the egg was laid can be approximated by[25]

$$C(t) = -0.0071t^4 + 0.95t^3 - 22t^2 + 95t \quad (25 \le t \le 50).$$

(An egg will typically hatch at around $t = 50$.) Suppose that at time $t = 0$ you have a collection of 100 newly laid eggs and that the number of eggs decreases linearly to zero at time $t = 50$ days. How fast is the total oxygen consumption of your collection of embryos changing after 40 days? (Round your answer to two significant digits.) Interpret the result. HINT [Total oxygen consumption = Oxygen consumption per egg × Number of eggs.]

---

[19] Source for data: Energy Information Administration (www.eia.doe.gov)/Pemex.

[20] Annual costs are adjusted for inflation. Sources: Department of Defense, Stephen Daggett, military analyst, Congressional Research Service/*New York Times*, April 19, 2002, p. A21.

[21] *Ibid.*

[22] Source: *Mathematics in Medicine and the Life Sciences* by F. C. Hoppensteadt and C. S. Peskin (Springer-Verlag, New York, 1992) pp. 20–22.

[23] *Ibid.*

[24] The model is derived from graphical data published in the article "The Brush Turkey" by Roger S. Seymour, *Scientific American,* December, 1991, pp. 108–114.

[25] *Ibid.*

COMMUNICATION AND REASONING EXERCISES

95. If f and g are functions of time, and at time $t = 3$, f equals 5 and is rising at a rate of 2 units per second, and g equals 4 and is rising at a rate of 5 units per second, then the product fg equals ____ and is rising at a rate of ____ units per second.

96. If f and g are functions of time, and at time $t = 2$, f equals 3 and is rising at a rate of 4 units per second, and g equals 5 and is rising at a rate of 6 units per second, then fg equals ____ and is rising at a rate of ____ units per second.

97. If f and g are functions of time, and at time $t = 3$, f equals 5 and is rising at a rate of 2 units per second, and g equals 4 and is rising at a rate of 5 units per second, then f/g equals ____ and is changing at a rate of ____ units per second.

98. If f and g are functions of time, and at time $t = 2$, f equals 3 and is rising at a rate of 4 units per second, and g equals 5 and is rising at a rate of 6 units per second, then f/g equals ____ and is changing at a rate of ____ units per second.

99. You have come across the following in a newspaper article: "Revenues of HAL Home Heating Oil Inc. are rising by \$4.2 million per year. This is due to an annual increase of 70¢ per gallon in the price HAL charges for heating oil and an increase in sales of 6 million gallons of oil per year." Comment on this analysis.

100. Your friend says that because average cost is obtained by dividing the cost function by the number of units x, it follows that the derivative of average cost is the same as marginal cost because the derivative of x is 1. Comment on this analysis.

101. ▼ Find a demand function $q(p)$ such that, at a price per item of $p = \$100$, revenue will rise if the price per item is increased.

102. ▼ What must be true about a demand function $q(p)$ so that, at a price per item of $p = \$100$, revenue will decrease if the price per item is increased?

103. ▼ You and I are both selling a steady 20 T-shirts per day. The price I am getting for my T-shirts is increasing twice as fast as yours, but your T-shirts are currently selling for twice the price of mine. Whose revenue is increasing faster: yours, mine, or neither? Explain.

104. ▼ You and I are both selling T-shirts for a steady \$20 per shirt. Sales of my T-shirts are increasing at twice the rate of yours, but you are currently selling twice as many as I am. Whose revenue is increasing faster: yours, mine, or neither? Explain.

105. ◆***Marginal Product*** *(from the GRE Economics Test)* Which of the following statements about average product and marginal product is correct?

(A) If average product is decreasing, marginal product must be less than average product.

(B) If average product is increasing, marginal product must be increasing.

(C) If marginal product is decreasing, average product must be less than marginal product.

(D) If marginal product is increasing, average product must be decreasing.

(E) If marginal product is constant over some range, average product must be constant over that range.

106. ◆***Marginal Cost*** *(based on a question from the GRE Economics Test)* Which of the following statements about average cost and marginal cost is correct?

(A) If average cost is increasing, marginal cost must be increasing.

(B) If average cost is increasing, marginal cost must be decreasing.

(C) If average cost is increasing, marginal cost must be more than average cost.

(D) If marginal cost is increasing, average cost must be increasing.

(E) If marginal cost is increasing, average cost must be larger than marginal cost.

Practice Problems 11.3, Part 1

1. The population of a metropolitan area is currently 86,200 people and is growing at a rate of about 930 people per year. The average annual income is about $20,800 per person and is growing at a rate of about $640 per year. Given this, estimate the rate at which total personal income in the metropolitan area is changing right now. Show how you arrived at your conclusion and label appropriately.

2. A bus company found that at the beginning of June, it was costing $7000 to run a particular route each month, but that that monthly cost was increasing at a rate of $40 per month. Also, at that point in time, there were 500 passengers taking the route each month, but that number was increasing at a rate of 4 passengers per month each month. Given this, determine the rate at which the company's per passenger cost for the route was changing as of the beginning of June. Label your result appropriately.

Practice Problems 11.3, Part 2

Suppose that $f(x)$ and $g(x)$ are two functions such that $f(1)=-3$, $f'(1)=2$, $g(1)=-4$, and $g'(1)=5$. Calculate $h'(1)$ for $h(x)$ as defined in each of the following.

1. $h(x)=f(x)\cdot g(x)$

2. $h(x)=x^2\cdot(g(x)+81)$

3. $h(x)=\dfrac{f(x)}{g(x)}$

4. $h(x)=\dfrac{\sqrt{x}}{f(x)}$

5. $h(x)=\dfrac{f(x)-g(x)}{x^4+1}$

Practice Problems 11.3, Part 3

1. The unit price p, in dollars, at which q thousand boxes of Scooby Snacks can be sold is given by $p = f(q)$. Suppose that $f(24) = 3.85$ and $f'(24) = -0.18$. Determine how fast the revenue from sales of boxes of Scooby Snacks is changing when 24 thousand boxes are sold, and label your result appropriately.

2. Suppose that $I(t)$ gives the amount of the annual budget of Calamity Community College that is spent on instructor salaries, and that $B(t)$ gives the total annual budget. Here, t represents years, with $t = 0$ corresponding to academic year 2013-2014.

a. What does the quantity $\dfrac{I(0)}{B(0)}$ represent in terms of the annual budget?

b. Suppose that CCC leadership is predicting that $\dfrac{d}{dt}\left[\dfrac{I(t)}{B(t)}\right]\Bigg|_{t=0} = 0.2$. What is being predicted? Be specific and include appropriate units in your interpretation.

c. For academic year 2013-2014, \$1,200,000 of the total budget of \$9,000,000 at CCC is spent on instructor salaries. Taking into account that the total budget is increasing at a rate of \$200,000 per year, how fast must the amount of money spent on instructor salaries be increasing so that the prediction in **b.** is valid?

11.4 The Chain Rule

We can now find the derivatives of expressions involving powers of x combined using addition, subtraction, multiplication, and division, but we still cannot take the derivative of an expression like $(3x + 1)^{0.5}$. For this we need one more rule. The function $h(x) = (3x + 1)^{0.5}$ is not a sum, difference, product, or quotient. To find out what it is, we can use the calculation thought experiment and think about the last operation we would perform in calculating $h(x)$.

1. Calculate $3x + 1$.

2. Take the 0.5 power (square root) of the answer.

The last operation is "take the 0.5 power." We do not yet have a rule for finding the derivative of the 0.5 power of a quantity other than x.

There is a way to build $h(x) = (3x + 1)^{0.5}$ out of two simpler functions: $u(x) = 3x + 1$ (the function that corresponds to the first step in the calculation above) and $f(x) = x^{0.5}$ (the function that corresponds to the second step):

$$\begin{aligned} h(x) &= (3x + 1)^{0.5} \\ &= [u(x)]^{0.5} && u(x) = 3x + 1 \\ &= f(u(x)). && f(x) = x^{0.5} \end{aligned}$$

We say that h is the **composite** of f and u. We read $f(u(x))$ as "f of u of x."

To compute $h(1)$, say, we first compute $3 \cdot 1 + 1 = 4$ and then take the square root of 4, giving $h(1) = 2$. To compute $f(u(1))$ we follow exactly the same steps: First compute $u(1) = 4$ and then $f(u(1)) = f(4) = 2$. We always compute $f(u(x))$ from the inside out: Given x, first compute $u(x)$ and then $f(u(x))$.

Now, f and u are functions *whose derivatives we know.* The *chain rule* allows us to use our knowledge of the derivatives of f and u to find the derivative of $f(u(x))$. For the purposes of stating the rule, let us avoid some of the nested parentheses by abbreviating $u(x)$ as u. Thus, we write $f(u)$ instead of $f(u(x))$ and remember that u is a function of x.

Chain Rule

If f is a differentiable function of u and u is a differentiable function of x, then the composite $f(u)$ is a differentiable function of x, and

$$\frac{d}{dx}[f(u)] = f'(u)\frac{du}{dx}. \qquad \text{Chain rule}$$

In words *The derivative of f(quantity) is the derivative of f, evaluated at that quantity, times the derivative of the quantity.*

Quick Examples

In the Quick Examples that follow, u, "the quantity," is some (unspecified) differentiable function of x.

1. Take $f(u) = u^2$. Then

$$\frac{d}{dx}(u^2) = 2u\frac{du}{dx}. \qquad \text{Because } f'(u) = 2u$$

The derivative of a quantity squared is two times the quantity, times the derivative of the quantity.

2. Take $f(u) = u^{0.5}$. Then

$$\frac{d}{dx}(u^{0.5}) = 0.5u^{-0.5}\frac{du}{dx}. \qquad \text{Because } f'(u) = 0.5u^{-0.5}$$

The derivative of a quantity raised to the 0.5 is 0.5 times the quantity raised to the −0.5, times the derivative of the quantity.

As the quick examples illustrate, for every power of a function u whose derivative we know, we now get a "generalized" differentiation rule. The following table gives more examples.

Original Rule	Generalized Rule	In Words
$\frac{d}{dx}(x^2) = 2x$	$\frac{d}{dx}(u^2) = 2u\frac{du}{dx}$	*The derivative of a quantity squared is twice the quantity, times the derivative of the quantity.*
$\frac{d}{dx}(x^3) = 3x^2$	$\frac{d}{dx}(u^3) = 3u^2\frac{du}{dx}$	*The derivative of a quantity cubed is 3 times the quantity squared, times the derivative of the quantity.*
$\frac{d}{dx}\left(\frac{1}{x}\right) = -\frac{1}{x^2}$	$\frac{d}{dx}\left(\frac{1}{u}\right) = -\frac{1}{u^2}\frac{du}{dx}$	*The derivative of 1 over a quantity is negative 1 over the quantity squared, times the derivative of the quantity.*
Power Rule	**Generalized Power Rule**	**In Words**
$\frac{d}{dx}(x^n) = nx^{n-1}$	$\frac{d}{dx}(u^n) = nu^{n-1}\frac{du}{dx}$	*The derivative of a quantity raised to the n is n times the quantity raised to the n − 1, times the derivative of the quantity.*
$\frac{d}{dx}\lvert x\rvert = \frac{\lvert x\rvert}{x}$	$\frac{d}{dx}\lvert u\rvert = \frac{\lvert u\rvert}{u}\frac{du}{dx}$	*The derivative of the absolute value of a quantity is the absolute value of the quantity divided by the quantity, times the derivative of the quantity.*

To motivate the chain rule, let us see why it is true in the special case when $f(u) = u^3$, where the chain rule tells us that

$$\frac{d}{dx}(u^3) = 3u^2\frac{du}{dx}. \quad \text{Generalized power rule with } n = 3$$

But we could have done this using the product rule instead:

$$\frac{d}{dx}(u^3) = \frac{d}{dx}(u \cdot u \cdot u) = \frac{du}{dx}u \cdot u + u\frac{du}{dx}u + u \cdot u\frac{du}{dx} = 3u^2\frac{du}{dx},$$

which gives us the same result. A similar argument works for $f(u) = u^n$, where $n = 2, 3, 4, \ldots$. We can then use the quotient rule and the chain rule for positive powers to verify the generalized power rule for *negative* powers as well. For the case of a general differentiable function *f*, the proof of the chain rule is beyond the scope of this book, but you can find one on the Website by following the path

Website → Everything → Chapter 11 → Proof of Chain Rule.

EXAMPLE 1 Using the Chain Rule

Compute the following derivatives.

a. $\frac{d}{dx}[(2x^2 + x)^3]$ **b.** $\frac{d}{dx}[(x^3 + x)^{100}]$ **c.** $\frac{d}{dx}\sqrt{3x + 1}$ **d.** $\frac{d}{dx}\lvert 4x^2 - x\rvert$

Solution

a. Using the calculation thought experiment, we see that the last operation we would perform in calculating $(2x^2 + x)^3$ is that of *cubing.* Thus we think of $(2x^2 + x)^3$ as *a quantity cubed.* There are two similar methods we can use to calculate its derivative.

Method 1: Using the formula We think of $(2x^2+x)^3$ as u^3, where $u = 2x^2+x$. By the formula,

$$\frac{d}{dx}(u^3) = 3u^2\frac{du}{dx}. \qquad \text{Generalized power rule}$$

Now substitute for u:

$$\frac{d}{dx}[(2x^2+x)^3] = 3(2x^2+x)^2\frac{d}{dx}(2x^2+x)$$
$$= 3(2x^2+x)^2(4x+1)$$

Method 2: Using the verbal form If we prefer to use the verbal form, we get:

The derivative of $(2x^2+x)$ *cubed is three times* $(2x^2+x)$ *squared, times the derivative of* $(2x^2+x)$.

In symbols,

$$\frac{d}{dx}[(2x^2+x)^3] = 3(2x^2+x)^2(4x+1),$$

as we obtained above.

b. First, the calculation thought experiment: If we were computing $(x^3+x)^{100}$, the last operation we would perform is *raising a quantity to the power* 100. Thus we are dealing with *a quantity raised to the power* 100, and so we must again use the generalized power rule. According to the verbal form of the generalized power rule, the derivative of a quantity raised to the power 100 is 100 times that quantity to the power 99, times the derivative of that quantity. In symbols,

$$\frac{d}{dx}[(x^3+x)^{100}] = 100(x^3+x)^{99}(3x^2+1).$$

c. We first rewrite the expression $\sqrt{3x+1}$ as $(3x+1)^{0.5}$ and then use the generalized power rule as in parts (a) and (b):

The derivative of a quantity raised to the 0.5 *is* 0.5 *times the quantity raised to the* −0.5*, times the derivative of the quantity.*

Thus,

$$\frac{d}{dx}[(3x+1)^{0.5}] = 0.5(3x+1)^{-0.5}\cdot 3 = 1.5(3x+1)^{-0.5}.$$

d. The calculation thought experiment tells us that $|4x^2-x|$ is the absolute value of a quantity, so we use the generalized rule for absolute values (above):

$$\frac{d}{dx}|u| = \frac{|u|}{u}\frac{du}{dx}, \text{ or, in words,}$$

The derivative of the absolute value of a quantity is the absolute value of the quantity divided by the quantity, times the derivative of the quantity.

Thus,

$$\frac{d}{dx}|4x^2-x| = \frac{|4x^2-x|}{4x^2-x}\cdot(8x-1). \qquad \frac{d}{dx}|u| = \frac{|u|}{u}\frac{du}{dx}$$

➡ **Before we go on...** The following are examples of common errors in solving Example 1(b):

$$\text{“}\frac{d}{dx}[(x^3+x)^{100}] = 100(3x^2+1)^{99}\text{”} \qquad \text{✗ } \textit{WRONG!}$$

$$\text{“}\frac{d}{dx}[(x^3+x)^{100}] = 100(x^3+x)^{99}.\text{”} \qquad \text{✗ } \textit{WRONG!}$$

Remember that the generalized power rule says that the derivative of a quantity to the power 100 is 100 times *that same quantity* raised to the power 99, *times the derivative of that quantity.* ■

Q: *It seems that there are now two formulas for the derivative of an nth power:*

1. $\frac{d}{dx}[x^n] = nx^{n-1}$
2. $\frac{d}{dx}[u^n] = nu^{n-1}\frac{du}{dx}$.

Which one do I use?

A: Formula 1 is actually a special case of Formula 2: Formula 1 is the original power rule, which applies only to a power of x. For instance, it applies to x^{10}, but it does not apply to $(2x+1)^{10}$ because the quantity that is being raised to a power is not x. Formula 2 applies to a power of any *function of* x, such as $(2x+1)^{10}$. It can even be used in place of the original power rule. For example, if we take $u = x$ in Formula 2, we obtain

$$\frac{d}{dx}[x^n] = nx^{n-1}\frac{dx}{dx}$$

$$= nx^{n-1}. \quad \text{The derivative of } x \text{ with respect to } x \text{ is } 1.$$

Thus, the generalized power rule really *is* a generalization of the original power rule, as its name suggests.

EXAMPLE 2 More Examples Using the Chain Rule

Find: **a.** $\frac{d}{dx}[(2x^5+x^2-20)^{-2/3}]$ **b.** $\frac{d}{dx}\left[\frac{1}{\sqrt{x+2}}\right]$ **c.** $\frac{d}{dx}\left[\frac{1}{x^2+x}\right]$

Solution Each of the given functions is, or can be rewritten as, a power of a function whose derivative we know. Thus, we can use the method of Example 1.

a. $\frac{d}{dx}[(2x^5+x^2-20)^{-2/3}] = -\frac{2}{3}(2x^5+x^2-20)^{-5/3}(10x^4+2x)$

b. $\frac{d}{dx}\left[\frac{1}{\sqrt{x+2}}\right] = \frac{d}{dx}(x+2)^{-1/2} = -\frac{1}{2}(x+2)^{-3/2}\cdot 1 = -\frac{1}{2(x+2)^{3/2}}$

c. $\frac{d}{dx}\left[\frac{1}{x^2+x}\right] = \frac{d}{dx}(x^2+x)^{-1} = -(x^2+x)^{-2}(2x+1) = -\frac{2x+1}{(x^2+x)^2}$

Before we go on... In Example 2(c), we could have used the quotient rule instead of the generalized power rule. We can think of the quantity $1/(x^2+x)$ in two different ways using the calculation thought experiment:

1. As 1 divided by something—in other words, as a quotient
2. As something raised to the -1 power

Of course, we get the same derivative using either approach. ■

We now look at some more complicated examples.

EXAMPLE 3 Harder Examples Using the Chain Rule

Find $\frac{dy}{dx}$ in each case. **a.** $y = [(x+1)^{-2.5} + 3x]^{-3}$ **b.** $y = (x+10)^3\sqrt{1-x^2}$

Solution

a. The calculation thought experiment tells us that the last operation we would perform in calculating y is raising the quantity $[(x+1)^{-2.5} + 3x]$ to the power -3. Thus, we use the generalized power rule.

$$\frac{dy}{dx} = -3[(x+1)^{-2.5} + 3x]^{-4}\frac{d}{dx}[(x+1)^{-2.5} + 3x]$$

We are not yet done; we must still find the derivative of $(x+1)^{-2.5} + 3x$. Finding the derivative of a complicated function in several steps helps to keep the problem manageable. Continuing, we have

$$\frac{dy}{dx} = -3[(x+1)^{-2.5} + 3x]^{-4}\frac{d}{dx}[(x+1)^{-2.5} + 3x]$$

$$= -3[(x+1)^{-2.5} + 3x]^{-4}\left(\frac{d}{dx}[(x+1)^{-2.5}] + \frac{d}{dx}(3x)\right).$$ Derivative of a sum

Now we have two derivatives left to calculate. The second of these we know to be 3, and the first is the derivative of a quantity raised to the -2.5 power. Thus

$$\frac{dy}{dx} = -3[(x+1)^{-2.5} + 3x]^{-4}[-2.5(x+1)^{-3.5}\cdot 1 + 3].$$

b. The expression $(x+10)^3\sqrt{1-x^2}$ is a product, so we use the product rule:

$$\frac{d}{dx}[(x+10)^3\sqrt{1-x^2}] = \left(\frac{d}{dx}[(x+10)^3]\right)\sqrt{1-x^2} + (x+10)^3\left(\frac{d}{dx}\sqrt{1-x^2}\right)$$

$$= 3(x+10)^2\sqrt{1-x^2} + (x+10)^3\frac{1}{2\sqrt{1-x^2}}(-2x)$$

$$= 3(x+10)^2\sqrt{1-x^2} - \frac{x(x+10)^3}{\sqrt{1-x^2}}.$$

APPLICATIONS

The next example is a new way of looking at Example 3 from Section 11.2.

EXAMPLE 4 Marginal Product

A consultant determines that *Precision Manufacturers'* annual profit (in dollars) is given by

$$P = -200{,}000 + 4{,}000q - 0.46q^2 - 0.00001q^3,$$

where q is the number of surgical lasers it sells each year. The consultant also informs Precision that the number of surgical lasers it can manufacture each year depends on the number n of assembly-line workers it employs according to the equation

$$q = 100n.$$ Each worker contributes 100 lasers per year.

Use the chain rule to find the marginal product $\frac{dP}{dn}$.

Solution We could calculate the marginal product by substituting the expression for q in the expression for P to obtain P as a function of n (as given in Example 3 from Section 11.2) and then finding dP/dn. Alternatively—and this will simplify the calculation—we can use the chain rule. To see how the chain rule applies, notice that P is a function of q, where q in turn is given as a function of n. By the chain rule,

$$\frac{dP}{dn} = P'(q)\frac{dq}{dn} \qquad \text{Chain rule}$$

$$= \frac{dP}{dq}\frac{dq}{dn}. \qquad \text{Notice how the "quantities" } dq \text{ appear to cancel.}$$

Now we compute

$$\frac{dP}{dq} = 4{,}000 - 0.92q - 0.00003q^2$$

and $$\frac{dq}{dn} = 100.$$

Substituting into the equation for $\frac{dP}{dn}$ gives

$$\frac{dP}{dn} = (4{,}000 - 0.92q - 0.00003q^2)(100)$$

$$= 400{,}000 - 92q - 0.003q^2.$$

Notice that the answer has q as a variable. We can express dP/dn as a function of n by substituting $100n$ for q:

$$\frac{dP}{dn} = 400{,}000 - 92(100n) - 0.003(100n)^2$$

$$= 400{,}000 - 9{,}200n - 30n^2.$$

The equation

$$\frac{dP}{dn} = \frac{dP}{dq}\frac{dq}{dn}$$

in the example above is an appealing way of writing the chain rule because it suggests that the "quantities" dq cancel. In general, we can write the chain rule as follows.

Chain Rule in Differential Notation

If y is a differentiable function of u, and u is a differentiable function of x, then

$$\frac{dy}{dx} = \frac{dy}{du}\frac{du}{dx}. \qquad \text{The terms } du \text{ cancel.}$$

Notice how the units of measurement also cancel:

$$\frac{\text{Units of } y}{\text{Units of } x} = \frac{\text{Units of } y}{\sout{\text{Units of } u}}\,\frac{\sout{\text{Units of } u}}{\text{Units of } x}.$$

Quick Examples

1. If $y = u^3$, where $u = 4x + 1$, then

$$\frac{dy}{dx} = \frac{dy}{du}\frac{du}{dx} = 3u^2 \cdot 4 = 12u^2 = 12(4x + 1)^2.$$

2. If $q = 43p^2$, where p (and hence q also) is a differentiable function of t, then

$$\frac{dq}{dt} = \frac{dq}{dp}\frac{dp}{dt}$$

$$= 86p\frac{dp}{dt}. \quad p \text{ is not specified, so we leave } dp/dt \text{ as is.}$$

EXAMPLE 5 Marginal Revenue

Suppose a company's weekly revenue R is given as a function of the unit price p, and p in turn is given as a function of weekly sales q (by means of a demand equation). If

$$\left.\frac{dR}{dp}\right|_{q=1,000} = \$40 \text{ per } \$1 \text{ increase in price}$$

and

$$\left.\frac{dp}{dq}\right|_{q=1,000} = -\$20 \text{ per additional item sold per week}$$

find the marginal revenue when sales are 1,000 items per week.

Solution The marginal revenue is $\frac{dR}{dq}$. By the chain rule, we have

$$\frac{dR}{dq} = \frac{dR}{dp}\frac{dp}{dq}. \quad \text{Units: Revenue per item} = \text{Revenue per \$1 price increase} \times \text{price increase per additional item.}$$

Because we are interested in the marginal revenue at a demand level of 1,000 items per week, we have

$$\left.\frac{dR}{dq}\right|_{q=1,000} = (40)(-20) = -\$800 \text{ per additional item sold.}$$

Thus, if the price is lowered to increase the demand from 1,000 to 1,001 items per week, the weekly revenue will drop by approximately $800.

Look again at the way the terms "du" appeared to cancel in the differential formula $\frac{dy}{dx} = \frac{dy}{du}\frac{du}{dx}$. In fact, the chain rule tells us more:

* The notion of "thinking of x as a function of y" will be made more precise in Section 11.6.

Manipulating Derivatives in Differential Notation

1. Suppose y is a function of x. Then, thinking of x as a function of y (as, for instance, when we can solve for x)* we have

$$\frac{dx}{dy} = \frac{1}{\left(\frac{dy}{dx}\right)}, \text{ provided } \frac{dy}{dx} \neq 0.$$ Notice again how $\frac{dy}{dx}$ behaves like a fraction.

Quick Example

In the demand equation $q = -0.2p - 8$, we have $\frac{dq}{dp} = -0.2$. Therefore,

$$\frac{dp}{dq} = \frac{1}{\left(\frac{dq}{dp}\right)} = \frac{1}{-0.2} = -5.$$

2. Suppose x and y are functions of t. Then, thinking of y as a function of x (as, for instance, when we can solve for t as a function of x, and hence obtain y as a function of x), we have

$$\frac{dy}{dx} = \frac{dy/dt}{dx/dt}.$$ The terms dt appear to cancel.

Quick Example

If $x = 3 - 0.2t$ and $y = 6 + 6t$, then

$$\frac{dy}{dx} = \frac{dy/dt}{dx/dt} = \frac{6}{-0.2} = -30.$$

To see why the above formulas work, notice that the second formula,

$$\frac{dy}{dx} = \frac{\left(\frac{dy}{dt}\right)}{\left(\frac{dx}{dt}\right)}$$

can be written as

$$\frac{dy}{dx}\frac{dx}{dt} = \frac{dy}{dt},$$ Multiply both sides by $\frac{dx}{dt}$.

which is just the differential form of the chain rule. For the first formula, use the second formula with y playing the role of t:

$$\frac{dy}{dx} = \frac{dy/dy}{dx/dy}$$

$$= \frac{1}{dx/dy}.$$ $\frac{dy}{dy} = \frac{d}{dy}[y] = 1$

FAQs

Using the Chain Rule

Q: *How do I decide whether or not to use the chain rule when taking a derivative?*

A: Use the calculation thought experiment (Section 11.3): Given an expression, consider the steps you would use in computing its value.

- If the last step is *raising a quantity to a power,* as in $\left(\frac{x^2-1}{x+4}\right)^4$, then the first step to use is the chain rule (in the form of the generalized power rule):

$$\frac{d}{dx}\left(\frac{x^2-1}{x+4}\right)^4 = 4\left(\frac{x^2-1}{x+4}\right)^3 \frac{d}{dx}\left(\frac{x^2-1}{x+4}\right).$$

Then use the appropriate rules to finish the computation. You may need to again use the calculation thought experiment to decide on the next step (here the quotient rule):

$$= 4\left(\frac{x^2-1}{x+4}\right)^3 \frac{(2x)(x+4)-(x^2-1)(1)}{(x+4)^2}.$$

- If the last step is *division,* as in $\frac{(x^2-1)}{(3x+4)^4}$, then the first step to use is the quotient rule:

$$\frac{d}{dx}\frac{(x^2-1)}{(3x+4)^4} = \frac{(2x)(3x+4)^4-(x^2-1)\frac{d}{dx}(3x+4)^4}{(3x+4)^8}.$$

Then use the appropriate rules to finish the computation (here the chain rule):

$$= \frac{(2x)(3x+4)^4-(x^2-1)[4(3x+4)^3(3)]}{(3x+4)^8}.$$

- If the last step is *multiplication, addition, subtraction, or multiplication by a constant,* then the first rule to use is the product rule, or the rule for sums, differences, or constant multiples as appropriate.

Q: *Every time I compute a derivative, I leave something out. How do I make sure I am really done when taking the derivative of a complicated-looking expression?*

A: Until you are an expert at taking derivatives, the key is to use one rule at a time and write out each step, rather than trying to compute the derivative in a single step. To illustrate this, try computing the derivative of $(x+10)^3\sqrt{1-x^2}$ in Example 3(b) in two ways: First try to compute it in a single step, and then compute it by writing out each step as shown in the example. How do your results compare? For more practice, try Exercises 87 and 88 following.

11.4 EXERCISES

▼ more advanced ◆ challenging

T indicates exercises that should be solved using technology

Calculate the derivatives of the functions in Exercises 1–50. HINT [See Example 1.]

1. $f(x) = (2x+1)^2$
2. $f(x) = (3x-1)^2$
3. $f(x) = (x-1)^{-1}$
4. $f(x) = (2x-1)^{-2}$
5. $f(x) = (2-x)^{-2}$
6. $f(x) = (1-x)^{-1}$
7. $f(x) = (2x+1)^{0.5}$
8. $f(x) = (-x+2)^{1.5}$
9. $f(x) = \dfrac{1}{3x-1}$
10. $f(x) = \dfrac{1}{(x+1)^2}$
11. $f(x) = (x^2+2x)^4$
12. $f(x) = (x^3-x)^3$
13. $f(x) = (2x^2-2)^{-1}$
14. $f(x) = (2x^3+x)^{-2}$
15. $g(x) = (x^2-3x-1)^{-5}$
16. $g(x) = (2x^2+x+1)^{-3}$
17. $h(x) = \dfrac{1}{(x^2+1)^3}$ HINT [See Example 2.]
18. $h(x) = \dfrac{1}{(x^2+x+1)^2}$ HINT [See Example 2.]
19. $r(x) = (0.1x^2-4.2x+9.5)^{1.5}$
20. $r(x) = (0.1x-4.2x^{-1})^{0.5}$
21. $r(s) = (s^2-s^{0.5})^4$
22. $r(s) = (2s+s^{0.5})^{-1}$
23. $f(x) = \sqrt{1-x^2}$
24. $f(x) = \sqrt{x+x^2}$
25. $f(x) = |3x-6|$ HINT [See Example 1(d).]
26. $f(x) = |-5x+1|$ HINT [See Example 1(d).]
27. $f(x) = |-x^3+5x|$
28. $f(x) = |x-x^4|$
29. $h(x) = 2[(x+1)(x^2-1)]^{-1/2}$ HINT [See Example 3.]
30. $h(x) = 3[(2x-1)(x-1)]^{-1/3}$ HINT [See Example 3.]
31. $h(x) = (3.1x-2)^2 - \dfrac{1}{(3.1x-2)^2}$
32. $h(x) = \left[3.1x^2 - 2 - \dfrac{1}{3.1x-2}\right]^2$
33. $f(x) = [(6.4x-1)^2 + (5.4x-2)^3]^2$
34. $f(x) = (6.4x-3)^{-2} + (4.3x-1)^{-2}$
35. $f(x) = (x^2-3x)^{-2}(1-x^2)^{0.5}$
36. $f(x) = (3x^2+x)(1-x^2)^{0.5}$
37. $s(x) = \left(\dfrac{2x+4}{3x-1}\right)^2$
38. $s(x) = \left(\dfrac{3x-9}{2x+4}\right)^3$
39. $g(z) = \left(\dfrac{z}{1+z^2}\right)^3$
40. $g(z) = \left(\dfrac{z^2}{1+z}\right)^2$
41. $f(x) = [(1+2x)^4 - (1-x)^2]^3$
42. $f(x) = [(3x-1)^2 + (1-x)^5]^2$
43. $f(x) = (3x-1)|3x-1|$
44. $f(x) = |(x-3)^{1/3}|$
45. $f(x) = |x-(2x-3)^{1/2}|$
46. $f(x) = (3-|3x-1|)^{-2}$
47. ▼ $r(x) = (\sqrt{2x+1} - x^2)^{-1}$
48. ▼ $r(x) = (\sqrt{x+1} + \sqrt{x})^3$
49. ▼ $f(x) = (1+(1+(1+2x)^3)^3)^3$
50. ▼ $f(x) = 2x + (2x + (2x+1)^3)^3$

Find the indicated derivatives in Exercises 51–58. In each case, the independent variable is a (unspecified) differentiable function of t. HINT [See Quick Example 2 on page 828.]

51. $y = x^{100} + 99x^{-1}$. Find $\dfrac{dy}{dt}$.
52. $y = x^{0.5}(1+x)$. Find $\dfrac{dy}{dt}$.
53. $s = \dfrac{1}{r^3} + r^{0.5}$. Find $\dfrac{ds}{dt}$.
54. $s = r + r^{-1}$. Find $\dfrac{ds}{dt}$.
55. $V = \dfrac{4}{3}\pi r^3$. Find $\dfrac{dV}{dt}$.
56. $A = 4\pi r^2$. Find $\dfrac{dA}{dt}$.
57. ▼ $y = x^3 + \dfrac{1}{x}$, $x = 2$ when $t = 1$, $\left.\dfrac{dx}{dt}\right|_{t=1} = -1$

    Find $\left.\dfrac{dy}{dt}\right|_{t=1}$.
58. ▼ $y = \sqrt{x} + \dfrac{1}{\sqrt{x}}$, $x = 9$ when $t = 1$, $\left.\dfrac{dx}{dt}\right|_{t=1} = -1$

    Find $\left.\dfrac{dy}{dt}\right|_{t=1}$.

In Exercises 59–64, compute the indicated derivative using the chain rule. HINT [See Quick Examples on page 829.]

59. $y = 3x-2$; $\dfrac{dx}{dy}$
60. $y = 8x+4$; $\dfrac{dx}{dy}$
61. $x = 2+3t$, $y = -5t$; $\dfrac{dy}{dx}$
62. $x = 1-t/2$, $y = 4t-1$; $\dfrac{dy}{dx}$
63. $y = 3x^2-2x$; $\left.\dfrac{dx}{dy}\right|_{x=1}$
64. $y = 3x - \dfrac{2}{x}$; $\left.\dfrac{dx}{dy}\right|_{x=2}$

APPLICATIONS

65. ***Marginal Product*** *Paramount Electronics* has an annual profit given by

$$P = -100{,}000 + 5{,}000q - 0.25q^2 \text{ dollars,}$$

where q is the number of laptop computers it sells each year. The number of laptop computers it can make and sell each year depends on the number n of electrical engineers Paramount employs, according to the equation

$$q = 30n + 0.01n^2.$$

Use the chain rule to find $\left.\frac{dP}{dn}\right|_{n=10}$ and interpret the result.
HINT [See Example 3.]

66. ***Marginal Product*** Refer back to Exercise 65. The average profit $\bar{P}$ per computer is given by dividing the total profit P by q:

$$\bar{P} = -\frac{100{,}000}{q} + 5{,}000 - 0.25q \text{ dollars.}$$

Determine the **marginal average product**, $d\bar{P}/dn$ at an employee level of 10 engineers. Interpret the result.
HINT [See Example 3.]

67. ***Food versus Education*** The percentage y (of total personal consumption) an individual spends on food is approximately

$$y = 35x^{-0.25} \text{ percentage points} \quad (6.5 \le x \le 17.5),$$

where x is the percentage the individual spends on education.[26] An individual finds that she is spending

$$x = 7 + 0.2t$$

percent of her personal consumption on education, where t is time in months since January 1. Use direct substitution to express the percentage y as a function of time t (do not simplify the expression) and then use the chain rule to estimate how fast the percentage she spends on food is changing on November 1. Be sure to specify the units.

68. ***Food versus Recreation*** The percentage y (of total personal consumption) an individual spends on food is approximately

$$y = 33x^{-0.63} \text{ percentage points} \quad (2.5 \le x \le 4.5),$$

where x is the percentage the individual spends on recreation.[27] A college student finds that he is spending

$$x = 3.5 + 0.1t$$

percent of his personal consumption on recreation, where t is time in months since January 1. Use direct substitution to express the percentage y as a function of time t (do not simplify the expression) and then use the chain rule to estimate how fast the percentage he spends on food is changing on November 1. Be sure to specify the units.

69. ***Marginal Revenue*** The weekly revenue from the sale of rubies at *Royal Ruby Retailers* (RRR) is increasing at a rate of \$40 per \$1 increase in price, and the price is decreasing at a rate of \$0.75 per additional ruby sold. What is the marginal revenue? (Be sure to state the units of measurement.) Interpret the result. HINT [See Example 5.]

70. ***Marginal Revenue*** The weekly revenue from the sale of emeralds at *Eduardo's Emerald Emporium* (EEE) is decreasing at a rate of €500 per €1 increase in price, and the price is decreasing at a rate of €0.45 per additional emerald sold. What is the marginal revenue? (Be sure to state the units of measurement.) Interpret the result. HINT [See Example 5.]

71. ***Crime Statistics*** The murder rate in large cities (over 1 million residents) can be related to that in smaller cities (500,000–1,000,000 residents) by the following linear model:[28]

$$y = 1.5x - 1.9 \quad (15 \le x \le 25),$$

where y is the murder rate (in murders per 100,000 residents each year) in large cities and x is the murder rate in smaller cities. During the period 1991–1998, the murder rate in small cities was decreasing at an average rate of 2 murders per 100,000 residents each year. Use the chain rule to estimate how fast the murder rate was changing in larger cities during that period. (Show how you used the chain rule in your answer.)

72. ***Crime Statistics*** Following is a quadratic model relating the murder rates described in the preceding exercise:

$$y = 0.1x^2 - 3x + 39 \quad (15 \le x \le 25).$$

In 1996, the murder rate in smaller cities was approximately 22 murders per 100,000 residents each year and was decreasing at a rate of approximately 2.5 murders per 100,000 residents each year. Use the chain rule to estimate how fast the murder rate was changing for large cities. (Show how you used the chain rule in your answer.)

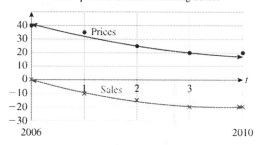

73. ***Existing Home Sales*** The following graph shows the approximate value of home prices and existing home sales in 2006–2010 as a percentage change from 2003, together with quadratic approximations.[29]

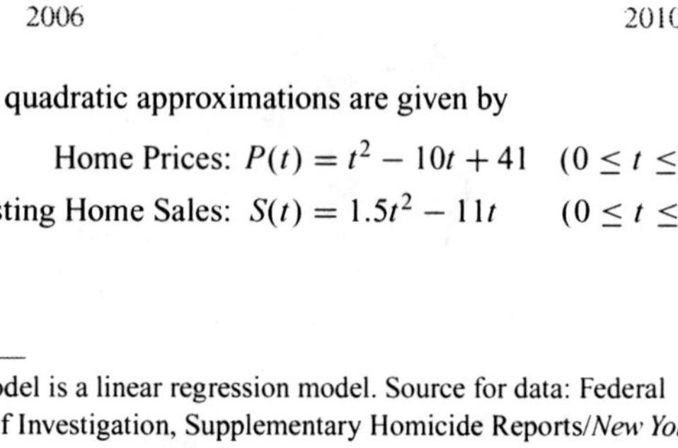

The quadratic approximations are given by

$$\text{Home Prices: } P(t) = t^2 - 10t + 41 \quad (0 \le t \le 4)$$
$$\text{Existing Home Sales: } S(t) = 1.5t^2 - 11t \quad (0 \le t \le 4),$$

[26] Model based on historical and projected data from 1908–2010. Sources: Historical data, Bureau of Economic Analysis; projected data, Bureau of Labor Statistics/*New York Times*, December 1, 2003, p. C2.

[27] *Ibid.*

[28] The model is a linear regression model. Source for data: Federal Bureau of Investigation, Supplementary Homicide Reports/*New York Times*, May 29, 2000, p. A12.

[29] Sources: Standard & Poors/Bloomberg Financial Markets/*New York Times*, September 29, 2007, p. C3. Projection is the authors'.

where t is time in years since the start of 2006. Use the chain rule to estimate $\left.\dfrac{dS}{dP}\right|_{t=2}$. What does the answer tell you about home sales and prices? HINT [See the second Quick Example on page 829.]

74. *Existing Home Sales Leading to the Financial Crisis* The following graph shows the approximate value of home prices and existing home sales in 2004–2007 (the 3 years prior to the 2008 economic crisis) as a percentage change from 2003, together with quadratic approximations.[30]

Home prices and sales of existing homes

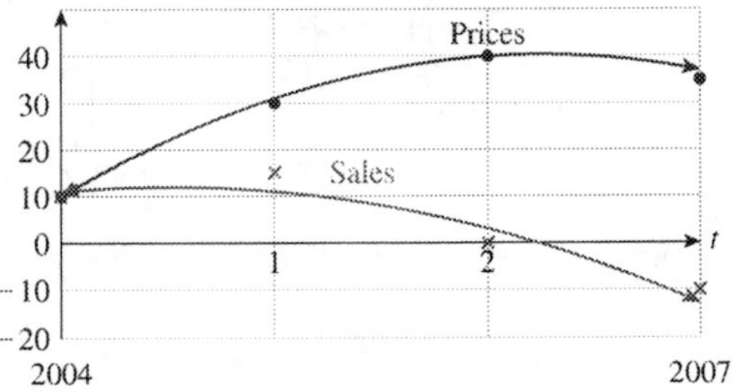

The quadratic approximations are given by

Home Prices: $P(t) = -6t^2 + 27t + 10 \quad (0 \le t \le 3)$

Existing Home Sales: $S(t) = -4t^2 + 4t + 11 \quad (0 \le t \le 3)$,

where t is time in years since the start of 2004. Use the chain rule to estimate $\left.\dfrac{dS}{dP}\right|_{t=2}$. What does the answer tell you about home sales and prices? HINT [See the second Quick Example on page 829.]

75. ▼ *Pollution* An offshore oil well is leaking oil and creating a circular oil slick. If the radius of the slick is growing at a rate of 2 miles/hour, find the rate at which the area is increasing when the radius is 3 miles. (The area of a disc of radius r is $A = \pi r^2$.) HINT [See Quick Example 2 on page 828.]

76. ▼ *Mold* A mold culture in a dorm refrigerator is circular and growing. The radius is growing at a rate of 0.3 cm/day. How fast is the area growing when the culture is 4 centimeters in radius? (The area of a disc of radius r is $A = \pi r^2$.) HINT [See Quick Example 2 on page 828.]

77. ▼ *Budget Overruns* The Pentagon is planning to build a new, spherical satellite. As is typical in these cases, the specifications keep changing, so that the size of the satellite keeps growing. In fact, the radius of the planned satellite is growing 0.5 feet per week. Its cost will be $1,000 per cubic foot. At the point when the plans call for a satellite 10 feet in radius, how fast is the cost growing? (The volume of a solid sphere of radius r is $V = \frac{4}{3}\pi r^3$.)

78. ▼ *Soap Bubbles* The soap bubble I am blowing has a radius that is growing at a rate of 4 cm/sec. How fast is the surface area growing when the radius is 10 cm? (The surface area of a sphere of radius r is $S = 4\pi r^2$.)

79. ▣ ▼ ***Revenue Growth*** The demand for the Cyberpunk II arcade video game is modeled by the logistic curve

$$q(t) = \frac{10,000}{1 + 0.5e^{-0.4t}}$$

where $q(t)$ is the total number of units sold t months after its introduction.

a. Use technology to estimate $q'(4)$.

b. Assume that the manufacturers of Cyberpunk II sell each unit for $800. What is the company's marginal revenue dR/dq?

c. Use the chain rule to estimate the rate at which revenue is growing 4 months after the introduction of the video game.

80. ▣ ▼ ***Information Highway*** The amount of information transmitted each month in the early years of the Internet (1988 to 1994) can be modeled by the equation

$$q(t) = \frac{2e^{0.69t}}{3 + 1.5e^{-0.4t}} \qquad (0 \le t \le 6),$$

where q is the amount of information transmitted each month in billions of data packets and t is the number of years since the start of 1988.[31]

a. Use technology to estimate $q'(2)$.

b. Assume that it costs $5 to transmit a million packets of data. What is the marginal cost $C'(q)$?

c. How fast was the cost increasing at the start of 1990?

Money Stock *Exercises 81–84 are based on the following demand function for money (taken from a question on the GRE Economics Test):*

$$M_d = 2 \times y^{0.6} \times r^{-0.3} \times p,$$

where

   $M_d = $ *demand for nominal money balances (money stock)*

   $y = $ *real income*

   $r = $ *an index of interest rates*

   $p = $ *an index of prices*

*These exercises also use the idea of **percentage rate of growth**:*

$$\text{Percentage Rate of Growth of } M = \frac{\text{Rate of Growth of } M}{M}$$
$$= \frac{dM/dt}{M}.$$

81. ◆ (from the GRE Economics Test) If the interest rate and price level are to remain constant while real income grows at 5 percent per year, the money stock must grow at what percent per year?

82. ◆ (from the GRE Economics Test) If real income and price level are to remain constant while the interest rate grows at 5 percent per year, the money stock must change by what percent per year?

---

[30]Sources: Standard & Poors /Bloomberg Financial Markets/*New York Times*, September 29, 2007, p. C3. Projection is the authors'.

[31]This is the authors' model, based on figures published in *New York Times*, Nov. 3, 1993.

83. ◆ (from the GRE Economics Test) If the interest rate is to remain constant while real income grows at 5 percent per year and the price level rises at 5 percent per year, the money stock must grow at what percent per year?

84. ◆ (from the GRE Economics Test) If real income grows by 5 percent per year, the interest rate grows by 2 percent per year, and the price level drops by 3 percent per year, the money stock must change by what percent per year?

COMMUNICATION AND REASONING EXERCISES

85. Complete the following: The derivative of 1 over a glob is -1 over . . . .

86. Complete the following: The derivative of the square root of a glob is 1 over . . . .

87. Say why the following was marked wrong and give the correct answer.

$$\frac{d}{dx}[(3x^3 - x)^3] = 3(9x^2 - 1)^2 \quad ✗ \ \textit{WRONG!}$$

88. Say why the following was marked wrong and give the correct answer.

$$\frac{d}{dx}\left[\left(\frac{3x^2-1}{2x-2}\right)^3\right] = 3\left(\frac{3x^2-1}{2x-2}\right)^2\left(\frac{6x}{2}\right) \quad ✗ \ \textit{WRONG!}$$

89. Name two major errors in the following graded test question and give the correct answer.

$$\frac{d}{dx}\left[\left(\frac{3x^2-1}{2x-2}\right)^3\right] = 3\left(\frac{6x}{2}\right)^2 \quad ✗ \ \textit{WRONG! SEE ME!}$$

90. Name two major errors in the following graded test question and give the correct answer.

$$\frac{d}{dx}[(3x^3 - x)(2x + 1)]^4 = 4[(9x^2 - 1)(2)]^3 \quad ✗ \ \textit{WRONG! SEE ME!}$$

91. ▼ Formulate a simple procedure for deciding whether to apply first the chain rule, the product rule, or the quotient rule when finding the derivative of a function.

92. ▼ Give an example of a function f with the property that calculating $f'(x)$ requires use of the following rules in the given order: (1) the chain rule, (2) the quotient rule, and (3) the chain rule.

93. ◆ Give an example of a function f with the property that calculating $f'(x)$ requires use of the chain rule five times in succession.

94. ◆ What can you say about the composite of two linear functions and what can you say about its derivative?

Practice Problems 11.4, Part 1

Suppose that $f(x)$ and $g(x)$ are differentiable functions such that $f(3)=4$, $g(3)=9$, $f'(3)=-2$, $f'(9)=7$, and $g'(3)=5$. Calculate $h'(3)$ for $h(x)$ as defined in each of the following.

1. $h(x)=\sqrt{f(x)\cdot g(x)}$

$h'(x)=(f(x)\cdot g(x))^{1/2}$

$1/2\,(f(x)\cdot g(x))$

2. $h(x)=f(x^2)+(g(x))^3$

3. $h(x)=\left(\dfrac{f(x)}{x^2+1}\right)^4$

Practice Problems 11.4, Part 2

According to observations, the length L (in mm) from nose to tip of tail of a Siberian tiger can be estimated by $L = 0.25w^{2.6}$, where w is the weight of the tiger, in kg. Furthermore, for tigers less than six months old, weight can be estimated by $w = 3 + 0.21d$, where d is the age of the tiger, in days.

1. Estimate the length of a Siberian tiger that weighs 60 kg. Round the result to two decimal places and label appropriately.

2. Estimate the rate at which the length of the tiger is changing with respect to weight if the tiger weighs 60 kg. Round the result to two decimal places and label appropriately.

3. Estimate the length of a Siberian tiger that is 100 days old. Round the result to two decimal places and label appropriately.

4. Estimate the rate at which the length of the tiger is changing with respect to age when the tiger is 100 days old. Round the result to two decimal places and label appropriately.

Practice Problems 11.4, Part 3

1. When Freddy goes to the movie theater, the number of ounces of soda he drinks, s, depends on the number of handfuls of popcorn he eats, p, as described by $s = 0.0003p^3 - 0.02p^2 + 2.9p + 4$. Also, the number of handfuls of popcorn he eats depends on how long the movie has been playing, t, in minutes, according to $p = 0.6t - 0.0025t^2$. Given this, estimate the rate (with respect to time) at which Freddy is consuming soda exactly 90 minutes into a movie. Label your final result appropriately, and give your answer accurate to three decimal places.

2. The weekly cost, in dollars, of producing x units of a product is given by $C = 0.0001x^3 - 0.08x^2 + 40x + 5000$. The number of units of the product that can be produced depends on the number of labor-hours, t, dedicated to production, according to $x = 2t - 0.0001t^2$. Given this, determine how fast weekly production costs are changing with respect to number of labor-hours when 500 labor-hours are dedicated to producing the product. Label your response appropriately.

Practice Problems 11.4, Part 4

A 26-foot ladder is placed against a wall. If the top of the ladder is sliding down at a rate of 2 feet per second, then estimate the rate at which the bottom of the ladder is moving away from the wall when the bottom of the ladder is 10 feet away from the wall. Here are some hints:

- draw a diagram—the height of the top of the ladder above ground is related to the distance the bottom of the ladder is from the base of the wall (call these quantities h and b, respectively, for the sake of giving names)
- both h and b change with respect to the amount of time, t, that the bottom of the ladder has been sliding away from the base of the wall
- you want to find $\frac{db}{dt}$, you are given $\frac{dh}{dt}$, and you can calculate $\frac{dh}{db}$ at the point in time you are interested in what's happening
- you don't need any techniques that we have not studied (except perhaps a little geometry), so use the tools we have developed

11.5 Derivatives of Logarithmic and Exponential Functions

At this point, we know how to take the derivative of any algebraic expression in x (involving powers, radicals, and so on). We now turn to the derivatives of logarithmic and exponential functions.

Derivative of the Natural Logarithm

$$\frac{d}{dx}[\ln x] = \frac{1}{x}$$ Recall that $\ln x = \log_e x$.

Quick Examples

1. $\frac{d}{dx}[3 \ln x] = 3 \cdot \frac{1}{x} = \frac{3}{x}$ Derivative of a constant times a function

2. $\frac{d}{dx}[x \ln x] = 1 \cdot \ln x + x \cdot \frac{1}{x}$ Product rule, because $x \ln x$ is a product

$= \ln x + 1.$

The above simple formula works only for the natural logarithm (the logarithm with base e). For logarithms with bases other than e, we have the following:

Derivative of the Logarithm with Base b

$$\frac{d}{dx}[\log_b x] = \frac{1}{x \ln b}$$ Notice that, if $b = e$, we get the same formula as previously.

Quick Examples

1. $\frac{d}{dx}[\log_3 x] = \frac{1}{x \ln 3} \approx \frac{1}{1.0986x}$

2. $\frac{d}{dx}[\log_2(x^4)] = \frac{d}{dx}(4 \log_2 x)$ We used the logarithm identity $\log_b(x^r) = r \log_b x$.

$= 4 \cdot \frac{1}{x \ln 2} \approx \frac{4}{0.6931x}$

Derivation of the formulas $\frac{d}{dx}[\ln x] = \frac{1}{x}$ and $\frac{d}{dx}[\log_b x] = \frac{1}{x \ln b}$

To compute $\frac{d}{dx}[\ln x]$, we need to use the definition of the derivative. We also use properties of the logarithm to help evaluate the limit.

$$\frac{d}{dx}[\ln x] = \lim_{h\to 0} \frac{\ln(x+h) - \ln x}{h}$$ Definition of the derivative

$$= \lim_{h\to 0} \frac{1}{h}[\ln(x+h) - \ln x]$$ Algebra

$$= \lim_{h\to 0} \frac{1}{h} \ln\left(\frac{x+h}{x}\right)$$ Properties of the logarithm

$$= \lim_{h\to 0} \frac{1}{h} \ln\left(1 + \frac{h}{x}\right)$$ Algebra

$$= \lim_{h\to 0} \ln\left(1 + \frac{h}{x}\right)^{1/h}$$ Properties of the logarithm

which we rewrite as

$$\lim_{h\to 0} \ln\left[\left(1 + \frac{1}{(x/h)}\right)^{x/h}\right]^{1/x}.$$

As $h \to 0^+$, the quantity x/h gets large and positive, and so the quantity in brackets approaches e (see the definition of e in Section 9.2), which leaves us with

$$\ln[e]^{1/x} = \frac{1}{x} \ln e = \frac{1}{x}$$

which is the derivative we are after.* What about the limit as $h \to 0^-$? We will glide over that case and leave it for the interested reader to pursue.†

The rule for the derivative of $\log_b x$ follows from the fact that $\log_b x = \ln x / \ln b$.

If we were to take the derivative of the natural logarithm of a *quantity* (a function of x), rather than just x, we would need to use the chain rule:

* We actually used the fact that the logarithm function is continuous when we took the limit.

† Here is an outline of the argument for negative h. Because x must be positive for $\ln x$ to be defined, we find that $x/h \to -\infty$ as $h \to 0^-$, and so we must consider the quantity $(1 + 1/m)^m$ for large *negative* m. It turns out the limit is still e (check it numerically!) and so the computation above still works.

Derivatives of Logarithms of Functions

Original Rule	*Generalized Rule*	*In Words*
$\frac{d}{dx}[\ln x] = \frac{1}{x}$	$\frac{d}{dx}[\ln u] = \frac{1}{u}\frac{du}{dx}$	*The derivative of the natural logarithm of a quantity is 1 over that quantity, times the derivative of that quantity.*
$\frac{d}{dx}[\log_b x] = \frac{1}{x \ln b}$	$\frac{d}{dx}[\log_b u] = \frac{1}{u \ln b}\frac{du}{dx}$	*The derivative of the log to base b of a quantity is 1 over the product of* ln *b and that quantity, times the derivative of that quantity.*

Quick Examples

1. $\frac{d}{dx}\ln[x^2+1] = \frac{1}{x^2+1}\frac{d}{dx}(x^2+1)$ $u = x^2 + 1$ (See the margin note.§)

$= \frac{1}{x^2+1}(2x) = \frac{2x}{x^2+1}$

2. $\frac{d}{dx}\log_2[x^3+x] = \frac{1}{(x^3+x)\ln 2}\frac{d}{dx}(x^3+x)$ $u = x^3 + x$

$= \frac{1}{(x^3+x)\ln 2}(3x^2+1) = \frac{3x^2+1}{(x^3+x)\ln 2}$

§ If we were to evaluate $\ln(x^2+1)$, the last operation we would perform would be to take the natural logarithm of a quantity. Thus, the calculation thought experiment tells us that we are dealing with ln *of a quantity*, and so we need the generalized logarithm rule as stated above.

EXAMPLE 1 Derivative of Logarithmic Function

Compute the following derivatives:

a. $\frac{d}{dx}[\ln\sqrt{x+1}]$ **b.** $\frac{d}{dx}[\ln[(1+x)(2-x)]]$ **c.** $\frac{d}{dx}[\ln|x|]$

Solution

a. The calculation thought experiment tells us that we have the natural logarithm of a quantity, so

$$\frac{d}{dx}[\ln\sqrt{x+1}] = \frac{1}{\sqrt{x+1}}\frac{d}{dx}\sqrt{x+1} \qquad \frac{d}{dx}\ln u = \frac{1}{u}\frac{du}{dx}$$

$$= \frac{1}{\sqrt{x+1}} \cdot \frac{1}{2\sqrt{x+1}} \qquad \frac{d}{dx}\sqrt{u} = \frac{1}{2\sqrt{u}}\frac{du}{dx}$$

$$= \frac{1}{2(x+1)}.$$

Q: *What happened to the square root?*

A: As with many problems involving logarithms, we could have done this one differently and much more easily if we had simplified the expression $\ln\sqrt{x+1}$ using the properties of logarithms *before* differentiating. Doing this, we get the following:

Part (a) redone by simplifying first:

$$\ln\sqrt{x+1} = \ln(x+1)^{1/2} = \frac{1}{2}\ln(x+1). \quad \text{Simplify the logarithm first.}$$

Thus,

$$\frac{d}{dx}[\ln\sqrt{x+1}] = \frac{d}{dx}\left[\frac{1}{2}\ln(x+1)\right]$$

$$= \frac{1}{2}\left[\frac{1}{x+1}\right]\cdot 1 = \frac{1}{2(x+1)}.$$

A *lot* easier!

b. This time, we simplify the expression $\ln[(1+x)(2-x)]$ before taking the derivative:

$$\ln[(1+x)(2-x)] = \ln(1+x) + \ln(2-x). \quad \text{Simplify the logarithm first.}$$

Thus,

$$\frac{d}{dx}[\ln[(1+x)(2-x)]] = \frac{d}{dx}[\ln[(1+x)]] + \frac{d}{dx}[\ln[(2-x)]]$$

$$= \frac{1}{1+x} - \frac{1}{2-x}. \quad \frac{d}{dx}\ln u = \frac{1}{u}\frac{du}{dx}$$

For practice, try doing this calculation without simplifying first. What other differentiation rule do you need to use?

c. Before we start, we note that $\ln x$ is defined only for positive values of x, so its domain is the set of positive real numbers. The domain of $\ln|x|$, on the other hand, is the set of *all* nonzero real numbers. For example, $\ln|-2| = \ln 2 \approx 0.6931$. For this reason, $\ln|x|$ often turns out to be more useful than the ordinary logarithm function.

$$\frac{d}{dx}[\ln|x|] = \frac{1}{|x|}\frac{d}{dx}|x| \quad \frac{d}{dx}\ln u = \frac{1}{u}\frac{du}{dx}$$

$$= \frac{1}{|x|}\frac{|x|}{x} \quad \text{Recall that } \frac{d}{dx}|x| = \frac{|x|}{x}.$$

$$= \frac{1}{x}$$

Before we go on... Figure 7(a) shows the graphs of $y = \ln |x|$ and $y = 1/x$. Figure 7(b) shows the graphs of $y = \ln |x|$ and $y = 1/|x|$. You should be able to see from these graphs why the derivative of $\ln |x|$ is $1/x$ and not $1/|x|$.

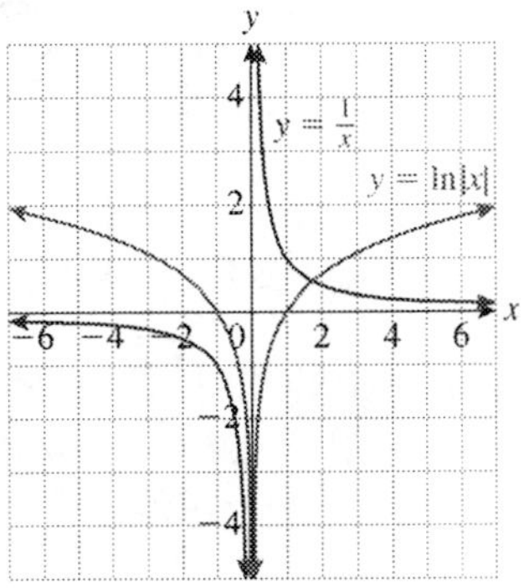

Figure 7(a)

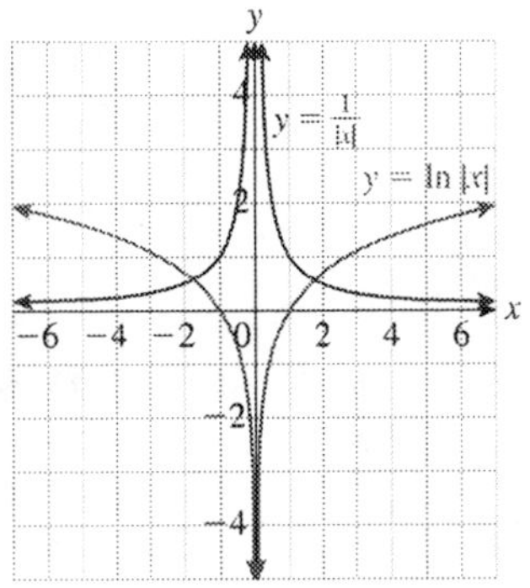

Figure 7(b)

This last example, in conjunction with the chain rule, gives us the following formulas.

Derivative of Logarithms of Absolute Values

Original Rule	*Generalized Rule*	*In Words*
$\frac{d}{dx}[\ln |x|] = \frac{1}{x}$	$\frac{d}{dx}[\ln |u|] = \frac{1}{u}\frac{du}{dx}$	*The derivative of the natural logarithm of the absolute value of a quantity is 1 over that quantity, times the derivative of that quantity.*
$\frac{d}{dx}[\log_b|x|] = \frac{1}{x \ln b}$	$\frac{d}{dx}[\log_b|u|] = \frac{1}{u \ln b}\frac{du}{dx}$	*The derivative of the log to base b of the absolute value of a quantity is 1 over the product of* ln b *and that quantity, times the derivative of that quantity.*

Note: Compare the above formulas with those on page 836. They tell us that we can simply ignore the absolute values in $\ln |u|$ or $\log_b |u|$ when taking the derivative.

Quick Examples

1. $\frac{d}{dx}[\ln |x^2 - 1|] = \frac{1}{x^2 - 1}\frac{d}{dx}(x^2 - 1)$ $\quad u = x^2 - 1$

$= \frac{1}{x^2 - 1}(2x) = \frac{2x}{x^2 - 1}$

2. $\frac{d}{dx}[\log_2|x^3+x|] = \frac{1}{(x^3+x)\ln 2}\frac{d}{dx}(x^3+x)$ $\quad u = x^3 + x$

$= \frac{1}{(x^3+x)\ln 2}(3x^2+1) = \frac{3x^2+1}{(x^3+x)\ln 2}$

We now turn to the derivatives of *exponential* functions—that is, functions of the form $f(x) = b^x$. We begin by showing how *not* to differentiate them.

Caution The derivative of b^x is *not* xb^{x-1}. The power rule applies only to *constant* exponents. In this case the exponent is decidedly *not* constant, and so the power rule does not apply.

The following shows the correct way of differentiating b^x, beginning with a special case.

Derivative of e^x

$$\frac{d}{dx}[e^x] = e^x$$

Quick Examples

1. $\frac{d}{dx}[3e^x] = 3\frac{d}{dx}[e^x] = 3e^x$ $\quad$ Constant multiple rule

2. $\frac{d}{dx}\left[\frac{e^x}{x}\right] = \frac{e^x x - e^x(1)}{x^2}$ $\quad$ Quotient rule

$= \frac{e^x(x-1)}{x^2}$

Thus, e^x has the amazing property that its derivative is itself!* For bases other than e, we have the following generalization:

* There is another—very simple—function that is its own derivative. What is it?

Derivative of b^x

If b is any positive number, then

$$\frac{d}{dx}[b^x] = b^x \ln b.$$

Note that if $b = e$, we obtain the previous formula.

Quick Example

$\frac{d}{dx}[3^x] = 3^x \ln 3$

Derivation of the Formula $\frac{d}{dx}[e^x] = e^x$

To find the derivative of e^x, we use a shortcut.* Write $g(x) = e^x$. Then

$$\ln g(x) = x.$$

Take the derivative of both sides of this equation to get

$$\frac{g'(x)}{g(x)} = 1$$

or

$$g'(x) = g(x) = e^x.$$

In other words, the exponential function with base *e* is its own derivative. The rule for exponential functions with other bases follows from the equality $b^x = e^{x\ln b}$ (why?) and the chain rule. (Try it.)

If we were to take the derivative of *e* raised to a *quantity*, not just *x*, we would need to use the chain rule, as follows.

* This shortcut is an example of a technique called *logarithmic differentiation*, which is occasionally useful. We will see it again in the next section.

Derivatives of Exponentials of Functions

Original Rule	*Generalized Rule*	*In Words*
$\frac{d}{dx}[e^x] = e^x$	$\frac{d}{dx}[e^u] = e^u\frac{du}{dx}$	*The derivative of e raised to a quantity is e raised to that quantity, times the derivative of that quantity.*
$\frac{d}{dx}[b^x] = b^x \ln b$	$\frac{d}{dx}[b^u] = b^u \ln b\frac{du}{dx}$	*The derivative of b raised to a quantity is b raised to that quantity, times* ln *b, times the derivative of that quantity.*

Quick Examples

1. $\frac{d}{dx}\left[e^{x^2+1}\right] = e^{x^2+1}\frac{d}{dx}[x^2+1]$ $\quad u = x^2 + 1$ (See margin note.†)

$= e^{x^2+1}(2x) = 2x\, e^{x^2+1}$

2. $\frac{d}{dx}[2^{3x}] = 2^{3x}\ln 2\frac{d}{dx}[3x]$ $\quad u = 3x$

$= 2^{3x}(\ln 2)(3) = (3\ln 2)2^{3x}$

3. $\frac{d}{dt}[30e^{1.02t}] = 30e^{1.02t}(1.02) = 30.6e^{1.02t}$ $\quad u = 1.02t$

4. If $1,000 is invested in an account earning 5% per year compounded continuously, then the rate of change of the account balance after *t* years is

$$\frac{d}{dt}[1{,}000e^{0.05t}] = 1{,}000(0.05)e^{0.05t} = 50e^{0.05t} \text{ dollars/year.}$$

† The calculation thought experiment tells us that we have *e* raised to a quantity.

APPLICATIONS

EXAMPLE 2 Epidemics

In the early stages of the AIDS epidemic during the 1980s, the number of cases in the United States was increasing by about 50% every 6 months. By the start of 1983, there were approximately 1,600 AIDS cases in the United States.[32] Had this trend continued, how many new cases per year would have been occurring by the start of 1993?

Solution To find the answer, we must first model this exponential growth using the methods of Chapter 9. Referring to Example 4 in Section 9.2, we find that t years after the start of 1983 the number of cases is

$$A = 1{,}600(2.25^t).$$

We are asking for the number of new cases each year. In other words, we want the rate of change, dA/dt:

$$\frac{dA}{dt} = 1{,}600(2.25)^t \ln 2.25 \text{ cases per year.}$$

At the start of 1993, $t = 10$, so the number of new cases per year is

$$\left.\frac{dA}{dt}\right|_{t=10} = 1{,}600(2.25)^{10} \ln 2.25 \approx 4{,}300{,}000 \text{ cases per year.}$$

Before we go on... In Example 2, the figure for the number of new cases per year is so large because we assumed that exponential growth—the 50% increase every 6 months—would continue. A more realistic model for the spread of a disease is the logistic model. (See Section 9.4, as well as the next example.) ■

EXAMPLE 3 Sales Growth

The sales of the *Cyberpunk II* video game can be modeled by the logistic curve

$$q(t) = \frac{10{,}000}{1 + 0.5e^{-0.4t}}$$

where $q(t)$ is the total number of units sold t months after its introduction. How fast is the game selling 2 years after its introduction?

Solution We are asked for $q'(24)$. We can find the derivative of $q(t)$ using the quotient rule, or we can first write

$$q(t) = 10{,}000(1 + 0.5e^{-0.4t})^{-1}$$

and then use the generalized power rule:

$$\begin{aligned} q'(t) &= -10{,}000(1 + 0.5e^{-0.4t})^{-2}(0.5e^{-0.4t})(-0.4) \\ &= \frac{2{,}000e^{-0.4t}}{(1 + 0.5e^{-0.4t})^2}. \end{aligned}$$

[32]Data based on regression of 1982–1986 figures. Source for data: Centers for Disease Control and Prevention. HIV/AIDS Surveillance Report, 2000;12 (No. 2).

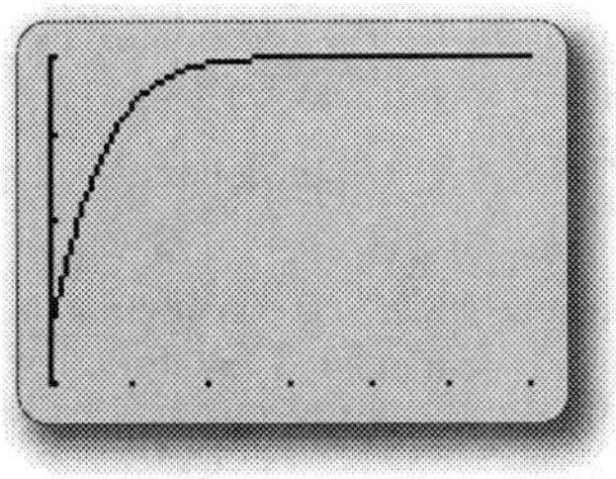

Figure 8

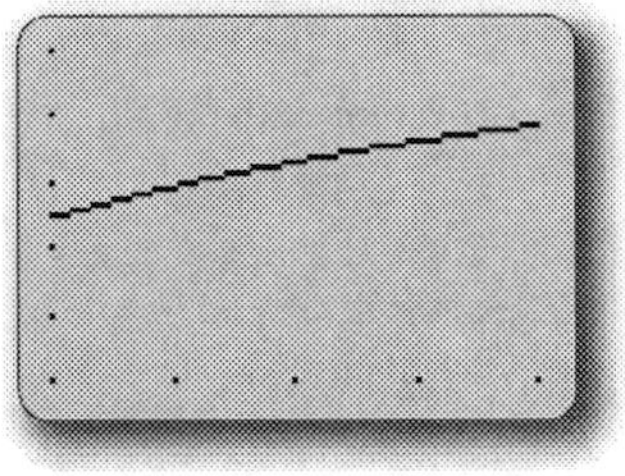

Figure 9

* We can also say this using limits: $\lim_{t \to +\infty} q(t) = 10{,}000$.

Thus,

$$q'(24) = \frac{2{,}000e^{-0.4(24)}}{(1 + 0.5e^{-0.4(24)})^2} \approx 0.135 \text{ units per month.}$$

So, after 2 years, sales are quite slow.

Before we go on... We can check the answer in Example 3 graphically. If we plot the total sales curve for $0 \le t \le 30$ and $6{,}000 \le q \le 10{,}000$, on a TI-83/84 Plus, for example, we get the graph shown in Figure 8. Notice that total sales level off at about 10,000 units.* We computed $q'(24)$, which is the slope of the curve at the point with t-coordinate 24. If we zoom in to the portion of the curve near $t = 24$, we obtain the graph shown in Figure 9, with $23 \le t \le 25$ and $9{,}999 \le q \le 10{,}000$. The curve is almost linear in this range. If we use the two endpoints of this segment of the curve, (23, 9,999.4948) and (25, 9,999.7730), we can approximate the derivative as

$$\frac{9{,}999.7730 - 9{,}999.4948}{25 - 23} = 0.1391$$

which is accurate to two decimal places. ■

11.5 EXERCISES

▼ more advanced ◆ challenging

T indicates exercises that should be solved using technology

Find the derivatives of the functions in Exercises 1–76. HINT [See Quick Examples on page 836.]

1. $f(x) = \ln(x - 1)$
2. $f(x) = \ln(x + 3)$
3. $f(x) = \log_2 x$
4. $f(x) = \log_3 x$
5. $g(x) = \ln|x^2 + 3|$
6. $g(x) = \ln|2x - 4|$
7. $h(x) = e^{x+3}$ HINT [See Quick Examples on page 840.]
8. $h(x) = e^{x^2}$ HINT [See Quick Examples on page 840.]
9. $f(x) = e^{-x}$
10. $f(x) = e^{1-x}$
11. $g(x) = 4^x$
12. $g(x) = 5^x$
13. $h(x) = 2^{x^2-1}$
14. $h(x) = 3^{x^2-x}$
15. $f(x) = x \ln x$
16. $f(x) = 3 \ln x$
17. $f(x) = (x^2 + 1) \ln x$
18. $f(x) = (4x^2 - x) \ln x$
19. $f(x) = (x^2 + 1)^5 \ln x$
20. $f(x) = (x + 1)^{0.5} \ln x$
21. $g(x) = \ln|3x - 1|$
22. $g(x) = \ln|5 - 9x|$
23. $g(x) = \ln|2x^2 + 1|$
24. $g(x) = \ln|x^2 - x|$
25. $g(x) = \ln(x^2 - 2.1x^{0.3})$
26. $g(x) = \ln(x - 3.1x^{-1})$
27. $h(x) = \ln[(-2x + 1)(x + 1)]$ HINT [See Example 1b.]
28. $h(x) = \ln[(3x + 1)(-x + 1)]$ HINT [See Example 1b.]
29. $h(x) = \ln\left(\frac{3x + 1}{4x - 2}\right)$
30. $h(x) = \ln\left(\frac{9x}{4x - 2}\right)$
31. $r(x) = \ln\left|\frac{(x + 1)(x - 3)}{-2x - 9}\right|$
32. $r(x) = \ln\left|\frac{-x + 1}{(3x - 4)(x - 9)}\right|$
33. $s(x) = \ln(4x - 2)^{1.3}$ HINT [See Example 1a.]
34. $s(x) = \ln(x - 8)^{-2}$ HINT [See Example 1a.]
35. $s(x) = \ln\left|\frac{(x + 1)^2}{(3x - 4)^3(x - 9)}\right|$
36. $s(x) = \ln\left|\frac{(x + 1)^2(x - 3)^4}{2x + 9}\right|$
37. $h(x) = \log_2(x + 1)$
38. $h(x) = \log_3(x^2 + x)$
39. $r(t) = \log_3(t + 1/t)$
40. $r(t) = \log_3\left(t + \sqrt{t}\right)$
41. $f(x) = (\ln|x|)^2$
42. $f(x) = \frac{1}{\ln|x|}$
43. $r(x) = \ln(x^2) - [\ln(x - 1)]^2$
44. $r(x) = (\ln(x^2))^2$
45. $f(x) = xe^x$
46. $f(x) = 2e^x - x^2e^x$
47. $r(x) = \ln(x + 1) + 3x^3e^x$
48. $r(x) = \ln|x + e^x|$
49. $f(x) = e^x \ln|x|$
50. $f(x) = e^x \log_2|x|$
51. $f(x) = e^{2x+1}$
52. $f(x) = e^{4x-5}$
53. $h(x) = e^{x^2-x+1}$
54. $h(x) = e^{2x^2-x+1/x}$
55. $s(x) = x^2e^{2x-1}$
56. $s(x) = \frac{e^{4x-1}}{x^3 - 1}$
57. $r(x) = (e^{2x-1})^2$
58. $r(x) = (e^{2x^2})^3$
59. $t(x) = 3^{2x-4}$
60. $t(x) = 4^{-x+5}$
61. $v(x) = 3^{2x+1} + e^{3x+1}$
62. $v(x) = e^{2x}4^{2x}$

63. $u(x) = \dfrac{3^{x^2}}{x^2+1}$

64. $u(x) = (x^2+1)4^{x^2-1}$

65. $g(x) = \dfrac{e^x + e^{-x}}{e^x - e^{-x}}$

66. $g(x) = \dfrac{1}{e^x + e^{-x}}$

67. ▼ $g(x) = e^{3x-1}e^{x-2}e^x$

68. ▼ $g(x) = e^{-x+3}e^{2x-1}e^{-x+11}$

69. ▼ $f(x) = \dfrac{1}{x \ln x}$

70. ▼ $f(x) = \dfrac{e^{-x}}{xe^x}$

71. ▼ $f(x) = [\ln(e^x)]^2 - \ln[(e^x)^2]$

72. ▼ $f(x) = e^{\ln x} - e^{2\ln(x^2)}$

73. ▼ $f(x) = \ln|\ln x|$

74. ▼ $f(x) = \ln|\ln|\ln x||$

75. ▼ $s(x) = \ln\sqrt{\ln x}$

76. ▼ $s(x) = \sqrt{\ln(\ln x)}$

Find the equations of the straight lines described in Exercises 77–82. Use graphing technology to check your answers by plotting the given curve together with the tangent line.

77. Tangent to $y = e^x \log_2 x$ at the point $(1, 0)$

78. Tangent to $y = e^x + e^{-x}$ at the point $(0, 2)$

79. Tangent to $y = \ln\sqrt{2x+1}$ at the point where $x = 0$

80. Tangent to $y = \ln\sqrt{2x^2+1}$ at the point where $x = 1$

81. At right angles to $y = e^{x^2}$ at the point where $x = 1$

82. At right angles to $y = \log_2(3x+1)$ at the point where $x = 1$

APPLICATIONS

83. ***Research and Development: Industry*** The total spent on research and development by industry in the United States during 1995–2007 can be approximated by

$$S(t) = 57.5 \ln t + 31 \text{ billion dollars} \quad (5 \le t \le 17),$$

where t is the year since 1990.[33] What was the total spent in 2000 ($t = 10$) and how fast was it increasing? HINT [See Quick Examples on page 834.]

84. ***Research and Development: Federal*** The total spent on research and development by the federal government in the United States during 1995–2007 can be approximated by

$$S(t) = 7.4 \ln t + 3 \text{ billion dollars} \quad (5 \le t \le 17),$$

where t is the year since 1990.[34] What was the total spent in 2005 ($t = 15$) and how fast was it increasing? HINT [See Quick Examples on page 834.]

85. ***Research and Development: Industry*** The function $S(t)$ in Exercise 83 can also be written (approximately) as

$$S(t) = 57.5 \ln(1.71t + 17.1) \text{ billion dollars} \quad (-5 \le t \le 7),$$

where this time t is the year since 2000. Use this alternative formula to estimate the amount spent in 2000 and its rate of change, and check your answers by comparing them with those in Exercise 83.

86. ***Research and Development: Federal*** The function $S(t)$ in Exercise 84 can also be written (approximately) as

$$S(t) = 7.4 \ln(1.5t + 15) \text{ billion dollars} \quad (-5 \le t \le 7),$$

where this time t is the year since 2000. Use this alternative formula to estimate the amount spent in 2005 and its rate of change, and check your answers by comparing them with those in Exercise 84.

87. ▼ ***Carbon Dating*** The age in years of a specimen that originally contained 10g of carbon 14 is given by

$$y = \log_{0.999879}(0.1x),$$

where x is the amount of carbon 14 it currently contains. Compute $\left.\dfrac{dy}{dx}\right|_{x=5}$ and interpret your answer. HINT [For the calculation, see Quick Examples on page 836.]

88. ▼ ***Iodine Dating*** The age in years of a specimen that originally contained 10g of iodine 131 is given by

$$y = \log_{0.999567}(0.1x),$$

where x is the amount of iodine 131 it currently contains. Compute $\left.\dfrac{dy}{dx}\right|_{x=8}$ and interpret your answer. HINT [For the calculation, see Quick Examples on page 836.]

89. ***New York City Housing Costs: Downtown*** The average price of a two-bedroom apartment in downtown New York City during the real estate boom from 1994 to 2004 can be approximated by

$$p(t) = 0.33e^{0.16t} \text{ million dollars} \quad (0 \le t \le 10),$$

where t is time in years ($t = 0$ represents 1994).[35] What was the average price of a two-bedroom apartment in downtown New York City in 2003, and how fast was it increasing? (Round your answers to two significant digits.) HINT [See Quick Example 3 on page 840.]

90. ***New York City Housing Costs: Uptown*** The average price of a two-bedroom apartment in uptown New York City during the real estate boom from 1994 to 2004 can be approximated by

$$p(t) = 0.14e^{0.10t} \text{ million dollars} \quad (0 \le t \le 10),$$

where t is time in years ($t = 0$ represents 1994).[36] What was the average price of a two-bedroom apartment in uptown

[33] Spending is in constant 2000 dollars. Source for data through 2006: National Science Foundation, Division of Science Resources Statistics, National Patterns of R&D Resources (www.nsf.gov/statistics) August 2008.

[34] Federal funding excluding grants to industry and nonprofit organizations. Spending is in constant 2000 dollars. Source for data through 2006: National Science Foundation, Division of Science Resources Statistics, National Patterns of R&D Resources (www.nsf.gov/statistics) August 2008.

[35] Model is based on a exponential regression. Source for data: Miller Samuel/*New York Times*, March 28, 2004, p. RE 11.

[36] *Ibid.*

New York City in 2002, and how fast was it increasing? (Round your answers to two significant digits.) HINT [See Quick Example 3 on page 840.]

91. ***Big Brother*** The following chart shows the total number of wiretaps authorized each year by U.S. state and federal courts from 1990 to 2009 ($t = 0$ represents 1990):[37]

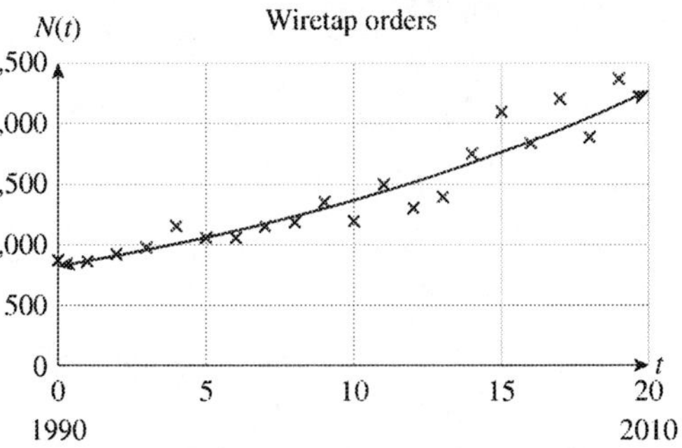

These data can be approximated with the model

$$N(t) = 820e^{0.051t} \quad (0 \le t \le 19).$$

a. Find $N(15)$ and $N'(15)$. Be sure to state the units of measurement. To how many significant digits should we round the answers? Why?

b. The number of people whose communications are intercepted averages around 100 per wiretap order. What does the answer to part (a) tell you about the number of people whose communications were intercepted?[38]

c. According to the model, the number of wiretaps orders each year (choose one)

(A) increased at a linear rate
(B) decreased at a quadratic rate
(C) increased at an exponential rate
(D) increased at a logarithmic rate

over the period shown.

92. ***Big Brother*** The following chart shows the total number of wiretaps authorized each year by U.S. state courts from 1990 to 2009 ($t = 0$ represents 1990):[39]

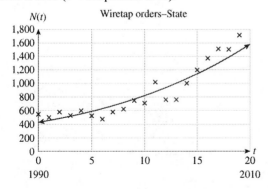

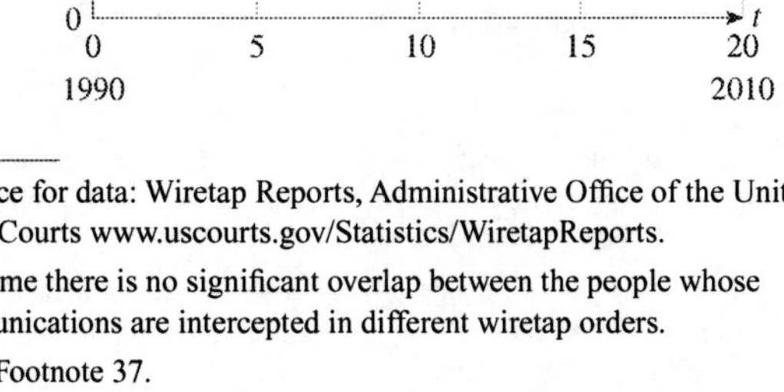

These data can be approximated with the model

$$N(t) = 430e^{0.065t} \quad (0 \le t \le 19).$$

a. Find $N(10)$ and $N'(10)$. Be sure to state the units of measurement. To how many significant digits should we round the answers? Why?

b. The number of people whose communications are intercepted averages around 100 per wiretap order. What does the answer to part (a) tell you about the number of people whose communications were intercepted?[40]

c. According to the model, the number of wiretaps orders each year (choose one)

(A) increased at a linear rate
(B) decreased at a quadratic rate
(C) increased at an exponential rate
(D) increased at a logarithmic rate

over the period shown.

93. ***Investments*** If \$10,000 is invested in a savings account offering 4% per year, compounded continuously, how fast is the balance growing after 3 years?

94. ***Investments*** If \$20,000 is invested in a savings account offering 3.5% per year, compounded continuously, how fast is the balance growing after 3 years?

95. ***Investments*** If \$10,000 is invested in a savings account offering 4% per year, compounded semiannually, how fast is the balance growing after 3 years?

96. ***Investments*** If \$20,000 is invested in a savings account offering 3.5% per year, compounded semiannually, how fast is the balance growing after 3 years?

97. ***SARS*** In the early stages of the deadly SARS (Severe Acute Respiratory Syndrome) epidemic in 2003, the number of cases was increasing by about 18% each day.[41] On March 17, 2003 (the first day for which statistics were reported by the World Health Organization) there were 167 cases. Find an exponential model that predicts the number of people infected t days after March 17, 2003, and use it to estimate how fast the epidemic was spreading on March 31, 2003. (Round your answer to the nearest whole number of new cases per day.) HINT [See Example 2.]

98. ***SARS*** A few weeks into the deadly SARS (Severe Acute Respiratory Syndrome) epidemic in 2003, the number of cases was increasing by about 4% each day.[42] On April 1, 2003 there were 1,804 cases. Find an exponential model that predicts the number $A(t)$ of people infected t days after April 1, 2003, and use it to estimate how fast the epidemic was spreading on April 30, 2003. (Round your answer to the nearest whole number of new cases per day.) HINT [See Example 2.]

[37] Source for data: Wiretap Reports, Administrative Office of the United States Courts www.uscourts.gov/Statistics/WiretapReports.

[38] Assume there is no significant overlap between the people whose communications are intercepted in different wiretap orders.

[39] See Footnote 37.

[40] See Footnote 38.

[41] World Health Organization (www.who.int).

[42] *Ibid.*

99. ▼ ***SAT Scores by Income*** The following bar graph shows U.S. math SAT scores as a function of household income:[43]

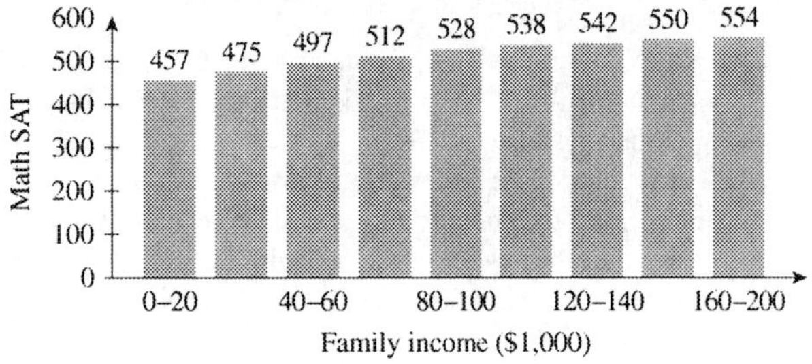

a. Which of the following best models the data (C is a constant)?

(A) $S(x) = C - 133e^{-0.0131x}$
(B) $S(x) = C + 133e^{-0.0131x}$
(C) $S(x) = C + 133e^{0.0131x}$
(D) $S(x) = C - 133e^{0.0131x}$

($S(x)$ is the average math SAT score of students whose household income is x thousand dollars per year.)

b. Use $S'(x)$ to predict how a student's math SAT score is affected by a $1,000 increase in parents' income for a student whose parents earn $45,000.

c. Does $S'(x)$ increase or decrease as x increases? Interpret your answer.

100. ***SAT Scores by Income*** The following bar graph shows U.S. critical reading SAT scores as a function of household income:[44]

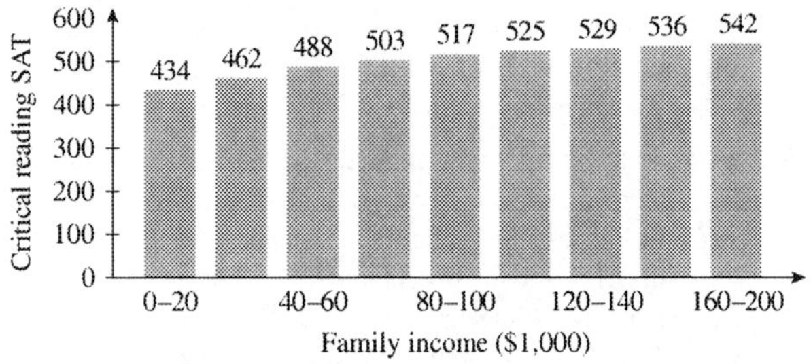

a. Which of the following best models the data (C is a constant)?

(A) $S(x) = C + \dfrac{1}{136e^{0.015x}}$

(B) $S(x) = C - 136e^{0.015x}$

(C) $S(x) = C - \dfrac{136}{e^{0.015x}}$

(D) $S(x) = C - \dfrac{e^{0.015x}}{136}$

($S(x)$ is the average critical reading SAT score of students whose household income is x thousand dollars per year.)

b. Use $S'(x)$ to predict how a student's critical reading SAT score is affected by a $1,000 increase in parents' income for a student whose parents earn $45,000.

c. Does $S'(x)$ increase or decrease as x increases? Interpret your answer.

101. ▼ ***Demographics: Average Age and Fertility*** The following graph shows a plot of average age of a population versus fertility rate (the average number of children each woman has in her lifetime) in the United States and Europe over the period 1950–2005.[45]

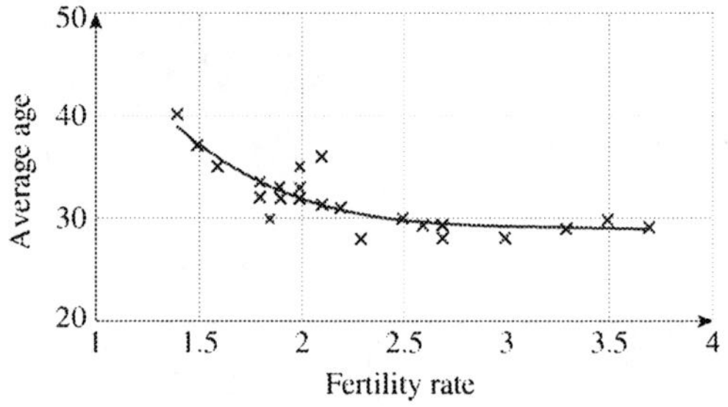

The equation of the accompanying curve is

$$a = 28.5 + 120(0.172)^x \quad (1.4 \le x \le 3.7),$$

where a is the average age (in years) of the population and x is the fertility rate.

a. Compute $a'(2)$. What does the answer tell you about average age and fertility rates?

b. Use the answer to part (a) to estimate how much the fertility rate would need to increase from a level of 2 children per woman to lower the average age of a population by about 1 year.

102. ▼ ***Demographics: Average Age and Fertility*** The following graph shows a plot of average age of a population versus fertility rate (the average number of children each woman has in her lifetime) in Europe over the period 1950–2005.[46]

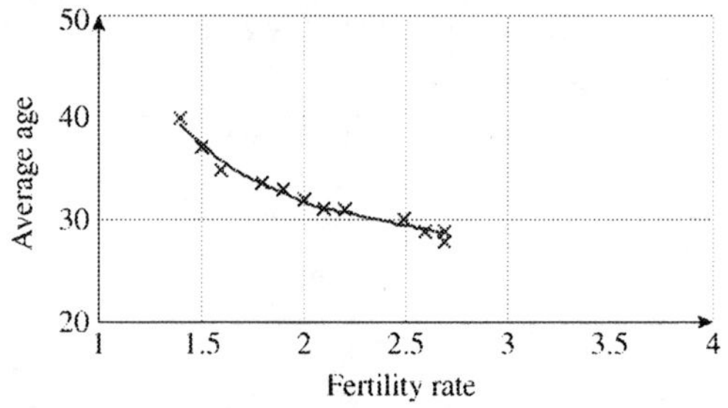

The equation of the accompanying curve is

$$g = 27.6 + 128(0.181)^x \quad (1.4 \le x \le 3.7),$$

where g is the average age (in years) of the population and x is the fertility rate.

a. Compute $g'(2.5)$. What does the answer tell you about average age and fertility rates?

[43] 2009 data. Source: College Board/*New York Times* http://economix .blogs.nytimes.com.

[44] *Ibid.*

[45] The separate data for Europe and the United States are collected in the same graph. 2005 figures are estimates. Source: United Nations World Population Division/*New York Times*, June 29, 2003, p. 3.

[46] All European countries including the Russian Federation. 2005 figures are estimates. Source: United Nations World Population Division/*New York Times*, June 29, 2003, p. 3.

b. Referring to the model that combines the data for Europe and the United States in Exercise 101, which population's average age is affected more by a changing fertility rate at the level of 2.5 children per woman?

103. ***Epidemics*** A flu epidemic described in Example 1 in Section 9.4 approximately followed the curve

$$P = \frac{150}{1 + 15{,}000e^{-0.35t}} \text{ million people,}$$

where P is the number of people infected and t is the number of weeks after the start of the epidemic. How fast is the epidemic growing (that is, how many new cases are there each week) after 20 weeks? After 30 weeks? After 40 weeks? (Round your answers to two significant digits.) HINT [See Example 3.]

104. ***Epidemics*** Another epidemic follows the curve

$$P = \frac{200}{1 + 20{,}000e^{-0.549t}} \text{ million people,}$$

where t is in years. How fast is the epidemic growing after 10 years? After 20 years? After 30 years? (Round your answers to two significant digits.) HINT [See Example 3.]

105. ***Subprime Mortgages during the Housing Bubble*** During the real estate run-up in 2000–2008, the percentage of mortgages issued in the U.S. that were subprime (normally classified as risky) could be approximated by

$$A(t) = \frac{15.0}{1 + 8.6e^{-0.59t}} \text{ percent} \quad (0 \le t \le 8)$$

t years after the start of 2000.[47]

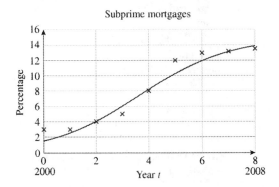

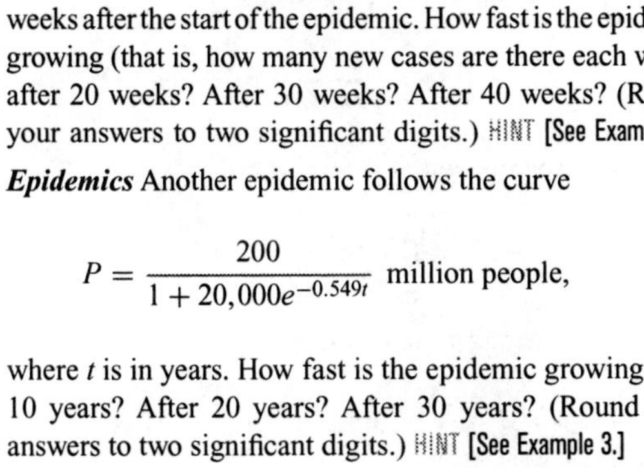

How fast, to the nearest 0.1%, was the percentage increasing at the start of 2003? How would you check that the answer is approximately correct by looking at the graph? HINT [See Example 3.]

106. ***Subprime Mortgage Debt during the Housing Bubble*** During the real estate run-up in 2000–2008, the value of subprime (normally classified as risky) mortgage debt outstanding in the U.S. was approximately

$$A(t) = \frac{1{,}350}{1 + 4.2e^{-0.53t}} \text{ billion dollars} \quad (0 \le t \le 8)$$

t years after the start of 2000.[48]

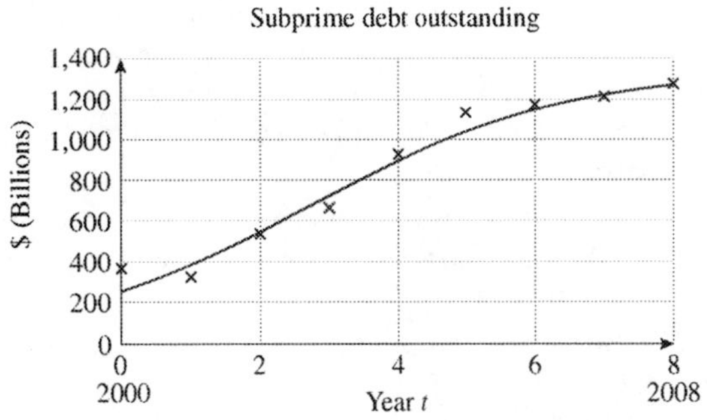

How fast, to the nearest $1 billion, was subprime mortgage debt increasing at the start of 2005? How would you check that the answer is approximately correct by looking at the graph? HINT [See Example 3.]

107. ***Subprime Mortgages during the Housing Bubble*** (Compare Exercise 105.) During the real estate run-up in 2000–2008, the percentage of mortgages issued in the U.S. that were subprime (normally classified as risky) could be approximated by

$$A(t) = \frac{15.0}{1 + 8.6(1.8)^{-t}} \text{ percent} \quad (0 \le t \le 8)$$

t years after the start of 2000.[49]

a. How fast, to the nearest 0.1%, was the percentage increasing at the start of 2003?

b. Compute $\lim_{t\to+\infty} A(t)$ and $\lim_{t\to+\infty} A'(t)$. What do the answers tell you about subprime mortgages?

108. ***Subprime Mortgage Debt during the Housing Bubble*** (Compare Exercise 106.) During the real estate run-up in 2000–2008, the value of subprime (normally classified as risky) mortgage debt outstanding in the U.S. could be approximated by

$$A(t) = \frac{1{,}350}{1 + 4.2(1.7)^{-t}} \text{ billion dollars} \quad (0 \le t \le 8)$$

t years after the start of 2000.[50]

a. How fast, to the nearest $1 billion, was subprime mortgage debt increasing at the start of 2005?

b. Compute $\lim_{t\to+\infty} A(t)$ and $\lim_{t\to+\infty} A'(t)$. What do the answers tell you about subprime mortgages?

[47] 2009 figure is an estimate. Sources: Mortgage Bankers Association, UBS.

[48] 2008–2009 figures are estimates. Source: www.data360.org/dataset.aspx? Data_Set_Id=9549.

[49] *Ibid.*

[50] *Ibid.*

109. ▼ ***Population Growth*** The population of Lower Anchovia was 4,000,000 at the start of 2010 and was doubling every 10 years. How fast was it growing per year at the start of 2010? (Round your answer to three significant digits.) HINT [Use the method of Example 2 in Section 9.2 to obtain an exponential model for the population.]

110. ▼ ***Population Growth*** The population of Upper Anchovia was 3,000,000 at the start of 2011 and doubling every 7 years. How fast was it growing per year at the start of 2011? (Round your answer to three significant digits.) HINT [Use the method of Example 2 in Section 9.2 to obtain an exponential model for the population.]

111. ▼ ***Radioactive Decay*** Plutonium 239 has a half-life of 24,400 years. How fast is a lump of 10 grams decaying after 100 years?

112. ▼ ***Radioactive Decay*** Carbon 14 has a half-life of 5,730 years. How fast is a lump of 20 grams decaying after 100 years?

113. ◆ ***Cellphone Revenues*** The number of cellphone subscribers in China for the period 2000–2005 was projected to follow the equation[51]

$$N(t) = 39t + 68 \text{ million subscribers}$$

in year t ($t = 0$ represents 2000). The average annual revenue per cellphone user was \$350 in 2000. Assuming that, due to competition, the revenue per cellphone user decreases continuously at an annual rate of 10%, give a formula for the annual revenue in year t. Hence, project the annual revenue and its rate of change in 2002. Round all answers to the nearest billion dollars or billion dollars per year.

114. ◆ ***Cellphone Revenues*** The annual revenue for cellphone use in China for the period 2000–2005 was projected to follow the equation[52]

$$R(t) = 14t + 24 \text{ billion dollars}$$

in year t ($t = 0$ represents 2000). At the same time, there were approximately 68 million subscribers in 2000. Assuming that the number of subscribers increases continuously at an annual rate of 10%, give a formula for the annual revenue per subscriber in year t. Hence, project to the nearest dollar the annual revenue per subscriber and its rate of change in 2002. (Be careful with units!)

[51]Based on a regression of projected figures (coefficients are rounded). Source: Intrinsic Technology/*New York Times*, Nov. 24, 2000, p. C1.

[52]Not allowing for discounting due to increased competition. Source: Ibid.

COMMUNICATION AND REASONING EXERCISES

115. Complete the following: The derivative of e raised to a glob is . . . .

116. Complete the following: The derivative of the natural logarithm of a glob is . . . .

117. Complete the following: The derivative of 2 raised to a glob is . . . .

118. Complete the following: The derivative of the base 2 logarithm of a glob is . . . .

119. What is wrong with the following?

$$\frac{d}{dx}\ln|3x+1| = \frac{3}{|3x+1|} \quad ✗ \textit{ WRONG!}$$

120. What is wrong with the following?

$$\frac{d}{dx}2^{2x} = (2)2^{2x} \quad ✗ \textit{ WRONG!}$$

121. What is wrong with the following?

$$\frac{d}{dx}3^{2x} = (2x)3^{2x-1} \quad ✗ \textit{ WRONG!}$$

122. What is wrong with the following?

$$\frac{d}{dx}\ln(3x^2 - 1) = \frac{1}{6x} \quad ✗ \textit{ WRONG!}$$

123. ▼ The number N of music downloads on campus is growing exponentially with time. Can $N'(t)$ grow linearly with time? Explain.

124. ▼ The number N of graphing calculators sold on campus is decaying exponentially with time. Can $N'(t)$ grow with time? Explain.

*The **percentage rate of change** or **fractional rate of change** of a function is defined to be the ratio $f'(x)/f(x)$. (It is customary to express this as a percentage when speaking about percentage rate of change.)*

125. ◆ Show that the fractional rate of change of the exponential function e^{kx} is equal to k, which is often called its **fractional growth rate**.

126. ◆ Show that the fractional rate of change of $f(x)$ is the rate of change of $\ln(f(x))$.

127. ◆ Let $A(t)$ represent a quantity growing exponentially. Show that the percentage rate of change, $A'(t)/A(t)$, is constant.

128. ◆ Let $A(t)$ be the amount of money in an account that pays interest that is compounded some number of times per year. Show that the percentage rate of growth, $A'(t)/A(t)$, is constant. What might this constant represent?

Practice Problems 11.5, Part 1

1. Suppose that $g(t) = 36te^{kt}$ for $t \geq 0$, where k is some constant. Find an appropriate value of k so that the graph of $g(t)$ has a horizontal tangent line at $t = 9$.

2. Students in a calculus course were given an exam, and each month thereafter they took an equivalent exam. The class average on the exam taken after t months is $F(t) = 86 - 6\ln(t+1)$. How many times has an equivalent exam been given if the average score is decreasing at a rate of one point per month?

Practice Problems 11.5, Part 2

Potentially Useful Fact: Recall that if $f(x) > 0$, then $e^{\ln f(x)} = f(x)$

(Another) Potentially Useful Fact: Recall that if $g(x) = \ln f(x)$, then $g'(x) = [\ln f(x)]'$

1. Let $w(x) = x^x$. Calculate $w'(x)$.

2. Let $y = (2x+1)^3(x^3 - 8)^5$. Calculate $\left.\frac{dy}{dx}\right|_{x=1}$ **without** using either the Product Rule or the Quotient Rule. (Hint: Consider using one of the facts above and properties of logarithms.)

11.6 Implicit Differentiation

Consider the equation $y^5 + y + x = 0$, whose graph is shown in Figure 10.

How did we obtain this graph? We did not solve for y as a function of x; that is impossible. In fact, we solved for x in terms of y to find points to plot. Nonetheless, the graph in Figure 10 is the graph of a function because it passes the vertical line test: Every vertical line crosses the graph no more than once, so for each value of x there is no more than one corresponding value of y. Because we cannot solve for y explicitly in terms of x, we say that the equation $y^5 + y + x = 0$ determines y as an **implicit function** of x.

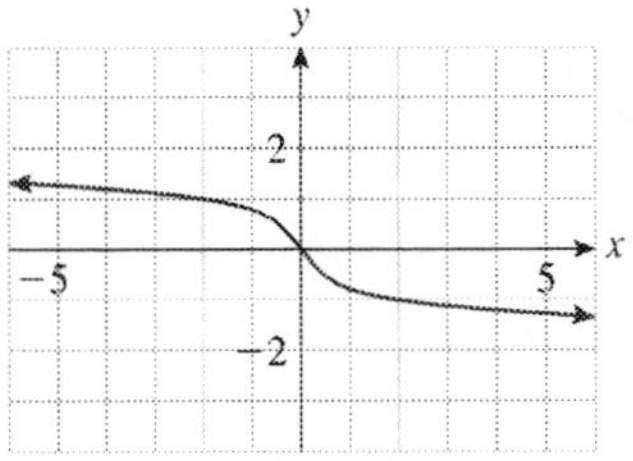

Figure 10

Now, suppose we want to find the slope of the tangent line to this curve at, say, the point $(2, -1)$ (which, you should check, is a point on the curve). In the following example we find, surprisingly, that it is possible to obtain a formula for dy/dx without having to first solve the equation for y.

EXAMPLE 1 Implicit Differentiation

Find $\dfrac{dy}{dx}$, given that $y^5 + y + x = 0$.

Solution We use the chain rule and a little cleverness. Think of y as a function of x and take the derivative with respect to x of both sides of the equation:

$$y^5 + y + x = 0 \qquad \text{Original equation}$$

$$\frac{d}{dx}[y^5 + y + x] = \frac{d}{dx}[0] \qquad \text{Derivative with respect to } x \text{ of both sides}$$

$$\frac{d}{dx}[y^5] + \frac{d}{dx}[y] + \frac{d}{dx}[x] = 0. \qquad \text{Derivative rules}$$

Now we must be careful. The derivative *with respect to x* of y^5 is *not* $5y^4$. Rather, because y is a function of x, we must use the chain rule, which tells us that

$$\frac{d}{dx}[y^5] = 5y^4\frac{dy}{dx}.$$

Thus, we get

$$5y^4\frac{dy}{dx} + \frac{dy}{dx} + 1 = 0.$$

We want to find dy/dx, so we *solve for it*:

$$(5y^4 + 1)\frac{dy}{dx} = -1 \qquad \text{Isolate } dy/dx \text{ on one side.}$$

$$\frac{dy}{dx} = -\frac{1}{5y^4 + 1}. \qquad \text{Divide both sides by } 5y^4 + 1.$$

➡ **Before we go on...** Note that we should not expect to obtain dy/dx as an explicit function of x if y was not an explicit function of x to begin with. For example, the formula we found for dy/dx in Example 1 is not a function of x because there is a y in

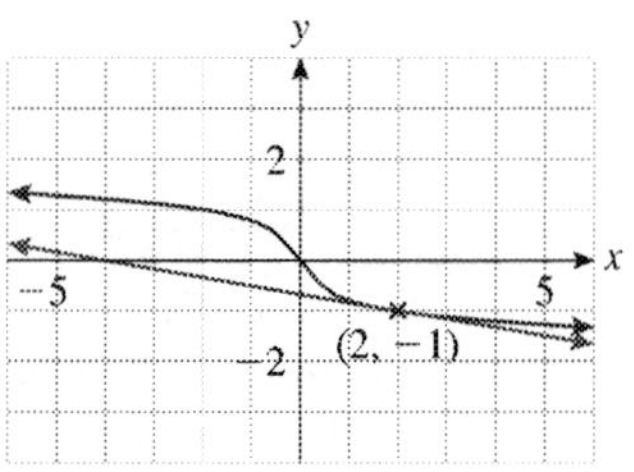

Figure 11

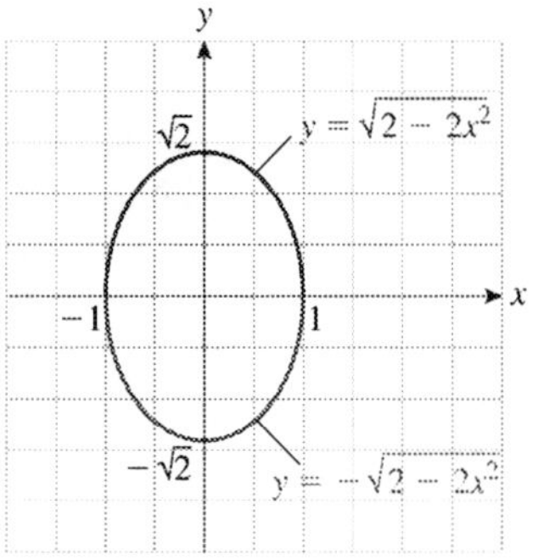

Figure 12

it. However, the result is still useful because we can evaluate the derivative at any point on the graph. For instance, at the point $(2, -1)$ on the graph, we get

$$\frac{dy}{dx} = -\frac{1}{5y^4 + 1} = -\frac{1}{5(-1)^4 + 1} = -\frac{1}{6}.$$

Thus, the slope of the tangent line to the curve $y^5 + y + x = 0$ at the point $(2, -1)$ is $-1/6$. Figure 11 shows the graph and this tangent line. ■

This procedure we just used—differentiating an equation to find dy/dx without first solving the equation for y—is called **implicit differentiation**.

In Example 1 we were given an equation in x and y that determined y as an (implicit) function of x, even though we could not solve for y. But an equation in x and y need not always determine y as a function of x. Consider, for example, the equation

$$2x^2 + y^2 = 2.$$

Solving for y yields $y = \pm\sqrt{2 - 2x^2}$. The $\pm$ sign reminds us that for some values of x there are two corresponding values for y. We can graph this equation by superimposing the graphs of

$$y = \sqrt{2 - 2x^2} \qquad \text{and} \qquad y = -\sqrt{2 - 2x^2}.$$

The graph, an *ellipse*, is shown in Figure 12.

The graph of $y = \sqrt{2 - 2x^2}$ constitutes the top half of the ellipse, and the graph of $y = -\sqrt{2 - 2x^2}$ constitutes the bottom half.

EXAMPLE 2 Slope of Tangent Line

Refer to Figure 12. Find the slope of the tangent line to the ellipse $2x^2 + y^2 = 2$ at the point $(1/\sqrt{2}, 1)$.

Solution Because $(1/\sqrt{2}, 1)$ is on the top half of the ellipse in Figure 12, we *could* differentiate the function $y = \sqrt{2 - 2x^2}$ to obtain the result, but it is actually easier to apply implicit differentiation to the original equation.

$$2x^2 + y^2 = 2 \qquad \text{Original equation}$$

$$\frac{d}{dx}[2x^2 + y^2] = \frac{d}{dx}[2] \qquad \text{Derivative with respect to } x \text{ of both sides}$$

$$4x + 2y\frac{dy}{dx} = 0$$

$$2y\frac{dy}{dx} = -4x \qquad \text{Solve for } dy/dx.$$

$$\frac{dy}{dx} = -\frac{4x}{2y} = -\frac{2x}{y}$$

To find the slope at $(1/\sqrt{2}, 1)$ we now substitute for x and y:

$$\left.\frac{dy}{dx}\right|_{(1/\sqrt{2},1)} = -\frac{2/\sqrt{2}}{1} = -\sqrt{2}.$$

Thus, the slope of the tangent to the ellipse at the point $(1/\sqrt{2}, 1)$ is $-\sqrt{2} \approx -1.414$.

EXAMPLE 3 Tangent Line for an Implicit Function

Find the equation of the tangent line to the curve $\ln y = xy$ at the point where $y = 1$.

Solution First, we use implicit differentiation to find dy/dx:

$$\frac{d}{dx}[\ln y] = \frac{d}{dx}[xy] \qquad \text{Take } d/dx \text{ of both sides.}$$

$$\frac{1}{y}\frac{dy}{dx} = (1)y + x\frac{dy}{dx}. \qquad \text{Chain rule on left, product rule on right}$$

To solve for dy/dx, we bring all the terms containing dy/dx to the left-hand side and all terms not containing it to the right-hand side:

$$\frac{1}{y}\frac{dy}{dx} - x\frac{dy}{dx} = y \qquad \text{Bring the terms with } dy/dx \text{ to the left.}$$

$$\frac{dy}{dx}\left(\frac{1}{y} - x\right) = y \qquad \text{Factor out } dy/dx.$$

$$\frac{dy}{dx}\left(\frac{1-xy}{y}\right) = y$$

$$\frac{dy}{dx} = y\left(\frac{y}{1-xy}\right) = \frac{y^2}{1-xy}. \qquad \text{Solve for } dy/dx.$$

The derivative gives the slope of the tangent line, so we want to evaluate the derivative at the point where $y = 1$. However, the formula for dy/dx requires values for both x and y. We get the value of x by substituting $y = 1$ in the original equation:

$$\ln y = xy$$

$$\ln 1 = x \cdot 1$$

But $\ln 1 = 0$, and so $x = 0$ for this point. Thus,

$$\left.\frac{dy}{dx}\right|_{(0,1)} = \frac{1^2}{1-(0)(1)} = 1.$$

Therefore, the tangent line is the line through $(x, y) = (0, 1)$ with slope 1, which is

$$y = x + 1.$$

Before we go on... Example 3 presents an instance of an implicit function in which it is simply not possible to solve for y. Try it. ■

Sometimes, it is easiest to differentiate a complicated function of x by first taking the logarithm and then using implicit differentiation—a technique called **logarithmic differentiation**.

EXAMPLE 4 Logarithmic Differentiation

Find $\frac{d}{dx}\left[\frac{(x+1)^{10}(x^2+1)^{11}}{(x^3+1)^{12}}\right]$ without using the product or quotient rules.

Solution Write

$$y = \frac{(x+1)^{10}(x^2+1)^{11}}{(x^3+1)^{12}}$$

and then take the natural logarithm of both sides:

$$\ln y = \ln\left[\frac{(x+1)^{10}(x^2+1)^{11}}{(x^3+1)^{12}}\right].$$

We can use properties of the logarithm to simplify the right-hand side:

$$\begin{aligned}\ln y &= \ln(x+1)^{10} + \ln(x^2+1)^{11} - \ln(x^3+1)^{12}\\ &= 10\ln(x+1) + 11\ln(x^2+1) - 12\ln(x^3+1).\end{aligned}$$

Now we can find $\frac{dy}{dx}$ using implicit differentiation:

$$\frac{1}{y}\frac{dy}{dx} = \frac{10}{x+1} + \frac{22x}{x^2+1} - \frac{36x^2}{x^3+1}$$ Take d/dx of both sides.

$$\frac{dy}{dx} = y\left(\frac{10}{x+1} + \frac{22x}{x^2+1} - \frac{36x^2}{x^3+1}\right)$$ Solve for dy/dx.

$$= \frac{(x+1)^{10}(x^2+1)^{11}}{(x^3+1)^{12}}\left(\frac{10}{x+1} + \frac{22x}{x^2+1} - \frac{36x^2}{x^3+1}\right).$$ Substitute for y.

➡ **Before we go on...** Redo Example 4 using the product and quotient rules (and the chain rule) instead of logarithmic differentiation and compare the answers. Compare also the amount of work involved in both methods. ■

APPLICATION

Productivity usually depends on both labor and capital. Suppose, for example, you are managing a surfboard manufacturing company. You can measure its productivity by counting the number of surfboards the company makes each year. As a measure of labor, you can use the number of employees, and as a measure of capital you can use its operating budget. The so-called *Cobb-Douglas* model uses a function of the form:

$$P = Kx^a y^{1-a},$$ Cobb-Douglas model for productivity

where P stands for the number of surfboards made each year, x is the number of employees, and y is the operating budget. The numbers K and a are constants that depend on the particular situation studied, with a between 0 and 1.

EXAMPLE 5 Cobb-Douglas Production Function

The surfboard company you own has the Cobb-Douglas production function

$$P = x^{0.3}y^{0.7}$$

where P is the number of surfboards it produces per year, x is the number of employees, and y is the daily operating budget (in dollars). Assume that the production level P is constant.

a. Find $\frac{dy}{dx}$.

b. Evaluate this derivative at $x = 30$ and $y = 10{,}000$, and interpret the answer.

Solution

a. We are given the equation $P = x^{0.3}y^{0.7}$, in which P is constant. We find $\frac{dy}{dx}$ by implicit differentiation.

$$0 = \frac{d}{dx}[x^{0.3}y^{0.7}]$$ d/dx of both sides

$$0 = 0.3x^{-0.7}y^{0.7} + x^{0.3}(0.7)y^{-0.3}\frac{dy}{dx} \qquad \text{Product and chain rules}$$

$$-0.7x^{0.3}y^{-0.3}\frac{dy}{dx} = 0.3x^{-0.7}y^{0.7} \qquad \text{Bring term with } dy/dx \text{ to left.}$$

$$\frac{dy}{dx} = -\frac{0.3x^{-0.7}y^{0.7}}{0.7x^{0.3}y^{-0.3}} \qquad \text{Solve for } dy/dx.$$

$$= -\frac{3y}{7x}. \qquad \text{Simplify.}$$

b. Evaluating this derivative at $x = 30$ and $y = 10{,}000$ gives

$$\left.\frac{dy}{dx}\right|_{x=30,\ y=10{,}000} = -\frac{3(10{,}000)}{7(30)} \approx -143.$$

To interpret this result, first look at the units of the derivative: We recall that the units of dy/dx are units of y per unit of x. Because y is the daily budget, its units are dollars; because x is the number of employees, its units are employees. Thus,

$$\left.\frac{dy}{dx}\right|_{x=30,\ y=10{,}000} \approx -\$143 \text{ per employee.}$$

Next, recall that dy/dx measures the rate of change of y as x changes. Because the answer is negative, the daily budget to maintain production at the fixed level is decreasing by approximately \$143 per additional employee at an employment level of 30 employees and a daily operating budget of \$10,000. In other words, increasing the workforce by one worker will result in a savings of approximately \$143 per day. Roughly speaking, *a new employee is worth \$143 per day* at the current levels of employment and production.

11.6 EXERCISES

▼ more advanced ◆ challenging

T indicates exercises that should be solved using technology

In Exercises 1–10, find dy/dx, using implicit differentiation. In each case, compare your answer with the result obtained by first solving for y as a function of x and then taking the derivative. HINT [See Example 1.]

1. $2x + 3y = 7$

2. $4x - 5y = 9$

3. $x^2 - 2y = 6$

4. $3y + x^2 = 5$

5. $2x + 3y = xy$

6. $x - y = xy$

7. $e^x y = 1$

8. $e^x y - y = 2$

9. $y \ln x + y = 2$

10. $\dfrac{\ln x}{y} = 2 - x$

In Exercises 11–30, find the indicated derivative using implicit differentiation. HINT [See Example 1.]

11. $x^2 + y^2 = 5;\ \dfrac{dy}{dx}$

12. $2x^2 - y^2 = 4;\ \dfrac{dy}{dx}$

13. $x^2y - y^2 = 4;\ \dfrac{dy}{dx}$

14. $xy^2 - y = x;\ \dfrac{dy}{dx}$

15. $3xy - \dfrac{y}{3} = \dfrac{2}{x};\ \dfrac{dy}{dx}$

16. $\dfrac{xy}{2} - y^2 = 3;\ \dfrac{dy}{dx}$

17. $x^2 - 3y^2 = 8;\ \dfrac{dx}{dy}$

18. $(xy)^2 + y^2 = 8;\ \dfrac{dx}{dy}$

19. $p^2 - pq = 5p^2q^2;\ \dfrac{dp}{dq}$

20. $q^2 - pq = 5p^2q^2;\ \dfrac{dp}{dq}$

21. $xe^y - ye^x = 1;\ \dfrac{dy}{dx}$

22. $x^2e^y - y^2 = e^x;\ \dfrac{dy}{dx}$

23. ▼ $e^{st} = s^2;\ \dfrac{ds}{dt}$

24. ▼ $e^{s^2t} - st = 1;\ \dfrac{ds}{dt}$

25. ▼ $\dfrac{e^x}{y^2} = 1 + e^y;\ \dfrac{dy}{dx}$

26. ▼ $\dfrac{x}{e^y} + xy = 9y;\ \dfrac{dy}{dx}$

27. ▼ $\ln(y^2 - y) + x = y;\ \dfrac{dy}{dx}$

28. ▼ $\ln(xy) - x \ln y = y;\ \dfrac{dy}{dx}$

29. ▼ $\ln(xy + y^2) = e^y;\ \dfrac{dy}{dx}$

30. ▼ $\ln(1 + e^{xy}) = y;\ \dfrac{dy}{dx}$

*In Exercises 31–42, use implicit differentiation to find **(a)** the slope of the tangent line, and **(b)** the equation of the tangent line at the indicated point on the graph. (Round answers to four decimal places as needed.) If only the x-coordinate is given, you must also find the y-coordinate.* HINT [See Examples 2, 3.]

31. $4x^2 + 2y^2 = 12, (1, -2)$

32. $3x^2 - y^2 = 11, (-2, 1)$

33. $2x^2 - y^2 = xy, (-1, 2)$

34. $2x^2 + xy = 3y^2, (-1, -1)$

35. $x^2y - y^2 + x = 1, (1, 0)$

36. $(xy)^2 + xy - x = 8, (-8, 0)$

37. $xy - 2000 = y, x = 2$

38. $x^2 - 10xy = 200, x = 10$

39. ▼ $\ln(x + y) - x = 3x^2, x = 0$

40. ▼ $\ln(x - y) + 1 = 3x^2, x = 0$

41. ▼ $e^{xy} - x = 4x, x = 3$

42. ▼ $e^{-xy} + 2x = 1, x = -1$

In Exercises 43–52, use logarithmic differentiation to find dy/dx. Do not simplify the result. HINT [See Example 4.]

43. $y = \dfrac{2x + 1}{4x - 2}$

44. $y = (3x + 2)(8x - 5)$

45. $y = \dfrac{(3x + 1)^2}{4x(2x - 1)^3}$

46. $y = \dfrac{x^2(3x + 1)^2}{(2x - 1)^3}$

47. $y = (8x - 1)^{1/3}(x - 1)$

48. $y = \dfrac{(3x + 2)^{2/3}}{3x - 1}$

49. $y = (x^3 + x)\sqrt{x^3 + 2}$

50. $y = \sqrt{\dfrac{x - 1}{x^2 + 2}}$

51. ▼ $y = x^x$

52. ▼ $y = x^{-x}$

APPLICATIONS

53. *Productivity* The number of CDs per hour that *Snappy Hardware* can manufacture at its plant is given by

$$P = x^{0.6}y^{0.4},$$

where x is the number of workers at the plant and y is the monthly budget (in dollars). Assume P is constant, and compute $\dfrac{dy}{dx}$ when $x = 100$ and $y = 200{,}000$. Interpret the result. HINT [See Example 5.]

54. *Productivity* The number of cellphone accessory kits (neon lights, matching covers, and earpods) per day that *USA Cellular Makeover Inc,* can manufacture at its plant in Cambodia is given by

$$P = x^{0.5}y^{0.5},$$

where x is the number of workers at the plant and y is the monthly budget (in dollars). Assume P is constant, and compute $\dfrac{dy}{dx}$ when $x = 200$ and $y = 100{,}000$. Interpret the result. HINT [See Example 5.]

55. *Demand* The demand equation for soccer tournament T-shirts is

$$xy - 2{,}000 = y,$$

where y is the number of T-shirts the Enormous State University soccer team can sell at a price of \$$x$ per shirt. Find $\left.\dfrac{dy}{dx}\right|_{x=5}$, and interpret the result.

56. *Cost Equations* The cost y (in cents) of producing x gallons of *Ectoplasm* hair gel is given by the cost equation

$$y^2 - 10xy = 200.$$

Evaluate $\dfrac{dy}{dx}$ at $x = 1$ and interpret the result.

57. *Housing Costs*[53] The cost C (in dollars) of building a house is related to the number k of carpenters used and the number e of electricians used by the formula

$$C = 15{,}000 + 50k^2 + 60e^2.$$

If the cost of the house is fixed at \$200,000, find $\left.\dfrac{dk}{de}\right|_{e=15}$ and interpret your result.

58. *Employment* An employment research company estimates that the value of a recent MBA graduate to an accounting company is

$$V = 3e^2 + 5g^3,$$

where V is the value of the graduate, e is the number of years of prior business experience, and g is the graduate school grade-point average. If V is fixed at 200, find $\dfrac{de}{dg}$ when $g = 3.0$ and interpret the result.

59. ▼ ***Grades*[54]** A productivity formula for a student's performance on a difficult English examination is

$$g = 4tx - 0.2t^2 - 10x^2 \quad (t < 30),$$

where g is the score the student can expect to obtain, t is the number of hours of study for the examination, and x is the student's grade-point average.

a. For how long should a student with a 3.0 grade-point average study in order to score 80 on the examination?

b. Find $\dfrac{dt}{dx}$ for a student who earns a score of 80, evaluate it when $x = 3.0$, and interpret the result.

60. ▼ ***Grades*** Repeat the preceding exercise using the following productivity formula for a basket-weaving examination:

$$g = 10tx - 0.2t^2 - 10x^2 \quad (t < 10).$$

Comment on the result.

[53]Based on an exercise in *Introduction to Mathematical Economics* by A. L. Ostrosky Jr., and J. V. Koch (Waveland Press, Springfield, Illinois, 1979).

[54]*Ibid.*

Exercises 61 and 62 are based on the following demand function for money (taken from a question on the GRE Economics Test):

$$M_d = (2) \times (y)^{0.6} \times (r)^{-0.3} \times (p)$$

where

M_d = *demand for nominal money balances (money stock)*

y = *real income*

r = *an index of interest rates*

p = *an index of prices.*

61. ◆ ***Money Stock*** If real income grows while the money stock and the price level remain constant, the interest rate must change at what rate? (First find dr/dy, then dr/dt; your answers will be expressed in terms of r, y, and $\dfrac{dy}{dt}$.)

62. ◆ ***Money Stock*** If real income grows while the money stock and the interest rate remain constant, the price level must change at what rate?

COMMUNICATION AND REASONING EXERCISES

63. Fill in the missing terms: The equation $x = y^3 + y - 3$ specifies ___ as a function of ___, and ___ as an implicit function of ___.

64. Fill in the missing terms: When $x \neq 0$ in the equation $xy = x^3 + 4$, it is possible to specify ___ as a function of ___. However, ___ is only an implicit function of ___.

65. ▼ Use logarithmic differentiation to give another proof of the product rule.

66. ▼ Use logarithmic differentiation to give a proof of the quotient rule.

67. ▼ If y is given explicitly as a function of x by an equation $y = f(x)$, compare finding dy/dx by implicit differentiation to finding it explicitly in the usual way.

68. ▼ Explain why one should not expect dy/dx to be a function of x if y is not a function of x.

69. ◆ If y is a function of x and $dy/dx \neq 0$ at some point, regard x as an implicit function of y and use implicit differentiation to obtain the equation

$$\frac{dx}{dy} = \frac{1}{dy/dx}.$$

70. ◆ If you are given an equation in x and y such that dy/dx is a function of x only, what can you say about the graph of the equation?

CHAPTER 11 REVIEW

KEY CONCEPTS

Website www.WanerMath.com

Go to the Website at www.WanerMath.com to find a comprehensive and interactive Web-based summary of Chapter 11.

11.1 Derivatives of Powers, Sums, and Constant Multiples

Power Rule: If n is any constant and $f(x) = x^n$, then $f'(x) = nx^{n-1}$. *p. 784*

Using the power rule for negative and fractional exponents *p. 785*

Sums, differences, and constant multiples *p. 787*

Combining the rules *p. 788*

$\frac{d}{dx}(cx) = c$, $\frac{d}{dx}(c) = 0$ *p. 790*

$f(x) = x^{1/3}$, $g(x) = x^{2/3}$, and $h(x) = |x|$ are not differentiable at $x = 0$. *p. 790*

L'Hospital's rule *p. 792*

11.2 A First Application: Marginal Analysis

Marginal cost function $C'(x)$ *p. 799*

Marginal revenue and profit functions $R'(x)$ and $P'(x)$ *p. 801*

What it means when the marginal profit is zero *p. 802*

Marginal product *p. 802*

Average cost of the first x items:

$\bar{C}(x) = \frac{C(x)}{x}$ *p. 805*

11.3 The Product and Quotient Rules

Product rule: $\frac{d}{dx}[f(x)g(x)] = f'(x)g(x) + f(x)g'(x)$ *p. 810*

Quotient rule: $\frac{d}{dx}\left[\frac{f(x)}{g(x)}\right] = \frac{f'(x)g(x) - f(x)g'(x)}{[g(x)]^2}$ *p. 810*

Using the product rule *p. 812*

Using the quotient rule *p. 813*

Calculation thought experiment *p. 815*

Application to revenue and average cost *p. 816*

11.4 The Chain Rule

Chain rule: $\frac{d}{dx}[f(u)] = f'(u)\frac{du}{dx}$ *p. 822*

Generalized power rule:

$\frac{d}{dx}[u^n] = nu^{n-1}\frac{du}{dx}$ *p. 823*

Using the chain rule *p. 823*

Application to marginal product *p. 826*

Chain rule in differential notation:

$\frac{dy}{dx} = \frac{dy}{du}\frac{du}{dx}$ *p. 827*

Manipulating derivatives in differential notation *p. 829*

11.5 Derivatives of Logarithmic and Exponential Functions

Derivative of the natural logarithm:

$\frac{d}{dx}[\ln x] = \frac{1}{x}$ *p. 834*

Derivative of logarithm with base b:

$\frac{d}{dx}[\log_b x] = \frac{1}{x \ln b}$ *p. 835*

Derivatives of logarithms of functions:

$\frac{d}{dx}[\ln u] = \frac{1}{u}\frac{du}{dx}$

$\frac{d}{dx}[\log_b u] = \frac{1}{u \ln b}\frac{du}{dx}$ *p. 836*

Derivatives of logarithms of absolute values:

$\frac{d}{dx}[\ln |x|] = \frac{1}{x}$ $\frac{d}{dx}[\ln |u|] = \frac{1}{u}\frac{du}{dx}$

$\frac{d}{dx}[\log_b |x|] = \frac{1}{x \ln b}$

$\frac{d}{dx}[\log_b |u|] = \frac{1}{u \ln b}\frac{du}{dx}$ *p. 838*

Derivative of e^x: $\frac{d}{dx}[e^x] = e^x$ *p. 839*

Derivative of b^x: $\frac{d}{dx}[b^x] = b^x \ln b$ *p. 839*

Derivatives of exponential functions *p. 840*

Application to epidemics *p. 841*

Application to sales growth (logistic function) *p. 841*

11.6 Implicit Differentiation

Implicit function of x *p. 848*

Implicit differentiation *p. 848*

Using implicit differentiation *p. 849*

Finding a tangent line *p. 849*

Logarithmic differentiation *p. 850*

REVIEW EXERCISES

In Exercises 1–26, find the derivative of the given function.

1. $f(x) = 10x^5 + \frac{1}{2}x^4 - x + 2$

2. $f(x) = \frac{10}{x^5} + \frac{1}{2x^4} - \frac{1}{x} + 2$

3. $f(x) = 3x^3 + 3\sqrt[3]{x}$

4. $f(x) = \frac{2}{x^{2.1}} - \frac{x^{0.1}}{2}$

5. $f(x) = x + \frac{1}{x^2}$

6. $f(x) = 2x - \frac{1}{x}$

7. $f(x) = \frac{4}{3x} - \frac{2}{x^{0.1}} + \frac{x^{1.1}}{3.2} - 4$

8. $f(x) = \frac{4}{x} + \frac{x}{4} - |x|$

9. $f(x) = e^x(x^2 - 1)$

10. $f(x) = \frac{x^2 + 1}{x^2 - 1}$

11. $f(x) = \frac{|x| + 1}{3x^2 + 1}$

12. $f(x) = (|x| + x)(2 - 3x^2)$

13. $f(x) = (4x - 1)^{-1}$

14. $f(x) = (x + 7)^{-2}$

15. $f(x) = (x^2 - 1)^{10}$

16. $f(x) = \frac{1}{(x^2 - 1)^{10}}$

17. $f(x) = [2 + (x + 1)^{-0.1}]^{4.3}$

18. $f(x) = [(x + 1)^{0.1} - 4x]^{-5.1}$

19. $f(x) = e^x(x^2 + 1)^{10}$

20. $f(x) = \left[\dfrac{x-1}{3x+1}\right]^3$ **21.** $f(x) = \dfrac{3^x}{x-1}$

22. $f(x) = 4^{-x}(x+1)$ **23.** $f(x) = e^{x^2-1}$

24. $f(x) = (x^2+1)e^{x^2-1}$ **25.** $f(x) = \ln(x^2-1)$

26. $f(x) = \dfrac{\ln(x^2-1)}{x^2-1}$

In Exercises 27–34, find all values of x (if any) where the tangent line to the graph of the given equation is horizontal.

27. $y = -3x^2 + 7x - 1$ **28.** $y = 5x^2 - 2x + 1$

29. $y = \dfrac{x}{2} + \dfrac{2}{x}$ **30.** $y = \dfrac{x^2}{2} - \dfrac{8}{x^2}$

31. $y = x - e^{2x-1}$ **32.** $y = e^{x^2}$

33. $y = \dfrac{x}{x+1}$ **34.** $y = \sqrt{x}(x-1)$

In Exercises 35–40, find dy/dx for the given equation.

35. $x^2 - y^2 = x$ **36.** $2xy + y^2 = y$

37. $e^{xy} + xy = 2$ **38.** $\ln\left(\dfrac{y}{x}\right) = y$

39. $y = \dfrac{(2x-1)^4(3x+4)}{(x+1)(3x-1)^3}$ **40.** $y = x^{x-1}3^x$

In Exercises 41–46, find the equation of the tangent line to the graph of the given equation at the specified point.

41. $y = (x^2 - 3x)^{-2}$; $x = 1$ **42.** $y = (2x^2 - 3)^{-3}$; $x = -1$

43. $y = x^2 e^{-x}$; $x = -1$ **44.** $y = \dfrac{x}{1+e^x}$; $x = 0$

45. $xy - y^2 = x^2 - 3$; $(-1, 1)$

46. $\ln(xy) + y^2 = 1$; $(-1, -1)$

APPLICATIONS: OHaganBooks.com

47. ***Sales*** OHaganBooks.com fits the cubic curve

$$w(t) = -3.7t^3 + 74.6t^2 + 135.5t + 6{,}300$$

to its weekly sales figures (see Chapter 10 Review Exercise 57; t is time in weeks), as shown in the following graph:

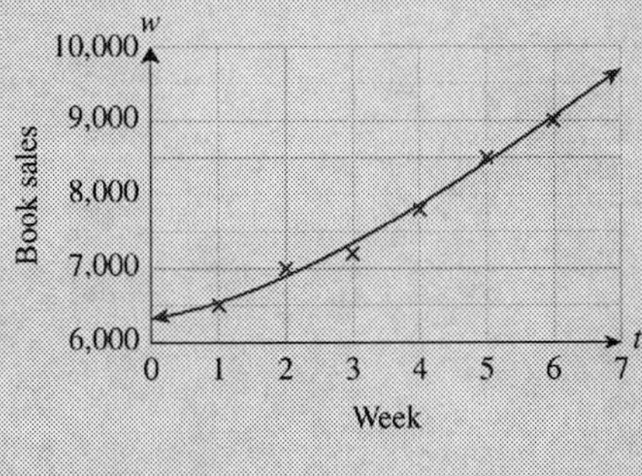

a. According to the cubic model, what was the rate of increase of sales at the beginning of the second week ($t = 1$)? (Round your answer to the nearest unit.)

b. If we extrapolate the model, what would be the rate of increase of weekly sales at the beginning of the eighth week ($t = 7$)?

c. Graph the function w for $0 \le t \le 20$. Would it be realistic to use the function to predict sales through week 20? Why?

d. By examining the graph, say why the choice of a quadratic model would result in radically different long-term predictions of sales.

48. ***Rising Sea Level*** Marjory Duffin is still toying with various models to fit to the New York sea level figures she had seen after purchasing a beachfront condominium in New York (see Chapter 10 Review Exercise 58). Following is a cubic curve she obtained using regression:

$$L(t) = -0.0001t^3 + 0.02t^2 + 2.2t \text{ mm}$$

(t is time in years since 1900). The curve and data are shown in the following graph:

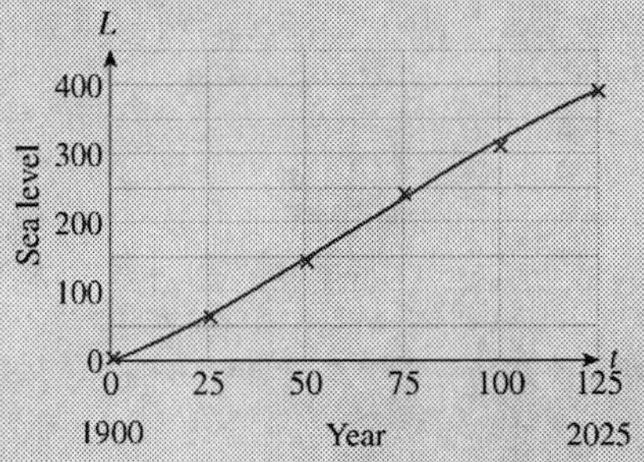

Sea Level Change since 1900

a. According to the cubic model, what was the rate at which the sea level was rising in 2000 ($t = 100$)? (Round your answer to two significant digits.)

b. If we extrapolate the model, what would be the rate at which the sea level is rising in 2025 ($t = 125$)?

c. Graph the function L for $0 \le t \le 200$. Why is it not realistic to use the function to predict the sea level through 2100?

d. James Stewart, a summer intern at Duffin House Publishers, differs. As he puts it, "The cubic curve came from doing regression on the actual data, and thus reflects the actual trend of the data. We can't argue against reality!" Comment on this assertion.

49. ***Cost*** As OHaganBooks.com's sales increase, so do its costs. If we take into account volume discounts from suppliers and shippers, the weekly cost of selling x books is

$$C(x) = -0.00002x^2 + 3.2x + 5{,}400 \text{ dollars.}$$

a. What is the marginal cost at a sales level of 8,000 books per week?

b. What is the average cost per book at a sales level of 8,000 books per week?

c. What is the marginal average cost ($d\bar{C}/dx$) at a sales level of 8,000 books per week?

d. Interpret the results of parts (a)–(c).

50. ***Cost*** OHaganBooks.com has been experiencing a run of bad luck with its summer college intern program in association with PCU (Party Central University), begun as a result of a suggestion by Marjory Duffin over dinner one evening. The frequent errors in filling orders, charges from movie download sites and dating sites, and beverages spilled on computer equipment have resulted in an estimated weekly cost to the company of

$$C(x) = 25x^2 - 5.2x + 4{,}000 \text{ dollars,}$$

where x is the number of college interns employed.

a. What is the marginal cost at a level of 10 interns?
b. What is the average cost per intern at a level of 10 interns?
c. What is the marginal average cost at a level of 10 interns?
d. Interpret the results of parts (a)–(c).

51. ***Revenue*** At the moment, OHaganBooks.com is selling 1,000 books per week and its sales are rising at a rate of 200 books per week. Also, it is now selling all its books for \$20 each, but its price is dropping at a rate of \$1 per week.

a. At what rate is OHaganBooks.com's weekly revenue rising or falling?
b. John O'Hagan would like to see the company's weekly revenue increase at a rate of \$5,000 per week. At what rate would sales have to have been increasing to accomplish that goal, assuming all the other information is as given above?

52. ***Revenue*** Due to ongoing problems with its large college intern program in association with PCU (see Exercise 50), OHaganBooks.com has arranged to transfer its interns to its competitor JungleBooks.com (whose headquarters happens to be across the road) for a small fee. At the moment, it is transferring 5 students per week, and this number is rising at a rate of 4 students per week. Also, it is now charging JungleBooks \$400 per intern, but this amount is decreasing at a rate of \$20 per week.

a. At what rate is OHaganBooks.com's weekly revenue from this transaction rising or falling?
b. Flush with success of the transfer program, John O'Hagan would like to see the company's resulting revenue increase at a rate of \$3,900 per week. At what rate would the transfer of interns have to increase to accomplish that goal, assuming all the other information is as given above?

53. ***Percentage Rate of Change of Revenue*** The percentage rate of change of a quantity Q is Q'/Q. Why is the percentage rate of change of revenue always equal to the sum of the percentage rates of change of unit price and weekly sales?

54. ***P/E Ratios*** At the beginning of last week, OHaganBooks.com stock was selling for \$100 per share, rising at a rate of \$50 per year. Its earnings amounted to \$1 per share, rising at a rate of \$0.10 per year. At what rate was its price-to-earnings (P/E) ratio, the ratio of its stock price to its earnings per share, rising or falling?

55. ***P/E Ratios*** Refer to Exercise 54. Jay Campbell, who recently invested in OHaganBooks.com stock, would have liked to see the P/E ratio increase at a rate of 100 points per year. How fast would the stock have to have been rising, assuming all the other information is as given in Exercise 54?

56. ***Percentage Rate of Change of P/E Ratios*** Refer to Exercise 54. The percentage rate of change of a quantity Q is Q'/Q. Why is the percentage rate of change of P/E always equal to the percentage rate of change of unit price minus the percentage rate of change of earnings?

57. ***Sales*** OHaganBooks.com decided that the cubic curve in Exercise 47 was not suitable for extrapolation, so instead it tried

$$s(t) = 6{,}000 + \frac{4{,}500}{1 + e^{-0.55(t-4.8)}}$$

as shown in the following graph:

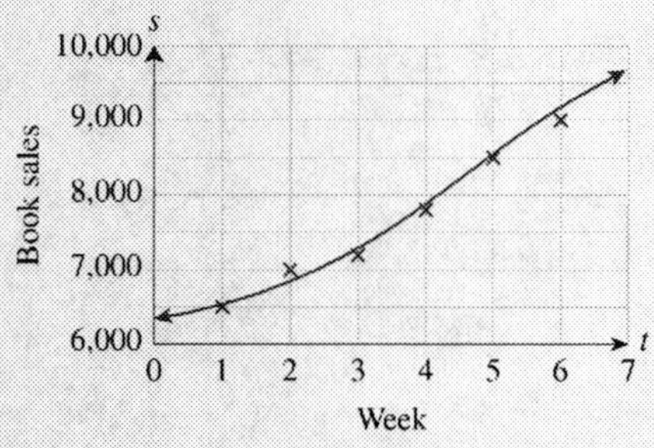

a. Compute $s'(t)$ and use the answer to estimate the rate of increase of weekly sales at the beginning of the seventh week ($t = 6$). (Round your answer to the nearest unit.)
b. Compute $\lim_{t\to+\infty} s'(t)$ and interpret the answer.

58. ***Rising Sea Level*** Upon some reflection, Marjory Duffin decided that the curve in Exercise 48 was not suitable for extrapolation, so instead she tried

$$L(t) = \frac{418}{1 + 17.2e^{-0.041t}} \qquad (0 \le t \le 125)$$

(t is time in years since 1900) as shown in the following graph:

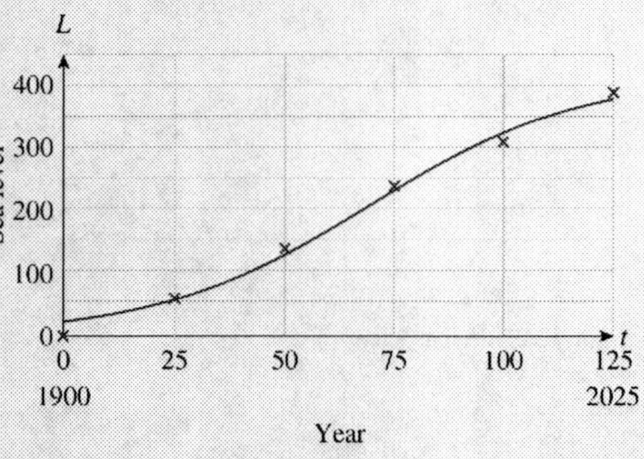

a. Compute $L'(t)$ and use the answer to estimate the rate at which the sea level was rising in 2000 ($t = 100$). (Round your answer to two decimal places.)
b. Compute $\lim_{t\to+\infty} L'(t)$ and interpret the answer.

59. ***Web Site Activity*** The number of "hits" on OHaganBooks.com's Web site was 1,000 per day at the beginning of the year, and was growing at a rate of 5% per week. If this growth rate continued for the whole year (52 weeks), find the rate of increase (in hits per day per week) at the end of the year.

60. ***Web Site Activity*** The number of "hits" on ShadyDownload.net during the summer intern program at OHaganBooks.com was 100 per day at the beginning of the intern program, and was growing at a rate of 15% per day. If this growth rate continued for the duration of the whole summer intern program (85 days), find the rate of increase (in hits per day per day) at the end of the program.

61. ***Demand and Revenue*** The price p that OHaganBooks.com charges for its latest leather-bound gift edition of *The Complete Larry Potter* is related to the demand q in weekly sales by the equation

$$250pq + q^2 = 13{,}500{,}000.$$

Suppose the price is set at \$50, which would make the demand 1,000 copies per week.

a. Using implicit differentiation, compute the rate of change of demand with respect to price, and interpret the result. (Round the answer to two decimal places.)

b. Use the result of part (a) to compute the rate of change of revenue with respect to price. Should the price be raised or lowered to increase revenue?

62. ***Demand and Revenue*** The price p that OHaganBooks.com charges for its latest leather-bound gift edition of *Lord of the Fields* is related to the demand q in weekly sales by the equation

$$100pq + q^2 = 5{,}000{,}000.$$

Suppose the price is set at \$40, which would make the demand 1,000 copies per week.

a. Using implicit differentiation, compute the rate of change of demand with respect to price, and interpret the result. (Round the answer to two decimal places.)

b. Use the result of part (a) to compute the rate of change of revenue with respect to price. Should the price be raised or lowered to increase revenue?

Case Study

Projecting Market Growth

Yuri Arcurs/Shutterstock

You are on the board of directors at *Fullcourt Academic Press,* a major textbook supplier to private schools, and various expansion strategies will be discussed at tomorrow's board meeting. TJM, the sales director of the high school division, has just burst into your office with his last-minute proposal based on data showing the number of private high school graduates in the U.S. each year over the past 18 years:[55]

Year	1995	1996	1997	1998	1999	2000	2001	2002	2003
Graduates (thousands)	245	254	265	273	279	279	285	296	301
Year	2004	2005	2006	2007	2008	2009	2010	2011	2012
Graduates (thousands)	307	307	307	314	314	315	315	316	316

He is asserts that, despite the unspectacular numbers in the past few years, the long-term trend appears to support a basic premise of his proposal for an expansion strategy: that the number of high school seniors in private schools in the U.S. will be growing at a rate of about 4,000 per year through 2015. He points out that the rate of increase predicted by the regression line is approximately 4,080 students per year, supporting his premise.

In order to decide whether to support TJM's proposal at tomorrow's board meeting, you would like to first determine whether the linear regression prediction of around 4,000 students per year is reasonable, especially in view of the more recent figures. You open your spreadsheet and graph the data with the regression line (Figure 13). The data suggest that the number of graduates began to "level off" (in the language of calculus, the *derivative appears to be decreasing*) toward the end of the

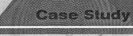

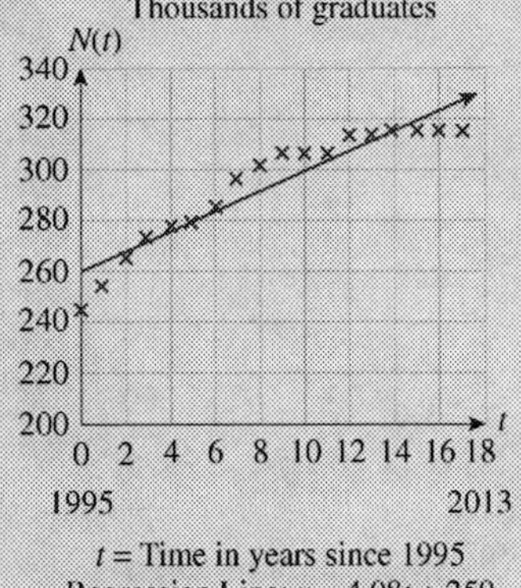

t = Time in years since 1995
Regression Line: $y = 4.08t + 259$

Figure 13

[55]Data through 2011 are National Center for Educational Statistics actual and projected data as of April 2010. Source: National Center for Educational Statistics http://nces.ed.gov/.

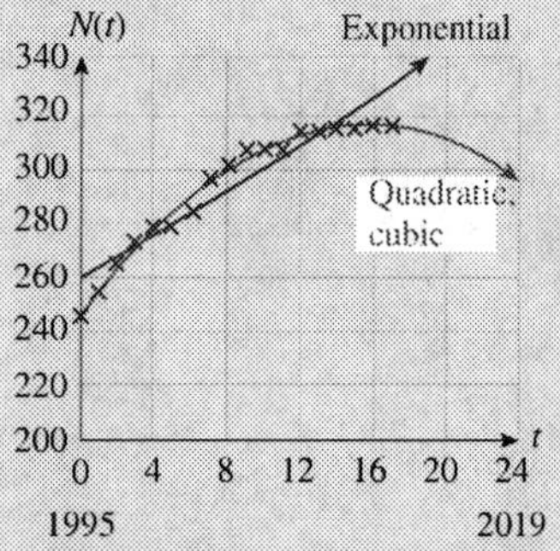

Figure 14

using Technology

You can obtain the best-fit logistic curve using technology.

TI-83/84 Plus

STAT EDIT

Enter 0–17 in L_1 and the values of $N(t)$ in L_2.

STAT CALC and select Option #B Logistic

To plot the regression curve with the data: Graph: Y= VARS 5 EQ 1, then ZOOM 9

[See the TI-83/84 Plus Technology Guide for Section 1.4 for more details on plotting the data and curve.]

Website

www.WanerMath.com

In the Function Ealuator and Grapher, enter the data as shown, press "Examples" until the logistic model `$1/(1+$2*$3^(-x))` shows in the first box, and press "Fit Curve". (You might need to press "Fit Curve" several times before it manages to find the curve. It also helps to read the instructions (link near the top of the Web page under the heading).)

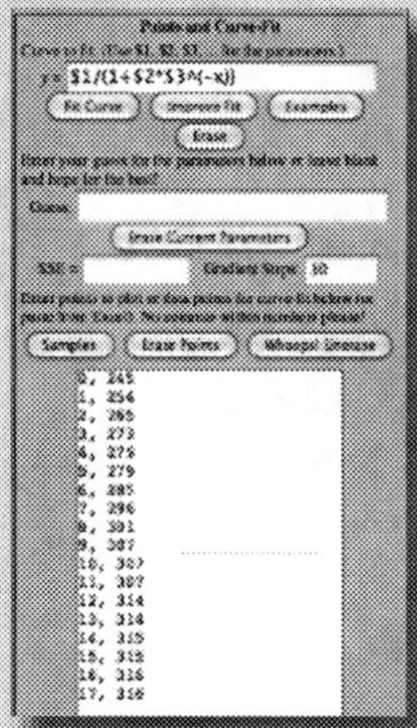

period. Moreover, you recall reading somewhere that the numbers of students in the lower grades have also begun to level off, so it is safe to predict that the slowing of growth in the senior class will continue over the next few years, contrary to what TJM has claimed. In order to make a meaningful prediction, you would really need some precise data about numbers in the lower grades, but the meeting is tomorrow and you would like a quick and easy way of extrapolating the data by "extending the curve to the right."

It would certainly be helpful if you had a mathematical model of the data in Figure 13 that you could use to project the current trend. But what kind of model should you use? The linear model is no good because it does not show any change in the derivative (the derivative of a linear function is constant). In addition, best-fit polynomial and exponential functions do not accurately reflect the leveling off, as you realize after trying to fit a few of them (Figure 14).

You then recall that a logistic curve can model the leveling-off property you desire, and so you try a model of the form

$$N(t) = \frac{M}{1 + Ab^{-t}}.$$

Figure 15 shows the best-fit logistic curve, which has a sum-of-squares error (SSE) of around 109. (See Section 1.4 or any of the regression examples in Chapter 9 for a discussion of SSE.)

$$N(t) = \frac{323.9}{1 + 0.3234(1.186)^{-t}} \qquad \text{SSE} \approx 109$$

Its graph shows the leveling off and also gives more reasonable long-term predictions.

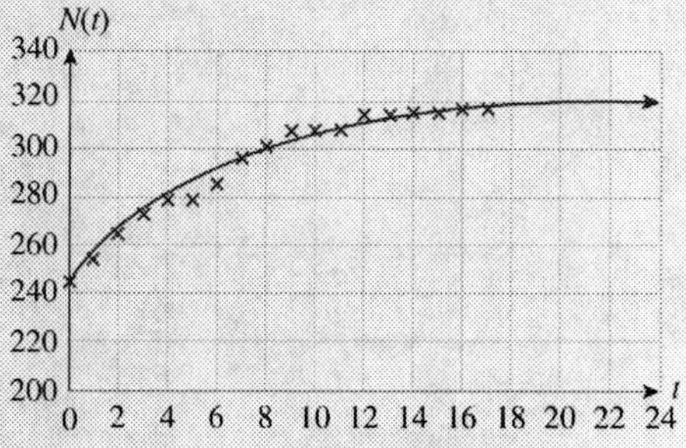

Figure 15

The rate of increase of high school students—pertinent to TJM's report—is given by the derivative, $N'(t)$:

$$N(t) = \frac{M}{1 + Ab^{-t}}$$

$$N'(t) = -\frac{M}{(1 + Ab^{-t})^2}\frac{d}{dt}[1 + Ab^{-t}]$$

$$= \frac{MAb^{-t}\ln b}{(1 + Ab^{-t})^2}.$$

The rate of increase in the number of high school students in 2015 ($t = 20$) is given by

$$N'(20) = \frac{(323.9)(0.3234)(1.186)^{-20}\ln 1.186}{(1 + 0.3234(1.186)^{-20})^2}$$

$$\approx 0.577 \text{ thousand students per year,}$$

or about 580 students per year—far less than the optimistic estimate of 4,000 in the proposal! Thus, TJM's prediction is suspect and further research will have to be done before the board can even consider the proposal.

To reassure yourself, you decide to look for another kind of S-shaped model as a backup. After flipping through a calculus book, you stumble across a function that is slightly more general than the one you have:

$$N(t) = \frac{M}{1 + Ab^{-t}} + C. \qquad \text{Shifted Logistic Curve*}$$

* To find a detailed discussion of scaled and shifted functions, visit the Website and follow Chapter 1 → New Functions from Old: Scaled and Shifted Functions.

The added term C has the effect of shifting the graph up C units. Turning once again to your calculus book (see the discussion of logistic regression in Section 9.4), you see that a best-fit curve is one that minimizes the sum-of-squares error, and you find the best-fit curve by again using the utility on the Website (this time, with the model `$1/(1+$2*$3^(-x))+$4` and initial guess 323.9, 0.3234, 1.186, 0; that is, keeping the current values and setting $c = 0$). You obtain the model

$$N(t) = \frac{135.5}{1 + 1.192(1.268)^{-t}} + 184.6. \qquad \text{SSE} \approx 100$$

The value of SSE has decreased only slightly, and, as seen in Figure 16, the shifted logistic curve seems almost identical to the unshifted curve, but does seem to level off slightly faster (compare the portions of the two curves on the extreme right).

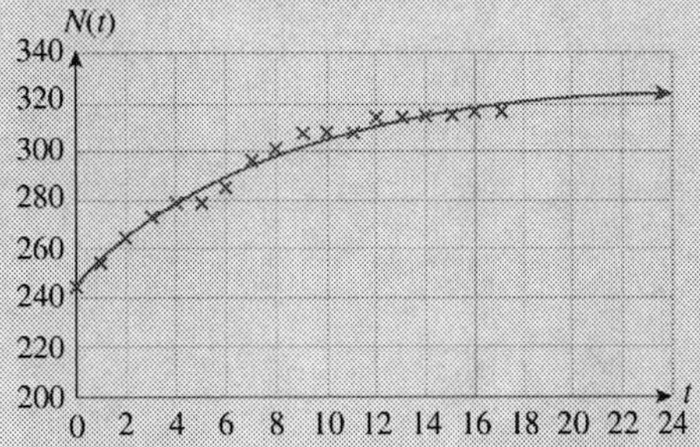

Figure 16

You decide to use the shifted model to obtain another estimate of the projected rate of change in 2015. As the two models differ by a constant, their derivatives are given by the same formula, so you compute

$$N'(20) = \frac{(135.5)(1.192)(1.268)^{-20}\ln 1.268}{(1 + 1.192(1.268)^{-20})^2}$$

$$\approx 0.325 \text{ thousand students per year,}$$

or about 325 students per year, even less than the prediction of the logistic model.

Q: *Why do the two models give very different predictions of the rate of change in 2015?*

A: The long-term prediction in any logistic model is highly sensitive to small changes in the data and/or the model. This is one reason why using regression curve-fitting models to make long-term projections can be a risky undertaking.

Q: *Then what is the point of using any model to project in the first place?*

A: Projections are always tricky as we cannot foresee the future. But a *good* model is not merely one that seems to fit the data well, but rather a model whose structure is based on the situation being modeled. For instance, a *good* model of student graduation rates should take into account such factors as the birth rate, current school populations at all levels, and the relative popularity of private schools as opposed to public schools. It is by using models of this kind that the National Center for Educational Statistics is able to make the projections shown in the data above.

EXERCISES

1. In 1994 there were 246,000 private high school graduates. What do the two logistic models (unshifted and shifted) "predict" for 1994? (Round answer to the nearest 1,000.) Which gives the better prediction?

2. What is the long-term prediction of each of the two models? (Round answer to the nearest 1,000.)

3. Find $\lim_{t \to +\infty} N'(t)$ for both models, and interpret the results.

4. T You receive a last-minute memo from TJM to the effect that, sorry, the 2011 and 2012 figures are not accurate. Use technology to re-estimate M, A, b, and C for the shifted logistic model in the absence of this data and obtain new estimates for the 2011 and 2012 data. What does the new model predict the rate of change in the number of high school seniors will be in 2015?

5. T ***Another Model*** Using the original data, find the best-fit shifted logistic curve of the form

$$N(t) = c + b\frac{a(t-m)}{1 + a|t-m|}. \qquad (a, b, c, m \text{ constant})$$

Its graph is shown below:

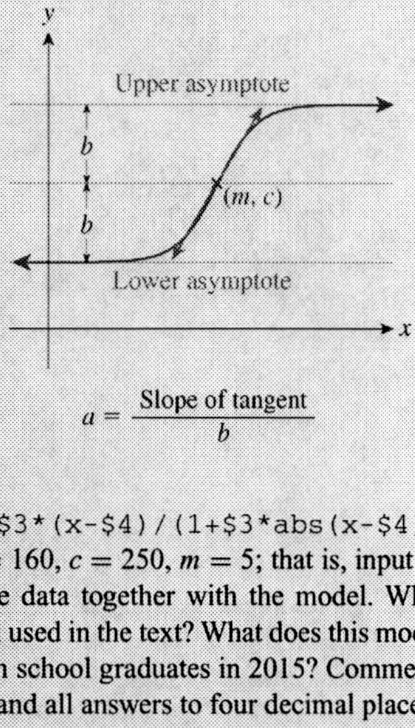

$$a = \frac{\text{Slope of tangent}}{b}$$

(Use the model `$1+$2*$3*(x-$4)/(1+$3*abs(x-$4))` and start with the following values: $a = 0.05$, $b = 160$, $c = 250$, $m = 5$; that is, input `250, 160, 0.05, 5` in the "Guess" field.) Graph the data together with the model. What is SSE? Is the model as accurate a fit as the model used in the text? What does this model predict will be the growth rate of the number of high school graduates in 2015? Comment on the answer. (Round the coefficients in the model and all answers to four decimal places.)

6. T ***Demand for Freon*** The demand for chlorofluorocarbon-12 (CFC-12)—the ozone-depleting refrigerant commonly known as Freon 12 (the name given to it by Du Pont)—has been declining significantly in response to regulation and concern about the ozone layer. The chart below shows the projected demand for CFC-12 for the period 1994–2005.[56]

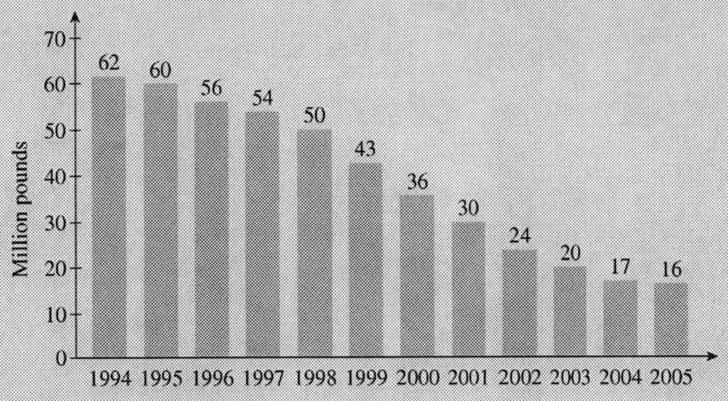

a. Use technology to obtain the best-fit equation of the form

$$N(t) = c + b\frac{a(t-m)}{1+a|t-m|}, \quad (a, b, c, m \text{ constant})$$

where t is the number of years since 1990. Use your function to estimate the total demand for CFC-12 from the start of the year 2000 to the start of 2010. [Start with the following values: $a = 1$, $b = -25$, $c = 35$, and $m = 10$, and round your answers to four decimal places.]

b. According to your model, how fast is the demand for Freon declining in 2000?

[56]Source: The Automobile Consulting Group (*New York Times*, December 26, 1993, p. F23). The exact figures were not given, and the chart is a reasonable facsimile of the chart that appeared in *New York Times*.

CHAPTER 11 QUIZ

1. A few weeks ago, Don and Moe were discussing brewing beer. Moe indicated that he would like to study how the microbes that influence the brewing process grow without any irradiation attempts. What Moe discovered was that under ideal laboratory conditions, the number of microbes in the flasks of brew grows at a rate of 65.3% per hour. Suppose that one particular experiment begins with 8,000 microbes present in a brew flask, and that these microbes are allowed to incubate without any irradiation interventions. How many microbes will be present after 4 hours, and what is the rate of growth of the microbe population exactly 4 hours after the experiment starts?

2. Suppose that *f* and *g* are two functions such that $f(5)=1$ and $g(5)=-3$. Suppose also that $f'(5)=4$ and $g'(5)=-2$. Let $y=g(x)\cdot\left(f(x)\right)^{3/2}$. Evaluate $\left.\frac{dy}{dx}\right|_{x=5}$.

3. A manufacturer of toaster ovens has total production costs of $2400 when 50 ovens are produced. Also, at that production level, the marginal cost is $25 per oven. Calculate the rate at which **average cost** per oven is changing at a production level of 50 ovens. Label your result appropriately.

4. In a recent clinical trial, a volunteer watched several consecutive hours of "The Bachelor" while her bodily systems were monitored. One of the things discovered, to the shock of no one, was that as she watched the show, the volunteer's brain cells were dying. In fact, the cells were dying at a very uniform rate so that the number $B(t)$ of living brain cells remaining after t hours was reasonably described by a model of the form $B(t) = B_0 e^{rt}$ billion brain cells, where r is some constant. If the volunteer had 20 billion living brain cells at the time she started the trial and at that time her brain cells were dying at a rate of 0.28 billion cells per hour, determine the rate at which her brain cells were dying (number of cells per hour) after 4 hours of watching the show. Show clearly how you arrived at your conclusion, and label appropriately.

5. Suppose that g is some differentiable function such that $g(0) = 4$ and $g'(0) = -5$. Define a function h by $h(x) = \dfrac{g(x)}{e^{-4x}}$. Calculate $h'(0)$. Show all steps and relevant calculations.

6. A company that manufactures and sells ballet slippers is currently producing and selling 1200 pairs of slippers each month at an average cost of $4 per pair. At that production level, marginal cost is $5 per pair. Each pair of slippers produced is sold for $20.

a. At that level of production and sales, how much profit or loss is the business experiencing? Is profit increasing or decreasing at that level?

b. At that level of production and sales, is average cost increasing or decreasing? Explain your contention.

7. Management at a fly-in lodge have established that the weekly profit, P, for the lodge depends on the number of cabins, n, that are rented for the week as given by $P(n) = -4n^2 + 108n - 228$ dollars. Also, records indicate that, on average, the number of cabins rented t weeks after the start of the year is given by $n(t) = -0.0015t^3 + 0.085t^2 - 0.44t + 8.4$. Given this, determine the rate at which weekly profit is changing 10 weeks after the start of the year. Show all relevant calculations and label your result appropriately.

8. The number of bacteria in a culture has been doubling every six hours and is currently 720,000. How fast is the bacteria population growing right now, in terms of number of bacteria per hour?

12

Further Applications of the Derivative

WW Website
www.WanerMath.com
At the Website you will find:

- Section-by-section tutorials, including game tutorials with randomized quizzes
- A detailed chapter summary
- A true/false quiz
- Additional review exercises
- Graphers, Excel tutorials, and other resources
- The following extra topic:
  Linear Approximation and Error Estimation

Case Study Production Lot Size Management

Your publishing company is planning the production of its latest best seller, which it predicts will sell 100,000 copies each month over the coming year. The book will be printed in several batches of the same number, evenly spaced throughout the year. Each print run has a setup cost of $5,000, a single book costs $1 to produce, and monthly storage costs for books awaiting shipment average 1¢ per book. **To meet the anticipated demand at minimum total cost to your company, how many printing runs should you plan?**

SERDAR/Alamy

Introduction

In this chapter we begin to see the power of calculus as an optimization tool. In Chapter 9 we saw how to price an item in order to get the largest revenue when the demand function is linear. Using calculus, we can handle nonlinear functions, which are much more general. In Section 12.1 we show how calculus can be used to solve the problem of finding the values of a variable that lead to a maximum or minimum value of a given function. In Section 12.2 we show how this helps us in various real-world applications.

Another theme in this chapter is that calculus can help us to draw and understand the graph of a function. By the time you have completed the material in Section 12.1, you will be able to locate and sketch some of the important features of a graph, such as where it rises and where it falls. In Section 12.3 we look at the *second derivative,* the derivative of the derivative function, and what it tells us about how the graph *curves*. We also see how the second derivative is used to model the notion of *acceleration*. In Section 12.4 we put a number of ideas together that help to explain what you see in a graph (drawn, for example, using graphing technology) and to locate its most important points.

algebra Review
For this chapter, you should be familiar with the algebra reviewed in **Chapter 0, sections 5 and 6.**

We also include sections on related rates and elasticity of demand. The first of these (Section 12.5) examines further the concept of the derivative as a rate of change. The second (Section 12.6) returns to the problem of optimizing revenue based on the demand equation, looking at it in a new way that leads to an important idea in economics—elasticity.

12.1 Maxima and Minima

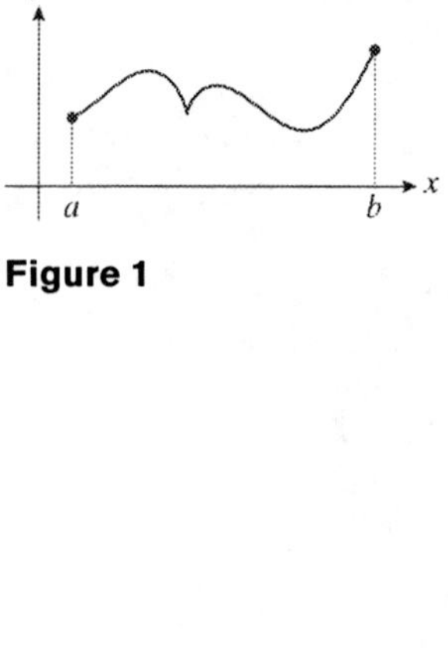

Figure 1

Figure 1 shows the graph of a function f whose domain is the closed interval $[a, b]$. A mathematician sees lots of interesting things going on here. There are hills and valleys, and even a small chasm (called a *cusp*) near the center. For many purposes, the important features of this curve are the highs and lows. Suppose, for example, you know that the price of the stock of a certain company will follow this graph during the course of a week. Although you would certainly make a handsome profit if you bought at time a and sold at time b, your best strategy would be to follow the old adage to "buy low and sell high," buying at all the lows and selling at all the highs.

Figure 2 shows the graph once again with the highs and lows marked. Mathematicians have names for these points: the highs (at the x-values p, r, and b) are referred to as **relative maxima**, and the lows (at the x-values a, q, and s) are referred to as **relative minima**. Collectively, these highs and lows are referred to as **relative extrema**. (A point of language: The singular forms of the plurals *minima, maxima,* and *extrema* are *minimum, maximum,* and *extremum*.)

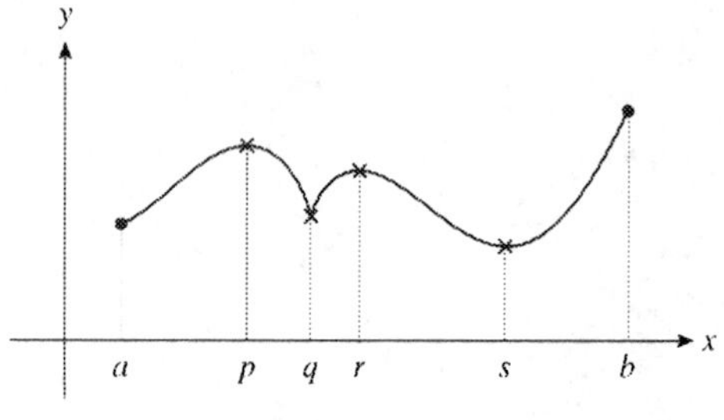

Figure 2

Why do we refer to these points as relative extrema? Take a look at the point corresponding to $x = r$. It is the highest point of the graph *compared to other points nearby*. If you were an extremely nearsighted mountaineer standing at the point

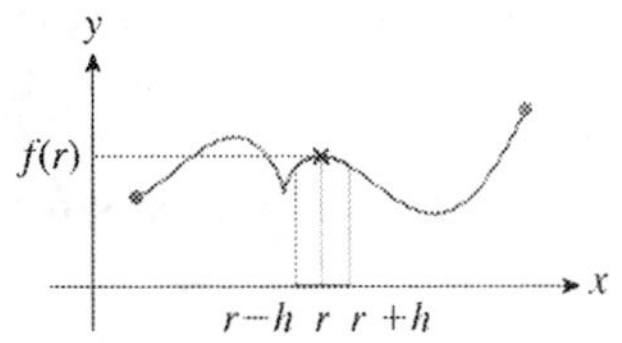

Figure 3

where $x = r$, you would *think* that you were at the highest point of the graph, not being able to see the distant peaks at $x = p$ and $x = b$.

Let's translate into mathematical terms. We are talking about the heights of various points on the curve. The height of the curve at $x = r$ is $f(r)$, so we are saying that $f(r)$ is greater than or equal to $f(x)$ for every x near r. In other words, *$f(r)$ is the greatest value that $f(x)$ has for all choices of x between $r - h$ and $r + h$* for some (possibly small) h. (See Figure 3.)

We can phrase the formal definition as follows.

Relative Extrema

f has a **relative maximum** at $x = r$ if there is some interval $(r - h, r + h)$ (even a very small one) for which $f(r) \geq f(x)$ for all x in $(r - h, r + h)$ for which $f(x)$ is defined.

f has a **relative minimum** at $x = r$ if there is some interval $(r - h, r + h)$ (even a very small one) for which $f(r) \leq f(x)$ for all x in $(r - h, r + h)$ for which $f(x)$ is defined.

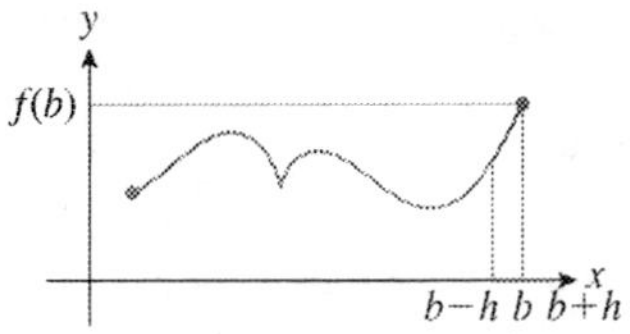

Figure 4

Quick Examples

In Figure 2, f has the following relative extrema:

1. Relative maxima at p and r.
2. A relative maximum at b. (See Figure 4.) Note that $f(x)$ is not defined for $x > b$. However, $f(b) \geq f(x)$ for every x in the interval $(b - h, b + h)$ *for which $f(x)$ is defined*—that is, for every x in $(b - h, b]$.*
3. Relative minima at a, q, and s.

* Our definition of relative extremum allows f to have a relative extremum at an endpoint of its domain; the definitions used in some books do not. In view of examples like the stock market investing strategy mentioned above, we find it more useful to allow endpoints as relative extrema.

Looking carefully at Figure 2, we can see that the lowest point on the whole graph is where $x = s$ and the highest point is where $x = b$. This means that $f(s)$ is the least value of f on the whole domain of f (the interval $[a, b]$) and $f(b)$ is the greatest value. We call these the *absolute* minimum and maximum.

Absolute Extrema

f has an **absolute maximum** at $x = r$ if $f(r) \geq f(x)$ for every x in the domain of f.

f has an **absolute minimum** at $x = r$ if $f(r) \leq f(x)$ for every x in the domain of f.

Quick Examples

1. In Figure 2, f has an absolute maximum at b and an absolute minimum at s.
2. If $f(x) = x^2$, then $f(x) \geq f(0)$ for every real number x. Therefore, $f(x) = x^2$ has an absolute minimum at $x = 0$. (See Figure 5.)
3. Generalizing (2), every quadratic function $f(x) = ax^2 + bx + c$ has an absolute extremum at its vertex $x = -b/(2a)$; an absolute minimum if $a > 0$, and an absolute maximum if $a < 0$.

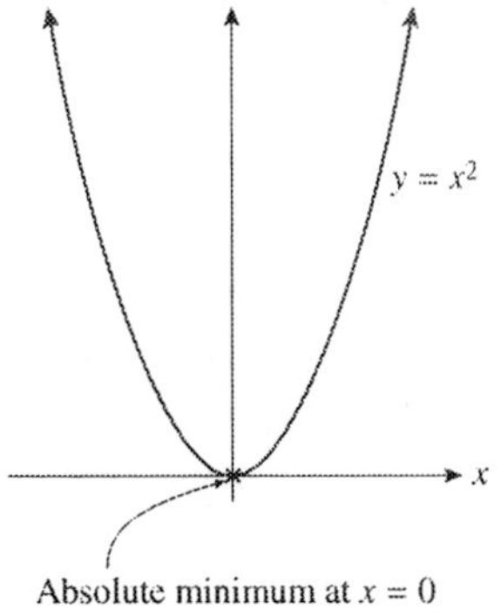

Figure 5

Note If f has an absolute extremum at $x = r$, then it automatically satisfies the requirement for a *relative* extremum there as well; take $h = 1$ (or any other value) in the definition of relative extremum. Thus, absolute extrema are special types of relative extrema. ■

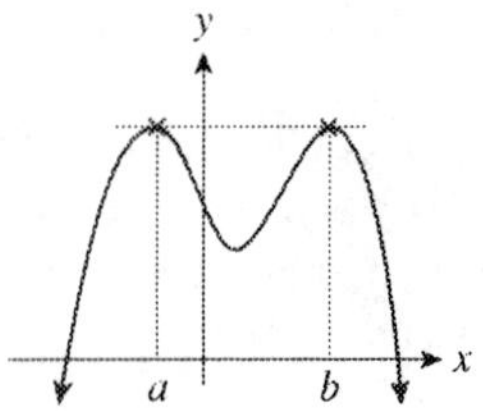

Absolute maxima at $x = a$ and $x = b$

Figure 6

Some graphs have no absolute extrema at all (think of the graph of $y = x$), while others might have an absolute minimum but no absolute maximum (like $y = x^2$), or vice versa. When f does have an absolute maximum, there is only one absolute maximum *value* of f, but this value may occur at different values of x, and similarly for absolute minima. (See Figure 6.)

Q: *At how many different values of x can f take on its absolute maximum value?*

A: An extreme case is that of a constant function; because we use $\geq$ in the definition of absolute maximum, a constant function has an absolute maximum (and minimum) at every point in its domain.

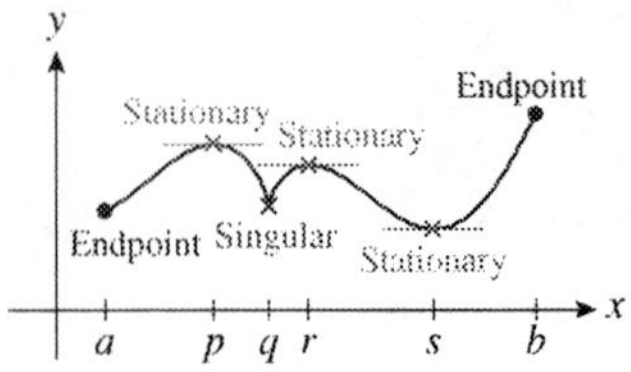

Figure 7

Now, how do we go about locating extrema? In many cases we can get a good idea by using graphing technology to zoom in on a maximum or minimum and approximate its coordinates. However, calculus gives us a way to find the exact locations of the extrema and at the same time to understand why the graph of a function behaves the way it does. In fact, it is often best to combine the powers of graphing technology with those of calculus, as we shall see.

In Figure 7 we see the graph from Figure 1 once more, but we have labeled each extreme point as one of three types. Notice that two extrema occur at endpoints and the others at **interior points;** that is, points other than endpoints. Let us look first at the extrema occurring at interior points: At the points labeled "Stationary," the tangent lines to the graph are horizontal, and so have slope 0, so f' (which gives the slope) is 0. Any time $f'(x) = 0$, we say that f has a **stationary point** at x because the rate of change of f is zero there. We call an extremum that occurs at a stationary point a **stationary extremum.** In general, to find the exact location of each stationary point, we need to solve the equation $f'(x) = 0$. Note that stationary points are always interior points, as f' is not defined at endpoints of the domain.

There is a relative minimum in Figure 7 at $x = q$, but there is no horizontal tangent there. In fact, there is no tangent line at all; $f'(q)$ is not defined. (Recall a similar situation with the graph of $f(x) = |x|$ at $x = 0$.) When $f'(x)$ does not exist for some interior point x in the domain of f, we say that f has a **singular point** at x. We shall call an extremum that occurs at a singular point a **singular extremum.** The points that are either stationary or singular we call collectively the **critical points** of f.

The remaining two extrema are at the **endpoints** of the domain (remember that we do allow relative extrema at endpoints). As we see in the figure, they are (almost) always either relative maxima or relative minima.

We bring all the above information together in Figure 8:

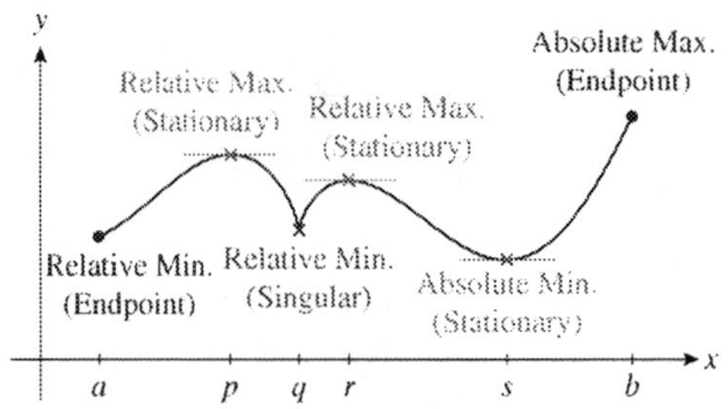

Figure 8

Q: *Are there any other types of relative extrema?*

A: No; relative extrema of a function always occur at critical points or endpoints. (A rigorous proof is beyond the scope of this book.)*

* Here is an outline of the argument. Suppose f has a maximum, say, at $x = a$, at some interior point of its domain. Then either f is differentiable there, or it is not. If it is not, then we have a singular point. If f is differentiable at $x = a$, then consider the slope of the secant line through the points where $x = a$ and $x = a + h$ for small positive h. Because f has a maximum at $x = a$, it is falling (or level) to the right of $x = a$, and so the slope of this secant line must be ≤ 0. Thus, we must have $f'(a) \leq 0$ in the limit as $h \to 0$. On the other hand, if h is small and *negative,* then the corresponding secant line must have slope ≥ 0 because f is also falling (or level) as we move left from $x = a$, and so $f'(a) \geq 0$. Because $f'(a)$ is both ≥ 0 and ≤ 0, it must be zero, and so we have a stationary point at $x = a$.

Locating Candidates for Extrema

If f is a real-valued function, then its extrema occur among the following types of points:

1. **Stationary Points:** f has a stationary point at x if x is in the interior of the domain and $f'(x) = 0$. To locate stationary points, set $f'(x) = 0$ and solve for x.
2. **Singular Points:** f has a singular point at x if x is in the interior of the domain and $f'(x)$ is not defined. To locate singular points, find values of x where $f'(x)$ is *not* defined, but $f(x)$ *is* defined.
3. **Endpoints:** These are the endpoints, if any, of the domain. Recall that closed intervals contain endpoints, but open intervals do not. If the domain of f is an open interval or the whole real line, then there are no endpoints.

Once we have a candidate for an extremum of f, we find the corresponding point (x, y) on the graph of f using $y = f(x)$.

Quick Examples

1. **Stationary Points:** Let $f(x) = x^3 - 12x$. Then to locate the stationary points, set $f'(x) = 0$ and solve for x. This gives $3x^2 - 12 = 0$, so f has stationary points at $x = \pm 2$. The corresponding points on the graph are $(-2, f(-2)) = (-2, 16)$ and $(2, f(2)) = (2, -16)$.
2. **Singular Points:** Let $f(x) = 3(x - 1)^{1/3}$. Then $f'(x) = (x - 1)^{-2/3} = 1/(x - 1)^{2/3}$. $f'(1)$ is not defined, although $f(1)$ *is* defined. Thus, the (only) singular point occurs at $x = 1$. The corresponding point on the graph is $(1, f(1)) = (1, 0)$.
3. **Endpoints:** Let $f(x) = 1/x$, with domain $(-\infty, 0) \cup [1, +\infty)$. Then the only endpoint in the domain of f occurs at $x = 1$. The corresponding point on the graph is $(1, 1)$. The natural domain of $1/x$, on the other hand, has no endpoints.

Remember, though, that the three types of points we identify above are only *candidates* for extrema. It is quite possible, as we shall see, to have a stationary point or a singular point that is neither a maximum nor a minimum. (It is also possible for an endpoint to be neither a maximum nor a minimum, but only in functions whose graphs are rather bizarre—see Exercise 65.)

Now let's look at some examples of finding maxima and minima. In all of these examples, we will use the following procedure: First, we find the derivative, which we examine to find the stationary points and singular points. Next, we make a table listing the x-coordinates of the critical points and endpoints, together with their y-coordinates. We use this table to make a rough sketch of the graph. From the table and rough sketch, we usually have enough data to be able to say where the extreme points are and what kind they are.

EXAMPLE 1 Maxima and Minima

Find the relative and absolute maxima and minima of

$$f(x) = x^2 - 2x$$

on the interval [0, 4].

Solution We first calculate $f'(x) = 2x - 2$. We use this derivative to locate the critical points (stationary and singular points).

Stationary Points To locate the stationary points, we solve the equation $f'(x) = 0$, or

$$2x - 2 = 0,$$

getting $x = 1$. The domain of the function is $[0, 4]$, so $x = 1$ is in the interior of the domain. Thus, the only candidate for a stationary relative extremum occurs when $x = 1$.

Singular Points We look for interior points where the derivative is not defined. However, the derivative is $2x - 2$, which is defined for every x. Thus, there are no singular points and hence no candidates for singular relative extrema.

Endpoints The domain is $[0, 4]$, so the endpoints occur when $x = 0$ and $x = 4$.

We record these values of x in a table, together with the corresponding y-coordinates (values of f):

x	0	1	4
$f(x) = x^2 - 2x$	0	−1	8

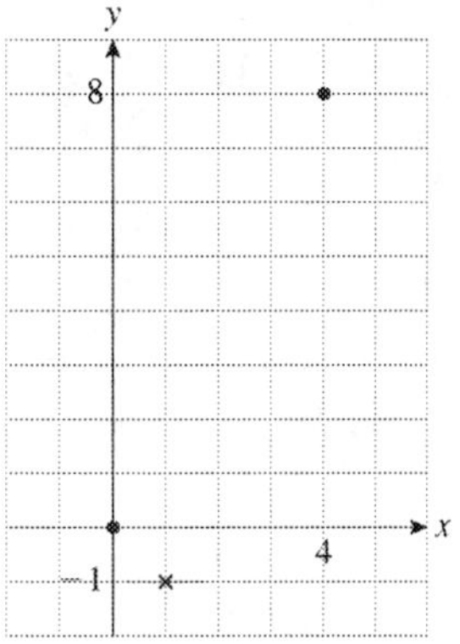

Figure 9

This gives us three points on the graph, (0, 0), (1, −1), and (4, 8), which we plot in Figure 9. We remind ourselves that the point (1, −1) is a stationary point of the graph by drawing in a part of the horizontal tangent line. Connecting these points must give us a graph something like that in Figure 10.

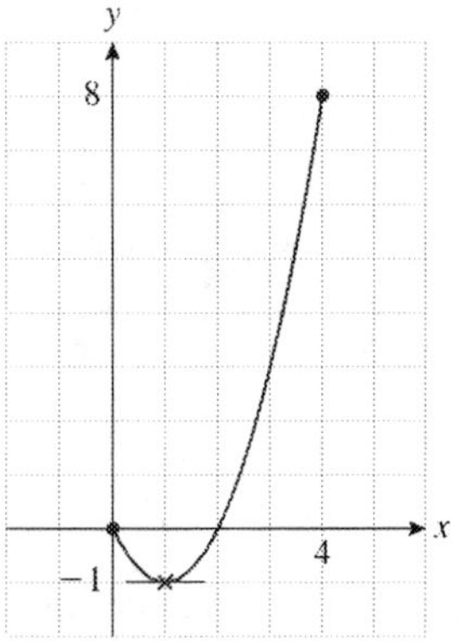

Figure 10

From Figure 10 we can see that f has the following extrema:

x	$y = x^2 - 2x$	*Classification*
0	0	Relative maximum (endpoint)
1	−1	Absolute minimum (stationary point)
4	8	Absolute maximum (endpoint)

➡ **Before we go on...** A little terminology: If the point (a, b) on the graph of f represents a maximum (or minimum) of f, we will sometimes say that ***f* has a maximum (or minimum) value of *b* at *x* = *a***, or simply that ***f* has a maximum (or minimum) at (*a*, *b*).** Thus, in the above example, we could have said the following:

- "f has a relative maximum value of 0 at $x = 0$," or "f has a relative maximum at (0, 0)."
- "f has an absolute minimum value of −1 at $x = 1$," or "f has an absolute minimum at (1, −1)."
- "f has an absolute maximum value of 8 at $x = 4$," or "f has an absolute maximum at (4, 8)."

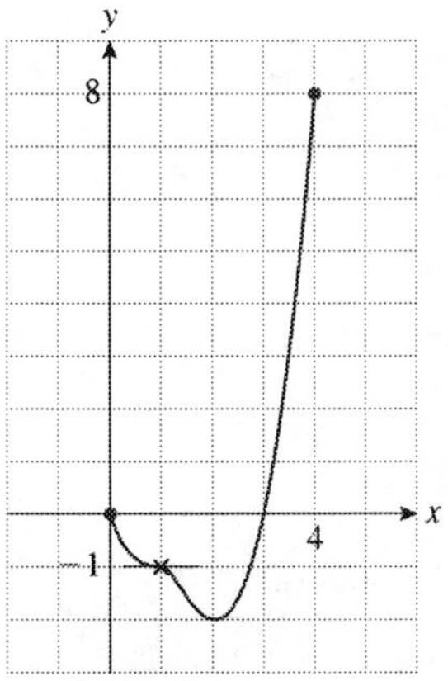

Figure 11

Q: *How can we be sure that the graph in Example 1 doesn't look like Figure 11?*

A: If it did, there would be another critical point somewhere between $x = 1$ and $x = 4$. But we already know that there aren't any other critical points. The table we made listed all of the possible extrema; there can be no more.

■

First Derivative Test

The **first derivative test*** gives another, very systematic, way of checking whether a critical point is a maximum or minimum. To motivate the first derivative test, consider again the critical point $x = 1$ in Example 1. If we look at some values of $f'(x)$ to the left and right of the critical point, we obtain the information shown in the following table:

* Why "first" derivative test? To distinguish it from a test based on the **second derivative** of a function, which we shall discuss in Section 12.3.

	Point to the Left	Critical Point	Point to the Right
x	0.5	1	2
$f'(x) = 2x - 2$	−1	0	2
Direction of Graph	↘	→	↗

At $x = 0.5$ (to the left of the critical point) we see that $f'(0.5) = -1 < 0$, so the graph has negative slope and f is decreasing. We note this with the downward pointing arrow. At $x = 2$ (to the right of the critical point), we find $f'(2) = 2 > 0$, so the graph has positive slope and f is increasing. In fact, because $f'(x) = 0$ only at $x = 1$, we know that $f'(x) < 0$ for all x in (0, 1), and we can say that f is decreasing on the interval (0, 1). Similarly, f is increasing on (1, 4).

So, starting at $x = 0$, the graph of f goes down until we reach $x = 1$ and then it goes back up, telling us that $x = 1$ must be a minimum. Notice how the minimum is suggested by the arrows to the left and right.

First Derivative Test for Extrema

Suppose that c is a critical point of the continuous function f, and that its derivative is defined for x close to, and on both sides of, $x = c$. Then, determine the sign of the derivative to the left and right of $x = c$.

1. If $f'(x)$ is positive to the left of $x = c$ and negative to the right, then f has a maximum at $x = c$.
2. If $f'(x)$ is negative to the left of $x = c$ and positive to the right, then f has a minimum at $x = c$.
3. If $f'(x)$ has the same sign on both sides of $x = c$, then f has neither a maximum nor a minimum at $x = c$.

Quick Examples

1. In Example 1 above, we saw that $f(x) = x^2 - 2x$ has a critical point at $x = 1$ with $f'(x)$ negative to the left of $x = 1$ and positive to the right (see the table). Therefore, f has a minimum at $x = 1$.

2. Here is a graph showing a function f with a singular point at $x = 1$:

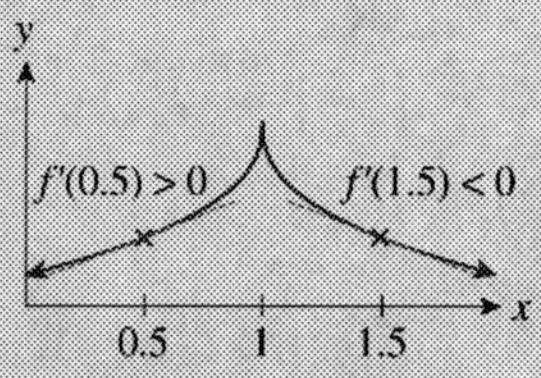

The graph gives us the information shown in the table:

	Point to the Left	Critical Point	Point to the Right
x	0.5	1	1.5
$f'(x)$	+	Undefined	−
Direction of Graph	↗		↘

Since $f'(x)$ is positive to the left of $x = 1$ and negative to the right, we see that f has maximum at $x = 1$. (Notice again how this is suggested by the direction of the arrows.)

EXAMPLE 2 Unbounded Interval

Find all extrema of $f(x) = 3x^4 - 4x^3$ on $[-1, \infty)$.

Solution We first calculate $f'(x) = 12x^3 - 12x^2$.

Stationary points We solve the equation $f'(x) = 0$, which is

$$12x^3 - 12x^2 = 0 \text{ or}$$
$$12x^2(x - 1) = 0.$$

There are two solutions, $x = 0$ and $x = 1$, and both are in the domain. These are our candidates for the x-coordinates of stationary extrema.

Singular points There are no points where $f'(x)$ is not defined, so there are no singular points.

Endpoints The domain is $[-1, \infty)$, so there is one endpoint, at $x = -1$.

We record these points in a table with the corresponding y-coordinates:

x	−1	0	1
$f(x) = 3x^4 - 4x^3$	7	0	−1

We will illustrate three methods we can use to determine which are minima, which are maxima, and which are neither:

1. Plot these points and sketch the graph by hand.

2. Use the first derivative test.

3. Use technology to help us.

Use the method you find most convenient.

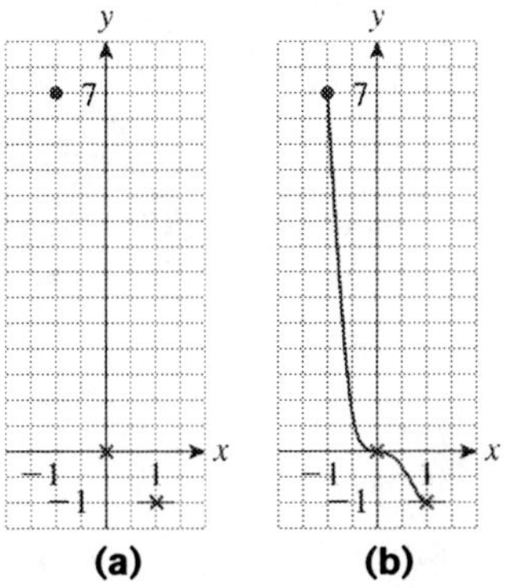

Figure 12

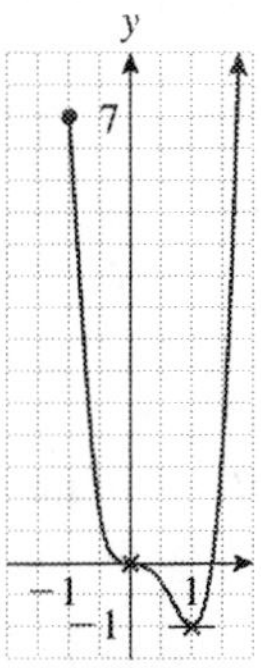

Figure 13

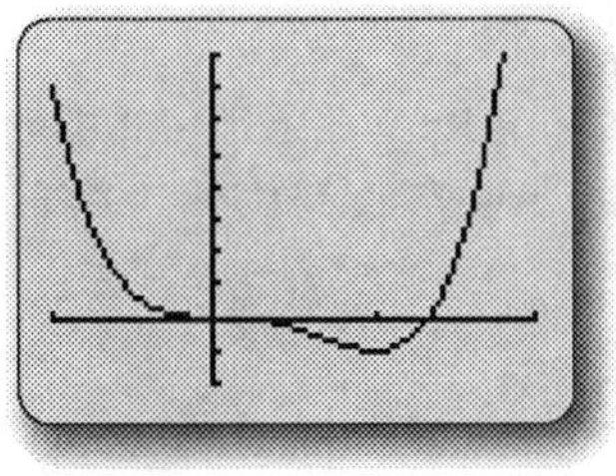
Figure 14

Using a Hand Plot: If we plot these points by hand, we obtain Figure 12(a), which suggests Figure 12(b).

We can't be sure what happens to the right of $x = 1$. Does the curve go up, or does it go down? To find out, let's plot a "test point" to the right of $x = 1$. Choosing $x = 2$, we obtain $y = 3(2)^4 - 4(2)^3 = 16$, so (2, 16) is another point on the graph. Thus, it must turn upward to the right of $x = 1$, as shown in Figure 13.

From the graph, we find that f has the following extrema:

A relative (endpoint) maximum at $(-1, 7)$

An absolute (stationary) minimum at $(1, -1)$

Using the First Derivative Test: List the critical and endpoints in a table, and add additional points as necessary so that each critical point has a noncritical point on either side. Then compute the derivative at each of these points, and draw an arrow to indicate the direction of the graph.

	Endpoint		Critical Point		Critical Point	
x	−1	−0.5	0	0.5	1	2
$f'(x) = 12x^3 - 12x^2$	−24	−1.5	0	−1.5	0	48
Direction of Graph		↘	→	↘	→	↗

Notice that the arrows now suggest the shape of the curve in Figure 13. The first derivative test tells us that the function has a relative maximum at $x = -1$, neither a maximum nor a minimum at $x = 0$, and a relative minimum at $x = 1$. Deciding which of these extrema are absolute and which are relative requires us to compute y-coordinates and plot the corresponding points on the graph by hand, as we did in the first method.

using Technology

If we use technology to show the graph, we should choose the viewing window so that it contains the three interesting points we found: $x = -1$, $x = 0$, and $x = 1$. Again, we can't be sure yet what happens to the right of $x = 1$; does the graph go up or down from that point? If we set the viewing window to an interval of $[-1, 2]$ for x and $[-2, 8]$ for y, we will leave enough room to the right of $x = 1$ and below $y = -1$ to see what the graph will do. The result will be something like Figure 14.

Now we can tell what happens to the right of $x = 1$: the function increases. We know that it cannot later decrease again because if it did, there would have to be another critical point where it turns around, and we found that there are no other critical points. ■

➡ **Before we go on...** Notice that the stationary point at $x = 0$ in Example 2 is neither a relative maximum nor a relative minimum. It is simply a place where the graph of f flattens out for a moment before it continues to fall. Notice also that f has no absolute maximum because $f(x)$ increases without bound as x gets large. ■

EXAMPLE 3 Singular Point

Find all extrema of $f(t) = t^{2/3}$ on $[-1, 1]$.

Solution First, $f'(t) = \frac{2}{3}t^{-1/3}$.

Stationary points We need to solve

$$\frac{2}{3}t^{-1/3} = 0.$$

We can rewrite this equation without the negative exponent:

$$\frac{2}{3t^{1/3}} = 0.$$

Now, the only way that a fraction can equal 0 is if the numerator is 0, so this fraction can never equal 0. Thus, there are no stationary points.

Singular Points The derivative

$$f'(t) = \frac{2}{3t^{1/3}}$$

is not defined for $t = 0$. However, 0 is in the interior of the domain of f (although f' is not defined at $t = 0$, f itself is). Thus, f has a singular point at $t = 0$.

Endpoints There are two endpoints, -1 and 1.

We now put these three points in a table with the corresponding y-coordinates:

t	-1	0	1
$f(t)$	1	0	1

Using a Hand Plot: The derivative, $f'(t) = 2/(3t^{1/3})$, is not defined at the singular point $t = 0$. To help us sketch the graph, let's use limits to investigate what happens to the derivative as we approach 0 from either side:

$$\lim_{t\to 0^-} f'(t) = \lim_{t\to 0^-} \frac{2}{3t^{1/3}} = -\infty$$

$$\lim_{t\to 0^+} f'(t) = \lim_{t\to 0^+} \frac{2}{3t^{1/3}} = +\infty.$$

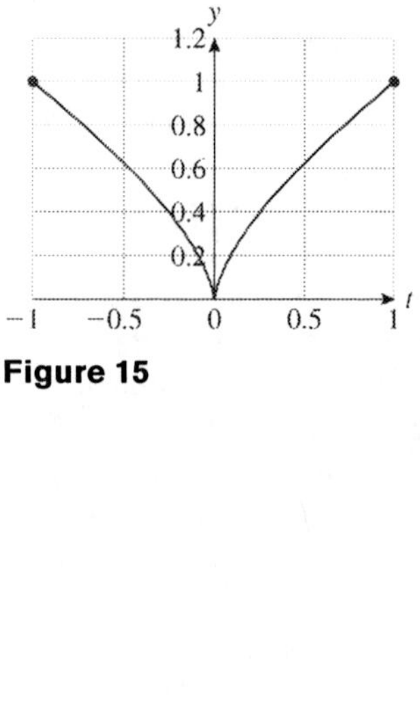

Figure 15

Thus, the graph decreases very steeply, approaching $t = 0$ from the left, and then rises very steeply as it leaves to the right. It would make sense to say that the tangent line at $x = 0$ is vertical, as seen in Figure 15.

From this graph, we find the following extrema for f:

An absolute (endpoint) maximum at $(-1, 1)$

An absolute (singular) minimum at $(0, 0)$

An absolute (endpoint) maximum at $(1, 1)$.

Notice that the absolute maximum value of f is achieved at two values of t: $t = -1$ and $t = 1$.

First Derivative Test: Here is the corresponding table for the first derivative test.

t	-0.5	0	0.5
$f'(t) = \frac{2}{3t^{1/3}}$	$-\frac{2}{3(0.5)^{1/3}}$	Undefined	$\frac{2}{3(0.5)^{1/3}}$
Direction of Graph	↘	↕	↗

(We drew a vertical arrow at $t = 0$ to indicate a vertical tangent.) Again, notice how the arrows suggest the shape of the curve in Figure 15, and the first derivative test confirms that we have a minimum at $x = 0$.

using Technology

Because there is only one critical point, at $t = 0$, it is clear from this table that f must decrease from $t = -1$ to $t = 0$ and then increase from $t = 0$ to $t = 1$. To graph f using technology, choose a viewing window with an interval of $[-1, 1]$ for t and $[0, 1]$ for y. The result will be something like Figure 15.* ■

* Many graphing calculators will give you only the right-hand half of the graph shown in Figure 15 because fractional powers of negative numbers are not, in general, real numbers. To obtain the whole curve, enter the formula as `Y=(x^2)^(1/3)`, a fractional power of the non-negative function x^2.

In Examples 1 and 3, we could have found the absolute maxima and minima without doing any graphing. In Example 1, after finding the critical points and endpoints, we created the following table:

x	0	1	4
$f(x)$	0	−1	8

From this table we can see that f must decrease from its value of 0 at $x = 0$ to -1 at $x = 1$, and then increase to 8 at $x = 4$. The value of 8 must be the largest value it takes on, and the value of -1 must be the smallest, on the interval $[0, 4]$. Similarly, in Example 3 we created the following table:

t	−1	0	1
$f(t)$	1	0	1

From this table we can see that the largest value of f on the interval $[-1, 1]$ is 1 and the smallest value is 0. We are taking advantage of the following fact, the proof of which uses some deep and beautiful mathematics (alas, beyond the scope of this book):

Extreme Value Theorem

If f is *continuous* on a *closed interval* $[a, b]$, then it will have an absolute maximum and an absolute minimum value on that interval. Each absolute extremum must occur at either an endpoint or a critical point. Therefore, the absolute maximum is the largest value in a table of the values of f at the endpoints and critical points, and the absolute minimum is the smallest value.

Quick Example

The function $f(x) = 3x - x^3$ on the interval $[0, 2]$ has one critical point at $x = 1$. The values of f at the critical point and the endpoints of the interval are given in the following table:

	Endpoint	Critical point	Endpoint
x	0	1	2
$f(x)$	0	2	−2

From this table we can say that the absolute maximum value of f on $[0, 2]$ is 2, which occurs at $x = 1$, and the absolute minimum value of f is -2, which occurs at $x = 2$.

As we can see in Example 2 and the following examples, if the domain is not a closed interval, then f may not have an absolute maximum and minimum, and a table of values as above is of little help in determining whether it does.

EXAMPLE 4 Domain Not a Closed Interval

Find all extrema of $f(x) = x + \frac{1}{x}$.

Solution Because no domain is specified, we take the domain to be as large as possible. The function is not defined at $x = 0$ but is at all other points, so we take its domain to be $(-\infty, 0) \cup (0, +\infty)$. We calculate

$$f'(x) = 1 - \frac{1}{x^2}.$$

Stationary Points Setting $f'(x) = 0$, we solve

$$1 - \frac{1}{x^2} = 0$$

to find $x = \pm 1$. Calculating the corresponding values of f, we get the two stationary points $(1, 2)$ and $(-1, -2)$.

Singular Points The only value of x for which $f'(x)$ is not defined is $x = 0$, but then f is not defined there either, so there are no singular points in the domain.

Endpoints The domain, $(-\infty, 0) \cup (0, +\infty)$, has no endpoints.

From this scant information, it is hard to tell what f does. If we are sketching the graph by hand, or using the first derivative test, we will need to plot additional "test points" to the left and right of the stationary points $x = \pm 1$.

using Technology

For the technology approach, let's choose a viewing window with an interval of $[-3, 3]$ for x and $[-4, 4]$ for y, which should leave plenty of room to see how f behaves near the stationary points. The result is something like Figure 16.

From this graph we can see that f has:

A relative (stationary) maximum at $(-1, -2)$

A relative (stationary) minimum at $(1, 2)$

Curiously, the relative maximum is lower than the relative minimum! Notice also that, because of the break in the graph at $x = 0$, the graph did not need to rise to get from $(-1, -2)$ to $(1, 2)$. ■

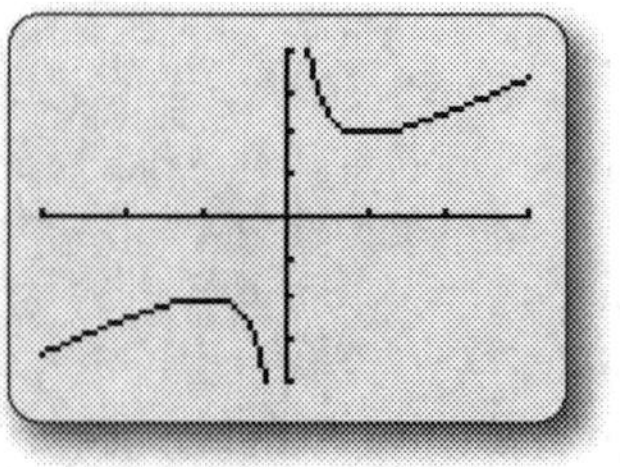

Figure 16

So far we have been solving the equation $f'(x) = 0$ to obtain our candidates for stationary extrema. However, it is often not easy—or even possible—to solve equations analytically. In the next example, we show a way around this problem by using graphing technology.

EXAMPLE 5 Finding Approximate Extrema Using Technology

Graph the function $f(x) = (x - 1)^{2/3} - \frac{x^2}{2}$ with domain $[-2, +\infty)$. Also graph its derivative and hence locate and classify all extrema of f, with coordinates accurate to two decimal places.

Solution In Example 4 of Section 10.5, we saw how to draw the graphs of f and f' using technology. Note that the technology formula to use for the graph of f is

```
((x-1)^2)^(1/3)-0.5*x^2
```

instead of

```
(x-1)^(2/3)-0.5*x^2
```

(Why?)

Figure 17 shows the resulting graphs of f and f'.

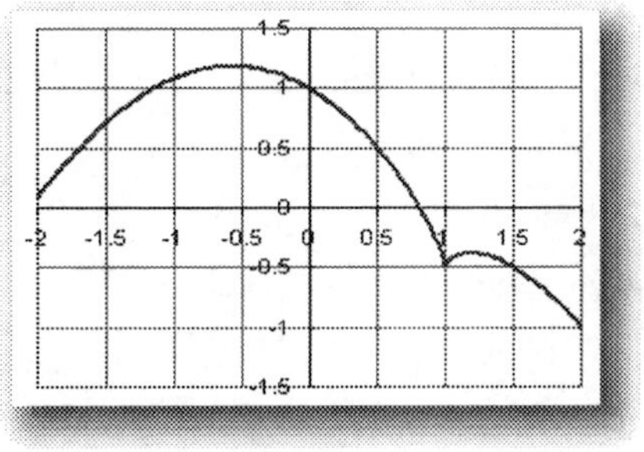

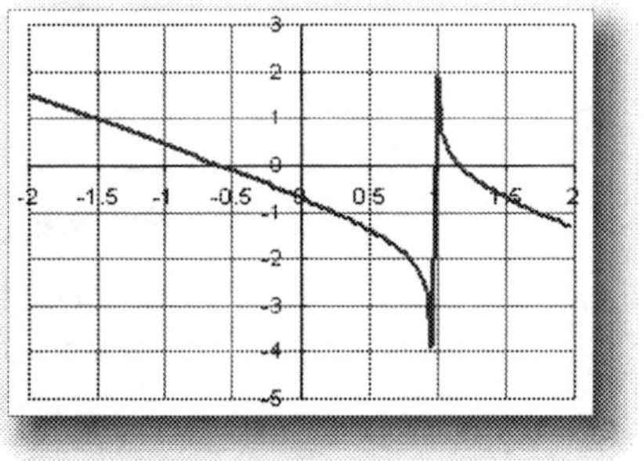

Graph of f | Graph of f'

Figure 17 **(a)** **(b)**

If we extend Xmax beyond $x = 2$, we find that the graph continues downward, apparently without any further interesting behavior.

Stationary Points The graph of f shows two stationary points, both maxima, at around $x = -0.6$ and $x = 1.2$. Notice that the graph of f' is zero at these points. Moreover, it is easier to locate these values accurately on the graph of f' because it is easier to pinpoint where a graph crosses the x-axis than to locate a stationary point. Zooming in to the stationary point at $x \approx -0.6$ results in Figure 18.

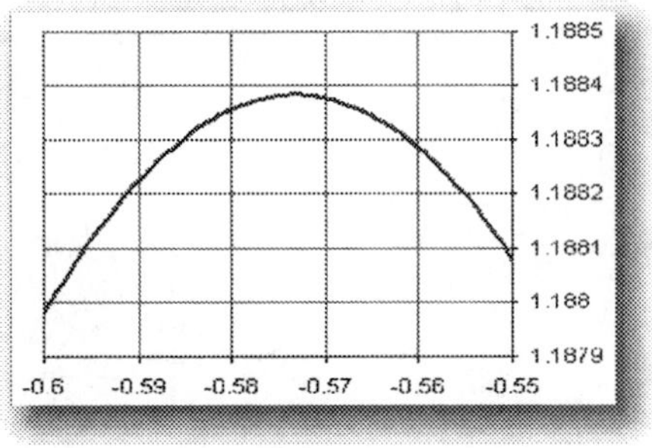

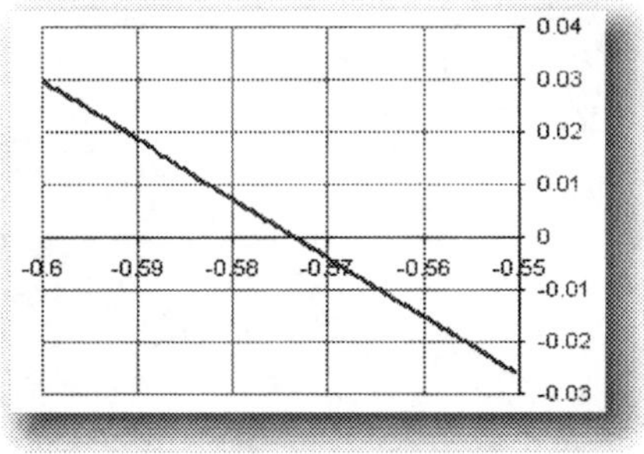

Graph of f | Graph of f'

Figure 18 **(a)** **(b)**

From the graph of f, we can see that the stationary point is somewhere between -0.58 and -0.57. The graph of f' shows more clearly that the zero of f', hence the stationary point of f lies somewhat closer to -0.57 than to -0.58. Thus, the stationary point occurs at $x \approx -0.57$, rounded to two decimal places.

In a similar way, we find the second stationary point at $x \approx 1.18$.

Singular Points Going back to Figure 17, we notice what appears to be a cusp (singular point) at the relative minimum around $x = 1$, and this is confirmed by a glance at the graph of f', which seems to take a sudden jump at that value. Zooming in closer suggests that the singular point occurs at exactly $x = 1$. In fact, we can calculate

$$f'(x) = \frac{2}{3(x-1)^{1/3}} - x.$$

From this formula we see clearly that $f'(x)$ is defined everywhere except at $x = 1$.

Endpoints The only endpoint in the domain is $x = -2$, which gives a relative minimum.

Thus, we have found the following approximate extrema for f:

A relative (endpoint) minimum at $(-2, 0.08)$

An absolute (stationary) maximum at $(-0.57, 1.19)$

A relative (singular) minimum at $(1, -0.5)$

A relative (stationary) maximum at $(1.18, -0.38)$.

12.1 EXERCISES

▼ more advanced ◆ challenging

T indicates exercises that should be solved using technology

In Exercises 1–12, locate and classify all extrema in each graph. (By classifying the extrema, we mean listing whether each extremum is a relative or absolute maximum or minimum.) Also, locate any stationary points or singular points that are not relative extrema. HINT [See Figure 8.]

1.

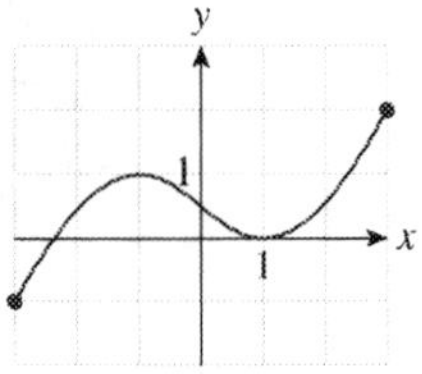

2.

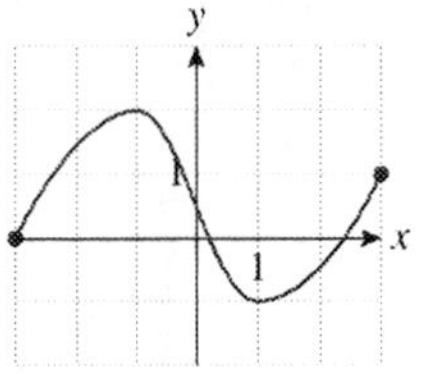

3.

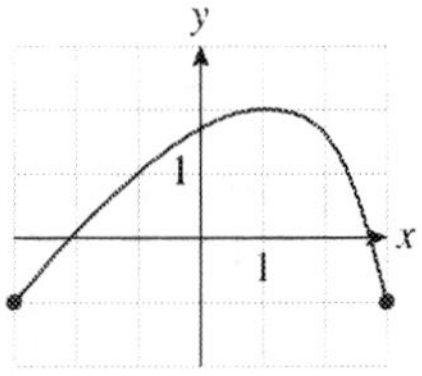

4.

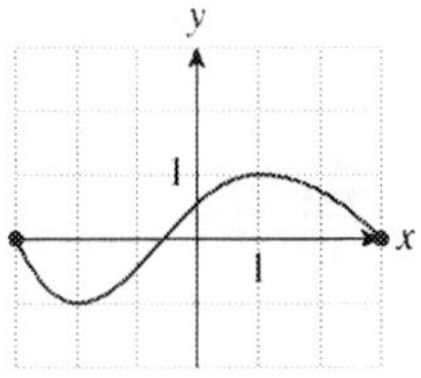

5.

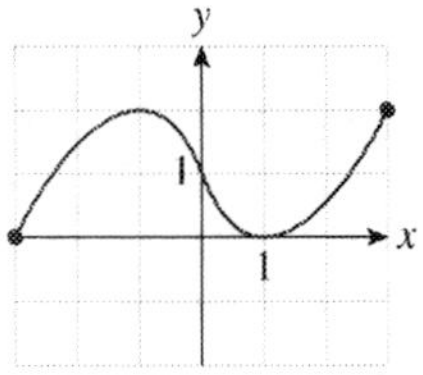

6.

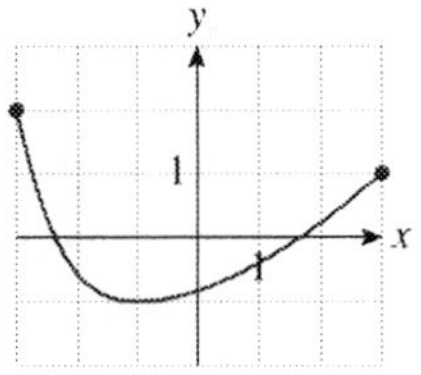

7.

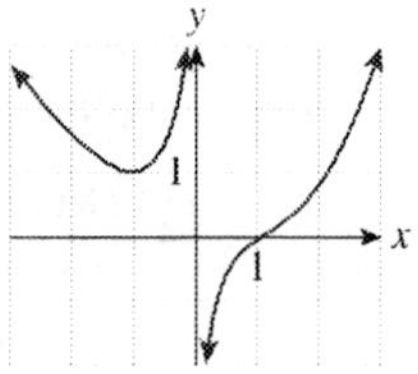

8.

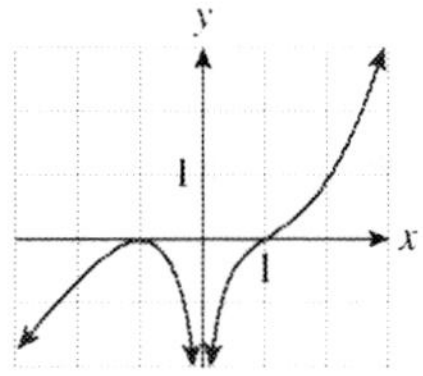

9.

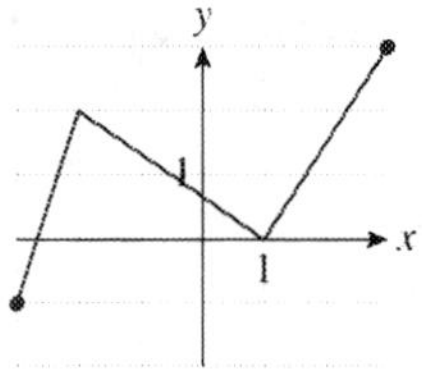

10.

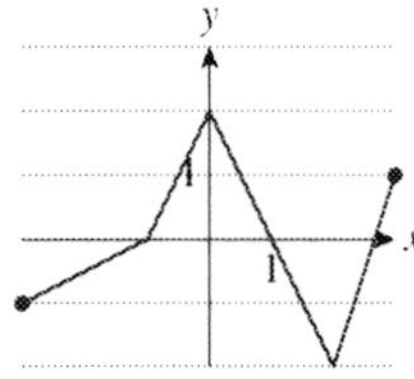

11.

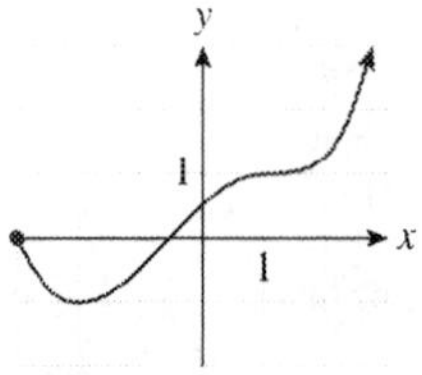

12.

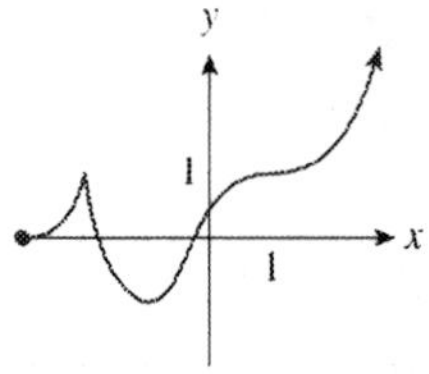

Find the exact location of all the relative and absolute extrema of each function in Exercises 13–44. HINT [See Example 1.]

13. $f(x) = x^2 - 4x + 1$ with domain $[0, 3]$

14. $f(x) = 2x^2 - 2x + 3$ with domain $[0, 3]$

15. $g(x) = x^3 - 12x$ with domain $[-4, 4]$

16. $g(x) = 2x^3 - 6x + 3$ with domain $[-2, 2]$

17. $f(t) = t^3 + t$ with domain $[-2, 2]$

— **18.** $f(t) = -2t^3 - 3t$ with domain $[-1, 1]$

19. $h(t) = 2t^3 + 3t^2$ with domain $[-2, +\infty)$ HINT [See Example 2.]

20. $h(t) = t^3 - 3t^2$ with domain $[-1, +\infty)$ HINT [See Example 2.]

21. $f(x) = x^4 - 4x^3$ with domain $[-1, +\infty)$

22. $f(x) = 3x^4 - 2x^3$ with domain $[-1, +\infty)$

23. $g(t) = \frac{1}{4}t^4 - \frac{2}{3}t^3 + \frac{1}{2}t^2$ with domain $(-\infty, +\infty)$

24. $g(t) = 3t^4 - 16t^3 + 24t^2 + 1$ with domain $(-\infty, +\infty)$

25. $h(x) = (x - 1)^{2/3}$ with domain $[0, 2]$ HINT [See Example 3.]

26. $h(x) = (x + 1)^{2/5}$ with domain $[-2, 0]$ HINT [See Example 3.]

27. $k(x) = \frac{2x}{3} + (x + 1)^{2/3}$ with domain $(-\infty, 0]$

28. $k(x) = \frac{2x}{5} - (x - 1)^{2/5}$ with domain $[0, +\infty)$

29. ▼ $f(t) = \frac{t^2 + 1}{t^2 - 1}$; $-2 \le t \le 2, t \ne \pm 1$

30. ▼ $f(t) = \frac{t^2 - 1}{t^2 + 1}$ with domain $[-2, 2]$

31. ▼ $f(x) = \sqrt{x}(x - 1)$; $x \ge 0$

32. ▼ $f(x) = \sqrt{x}(x + 1)$; $x \ge 0$

33. ▼ $g(x) = x^2 - 4\sqrt{x}$

34. ▼ $g(x) = \frac{1}{x} - \frac{1}{x^2}$

35. ▼ $g(x) = \frac{x^3}{x^2 + 3}$

36. ▼ $g(x) = \frac{x^3}{x^2 - 3}$

37. ▼ $f(x) = x - \ln x$ with domain $(0, +\infty)$

38. ▼ $f(x) = x - \ln x^2$ with domain $(0, +\infty)$

39. ▼ $g(t) = e^t - t$ with domain $[-1, 1]$

40. ▼ $g(t) = e^{-t^2}$ with domain $(-\infty, +\infty)$

41. ▼ $f(x) = \frac{2x^2 - 24}{x + 4}$

42. ▼ $f(x) = \frac{x - 4}{x^2 + 20}$

43. ▼ $f(x) = xe^{1-x^2}$

44. ▼ $f(x) = x \ln x$ with domain $(0, +\infty)$

In Exercises 45–48, use graphing technology and the method in Example 5 to find the x-coordinates of the critical points, accurate to two decimal places. Find all relative and absolute maxima and minima. HINT [See Example 5.]

45. ▣ $y = x^2 + \frac{1}{x - 2}$ with domain $(-3, 2) \cup (2, 6)$

46. ▣ $y = x^2 - 10(x - 1)^{2/3}$ with domain $(-4, 4)$

47. ▣ $f(x) = (x - 5)^2(x + 4)(x - 2)$ with domain $[-5, 6]$

48. ▣ $f(x) = (x + 3)^2(x - 2)^2$ with domain $[-5, 5]$

In Exercises 49–56, the graph of the derivative of a function f is shown. Determine the x-coordinates of all stationary and singular points of f, and classify each as a relative maximum, relative minimum, or neither. (Assume that f(x) is defined and continuous everywhere in $[-3, 3]$.) HINT [See Example 5.]

49. ▼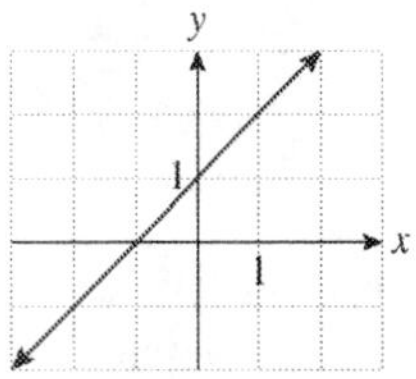

50. ▼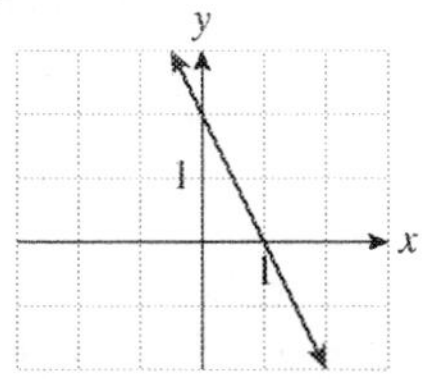

51. ▼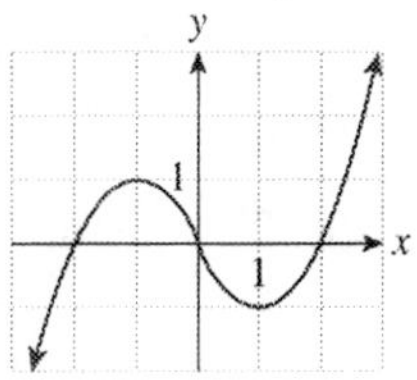

52. ▼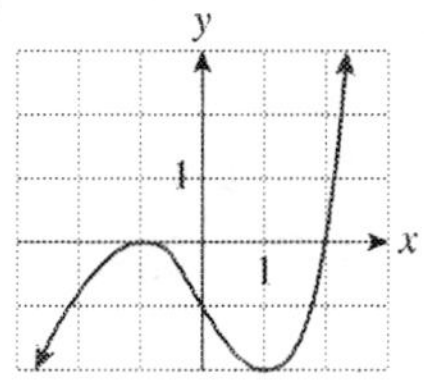

53. ▼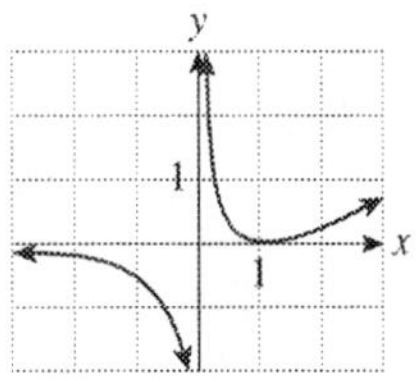

54. ▼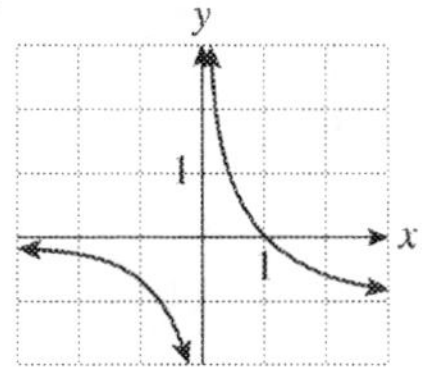

55. ▼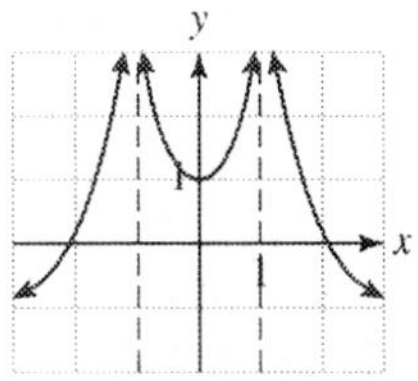

56. ▼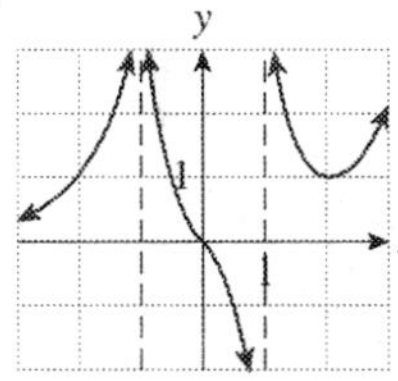

COMMUNICATION AND REASONING EXERCISES

57. Draw the graph of a function f with domain the set of all real numbers, such that f is not linear and has no relative extrema.

58. Draw the graph of a function g with domain the set of all real numbers, such that g has a relative maximum and minimum but no absolute extrema.

59. Draw the graph of a function that has stationary and singular points but no relative extrema.

60. Draw the graph of a function that has relative, not absolute, maxima and minima, but has no stationary or singular points.

61. If a stationary point is not a relative maximum, then must it be a relative minimum? Explain your answer.

62. If one endpoint is a relative maximum, must the other be a relative minimum? Explain your answer.

63. T We said that if f is continuous on a closed interval $[a, b]$, then it will have an absolute maximum and an absolute minimum. Draw the graph of a function with domain [0, 1] having an absolute maximum but no absolute minimum.

64. T Refer to Exercise 63. Draw the graph of a function with domain [0, 1] having no absolute extrema.

65. T Must endpoints always be extrema? Consider the following function (based on the trigonometric sine function—see Chapter 16 for a discussion of its properties):

$$f(x) = \begin{cases} x \sin \dfrac{1}{x} & \text{if } x > 0 \\ 0 & \text{if } x = 0 \end{cases}.$$

Technology formula: `x*sin(1/x)`

Graph this function using the technology formula above for $0 \le x \le h$, choosing smaller and smaller values of h, and decide whether f has a either a relative maximum or relative minimum at the endpoint $x = 0$. Explain your answer. (Note: Very few graphers can draw this curve accurately; the grapher on the Website does a good job (you can increase the number of points to plot for more beautiful results), the grapher that comes with Mac computers is probably among the best, while the TI-83/84 Plus is probably among the worst.)

66. T Refer to the preceding exercise, and consider the function

$$f(x) = \begin{cases} x^2 \sin \dfrac{1}{x} & \text{if } x \ne 0 \\ 0 & \text{if } x = 0 \end{cases}.$$

Technology formula: `x^2*sin(1/x)`

Graph this function using the technology formula above for $-h \le x \le h$, choosing smaller and smaller values of h, and decide **(a)** whether $x = 0$ is a stationary point, and **(b)** whether f has either a relative maximum or a relative minimum at $x = 0$. Explain your answers. HINT [For part (a), use technology to estimate the derivative at $x = 0$.]

Practice Problems 12.1, Part 1

1. If an object is launched straight up into the air from a starting height of h_0 feet, then the height of the object after t seconds is approximately $h(t) = -16t^2 + v_0 t + h_0$ feet, where v_0 is the initial velocity of the object. Find the starting height and initial velocity of an object that attains a maximum height of 562 feet four seconds after being launched.

2. The concentration of a certain drug in the bloodstream t hours after the drug is administered is given by $c(t) = 35te^{-bt}$ ng/ml, where b is some positive constant. Suppose that the drug reaches maximum concentration exactly seven hours after being administered. Find the constant b.

Practice Problems 12.1, Part 2

1. Suppose that $P(t)$ gives the price of a share of Agrosystems Inc. stock over a period of several days. The graph to the right gives $P'(t)$, the rate of change of stock price. Given this, determine the points in time where the stock achieved a (relative) maximum or (relative) minimum price. Identify each time as to whether a maximum or minimum price occurs.

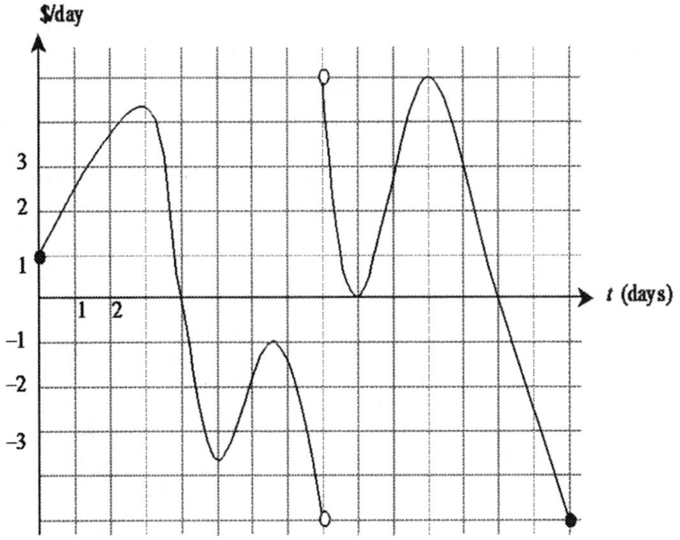

2. Some people in the state legislature believe that the function $R(x) = (100 - x)\sqrt{x}$ describes the amount of revenue the state takes in from income taxes if x represents the percentage of income taken for taxes. Assuming this is correct, what income tax rate would result in maximum revenue to the state? Use calculus to draw your conclusion.

Practice Problems 12.1, Part 3

The owner of a retail lumber store wants to construct a fence to enclose a rectangular outdoor storage area adjacent to the store, using all of one wall of the store as part of one side of the storage area. The wall of the store is 100 feet long.

1. Find the dimensions of the enclosure of maximum area if 340 feet of fencing is to be used. Use calculus to draw your conclusion.

2. Find the dimensions of the enclosure of maximum area if 240 feet of fencing is to be used.

12.2 Applications of Maxima and Minima

In many applications we would like to find the largest or smallest possible value of some quantity—for instance, the greatest possible profit or the lowest cost. We call this the *optimal* (best) value. In this section we consider several such examples and use calculus to find the optimal value in each.

In all applications the first step is to translate a written description into a mathematical problem. In the problems we look at in this section, there are *unknowns* that we are asked to find, there is an expression involving those unknowns that must be made as large or as small as possible—the **objective function**—and there may be **constraints**—equations or inequalities relating the variables.*

* If you have studied linear programming, you will notice a similarity here, but unlike the situation in linear programming, neither the objective function nor the constraints need be linear.

EXAMPLE 1 Minimizing Average Cost

Gymnast Clothing manufactures expensive hockey jerseys for sale to college bookstores in runs of up to 500. Its cost (in dollars) for a run of x hockey jerseys is

$$C(x) = 2,000 + 10x + 0.2x^2.$$

How many jerseys should Gymnast produce per run in order to minimize average cost?†

† Why don't we seek to minimize total cost? The answer would be uninteresting; to minimize total cost, we would make *no* jerseys at all. Minimizing the average cost is a more practical objective.

Solution Here is the procedure we will follow to solve problems like this.

1. ***Identify the unknown(s).*** There is one unknown: x, the number of hockey jerseys Gymnast should produce per run. (We know this because the question is, How many jerseys . . . ?)
2. ***Identify the objective function.*** The objective function is the quantity that must be made as small (in this case) as possible. In this example it is the average cost, which is given by

$$\bar{C}(x) = \frac{C(x)}{x} = \frac{2,000 + 10x + 0.2x^2}{x}$$
$$= \frac{2,000}{x} + 10 + 0.2x \text{ dollars/jersey.}$$

3. ***Identify the constraints (if any).*** At most 500 jerseys can be manufactured in a run. Also, $\bar{C}(0)$ is not defined. Thus, x is constrained by

$$0 < x \leq 500.$$

Put another way, the domain of the objective function $\bar{C}(x)$ is (0, 500].

4. ***State and solve the resulting optimization problem.*** Our optimization problem is:

$$\text{Minimize } \bar{C}(x) = \frac{2{,}000}{x} + 10 + 0.2x \qquad \text{Objective function}$$

$$\text{subject to } 0 < x \leq 500. \qquad \text{Constraint}$$

We now solve this problem as in Section 12.1. We first calculate

$$\bar{C}'(x) = -\frac{2{,}000}{x^2} + 0.2.$$

We solve $\bar{C}'(x) = 0$ to find $x = \pm 100$. We reject $x = -100$ because -100 is not in the domain of $\bar{C}$ (and makes no sense), so we have one stationary point, at $x = 100$. There, the average cost is $\bar{C}(100) = \$50$ per jersey.

The only point at which the formula for $\bar{C}'$ is not defined is $x = 0$, but that is not in the domain of $\bar{C}$, so we have no singular points. We have one endpoint in the domain, at $x = 500$. There, the average cost is $\bar{C}(500) = \$114$.

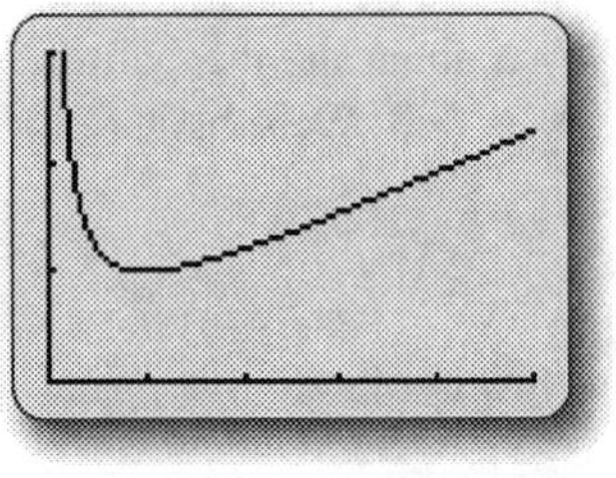

Figure 19

using Technology

Let's plot $\bar{C}$ in a viewing window with the intervals [0, 500] for x and [0, 150] for y, which will show the whole domain and the two interesting points we've found so far. The result is Figure 19.

From the graph of $\bar{C}$, we can see that the stationary point at $x = 100$ gives the absolute minimum. We can therefore say that Gymnast Clothing should produce 100 jerseys per run, for a lowest possible average cost of \$50 per jersey. ■

EXAMPLE 2 Maximizing Area

Slim wants to build a rectangular enclosure for his pet rabbit, Killer, against the side of his house, as shown in Figure 20. He has bought 100 feet of fencing. What are the dimensions of the largest area that he can enclose?

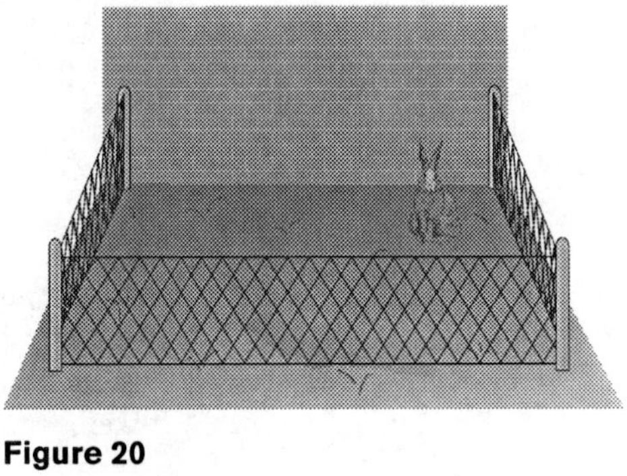

Figure 20

Solution

1. ***Identify the unknown(s).*** To identify the unknown(s), we look at the question: What are the *dimensions* of the largest area he can enclose? Thus, the unknowns are the dimensions of the fence. We call these x and y, as shown in Figure 21.

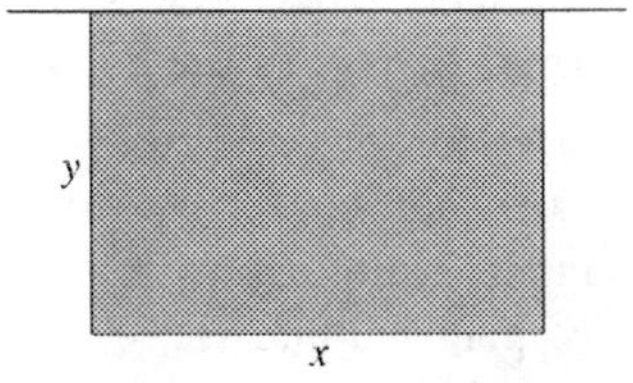

Figure 21

2. ***Identify the objective function.*** We look for what it is that we are trying to maximize (or minimize). The phrase "largest area" tells us that our object is to *maximize the area*, which is the product of length and width, so our objective function is

$$A = xy, \text{ where } A \text{ is the area of the enclosure.}$$

3. ***Identify the constraints (if any).*** What stops Slim from making the area as large as he wants? He has only 100 feet of fencing to work with. Looking again at Figure 21, we see that the sum of the lengths of the three sides must equal 100, so

$$x + 2y = 100.$$

One more point: Because x and y represent the lengths of the sides of the enclosure, neither can be a negative number.

4. ***State and solve the resulting optimization problem.*** Our mathematical problem is:

Maximize $A = xy$ Objective function

subject to $x + 2y = 100$, $x \geq 0$, and $y \geq 0$. Constraints

We know how to find maxima and minima of a function of one variable, but A appears to depend on two variables. We can remedy this by using a constraint to express one variable in terms of the other. Let's take the constraint $x + 2y = 100$ and solve for x in terms of y:

$$x = 100 - 2y.$$

Substituting into the objective function gives

$$A = xy = (100 - 2y)y = 100y - 2y^2$$

and we have eliminated x from the objective function. What about the inequalities? One says that $x \geq 0$, but we want to eliminate x from this as well. We substitute for x again, getting

$$100 - 2y \geq 0.$$

Solving this inequality for y gives $y \leq 50$. The second inequality says that $y \geq 0$. Now, we can restate our problem with x eliminated:

Maximize $A(y) = 100y - 2y^2$ subject to $0 \leq y \leq 50$.

We now proceed with our usual method of solving such problems. We calculate $A'(y) = 100 - 4y$. Solving $100 - 4y = 0$, we get one stationary point at $y = 25$. There, $A(25) = 1{,}250$. There are no points at which $A'(y)$ is not defined, so there are no singular points. We have two endpoints, at $y = 0$ and $y = 50$. The corresponding areas are $A(0) = 0$ and $A(50) = 0$. We record the three points we found in a table:

y	0	25	50
$A(y)$	0	1,250	0

It's clear now how A must behave: It increases from 0 at $y = 0$ to 1,250 at $y = 25$ and then decreases back to 0 at $y = 50$. Thus, the largest possible value of A is 1,250 square feet, which occurs when $y = 25$. To completely answer the question that was asked, we need to know the corresponding value of x. We have $x = 100 - 2y$, so $x = 50$ when $y = 25$. Thus, Slim should build his enclosure 50 feet across and 25 feet deep (with the "missing" 50-foot side being formed by part of the house).

➡ **Before we go on...** Notice that the problem in Example 2 came down to finding the absolute maximum value of A on the closed and bounded interval [0, 50]. As we noted in the preceding section, the table of values of A at its critical points and the endpoints of the interval gives us enough information to find the absolute maximum. ■

Let's stop for a moment and summarize the steps we've taken in these two examples.

Solving an Optimization Problem

1. **Identify the unknown(s), possibly with the aid of a diagram.** These are usually the quantities asked for in the problem.
2. **Identify the objective function.** This is the quantity you are asked to maximize or minimize. You should name it explicitly, as in "Let S = surface area."
3. **Identify the constraint(s).** These can be equations relating variables or inequalities expressing limitations on the values of variables.
4. **State the optimization problem.** This will have the form "Maximize [minimize] the objective function subject to the constraint(s)."
5. **Eliminate extra variables.** If the objective function depends on several variables, solve the constraint equations to express all variables in terms of one particular variable. Substitute these expressions into the objective function to rewrite it as a function of a single variable. In short, if there is only one constraint equation:

   Solve the constraint for one of the unknowns and substitute into the objective.

   Also substitute the expressions into any inequality constraints to help determine the domain of the objective function.
6. **Find the absolute maximum (or minimum) of the objective function.** Use the techniques of the preceding section.

Now for some further examples.

EXAMPLE 3 Maximizing Revenue

Cozy Carriage Company builds baby strollers. Using market research, the company estimates that if it sets the price of a stroller at p dollars, then it can sell $q = 300{,}000 - 10p^2$ strollers per year.* What price will bring in the greatest annual revenue?

* This equation is, of course, the demand equation for the baby strollers. However, coming up with a suitable demand equation in real life is hard, to say the least. In this regard, the very entertaining and also insightful article, *Camels and Rubber Duckies* by Joel Spolsky at www.joelonsoftware.com/articles/CamelsandRubberDuckies.html is a must-read.

Solution The question we are asked identifies our main unknown, the price p. However, there is another quantity that we do not know, q, the number of strollers the company will sell per year. The question also identifies the objective function, revenue, which is

$$R = pq.$$

Including the equality constraint given to us, that $q = 300{,}000 - 10p^2$, and the "reality" inequality constraints $p \geq 0$ and $q \geq 0$, we can write our problem as

$$\text{Maximize } R = pq \text{ subject to } q = 300{,}000 - 10p^2,\ p \geq 0, \text{ and } q \geq 0.$$

We are given q in terms of p, so let's substitute to eliminate q:

$$R = pq = p(300{,}000 - 10p^2) = 300{,}000p - 10p^3.$$

Substituting in the inequality $q \geq 0$, we get

$$300{,}000 - 10p^2 \geq 0.$$

Thus, $p^2 \leq 30{,}000$, which gives $-100\sqrt{3} \leq p \leq 100\sqrt{3}$. When we combine this with $p \geq 0$, we get the following restatement of our problem:

$$\text{Maximize } R(p) = 300{,}000p - 10p^3 \text{ such that } 0 \leq p \leq 100\sqrt{3}.$$

We solve this problem in much the same way we did the preceding one. We calculate $R'(p) = 300{,}000 - 30p^2$. Setting $300{,}000 - 30p^2 = 0$, we find one stationary point at $p = 100$. There are no singular points and we have the endpoints $p = 0$ and $p = 100\sqrt{3}$. Putting these points in a table and computing the corresponding values of R, we get the following:

p	0	100	$100\sqrt{3}$
$R(p)$	0	20,000,000	0

Thus, Cozy Carriage should price its strollers at $100 each, which will bring in the largest possible revenue of $20,000,000.

Figure 22

EXAMPLE 4 Optimizing Resources

The Metal Can Company has an order to make cylindrical cans with a volume of 250 cubic centimeters. What should be the dimensions of the cans in order to use the least amount of metal in their production?

Solution We are asked to find the dimensions of the cans. It is traditional to take as the dimensions of a cylinder the height h and the radius of the base r, as in Figure 22.

We are also asked to minimize the amount of metal used in the can, which is the area of the surface of the cylinder. We can look up the formula or figure it out ourselves: Imagine removing the circular top and bottom and then cutting vertically and flattening out the hollow cylinder to get a rectangle, as shown in Figure 23.

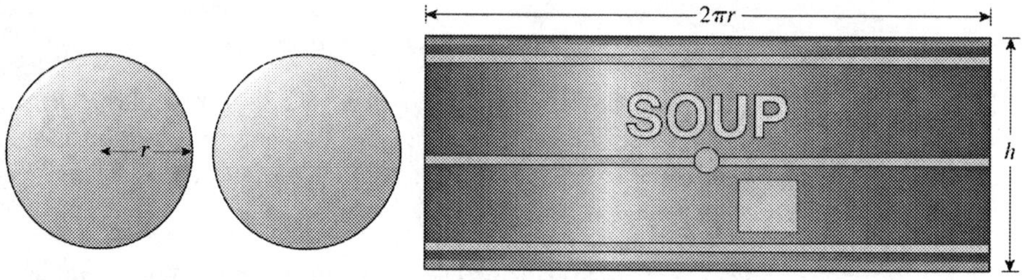

Figure 23

Our objective function is the (total) surface area S of the can. The area of each disc is πr^2, while the area of the rectangular piece is $2\pi rh$. Thus, our objective function is

$$S = 2\pi r^2 + 2\pi rh.$$

As usual, there is a constraint: The volume must be exactly 250 cubic centimeters. The formula for the volume of a cylinder is $V = \pi r^2 h$, so

$$\pi r^2 h = 250.$$

It is easiest to solve this constraint for h in terms of r:

$$h = \frac{250}{\pi r^2}.$$

Substituting in the objective function, we get

$$S = 2\pi r^2 + 2\pi r\frac{250}{\pi r^2} = 2\pi r^2 + \frac{500}{r}.$$

Now r cannot be negative or 0, but it can become very large (a very wide but very short can could have the right volume). We therefore take the domain of $S(r)$ to be $(0, +\infty)$, so our mathematical problem is as follows:

$$\text{Minimize } S(r) = 2\pi r^2 + \frac{500}{r} \text{ subject to } r > 0.$$

Now we calculate

$$S'(r) = 4\pi r - \frac{500}{r^2}.$$

To find stationary points, we set this equal to 0 and solve:

$$\begin{aligned} 4\pi r - \frac{500}{r^2} &= 0 \\ 4\pi r &= \frac{500}{r^2} \\ 4\pi r^3 &= 500 \\ r^3 &= \frac{125}{\pi}. \end{aligned}$$

So

$$r = \sqrt[3]{\frac{125}{\pi}} = \frac{5}{\sqrt[3]{\pi}} \approx 3.41.$$

The corresponding surface area is approximately $S(3.41) \approx 220$. There are no singular points or endpoints in the domain.

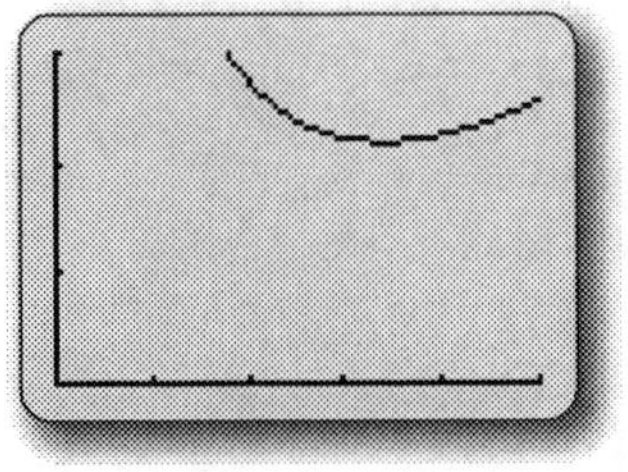

Figure 24

using Technology

To see how S behaves near the one stationary point, let's graph it in a viewing window with interval $[0, 5]$ for r and $[0, 300]$ for S. The result is Figure 24.

From the graph we can clearly see that the smallest surface area occurs at the stationary point at $r \approx 3.41$. The height of the can will be

$$h = \frac{250}{\pi r^2} \approx 6.83.$$

Thus, the can that uses the least amount of metal has a height of approximately 6.83 centimeters and a radius of approximately 3.41 centimeters. Such a can will use approximately 220 square centimeters of metal.

Before we go on... We obtained the value of r in Example 4 by solving the equation

$$4\pi r = \frac{500}{r^2}.$$

This time, let us do things differently: Divide both sides by 4π to obtain

$$r = \frac{500}{4\pi r^2} = \frac{125}{\pi r^2}$$

and compare what we got with the expression for h:

$$h = \frac{250}{\pi r^2},$$

which we see is exactly twice the expression for r. Put another way, the height is exactly equal to the diameter so that the can looks square when viewed from the side. Have you ever seen cans with that shape? Why do you think most cans do not have this shape? ■

EXAMPLE 5 Allocation of Labor

The Gym Sock Company manufactures cotton athletic socks. Production is partially automated through the use of robots. Daily operating costs amount to \$50 per laborer and \$30 per robot. The number of pairs of socks the company can manufacture in a day is given by a Cobb-Douglas* production formula

* Cobb-Douglas production formulas were discussed in Section 11.6.

$$q = 50n^{0.6}r^{0.4},$$

where q is the number of pairs of socks that can be manufactured by n laborers and r robots. Assuming that the company wishes to produce 1,000 pairs of socks per day at a minimum cost, how many laborers and how many robots should it use?

Solution The unknowns are the number of laborers n and the number of robots r. The objective is to minimize the daily cost:

$$C = 50n + 30r.$$

The constraints are given by the daily quota

$$1{,}000 = 50n^{0.6}r^{0.4}$$

and the fact that n and r are nonnegative. We solve the constraint equation for one of the variables; let's solve for n:

$$n^{0.6} = \frac{1{,}000}{50r^{0.4}} = \frac{20}{r^{0.4}}.$$

Taking the $1/0.6$ power of both sides gives

$$n = \left(\frac{20}{r^{0.4}}\right)^{1/0.6} = \frac{20^{1/0.6}}{r^{0.4/0.6}} = \frac{20^{5/3}}{r^{2/3}} \approx \frac{147.36}{r^{2/3}}.$$

Substituting in the objective equation gives us the cost as a function of r:

$$C(r) \approx 50\left(\frac{147.36}{r^{2/3}}\right) + 30r$$
$$= 7{,}368r^{-2/3} + 30r.$$

The only remaining constraint on r is that $r > 0$. To find the minimum value of $C(r)$, we first take the derivative:

$$C'(r) \approx -4{,}912r^{-5/3} + 30.$$

Setting this equal to zero, we solve for r:

$$r^{-5/3} \approx 0.006107$$
$$r \approx (0.006107)^{-3/5} \approx 21.3.$$

The corresponding cost is $C(21.3) \approx \$1{,}600$. There are no singular points or endpoints in the domain of C.

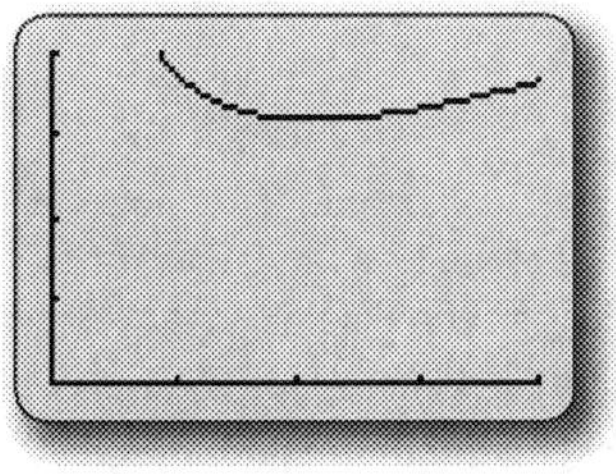

Figure 25

using Technology

To see how C behaves near its stationary point, let's draw its graph in a viewing window with an interval of [0, 40] for r and [0, 2,000] for C. The result is Figure 25.

From the graph we can see that C does have its minimum at the stationary point. The corresponding value of n is

$$n \approx \frac{147.36}{r^{2/3}} \approx 19.2.$$

At this point, our solution appears to be this: Use (approximately) 19.2 laborers and (approximately) 21.3 robots to meet the manufacturing quota at a minimum cost. However, we are not interested in fractions of robots or people, so we need to find integer solutions for n and r. If we round these numbers, we get the solution $(n, r) = (19, 21)$. However, a quick calculation shows that

$$q = 50(19)^{0.6}(21)^{0.4} \approx 989 \text{ pairs of socks,}$$

which fails to meet the quota of 1,000. Thus, we need to round at least one of the quantities n and r *upward* in order to meet the quota. The three possibilities, with corresponding values of q and C, are as follows:

$$(n, r) = (20, 21), \text{ with } q \approx 1{,}020 \text{ and } C = \$1{,}630$$
$$(n, r) = (19, 22), \text{ with } q \approx 1{,}007 \text{ and } C = \$1{,}610$$
$$(n, r) = (20, 22), \text{ with } q \approx 1{,}039 \text{ and } C = \$1{,}660.$$

Of these, the solution that meets the quota at a minimum cost is $(n, r) = (19, 22)$. Thus, the Gym Sock Co. should use 19 laborers and 22 robots, at a cost of $50 \times 19 + 30 \times 22 = \$1{,}610$, to manufacture $50 \times 19^{0.6} \times 22^{0.4} \approx 1{,}007$ pairs of socks.

FAQs

Constraints and Objectives

Q: *How do I know whether or not there are constraints in an applied optimization problem?*

A: There are usually at least *inequality* constraints; the variables usually represent real quantities, such as length or number of items, and so cannot be negative, leading to constraints like $x \geq 0$ (or $0 \leq x \leq 100$ in the event that there is an upper limit). *Equation* constraints usually arise when there is more than one unknown in the objective, and dictate how one unknown is related to others; as in, say "the length is twice the width," or "the demand is 8 divided by the price" (a demand equation).

Q: *How do I know what to use as the objective, and what to use as the constraint(s)?*

A: To identify the objective, look for a phrase such as "find the maximum (or minimum) value of." The amount you are trying to maximize or minimize is the objective. For example,

- *. . . at the least cost. . .* The objective function is the equation for cost, $C = \ldots$.
- *. . . the greatest area. . .* The objective function is the equation for area, $A = \ldots$.

To determine the constraint *inequalities*, ask yourself what limitations are placed on the unknown variables as above—are they nonnegative? are there upper limits? To identify the constraint *equations*, look for sentences that dictate restrictions in the form of relationships between the variables, as in the answer to the first question above.

12.2 EXERCISES

▼ more advanced ◆ challenging

T indicates exercises that should be solved using technology

Solve the optimization problems in Exercises 1–8. HINT [See Example 2.]

1. Maximize $P = xy$ subject to $x + y = 10$.
2. Maximize $P = xy$ subject to $x + 2y = 40$.
3. Minimize $S = x + y$ subject to $xy = 9$ and both x and $y > 0$.
4. Minimize $S = x + 2y$ subject to $xy = 2$ and both x and $y > 0$.
5. Minimize $F = x^2 + y^2$ subject to $x + 2y = 10$.
6. Minimize $F = x^2 + y^2$ subject to $xy^2 = 16$.
7. Maximize $P = xyz$ subject to $x + y = 30$, $y + z = 30$, and $x, y, z \geq 0$.
8. Maximize $P = xyz$ subject to $x + z = 12$, $y + z = 12$, and $x, y, z \geq 0$.
9. For a rectangle with perimeter 20 to have the largest area, what dimensions should it have?
10. For a rectangle with area 100 to have the smallest perimeter, what dimensions should it have?

APPLICATIONS

11. ***Average Cost: iPods*** Assume that it costs Apple approximately

$$C(x) = 22{,}500 + 100x + 0.01x^2$$

dollars to manufacture x 32GB iPods in a day.[1] How many iPods should be manufactured in order to minimize average cost? What is the resulting average cost of an iPod? (Give your answer to the nearest dollar.) HINT [See Example 1.]

12. ***Average Cost: Xboxes*** Assume that it costs Microsoft approximately

$$C(x) = 14{,}400 + 550x + 0.01x^2$$

dollars to manufacture x Xbox 360s in a day.[2] How many Xboxes should be manufactured in order to minimize average cost? What is the resulting average cost of an Xbox? (Give your answer to the nearest dollar.) HINT [See Example 1.]

13. ***Pollution Control*** The cost of controlling emissions at a firm rises rapidly as the amount of emissions reduced increases. Here is a possible model:

$$C(q) = 4{,}000 + 100q^2$$

where q is the reduction in emissions (in pounds of pollutant per day) and C is the daily cost to the firm (in dollars) of this reduction. What level of reduction corresponds to the lowest average cost per pound of pollutant, and what would be the resulting average cost to the nearest dollar?

14. ***Pollution Control*** Repeat the preceding exercise using the following cost function:

$$C(q) = 2{,}000 + 200q^2.$$

15. ***Pollution Control*** (Compare Exercise 13.) The cost of controlling emissions at a firm is given by

$$C(q) = 4{,}000 + 100q^2,$$

where q is the reduction in emissions (in pounds of pollutant per day) and C is the daily cost to the firm (in dollars) of this reduction. Government clean-air subsidies amount to \$500 per pound of pollutant removed. How many pounds of pollutant should the firm remove each day in order to minimize *net* cost (cost minus subsidy)?

16. ***Pollution Control*** (Compare Exercise 14.) Repeat the preceding exercise, using the following cost function:

$$C(q) = 2{,}000 + 200q^2$$

with government subsidies amounting to \$100 per pound of pollutant removed per day.

17. ***Fences*** I would like to create a rectangular vegetable patch. The fencing for the east and west sides costs \$4 per foot, and the fencing for the north and south sides costs only \$2 per foot. I have a budget of \$80 for the project. What are the dimensions of the vegetable patch with the largest area I can enclose? HINT [See Example 2.]

18. ***Fences*** I would like to create a rectangular orchid garden that abuts my house so that the house itself forms the northern boundary. The fencing for the southern boundary costs \$4 per foot, and the fencing for the east and west sides costs \$2 per foot. If I have a budget of \$80 for the project, what are the dimensions of the garden with the largest area I can enclose? HINT [See Example 2.]

19. ***Fences*** You are building a right-angled triangular flower garden along a stream as shown in the figure. (The borders can be in any directions as long as they are at right angles as shown.)

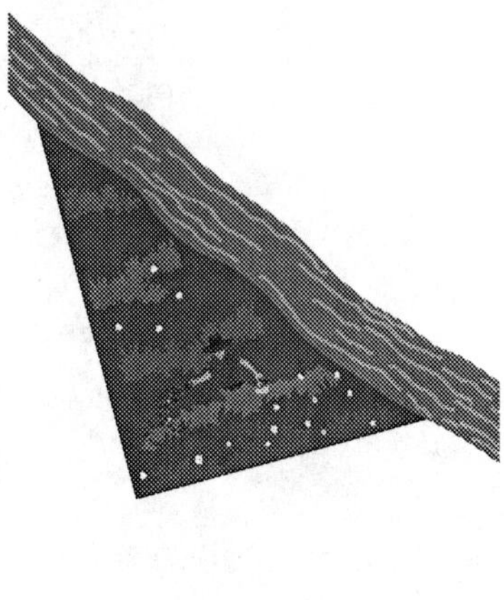

[1] Not the actual cost equation; the authors do not know Apple's actual cost equation. The marginal cost in the model given is in rough agreement with the actual marginal cost for reasonable values of x for one of the 2007 models. Source for cost data: *Manufacturing & Technology News*, July 31, 2007 Volume 14, No. 14 (www.manufacturingnews.com).

[2] Not the actual cost equation; the authors do not know Microsoft's actual cost equation. The marginal cost in the model given is in rough agreement with the actual marginal cost for reasonable values of x. Source for estimate of marginal cost: iSuppli (www.isuppli.com).

The fencing of the left border costs \$5 per foot, while the fencing of the lower border costs \$1 per foot. (No fencing is required along the river.) You want to spend \$100 and enclose as much area as possible. What are the dimensions of your garden, and what area does it enclose? HINT [The area of a right-triangle is given by $A = xy/2$.]

20. ***Fences*** Repeat Exercise 19, this time assuming that the fencing of the left border costs \$8 per foot, while the fencing of the lower border costs \$2 per foot, and that you can spend \$400.

21. ▼ ***Fences*** (Compare Exercise 17.) For tax reasons, I need to create a rectangular vegetable patch with an area of exactly 242 sq. ft. The fencing for the east and west sides costs \$4 per foot, and the fencing for the north and south sides costs only \$2 per foot. What are the dimensions of the vegetable patch with the least expensive fence? HINT [Compare Exercise 3.]

22. ▼ ***Fences*** (Compare Exercise 18.) For reasons too complicated to explain, I need to create a rectangular orchid garden with an area of exactly 324 sq. ft. abutting my house so that the house itself forms the northern boundary. The fencing for the southern boundary costs \$4 per foot, and the fencing for the east and west sides costs \$2 per foot. What are the dimensions of the orchid garden with the least expensive fence? HINT [Compare Exercise 4.]

23. ***Revenue*** *Hercules Films* is deciding on the price of the video release of its film *Son of Frankenstein.* Its marketing people estimate that at a price of p dollars, it can sell a total of $q = 200{,}000 - 10{,}000p$ copies. What price will bring in the greatest revenue? HINT [See Example 3.]

24. ***Profit*** *Hercules Films* is also deciding on the price of the video release of its film *Bride of the Son of Frankenstein.* Again, marketing estimates that at a price of p dollars, it can sell $q = 200{,}000 - 10{,}000p$ copies, but each copy costs \$4 to make. What price will give the greatest *profit*?

25. ***Revenue: Cellphones*** Worldwide quarterly sales of Nokia cellphones were approximately $q = -p + 156$ million phones when the wholesale price was \$$p$. At what wholesale price should Nokia have sold its phones to maximize its quarterly revenue? What would have been the resulting revenue?[3]

26. ***Revenue: Cellphones*** Worldwide annual sales of all cellphones were approximately $-10p + 1{,}600$ million phones when the wholesale price was \$$p$. At what wholesale price should cellphones have been sold to maximize annual revenue? What would have been the resulting revenue?[4]

27. ***Revenue: Monorail Service*** The demand, in rides per day, for monorail service in Las Vegas in 2005 can be approximated by $q = -4{,}500p + 41{,}500$ when the fare was \$$p$. What price should have been charged to maximize total revenue?[5]

28. ***Revenue: Mars Monorail*** The demand, in rides per day, for monorail service in the three urbynes (or districts) of Utarek, Mars, can be approximated by $q = -2p + 24$ million riders when the fare is Ƶp. What price should be charged to maximize total revenue?[6]

29. ***Revenue*** Assume that the demand for tuna in a small coastal town is given by

$$p = \frac{500{,}000}{q^{1.5}},$$

where q is the number of pounds of tuna that can be sold in a month at p dollars per pound. Assume that the town's fishery wishes to sell at least 5,000 pounds of tuna per month.

a. How much should the town's fishery charge for tuna in order to maximize monthly revenue? HINT [See Example 3, and don't neglect endpoints.]

b. How much tuna will it sell per month at that price?

c. What will be its resulting revenue?

30. ***Revenue*** In the 1930s the economist Henry Schultz devised the following demand function for corn:

$$p = \frac{6{,}570{,}000}{q^{1.3}},$$

where q is the number of bushels of corn that could be sold at p dollars per bushel in one year.[7] Assume that at least 10,000 bushels of corn per year must be sold.

a. How much should farmers charge per bushel of corn to maximize annual revenue? HINT [See Example 3, and don't neglect endpoints.]

b. How much corn can farmers sell per year at that price?

c. What will be the farmers' resulting revenue?

31. ***Revenue*** During the 1950s the wholesale price for chicken in the United States fell from 25¢ per pound to 14¢ per pound, while per capita chicken consumption rose from 22 pounds per year to 27.5 pounds per year.[8] Assuming that the demand for chicken depended linearly on the price, what wholesale price for chicken would have maximized revenues for poultry farmers, and what would that revenue have amounted to?

32. ***Revenue*** Your underground used-book business is booming. Your policy is to sell all used versions of *Calculus and You* at the same price (regardless of condition). When you set the price at \$10, sales amounted to 120 volumes during the first week of classes. The following semester, you set the price at \$30 and sales dropped to zero. Assuming that the demand for

[3] Demand equation based on second- and fourth-quarter sales. Source: Embedded.com/Company reports December, 2004.

[4] Demand equation based on estimated 2004 sales and projected 2008 sales. Source: I-Stat/NDR, December 2004.

[5] Source for ridership data: *New York Times*, February 10, 2007, p. A9.

[6] The zonar (Ƶ) is the official currency in the city-state of Utarek, Mars (formerly www.Marsnext.com, a now extinct virtual society).

[7] Based on data for the period 1915–1929. Source: Henry Schultz (1938), *The Theory and Measurement of Demand,* University of Chicago Press, Chicago.

[8] Data are provided for the years 1951–1958. Source: U.S. Department of Agriculture, *Agricultural Statistics.*

books depends linearly on the price, what price gives you the maximum revenue, and what does that revenue amount to?

33. ***Profit: Cellphones*** (Compare Exercise 25.) Worldwide quarterly sales of Nokia cellphones were approximately $q = -p + 156$ million phones when the wholesale price was \$$p$. Assuming that it cost Nokia \$40 to manufacture each cellphone, at what wholesale price should Nokia have sold its phones to maximize its quarterly profit? What would have been the resulting profit?[9] (The actual wholesale price was \$105 in the fourth quarter of 2004.) HINT [See Example 3, and recall that Profit = Revenue − Cost.]

34. ***Profit: Cellphones*** (Compare Exercise 26.) Worldwide annual sales of all cellphones were approximately $-10p + 1{,}600$ million phones when the wholesale price was \$$p$. Assuming that it costs \$30 to manufacture each cellphone, at what wholesale price should cellphones have been sold to maximize annual profit? What would have been the resulting profit?[10] HINT [See Example 3, and recall that Profit = Revenue − Cost.]

35. ▼ ***Profit*** The demand equation for your company's virtual reality video headsets is

$$p = \frac{1{,}000}{q^{0.3}},$$

where q is the total number of headsets that your company can sell in a week at a price of p dollars. The total manufacturing and shipping cost amounts to \$100 per headset.

   a. What is the greatest profit your company can make in a week, and how many headsets will your company sell at this level of profit? (Give answers to the nearest whole number.)
   b. How much, to the nearest \$1, should your company charge per headset for the maximum profit?

36. ▼ ***Profit*** Due to sales by a competing company, your company's sales of virtual reality video headsets have dropped, and your financial consultant revises the demand equation to

$$p = \frac{800}{q^{0.35}},$$

where q is the total number of headsets that your company can sell in a week at a price of p dollars. The total manufacturing and shipping cost still amounts to \$100 per headset.

   a. What is the greatest profit your company can make in a week, and how many headsets will your company sell at this level of profit? (Give answers to the nearest whole number.)
   b. How much, to the nearest \$1, should your company charge per headset for the maximum profit?

37. ***Paint Cans*** A company manufactures cylindrical paint cans with open tops with a volume of 27,000 cubic centimeters. What should be the dimensions of the cans in order to use the least amount of metal in their production? HINT [See Example 4.]

38. ***Metal Drums*** A company manufactures cylindrical metal drums with open tops with a volume of 1 cubic meter. What should be the dimensions of the drum in order to use the least amount of metal in their production? HINT [See Example 4.]

39. ***Tin Cans*** A company manufactures cylindrical tin cans with closed tops with a volume of 250 cubic centimeters. The metal used to manufacture the cans costs \$0.01 per square cm for the sides and \$0.02 per square cm for the (thicker) top and bottom. What should be the dimensions of the cans in order to minimize the cost of metal in their production? What is the ratio height/radius? HINT [See Example 4.]

40. ***Metal Drums*** A company manufactures cylindrical metal drums with open tops with a volume of 2 cubic meters. The metal used to manufacture the cans costs \$2 per square meter for the sides and \$3 per square meter for the (thicker) bottom. What should be the dimensions of the drums in order to minimize the cost of metal in their production? What is the ratio height/radius? HINT [See Example 4.]

41. ▼ ***Box Design*** *Chocolate Box Company* is going to make open-topped boxes out of 6 × 16-inch rectangles of cardboard by cutting squares out of the corners and folding up the sides. What is the largest volume box it can make this way?

42. ▼ ***Box Design*** *Vanilla Box Company* is going to make open-topped boxes out of 12 × 12-inch rectangles of cardboard by cutting squares out of the corners and folding up the sides. What is the largest volume box it can make this way?

43. ▼ ***Box Design*** A packaging company is going to make closed boxes, with square bases, that hold 125 cubic centimeters. What are the dimensions of the box that can be built with the least material?

44. ▼ ***Box Design*** A packaging company is going to make open-topped boxes, with square bases, that hold 108 cubic centimeters. What are the dimensions of the box that can be built with the least material?

45. ▼ ***Luggage Dimensions*** American Airlines requires that the total outside dimensions (length + width + height) of a checked bag not exceed 62 inches.[11] Suppose you want to check a bag whose height equals its width. What is the largest volume bag of this shape that you can check on an American flight?

46. ▼ ***Carry-on Dimensions*** American Airlines requires that the total outside dimensions (length + width + height) of a carry-on bag not exceed 45 inches.[12] Suppose you want to carry on a bag whose length is twice its height. What is the largest volume bag of this shape that you can carry on an American flight?

47. ▼ ***Luggage Dimensions*** *Fly-by-Night Airlines* has a peculiar rule about luggage: The length and width of a bag must add up to at most 45 inches, and the width and height must also add up to at most 45 inches. What are the dimensions of the bag with the largest volume that Fly-by-Night will accept?

[9] See Exercise 25.

[10] See Exercise 26.

[11] According to information on its Web site (www.aa.com/).

[12] *Ibid.*

48. ▼ ***Luggage Dimensions*** *Fair Weather Airlines* has a similar rule. It will accept only bags for which the sum of the length and width is at most 36 inches, while the sum of length, height, and twice the width is at most 72 inches. What are the dimensions of the bag with the largest volume that Fair Weather will accept?

49. ▼ ***Package Dimensions*** The U.S. Postal Service (USPS) will accept packages only if the length plus girth is no more than 108 inches.[13] (See the figure.)

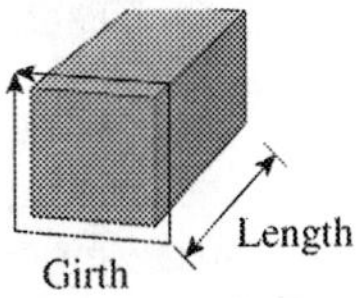

Assuming that the front face of the package (as shown in the figure) is square, what is the largest volume package that the USPS will accept?

50. ▼ ***Package Dimensions*** United Parcel Service (UPS) will accept only packages with a length of no more than 108 inches and length plus girth of no more than 165 inches.[14] (See figure for the preceding exercise.) Assuming that the front face of the package (as shown in the figure) is square, what is the largest volume package that UPS will accept?

51. ▼ ***Cellphone Revenues*** The number of cellphone subscribers in China in the years 2000–2005 was projected to follow the equation $N(t) = 39t + 68$ million subscribers in year t ($t = 0$ represents January 2000). The average annual revenue per cellphone user was \$350 in 2000.[15] If we assume that due to competition the revenue per cellphone user decreases continuously at an annual rate of 30%, we can model the annual revenue as

$$R(t) = 350(39t + 68)e^{-0.3t} \text{ million dollars.}$$

Determine **a.** when to the nearest 0.1 year the revenue was projected to peak and **b.** the revenue, to the nearest \$1 million, at that time.

52. ▼ ***Cellphone Revenues*** (Refer to Exercise 51.) If we assume instead that the revenue per cellphone user decreases continuously at an annual rate of 20%, we obtain the revenue model

$$R(t) = 350(39t + 68)e^{-0.2t} \text{ million dollars.}$$

Determine **a.** when to the nearest 0.1 year the revenue was projected to peak and **b.** the revenue, to the nearest \$1 million, at that time.

53. ▼ ***Research and Development*** Spending on research and development by drug companies in the United States t years after 1970 can be modeled by

$$S(t) = 2.5e^{0.08t} \text{ billion dollars} \quad (0 \le t \le 31).$$

The number of new drugs approved by the Federal Drug Administration (FDA) over the same period can be modeled by

$$D(t) = 10 + t \text{ drugs per year}^{16} \quad (0 \le t \le 31).$$

When was the function $D(t)/S(t)$ at a maximum? What is the maximum value of $D(t)/S(t)$? What does the answer tell you about the cost of developing new drugs?

54. ▼ ***Research and Development*** (Refer to Exercise 53.) If the number of new drugs approved by the FDA had been $10 + 2t$ new drugs each year, when would the function $D(t)/S(t)$ have reached a maximum? What does the answer tell you about the cost of developing new drugs?

55. ▼ ***Asset Appreciation*** As the financial consultant to a classic auto dealership, you estimate that the total value (in dollars) of its collection of 1959 Chevrolets and Fords is given by the formula

$$v = 300{,}000 + 1{,}000t^2 \quad (t \ge 5),$$

where t is the number of years from now. You anticipate a continuous inflation rate of 5% per year, so that the discounted (present) value of an item that will be worth \$$v$ in t years' time is

$$p = ve^{-0.05t}.$$

When would you advise the dealership to sell the vehicles to maximize their discounted value?

56. ▼ ***Plantation Management*** The value of a fir tree in your plantation increases with the age of the tree according to the formula

$$v = \frac{20t}{1 + 0.05t},$$

where t is the age of the tree in years. Given a continuous inflation rate of 5% per year, the discounted (present) value of a newly planted seedling is

$$p = ve^{-0.05t}.$$

At what age (to the nearest year) should you harvest your trees in order to ensure the greatest possible discounted value?

57. ▼ ***Marketing Strategy*** *FeatureRich Software Company* has a dilemma. Its new program, Doors-X 10.27, is almost ready to go on the market. However, the longer the company works on it, the better it can make the program and the more it can charge for it. The company's marketing analysts estimate that if it delays t days, it can set the price at $100 + 2t$ dollars. On the other hand, the longer it delays, the more market share it will lose to its main competitor (see the next exercise) so that if it delays t days it will be able to sell $400{,}000 - 2{,}500t$ copies of

[13] The requirement for packages sent other than Parcel Post, as of August 2011 (www.usps.com/).

[14] The requirement as of August, 2011 (www.ups.com/).

[15] Based on a regression of projected figures (coefficients are rounded). Source: Intrinsic Technology/*New York Times*, Nov. 24, 2000, p. C1.

[16] The exponential model for R&D is based on the 1970 and 2001 spending in constant 2001 dollars, while the linear model for new drugs approved is based on the 6-year moving average from data from 1970 to 2000. Source for data: Pharmaceutical Research and Manufacturers of America, FDA/*New York Times*, April 19, 2002, p. C1.

the program. How many days should FeatureRich delay the release in order to get the greatest revenue?

58. ▼ ***Marketing Strategy*** *FeatureRich Software's* main competitor (see previous exercise) is Moon Systems, and Moon is in a similar predicament. Its product, Walls-Y 11.4, could be sold now for $200, but for each day Moon delays, it could increase the price by $4. On the other hand, it could sell 300,000 copies now, but each day it waits will cut sales by 1,500. How many days should Moon delay the release in order to get the greatest revenue?

59. ▼ ***Average Profit*** The *FeatureRich Software Company* sells its graphing program, Dogwood, with a volume discount. If a customer buys x copies, then he or she pays[17] $\$500\sqrt{x}$. It cost the company $10,000 to develop the program and $2 to manufacture each copy. If a single customer were to buy all the copies of Dogwood, how many copies would the customer have to buy for FeatureRich Software's average profit per copy to be maximized? How are average profit and marginal profit related at this number of copies?

60. ▼ ***Average Profit*** Repeat the preceding exercise with the charge to the customer $\$600\sqrt{x}$ and the cost to develop the program $9,000.

61. ***Resource Allocation*** Your company manufactures automobile alternators, and production is partially automated through the use of robots. Daily operating costs amount to $100 per laborer and $16 per robot. In order to meet production deadlines, the company calculates that the numbers of laborers and robots must satisfy the constraint

$$xy = 10{,}000,$$

where x is the number of laborers and y is the number of robots. Assuming that the company wishes to meet production deadlines at a minimum cost, how many laborers and how many robots should it use? HINT [See Example 5.]

62. ***Resource Allocation*** Your company is the largest sock manufacturer in the Solar System, and production is automated through the use of androids and robots. Daily operating costs amount to ₩200 per android and ₩8 per robot.[18] In order to meet production deadlines, the company calculates that the numbers of androids and robots must satisfy the constraint

$$xy = 1{,}000{,}000,$$

where x is the number of androids and y is the number of robots. Assuming that the company wishes to meet production deadlines at a minimum cost, how many androids and how many robots should it use? HINT [See Example 5.]

63. ▼ ***Resource Allocation*** Your automobile assembly plant has a Cobb-Douglas production function given by

$$q = x^{0.4}y^{0.6},$$

where q is the number of automobiles it produces per year, x is the number of employees, and y is the daily operating budget (in dollars). Annual operating costs amount to an average of $20,000 per employee plus the operating budget of $\$365y$. Assume that you wish to produce 1,000 automobiles per year at a minimum cost. How many employees should you hire? HINT [See Example 5.]

64. ▼ ***Resource Allocation*** Repeat the preceding exercise using the production formula

$$q = x^{0.5}y^{0.5}.$$

HINT [See Example 5.]

65. ▼ ***Incarceration Rate*** The incarceration rate (the number of persons in prison per 100,000 residents) in the United States can be approximated by

$$N(t) = 0.04t^3 - 2t^2 + 40t + 460 \quad (0 \le t \le 18)$$

(t is the year since 1990).[19] When, to the nearest year, was the incarceration rate increasing most rapidly? When was it increasing least rapidly? HINT [You are being asked to find the extreme values of the rate of change of the incarceration rate.]

66. ▼ ***Prison Population*** The prison population in the United States can be approximated by

$$N(t) = 0.02t^3 - 2t^2 + 100t + 1{,}100 \text{ thousand people} \quad (0 \le t \le 18)$$

(t is the year since 1990).[20] When, to the nearest year, was the prison population increasing most rapidly? When was it increasing least rapidly? HINT [You are being asked to find the extreme values of the rate of change of the prison population.]

67. ▼ ***Embryo Development*** The oxygen consumption of a bird embryo increases from the time the egg is laid through the time the chick hatches. In a typical galliform bird, the oxygen consumption can be approximated by

$$c(t) = -0.065t^3 + 3.4t^2 - 22t + 3.6 \text{ milliliters per day} \quad (8 \le t \le 30),$$

where t is the time (in days) since the egg was laid.[21] (An egg will typically hatch at around $t = 28$.) When, to the nearest day, is $c'(t)$ a maximum? What does the answer tell you?

68. ▼ ***Embryo Development*** The oxygen consumption of a turkey embryo increases from the time the egg is laid through the time the chick hatches. In a brush turkey, the oxygen consumption can be approximated by

$$c(t) = -0.028t^3 + 2.9t^2 - 44t + 95 \text{ milliliters per day} \quad (20 \le t \le 50),$$

[17] This is similar to the way site licenses have been structured for the program Maple®.

[18] ₩ are Neptunian Standard Solar Units of currency.

[19] Source for data: Sourcebook of Criminal Justice Statistics Online (www.albany.edu/sourcebook).

[20] *Ibid.*

[21] The model approximates graphical data published in the article "The Brush Turkey" by Roger S. Seymour, *Scientific American*, December, 1991, pp. 108–114.

where t is the time (in days) since the egg was laid.[22] (An egg will typically hatch at around $t = 50$.) When, to the nearest day, is $c'(t)$ a maximum? What does the answer tell you?

69. ▣ ▽ *Subprime Mortgages during the Housing Bubble* During the real estate run-up in 2000–2008, the percentage of mortgages issued in the United States that were subprime (normally classified as risky) could be approximated by

$$A(t) = \frac{15.0}{1 + 8.6(1.8)^{-t}} \text{ percent} \quad (0 \le t \le 8)$$

t years after the start of 2000.[23] Graph the *derivative* of $A(t)$ and determine the year during which this derivative had an absolute maximum and also its value at that point. What does the answer tell you?

70. ▣ ▽ *Subprime Mortgage Debt during the Housing Bubble* During the real estate run-up in 2000–2008, the value of subprime (normally classified as risky) mortgage debt outstanding in the United States was approximately

$$A(t) = \frac{1,350}{1 + 4.2(1.7)^{-t}} \text{ billion dollars} \quad (0 \le t \le 8)$$

t years after the start of 2000.[24] Graph the *derivative* of $A(t)$ and determine the year during which this derivative had an absolute maximum and also its value at that point. What does the answer tell you?

71. ▣ ▽ *Asset Appreciation* You manage a small antique company that owns a collection of Louis XVI jewelry boxes. Their value v is increasing according to the formula

$$v = \frac{10,000}{1 + 500e^{-0.5t}},$$

where t is the number of years from now. You anticipate an inflation rate of 5% per year, so that the present value of an item that will be worth $\$v$ in t years' time is given by

$$p = v \cdot (1.05)^{-t}.$$

When (to the nearest year) should you sell the jewelry boxes to maximize their present value? How much (to the nearest constant dollar) will they be worth at that time?

72. ▣ ▽ *Harvesting Forests* The following equation models the approximate volume in cubic feet of a typical Douglas fir tree of age t years.[25]

$$V = \frac{22,514}{1 + 22,514t^{-2.55}}$$

The lumber will be sold at $10 per cubic foot, and you do not expect the price of lumber to appreciate in the foreseeable future. On the other hand, you anticipate a general inflation

rate of 5% per year, so that the present value of an item that will be worth $\$v$ in t years' time is given by

$$p = v \cdot (1.05)^{-t}.$$

At what age (to the nearest year) should you harvest a Douglas fir tree in order to maximize its present value? How much (to the nearest constant dollar) will a Douglas fir tree be worth at that time?

73. ◆ *Agriculture* The fruit yield per tree in an orchard containing 50 trees is 100 pounds per tree each year. Due to crowding, the yield decreases by 1 pound per season for every additional tree planted. How many additional trees should be planted for a maximum total annual yield?

74. ◆ *Agriculture* Two years ago your orange orchard contained 50 trees and the yield per tree was 75 bags of oranges. Last year you removed 10 of the trees and noticed that the yield per tree increased to 80 bags. Assuming that the yield per tree depends linearly on the number of trees in the orchard, what should you do this year to maximize your total yield?

75. ◆ *Revenue* (based on a question on the GRE Economics Test[26]) If total revenue (*TR*) is specified by $TR = a + bQ - cQ^2$, where Q is quantity of output and a, b, and c are positive parameters, then *TR* is maximized for this firm when it produces Q equal to:

(A) $b/2ac$. **(B)** $b/4c$. **(C)** $(a+b)/c$. **(D)** $b/2c$. **(E)** $c/2b$.

76. ◆ *Revenue* (based on a question on the GRE Economics Test) If total demand (Q) is specified by $Q = -aP + b$, where P is unit price and a and b are positive parameters, then total revenue is maximized for this firm when it charges P equal to:

(A) $b/2a$. **(B)** $b/4a$. **(C)** a/b. **(D)** $a/2b$. **(E)** $-b/2a$.

COMMUNICATION AND REASONING EXERCISES

77. You are interested in knowing the height of the tallest condominium complex that meets the city zoning requirements that the height H should not exceed eight times the distance D from the road and that it must provide parking for at least 50 cars. The objective function of the associated optimization problem is then:

(A) H. **(B)** $H - 8D$. **(C)** D. **(D)** $D - 8H$.

One of the constraints is:

(A) $8H = D$. **(B)** $8D = H$.
(C) $H'(D) = 0$. **(D)** $D'(H) = 0$.

78. You are interested in building a condominium complex with a height H of at least 8 times the distance D from the road and parking area of at least 1,000 sq. ft. at the cheapest cost C. The objective function of the associated optimization problem is then:

(A) H. **(B)** D. **(C)** C. **(D)** $H + D - C$.

---

[22] The model approximates graphical data published in the article "The Brush Turkey" by Roger S. Seymour, *Scientific American,* December, 1991, pp. 108–114.

[23] Sources: Mortgage Bankers Association, UBS.

[24] Source: www.data360.org/dataset.aspx?Data_Set_Id=9549.

[25] The model is the authors' and is based on data in *Environmental and Natural Resource Economics* by Tom Tietenberg, third edition (New York: HarperCollins, 1992), p. 282.

[26] Source: GRE Economics Test, by G. Gallagher, G. E. Pollock, W. J. Simeone, G. Yohe (Piscataway, NJ: Research and Education Association, 1989).

One of the constraints is:

(A) $H - 8D = 0.$ **(B)** $H + D - C = 0.$
(C) $C'(D) = 0.$ **(D)** $8H = D.$

79. Explain why the following problem is uninteresting: A packaging company wishes to make cardboard boxes with open tops by cutting square pieces from the corners of a square sheet of cardboard and folding up the sides. What is the box with the least surface area it can make this way?

80. Explain why finding the production level that minimizes a cost function is frequently uninteresting. What would a more interesting objective be?

81. Your friend Margo claims that all you have to do to find the absolute maxima and minima in applications is set the derivative equal to zero and solve. "All that other stuff about endpoints and so on is a waste of time just to make life hard for us," according to Margo. Explain why she is wrong, and find at least one exercise in this exercise set to illustrate your point.

82. You are having a hard time persuading your friend Marco that maximizing revenue is not the same as maximizing profit. "How on earth can you expect to obtain the largest profit if you are not taking in the largest revenue?" Explain why he is wrong, and find at least one exercise in this exercise set to illustrate your point.

83. ▼ If demand q decreases as price p increases, what does the minimum value of dq/dp measure?

84. ▼ Explain how you would solve an optimization problem of the following form. Maximize $P = f(x, y, z)$ subject to $z = g(x, y)$ and $y = h(x)$.

Practice Problems 12.2, Part 1

At a price of \$8 per ticket, a theater group can fill every seat in the theater, which has a seating capacity of 990. For every additional dollar charged, the number of people buying tickets decreases by 60.

1. Define a function, $n(p)$, that gives the number of tickets that will be sold for the performance if a single ticket costs \$$p$.

2. Define a function, $R(p)$, that gives the revenue for the performance if a single ticket costs \$$p$.

3. Using $R'(p)$, determine the ticket price that maximizes revenue. Also, compute the maximum possible revenue for the performance.

Practice Problems 12.2, Part 2

A closed box with a square base is to have a volume of 24 cubic feet. The material for the sides, top, and base costs \$0.25, \$0.50, and \$1 per square foot, respectively.

1. Let x denote the length, in feet, of one of the edges of the base of the box, and let $C(x)$ denote the corresponding cost of the box, in dollars. Write a formula for $C(x)$.

2. Using $C'(x)$, determine the dimensions of the box of least cost, and calculate the corresponding cost.

Practice Problems 12.2, Part 3

A closed box with a square base is to have a volume of 24 cubic feet.

1. Let x denote the length, in feet, of one of the edges of the base of the box, and let $A(x)$ denote the corresponding amount of material needed to construct the box, in square feet. Write a formula for $A(x)$.

2. Using $A'(x)$, determine the dimensions of the box that requires the minimum amount of material to construct, and calculate the corresponding amount of material. (Note: Compare this to your results from the problem on p. 892B.)

Practice Problems 12.2, Part 4

For these problems, set up an appropriate function modeling the situation, use the derivative to locate critical points, and draw the appropriate conclusion.

1. The cost per hour for fuel to run a train is $\frac{v^2}{2}$ dollars, where v is the average speed of the train, in miles per hour. Other costs, including labor, are \$400 per hour. At what average speed should the train travel on a 520-mile trip to minimize the total cost for the trip?

2. An open box is to be made from a square sheet of tin 18 centimeters on a side by cutting small squares from each of the corners and turning up the edges. What are the dimensions of the resulting box if its volume is to be maximized?

Practice Problems 12.2, Part 5

A participant in an orienteering event must get to a specific tree in the woods as fast as possible. If she travels 300 meters east along a trail, she will then be 600 meters directly south of the tree. She can run at a rate of 120 meters per minute along the trail, but she can only move through the woods at a rate of 50 meters per minute. Your task is to determine the path she should take in order to get to the tree as quickly as possible. Define a function that is appropriate for this task and use derivatives to establish your conclusion. Clearly state your conclusion (use a diagram if appropritate).

Practice Problems 12.2, Part 6

Suppose that the total cost to produce and sell x thousand units of a product, $0 \le x \le 15$, is $C(x) = x^3 - 20x^2 + 179x + 242$ thousand dollars. Let $\overline{C}(x)$ denote the corresponding average cost function.

1. Using $\overline{C}'(x)$, determine the level of production and sales where average cost is minimized. Give your result to the nearest unit of product and calculate the corresponding minimum average cost (label appropriately).

2. Find all values of x so that $\overline{C}(x) = C'(x)$, accurate to three decimal places. (Compare your findings to your conclusion above.)

12.3 Higher Order Derivatives: Acceleration and Concavity

The **second derivative** is simply the derivative of the derivative function. To explain why we would be interested in such a thing, we start by discussing one of its interpretations.

Acceleration

Recall that if $s(t)$ represents the position of a car at time t, then its velocity is given by the derivative: $v(t) = s'(t)$. But one rarely drives a car at a constant speed; the velocity itself may be changing. The rate at which the velocity is changing is the **acceleration**. Because the derivative measures the rate of change, acceleration is the derivative of velocity: $a(t) = v'(t)$. Because v is the derivative of s, we can express the acceleration in terms of s:

$$a(t) = v'(t) = (s')'(t) = s''(t).$$

That is, a is the derivative of the derivative of s; in other words, the second derivative of s, which we write as s''. (In this context you will often hear the derivative s' referred to as the **first derivative**.)

Second Derivative, Acceleration

If a function f has a derivative that is in turn differentiable, then its **second derivative** is the derivative of the derivative of f, written as f''. If $f''(a)$ exists, we say that f is **twice differentiable at** $x = a$.

Quick Examples

1. If $f(x) = x^3 - x$, then $f'(x) = 3x^2 - 1$, so $f''(x) = 6x$ and $f''(-2) = -12$.
2. If $f(x) = 3x + 1$, then $f'(x) = 3$, so $f''(x) = 0$.
3. If $f(x) = e^x$, then $f'(x) = e^x$, so $f''(x) = e^x$ as well.

The **acceleration** of a moving object is the derivative of its velocity—that is, the second derivative of the position function.

Quick Example

If t is time in hours and the position of a car at time t is $s(t) = t^3 + 2t^2$ miles, then the car's velocity is $v(t) = s'(t) = 3t^2 + 4t$ miles per hour and its acceleration is $a(t) = s''(t) = v'(t) = 6t + 4$ miles per hour per hour.

Differential Notation for the Second Derivative

We have written the second derivative of $f(x)$ as $f''(x)$. We could also use differential notation:

$$f''(x) = \frac{d^2f}{dx^2}.$$

This notation comes from writing the second derivative as the derivative of the derivative in differential notation:

$$f''(x) = \frac{d}{dx}\left[\frac{df}{dx}\right] = \frac{d^2f}{dx^2}.$$

Similarly, if $y = f(x)$, we write $f''(x)$ as $\frac{d}{dx}\left[\frac{dy}{dx}\right] = \frac{d^2y}{dx^2}$. For example, if $y = x^3$, then $\frac{d^2y}{dx^2} = 6x$.

An important example of acceleration is the acceleration due to gravity.

EXAMPLE 1 Acceleration Due to Gravity

According to the laws of physics, the height of an object near the surface of the earth falling in a vacuum from an initial rest position 100 feet above the ground under the influence of gravity is approximately

$$s(t) = 100 - 16t^2 \text{ feet}$$

in t seconds. Find its acceleration.

Solution The velocity of the object is

$$v(t) = s'(t) = -32t \text{ ft/sec.}$$ Differential notation: $v = \frac{ds}{dt} = -32t$ ft/sec

The reason for the negative sign is that the height of the object is decreasing with time, so its velocity is negative. Hence, the acceleration is

$$a(t) = s''(t) = -32 \text{ ft/sec}^2.$$ Differential notation: $a = \frac{d^2s}{dt^2} = -32$ ft/sec^2

(We write ft/sec^2 as an abbreviation for feet/second/second—that is, feet per second per second. It is often read "feet per second squared.") Thus, the *downward* velocity is increasing by 32 ft/sec every second. We say that 32 ft/sec^2 is the **acceleration due to gravity**. In the absence of air resistance, all falling bodies near the surface of the earth, no matter what their weight, will fall with this acceleration.*

Before we go on... In very careful experiments using balls rolling down inclined planes, Galileo made one of his most important discoveries—that the acceleration due to gravity is constant and does not depend on the weight or composition of the object falling.† A famous, though probably apocryphal, story has him dropping cannonballs of different weights off the Leaning Tower of Pisa to prove his point.§ ■

* On other planets the acceleration due to gravity is different. For example, on Jupiter, it is about three times as large as on Earth.

† An interesting aside: Galileo's experiments depended on getting extremely accurate timings. Because the timepieces of his day were very inaccurate, he used the most accurate time measurement he could: He sang and used the beat as his stopwatch.

§ Here is a true story: The point was made again during the Apollo 15 mission to the moon (July 1971) when astronaut David R. Scott dropped a feather and a hammer from the same height. The moon has no atmosphere, so the two hit the surface of the moon simultaneously.

EXAMPLE 2 Acceleration of Sales

For the first 15 months after the introduction of a new video game, the total sales can be modeled by the curve

$$S(t) = 20e^{0.4t} \text{ units sold,}$$

where t is the time in months since the game was introduced. After about 25 months total sales follow more closely the curve

$$S(t) = 100{,}000 - 20e^{17-0.4t}.$$

How fast are total sales accelerating after 10 months? How fast are they accelerating after 30 months? What do these numbers mean?

Solution By acceleration we mean the rate of change of the rate of change, which is the second derivative. During the first 15 months, the first derivative of sales is

$$\frac{dS}{dt} = 8e^{0.4t}$$

and so the second derivative is

$$\frac{d^2S}{dt^2} = 3.2e^{0.4t}.$$

Thus, after 10 months the acceleration of sales is

$$\left.\frac{d^2S}{dt^2}\right|_{t=10} = 3.2e^4 \approx 175 \text{ units/month/month, or units/month}^2.$$

We can also compute total sales

$$S(10) = 20e^4 \approx 1{,}092 \text{ units}$$

and the rate of change of sales

$$\left.\frac{dS}{dt}\right|_{t=10} = 8e^4 \approx 437 \text{ units/month.}$$

What do these numbers mean? By the end of the tenth month, a total of 1,092 video games have been sold. At that time the game is selling at the rate of 437 units per month. This rate of sales is increasing by 175 units per month per month. More games will be sold each month than the month before.

Analysis of the sales after 30 months is done similarly, using the formula

$$S(t) = 100{,}000 - 20e^{17-0.4t}.$$

The derivative is

$$\frac{dS}{dt} = 8e^{17-0.4t}$$

and the second derivative is

$$\frac{d^2S}{dt^2} = -3.2e^{17-0.4t}.$$

After 30 months,

$$S(30) = 100{,}000 - 20e^{17-12} \approx 97{,}032 \text{ units}$$

$$\left.\frac{dS}{dt}\right|_{t=30} = 8e^{17-12} \approx 1{,}187 \text{ units/month}$$

$$\left.\frac{d^2S}{dt^2}\right|_{t=30} = -3.2e^{17-12} \approx -475 \text{ units/month}^2.$$

By the end of the thirtieth month, 97,032 video games have been sold, the game is selling at a rate of 1,187 units per month, and the rate of sales is *decreasing* by 475 units per month. Fewer games are sold each month than the month before.

Geometric Interpretation of Second Derivative: Concavity

The first derivative of f tells us where the graph of f is rising [where $f'(x) > 0$] and where it is falling [where $f'(x) < 0$]. The second derivative tells in what direction the graph of f *curves* or *bends*. Consider the graphs in Figures 26 and 27.

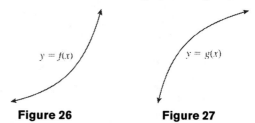

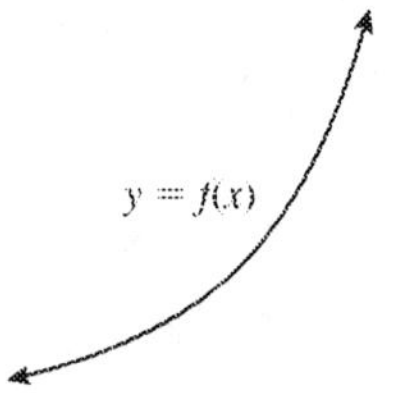

Figure 26

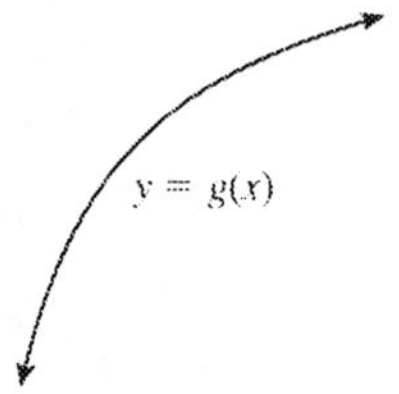

Figure 27

Think of a car driving from left to right along each of the roads shown in the two figures. A car driving along the graph of f in Figure 26 will turn to the left (upward); a car driving along the graph of g in Figure 27 will turn to the right (downward). We say that the graph of f is **concave up** and the graph of g is **concave down**. Now think about the derivatives of f and g. The derivative $f'(x)$ starts small but *increases* as the graph gets steeper. Because $f'(x)$ is increasing, its derivative $f''(x)$ must be positive. On the other hand, $g'(x)$ *decreases* as we go to the right. Because $g'(x)$ is decreasing, its derivative $g''(x)$ must be negative. Summarizing, we have the following.

Concavity and the Second Derivative

A curve is **concave up** if its slope is increasing, in which case the second derivative is positive. A curve is **concave down** if its slope is decreasing, in which case the second derivative is negative. A point in the domain of f where the graph of f changes concavity, from concave up to concave down or vice versa, is called a **point of inflection**. At a point of inflection, the second derivative is either zero or undefined.

Locating Points of Inflection

To locate possible points of inflection, list points where $f''(x) = 0$ and also interior points where $f''(x)$ is not defined.

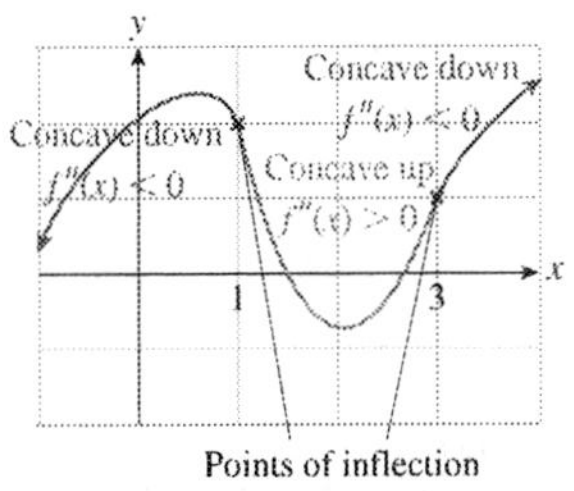

Figure 28

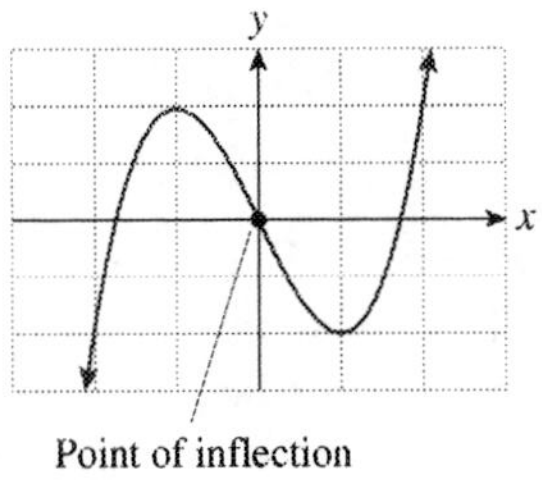

Figure 29

Quick Examples

1. The graph of the function f shown in Figure 28 is concave up when $1 < x < 3$, so $f''(x) > 0$ for $1 < x < 3$. It is concave down when $x < 1$ and $x > 3$, so $f''(x) < 0$ when $x < 1$ and $x > 3$. It has points of inflection at $x = 1$ and $x = 3$.
2. Consider $f(x) = x^3 - 3x$, whose graph is shown in Figure 29. $f''(x) = 6x$ is negative when $x < 0$ and positive when $x > 0$. The graph of f is concave down when $x < 0$ and concave up when $x > 0$. f has a point of inflection at $x = 0$, where the second derivative is 0.

The following example shows one of the reasons it's useful to look at concavity.

EXAMPLE 3 Inflation

Figure 30 shows the value of the U.S. Consumer Price Index (CPI) from January 2010 through April 2011.[27]

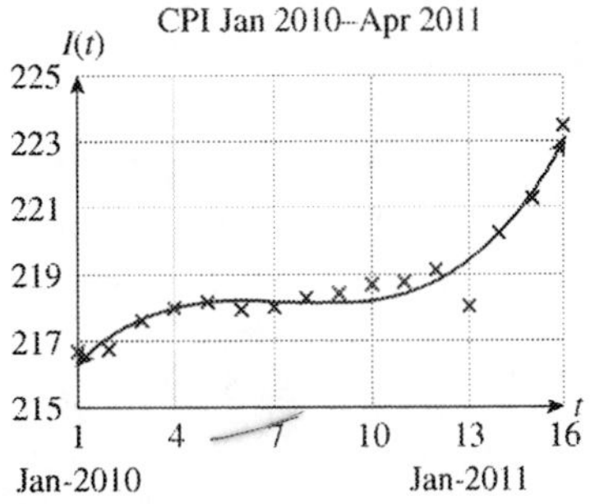

Figure 30

The approximating curve shown on the figure is given by

$$I(t) = 0.0081t^3 - 0.18t^2 + 1.3t + 215 \qquad (1 \le t \le 16),$$

where t is time in months ($t = 1$ represents January 2010). When the CPI is increasing, the U.S. economy is **experiencing inflation**. In terms of the model, this means that the derivative is positive: $I'(t) > 0$. Notice that $I'(t) > 0$ for most of the period shown (the graph is sloping upward), so the U.S. economy experienced inflation for most of $1 \le t \le 16$. We could measure **inflation** by the first derivative $I'(t)$ of the CPI, but we traditionally measure it as a ratio:

$$\text{Inflation rate} = \frac{I'(t)}{I(t)}, \qquad \text{Relative rate of change of the CPI}$$

expressed as a percentage per unit time (per month in this case).

a. Use the model to estimate the inflation rate in March 2010.

b. Was inflation slowing or speeding up in March 2010?

c. When was inflation slowing? When was inflation speeding up? When was inflation slowest?

[27] The CPI is compiled by the Bureau of Labor Statistics and is based upon a 1982 value of 100. For instance, a CPI of 200 means the CPI has doubled since 1982. Source: InflationData.com (www.inflationdata.com).

Solution

a. We need to compute $I'(t)$:

$$I'(t) = 0.0243t^2 - 0.36t + 1.3.$$

Thus, the inflation rate in March 2010 was given by

$$\text{Inflation rate} = \frac{I'(3)}{I(3)} = \frac{0.0243(3)^2 - 0.36(3) + 1.3}{0.0081(3)^3 - 0.18(3)^2 + 1.3(3) + 215}$$

$$= \frac{0.4387}{217.4987} \approx 0.0020,$$

or 0.20% per month.*

b. We say that inflation is "slowing" when the CPI is decelerating ($I''(t) < 0$; the index rises at a slower rate or falls at a faster rate†). Similarly, inflation is "speeding up" when the CPI is accelerating ($I''(t) > 0$; the index rises at a faster rate or falls at a slower rate). From the formula for $I'(t)$, the second derivative is

$$I''(t) = 0.0486t - 0.36$$
$$I''(3) = 0.0486(3) - 0.36 = -0.2142.$$

Because this quantity is negative, we conclude that inflation was slowing down in March 2010.

c. When inflation is slowing, $I''(t)$ is negative, so the graph of the CPI is concave down. When inflation is speeding up, it is concave up. At the point at which it switches, there is a point of inflection (Figure 31).

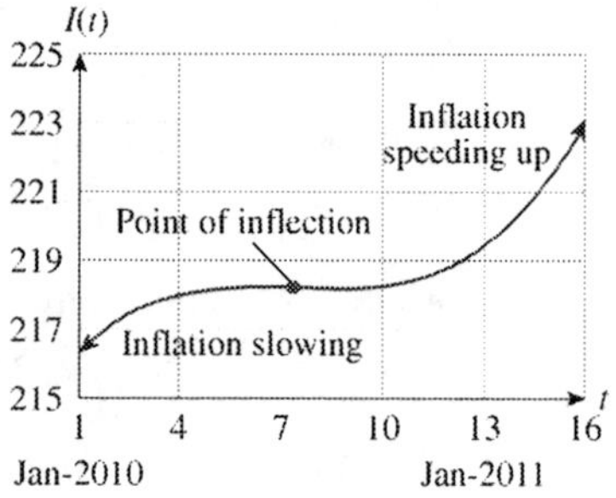

Figure 31

The point of inflection occurs when $I''(t) = 0$; that is,

$$0.0486t - 0.36 = 0$$
$$t = \frac{0.36}{0.0486} \approx 7.4.$$

Thus, inflation was slowing when $t < 7.4$ (that is, until around the middle of July), and speeding up when $t > 7.4$ (after that time). Inflation was slowest at the point when it stopped slowing down and began to speed up, $t \approx 7.4$ (in fact there was slight deflation at that particular point as $I'(7.4)$ is negative); notice that the graph has the least slope at that point.

* The 0.20% monthly inflation rate corresponds to a $12 \times 0.20 =$ 2.40% annual inflation rate. This result could be obtained directly by changing the units of the *t*-axis from months to years and then redoing the calculation.

† When the CPI is falling, the inflation rate is negative and we experience *deflation*.

EXAMPLE 4 The Point of Diminishing Returns

After the introduction of a new video game, the total worldwide sales are modeled by the curve

$$S(t) = \frac{1}{1 + 50e^{-0.2t}} \text{ million units sold,}$$

where t is the time in months since the game was introduced (compare Example 2). The graphs of $S(t)$, $S'(t)$, and $S''(t)$ are shown in Figure 32. Where is the graph of S concave up, and where is it concave down? Where are any points of inflection? What does this all mean?

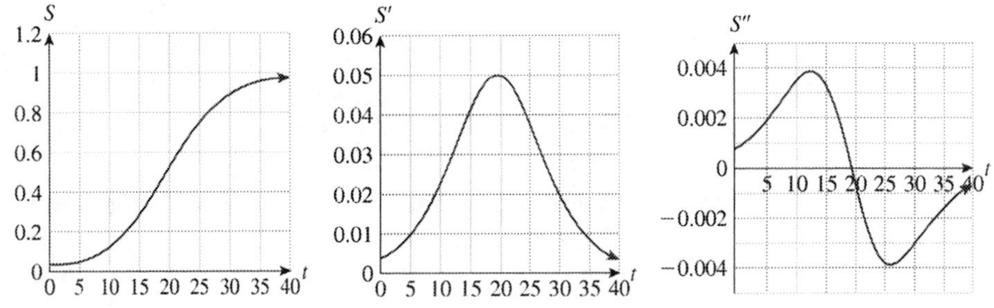

(a) Graph of S (b) Graph of S' (c) Graph of S''

Figure 32

Solution Look at the graph of S. We see that the graph of S is concave up in the early months and then becomes concave down later. The point of inflection, where the concavity changes, is somewhere between 15 and 25 months.

Now look at the graph of S''. This graph crosses the t-axis very close to $t = 20$, is positive before that point, and negative after that point. Because positive values of S'' indicate S is concave up and negative values concave down, we conclude that the graph of S is concave up for about the first 20 months; that is, for $0 < t < 20$ and concave down for $20 < t < 40$. The concavity switches at the point of inflection, which occurs at about $t = 20$ (when $S''(t) = 0$; a more accurate answer is $t \approx 19.56$).

What does this all mean? Look at the graph of S', which shows sales per unit time, or monthly sales. From this graph we see that monthly sales are increasing for $t < 20$: more units are being sold each month than the month before. Monthly sales reach a peak of 0.05 million $= 50{,}000$ games per month at the point of inflection $t = 20$ and then begin to drop off. Thus, the point of inflection occurs at the time when monthly sales stop increasing and start to fall off; that is, the time when monthly sales peak. The point of inflection is sometimes called the **point of diminishing returns**. Although the total sales figure continues to rise (see the graph of S: game units continue to be sold), the *rate* at which units are sold starts to drop. (See Figure 33.)

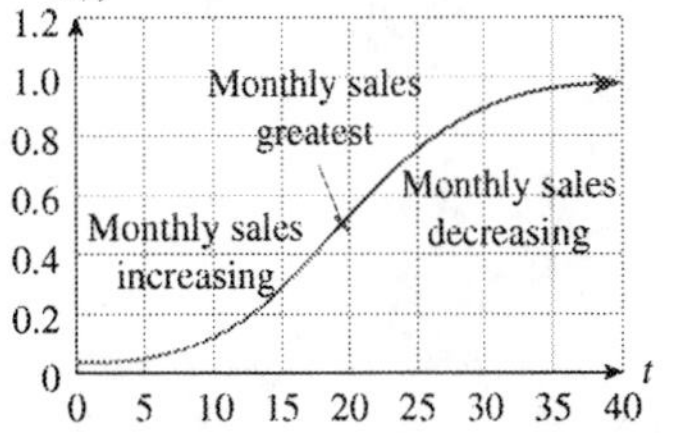

Figure 33

using Technology

You can use a TI-83/84 Plus, a downloadable Excel sheet at the Website, or the Function Evaluator and Grapher at the Website to graph the second derivative of the function in Example 4:

TI-83/84 Plus

```
Y1=1/(1+50*e^(-0.2X))
Y2=nDeriv(Y1,X,X)
Y3=nDeriv(Y2,X,X)
```

Website

www.WanerMath.com

In the Function Evaluator and Grapher, enter the functions as shown.

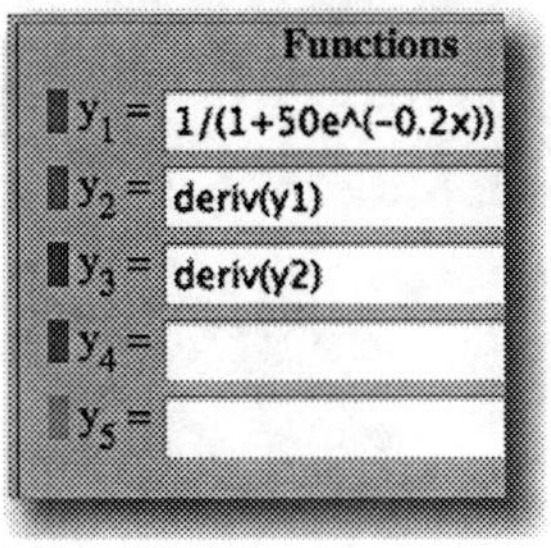

(Use Ymin = 0, yMax = 0.1 for a nice view of S' and Ymin = −0.01 and yMax = 0.01 for S''.)

For an Excel utility, try:

On Line Utilities
↓
Excel First and Second Derivative Graphing Utility

(This utility needs macros, so ensure they are enabled.)

The Second Derivative Test for Relative Extrema

The second derivative often gives us a way of knowing whether or not a stationary point is a relative extremum. Figure 34 shows a graph with two stationary points: a relative maximum at $x = a$ and a relative minimum at $x = b$.

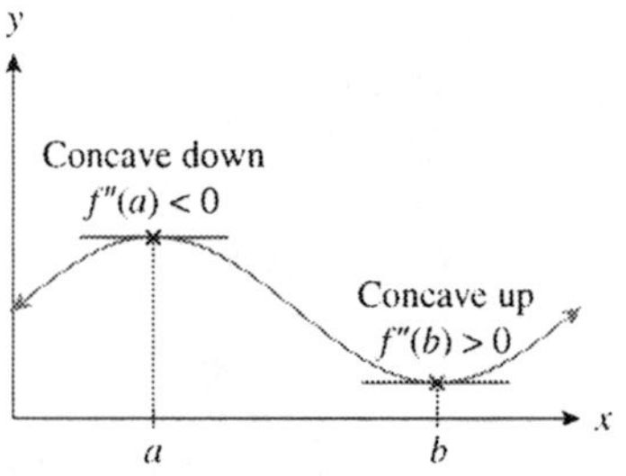

Figure 34

Notice that the curve is *concave down* at the relative maximum ($x = a$), so that $f''(a) < 0$, and *concave up* at the relative minimum ($x = b$), so that $f''(b) > 0$. This suggests the following (compare the First Derivative Test in Section 12.1).

Second Derivative Test for Relative Extrema

Suppose that the function f has a stationary point at $x = c$, and that $f''(c)$ exists. Determine the sign of $f''(c)$.

1. If $f''(c) > 0$, then f has a relative minimum at $x = c$.

2. If $f''(c) < 0$, then f has a relative maximum at $x = c$.

If $f''(c) = 0$, then the test is inconclusive and you need to use one of the methods of Section 12.1 (such as the first derivative test) to determine whether or not f has a relative extremum at $x = c$.

Quick Examples

1. $f(x) = x^2 - 2x$ has $f'(x) = 2x - 2$ and hence a stationary point at $x = 1$. $f''(x) = 2$, and so $f''(1) = 2$, which is positive, so f has a relative minimum at $x = 1$.

2. Let $f(x) = x^3 - 3x^2 - 9x$. Then

$f'(x) = 3x^2 - 6x - 9 = 3(x + 1)(x - 3)$

Stationary points at $x = -1$, $x = 3$

$f''(x) = 6x - 6$

$f''(-1) = -12$, so there is a relative maximum at $x = -1$

$f''(3) = 12$, so there is a relative minimum at $x = 3$.

3. $f(x) = x^4$ has $f'(x) = 4x^3$ and hence a stationary point at $x = 0$. $f''(x) = 12x^2$ and so $f''(0) = 0$, telling us that the second derivative test is inconclusive. However, we can see from the graph of f or the first derivative test that f has a minimum at $x = 0$.

Higher Order Derivatives

There is no reason to stop at the second derivative; we could once again take the *derivative* of the second derivative to obtain the **third derivative**, f''', and we could take the derivative once again to obtain the **fourth derivative**, written $f^{(4)}$, and then continue to obtain $f^{(5)}$, $f^{(6)}$, and so on (assuming we get a differentiable function at each stage).

Higher Order Derivatives

We define

$$f'''(x) = \frac{d}{dx}[f''(x)]$$

$$f^{(4)}(x) = \frac{d}{dx}[f'''(x)]$$

$$f^{(5)}(x) = \frac{d}{dx}[f^{(4)}(x)],$$

and so on, assuming all these derivatives exist.

Different Notations

$$f'(x), f''(x), f'''(x), f^{(4)}(x), \dots, f^{(n)}(x), \dots$$

$$\frac{df}{dx}, \frac{d^2f}{dx^2}, \frac{d^3f}{dx^3}, \frac{d^4f}{dx^4}, \dots, \frac{d^nf}{dx^n}, \dots$$

$$\frac{dy}{dx}, \frac{d^2y}{dx^2}, \frac{d^3y}{dx^3}, \frac{d^4y}{dx^4}, \dots, \frac{d^ny}{dx^n}, \dots \quad \text{When } y = f(x)$$

$$y, y', y'', y''', y^{(4)}, \dots, y^{(n)}, \dots \quad \text{When } y = f(x)$$

Quick Examples

1. If $f(x) = x^3 - x$, then $f'(x) = 3x^2 - 1$, $f''(x) = 6x$, $f'''(x) = 6$, $f^{(4)}(x) = f^{(5)}(x) = \cdots = 0$.
2. If $f(x) = e^x$, then $f'(x) = e^x$, $f''(x) = e^x$, $f'''(x) = e^x$, $f^{(4)}(x) = f^{(5)}(x) = \cdots = e^x$.

Q: *We know that the second derivative can be interpreted as acceleration. How do we interpret the third derivative; and the fourth, fifth, and so on?*

A: Think of a car traveling down the road (with position $s(t)$ at time t) in such a way that its acceleration $\frac{d^2s}{dt^2}$ is changing with time (for instance, the driver may be slowly increasing pressure on the accelerator, causing the car to accelerate at a greater and greater rate). Then $\frac{d^3s}{dt^3}$ is the rate of change of acceleration. $\frac{d^4s}{dt^4}$ would then be the *acceleration* of the acceleration, and so on.

Q: *How are these higher order derivatives reflected in the graph of a function f?*

A: Because the concavity is measured by f'', its derivative f''' tells us the rate of change of concavity. Similarly, $f^{(4)}$ would tell us the *acceleration* of concavity, and so on. These properties are very subtle and hard to discern by simply looking at the curve; the higher the order, the more subtle the property. There is a remarkable theorem by Taylor* that tells us that, for a large class of functions (including polynomial, exponential, logarithmic, and trigonometric functions) the values of all orders of derivative $f(a)$, $f'(a)$, $f''(a)$, $f'''(a)$, and so on at the single point $x = a$ are enough to describe the entire graph (even at points very far from $x = a$)! In other words, the smallest piece of a graph near any point a contains sufficient information to "clone" the entire graph!

* Brook Taylor (1685–1731) was an English mathematician.

FAQs

Interpreting Points of Inflection and Using the Second Derivative Test

Q: *It says in Example 4 that monthly sales reach a maximum at the point of inflection (second derivative is zero), but the second derivative test says that, for a maximum, the second derivative must be negative. What is going on here?*

A: What is a maximum in Example 4 is the *rate of change of* sales: which is measured in sales per unit time (monthly sales in the example). In other words, it is the *derivative* of the total sales function that is a maximum, so we located the maximum by setting its derivative (which is the *second* derivative of total sales) equal to zero. In general: To find relative (stationary) extrema of the *original* function, set $f'(x)$ equal to zero and solve for x as usual. The second derivative test can then be used to test the stationary point obtained. To find relative (stationary) extrema of the *rate of change of f*, set $f''(x) = 0$ and solve for x.

Q: *I used the second derivative test and it was inconclusive. That means that there is neither a relative maximum nor a relative minimum at $x = a$, right?*

A: Wrong. If (as is often the case) the second derivative is zero at a stationary point, all it means is that the second derivative test itself cannot determine whether the given point is a relative maximum, minimum, or neither. For instance, $f(x) = x^4$ has a stationary minimum at $x = 0$, but the second derivative test is inconclusive. In such cases, one should use another test (such as the first derivative test) to decide if the point is a relative maximum, minimum, or neither.

12.3 EXERCISES

▼ more advanced ◆ challenging

T indicates exercises that should be solved using technology

In Exercises 1–10, calculate $\frac{d^2y}{dx^2}$. HINT [See Quick Examples on page 892.]

1. $y = 3x^2 - 6$

2. $y = -x^2 + x$

3. $y = \frac{2}{x}$

4. $y = -\frac{2}{x^2}$

5. $y = 4x^{0.4} - x$

6. $y = 0.2x^{-0.1}$

7. $y = e^{-(x-1)} - x$

8. $y = e^{-x} + e^x$

9. $y = \frac{1}{x} - \ln x$

10. $y = x^{-2} + \ln x$

In Exercises 11–16, the position s of a point (in feet) is given as a function of time t (in seconds). Find (a) its acceleration as a function of t and (b) its acceleration at the specified time. HINT [See Example 1.]

11. $s = 12 + 3t - 16t^2$; $t = 2$

12. $s = -12 + t - 16t^2$; $t = 2$

13. $s = \frac{1}{t} + \frac{1}{t^2}$; $t = 1$ **14.** $s = \frac{1}{t} - \frac{1}{t^2}$; $t = 2$

15. $s = \sqrt{t} + t^2$; $t = 4$ **16.** $s = 2\sqrt{t} + t^3$; $t = 1$

In Exercises 17–24, the graph of a function is given. Find the approximate coordinates of all points of inflection of each function (if any). HINT [See Quick Examples on page 896.]

17.
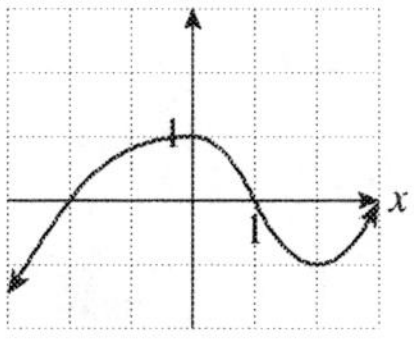

18.
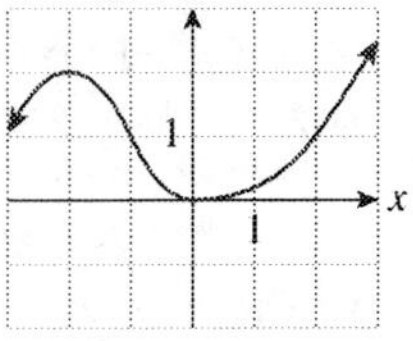

19.
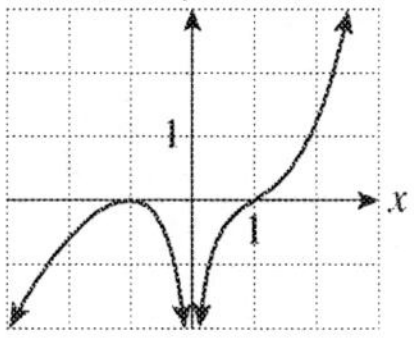

20.
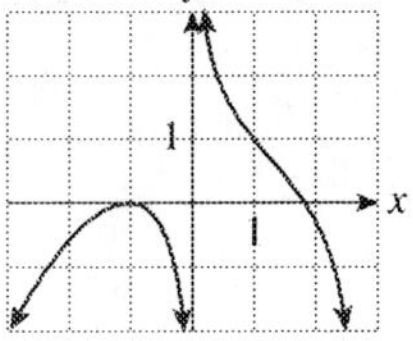

21.
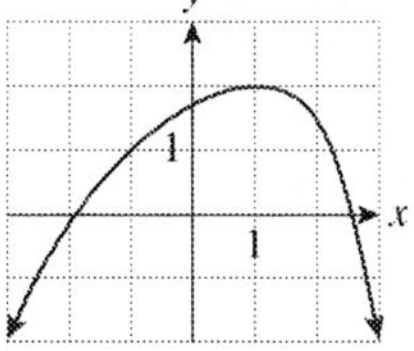

22.
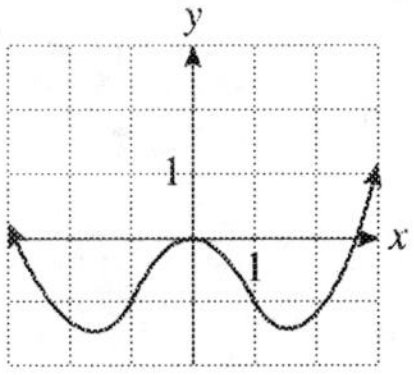

23.
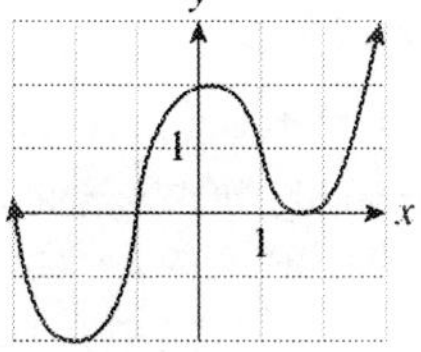

24.
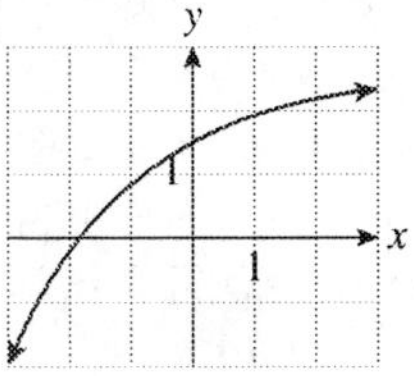

In Exercises 25–28, the graph of the derivative, $f'(x)$, *is given. Determine the x-coordinates of all points of inflection of $f(x)$, if any. (Assume that $f(x)$ is defined and continuous everywhere in $[-3, 3]$.)* HINT [See the **Before we go on** discussion in Example 4.]

25.
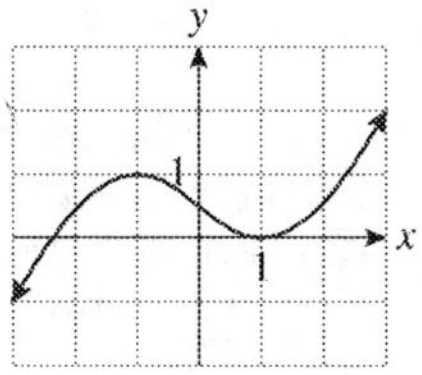

26.
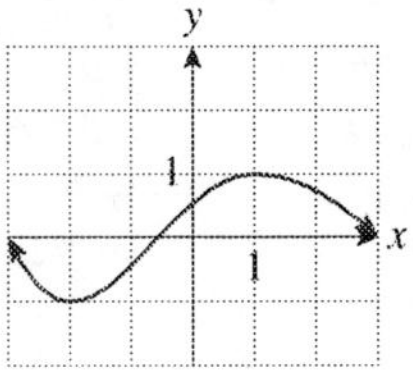

27.
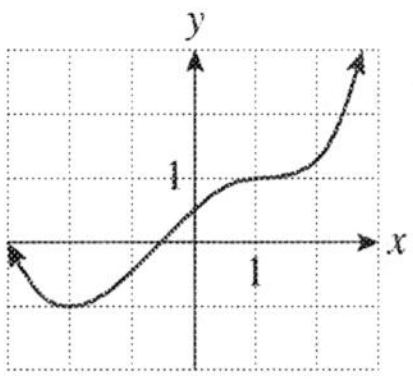

28.
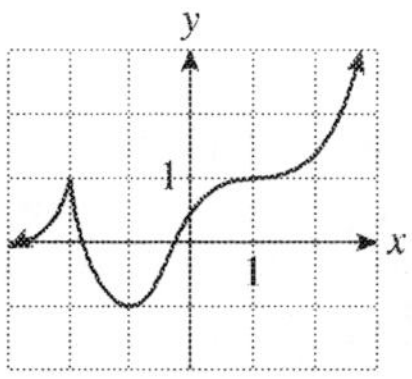

In Exercises 29–32, the graph of the second derivative, $f''(x)$, *is given. Determine the x-coordinates of all points of inflection of $f(x)$, if any. (Assume that $f(x)$ is defined and continuous everywhere in $[-3, 3]$.)* HINT [Remember that a point of inflection of f corresponds to a point at which f'' changes sign, from positive to negative or vice versa. This could be a point where its graph crosses the x-axis, or a point where its graph is broken: positive on one side of the break and negative on the other.]

29.
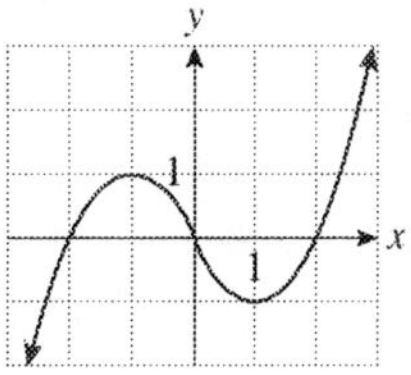

30.
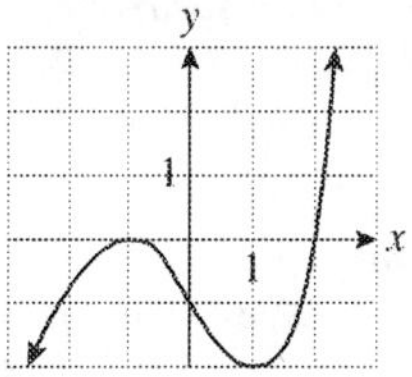

31.
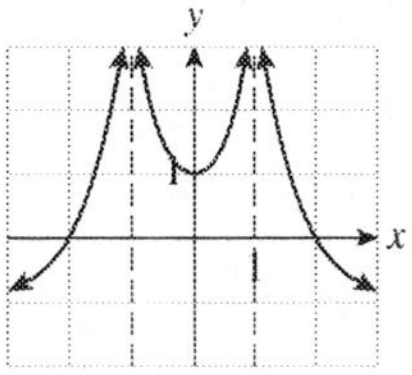

32.
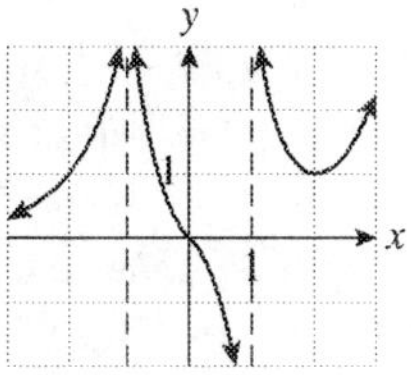

In Exercises 33–44, find the x-coordinates of all critical points of the given function. Determine whether each critical point is a relative maximum, minimum, or neither by first applying the second derivative test, and, if the test fails, by some other method. HINT [See Quick Examples on page 899.]

33. $f(x) = x^2 - 4x + 1$ **34.** $f(x) = 2x^2 - 2x + 3$

35. $g(x) = x^3 - 12x$ **36.** $g(x) = 2x^3 - 6x + 3$

37. $f(t) = t^3 - t$ **38.** $f(t) = -2t^3 + 3t$

39. $f(x) = x^4 - 4x^3$ **40.** $f(x) = 3x^4 - 2x^3$

41. $f(x) = e^{-x^2}$ **42.** $f(x) = e^{2-x^2}$

43. $f(x) = xe^{1-x^2}$ **44.** $f(x) = xe^{-x^2}$

In Exercises 45–54, calculate the derivatives of all orders: $f'(x), f''(x), f'''(x), f^{(4)}(x), \ldots, f^{(n)}(x), \ldots$ HINT [See Quick Examples on page 900.]

45. $f(x) = 4x^2 - x + 1$ **46.** $f(x) = -3x^3 + 4x$

47. $f(x) = -x^4 + 3x^2$ **48.** $f(x) = x^4 + x^3$

49. $f(x) = (2x + 1)^4$ **50.** $f(x) = (-2x + 1)^3$

51. $f(x) = e^{-x}$ **52.** $f(x) = e^{2x}$

53. $f(x) = e^{3x-1}$ **54.** $f(x) = 2e^{-x+3}$

APPLICATIONS

55. ***Acceleration on Mars*** If a stone is dropped from a height of 40 meters above the Martian surface, its height in meters after t seconds is given by $s = 40 - 1.9t^2$. What is its acceleration? HINT [See Example 1.]

56. ***Acceleration on the Moon*** If a stone is thrown up at 10 m per second from a height of 100 meters above the surface of the Moon, its height in meters after t seconds is given by $s = 100 + 10t - 0.8t^2$. What is its acceleration? HINT [See Example 1.]

57. ***Motion in a Straight Line*** The position of a particle moving in a straight line is given by $s = t^3 - t^2$ ft after t seconds. Find an expression for its acceleration after a time t. Is its velocity increasing or decreasing when $t = 1$?

58. ***Motion in a Straight Line*** The position of a particle moving in a straight line is given by $s = 3e^t - 8t^2$ ft after t seconds. Find an expression for its acceleration after a time t. Is its velocity increasing or decreasing when $t = 1$?

59. ***Bottled Water Sales*** Annual sales of bottled water in the United States in the period 2000–2010 could be approximated by

$$R(t) = -45t^2 + 900t + 4{,}200 \text{ million gallons} \quad (0 \le t \le 10),$$

where t is time in years since 2000.[28] According to the model, were annual sales of bottled water accelerating or decelerating in 2009? How fast? HINT [See Example 2.]

60. ***Bottled Water Sales*** Annual U.S. per capita sales of bottled water in the period 2000–2010 could be approximated by

$$Q(t) = -0.18t^2 + 3t + 15 \text{ gallons} \quad (0 \le t \le 10),$$

where t is time in years since 2000.[29] According to the model, were annual U.S. per capita sales of bottled water accelerating or decelerating in 2009? How fast?

61. ***Embryo Development*** The daily oxygen consumption of a bird embryo increases from the time the egg is laid through the time the chick hatches. In a typical galliform bird, the oxygen consumption can be approximated by

$$c(t) = -0.065t^3 + 3.4t^2 - 22t + 3.6 \text{ ml} \quad (8 \le t \le 30),$$

where t is the time (in days) since the egg was laid.[30] (An egg will typically hatch at around $t = 28$.) Use the model to estimate the following (give the units of measurement for each answer and round all answers to two significant digits):

a. The daily oxygen consumption 20 days after the egg was laid

b. The rate at which the oxygen consumption is changing 20 days after the egg was laid

c. The rate at which the oxygen consumption is accelerating 20 days after the egg was laid

62. ***Embryo Development*** The daily oxygen consumption of a turkey embryo increases from the time the egg is laid through the time the chick hatches. In a brush turkey, the oxygen consumption can be approximated by

$$c(t) = -0.028t^3 + 2.9t^2 - 44t + 95 \text{ ml} \quad (20 \le t \le 50),$$

where t is the time (in days) since the egg was laid.[31] (An egg will typically hatch at around $t = 50$.) Use the model to estimate the following (give the units of measurement for each answer and round all answers to two significant digits):

a. The daily oxygen consumption 40 days after the egg was laid

b. The rate at which the oxygen consumption is changing 40 days after the egg was laid

c. The rate at which the oxygen consumption is accelerating 40 days after the egg was laid

63. ***Inflation*** The following graph shows the approximate value of the United States Consumer Price Index (CPI) from December 2006 through July 2007.[32]

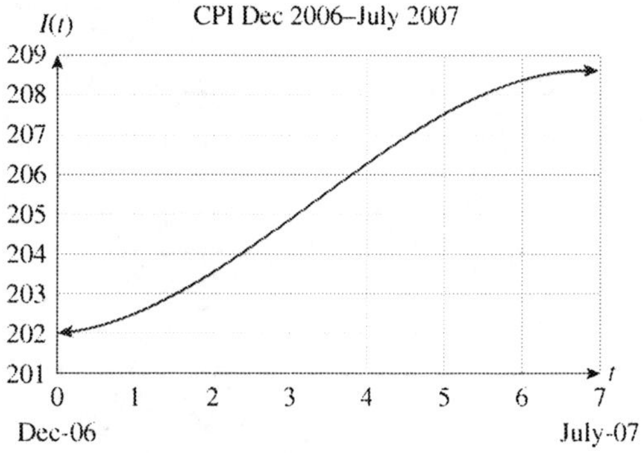

The approximating curve shown on the figure is given by

$$I(t) = -0.04t^3 + 0.4t^2 + 0.1t + 202 \quad (0 \le t \le 7),$$

where t is time in months ($t = 0$ represents December 2006).

a. Use the model to estimate the monthly inflation rate in February 2007 ($t = 2$). [Recall that the inflation *rate* is $I'(t)/I(t)$.]

b. Was inflation slowing or speeding up in February 2007?

c. When was inflation speeding up? When was inflation slowing? HINT [See Example 3.]

64. ***Inflation*** The following graph shows the approximate value of the U.S. Consumer Price Index (CPI) from September 2004 through November 2005.[33]

[28] Source for data: Beverage Marketing Corporation (www.bottledwater.org).

[29] *Ibid.*

[30] The model approximates graphical data published in the article "The Brush Turkey" by Roger S. Seymour, *Scientific American*, December, 1991, pp. 108–114.

[31] *Ibid.*

[32] The CPI is compiled by the Bureau of Labor Statistics and is based upon a 1982 value of 100. For instance, a CPI of 200 means the CPI has doubled since 1982. Source: InflationData.com (www.inflationdata.com).

[33] *Ibid.*

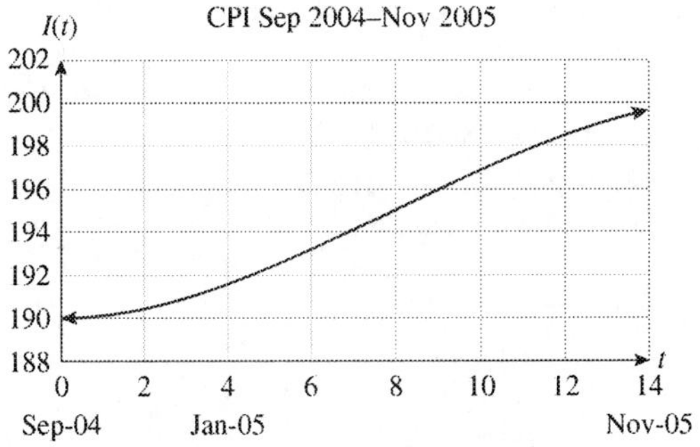

The approximating curve shown on the figure is given by

$$I(t) = -0.005t^3 + 0.12t^2 - 0.01t + 190 \quad (0 \le t \le 14),$$

where t is time in months ($t = 0$ represents September 2004).

a. Use the model to estimate the monthly inflation rate in July 2005 ($t = 10$). [Recall that the inflation *rate* is $I'(t)/I(t)$.]

b. Was inflation slowing or speeding up in July 2005?

c. When was inflation speeding up? When was inflation slowing? HINT [See Example 3.]

65. ***Inflation*** The following graph shows the approximate value of the U.S. Consumer Price Index (CPI) from July 2005 through March 2006.[34]

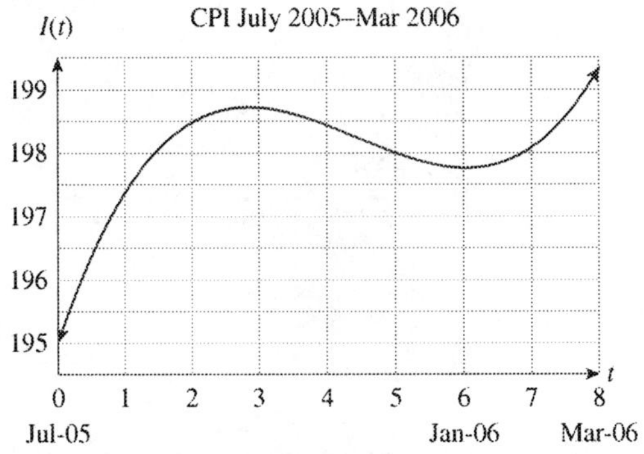

The approximating curve shown on the figure is given by

$$I(t) = 0.06t^3 - 0.8t^2 + 3.1t + 195 \quad (0 \le t \le 8),$$

where t is time in months ($t = 0$ represents July 2005).

a. Use the model to estimate the monthly inflation rates in December 2005 and February 2006 ($t = 5$ and $t = 7$).

b. Was inflation slowing or speeding up in February 2006?

c. When was inflation speeding up? When was inflation slowing?

66. ***Inflation*** The following graph shows the approximate value of the U.S. Consumer Price Index (CPI) from March 2006 through May 2007.[35]

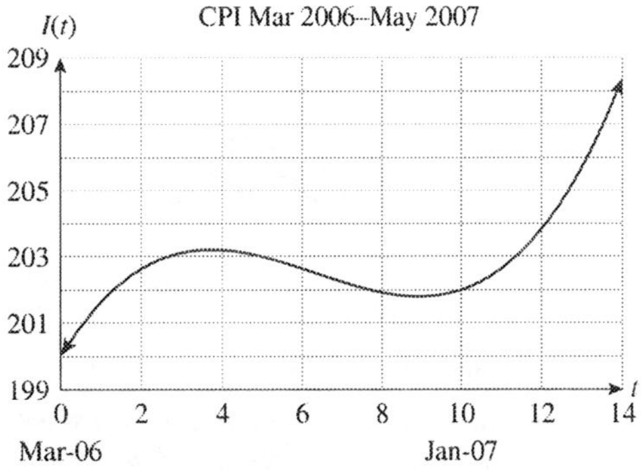

The approximating curve shown on the figure is given by

$$I(t) = 0.02t^3 - 0.38t^2 + 2t + 200 \quad (0 \le t \le 14),$$

where t is time in months ($t = 0$ represents March, 2006).

a. Use the model to estimate the monthly inflation rates in September 2006 and January 2007 ($t = 6$ and $t = 10$).

b. Was inflation slowing or speeding up in January 2007?

c. When was inflation speeding up? When was inflation slowing?

67. ***Scientific Research*** The percentage of research articles in the prominent journal *Physical Review* that were written by researchers in the United States during the years 1983–2003 can be modeled by

$$P(t) = 25 + \frac{36}{1 + 0.06(0.7)^{-t}},$$

where t is time in years since 1983.[36] The graphs of P, P', and P'' are shown here:

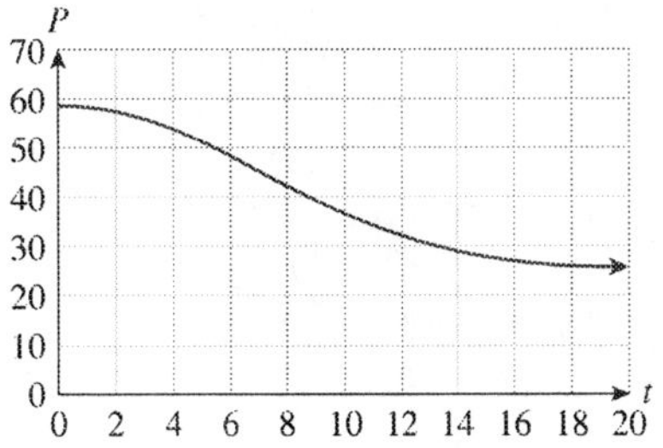

Graph of P

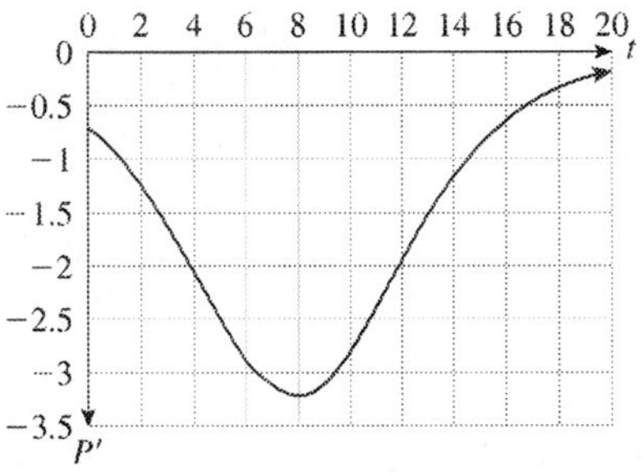

Graph of P'

[34]The CPI is compiled by the Bureau of Labor Statistics and is based upon a 1982 value of 100. For instance, a CPI of 200 means the CPI has doubled since 1982. Source: InflationData.com (www.inflationdata.com).

[35]*Ibid.*

[36]Source: The American Physical Society/*New York Times*, May 3, 2003, p. A1.

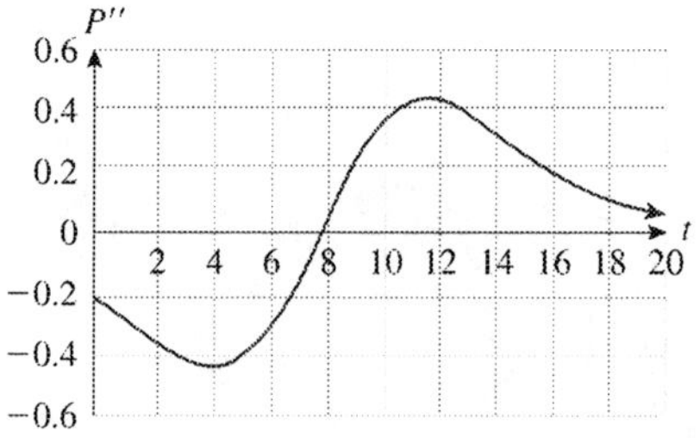

Graph of P''

Determine, to the nearest whole number, the values of t for which the graph of P is concave up and where it is concave down, and locate any points of inflection. What does the point of inflection tell you about science articles? HINT [See Example 4.]

68. ***Scientific Research*** The number of research articles in the prominent journal *Physical Review* that were written by researchers in Europe during the years 1983–2003 can be modeled by

$$P(t) = \frac{7.0}{1 + 5.4(1.2)^{-t}},$$

where t is time in years since 1983.[37] The graphs of P, P', and P'' are shown here:

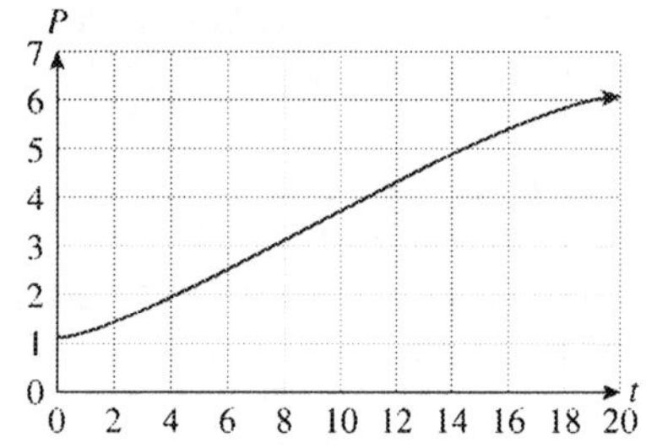

Graph of P

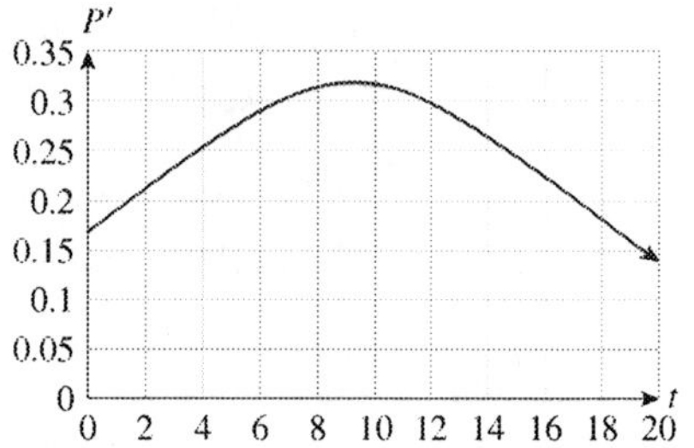

Graph of P'

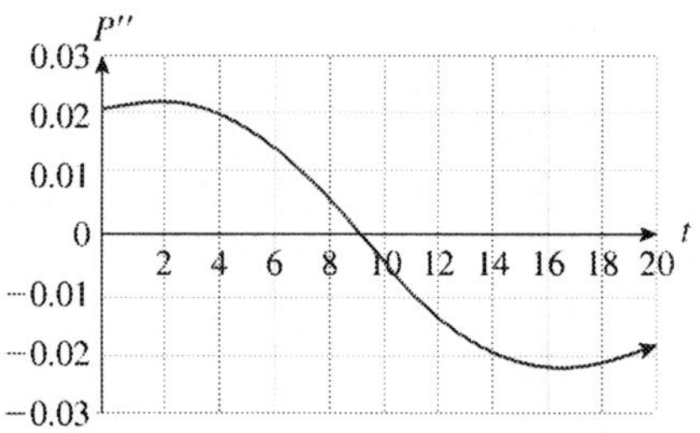

Graph of P''

Determine, to the nearest whole number, the values of t for which the graph of P is concave up and where it is concave down, and locate any points of inflection. What does the point of inflection tell you about science articles?

69. ***Embryo Development*** Here are sketches of the graphs of c, c', and c'' from Exercise 61:

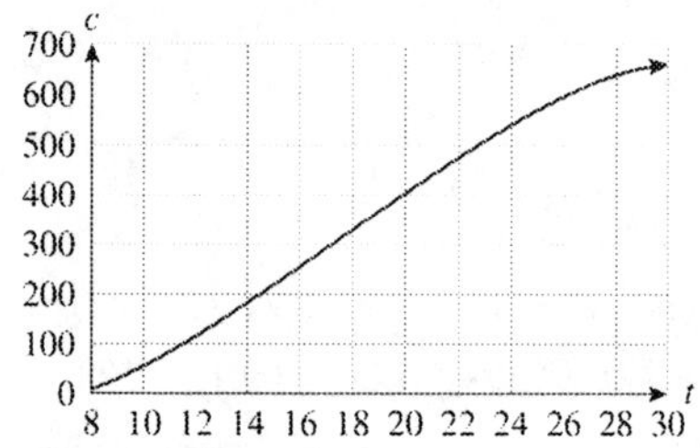

Graph of c

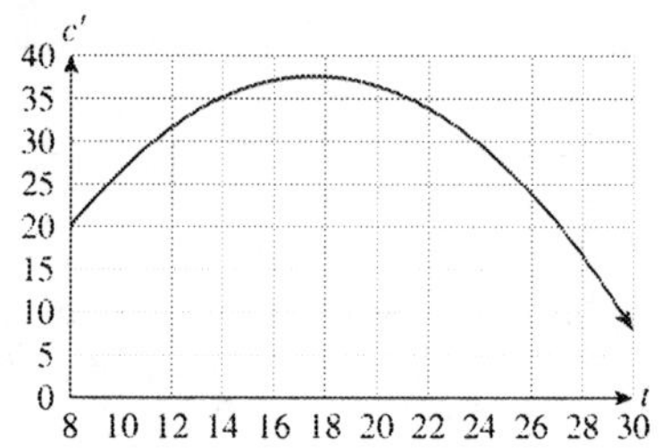

Graph of c'

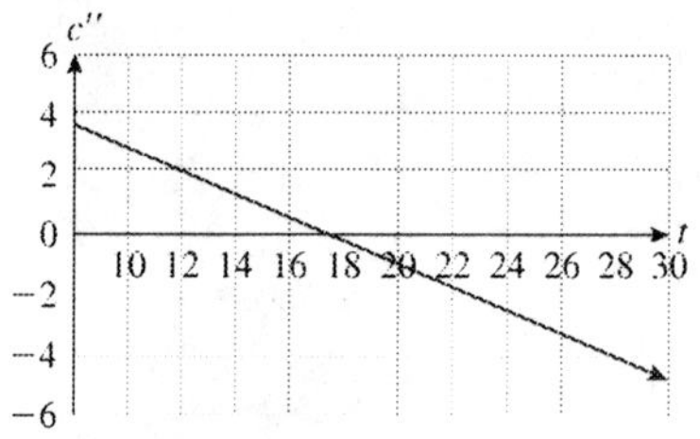

Graph of c''

Multiple choice:

a. The graph of c' **(A)** has a point of inflection. **(B)** has no points of inflection.

b. At around 18 days after the egg is laid, daily oxygen consumption is: **(A)** at a maximum. **(B)** increasing at a maximum rate. **(C)** just beginning to decrease.

c. For $t > 18$ days, the oxygen consumption is **(A)** increasing at a decreasing rate. **(B)** decreasing at an increasing rate. **(C)** increasing at an increasing rate.

70. ***Embryo Development*** Here are sketches of the graphs of c, c', and c'' from Exercise 62:

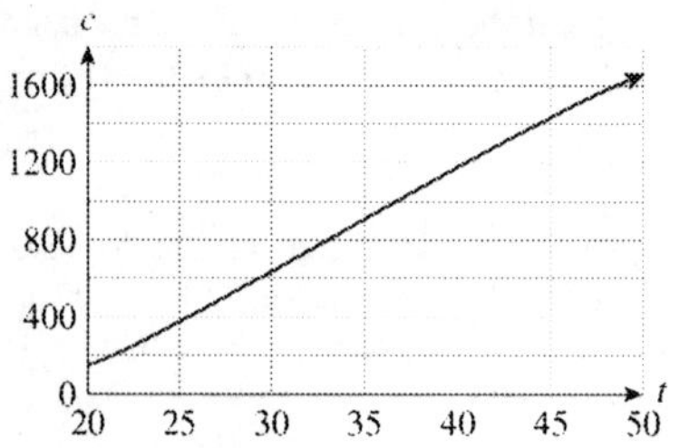

Graph of c

[37] Source: The American Physical Society/*New York Times*, May 3, 2003, p. A1.

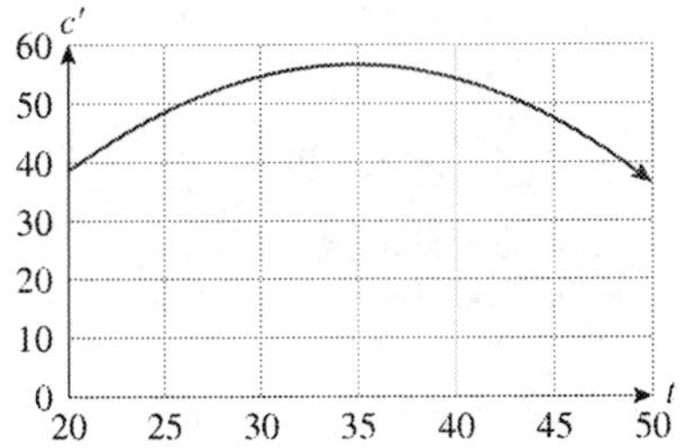

Graph of c'

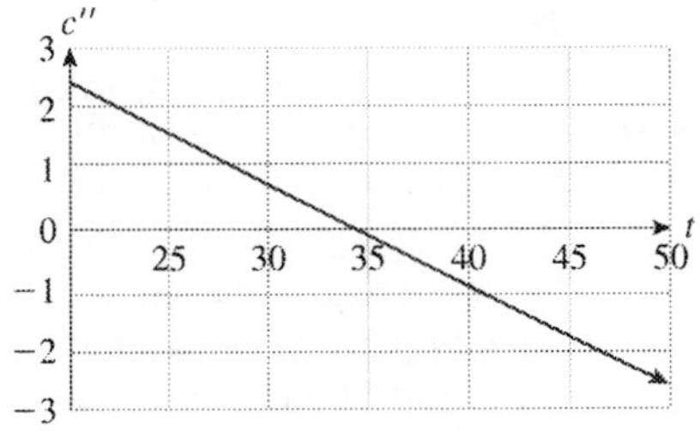

Graph of c''

Multiple choice:

a. The graph of c: **(A)** has points of inflection. **(B)** has no points of inflection. **(C)** may or may not have a point of inflection, but the graphs do not provide enough information.

b. At around 35 days after the egg is laid, the rate of change of daily oxygen consumption is: **(A)** at a maximum. **(B)** increasing at a maximum rate. **(C)** just becoming negative.

c. For $t < 35$ days, the oxygen consumption is: **(A)** increasing at an increasing rate. **(B)** increasing at a decreasing rate. **(C)** decreasing at an increasing rate.

71. ***Subprime Mortgages during the Housing Bubble*** During the real estate run-up in 2000–2008, the percentage of mortgages issued in the United States that were subprime (normally classified as risky) could be approximated by

$$A(t) = \frac{15.0}{1 + 8.6(1.8)^{-t}} \text{ percent} \quad (0 \le t \le 8)$$

t years after the start of 2000.[38] Graph the function as well as its first and second derivatives. Determine, to the nearest whole number, the values of t for which the graph of A is concave up and concave down, and the t-coordinate of any points of inflection. What does the point of inflection tell you about subprime mortgages? HINT [To graph the second derivative, see the note in the margin after Example 4.]

72. ***Subprime Mortgage Debt during the Housing Bubble*** During the real estate run-up in 2000–2008, the value of subprime (normally classified as risky) mortgage debt outstanding in the United States was approximately

$$A(t) = \frac{1{,}350}{1 + 4.2(1.7)^{-t}} \text{ billion dollars} \quad (0 \le t \le 8)$$

t years after the start of 2000.[39] Graph the function as well as its first and second derivatives. Determine, to the nearest whole number, the values of t for which the graph of A is concave up and concave down, and the t-coordinate of any points of inflection. What does the point of inflection tell you about subprime mortgages? HINT [To graph the second derivative, see the note in the margin after Example 4.]

73. ***Epidemics*** The following graph shows the total number n of people (in millions) infected in an epidemic as a function of time t (in years):

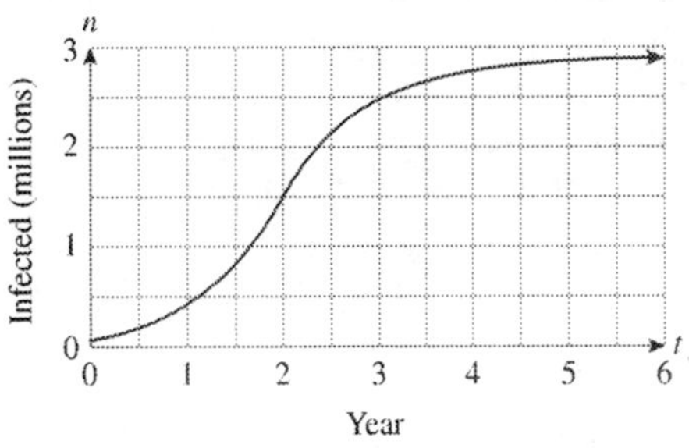

a. When to the nearest year was the rate of new infection largest?

b. When could the Centers for Disease Control and Prevention announce that the rate of new infection was beginning to drop? HINT [See Example 4.]

74. ***Sales*** The following graph shows the total number of *Pomegranate Q4* computers sold since their release (t is in years):

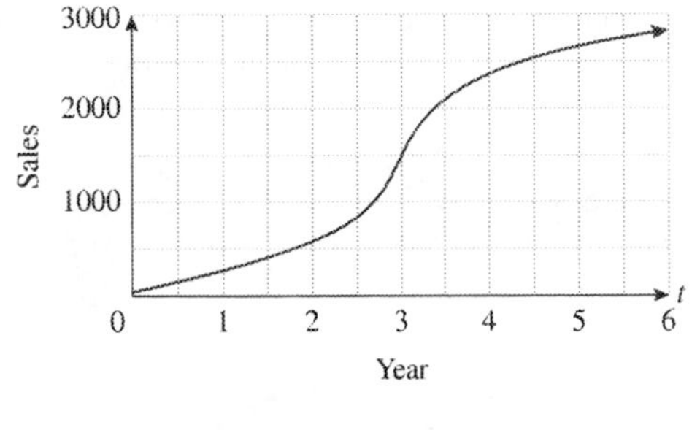

a. When were the computers selling fastest?

b. Explain why this graph might look as it does. HINT [See Example 4.]

[38] Sources: Mortgage Bankers Association, UBS.

[39] 2008 figure is an estimate.
Source: www.data360.org/dataset.aspx?Data_Set_Id=9549.

75. *Industrial Output* The following graph shows the yearly industrial output (measured in billions of zonars) of the city-state of Utarek, Mars over a seven-year period:

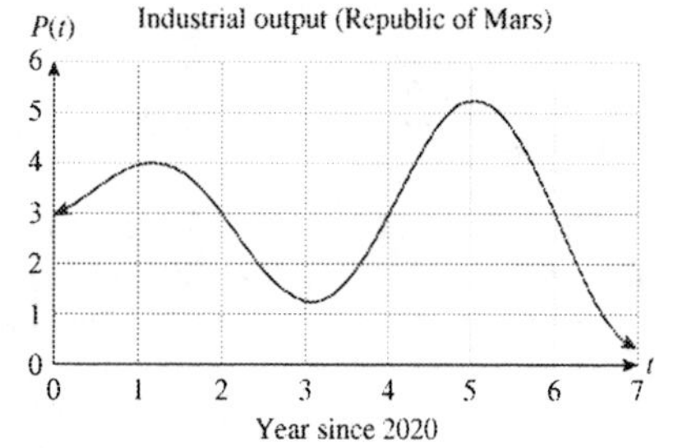

Industrial output (Republic of Mars)

Year since 2020

a. When to the nearest year did the rate of change of yearly industrial output reach a maximum?

b. When to the nearest year did the rate of change of yearly industrial output reach a minimum?

c. When to the nearest year does the graph first change from concave down to concave up? The result tells you that:

    (A) In that year the rate of change of industrial output reached a minimum compared with nearby years.

    (B) In that year the rate of change of industrial output reached a maximum compared with nearby years.

76. *Profits* The following graph shows the yearly profits of Gigantic Conglomerate, Inc. (GCI) from 2020 to 2035:

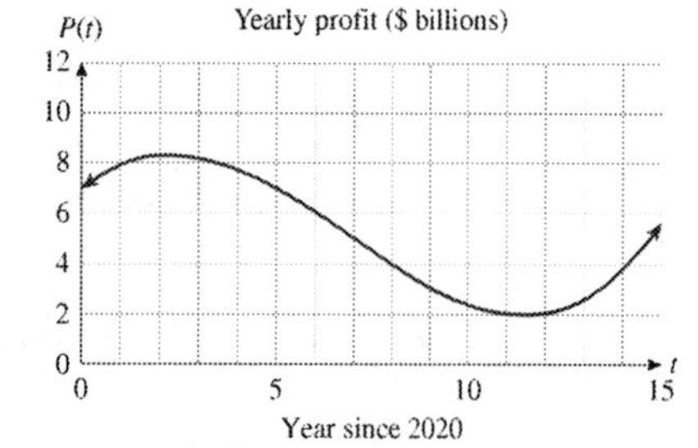

Yearly profit ($ billions)

Year since 2020

a. Approximately when were the profits rising most rapidly?

b. Approximately when were the profits falling most rapidly?

c. Approximately when could GCI's board of directors legitimately tell stockholders that they had "turned the company around"?

77. *Education and Crime* The following graph compares the total U.S. prison population and the average combined SAT score in the United States during the 1970s and 1980s:

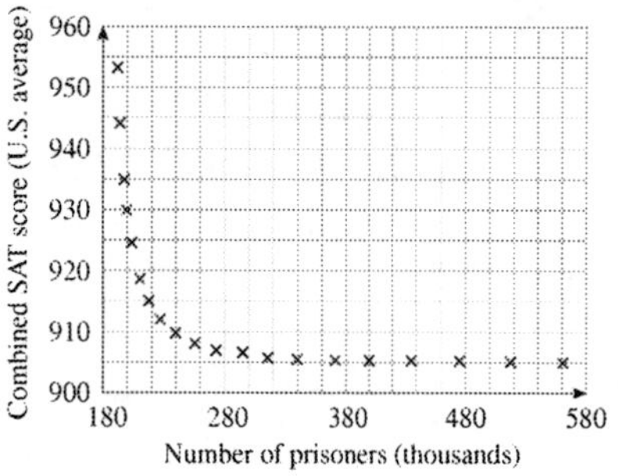

Number of prisoners (thousands)

These data can be accurately modeled by

$$S(n) = 904 + \frac{1{,}326}{(n - 180)^{1.325}} \quad (192 \le n \le 563).$$

Here, $S(n)$ is the combined U.S. average SAT score at a time when the total U.S. prison population was n thousand.[40]

a. Are there any points of inflection on the graph of S?

b. What does the concavity of the graph of S tell you about prison populations and SAT scores?

78. ▼ *Education and Crime* Refer back to the model in the preceding exercise.

a. Are there any points of inflection on the graph of S'?

b. What does the concavity of the graph of S' tell you about prison populations and SAT scores?

79. ▼ *Patents* In 1965, the economist F. M. Scherer modeled the number, n, of patents produced by a firm as a function of the size, s, of the firm (measured in annual sales in millions of dollars). He came up with the following equation based on a study of 448 large firms:[41]

$$n = -3.79 + 144.42s - 23.86s^2 + 1.457s^3.$$

a. Find $\dfrac{d^2n}{ds^2}\Big|_{s=3}$. Is the rate at which patents are produced as the size of a firm goes up increasing or decreasing with size when $s = 3$? Comment on Scherer's words, ". . . we find diminishing returns dominating."

b. Find $\dfrac{d^2n}{ds^2}\Big|_{s=7}$ and interpret the answer.

c. Find the s-coordinate of any points of inflection and interpret the result.

80. ▼ *Returns on Investments* A company finds that the number of new products it develops per year depends on the size of its annual R&D budget, x (in thousands of dollars), according to the formula

$$n(x) = -1 + 8x + 2x^2 - 0.4x^3.$$

a. Find $n''(1)$ and $n''(3)$, and interpret the results.

b. Find the size of the budget that gives the largest rate of return as measured in new products per dollar (again, called the point of diminishing returns).

81. ▣ ▼ *Oil Imports from Mexico* Daily oil production in Mexico and daily U.S. oil imports from Mexico during 2005–2009 can be approximated by

$$P(t) = 3.9 - 0.10t \text{ million barrels} \quad (5 \le t \le 9)$$
$$I(t) = 2.1 - 0.11t \text{ million barrels} \quad (5 \le t \le 9),$$

[40] Based on data for the years 1967–1989. Sources: *Sourcebook of Criminal Justice Statistics*, 1990, p. 604/Educational Testing Service.

[41] Source: F. M. Scherer, "Firm Size, Market Structure, Opportunity, and the Output of Patented Inventions," *American Economic Review* 55 (December 1965): pp. 1097–1125.

where t is time in years since the start of 2000.[42]

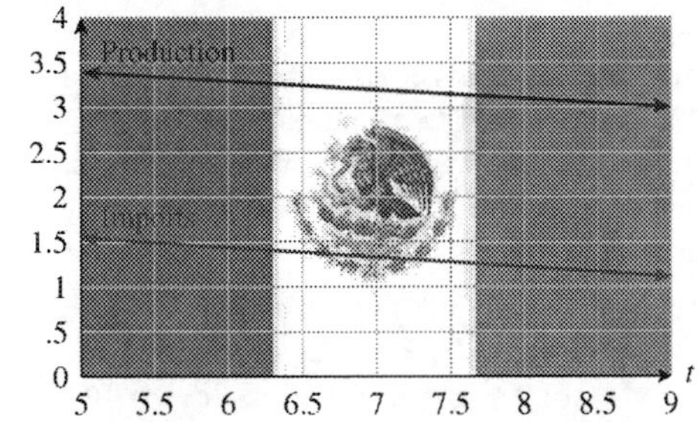

Graph the function $I(t)/P(t)$ and its derivative. Is the graph of $I(t)/P(t)$ concave up or concave down? The concavity of $I(t)/P(t)$ tells you that

(A) the percentage of oil produced in Mexico that was exported to the United States was decreasing.
(B) the percentage of oil produced in Mexico that was not exported to the United States was increasing.
(C) the percentage of oil produced in Mexico that was exported to the United States was decreasing at a slower rate.
(D) the percentage of oil produced in Mexico that was exported to the United States was decreasing at a faster rate.

82. ***Oil Imports from Mexico*** Repeat Exercise 81 using instead the models for 2000–2004 shown below:

$$P(t) = 3.0 + 0.13t \text{ million barrels} \quad (0 \le t \le 4)$$
$$I(t) = 1.4 + 0.06t \text{ million barrels} \quad (0 \le t \le 4)$$

(t is time in years since the start of 2000).[43]

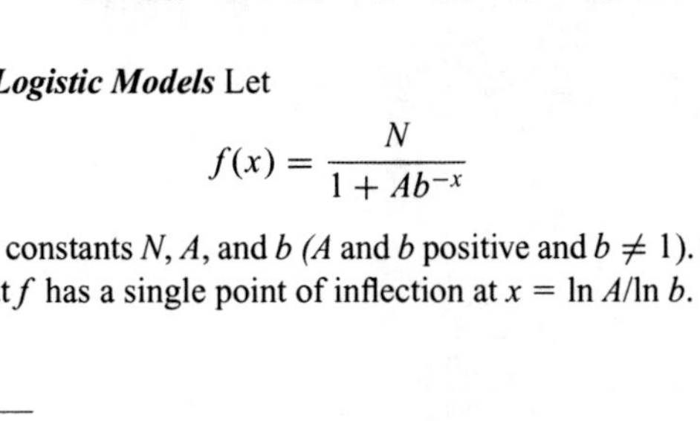

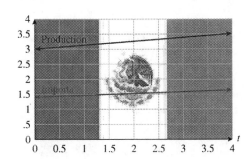

83. ◆ ***Logistic Models*** Let

$$f(x) = \frac{N}{1 + Ab^{-x}}$$

for constants N, A, and b (A and b positive and $b \neq 1$). Show that f has a single point of inflection at $x = \ln A/\ln b$.

84. ◆ ***Logistic Models*** Let

$$f(x) = \frac{N}{1 + Ae^{-kx}}$$

for constants N, A, and k (A and k positive). Show that f has a single point of inflection at $x = \ln A/k$.

85. ***Population: Puerto Rico*** The population of Puerto Rico in 1950–2025 can be approximated by

$$P(t) = \frac{4{,}500}{1 + 1.1466\,(1.0357)^{-t}} \text{ thousand people} \quad (0 \le t \le 75)$$

(t is the year since 1950).[44] Use the result of Exercise 83 to find the location of the point of inflection in the graph of P. What does the result tell you about the population of Puerto Rico?

86. ***Population: Virgin Islands*** The population of the Virgin Islands in 1950–2025 can be approximated by

$$P(t) = \frac{110}{1 + 2.3596\,(1.0767)^{-t}} \text{ thousand people} \quad (0 \le t \le 75)$$

(t is the year since 1950).[45] Use the result of Exercise 83 to find the location of the point of inflection in the graph of P. What does the result tell you about the population of the Virgin Islands?

87. ***Asset Appreciation*** You manage a small antique store that owns a collection of Louis XVI jewelry boxes. Their value v is increasing according to the formula

$$v = \frac{10{,}000}{1 + 500e^{-0.5t}},$$

where t is the number of years from now. You anticipate an inflation rate of 5% per year, so that the present value of an item that will be worth \$$v$ in t years' time is given by

$$p = v \cdot (1.05)^{-t}.$$

What is the greatest rate of increase of the value of your antiques, and when is this rate attained?

88. ***Harvesting Forests*** The following equation models the approximate volume in cubic feet of a typical Douglas fir tree of age t years[46]:

$$V = \frac{22{,}514}{1 + 22{,}514t^{-2.55}}.$$

The lumber will be sold at \$10 per cubic foot, and you do not expect the price of lumber to appreciate in the foreseeable

[42] Source for data: Energy Information Administration/Pemex (www.eia.doe.gov).

[43] *Ibid.*

[44] Figures from 2010 on are U.S. census projections. Source for data: The 2008 Statistical Abstract (www.census.gov/).

[45] *Ibid.*

[46] The model is the authors', and is based on data in *Environmental and Natural Resource Economics* by Tom Tietenberg, third edition (New York: HarperCollins, 1992), p. 282.

future. On the other hand, you anticipate a general inflation rate of 5% per year, so that the present value of an item that will be worth $\$v$ in t years time is given by

$$p = v \cdot (1.05)^{-t}.$$

What is the largest rate of increase of the value of a fir tree, and when is this rate attained?

89. ▼ ***Asset Appreciation*** As the financial consultant to a classic auto dealership, you estimate that the total value of its collection of 1959 Chevrolets and Fords is given by the formula

$$v = 300{,}000 + 1{,}000t^2,$$

where t is the number of years from now. You anticipate a continuous inflation rate of 5% per year, so that the discounted (present) value of an item that will be worth $\$v$ in t years' time is given by

$$p = ve^{-0.05t}.$$

When is the value of the collection of classic cars increasing most rapidly? When is it decreasing most rapidly?

90. ▼ ***Plantation Management*** The value of a fir tree in your plantation increases with the age of the tree according to the formula

$$v = \frac{20t}{1 + 0.05t},$$

where t is the age of the tree in years. Given a continuous inflation rate of 5% per year, the discounted (present) value of a newly planted seedling is

$$p = ve^{-0.05t}.$$

When is the discounted value of a tree increasing most rapidly? Decreasing most rapidly?

COMMUNICATION AND REASONING EXERCISES

91. Complete the following: If the graph of a function is concave up on its entire domain, then its second derivative is ______ on the domain.

92. Complete the following: If the graph of a function is concave up on its entire domain, then its first derivative is ______ on the domain.

93. Daily sales of *Kent's Tents* reached a maximum in January 2002 and declined to a minimum in January 2003 before starting to climb again. The graph of daily sales shows a point of inflection at June 2002. What is the significance of the point of inflection?

94. The graph of daily sales of *Luddington's Wellington* boots is concave down, although sales continue to increase. What properties of the graph of daily sales versus time are reflected in the following behaviors?

a. a point of inflection next year
b. a horizontal asymptote

95. ▼ Company A's profits satisfy $P(0) = \$1$ million, $P'(0) = \$1$ million per year, and $P''(0) = -\$1$ million per year per year. Company B's profits satisfy $P(0) = \$1$ million, $P'(0) = -\$1$ million per year, and $P''(0) = \$1$ million per year per year. There are no points of inflection in either company's profit curve. Sketch two pairs of profit curves: one in which Company A ultimately outperforms Company B and another in which Company B ultimately outperforms Company A.

96. ▼ Company C's profits satisfy $P(0) = \$1$ million, $P'(0) = \$1$ million per year, and $P''(0) = -\$1$ million per year per year. Company D's profits satisfy $P(0) = \$0$ million, $P'(0) = \$0$ million per year, and $P''(0) = \$1$ million per year per year. There are no points of inflection in either company's profit curve. Sketch two pairs of profit curves: one in which Company C ultimately outperforms Company D and another in which Company D ultimately outperforms Company C.

97. ▼ Explain geometrically why the derivative of a function has a relative extremum at a point of inflection, if it is defined there. Which points of inflection give rise to relative maxima in the derivative?

98. ▼ If we regard position, s, as a function of time, t, what is the significance of the *third* derivative, $s'''(t)$? Describe an everyday scenario in which this arises.

Practice Problems 12.3, Part 1

1. The figure to the right shows a vase. Assume that the vase is being filled with water at a constant rate. Sketch a graph that shows the height of the water in the vase as a function of time, and mark on your graph the point when the water level is at the widest part of the vase and when the water level is at the narrowest part of the vase.

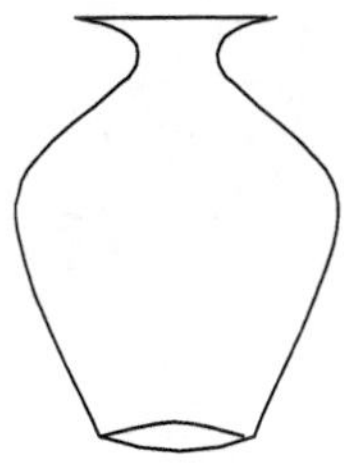

2. The distance s (in feet) covered by a car t seconds after starting from rest is given by $s=-t^3+8t^2+20t$ for $0\le t\le 6$.

a. What is the velocity of the car exactly 2 seconds after starting from rest?

b. Does the car ever start to decelerate? If so, determine when. If not, then explain why.

Practice Problems 12.3, Part 2

A car is moving along a straight stretch of road. The acceleration of the car is given by the graph to the right. Assume that the velocity of the car is always positive.

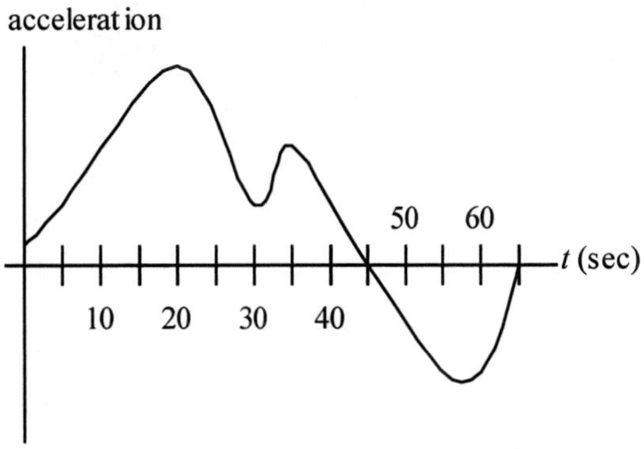

1. At what point in time was the car moving most rapidly? Explain your claim.

2. Sketch a possible graph of the velocity of the car as a function of time. You don't need to include scale on your vertical axis, but label all significant times on your graph.

3. Notice that the acceleration of the car has a relative maximum value at about $t = 20$ seconds. Make a plausible proposal for what could be happening with the car at that moment (i.e., "at that point in time the car crashed into a tree" or some physical action that could account for what the graph shows).

Practice Problems 12.3, Part 3

1. Suppose that $C(t)$ gives the concentration in the blood of a drug (in ng/ml) t hours after a dose of the drug is administered, and that $C'(t) = (40 - 12t)e^{-0.3t}$ and $C''(t) = (3.6t - 24)e^{-0.3t}$.

a. Determine how long it takes for the drug dose to reach peak concentration.

b. Find the locations (values of t) of all inflection points for the graph of $C(t)$. For each, explain the significance in terms of drug concentration.

2. Suppose that $g(x)$ is some function. The graph of $g'(x)$ is given to the right. At which of the marked values of x is

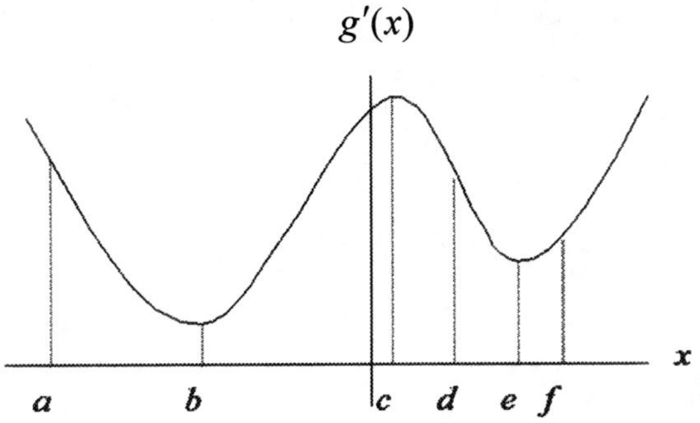

a. $g(x)$ greatest?

b. $g(x)$ least?

c. $g'(x)$ greatest?

d. $g'(x)$ least?

e. $g''(x)$ greatest

f. $g''(x)$ least?

Practice Problems 12.3, Part 4

In an effort to capitalize on the notoriety of a recent craze in California, Maria has decided to produce and sell stuffed toys, to be called "Maria's Math Monkeys". Preliminary market research suggests that the total revenue generated from selling x thousand of these items is reasonably approximated by $R(x) = 2.7x^2 - 0.04x^3$ thousands of dollars for $0 \le x \le 60$.

1. Use calculus to determine the level of sales that results in maximum revenue.

2. Use calculus to determine the level of sales where revenue is increasing most rapidly.

12.4 Analyzing Graphs

Mathematical curves are beautiful—their subtle form can be imitated by only the best of artists—and calculus gives us the tools we need to probe their secrets. While it is easy to use graphing technology to draw a graph, we must use calculus to understand what we are seeing. Following is a list of some of the most interesting features of the graph of a function.

Features of a Graph

1. ***The x- and y-intercepts:*** If $y = f(x)$, find the x-intercept(s) by setting $y = 0$ and solving for x; find the y-intercept by setting $x = 0$ and solving for y:

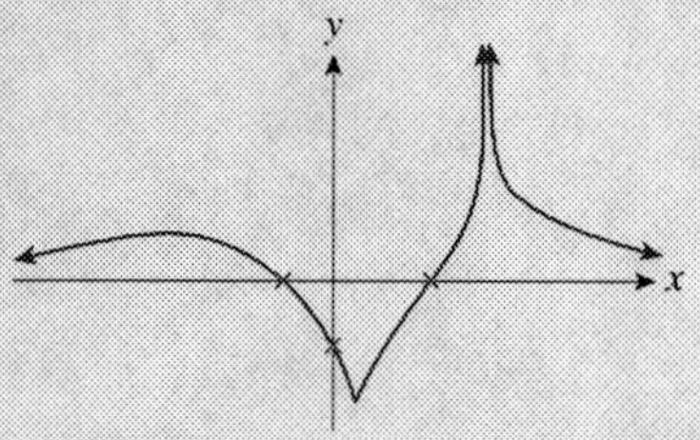

2. ***Extrema:*** Use the techniques of Section 12.1 to locate the maxima and minima:

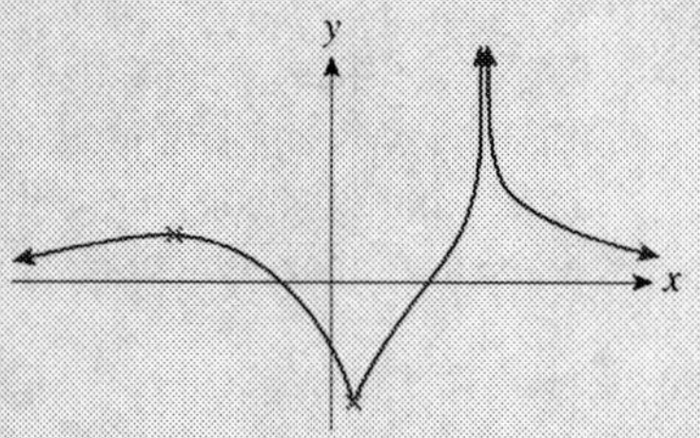

3. ***Points of inflection:*** Use the techniques of Section 12.2 to locate the points of inflection:

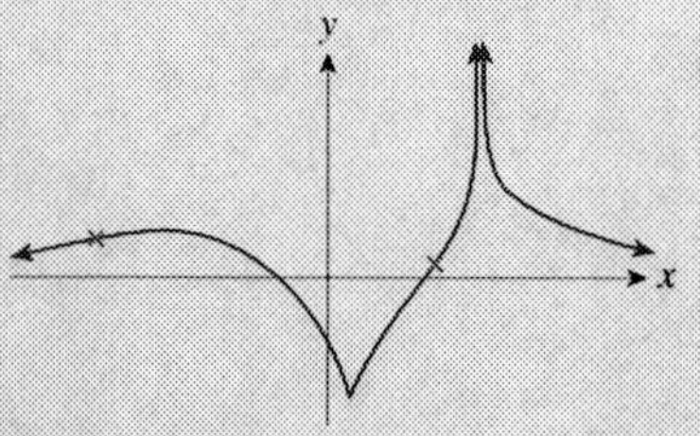

4. ***Behavior near points where the function is not defined:*** If $f(x)$ is not defined at $x = a$, consider $\lim_{x\to a^-} f(x)$ and $\lim_{x\to a^+} f(x)$ to see how the graph of f behaves as x approaches a:

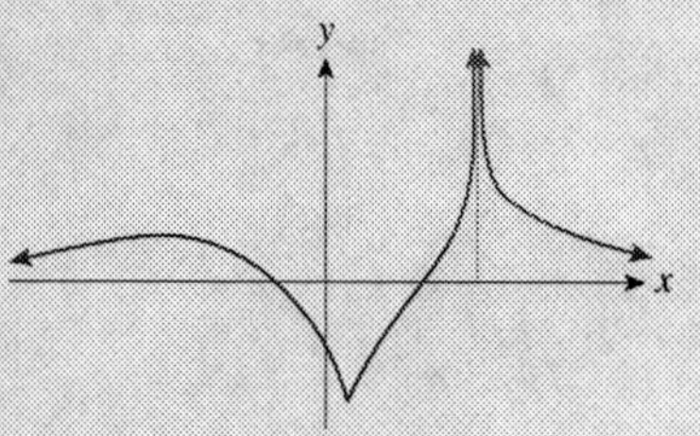

5. ***Behavior at infinity:*** Consider $\lim_{x \to -\infty} f(x)$ and $\lim_{x \to +\infty} f(x)$ if appropriate, to see how the graph of f behaves far to the left and right:

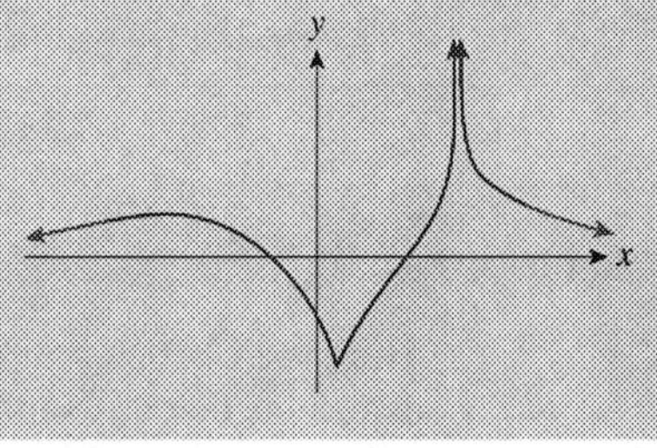

Note It is sometimes difficult or impossible to solve all of the equations that come up in Steps 1, 2, and 3 of the previous analysis. As a consequence, we might not be able to say exactly where the x-intercept, extrema, or points of inflection are. When this happens, we will use graphing technology to assist us in determining accurate numerical approximations. ■

EXAMPLE 1 Analyzing a Graph

Analyze the graph of $f(x) = \dfrac{1}{x} - \dfrac{1}{x^2}$.

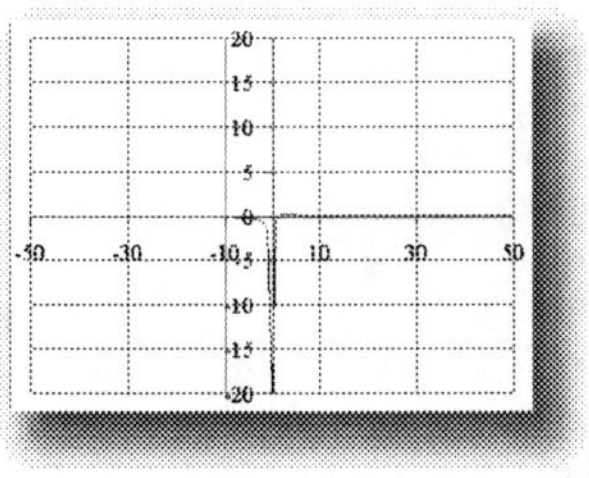

$-50 \le x \le 50, -20 \le y \le 20$

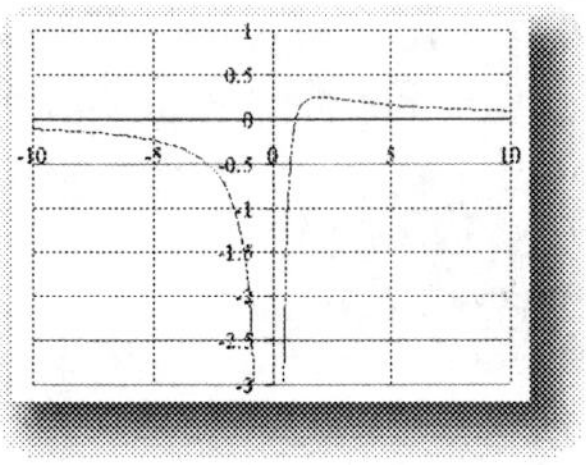

$-10 \le x \le 10, -3 \le y \le 1$

Figure 35

Solution The graph, as drawn using graphing technology, is shown in Figure 35, using two different viewing windows. (Note that $x = 0$ is not in the domain of f.) The second window in Figure 35 seems to show the features of the graph better than the first. Does the second viewing window include *all* the interesting features of the graph? Or are there perhaps some interesting features to the right of $x = 10$ or to the left of $x = -10$? Also, where exactly do features like maxima, minima, and points of inflection occur? In our five-step process of analyzing the interesting features of the graph, we will be able to sketch the curve by hand, and also answer these questions.

1. ***The x- and y-intercepts:*** We consider $y = \dfrac{1}{x} - \dfrac{1}{x^2}$. To find the x-intercept(s), we set $y = 0$ and solve for x:

$$0 = \frac{1}{x} - \frac{1}{x^2}$$

$$\frac{1}{x} = \frac{1}{x^2}.$$

Multiplying both sides by x^2 (we know that x cannot be zero, so we are not multiplying both sides by 0) gives

$$x = 1.$$

Thus, there is one x-intercept (which we can see in Figure 35) at $x = 1$.

For the y-intercept, we would substitute $x = 0$ and solve for y. However, we cannot substitute $x = 0$; because $f(0)$ is not defined, the graph does not meet the y-axis.

We add features to our freehand sketch as we go. Figure 36 shows what we have so far.

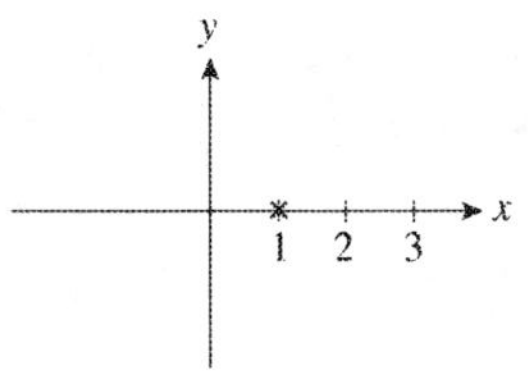

Figure 36

2. ***Relative extrema:*** We calculate $f'(x) = -\frac{1}{x^2} + \frac{2}{x^3}$. To find any stationary points, we set the derivative equal to 0 and solve for x:

$$-\frac{1}{x^2} + \frac{2}{x^3} = 0$$
$$\frac{1}{x^2} = \frac{2}{x^3}$$
$$x = 2.$$

Thus, there is one stationary point, at $x = 2$. We can use a test point to the right to determine that this stationary point is a relative maximum:

x	1 (Intercept)	2	3 (Test point)
$y = \frac{1}{x} - \frac{1}{x^2}$	0	$\frac{1}{4}$	$\frac{2}{9}$

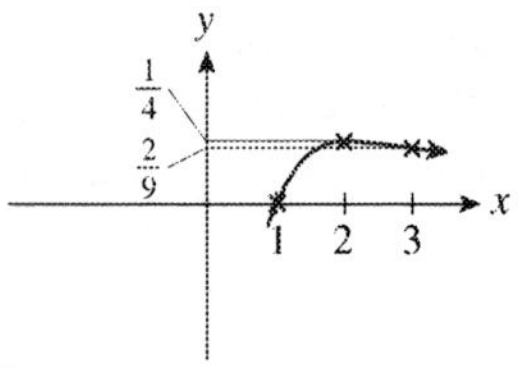

Figure 37

The only possible singular point is at $x = 0$ because $f'(0)$ is not defined. However, $f(0)$ is not defined either, so there are no singular points. Figure 37 shows our graph so far.

3. ***Points of inflection:*** We calculate $f''(x) = \frac{2}{x^3} - \frac{6}{x^4}$. To find points of inflection, we set the second derivative equal to 0 and solve for x:

$$\frac{2}{x^3} - \frac{6}{x^4} = 0$$
$$\frac{2}{x^3} = \frac{6}{x^4}$$
$$2x = 6$$
$$x = 3.$$

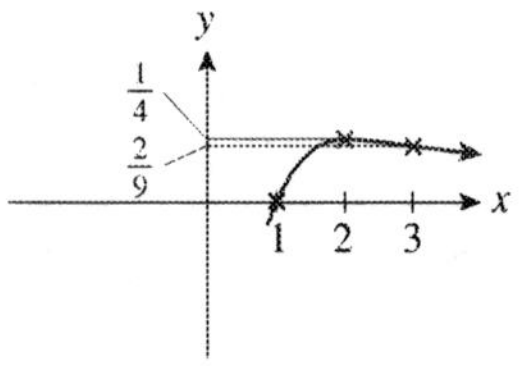

Figure 38

Figure 35 confirms that the graph of f changes from being concave down to being concave up at $x = 3$, so this is a point of inflection. $f''(x)$ is not defined at $x = 0$, but that is not in the domain, so there are no other points of inflection. In particular, the graph must be concave down in the whole region $(-\infty, 0)$, as we can see by calculating the second derivative at any one point in that interval: $f''(-1) = -8 < 0$.

Figure 38 shows our graph so far (we extended the curve near $x = 3$ to suggest a point of inflection at $x = 3$).

4. ***Behavior near points where f is not defined:*** The only point where $f(x)$ is not defined is $x = 0$. From the graph, $f(x)$ appears to go to $-\infty$ as x approaches 0 from either side. To calculate these limits, we rewrite $f(x)$:

$$f(x) = \frac{1}{x} - \frac{1}{x^2} = \frac{x-1}{x^2}.$$

Now, if x is close to 0 (on either side), the numerator $x - 1$ is close to -1 and the denominator is a very small but positive number. The quotient is therefore a negative number of very large magnitude. Therefore,

$$\lim_{x \to 0^-} f(x) = -\infty$$

and

$$\lim_{x \to 0^+} f(x) = -\infty.$$

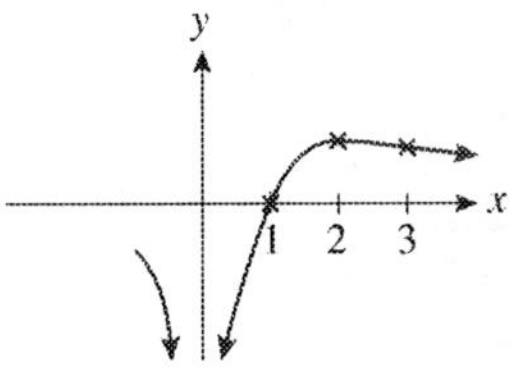

Figure 39

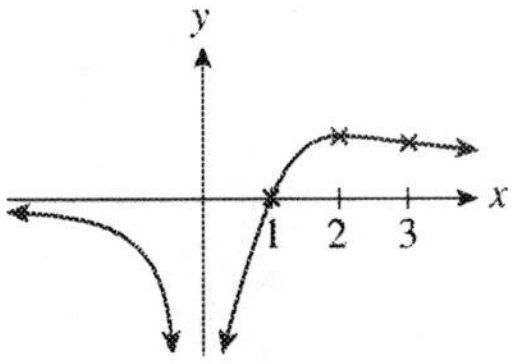

Figure 40

From these limits, we see the following:

(1) Immediately to the *left* of $x = 0$, the graph plunges down toward $-\infty$.

(2) Immediately to the *right* of $x = 0$, the graph also plunges down toward $-\infty$.

Figure 39 shows our graph with these features added. We say that f has a **vertical asymptote** at $x = 0$, meaning that the points on the graph of f get closer and closer to points on a vertical line (the y-axis in this case) further and further from the origin.

5. ***Behavior at infinity:*** Both $1/x$ and $1/x^2$ go to 0 as x goes to $-\infty$ or $+\infty$; that is,

$$\lim_{x \to -\infty} f(x) = 0$$

and

$$\lim_{x \to +\infty} f(x) = 0.$$

Thus, on the extreme left and right of our picture, the height of the curve levels off toward zero. Figure 40 shows the completed freehand sketch of the graph.

We say that f has a **horizontal asymptote** at $y = 0$. (Notice another thing: We haven't plotted a single point to the left of the y-axis, and yet we have a pretty good idea of what the curve looks like there! Compare the technology-drawn curve in Figure 35.)

In summary, there is one x-intercept at $x = 1$; there is one relative maximum (which, we can now see, is also an absolute maximum) at $x = 2$; there is one point of inflection at $x = 3$, where the graph changes from being concave down to concave up. There is a vertical asymptote at $x = 0$, on both sides of which the graph goes down toward $-\infty$, and a horizontal asymptote at $y = 0$.

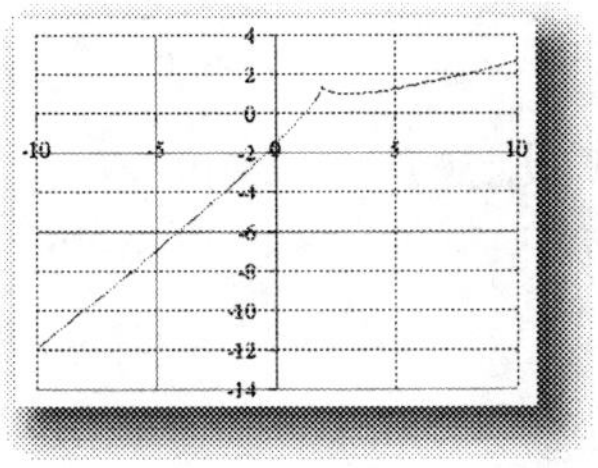

Technology:
2*x/3-((x-2)^2)^(1/3)

Figure 41

EXAMPLE 2 Analyzing a Graph

Analyze the graph of $f(x) = \dfrac{2x}{3} - (x-2)^{2/3}$.

Solution Figure 41 shows a technology-generated version of the graph. Note that in the technology formulation $(x-2)^{2/3}$ is written as $[(x-2)^2]^{1/3}$ to avoid problems with some graphing calculators and Excel.

Let us now re-create this graph by hand, and in the process identify the features we see in Figure 41.

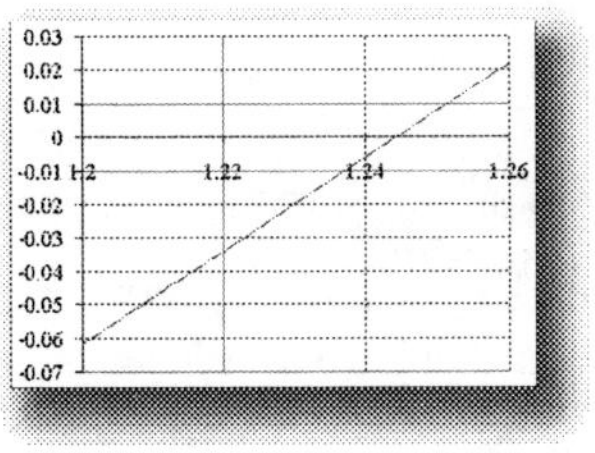

Figure 42

1. ***The x- and y-intercepts:*** We consider $y = \dfrac{2x}{3} - (x-2)^{2/3}$. For the y-intercept, we set $x = 0$ and solve for y:

$$y = \frac{2(0)}{3} - (0-2)^{2/3} = -2^{2/3} \approx -1.59.$$

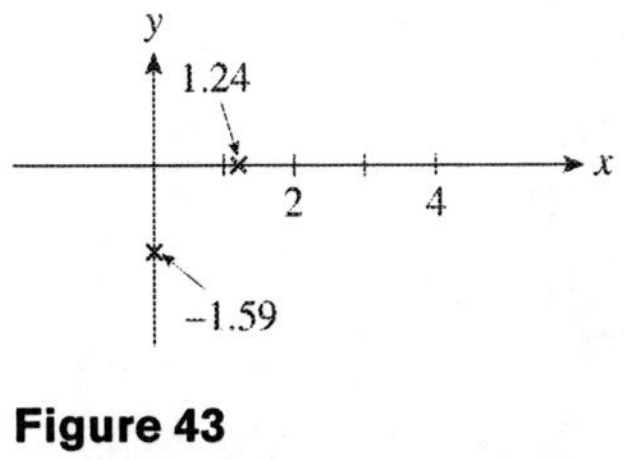

Figure 43

To find the x-intercept(s), we set $y = 0$ and solve for x. However, if we attempt this, we will find ourselves with a cubic equation that is hard to solve. (Try it!) Following the advice in the note on page 911, we use graphing technology to locate the x-intercept we see in Figure 41 by zooming in (Figure 42). From Figure 42, we find $x \approx 1.24$. We shall see in the discussion to follow that there can be no other x-intercepts.

Figure 43 shows our freehand sketch so far.

2. ***Relative extrema:*** We calculate

$$f'(x) = \frac{2}{3} - \frac{2}{3}(x-2)^{-1/3}$$
$$= \frac{2}{3} - \frac{2}{3(x-2)^{1/3}}.$$

To find any stationary points, we set the derivative equal to 0 and solve for x:

$$\frac{2}{3} - \frac{2}{3(x-2)^{1/3}} = 0$$
$$(x-2)^{1/3} = 1$$
$$x - 2 = 1^3 = 1$$
$$x = 3.$$

To check for singular points, look for points where $f(x)$ is defined and $f'(x)$ is not defined. The only such point is $x = 2$: $f'(x)$ is not defined at $x = 2$, whereas $f(x)$ is defined there, so we have a singular point at $x = 2$.

x	2 (Singular point)	3 (Stationary point)	4 (Test point)
$y = \frac{2x}{3} - (x-2)^{2/3}$	$\frac{4}{3}$	1	1.079

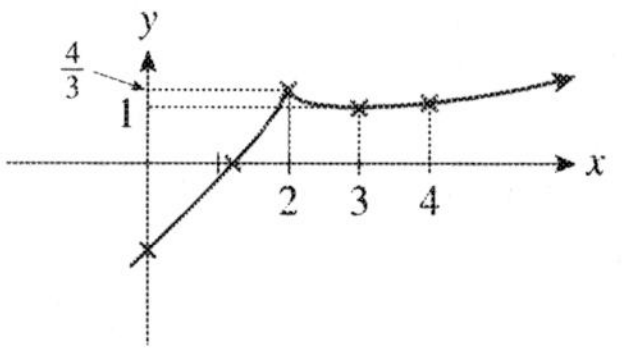

Figure 44

Figure 44 shows our graph so far.

We see that there is a singular relative maximum at (2, 4/3) (we will confirm that the graph eventually gets higher on the right) and a stationary relative minimum at $x = 3$.

3. ***Points of inflection:*** We calculate

$$f''(x) = \frac{2}{9(x-2)^{4/3}}.$$

To find points of inflection, we set the second derivative equal to 0 and solve for x. But the equation

$$0 = \frac{2}{9(x-2)^{4/3}}$$

has no solution for x, so there are no points of inflection on the graph.

4. ***Behavior near points where f is not defined:*** Because $f(x)$ is defined everywhere, there are no such points to consider. In particular, there are no vertical asymptotes.

5. ***Behavior at infinity:*** We estimate the following limits numerically:

$$\lim_{x\to-\infty}\left[\frac{2x}{3} - (x-2)^{2/3}\right] = -\infty$$

and

$$\lim_{x\to+\infty}\left[\frac{2x}{3} - (x-2)^{2/3}\right] = +\infty.$$

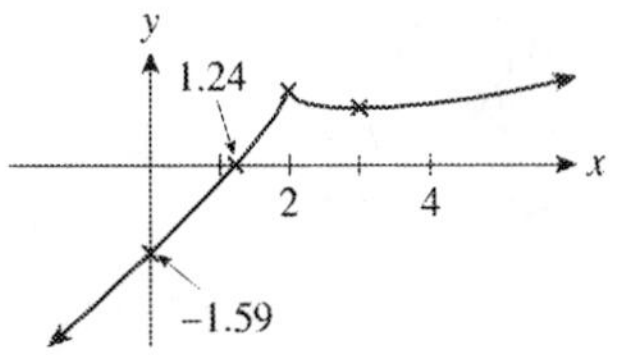

Figure 45

Thus, on the extreme left the curve goes down toward $-\infty$, and on the extreme right the curve rises toward $+\infty$. In particular, there are no horizontal asymptotes. (There can also be no other x-intercepts.)

Figure 45 shows the completed graph.

12.4 EXERCISES

▼ more advanced ◆ challenging

T indicates exercises that should be solved using technology

In Exercises 1–26, sketch the graph of the given function, indicating (a) x- and y-intercepts, (b) extrema, (c) points of inflection, (d) behavior near points where the function is not defined, and (e) behavior at infinity. Where indicated, technology should be used to approximate the intercepts, coordinates of extrema, and/or points of inflection to one decimal place. Check your sketch using technology. HINT [See Example 1.]

1. $f(x) = x^2 + 2x + 1$
2. $f(x) = -x^2 - 2x - 1$
3. $g(x) = x^3 - 12x$, domain $[-4, 4]$
4. $g(x) = 2x^3 - 6x$, domain $[-4, 4]$
5. $h(x) = 2x^3 - 3x^2 - 36x$ [Use technology for x-intercepts.]
6. $h(x) = -2x^3 - 3x^2 + 36x$ [Use technology for x-intercepts.]
7. $f(x) = 2x^3 + 3x^2 - 12x + 1$ [Use technology for x-intercepts.]
8. $f(x) = 4x^3 + 3x^2 + 2$ [Use technology for x-intercepts.]
9. $k(x) = -3x^4 + 4x^3 + 36x^2 + 10$ [Use technology for x-intercepts.]
10. $k(x) = 3x^4 + 4x^3 - 36x^2 - 10$ [Use technology for x-intercepts.]
11. $g(t) = \frac{1}{4}t^4 - \frac{2}{3}t^3 + \frac{1}{2}t^2$
12. $g(t) = 3t^4 - 16t^3 + 24t^2 + 1$
13. $f(x) = x + \frac{1}{x}$
14. $f(x) = x^2 + \frac{1}{x^2}$
15. $g(x) = x^3/(x^2 + 3)$
16. $g(x) = x^3/(x^2 - 3)$
17. $f(t) = \frac{t^2 + 1}{t^2 - 1}$, domain $[-2, 2]$, $t \neq \pm 1$
18. $f(t) = \frac{t^2 - 1}{t^2 + 1}$, domain $[-2, 2]$
19. $k(x) = \frac{2x}{3} + (x + 1)^{2/3}$ [Use technology for x-intercepts. HINT [See Example 2.]
20. $k(x) = \frac{2x}{5} - (x - 1)^{2/5}$ [Use technology for x-intercepts. HINT [See Example 2.]
21. $f(x) = x - \ln x$, domain $(0, +\infty)$
22. $f(x) = x - \ln x^2$, domain $(0, +\infty)$
23. $f(x) = x^2 + \ln x^2$ [Use technology for x-intercepts.]
24. $f(x) = 2x^2 + \ln x$ [Use technology for x-intercepts.]
25. $g(t) = e^t - t$, domain $[-1, 1]$
26. $g(t) = e^{-t^2}$

T *In Exercises 27–30, use technology to sketch the graph of the given function, labeling all relative and absolute extrema and points of inflection, and vertical and horizontal asymptotes. The coordinates of the extrema and points of inflection should be accurate to two decimal places.* HINT [To locate extrema accurately, plot the first derivative; to locate points of inflection accurately, plot the second derivative.]

27. ▼ $f(x) = x^4 - 2x^3 + x^2 - 2x + 1$
28. ▼ $f(x) = x^4 + x^3 + x^2 + x + 1$
29. ▼ $f(x) = e^x - x^3$
30. ▼ $f(x) = e^x - \frac{x^4}{4}$

APPLICATIONS

31. ***Home Prices*** The following graph approximates historical and projected median home prices in the United States for the period 2000–2020:[47]

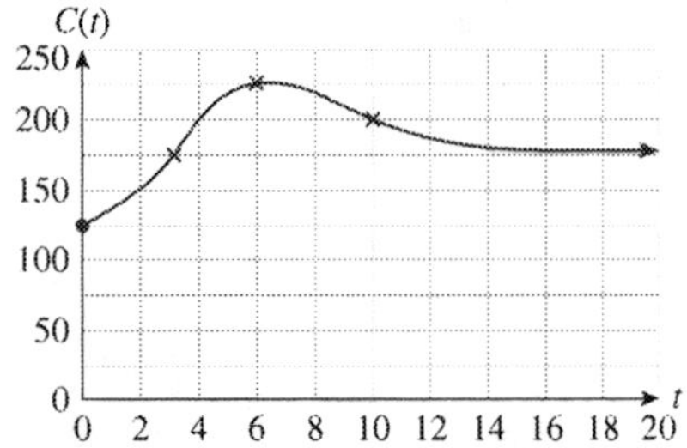

Here, t is time in years since the start of 2000 and $C(t)$ is the median home price in thousands of dollars. The locations of extrema and points of inflection are indicated on the graph. Analyze the graph's important features and interpret each feature in terms of the median home price.

32. ***Housing Starts*** The following graph approximates historical and projected numbers of housing starts of single-family homes each year in the United States for the period 2000–2020:[48]

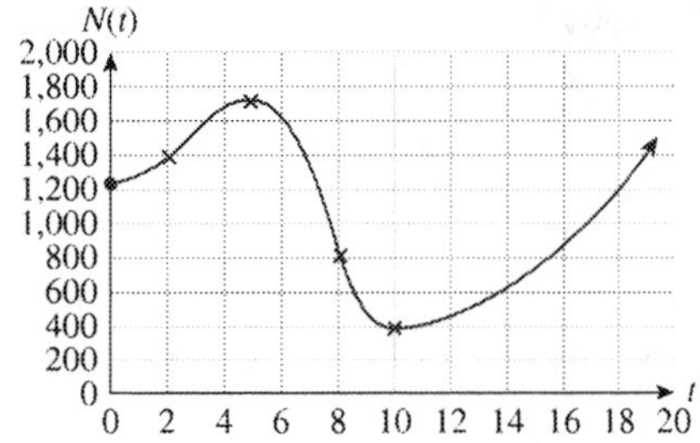

Here, t is time in years since 2000 and $N(t)$ is the number, in thousands, of housing starts per year. The locations of extrema and points of inflection are indicated on the graph. Analyze the graph's important features and interpret each feature in terms of the number of housing starts.

33. ***Consumer Price Index*** The following graph shows the approximate value of the U.S. Consumer Price Index (CPI) from July 2005 through March 2006.[49]

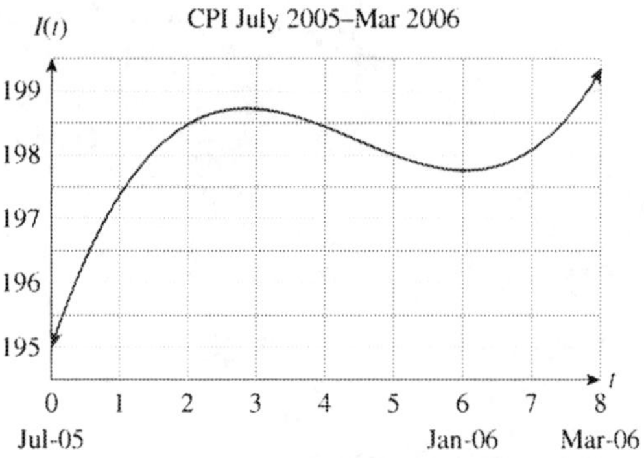

The approximating curve shown on the figure is given by

$$I(t) = 0.06t^3 - 0.8t^2 + 3.1t + 195 \quad (0 \le t \le 8),$$

where t is time in months ($t = 0$ represents July 2005).

a. Locate the intercepts, extrema, and points of inflection of the curve and interpret each feature in terms of the CPI. (Approximate all coordinates to one decimal place.) HINT [See Example 1.]

b. Recall from Section 12.2 that the inflation rate is defined to be $\dfrac{I'(t)}{I(t)}$. What do the stationary extrema of the curve shown above tell you about the inflation rate?

34. ***Consumer Price Index*** The following graph shows the approximate value of the U.S. Consumer Price Index (CPI) from March 2006 through May 2007.[50]

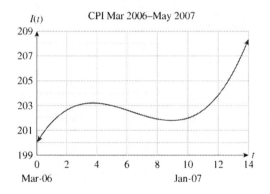

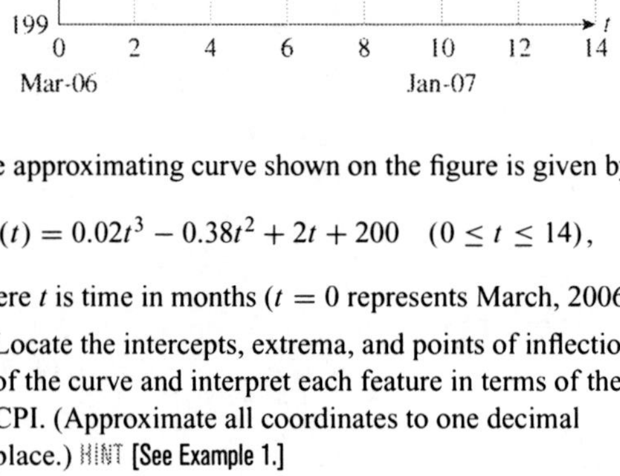

The approximating curve shown on the figure is given by

$$I(t) = 0.02t^3 - 0.38t^2 + 2t + 200 \quad (0 \le t \le 14),$$

where t is time in months ($t = 0$ represents March, 2006).

a. Locate the intercepts, extrema, and points of inflection of the curve and interpret each feature in terms of the CPI. (Approximate all coordinates to one decimal place.) HINT [See Example 1.]

[47] Values from 2012 on are authors' projections. Source for data through 2011: Zillow (www.zillow.com).

[48] Values from 2011 on are authors' projections. Source for data through 2010: U.S. Census Bureau (www.census.gov).

[49] The CPI is compiled by the Bureau of Labor Statistics and is based upon a 1982 value of 100. For instance, a CPI of 200 means the CPI has doubled since 1982. Source: InflationData.com. (www.inflationdata.com).

[50] *Ibid.*

b. Recall from Section 12.2 that the inflation rate is defined to be $\frac{I'(t)}{I(t)}$. What do the stationary extrema of the curve shown above tell you about the inflation rate?

35. ***Motion in a Straight Line*** The distance of a UFO from an observer is given by $s = 2t^3 - 3t^2 + 100$ feet after t seconds ($t \geq 0$). Obtain the extrema, points of inflection, and behavior at infinity. Sketch the curve and interpret these features in terms of the movement of the UFO.

36. ***Motion in a Straight Line*** The distance of the Mars orbiter from your location in Utarek, Mars is given by $s = 2(t-1)^3 - 3(t-1)^2 + 100$ km after t seconds ($t \geq 0$). Obtain the extrema, points of inflection, and behavior at infinity. Sketch the curve and interpret these features in terms of the movement of the Mars orbiter.

37. ***Average Cost: iPods*** Assume that it costs Apple approximately

$$C(x) = 22{,}500 + 100x + 0.01x^2$$

dollars to manufacture x 32 GB iPods in a day.[51] Obtain the average cost function, sketch its graph, and analyze the graph's important features. Interpret each feature in terms of iPods. HINT [Recall that the average cost function is $\bar{C}(x) = C(x)/x$.]

38. ***Average Cost: Xboxes*** Assume that it costs Microsoft approximately

$$C(x) = 14{,}400 + 550x + 0.01x^2$$

dollars to manufacture x Xbox 360s in a day.[52] Obtain the average cost function, sketch its graph, and analyze the graph's important features. Interpret each feature in terms of Xboxes. HINT [Recall that the average cost function is $\bar{C}(x) = C(x)/x$.]

39. ***Subprime Mortgages during the Housing Bubble*** During the real estate run-up in 2000–2008, the percentage of mortgages issued in the United States that were subprime (normally classified as risky) could be approximated by

$$A(t) = \frac{15.0}{1 + 8.6(1.8)^{-t}} \text{ percent} \qquad (0 \leq t \leq 8)$$

t years after the start of 2000.[53] Graph the *derivative* $A'(t)$ of $A(t)$ using an extended domain of $0 \leq t \leq 15$. Determine the approximate coordinates of the maximum and determine the behavior of $A'(t)$ at infinity. What do the answers tell you?

40. ***Subprime Mortgage Debt during the Housing Bubble*** During the real estate run-up in 2000–2008, the value of subprime (normally classified as risky) mortgage debt outstanding in the United States was approximately

$$A(t) = \frac{1{,}350}{1 + 4.2(1.7)^{-t}} \text{ billion dollars} \qquad (0 \leq t \leq 8)$$

t years after the start of 2000.[54] Graph the *derivative* $A'(t)$ of $A(t)$ using an extended domain of $0 \leq t \leq 15$. Determine the approximate coordinates of the maximum and determine the behavior of $A'(t)$ at infinity. What do the answers tell you?

COMMUNICATION AND REASONING EXERCISES

41. A function is *bounded* if its entire graph lies between two horizontal lines. Can a bounded function have vertical asymptotes? Can a bounded function have horizontal asymptotes? Explain.

42. A function is *bounded above* if its entire graph lies below some horizontal line. Can a bounded above function have vertical asymptotes? Can a bounded above function have horizontal asymptotes? Explain.

43. If the graph of a function has a vertical asymptote at $x = a$ in such a way that y increases to $+\infty$ as $x \to a$, what can you say about the graph of its derivative? Explain.

44. If the graph of a function has a horizontal asymptote at $y = a$ in such a way that y decreases to a as $x \to +\infty$, what can you say about the graph of its derivative? Explain.

45. Your friend tells you that he has found a continuous function defined on $(-\infty, +\infty)$ with exactly two critical points, each of which is a relative maximum. Can he be right?

46. Your other friend tells you that she has found a continuous function with two critical points, one a relative minimum and one a relative maximum, and no point of inflection between them. Can she be right?

47. By thinking about extrema, show that, if $f(x)$ is a polynomial, then between every pair of zeros (x-intercepts) of $f(x)$ there is a zero of $f'(x)$.

48. If $f(x)$ is a polynomial of degree 2 or higher, show that between every pair of relative extrema of $f(x)$ there is a point of inflection of $f(x)$.

[51] Not the actual cost equation; the authors do not know Apple's actual cost equation. The marginal cost in the model given is in rough agreement with the actual marginal cost for reasonable values of x for one of the 2007 models. Source for cost data: *Manufacturing & Technology News,* July 31, 2007 Volume 14, No. 14 (www.manufacturingnews.com).

[52] Not the actual cost equation; the authors do not know Microsoft's actual cost equation. The marginal cost in the model given is in rough agreement with the actual marginal cost for reasonable values of x. Source for estimate of marginal cost: iSuppli: (www.isuppli.com/news/xbox/).

[53] 2009 figure is an estimate. Sources: Mortgage Bankers Association, UBS.

[54] 2008–2009 figure are estimates. Source: www.data360.org/dataset.aspx?Data_Set_Id=9549.

12.5 Related Rates

We start by recalling some basic facts about the rate of change of a quantity:

Rate of Change of Q

If Q is a quantity changing over time t, then the derivative dQ/dt is the rate at which Q changes over time.

Quick Examples

1. If A is the area of an expanding circle, then dA/dt is the rate at which the area is increasing.
2. *Words:* The radius r of a sphere is currently 3 cm and increasing at a rate of 2 cm/sec.

   Symbols: $r = 3$ cm and $dr/dt = 2$ cm/sec.

In this section we are concerned with what are called **related rates** problems. In such a problem we have two (sometimes more) related quantities, we know the rate at which one is changing, and we wish to find the rate at which another is changing. A typical example is the following.

EXAMPLE 1 The Expanding Circle

The radius of a circle is increasing at a rate of 10 cm/sec. How fast is the area increasing at the instant when the radius has reached 5 cm?

Solution We have two related quantities: the radius of the circle, r, and its area, A. The first sentence of the problem tells us that r is increasing at a certain rate. When we see a sentence referring to speed or change, it is very helpful to rephrase the sentence using the phrase "the rate of change of." Here, we can say

The rate of change of r is 10 cm/sec.

Because the rate of change is the derivative, we can rewrite this sentence as the equation

$$\frac{dr}{dt} = 10.$$

Similarly, the second sentence of the problem asks how A is changing. We can rewrite that question:

What is the rate of change of A when the radius is 5 *cm?*

Using mathematical notation, the question is:

$$\text{What is } \frac{dA}{dt} \text{ when } r = 5?$$

Thus, knowing one rate of change, dr/dt, we wish to find a related rate of change, dA/dt. To find exactly how these derivatives are related, we need the equation relating the variables, which is

$$A = \pi r^2.$$

To find the relationship between the derivatives, we take the derivative of both sides of this equation *with respect to t*. On the left we get dA/dt. On the right we need to remember that r is a function of t and use the chain rule. We get

$$\frac{dA}{dt} = 2\pi r \frac{dr}{dt}.$$

Now we substitute the given values $r = 5$ and $dr/dt = 10$. This gives

$$\left.\frac{dA}{dt}\right|_{r=5} = 2\pi(5)(10) = 100\pi \approx 314 \text{ cm}^2/\text{sec}.$$

Thus, the area is increasing at the rate of 314 cm^2/sec when the radius is 5 cm.

We can organize our work as follows:

Solving a Related Rates Problem

A. The Problem

1. List the related, changing quantities.
2. Restate the problem in terms of rates of change. Rewrite the problem using mathematical notation for the changing quantities and their derivatives.

B. The Relationship

1. Draw a diagram, if appropriate, showing the changing quantities.
2. Find an equation or equations relating the changing quantities.
3. Take the derivative with respect to time of the equation(s) relating the quantities to get the **derived equation(s)**, which relate the rates of change of the quantities.

C. The Solution

1. Substitute into the derived equation(s) the given values of the quantities and their derivatives.
2. Solve for the derivative required.

We can illustrate the procedure with the "ladder problem" found in almost every calculus textbook.

EXAMPLE 2 The Falling Ladder

Jane is at the top of a 5-foot ladder when it starts to slide down the wall at a rate of 3 feet per minute. Jack is standing on the ground behind her. How fast is the base of the ladder moving when it hits him if Jane is 4 feet from the ground at that instant?

Solution The first sentence talks about (the top of) the ladder sliding down the wall. Thus, one of the changing quantities is the height of the top of the ladder. The question asked refers to the motion of the base of the ladder, so another changing quantity is the distance of the base of the ladder from the wall. Let's record these variables and follow the outline above to obtain the solution.

A. The Problem

1. The changing quantities are

h = height of the top of the ladder
b = distance of the base of the ladder from the wall

2. We rephrase the problem in words, using the phrase "rate of change":

The rate of change of the height of the top of the ladder is -3 *feet per minute. What is the rate of change of the distance of the base from the wall when the top of the ladder is* 4 *feet from the ground?*

We can now rewrite the problem mathematically:

$$\frac{dh}{dt} = -3. \text{ Find } \frac{db}{dt} \text{ when } h = 4.$$

Figure 46

B. The Relationship

1. Figure 46 shows the ladder and the variables h and b. Notice that we put in the figure the fixed length, 5, of the ladder, but any changing quantities, like h and b, we leave as variables. We shall not use any specific values for h or b until the very end.

2. From the figure, we can see that h and b are related by the Pythagorean theorem:

$$h^2 + b^2 = 25.$$

3. Taking the derivative with respect to time of the equation above gives us the derived equation:

$$2h\frac{dh}{dt} + 2b\frac{db}{dt} = 0.$$

C. The Solution

1. We substitute the known values $dh/dt = -3$ and $h = 4$ into the derived equation:

$$2(4)(-3) + 2b\frac{db}{dt} = 0.$$

We would like to solve for db/dt, but first we need the value of b, which we can determine from the equation $h^2 + b^2 = 25$, using the value $h = 4$:

$$16 + b^2 = 25$$
$$b^2 = 9$$
$$b = 3.$$

Substituting into the derived equation, we get

$$-24 + 2(3)\frac{db}{dt} = 0.$$

2. Solving for db/dt gives

$$\frac{db}{dt} = \frac{24}{6} = 4.$$

Thus, the base of the ladder is sliding away from the wall at 4 ft/min when it hits Jack.

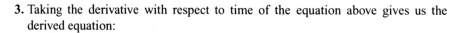

EXAMPLE 3 Average Cost

The cost to manufacture x cellphones in a day is

$$C(x) = 10{,}000 + 20x + \frac{x^2}{10{,}000} \text{ dollars.}$$

The daily production level is currently $x = 5{,}000$ cellphones and is increasing at a rate of 100 units per day. How fast is the average cost changing?

Solution

A. The Problem

1. The changing quantities are the production level x and the average cost, $\bar{C}$.

2. We rephrase the problem as follows:

> *The daily production level is* $x = 5{,}000$ *units and the rate of change of* x *is* 100 *units/day. What is the rate of change of the average cost,* $\bar{C}$*?*

In mathematical notation,

$$x = 5{,}000 \text{ and } \frac{dx}{dt} = 100. \text{ Find } \frac{d\bar{C}}{dt}.$$

B. The Relationship

1. In this example the changing quantities cannot easily be depicted geometrically.

2. We are given a formula for the *total* cost. We get the *average* cost by dividing the total cost by x:

$$\bar{C} = \frac{C}{x}.$$

So,

$$\bar{C} = \frac{10{,}000}{x} + 20 + \frac{x}{10{,}000}.$$

3. Taking derivatives with respect to t of both sides, we get the derived equation:

$$\frac{d\bar{C}}{dt} = \left(-\frac{10{,}000}{x^2} + \frac{1}{10{,}000}\right)\frac{dx}{dt}.$$

C. The Solution

Substituting the values from part A into the derived equation, we get

$$\frac{d\bar{C}}{dt} = \left(-\frac{10{,}000}{5{,}000^2} + \frac{1}{10{,}000}\right)100$$

$$= -0.03 \text{ dollars/day.}$$

Thus, the average cost is decreasing by 3¢ per day.

The scenario in the following example is similar to Example 5 in Section 12.2.

EXAMPLE 4 Allocation of Labor

The Gym Sock Company manufactures cotton athletic socks. Production is partially automated through the use of robots. The number of pairs of socks the company can manufacture in a day is given by a Cobb-Douglas production formula:

$$q = 50n^{0.6}r^{0.4},$$

where q is the number of pairs of socks that can be manufactured by n laborers and r robots. The company currently produces 1,000 pairs of socks each day and employs 20 laborers. It is bringing one new robot on line every month. At what rate are laborers being laid off, assuming that the number of socks produced remains constant?

Solution

A. The Problem

1. The changing quantities are the number of laborers n and the number of robots r.

2. $\frac{dr}{dt} = 1$. Find $\frac{dn}{dt}$ when $n = 20$.

B. The Relationship

1. No diagram is appropriate here.

2. The equation relating the changing quantities:

$$1{,}000 = 50n^{0.6}r^{0.4} \qquad \text{Productivity is constant at 1,000 pairs of socks each day.}$$

or

$$20 = n^{0.6}r^{0.4}.$$

3. The derived equation is

$$0 = 0.6n^{-0.4}\left(\frac{dn}{dt}\right)r^{0.4} + 0.4n^{0.6}r^{-0.6}\left(\frac{dr}{dt}\right)$$

$$= 0.6\left(\frac{r}{n}\right)^{0.4}\left(\frac{dn}{dt}\right) + 0.4\left(\frac{n}{r}\right)^{0.6}\left(\frac{dr}{dt}\right).$$

We solve this equation for dn/dt because we shall want to find dn/dt below and because the equation becomes simpler when we do this:

$$0.6\left(\frac{r}{n}\right)^{0.4}\left(\frac{dn}{dt}\right) = -0.4\left(\frac{n}{r}\right)^{0.6}\left(\frac{dr}{dt}\right)$$

$$\frac{dn}{dt} = -\frac{0.4}{0.6}\left(\frac{n}{r}\right)^{0.6}\left(\frac{n}{r}\right)^{0.4}\left(\frac{dr}{dt}\right)$$

$$= -\frac{2}{3}\left(\frac{n}{r}\right)\left(\frac{dr}{dt}\right).$$

C. The Solution

Substituting the numbers in A into the last equation in B, we get

$$\frac{dn}{dt} = -\frac{2}{3}\left(\frac{20}{r}\right)(1).$$

We need to compute r by substituting the known value of n in the original formula:

$$20 = n^{0.6}r^{0.4}$$
$$20 = 20^{0.6}r^{0.4}$$
$$r^{0.4} = \frac{20}{20^{0.6}} = 20^{0.4}$$
$$r = 20.$$

Thus,

$$\frac{dn}{dt} = -\frac{2}{3}\left(\frac{20}{20}\right)(1) = -\frac{2}{3} \text{ laborers per month.}$$

The company is laying off laborers at a rate of 2/3 per month, or two every three months.

We can interpret this result as saying that, at the current level of production and number of laborers, one robot is as productive as 2/3 of a laborer, or 3 robots are as productive as 2 laborers.

12.5 EXERCISES

▼ more advanced ◆ challenging

indicates exercises that should be solved using technology

Rewrite the statements and questions in Exercises 1–8 in mathematical notation. HINT [See Quick Examples on page 918.]

1. The population P is currently 10,000 and growing at a rate of 1,000 per year.
2. There are presently 400 cases of Bangkok flu, and the number is growing by 30 new cases every month.
3. The annual revenue of your tie-dye T-shirt operation is currently \$7,000 but is decreasing by \$700 each year. How fast are annual sales changing?
4. A ladder is sliding down a wall so that the distance between the top of the ladder and the floor is decreasing at a rate of 3 feet per second. How fast is the base of the ladder receding from the wall?
5. The price of shoes is rising \$5 per year. How fast is the demand changing?
6. Stock prices are rising \$1,000 per year. How fast is the value of your portfolio increasing?
7. The average global temperature is 60°F and rising by 0.1°F per decade. How fast are annual sales of Bermuda shorts increasing?
8. The country's population is now 260,000,000 and is increasing by 1,000,000 people per year. How fast is the annual demand for diapers increasing?

APPLICATIONS

9. ***Sun Spots*** The area of a circular sun spot is growing at a rate of 1,200 km²/sec.
   a. How fast is the radius growing at the instant when it equals 10,000 km? HINT [See Example 1.]
   b. How fast is the radius growing at the instant when the sun spot has an area of 640,000 km²? HINT [Use the area formula to determine the radius at that instant.]
10. ***Puddles*** The radius of a circular puddle is growing at a rate of 5 cm/sec.
    a. How fast is its area growing at the instant when the radius is 10 cm? HINT [See Example 1.]
    b. How fast is the area growing at the instant when it equals 36 cm²? HINT [Use the area formula to determine the radius at that instant.]
11. ***Balloons*** A spherical party balloon is being inflated with helium pumped in at a rate of 3 cubic feet per minute. How fast is the radius growing at the instant when the radius has reached 1 foot? (The volume of a sphere of radius r is $V = \frac{4}{3}\pi r^3$.) HINT [See Example 1.]
12. ***More Balloons*** A rather flimsy spherical balloon is designed to pop at the instant its radius has reached 10 centimeters. Assuming the balloon is filled with helium at a rate of 10 cubic centimeters per second, calculate how fast the radius is growing at the instant it pops. (The volume of a sphere of radius r is $V = \frac{4}{3}\pi r^3$.) HINT [See Example 1.]

13. ***Sliding Ladders*** The base of a 50-foot ladder is being pulled away from a wall at a rate of 10 feet per second. How fast is the top of the ladder sliding down the wall at the instant when the base of the ladder is 30 feet from the wall? HINT [See Example 2.]

14. ***Sliding Ladders*** The top of a 5-foot ladder is sliding down a wall at a rate of 10 feet per second. How fast is the base of the ladder sliding away from the wall at the instant when the top of the ladder is 3 feet from the ground? HINT [See Example 2.]

15. ***Average Cost*** The average cost function for the weekly manufacture of portable CD players is given by

$$\bar{C}(x) = 150{,}000x^{-1} + 20 + 0.0001x \text{ dollars per player,}$$

where x is the number of CD players manufactured that week. Weekly production is currently 3,000 players and is increasing at a rate of 100 players per week. What is happening to the average cost? HINT [See Example 3.]

16. ***Average Cost*** Repeat the preceding exercise, using the revised average cost function

$$\bar{C}(x) = 150{,}000x^{-1} + 20 + 0.01x \text{ dollars per player.}$$

HINT [See Example 3.]

17. ***Demand*** Demand for your tie-dyed T-shirts is given by the formula

$$q = 500 - 100p^{0.5},$$

where q is the number of T-shirts you can sell each month at a price of p dollars. If you currently sell T-shirts for \$15 each and you raise your price by \$2 per month, how fast will the demand drop? (Round your answer to the nearest whole number.)

18. ***Supply*** The number of portable CD players you are prepared to supply to a retail outlet every week is given by the formula

$$q = 0.1p^2 + 3p,$$

where p is the price it offers you. The retail outlet is currently offering you \$40 per CD player. If the price it offers decreases at a rate of \$2 per week, how will this affect the number you supply?

19. ***Revenue*** You can now sell 50 cups of lemonade per week at 30¢ per cup, but demand is dropping at a rate of 5 cups per week each week. Assuming that raising the price does not affect demand, how fast do you have to raise your price if you want to keep your weekly revenue constant? HINT [Revenue = Price × Quantity.]

20. ***Revenue*** You can now sell 40 cars per month at \$20,000 per car, and demand is increasing at a rate of 3 cars per month each month. What is the fastest you could drop your price before your monthly revenue starts to drop? HINT [Revenue = Price × Quantity.]

21. ▼ ***Oil Revenues*** Daily oil production by Pemex, Mexico's national oil company, can be approximated by

$$q(t) = -0.022t^2 + 0.2t + 2.9 \text{ million barrels} \quad (1 \le t \le 9),$$

where t is time in years since the start of 2000.[55]

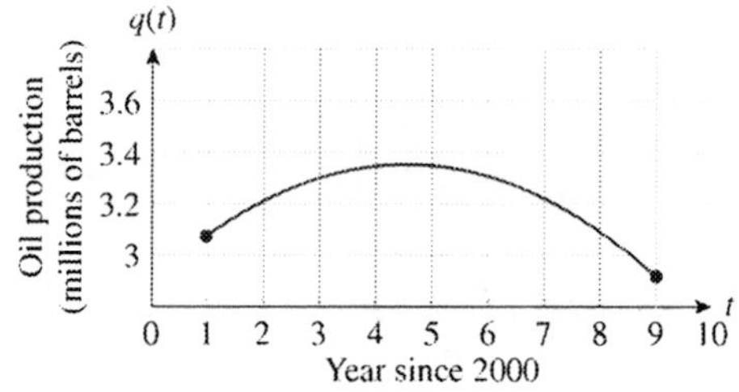

At the start of 2008 the price of oil was \$90 per barrel and increasing at a rate of \$80 per year.[56] How fast was Pemex's oil (daily) revenue changing at that time?

22. ▼ ***Oil Expenditures*** Daily oil imports to the United States from Mexico can be approximated by

$$q(t) = -0.015t^2 + 0.1t + 1.4 \text{ million barrels} \quad (0 \le t \le 8),$$

where t is time in years since the start of 2000.[57]

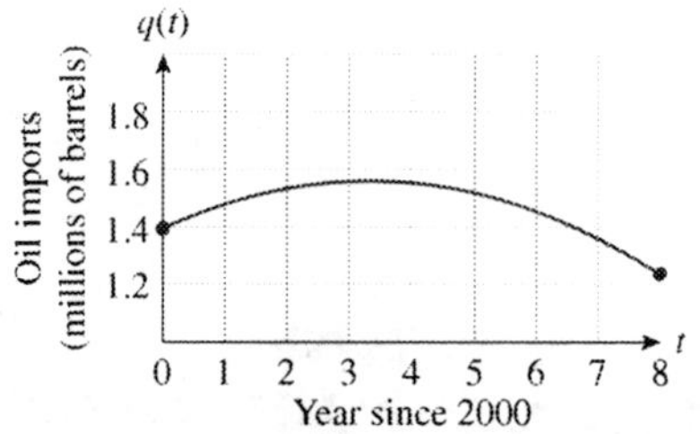

At the start of 2004 the price of oil was \$30 per barrel and increasing at a rate of \$40 per year.[58] How fast was (daily) oil expenditure for imports from Mexico changing at that time?

23. ***Resource Allocation*** Your company manufactures automobile alternators, and production is partially automated through the use of robots. In order to meet production deadlines, your company calculates that the numbers of laborers and robots must satisfy the constraint

$$xy = 10{,}000,$$

where x is the number of laborers and y is the number of robots. Your company currently uses 400 robots and is increasing robot deployment at a rate of 16 per month. How fast is it laying off laborers? HINT [See Example 4.]

24. ***Resource Allocation*** Your company is the largest sock manufacturer in the Solar System, and production is automated through the use of androids and robots. In order to meet production deadlines, your company calculates that the numbers of androids and robots must satisfy the constraint

$$xy = 1{,}000{,}000,$$

[55] Source for data: Energy Information Administration/Pemex (www.eia.doe.gov).

[56] Based on NYMEX crude oil futures; average rate of change during January–June, 2008.

[57] Source for data: Energy Information Administration/Pemex (www.eia.doe.gov).

[58] Based on NYMEX crude oil futures; average rate of change during 2004–2005.

where x is the number of androids and y is the number of robots. Your company currently uses 5000 androids and is increasing android deployment at a rate of 200 per month. How fast is it scrapping robots? HINT [See Example 4.]

25. *Production* The automobile assembly plant you manage has a Cobb-Douglas production function given by

$$P = 10x^{0.3}y^{0.7},$$

where P is the number of automobiles it produces per year, x is the number of employees, and y is the daily operating budget (in dollars). You maintain a production level of 1,000 automobiles per year. If you currently employ 150 workers and are hiring new workers at a rate of 10 per year, how fast is your daily operating budget changing? HINT [See Example 4.]

26. *Production* Refer back to the Cobb-Douglas production formula in the preceding exercise. Assume that you maintain a constant workforce of 200 workers and wish to increase production in order to meet a demand that is increasing by 100 automobiles per year. The current demand is 1000 automobiles per year. How fast should your daily operating budget be increasing? HINT [See Example 4.]

27. *Demand* Assume that the demand equation for tuna in a small coastal town is

$$pq^{1.5} = 50{,}000,$$

where q is the number of pounds of tuna that can be sold in one month at the price of p dollars per pound. The town's fishery finds that the demand for tuna is currently 900 pounds per month and is increasing at a rate of 100 pounds per month each month. How fast is the price changing?

28. *Demand* The demand equation for rubies at *Royal Ruby Retailers* is

$$q + \frac{4}{3}p = 80,$$

where q is the number of rubies RRR can sell per week at p dollars per ruby. RRR finds that the demand for its rubies is currently 20 rubies per week and is dropping at a rate of one ruby per week. How fast is the price changing?

29. ▼ ***Ships Sailing Apart*** The H.M.S. *Dreadnaught* is 40 miles south of Montauk and steaming due south at 20 miles/hour, while the U.S.S. *Mona Lisa* is 50 miles east of Montauk and steaming due east at an even 30 miles/hour. How fast is their distance apart increasing?

30. ▼ ***Near Miss*** My aunt and I were approaching the same intersection, she from the south and I from the west. She was traveling at a steady speed of 10 miles/hour, while I was approaching the intersection at 60 miles/hour. At a certain instant in time, I was one tenth of a mile from the intersection, while she was one twentieth of a mile from it. How fast were we approaching each other at that instant?

31. ▼ ***Baseball*** A baseball diamond is a square with side 90 ft.

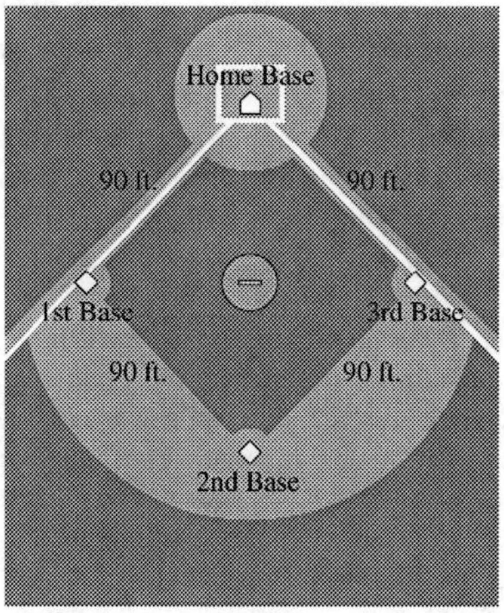

A batter at home base hits the ball and runs toward first base with a speed of 24 ft/sec. At what rate is his distance from third base increasing when he is halfway to first base?

32. ▼ ***Baseball*** Refer to Exercise 31. Another player is running from third base to home at 30 ft/sec. How fast is her distance from second base increasing when she is 60 feet from third base?

33. ▼ ***Movement along a Graph*** A point on the graph of $y = 1/x$ is moving along the curve in such a way that its x-coordinate is increasing at a rate of 4 units per second. What is happening to the y-coordinate at the instant the y-coordinate is equal to 2?

34. ▼ ***Motion around a Circle*** A point is moving along the circle $x^2 + (y - 1)^2 = 8$ in such a way that its x-coordinate is decreasing at a rate of 1 unit per second. What is happening to the y-coordinate at the instant when the point has reached $(-2, 3)$?

35. ▼ ***Education*** In 1991, the expected income of an individual depended on his or her educational level according to the following formula:

$$I(n) = 2.929n^3 - 115.9n^2 + 1{,}530n - 6{,}760 \text{ thousand dollars } (12 \le n \le 15).$$

Here, n is the number of school years completed and $I(n)$ is the individual's expected income in thousands of dollars.[59] It is 1991, and you have completed 13 years of school and are currently a part-time student. Your schedule is such that you will complete the equivalent of one year of college every three years. Assuming that your salary is linked to the above model, how fast is your income going up? (Round your answer to the nearest \$1.)

[59]The model is a based on Table 358, U.S. Department of Education, *Digest of Education Statistics, 1991*, Washington, DC: Government Printing Office, 1991.

36. ***Education*** Refer back to the model in the preceding exercise. Assume that you have completed 14 years of school and that your income is increasing by \$5,000 per year. How much schooling per year is this rate of increase equivalent to?

37. ***Employment*** An employment research company estimates that the value of a recent MBA graduate to an accounting company is

$$V = 3e^2 + 5g^3,$$

where V is the value of the graduate, e is the number of years of prior business experience, and g is the graduate school grade-point average. A company that currently employs graduates with a 3.0 average wishes to maintain a constant employee value of $V = 200$, but finds that the grade-point average of its new employees is dropping at a rate of 0.2 per year. How fast must the experience of its new employees be growing in order to compensate for the decline in grade point average?

38. ***Grades***[60] A production formula for a student's performance on a difficult English examination is given by

$$g = 4hx - 0.2h^2 - 10x^2,$$

where g is the grade the student can expect to obtain, h is the number of hours of study for the examination, and x is the student's grade point average. The instructor finds that students' grade point averages have remained constant at 3.0 over the years, and that students currently spend an average of 15 hours studying for the examination. However, scores on the examination are dropping at a rate of 10 points per year. At what rate is the average study time decreasing?

39. ***Cones*** A right circular conical vessel is being filled with green industrial waste at a rate of 100 cubic meters per second. How fast is the level rising after 200π cubic meters have been poured in? The cone has a height of 50 m and a radius of 30 m at its brim. (The volume of a cone of height h and cross-sectional radius r at its brim is given by $V = \frac{1}{3}\pi r^2 h$.)

40. ***More Cones*** A circular conical vessel is being filled with ink at a rate of 10 cm^3/sec. How fast is the level rising after 20 cm^3 have been poured in? The cone has height 50 cm and radius 20 cm at its brim. (The volume of a cone of height h and cross-sectional radius r at its brim is given by $V = \frac{1}{3}\pi r^2 h$.)

41. ***Cylinders*** The volume of paint in a right cylindrical can is given by $V = 4t^2 - t$ where t is time in seconds and V is the volume in cm^3. How fast is the level rising when the height is 2 cm? The can has a height of 4 cm and a radius of 2 cm. HINT [To get h as a function of t, first solve the volume $V = \pi r^2 h$ for h.]

42. ***Cylinders*** A cylindrical bucket is being filled with paint at a rate of 6 cm^3 per minute. How fast is the level rising when the bucket starts to overflow? The bucket has a radius of 30 cm and a height of 60 cm.

43. ***Computers vs. Income*** The demand for personal computers in the home goes up with household income. For a given community, we can approximate the average number of computers in a home as

$$q = 0.3454 \ln x - 3.047 \quad (10{,}000 \le x \le 125{,}000),$$

where x is mean household income.[61] Your community has a mean income of \$30,000, increasing at a rate of \$2,000 per year. How many computers per household are there, and how fast is the number of computers in a home increasing? (Round your answer to four decimal places.)

44. ***Computers vs. Income*** Refer back to the model in the preceding exercise. The average number of computers per household in your town is 0.5 and is increasing at a rate of 0.02 computers per household per year. What is the average household income in your town, and how fast is it increasing? (Round your answers to the nearest \$10).

Education and Crime *The following graph compares the total U.S. prison population and the average combined SAT score in the United States during the 1970s and 1980s:*

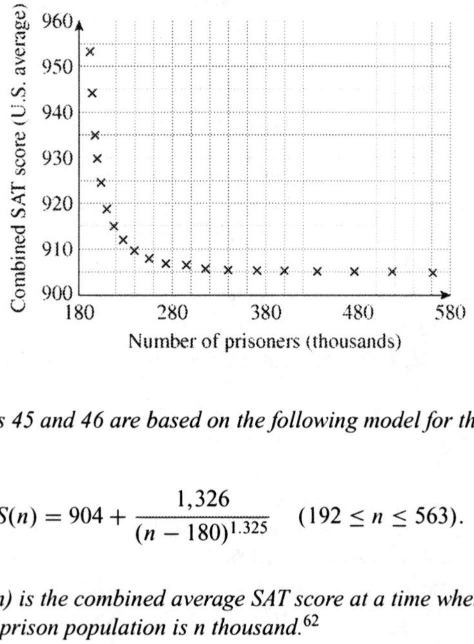

Exercises 45 and 46 are based on the following model for these data:

$$S(n) = 904 + \frac{1{,}326}{(n - 180)^{1.325}} \quad (192 \le n \le 563).$$

Here, S(n) is the combined average SAT score at a time when the total prison population is n thousand.[62]

45. In 1985, the U.S. prison population was 475,000 and increasing at a rate of 35,000 per year. What was the average SAT score, and how fast, and in what direction, was it changing? (Round your answers to two decimal places.)

60 Based on an Exercise in *Introduction to Mathematical Economics* by A.L. Ostrosky Jr. and J.V. Koch (Waveland Press, Illinois, 1979).

61 The model is a regression model. Source for data: Income distribution: Computer data: Forrester Research/*New York Times*, August 8, 1999, p. BU4.

62 Based on data for the years 1967–1989. Sources: Sourcebook of Criminal Justice Statistics, 1990, p. 604/Educational Testing Service.

46. ▼ In 1970, the U.S. combined SAT average was 940 and dropping by 10 points per year. What was the U.S. prison population, and how fast, and in what direction, was it changing? (Round your answers to the nearest 100.)

Divorce Rates *A study found that the divorce rate d (given as a percentage) appears to depend on the ratio r of available men to available women.*[63] *This function can be approximated by*

$$d(r) = \begin{cases} -40r + 74 & \text{if } r \le 1.3 \\ \dfrac{130r}{3} - \dfrac{103}{3} & \text{if } r > 1.3 \end{cases}.$$

Exercises 47 and 48 are based on this model.

47. ◆ There are currently 1.1 available men per available woman in Littleville, and this ratio is increasing by 0.05 per year. What is happening to the divorce rate?

48. ◆ There are currently 1.5 available men per available woman in Largeville, and this ratio is decreasing by 0.03 per year. What is happening to the divorce rate?

COMMUNICATION AND REASONING EXERCISES

49. Why is this section titled "related rates"?

50. If you know how fast one quantity is changing and need to compute how fast a second quantity is changing, what kind of information do you need?

51. In a related rates problem, there is no limit to the number of changing quantities we can consider. Illustrate this by creating a related rates problem with four changing quantities.

[63] The cited study, by Scott J. South and associates, appeared in the *American Sociological Review* (February, 1995). Figures are rounded. Source: *New York Times*, February 19, 1995, p. 40.

52. If three quantities are related by a single equation, how would you go about computing how fast one of them is changing based on a knowledge of the other two?

53. ▼ The demand and unit price for your store's checkered T-shirts are changing with time. Show that the percentage rate of change of revenue equals the sum of the percentage rates of change of price and demand. (The percentage rate of change of a quantity Q is $Q'(t)/Q(t)$.)

54. ▼ The number N of employees and the total floor space S of your company are both changing with time. Show that the percentage rate of change of square footage per employee equals the percentage rate of change of S minus the percentage rate of change of N. (The percentage rate of change of a quantity Q is $Q'(t)/Q(t)$.)

55. ▼ In solving a related rates problem, a key step is solving the derived equation for the unknown rate of change (once we have substituted the other values into the equation). Call the unknown rate of change X. The derived equation is what kind of equation in X?

56. ▼ On a recent exam, you were given a related rates problem based on an algebraic equation relating two variables x and y. Your friend told you that the correct relationship between dx/dt and dy/dt was given by

$$\left(\frac{dx}{dt}\right) = \left(\frac{dy}{dt}\right)^2.$$

Could he be correct?

57. ▼ Transform the following into a mathematical statement about derivatives: If my grades are improving at twice the speed of yours, then your grades are improving at half the speed of mine.

58. ▼ If two quantities x and y are related by a linear equation, how are their rates of change related?

12.6 Elasticity

You manufacture an extremely popular brand of sneakers and want to know what will happen if you increase the selling price. Common sense tells you that demand will drop as you raise the price. But will the drop in demand be enough to cause your revenue to fall? Or will it be small enough that your revenue will rise because of the higher selling price? For example, if you raise the price by 1%, you might suffer only a 0.5% loss in sales. In this case, the loss in sales will be more than offset by the increase in price and your revenue will rise. In such a case, we say that the demand is **inelastic**, because it is not very sensitive to the increase in price. On the other hand, if your 1% price increase results in a 2% drop in demand, then raising the price will cause a drop in revenues. We then say that the demand is **elastic** because it reacts strongly to a price change.

We can use calculus to measure the response of demand to price changes if we have a demand equation for the item we are selling.* We need to know the *percentage drop in demand per percentage increase in price.* This ratio is called the **elasticity of demand**, or **price elasticity of demand**, and is usually denoted by E. Let's derive a formula for E in terms of the demand equation.

Assume that we have a demand equation

$$q = f(p),$$

where q stands for the number of items we would sell (per week, per month, or what have you) if we set the price per item at p. Now suppose we increase the price p by a very small amount, Δp. Then our percentage increase in price is $(\Delta p/p) \times 100\%$. This increase in p will presumably result in a decrease in the demand q. Let's denote this corresponding decrease in q by $-\Delta q$ (we use the minus sign because, by convention, Δq stands for the *increase* in demand). Thus, the percentage decrease in demand is $(-\Delta q/q) \times 100\%$.

Now E is the ratio

$$E = \frac{\text{Percentage decrease in demand}}{\text{Percentage increase in price}}$$

so

$$E = \frac{-\frac{\Delta q}{q} \times 100\%}{\frac{\Delta p}{p} \times 100\%}.$$

Canceling the 100%s and reorganizing, we get

$$E = -\frac{\Delta q}{\Delta p} \cdot \frac{p}{q}.$$

* Coming up with a good demand equation is not always easy. We saw in Chapter 1 that it is possible to find a linear demand equation if we know the sales figures at two different prices. However, such an equation is only a first approximation. To come up with a more accurate demand equation, we might need to gather data corresponding to sales at several different prices and use curve-fitting techniques like regression. Another approach would be an analytic one, based on mathematical modeling techniques that an economist might use.

That said, we refer you again to *Camels and Rubber Duckies* by Joel Spolsky at www.joelonsoftware.com/articles/CamelsandRubberDuckies.html just in case you think there is nothing more to demand curves.

Q: *What small change in price will we use for Δp?*

A: It should probably be pretty small. If, say, we increased the price of sneakers to \$1 million per pair, the sales would likely drop to zero. But knowing this tells us nothing about how the market would respond to a modest increase in price. In fact, we'll do the usual thing we do in calculus and let Δp approach 0.

In the expression for E, if we let Δp go to 0, then the ratio $\Delta q/\Delta p$ goes to the derivative dq/dp. This gives us our final and most useful definition of the elasticity.

Price Elasticity of Demand

The **price elasticity of demand** E is the percentage rate of decrease of demand per percentage increase in price. E is given by the formula

$$E = -\frac{dq}{dp} \cdot \frac{p}{q}.$$

We say that the demand is **elastic** if $E > 1$, is **inelastic** if $E < 1$, and has **unit elasticity** if $E = 1$.

Quick Example

Suppose that the demand equation is $q = 20{,}000 - 2p$, where p is the price in dollars. Then

$$E = -(-2)\frac{p}{20{,}000 - 2p} = \frac{p}{10{,}000 - p}.$$

If $p = \$2{,}000$, then $E = 1/4$, and demand is inelastic at this price.
If $p = \$8{,}000$, then $E = 4$, and demand is elastic at this price.
If $p = \$5{,}000$, then $E = 1$, and the demand has unit elasticity at this price.

We are generally interested in the price that maximizes revenue and, in ordinary cases, the price that maximizes revenue must give unit elasticity. One way of seeing this is as follows:* If the demand is inelastic (which ordinarily occurs at a low unit price), then raising the price by a small percentage—1% say—results in a smaller percentage drop in demand. For example, in the Quick Example above, if $p = \$2{,}000$, then the demand would drop by only $\frac{1}{4}$% for every 1% increase in price. To see the effect on revenue, we use the fact† that, for small changes in price,

* For another—more rigorous—argument, see Exercise 29.

† See, for example, Exercise 53 in Section 12.5.

$$\begin{aligned}\text{Percentage change in revenue} &\approx \text{Percentage change in price} \\ &\quad + \text{Percentage change in demand} \\ &= 1 + \left(-\frac{1}{4}\right) = \frac{3}{4}\%.\end{aligned}$$

Thus, the revenue will increase by about 3/4%. Put another way:

If the demand is inelastic, raising the price increases revenue.

On the other hand, if the price is elastic (which ordinarily occurs at a high unit price), then increasing the price slightly will lower the revenue, so:

If the demand is elastic, lowering the price increases revenue.

The price that results in the largest revenue must therefore be at unit elasticity.

EXAMPLE 1 Price Elasticity of Demand: Dolls

Suppose that the demand equation for *Bobby Dolls* is given by $q = 216 - p^2$, where p is the price per doll in dollars and q is the number of dolls sold per week.

a. Compute the price elasticity of demand when $p = \$5$ and $p = \$10$, and interpret the results.

b. Find the range of prices for which the demand is elastic and the range for which the demand is inelastic.

c. Find the price at which the weekly revenue is maximized. What is the maximum weekly revenue?

Solution

a. The price elasticity of demand is

$$E = -\frac{dq}{dp} \cdot \frac{p}{q}.$$

Taking the derivative and substituting for q gives

$$E = 2p \cdot \frac{p}{216 - p^2} = \frac{2p^2}{216 - p^2}.$$

When $p = \$5$,

$$E = \frac{2(5)^2}{216 - 5^2} = \frac{50}{191} \approx 0.26.$$

Thus, when the price is set at \$5, the demand is dropping at a rate of 0.26% per 1% increase in the price. Because $E < 1$, the demand is inelastic at this price, so raising the price will increase revenue.

When $p = \$10$,

$$E = \frac{2(10)^2}{216 - 10^2} = \frac{200}{116} \approx 1.72.$$

Thus, when the price is set at \$10, the demand is dropping at a rate of 1.72% per 1% increase in the price. Because $E > 1$, demand is elastic at this price, so raising the price will decrease revenue; lowering the price will increase revenue.

b. and **c.** We answer part (c) first. Setting $E = 1$, we get

$$\frac{2p^2}{216 - p^2} = 1$$

$$p^2 = 72.$$

Thus, we conclude that the maximum revenue occurs when $p = \sqrt{72} \approx \$8.49$. We can now answer part (b): The demand is elastic when $p > \$8.49$ (the price is too high), and the demand is inelastic when $p < \$8.49$ (the price is too low). Finally, we calculate the maximum weekly revenue, which equals the revenue corresponding to the price of \$8.49:

$$R = qp = (216 - p^2)p = (216 - 72)\sqrt{72} = 144\sqrt{72} \approx \$1{,}222.$$

using Technology

See the Technology Guides at the end of the chapter to find out how to automate computations like those in part (a) of Example 1 using a graphing calculator or Excel. Here is an outline:

TI-83/84 Plus

```
Y1=216-X^2
Y2=-nDeriv(Y1,X,X)*X/Y1
```

[2ND] [TABLE] Enter $x = 5$

[More details on page 943.]

Spreadsheet

Enter values of p: 4.9, 4.91, . . . , 5.0, 5.01, . . . , 5.1 in A5–A25.

In B5 enter `216-A5^2` and copy down to B25.

In C5 enter `=(A6-A5)/A5` and paste the formula in C5–D24.

In E5 enter =−D5/C5 and copy down to E24. This column contains the values of E for the values of p in column A.

[More details on page 943.]

The concept of elasticity can be applied in other situations. In the following example we consider *income* elasticity of demand—the percentage increase in demand for a particular item per percentage increase in personal income.

EXAMPLE 2 Income Elasticity of Demand: Porsches

You are the sales director at *Suburban Porsche* and have noticed that demand for Porsches depends on income according to

$$q = 0.005e^{-0.05x^2+x} \qquad (1 \le x \le 10).$$

Here, x is the income of a potential customer in hundreds of thousands of dollars and q is the probability that the person will actually purchase a Porsche.* The **income elasticity of demand** is

$$E = \frac{dq}{dx}\frac{x}{q}.$$

Compute and interpret E for $x = 2$ and 9.

* In other words, q is the fraction of visitors to your showroom having income x who actually purchase a Porsche.

Solution

Q: *Why is there no negative sign in the formula?*

A: Because we anticipate that the demand will increase as income increases, the ratio

$$\frac{\text{Percentage increase in demand}}{\text{Percentage increase in income}}$$

will be positive, so there is no need to introduce a negative sign.

Turning to the calculation, since $q = 0.005e^{-0.05x^2+x}$,

$$\frac{dq}{dx} = 0.005e^{-0.05x^2+x}(-0.1x+1)$$

and so

$$\begin{aligned} E &= \frac{dq}{dx}\frac{x}{q} \\ &= 0.005e^{-0.05x^2+x}(-0.1x+1)\frac{x}{0.005e^{-0.05x^2+x}} \\ &= x(-0.1x+1). \end{aligned}$$

When $x = 2$, $E = 2[-0.1(2)+1)] = 1.6$. Thus, at an income level of \$200,000, the probability that a customer will purchase a Porsche increases at a rate of 1.6% per 1% increase in income.

When $x = 9$, $E = 9[-0.1(9)+1)] = 0.9$. Thus, at an income level of \$900,000, the probability that a customer will purchase a Porsche increases at a rate of 0.9% per 1% increase in income.

12.6 EXERCISES

▼ more advanced ◆ challenging

T indicates exercises that should be solved using technology

APPLICATIONS

1. ***Demand for Oranges*** The weekly sales of *Honolulu Red Oranges* is given by $q = 1{,}000 - 20p$. Calculate the price elasticity of demand when the price is \$30 per orange (yes, \$30 per orange[64]). Interpret your answer. Also, calculate the price that gives a maximum weekly revenue, and find this maximum revenue. HINT [See Example 1.]

2. ***Demand for Oranges*** Repeat the preceding exercise for weekly sales of $1{,}000 - 10p$. HINT [See Example 1.]

3. ***Tissues*** The consumer demand equation for tissues is given by $q = (100 - p)^2$, where p is the price per case of tissues and q is the demand in weekly sales.

   a. Determine the price elasticity of demand E when the price is set at \$30, and interpret your answer.

   b. At what price should tissues be sold in order to maximize the revenue?

   c. Approximately how many cases of tissues would be demanded at that price?

4. ***Bodybuilding*** The consumer demand curve for *Professor Stefan Schwarzenegger* dumbbells is given by $q = (100 - 2p)^2$, where p is the price per dumbbell, and q is the demand in weekly sales. Find the price Professor Schwarzenegger should charge for his dumbbells in order to maximize revenue.

5. ***T-Shirts*** The Physics Club sells $E = mc^2$ T-shirts at the local flea market. Unfortunately, the club's previous administration has been losing money for years, so you decide to do an analysis of the sales. A quadratic regression based on old sales data reveals the following demand equation for the T-shirts:

$$q = -2p^2 + 33p \quad (9 \le p \le 15).$$

   Here, p is the price the club charges per T-shirt, and q is the number it can sell each day at the flea market.

   a. Obtain a formula for the price elasticity of demand for $E = mc^2$ T-shirts.

[64] They are very hard to find, and their possession confers considerable social status.

b. Compute the elasticity of demand if the price is set at $10 per shirt. *Interpret the result.*

c. How much should the Physics Club charge for the T-shirts in order to obtain the maximum daily revenue? What will this revenue be?

6. *Comics* The demand curve for original *Iguanawoman* comics is given by

$$q = \frac{(400 - p)^2}{100} \quad (0 \le p \le 400),$$

where q is the number of copies the publisher can sell per week if it sets the price at $p.

a. Find the price elasticity of demand when the price is set at $40 per copy.

b. Find the price at which the publisher should sell the books in order to maximize weekly revenue.

c. What, to the nearest $1, is the maximum weekly revenue the publisher can realize from sales of *Iguanawoman* comics?

7. *College Tuition* A study of about 1,800 U.S. colleges and universities resulted in the demand equation $q = 9,900 - 2.2p$, where q is the enrollment at a college or university, and p is the average annual tuition (plus fees) it charges.[65]

a. The study also found that the average tuition charged by universities and colleges was $2,900. What is the corresponding price elasticity of demand? Is the price elastic or inelastic? Should colleges charge more or less on average to maximize revenue?

b. Based on the study, what would you advise a college to charge its students in order to maximize total revenue, and what would the revenue be?

8. *Demand for Fried Chicken* A fried chicken franchise finds that the demand equation for its new roast chicken product, "Roasted Rooster," is given by

$$p = \frac{40}{q^{1.5}},$$

where p is the price (in dollars) per quarter-chicken serving and q is the number of quarter-chicken servings that can be sold per hour at this price. Express q as a function of p and find the price elasticity of demand when the price is set at $4 per serving. Interpret the result.

9. *Paint-By-Number* The estimated monthly sales of *Mona Lisa* paint-by-number sets is given by the formula $q = 100e^{-3p^2+p}$, where q is the demand in monthly sales and p is the retail price in hundreds of yen.

a. Determine the price elasticity of demand E when the retail price is set at ¥300 and interpret your answer.

b. At what price will revenue be a maximum?

c. Approximately how many paint-by-number sets will be sold per month at the price in part (b)?

---

10. *Paint-By-Number* Repeat the preceding exercise using the demand equation $q = 100e^{p-3p^2/2}$.

11. ▼ *Linear Demand Functions* A general linear demand function has the form $q = mp + b$ (m and b constants, $m \neq 0$).

a. Obtain a formula for the price elasticity of demand at a unit price of p.

b. Obtain a formula for the price that maximizes revenue.

12. ▼ *Exponential Demand Functions* A general exponential demand function has the form $q = Ae^{-bp}$ (A and b nonzero constants).

a. Obtain a formula for the price elasticity of demand at a unit price of p.

b. Obtain a formula for the price that maximizes revenue.

13. ▼ *Hyperbolic Demand Functions* A general hyperbolic demand function has the form $q = \dfrac{k}{p^r}$ (r and k nonzero constants).

a. Obtain a formula for the price elasticity of demand at unit price p.

b. How does E vary with p?

c. What does the answer to part (b) say about the model?

14. ▼ *Quadratic Demand Functions* A general quadratic demand function has the form $q = ap^2 + bp + c$ (a, b, and c constants with $a \neq 0$).

a. Obtain a formula for the price elasticity of demand at a unit price p.

b. Obtain a formula for the price or prices that could maximize revenue.

15. ▼ *Modeling Linear Demand* You have been hired as a marketing consultant to *Johannesburg Burger Supply, Inc.*, and you wish to come up with a unit price for its hamburgers in order to maximize its weekly revenue. To make life as simple as possible, you assume that the demand equation for Johannesburg hamburgers has the linear form $q = mp + b$, where p is the price per hamburger, q is the demand in weekly sales, and m and b are certain constants you must determine.

a. Your market studies reveal the following sales figures: When the price is set at $2.00 per hamburger, the sales amount to 3,000 per week, but when the price is set at $4.00 per hamburger, the sales drop to zero. Use these data to calculate the demand equation.

b. Now estimate the unit price that maximizes weekly revenue and predict what the weekly revenue will be at that price.

16. ▼ *Modeling Linear Demand* You have been hired as a marketing consultant to *Big Book Publishing, Inc.*, and you have been approached to determine the best selling price for the hit calculus text by Whiner and Istanbul entitled *Fun with Derivatives*. You decide to make life easy and assume that the demand equation for *Fun with Derivatives* has the linear form $q = mp + b$, where p is the price per book, q is the demand in annual sales, and m and b are certain constants you must determine.

---

[65]Based on a study by A.L. Ostrosky Jr. and J.V. Koch, as cited in their book *Introduction to Mathematical Economics* (Waveland Press, Illinois, 1979) p. 133.

a. Your market studies reveal the following sales figures: When the price is set at \$50.00 per book, the sales amount to 10,000 per year; when the price is set at \$80.00 per book, the sales drop to 1000 per year. Use these data to calculate the demand equation.

b. Now estimate the unit price that maximizes annual revenue and predict what Big Book Publishing, Inc.'s annual revenue will be at that price.

17. ***Income Elasticity of Demand: Live Drama*** The likelihood that a child will attend a live theatrical performance can be modeled by

$$q = 0.01(-0.0078x^2 + 1.5x + 4.1) \qquad (15 \le x \le 100).$$

Here, q is the fraction of children with annual household income x thousand dollars who will attend a live dramatic performance at a theater during the year.[66] Compute the income elasticity of demand at an income level of \$20,000 and interpret the result. (Round your answer to two significant digits.) HINT [See Example 2.]

18. ***Income Elasticity of Demand: Live Concerts*** The likelihood that a child will attend a live musical performance can be modeled by

$$q = 0.01(0.0006x^2 + 0.38x + 35) \quad (15 \le x \le 100).$$

Here, q is the fraction of children with annual household income x who will attend a live musical performance during the year.[67] Compute the income elasticity of demand at an income level of \$30,000 and interpret the result. (Round your answer to two significant digits.) HINT [See Example 2.]

19. ***Income Elasticity of Demand: Broadband in 2010*** The following graph shows the percentage q of people in households with annual income x thousand dollars using broadband Internet access in 2010, together with the exponential curve $q = -74e^{-0.021x} + 92$.[68]

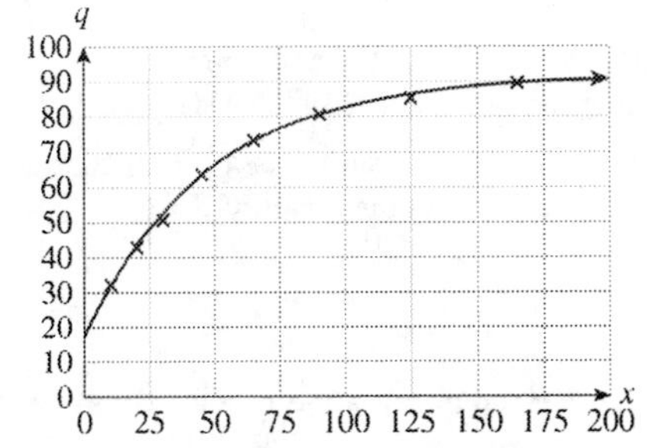

a. Find an equation for the income elasticity of demand for broadband usage, and use it to compute the elasticity for a household with annual income \$100,000 to two decimal places. Interpret the result.

b. What does the model predict as the elasticity of demand for households with very large incomes?

20. ***Income Elasticity of Demand: Broadband in 2007*** The following graph shows the percentage q of people in households with annual income x thousand dollars using broadband Internet access in 2007, together with the exponential curve $q = -86e^{-0.013x} + 92$.[69]

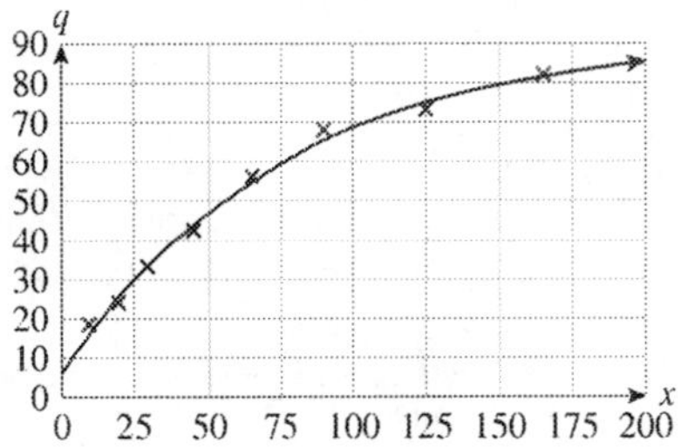

a. Find an equation for the income elasticity of demand for broadband usage, and use it to compute the elasticity for a household with annual income \$60,000 to two decimal places. Interpret the result.

b. What does the model predict as the elasticity of demand for households with very large incomes?

21. ***Income Elasticity of Demand: Computer Usage in the 1990s*** The following graph shows the probability q that a household in the 1990s with annual income x dollars had a computer, together with the logarithmic curve $q = 0.3454 \ln x - 3.047$.[70]

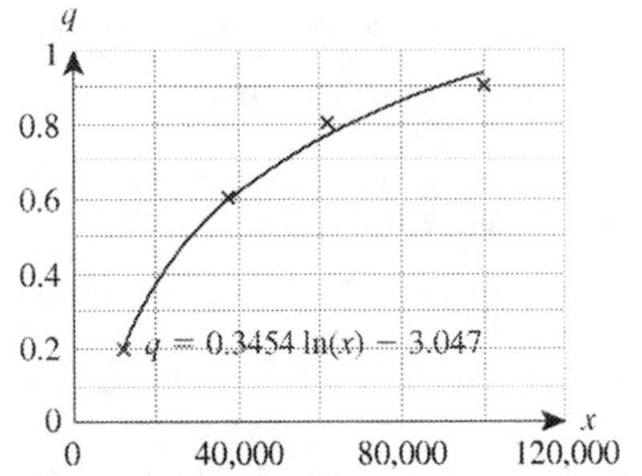

a. Compute the income elasticity of demand for computers, to two decimal places, for a household income of \$60,000 and interpret the result.

b. As household income increases, how is income elasticity of demand affected?

c. How reliable is the given model of demand for incomes well above \$120,000? Explain.

d. What can you say about E for incomes much larger than those shown?

---

[66] Based on a quadratic regression of data from a 2001 survey. Source for data: New York Foundation of the Arts (www.nyfa.org/culturalblueprint).

[67] *Ibid.*

[68] Source for data: *Digital Nation: Expanding Internet Usage,* National Telecommunications and Information Administration (U.S. Department of Commerce) (http://search.ntia.doc.gov).

[69] *Ibid.*

[70] Source for data: Income distribution computer data: Forrester Research/*New York Times*, August 8, 1999, p. BU4.

22. ***Income Elasticity of Demand: Internet Usage in the 1990s*** The following graph shows the probability q that a person in the 1990s with household annual income x dollars used the Internet, together with the logarithmic curve $q = 0.2802 \ln x - 2.505$.[71]

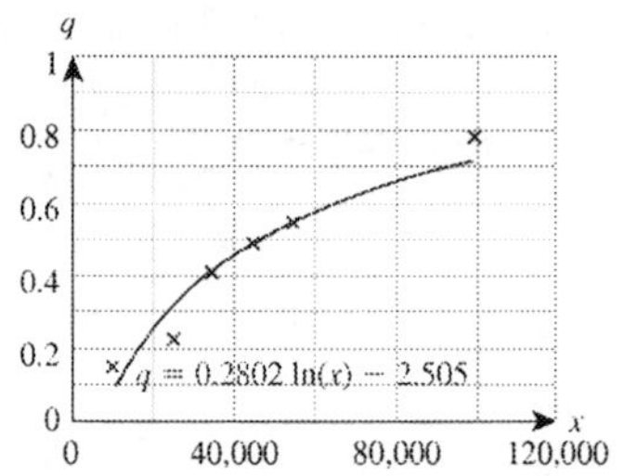

a. Compute the income elasticity of demand for Internet usage, to two decimal places, for a household income of \$60,000 and interpret the result.

b. As household income increases, how is income elasticity of demand affected?

c. The logarithmic model shown above is not appropriate for incomes well above \$100,000. Suggest a model that might be more appropriate.

d. In the model you propose, how would E behave for very large incomes?

23. ▼ ***Income Elasticity of Demand*** *(based on a question on the GRE Economics Test)* If $Q = aP^{\alpha}Y^{\beta}$ is the individual's demand function for a commodity, where P is the (fixed) price of the commodity, Y is the individual's income, and a, α, and β are parameters, explain why β can be interpreted as the income elasticity of demand.

24. ▼ ***College Tuition*** *(from the GRE Economics Test)* A time-series study of the demand for higher education, using tuition charges as a price variable, yields the following result:

$$\frac{dq}{dp} \cdot \frac{p}{q} = -0.4,$$

where p is tuition and q is the quantity of higher education. Which of the following is suggested by the result?

(A) As tuition rises, students want to buy a greater quantity of education.

(B) As a determinant of the demand for higher education, income is more important than price.

(C) If colleges lowered tuition slightly, their total tuition receipts would increase.

(D) If colleges raised tuition slightly, their total tuition receipts would increase.

(E) Colleges cannot increase enrollments by offering larger scholarships.

25. ▼ ***Modeling Exponential Demand*** As the new owner of a supermarket, you have inherited a large inventory of unsold imported Limburger cheese, and you would like to set the price so that your revenue from selling it is as large as possible. Previous sales figures of the cheese are shown in the following table:

Price per Pound, p	\$3.00	\$4.00	\$5.00
Monthly Sales in Pounds, q	407	287	223

a. Use the sales figures for the prices \$3 and \$5 per pound to construct a demand function of the form $q = Ae^{-bp}$, where A and b are constants you must determine. (Round A and b to two significant digits.)

b. Use your demand function to find the price elasticity of demand at each of the prices listed.

c. At what price should you sell the cheese in order to maximize monthly revenue?

d. If your total inventory of cheese amounts to only 200 pounds, and it will spoil one month from now, how should you price it in order to receive the greatest revenue? Is this the same answer you got in part (c)? If not, give a brief explanation.

26. ▼ ***Modeling Exponential Demand*** Repeat the preceding exercise, but this time use the sales figures for \$4 and \$5 per pound to construct the demand function.

COMMUNICATION AND REASONING EXERCISES

27. Complete the following: When demand is inelastic, revenue will decrease if____ .

28. Complete the following: When demand has unit elasticity, revenue will decrease if____ .

29. ▼ Given that the demand q is a differentiable function of the unit price p, show that the revenue $R = pq$ has a stationary point when

$$q + p\frac{dq}{dp} = 0.$$

Deduce that the stationary points of R are the same as the points of unit price elasticity of demand. (Ordinarily, there is only one such stationary point, corresponding to the absolute maximum of R.) HINT [Differentiate R with respect to p.]

30. ▼ Given that the demand q is a differentiable function of income x, show that the quantity $R = q/x$ has a stationary point when

$$q - x\frac{dq}{dx} = 0.$$

Deduce that stationary points of R are the same as the points of unit income elasticity of demand. HINT [Differentiate R with respect to x.]

31. ◆ Your calculus study group is discussing price elasticity of demand, and a member of the group asks the following question: "Since elasticity of demand measures the response of demand to change in unit price, what is the difference between elasticity of demand and the quantity $-dq/dp$?" How would you respond?

32. ◆ Another member of your study group claims that unit price elasticity of demand need not always correspond to maximum revenue. Is he correct? Explain your answer.

[71] Sources: Luxembourg Income Study/*New York Times*, August 14, 1995, p. A9, Commerce Department, Deloitte & Touche Survey/*New York Times*, November 24, 1999, p. C1.

Practice Problems 12.6, Part 1

1.) Raising the price of hotel rooms from $75 to $80 per night reduces weekly sales from 100 rooms to 90 rooms.

a.) What is the elasticity of demand for rooms at a price of $75?

b.) Should the owner raise the price? Why?

2.) The elasticity of demand for a good is $E = 0.5$. What is the effect on demand of:

a.) A 3% price increase?

b.) A 6% price decrease?

Practice Problems 12.6, Part 2

1. Suppose that the equation $635p^2 - q^2 = 100$ describes the relations ship between price and demand for some product. Assume that p is in dollars per unit and q is in units of product. Calculate point elasticity at $q = 25$.

2. Suppose that $q = \sqrt{144 - p}$ describes a demand function. Find all values of p where demand is unit elastic.

CHAPTER 12 REVIEW

KEY CONCEPTS

WM Website www.WanerMath.com

Go to the Website at www.WanerMath.com to find a comprehensive and interactive Web-based summary of Chapter 12.

12.1 Maxima and Minima

Relative maximum, relative minimum *p. 865*

Absolute maximum, absolute minimum *p. 865*

Stationary points, singular points, endpoints *p. 867*

Finding and classifying maxima and minima *p. 868*

First derivative test for relative extrema *p. 869*

Extreme value theorem *p. 873*

Using technology to locate approximate extrema *p. 874*

12.2 Applications of Maxima and Minima

Minimizing average cost *p. 878*

Maximizing area *p. 879*

Steps in solving optimization problems *p. 881*

Maximizing revenue *p. 881*

Optimizing resources *p. 882*

Allocation of labor *p. 884*

12.3 Higher Order Derivatives: Acceleration and Concavity

The second derivative of a function f is the derivative of the derivative of f, written as f'' *p. 892*

The acceleration of a moving object is the second derivative of the position function *p. 892*

Acceleration due to gravity *p. 893*

Acceleration of sales *p. 894*

Concave up, concave down, point of inflection *p. 895*

Locating points of inflection *p. 895*

Application to inflation *p. 896*

Second derivative test for relative extrema *p. 899*

Higher order derivatives *p. 900*

12.4 Analyzing Graphs

Features of a graph: x- and y-intercepts, relative extrema, points of inflection; behavior near points where the function is not defined, behavior at infinity *pp. 910–911*

Analyzing a graph *p. 911*

12.5 Related Rates

If Q is a quantity changing over time t, then the derivative dQ/dt is the rate at which Q changes over time *p. 918*

The expanding circle *p. 918*

Steps in solving related rates problems *p. 919*

The falling ladder *p. 919*

Average cost *p. 921*

Allocation of labor *p. 922*

12.6 Elasticity

Price elasticity of demand $E = -\frac{dq}{dp} \cdot \frac{p}{q}$; demand is elastic if $E > 1$, inelastic if $E < 1$, has unit elasticity if $E = 1$ *p. 928*

Computing and interpreting elasticity, and maximizing revenue *p. 929*

Using technology to compute elasticity *p. 930*

Income elasticity of demand *p. 930*

REVIEW EXERCISES

In Exercises 1–8, find all the relative and absolute extrema of the given functions on the given domain (if supplied) or on the largest possible domain (if no domain is supplied).

1. $f(x) = 2x^3 - 6x + 1$ on $[-2, +\infty)$
2. $f(x) = x^3 - x^2 - x - 1$ on $(-\infty, \infty)$
3. $g(x) = x^4 - 4x$ on $[-1, 1]$
4. $f(x) = \frac{x+1}{(x-1)^2}$ for $-2 \le x \le 2, x \ne 1$
5. $g(x) = (x-1)^{2/3}$
6. $g(x) = x^2 + \ln x$ on $(0, +\infty)$
7. $h(x) = \frac{1}{x} + \frac{1}{x^2}$
8. $h(x) = e^{x^2} + 1$

In Exercises 9–12, the graph of the function f or its derivative is given. Find the approximate x-coordinates of all relative extrema and points of inflection of the original function f (if any).

9. Graph of f:

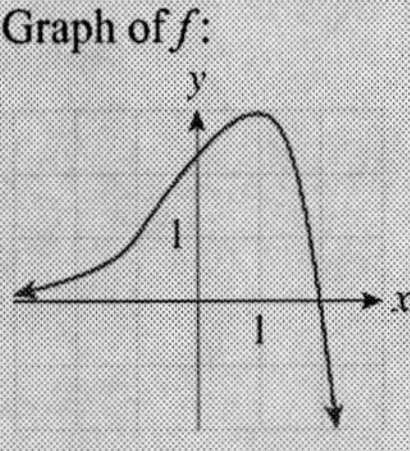

10. Graph of f:

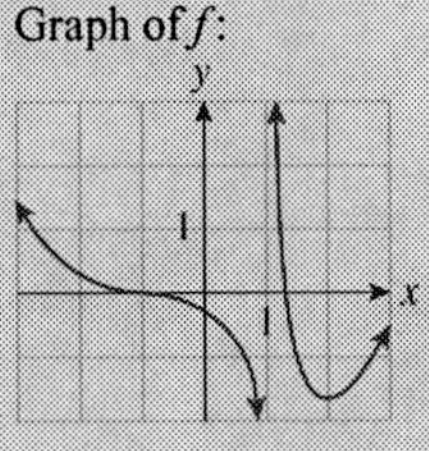

11. Graph of f':

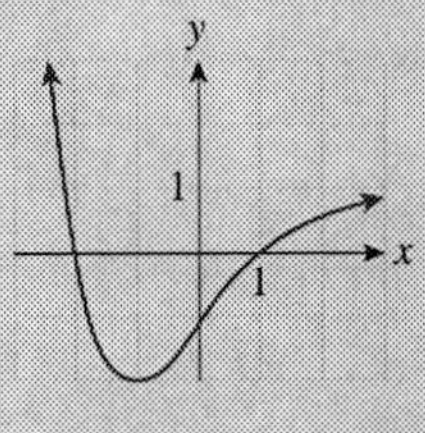

12. Graph of f':

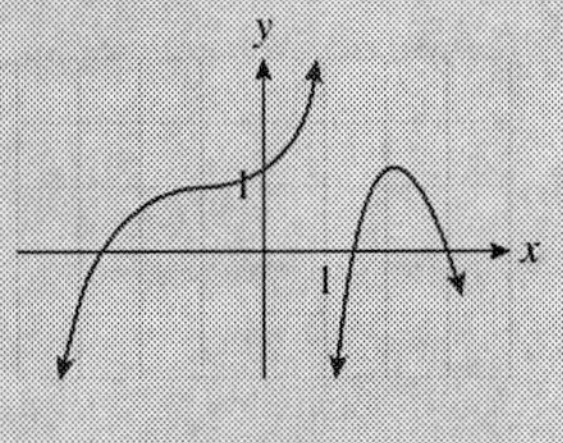

In Exercises 13 and 14, the graph of the second derivative of a function f is given. Find the approximate x-coordinates of all points of inflection of the original function f (if any).

13. Graph of f''

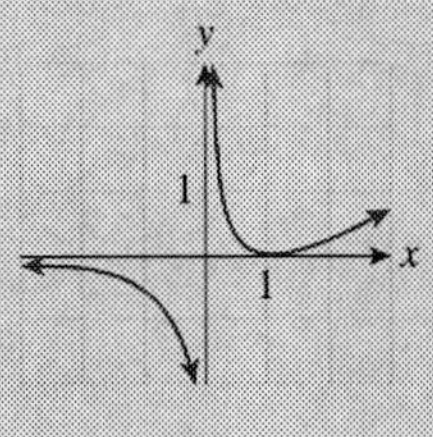

14. Graph of f''

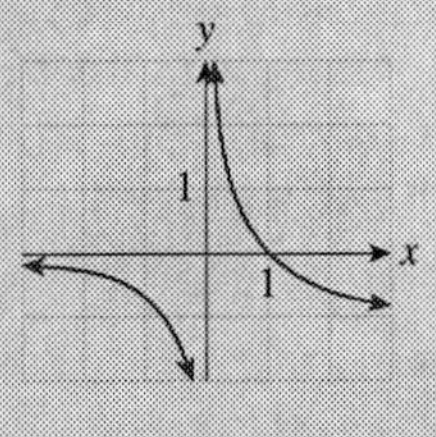

*In Exercises 15 and 16, the position s of a point (in meters) is given as a function of time t (in seconds). Find **(a)** its acceleration as a function of t and **(b)** its acceleration at the specified time.*

15. $s = \frac{2}{3t^2} - \frac{1}{t}; t = 1$

16. $s = \frac{4}{t^2} - \frac{3t}{4}; t = 2$

In Exercises 17–22, sketch the graph of the given function, indicating all relative and absolute extrema and points of inflection. Find the coordinates of these points exactly, where possible. Also indicate any horizontal and vertical asymptotes.

17. $f(x) = x^3 - 12x$ on $[-2, +\infty)$

18. $g(x) = x^4 - 4x$ on $[-1, 1]$

19. $f(x) = \frac{x^2 - 3}{x^3}$

20. $f(x) = (x - 1)^{2/3} + \frac{2x}{3}$

21. $g(x) = (x - 3)\sqrt{x}$

22. $g(x) = (x + 3)\sqrt{x}$

APPLICATIONS: OHaganBooks.com

23. *Revenue* Demand for the latest best-seller at OHaganBooks.com, *A River Burns through It*, is given by

$$q = -p^2 + 33p + 9 \quad (18 \le p \le 28)$$

copies sold per week when the price is p dollars. What price should the company charge to obtain the largest revenue?

24. *Revenue* Demand for *The Secret Loves of John O*, a romance novel by Margó Dufón that flopped after two weeks on the market, is given by

$$q = -2p^2 + 5p + 6 \quad (0 \le p \le 3.3)$$

copies sold per week when the price is p dollars. What price should OHaganBooks charge to obtain the largest revenue?

25. *Profit* Taking into account storage and shipping, it costs OHaganBooks.com

$$C = 9q + 100$$

dollars to sell q copies of *A River Burns through It* in a week (see Exercise 23).

a. If demand is as in Exercise 23, express the weekly profit earned by OHaganBooks.com from the sale of *A River Burns through It* as a function of unit price p.

b. What price should the company charge to get the largest weekly profit? What is the maximum possible weekly profit?

c. Compare your answer in part (b) with the price the company should charge to obtain the largest revenue (Exercise 23). Explain any difference.

26. *Profit* Taking into account storage and shipping, it costs OHaganBooks.com

$$C = 3q$$

dollars to sell q copies of Margó Dufón's *The Secret Loves of John O* in a week (see Exercise 24).

a. If demand is as in Exercise 24, express the weekly profit earned by OHaganBooks.com from the sale of *The Secret Loves of John O* as a function of unit price p.

b. What price should the company charge to get the largest weekly profit? What is the maximum possible weekly profit?

c. Compare your answer in part (b) with the price the company should charge to obtain the largest revenue (Exercise 24). Explain any difference.

27. *Box Design* The sales department at OHaganBooks.com, which has decided to send chocolate lobsters to each of its customers, is trying to design a shipping box with a square base. It has a roll of cardboard 36 inches wide from which to make the boxes. Each box will be obtained by cutting out corners from a rectangle of cardboard as shown in the following diagram:

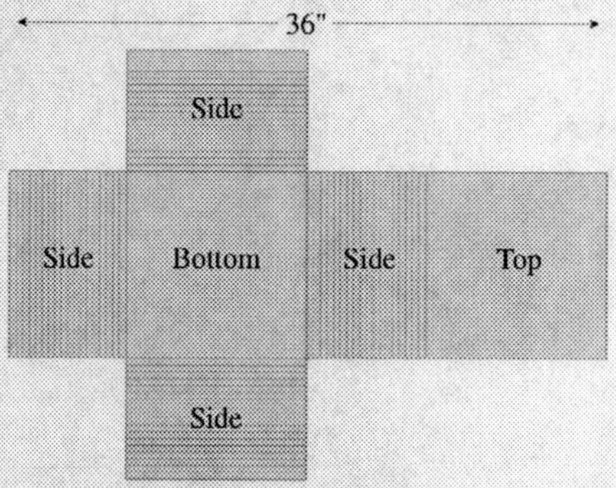

(Notice that the top and bottom of each box will be square, but the sides will not necessarily be square.) What are the dimensions of the boxes with the largest volume that can be made in this way? What is the maximum volume?

28. *Box Redesign* The sales department at OHaganBooks.com was not pleased with the result of the box design in the preceding exercise; the resulting box was too large for the chocolate lobsters, so, following a suggestion by a math major student intern, the department decided to redesign the boxes to meet the following specifications: As in Exercise 27, each box would be obtained by cutting out corners from a rectangle of cardboard as shown in the following diagram:

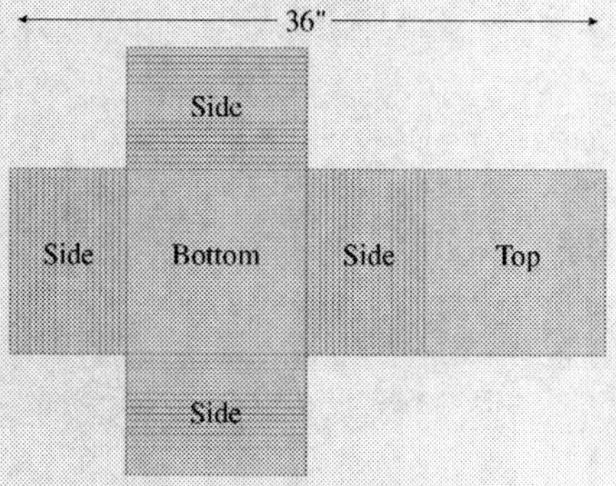

(Notice that the top and bottom of each box would be square, but not necessarily the sides.) The dimensions would be such that the total surface area of the sides plus the bottom of the box would be as large as possible. What are the dimensions of the boxes with the largest area that can be made in this way? How does this box compare with that obtained in Exercise 27?

29. ***Elasticity of Demand*** (Compare Exercise 23.) Demand for the latest best-seller at OHaganBooks.com, *A River Burns through It*, is given by

$$q = -p^2 + 33p + 9 \qquad (18 \le p \le 28)$$

copies sold per week when the price is p dollars.

a. Find the price elasticity of demand as a function of p.
b. Find the elasticity of demand for this book at a price of \$20 and at a price of \$25. (Round your answers to two decimal places.) Interpret the answers.
c. What price should the company charge to obtain the largest revenue?

30. ***Elasticity of Demand*** (Compare Exercise 24.) Demand for *The Secret Loves of John O*, a romance novel by Margó Dufón that flopped after two weeks on the market, is given by

$$q = -2p^2 + 5p + 6 \qquad (0 \le p \le 3.3)$$

copies sold per week when the price is p dollars.

a. Find the price elasticity of demand as a function of p.
b. Find the elasticity of demand for this book at a price of \$2 and at a price of \$3. (Round your answers to two decimal places.) Interpret the answers.
c. What price should the company charge to obtain the largest revenue?

31. ***Elasticity of Demand*** Last year OHaganBooks.com experimented with an online subscriber service, Red On Line (ROL), for its electronic book service. The consumer demand for ROL was modeled by the equation

$$q = 1{,}000e^{-p^2+p},$$

where p was the monthly access charge and q is the number of subscribers.

a. Obtain a formula for the price elasticity of demand, E, for ROL services.
b. Compute the elasticity of demand if the monthly access charge is set at \$2 per month. Interpret the result.
c. How much should the company have charged in order to obtain the maximum monthly revenue? What would this revenue have been?

32. ***Elasticity of Demand*** JungleBooks.com (one of OHaganBooks' main competitors) responded with its own online subscriber service, Better On Line (BOL), for its electronic book service. The consumer demand for BOL was modeled by the equation

$$q = 2{,}000e^{-3p^2+2p},$$

where p was the monthly access charge and q is the number of subscribers.

a. Obtain a formula for the price elasticity of demand, E, for BOL services.
b. Compute the elasticity of demand if the monthly access charge is set at \$2 per month. Interpret the result.
c. How much should the company have charged in order to obtain the maximum monthly revenue? What would this revenue have been?

33. ***Sales*** OHaganBooks.com modeled its weekly sales over a period of time with the function

$$s(t) = 6{,}053 + \frac{4{,}474}{1 + e^{-0.55(t-4.8)}},$$

where t is the time in weeks. Following are the graphs of s, s', and s'':

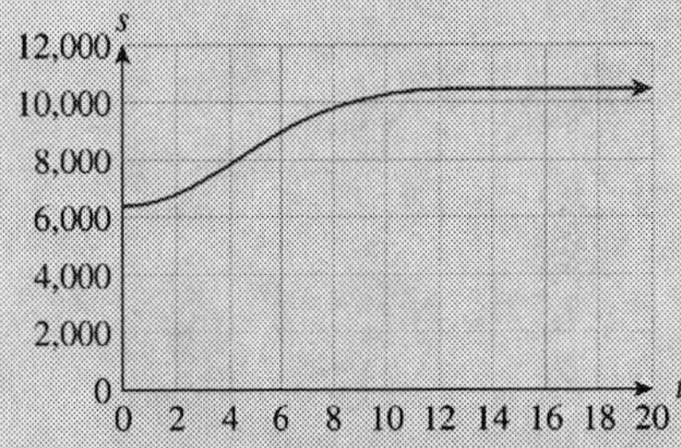

Graph of s

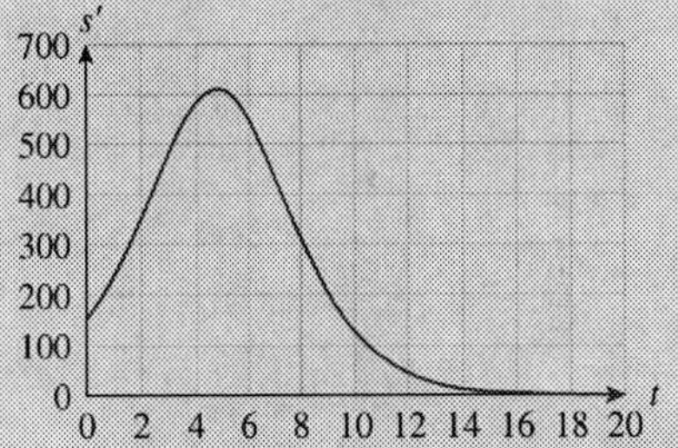

Graph of s'

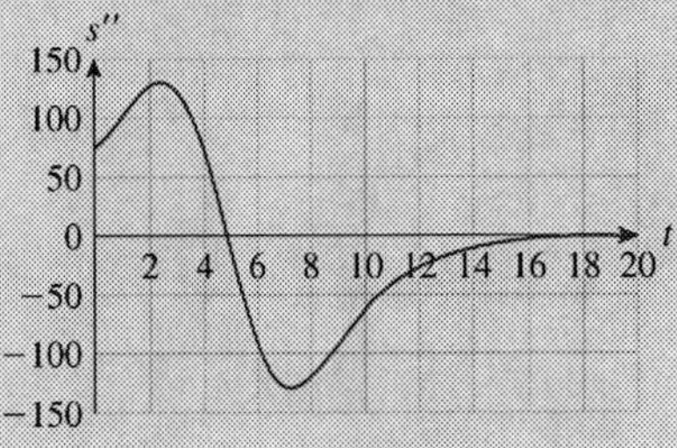

Graph of s''

a. Estimate when, to the nearest week, the weekly sales were growing fastest.
b. To what features on the graphs of s, s', and s'' does your answer to part (a) correspond?
c. The graph of s has a horizontal asymptote. What is the approximate value (s-coordinate) of this asymptote, and what is its significance in terms of weekly sales at OHaganBooks.com?

d. The graph of s' has a horizontal asymptote. What is the value (s'-coordinate) of this asymptote, and what is its significance in terms of weekly sales at OHaganBooks.com?

34. ***Sales*** The quarterly sales of OHagan *oPods* (OHaganBooks' answer to the *iPod*; a portable audio book unit with an incidental music feature) from the fourth quarter of 2009 can be roughly approximated by the function

$$N(t) = \frac{1{,}100}{1 + 9(1.8)^{-t}}\, oPods \ (t \geq 0),$$

where t is time in quarters since the fourth quarter of 2009. Following are the graphs of N, N', and N'':

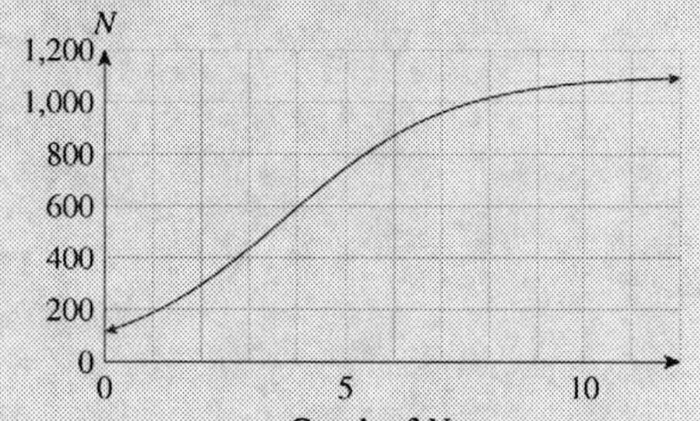

Graph of N

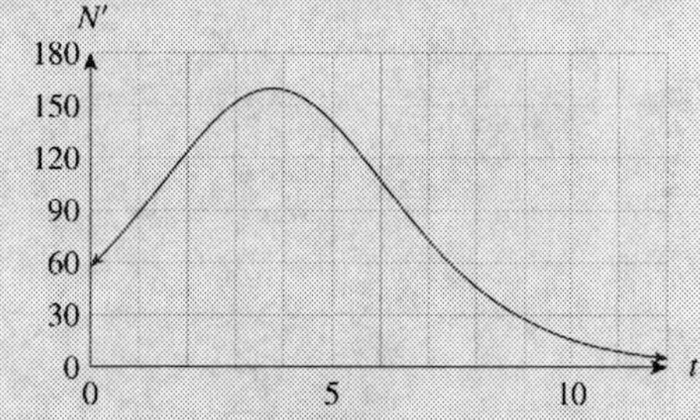

Graph of N'

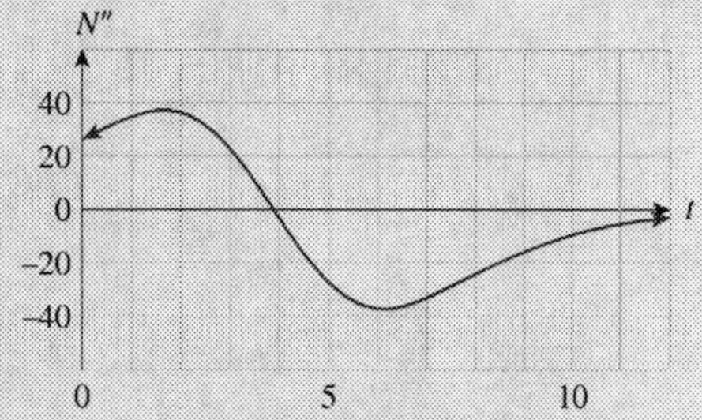

Graph of N''

a. Estimate when, to the nearest quarter, the quarterly sales were growing fastest.

b. To what features on the graphs of N, N', and N'' does your answer to part (a) correspond?

c. The graph of N has a horizontal asymptote. What is the approximate value (N-coordinate) of this asymptote, and what is its significance in terms of quarterly sales of *oPods*?

d. The graph of N' has a horizontal asymptote. What is the value (N'-coordinate) of this asymptote, and what is its significance in terms of quarterly sales of *oPods*?

35. ***Chance Encounter*** Marjory Duffin is walking north towards the corner entrance of OHaganBooks.com company headquarters at 5 ft/sec, while John O'Hagan is walking west toward the same entrance, also at 5 ft/sec. How fast is their distance apart decreasing when

a. each of them is 2 ft from the corner?

b. each of them is 1 ft from the corner?

c. each of them is h ft from the corner?

d. they collide on the corner?

36. ***Company Logos*** OHaganBooks.com's Web site has an animated graphic with its name in a rectangle whose height and width change; on either side of the rectangle are semicircles, as in the figure, whose diameters are the same as the height of the rectangle.

For reasons too complicated to explain, the designer wanted the combined area of the rectangle and semicircles to remain constant. At one point during the animation, the width of the rectangle is 1 inch, growing at a rate of 0.5 inches per second, while the height is 3 inches. How fast is the height changing?

SERDAR/Alamy

Production Lot Size Management

Your publishing company, *Knockem Dead Paperbacks, Inc.,* is about to release its next best-seller, *Henrietta's Heaving Heart* by Celestine A. Lafleur. The company expects to sell 100,000 books each month in the next year. You have been given the job of scheduling print runs to meet the anticipated demand and minimize total costs to the company. Each print run has a setup cost of $5,000, each book costs $1 to produce, and monthly storage costs for books awaiting shipment average 1¢ per book. What will you do?

If you decide to print all 1,200,000 books (the total demand for the year, 100,000 books per month for 12 months) in a single run at the start of the year and sales run as predicted, then the number of books in stock would begin at 1,200,000 and decrease to zero by the end of the year, as shown in Figure 47.

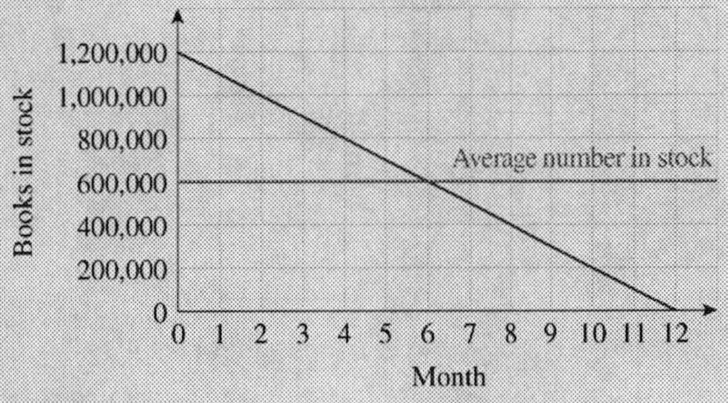

Figure 47

On average, you would be storing 600,000 books for 12 months at 1¢ per book, giving a total storage cost of $600{,}000 \times 12 \times .01 = \$72{,}000$. The setup cost for the single print run would be $5,000. When you add to these the total cost of producing 1,200,000 books at $1 per book, your total cost would be $1,277,000.

If, on the other hand, you decide to cut down on storage costs by printing the book in two runs of 600,000 each, you would get the picture shown in Figure 48.

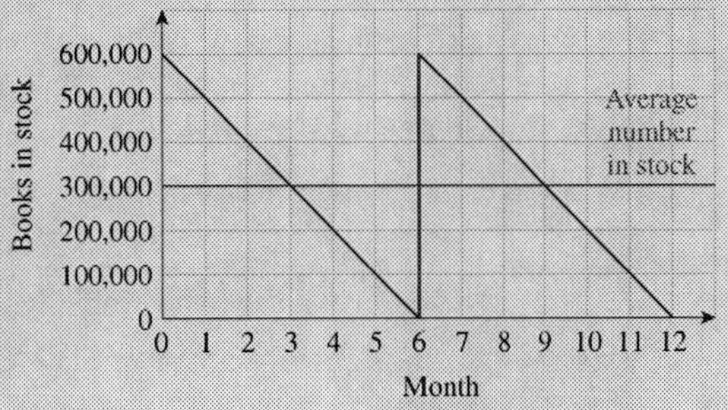

Figure 48

Now, the storage cost would be cut in half because on average there would be only 300,000 books in stock. Thus, the total storage cost would be $36,000, and the setup cost would double to $10,000 (because there would now be two runs). The production costs would be the same: 1,200,000 books @ $1 per book. The total cost would therefore be reduced to $1,246,000, a savings of $31,000 compared to your first scenario.

"Aha!" you say to yourself, after doing these calculations. "Why not drastically cut costs by setting up a run every month?" You calculate that the setup costs alone would be $12 \times \$5{,}000 = \$60{,}000$, which is already more than the setup plus storage costs for two runs, so a run every month will cost too much. Perhaps, then, you should investigate three runs, four runs, and so on, until you find the lowest cost. This strikes you as too laborious a process, especially considering that you will have to do it all over again when planning for Lafleur's sequel, *Lorenzo's Lost Love,* due to be released next year. Realizing that this is an optimization problem, you decide to use some calculus to help you come up with a *formula* that you can use for all future plans. So you get to work.

Instead of working with the number 1,200,000, you use the letter N so that you can be as flexible as possible. (What if *Lorenzo's Lost Love* sells more copies?) Thus, you have a total of N books to be produced for the year. You now calculate the total cost of using x print runs per year. Because you are to produce a total of N books in x print runs, you will have to produce N/x books in each print run. N/x is called the **lot size**. As you can see from the diagrams above, the average number of books in storage will be half that amount, $N/(2x)$.

Now you can calculate the total cost for a year. Write P for the setup cost of a single print run ($P = \$5{,}000$ in your case) and c for the *annual* cost of storing a book (to convert all of the time measurements to years; $c = \$0.12$ here). Finally, write b for the cost of producing a single book ($b = \$1$ here). The costs break down as follows.

Setup Costs: x print runs @ P dollars per run:	Px
Storage Costs: $N/(2x)$ books stored @ c dollars per year:	$cN/(2x)$
Production Costs: N books @ b dollars per book:	Nb
Total Cost:	$Px + \dfrac{cN}{2x} + Nb$

Remember that P, N, c, and b are all constants and x is the only variable. Thus, your cost function is

$$C(x) = Px + \frac{cN}{2x} + Nb$$

and you need to find the value of x that will minimize $C(x)$. But that's easy! All you need to do is find the relative extrema and select the absolute minimum (if any).

The domain of $C(x)$ is $(0, +\infty)$ because there is an x in the denominator and x can't be negative. To locate the extrema, you start by locating the critical points:

$$C'(x) = P - \frac{cN}{2x^2}.$$

The only singular point would be at $x = 0$, but 0 is not in the domain. To find stationary points, you set $C'(x) = 0$ and solve for x:

$$P - \frac{cN}{2x^2} = 0$$

$$2x^2 = \frac{cN}{P}$$

so

$$x = \sqrt{\frac{cN}{2P}}.$$

There is only one stationary point, and there are no singular points or endpoints. To graph the function you will need to put in numbers for the various constants. Substituting $N = 1{,}200{,}000$, $P = 5{,}000$, $c = 0.12$, and $b = 1$, you get

$$C(x) = 5{,}000x + \frac{72{,}000}{x} + 1{,}200{,}000$$

with the stationary point at

$$x = \sqrt{\frac{(0.12)(1{,}200{,}000)}{2(5000)}} \approx 3.79.$$

The total cost at the stationary point is

$$C(3.79) \approx 1{,}237{,}900.$$

You now graph $C(x)$ in a window that includes the stationary point, say, $0 \le x \le 12$ and $1{,}100{,}000 \le C \le 1{,}500{,}000$, getting Figure 49.

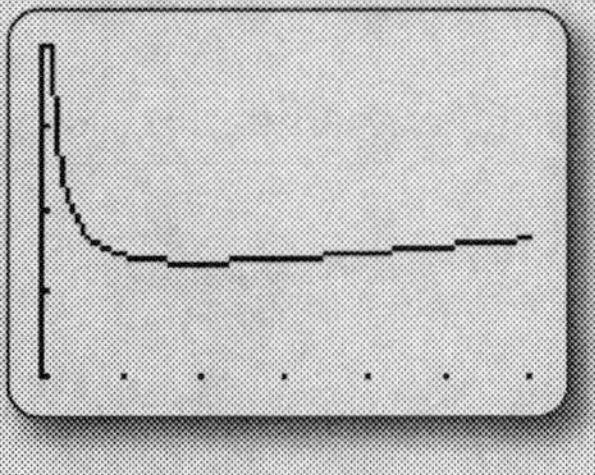

Figure 49

From the graph, you can see that the stationary point is an absolute minimum. In the graph it appears that the graph is always concave up, which also tells you that your stationary point is a minimum. You can check the concavity by computing the second derivative:

$$C''(x) = \frac{cN}{x^3} > 0.$$

The second derivative is always positive because c, N, and x are all positive numbers, so indeed the graph is always concave up. Now you also know that it works regardless of the particular values of the constants.

So now you are practically done! You know that the absolute minimum cost occurs when you have $x \approx 3.79$ print runs per year. Don't be disappointed that the answer is not a whole number; whole number solutions are rarely found in real scenarios. What the answer (and the graph) do indicate is that either three or four print runs per year will cost the least money. If you take $x = 3$, you get a total cost of

$$C(3) = \$1{,}239{,}000.$$

If you take $x = 4$, you get a total cost of

$$C(4) = \$1{,}238{,}000.$$

So, four print runs per year will allow you to minimize your total costs.

EXERCISES

1. *Lorenzo's Lost Love* will sell 2,000,000 copies in a year. The remaining costs are the same. How many print runs should you use now?
2. In general, what happens to the number of runs that minimizes cost if both the setup cost and the total number of books are doubled?
3. In general, what happens to the number of runs that minimizes cost if the setup cost increases by a factor of 4?
4. Assuming that the total number of copies and storage costs are as originally stated, find the setup cost that would result in a single print run.
5. Assuming that the total number of copies and setup cost are as originally stated, find the storage cost that would result in a print run each month.

6. In Figure 48 we assumed that all the books in each run were manufactured in a very short time; otherwise the figure might have looked more like the following graph, which shows the inventory, assuming a slower rate of production.

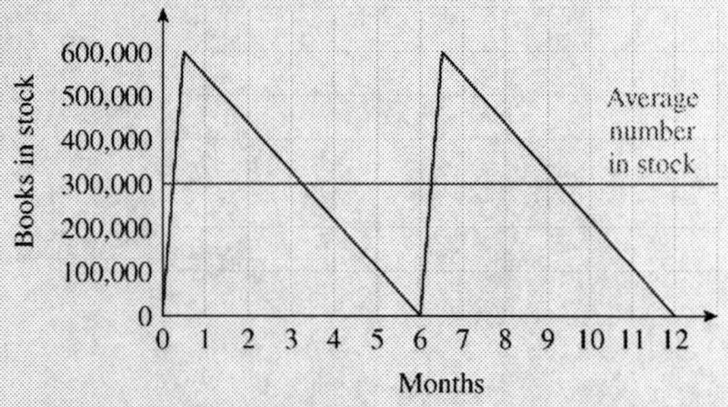

How would this affect the answer?

7. Referring to the general situation discussed in the text, find the cost as a function of the total number of books produced, assuming that the number of runs is chosen to minimize total cost. Also find the average cost per book.

8. Let $\bar{C}$ be the average cost function found in the preceding exercise. Calculate $\lim_{N\to+\infty} \bar{C}(N)$ and interpret the result.

TI-83/84 Plus Technology Guide

Section 12.6

Example 1(a) (page 929) Suppose that the demand equation for *Bobby Dolls* is given by $q = 216 - p^2$, where p is the price per doll in dollars and q is the number of dolls sold per week. Compute the price elasticity of demand when $p = \$5$ and $p = \$10$, and interpret the results.

Solution with Technology

The TI-83/84 Plus function `nDeriv` can be used to compute approximations of the elasticity E at various prices.

1. Set

Y_1= `216-X`^{2} — Demand equation

Y_2= `-nDeriv(`Y_1`,X,X)* X/`Y_1 — Formula for E

2. Use the table feature to list the values of elasticity for a range of prices. For part (a) we chose values of X close to 5:

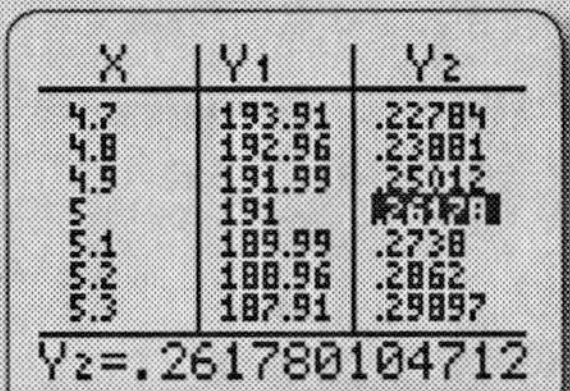

SPREADSHEET Technology Guide

Section 12.6

Example 1(a) (page 929) Suppose that the demand equation for *Bobby Dolls* is given by $q = 216 - p^2$, where p is the price per doll in dollars and q is the number of dolls sold per week. Compute the price elasticity of demand when $p = \$5$ and $p = \$10$, and interpret the results.

Solution with Technology

To approximate E in a spreadsheet, we can use the following approximation of E.

$$E \approx \frac{\text{Percentage decrease in demand}}{\text{Percentage increase in price}} \approx -\frac{\left(\frac{\Delta q}{q}\right)}{\left(\frac{\Delta p}{p}\right)}$$

The smaller Δp is, the better the approximation. Let's use $\Delta p = 1¢$, or 0.01 (which is small compared with the typical prices we consider—around \$5 to \$10).

1. We start by setting up our worksheet to list a range of prices, in increments of Δp, on either side of a price in which we are interested, such as $p_0 = \$5$:

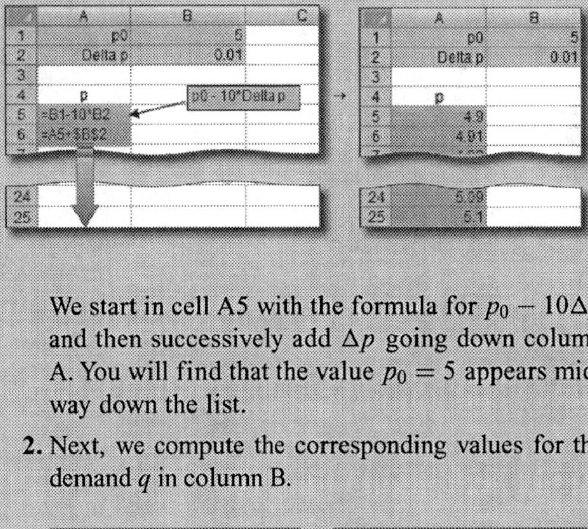

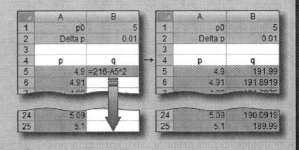

We start in cell A5 with the formula for $p_0 - 10\Delta p$ and then successively add Δp going down column A. You will find that the value $p_0 = 5$ appears midway down the list.

2. Next, we compute the corresponding values for the demand q in column B.

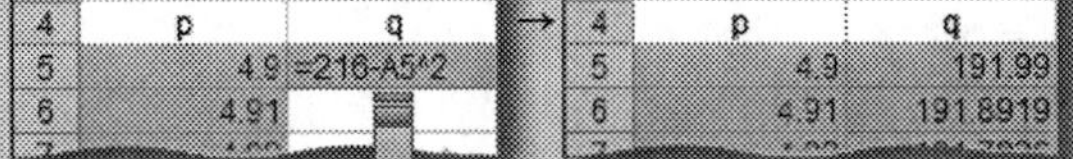

3. We add two new columns for the percentage changes in p and q. The formula shown in cell C5 is copied down columns C and D, to Row 24. (Why not row 25?)

	A	B	C	D
1	p0	5		
2	Delta p	0.01		
3				
4	p	q	Δp/p	Δq/q
5	4.9	191.99	=(A6-A5)/A5	
6	4.91	191.8919		
7	[illegible]	[illegible]		
24	5.09	190.0919		
25	5.1	189.99		

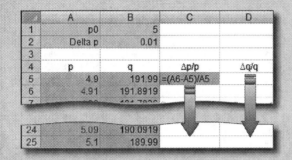

4. The elasticity can now be computed in column E as shown:

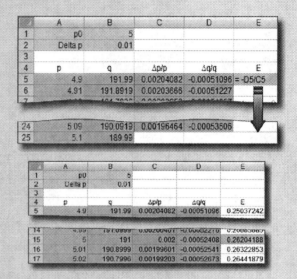

	A	B	C	D	E
1	p0	5			
2	Delta p	0.01			
3					
4	p	q	Δp/p	Δq/q	E
5	4.9	191.99	0.00204082	-0.00051096	=-D5/C5
6	4.91	191.8919	0.00203666	-0.00051227	
7	[illegible]	[illegible]	[illegible]	[illegible]	
24	5.09	190.0919	0.00196464	-0.00053506	
25	5.1	189.99			

	A	B	C	D	E
1	p0	5			
2	Delta p	0.01			
3					
4	p	q	Δp/p	Δq/q	E
5	4.9	191.99	0.00204082	-0.00051096	0.25037242
14	[illegible]	[illegible]	[illegible]	[illegible]	[illegible]
15	5	191	0.002	-0.00052408	0.26204188
16	5.01	190.8999	0.00199601	-0.00052541	0.26322853
17	5.02	190.7996	0.00199203	-0.00052673	0.26441879

CHAPTER 12 QUIZ

1. To the right is the graph of $y = f'(t)$ for some function $f(t)$. Use the graph to answer the questions that follow. Assume that gridlines each mark one unit.

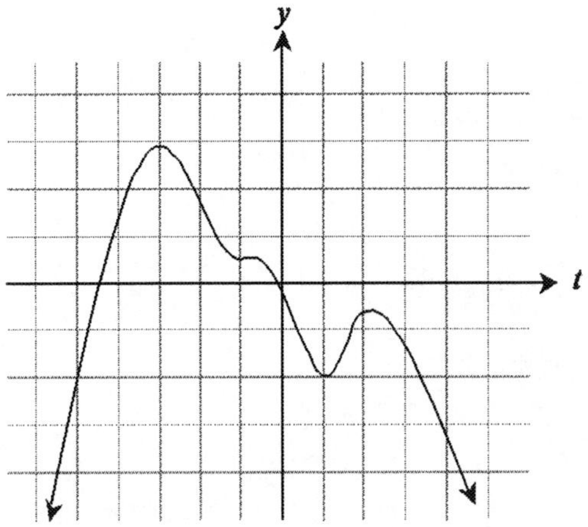

   a. Does the graph of $y = f(t)$ have any horizontal tangent lines? If so, where?

   b. Estimate the slope of the graph of $y = f(t)$ at the point where $t = -1$.

   c. Estimate all intervals where $f(t)$ is increasing.

   d. Which is larger: $f(1)$ or $f(4)$? Explain.

   e. Estimate all intervals where the graph of $y = f(t)$ is concave up.

2. For what values of a and b will the function defined by $f(x) = a(x - b\ln x)$ have $f(2) = 5$ as a relative minimum value? If rounding is necessary, then give estimates accurate to three decimal places.

3. Carefully sketch the graph of a function *f* that satisfies all of the conditions given in the following table. Be sure to label your graph completely. You should label all critical points and identify inflection points. There are many ways to construct a correct graph.

	$-5<x<-3$	$x=-3$	$-3<x<-2$	$x=-2$	$-2<x<1$	$x=1$	$1<x<3$	$x=3$
f	positive	4	positive	3	positive	0	positive	undef
f'	positive	0	negative	negative	negative	0	positive	undef
f''	negative	negative	negative	0	positive	positive	positive	undef

4. The U.S. Postal Service stipulates that any boxes sent through the mail must have a length plus girth (distance around the face) totaling no more than 108 inches. Find the dimensions of the box with maximum possible volume that can be sent through the U.S. mail, assuming that the width and height of the box are equal. Set up an appropriate model for this problem, and use the corresponding derivative function to justify your conclusion.

5. Let $r(t)$ be your instructor's heart rate, in beats per minute, t minutes since the start of class. The graph to the right shows the **rate of change** of $r(t)$, $r'(t)$. Sketch a possible graph of $r(t)$ for $0 \le t \le 50$. You don't need to put scale on your vertical axis, but you do need to indicate all appropriate values of t where $r(t)$ has a relative extreme value or the graph of $r(t)$ has an inflection point. Mark these times clearly on your graph.

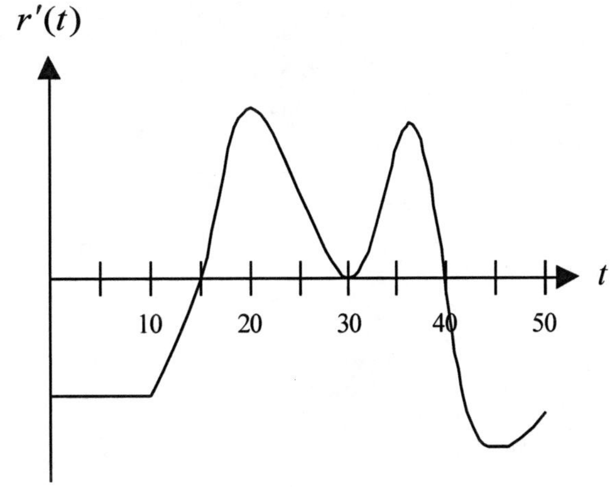

6. A model rocket is launched straight into the air and its velocity t seconds after engine ignition is described by $v(t) = \dfrac{50t}{a + t^2}$ feet per second, where a is some positive number. If the rocket begins to decelerate at exactly $t = 2$ seconds, then what is a?

7. At a fishery, it is estimated that t weeks after 300 fish are transferred to a rearing pond, the average weight of an individual fish will be $w(t) = 3 + t - 0.05t^2$ pounds. Furthermore, it is estimated that the proportion (fraction) of the fish that will still be alive after t weeks is given by $p(t) = \dfrac{31}{31+t}$. The *total yield* of the pond at a particular point is the total weight of all fish still living at that time. Let $y(t)$ denote the total yield of the pond after t weeks, and assume that $0 \le t \le 10$.

a. Give a formula for $y(t)$.

b. Find all critical points for $y(t)$ and subsequently determine when the fish should be harvested from the pond in order to maximize total yield.

8. Chuck's Cable Company currently has 80,000 subscribers, but that number is decreasing at a rate of 3000 subscribers per year due to rate increases of 2% per year. Right now, subscribers pay \$600 per year for service. Determine when the cable company will have the maximum possible revenue if these trends continue.

15

Functions of Several Variables

Website
www.WanerMath.com
At the Website you will find:

- A detailed chapter summary
- A true/false quiz
- A surface grapher
- An Excel surface grapher
- A linear multiple regression utility
- The following optional extra sections:

  Maxima and Minima: Boundaries and the Extreme Value Theorem

  The Chain Rule for Functions of Several Variables

Case Study Modeling College Population

College Malls, Inc. is planning to build a national chain of shopping malls in college neighborhoods. The company is planning to lease only to stores that target the specific age demographics of the national college student population. To decide which age brackets to target, the company has asked you, a paid consultant, for an analysis of the college population by student age, and of its trends over time. **How can you analyze the relevant data?**

david pearson/Alamy

Introduction

We have studied functions of a single variable extensively. But not every useful function is a function of only one variable. In fact, most are not. For example, if you operate an online bookstore in competition with Amazon.com, BN.com, and BooksAMillion.com, your sales may depend on those of your competitors. Your company's daily revenue might be modeled by a function such as

$$R(x, y, z) = 10{,}000 - 0.01x - 0.02y - 0.01z + 0.00001yz,$$

where x, y, and z are the online daily revenues of Amazon.com, BN.com, and BooksAMillion.com, respectively. Here, R is a function of three variables because it *depends on* x, y, and z. As we shall see, the techniques of calculus extend readily to such functions. Among the applications we shall look at is optimization: finding, where possible, the maximum or minimum of a function of two or more variables.

15.1 Functions of Several Variables from the Numerical, Algebraic, and Graphical Viewpoints

Numerical and Algebraic Viewpoints

Recall that a function of one variable is a rule for manufacturing a new number $f(x)$ from a single independent variable x. A function of two or more variables is similar, but the new number now depends on more than one independent variable.

Function of Several Variables

A **real-valued function, f, of x, y, z, . . .** is a rule for manufacturing a new number, written $f(x, y, z, \ldots)$, from the values of a sequence of independent variables $(x, y, z, \ldots)$. The function f is called a **real-valued function of two variables** if there are two independent variables, a **real-valued function of three variables** if there are three independent variables, and so on.

Quick Examples

1. $f(x, y) = x - y$ — Function of two variables
   $f(1, 2) = 1 - 2 = -1$ — Substitute 1 for x and 2 for y.
   $f(2, -1) = 2 - (-1) = 3$ — Substitute 2 for x and −1 for y.
   $f(y, x) = y - x$ — Substitute y for x and x for y.
2. $g(x, y) = x^2 + y^2$ — Function of two variables
   $g(-1, 3) = (-1)^2 + 3^2 = 10$ — Substitute −1 for x and 3 for y.
3. $h(x, y, z) = x + y + xz$ — Function of three variables
   $h(2, 2, -2) = 2 + 2 + 2(-2) = 0$ — Substitute 2 for x, 2 for y, and −2 for z.

Note It is often convenient to use $x_1, x_2, x_3, \ldots$ for the independent variables, so that, for instance, the third example above would be $h(x_1, x_2, x_3) = x_1 + x_2 + x_1x_3$. ■

Figure 1 illustrates the concept of a function of two variables: In goes a pair of numbers and out comes a single number.

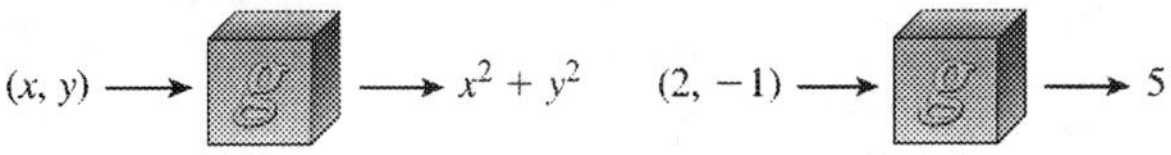

Figure 1

As with functions of one variable, functions of several variables can be represented numerically (using a table of values), algebraically (using a formula as in the above examples), and sometimes graphically (using a graph).

Let's now look at a number of examples of interesting functions of several variables.

EXAMPLE 1 Cost Function

Roy Mehta/The Image Bank/Getty Images

You own a company that makes two models of speakers: the Ultra Mini and the Big Stack. Your total monthly cost (in dollars) to make x Ultra Minis and y Big Stacks is given by

$$C(x, y) = 10{,}000 + 20x + 40y.$$

What is the significance of each term in this formula?

Solution The terms have meanings similar to those we saw for linear cost functions of a single variable. Let us look at the terms one at a time.

Constant Term Consider the monthly cost of making no speakers at all ($x = y = 0$). We find

$$C(0, 0) = 10{,}000. \qquad \text{Cost of making no speakers is \$10,000.}$$

Thus, the constant term 10,000 is the **fixed cost**, the amount you have to pay each month even if you make no speakers.

Coefficients of x and y Suppose you make a certain number of Ultra Minis and Big Stacks one month and the next month you increase production by one Ultra Mini. The costs are

$$\begin{aligned} C(x, y) &= 10{,}000 + 20x + 40y && \text{First month} \\ C(x + 1, y) &= 10{,}000 + 20(x + 1) + 40y && \text{Second month} \\ &= 10{,}000 + 20x + 20 + 40y \\ &= C(x, y) + 20. \end{aligned}$$

Thus, each Ultra Mini adds \$20 to the total cost. We say that \$20 is the **marginal cost** of each Ultra Mini. Similarly, because of the term $40y$, each Big Stack adds \$40 to the total cost. The marginal cost of each Big Stack is \$40.

This cost function is an example of a *linear function of two variables*. The coefficients of x and y play roles similar to that of the slope of a line. In particular, they give the rates of change of the function as each variable increases while the other stays constant (think about it). We shall say more about linear functions below.

using Technology

See the Technology Guides at the end of the chapter to see how you can use a TI-83/84 Plus and a spreadsheet to display various values of $C(x, y)$ in Example 1. Here is an outline:

TI-83/84 Plus

`Y1=10000+20X+40Y`

To evaluate $C(10, 30)$:

`10 → X`

`30 → Y`

`Y1` [More details on page 1147.]

Spreadsheet

x-values down column A starting in A2

y-values down column B starting in B2

`=10000+20*A2+40*B2`

in C2; copy down column C. [More details on page 1147.]

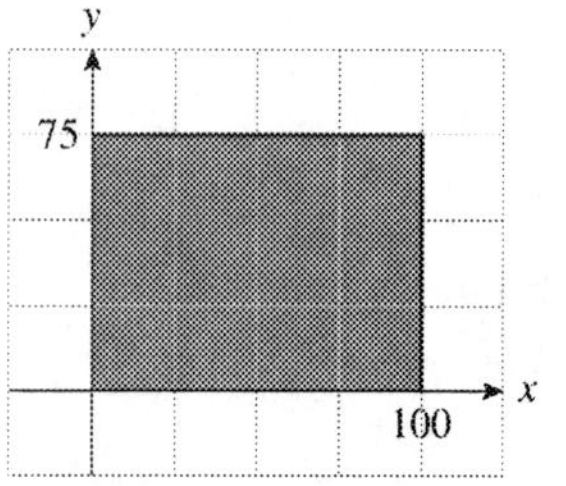

Figure 2

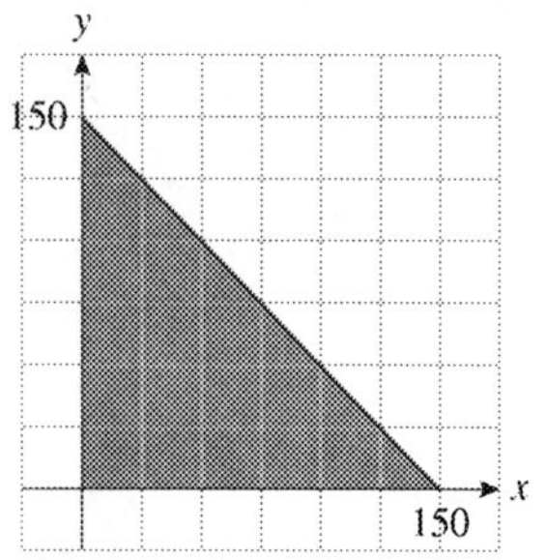

Figure 3

Before we go on... In Example 1 which values of x and y may we substitute into $C(x, y)$? Certainly we must have $x \geq 0$ and $y \geq 0$ because it makes no sense to speak of manufacturing a negative number of speakers. Also, there is certainly some upper bound to the number of speakers that can be made in a month. The bound might take one of several forms. The number of each model may be bounded—say $x \leq 100$ and $y \leq 75$. The inequalities $0 \leq x \leq 100$ and $0 \leq y \leq 75$ describe the region in the plane shaded in Figure 2.

Another possibility is that the *total* number of speakers is bounded—say, $x + y \leq 150$. This, together with $x \geq 0$ and $y \geq 0$, describes the region shaded in Figure 3.

In either case, the region shown represents the pairs (x, y) for which $C(x, y)$ is defined. Just as with a function of one variable, we call this region the **domain** of the function. As before, when the domain is not given explicitly, we agree to take the largest domain possible. ■

EXAMPLE 2 Faculty Salaries

David Katz came up with the following function for the salary of a professor with 10 years of teaching experience in a large university.

$$S(x, y, z) = 13{,}005 + 230x + 18y + 102z$$

Here, S is the salary in 1969–1970 in dollars per year, x is the number of books the professor has published, y is the number of articles published, and z is the number of "excellent" articles published.[1] What salary do you expect that a professor with 10 years' experience earned in 1969–1970 if she published 2 books, 20 articles, and 3 "excellent" articles?

Solution All we need to do is calculate

$$\begin{aligned} S(2, 20, 3) &= 13{,}005 + 230(2) + 18(20) + 102(3) \\ &= \$14{,}131. \end{aligned}$$

Before we go on... In Example 1, we gave a linear function of two variables. In Example 2 we have a linear function of three variables. Katz came up with his model by surveying a large number of faculty members and then finding the linear function "best" fitting the data. Such models are called **multiple linear regression** models. In the Case Study at the end of this chapter, we shall see a spreadsheet method of finding the coefficients of a multiple regression model from a set of observed data.

What does this model say about the value of a single book or a single article? If a book takes 15 times as long to write as an article, how would you recommend that a professor spend her writing time? ■

Here are two simple kinds of functions of several variables.

Linear Function

A function f of n variables is **linear** if f has the property that

$$f(x_1, x_2, \ldots, x_n) = a_0 + a_1x_1 + \cdots + a_nx_n \quad (a_0, a_1, a_2, \ldots, a_n \text{ constants}).$$

[1]David A. Katz, "Faculty Salaries, Promotions and Productivity at a Large University," *American Economic Review*, June 1973, pp. 469–477. Prof. Katz's equation actually included other variables, such as the number of dissertations supervised; our equation assumes that all of these are zero.

Quick Examples

1. $f(x, y) = 3x - 5y$ — Linear function of x and y
2. $C(x, y) = 10{,}000 + 20x + 40y$ — Example 1
3. $S(x_1, x_2, x_3) = 13{,}005 + 230x_1 + 18x_2 + 102x_3$ — Example 2

Interaction Function

If we add to a linear function one or more terms of the form bx_ix_j (b a nonzero constant and $i \neq j$), we get a **second-order interaction function**.

Quick Examples

1. $C(x, y) = 10{,}000 + 20x + 40y + 0.1xy$
2. $R(x_1, x_2, x_3) = 10{,}000 - 0.01x_1 - 0.02x_2 - 0.01x_3 + 0.00001x_2x_3$

So far, we have been specifying functions of several variables **algebraically**—by using algebraic formulas. If you have ever studied statistics, you are probably familiar with statistical tables. These tables may also be viewed as representing functions **numerically**, as the next example shows.

EXAMPLE 3 Function Represented Numerically: Body Mass Index

The following table lists some values of the "body mass index," which gives a measure of the massiveness of your body, taking height into account.* The variable w represents your weight in pounds, and h represents your height in inches. An individual with a body mass index of 25 or above is generally considered overweight.

* It is interesting that weight-lifting competitions are usually based on weight, rather than body mass index. As a consequence, taller people are at a significant disadvantage in these competitions because they must compete with shorter, stockier people of the same weight. (An extremely thin, very tall person can weigh as much as a muscular short person, although his body mass index would be significantly lower.)

$h \downarrow$ \ $w \rightarrow$	130	140	150	160	170	180	190	200	210
60	25.2	27.1	29.1	31.0	32.9	34.9	36.8	38.8	40.7
61	24.4	26.2	28.1	30.0	31.9	33.7	35.6	37.5	39.4
62	23.6	25.4	27.2	29.0	30.8	32.7	34.5	36.3	38.1
63	22.8	24.6	26.4	28.1	29.9	31.6	33.4	35.1	36.9
64	22.1	23.8	25.5	27.2	28.9	30.7	32.4	34.1	35.8
65	21.5	23.1	24.8	26.4	28.1	29.7	31.4	33.0	34.7
66	20.8	22.4	24.0	25.6	27.2	28.8	30.4	32.0	33.6
67	20.2	21.8	23.3	24.9	26.4	28.0	29.5	31.1	32.6
68	19.6	21.1	22.6	24.1	25.6	27.2	28.7	30.2	31.7
69	19.0	20.5	22.0	23.4	24.9	26.4	27.8	29.3	30.8
70	18.5	19.9	21.4	22.8	24.2	25.6	27.0	28.5	29.9
71	18.0	19.4	20.8	22.1	23.5	24.9	26.3	27.7	29.1
72	17.5	18.8	20.2	21.5	22.9	24.2	25.6	26.9	28.3
73	17.0	18.3	19.6	20.9	22.3	23.6	24.9	26.2	27.5
74	16.6	17.8	19.1	20.4	21.7	22.9	24.2	25.5	26.7
75	16.1	17.4	18.6	19.8	21.1	22.3	23.6	24.8	26.0
76	15.7	16.9	18.1	19.3	20.5	21.7	22.9	24.2	25.4

using Technology

See the Technology Guides at the end of the chapter to see how to use a spreadsheet to create the table in Example 3. Here is an outline:

Spreadsheet
w-values 130 to 210 in B1–J1
h-values 60 to 76 in A2–A18
`=0.45*B$1/(0.0254*$A2)^2`
in B2; copy down and across through J18. [More details on page 1147.]

As the table shows, the value of the body mass index depends on two quantities: w and h. Let us write $M(w, h)$ for the body mass index function. What are $M(140, 62)$ and $M(210, 63)$?

Solution We can read the answers from the table:

$$M(140, 62) = 25.4 \qquad w = 140 \text{ lb}, h = 62 \text{ in}$$

and $$M(210, 63) = 36.9. \qquad w = 210 \text{ lb}, h = 63 \text{ in}$$

The function $M(w, h)$ is actually given by the formula

$$M(w, h) = \frac{0.45w}{(0.0254h)^2}.$$

[The factor 0.45 converts the weight to kilograms, and 0.0254 converts the height to meters. If w is in kilograms and h is in meters, the formula is simpler: $M(w, h) = w/h^2$.]

Geometric Viewpoint: Three-Dimensional Space and the Graph of a Function of Two Variables

Just as functions of a single variable have graphs, so do functions of two or more variables. Recall that the graph of $f(x)$ consists of all points $(x, f(x))$ in the xy-plane. By analogy, we would like to say that the graph of a function of *two* variables, $f(x, y)$, consists of all points of the form $(x, y, f(x, y))$. Thus, we need three axes: the x-, y-, and z-axes. In other words, our graph will live in **three-dimensional space**, or **3-space**.*

Just as we had two mutually perpendicular axes in two-dimensional space (the xy-plane; see Figure 4(a)), so we have three mutually perpendicular axes in three-dimensional space (Figure 4(b)).

* If we were dealing instead with a function of *three* variables, then we would need to go to *four-dimensional* space. Here we run into visualization problems (to say the least!) so we won't discuss the graphs of functions of three or more variables in this text.

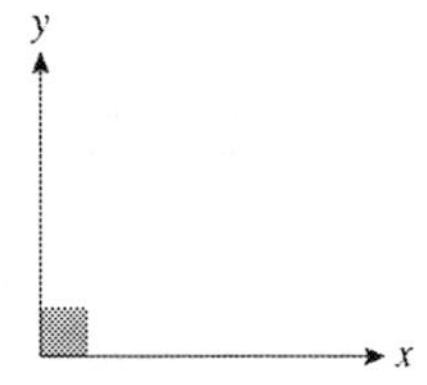

Two-dimensional space

Figure 4(a)

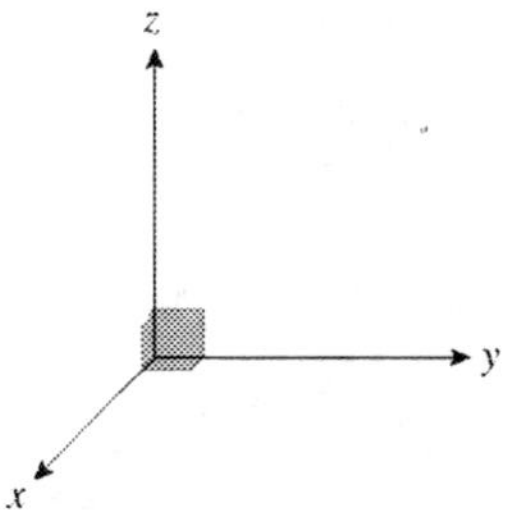

Three-dimensional space

Figure 4(b)

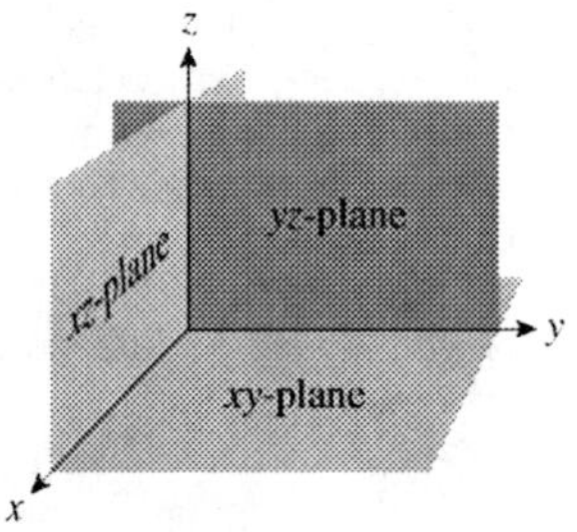

Figure 5

In both 2-space and 3-space, the axis labeled with the last letter goes up. Thus, the z-direction is the "up" direction in 3-space, rather than the y-direction.

Three important planes are associated with these axes: the xy-plane, the yz-plane, and the xz-plane. These planes are shown in Figure 5. Any two of these planes intersect in one of the axes (for example, the xy- and xz-planes intersect in the x-axis) and all three meet at the origin. Notice that the xy-plane consists of all points with z-coordinate zero, the xz-plane consists of all points with $y = 0$, and the yz-plane consists of all points with $x = 0$.

In 3-space, each point has *three* coordinates, as you might expect: the x-coordinate, the y-coordinate, and the z-coordinate. To see how this works, look at the following examples.

EXAMPLE 4 Plotting Points in Three Dimensions

Locate the points $P(1, 2, 3)$, $Q(-1, 2, 3)$, $R(1, -1, 0)$, and $S(1, 2, -2)$ in 3-space.

Solution To locate P, the procedure is similar to the one we used in 2-space: Start at the origin, proceed 1 unit in the x direction, then proceed 2 units in the y direction, and finally, proceed 3 units in the z direction. We wind up at the point P shown in Figures 6(a) and 6(b).

Here is another, extremely useful way of thinking about the location of P. First, look at the x- and y-coordinates, obtaining the point $(1, 2)$ in the xy-plane. The point we want is then 3 units vertically above the point $(1, 2)$ because the z-coordinate of a point is just its height above the xy-plane. This strategy is shown in Figure 6(c).

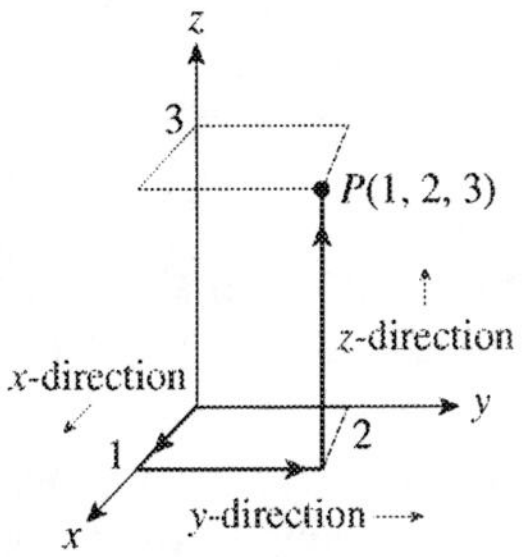

Figure 6(a)

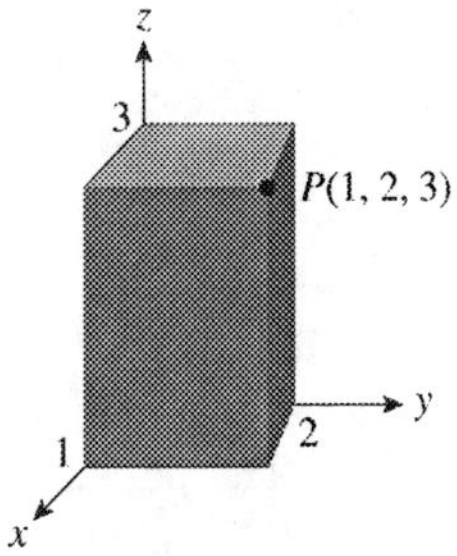

Figure 6(b)

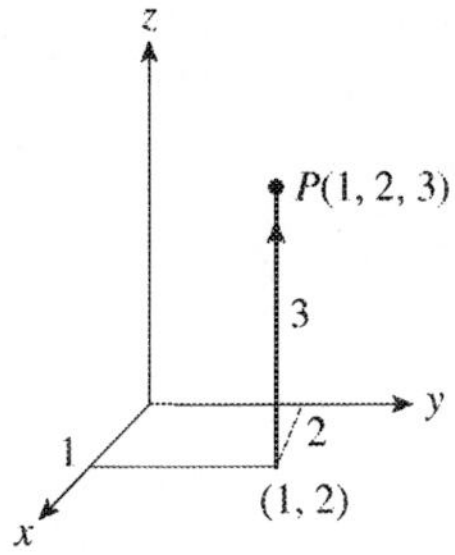

Figure 6(c)

Plotting the points Q, R, and S is similar, using the convention that negative coordinates correspond to moves back, left, or down. (See Figure 7.)

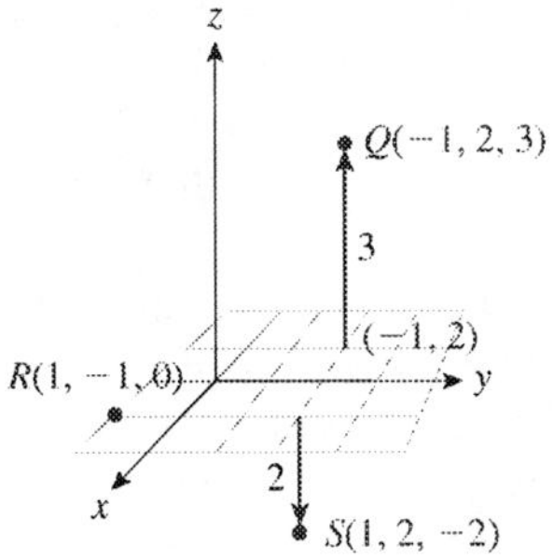

Figure 7

Our next task is to describe the graph of a function $f(x, y)$ of two variables.

Graph of a Function of Two Variables

The **graph of the function f of two variables** is the set of all points $(x, y, f(x, y))$ in three-dimensional space, where we restrict the values of (x, y) to lie in the domain of f. In other words, the graph is the set of all the points (x, y, z) with $z = f(x, y)$.

Note For *every* point (x, y) in the domain of f, the z-coordinate of the corresponding point on the graph is given by evaluating the function at (x, y). Thus, there will be a point of the graph on the vertical line through *every* point in the domain of f, so that the graph is usually a *surface* of some sort (see the figure).

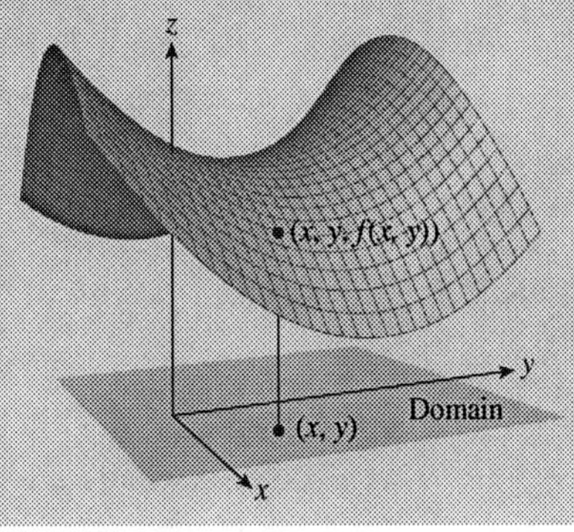

EXAMPLE 5 Graph of a Function of Two Variables

Describe the graph of $f(x, y) = x^2 + y^2$.

Solution Your first thought might be to make a table of values. You could choose some values for x and y and then, for each such pair, calculate $z = x^2 + y^2$. For example, you might get the following table:

$y \downarrow$ \ $x \rightarrow$	**−1**	**0**	**1**
−1	2	1	2
0	1	0	1
1	2	1	2

$f(x, y) = x^2 + y^2$

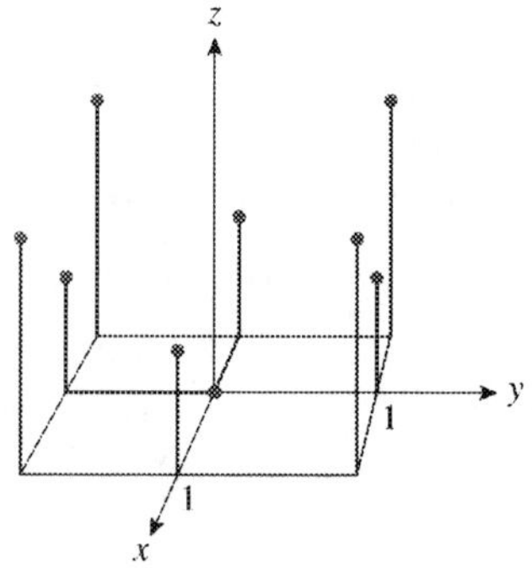

Figure 8

This gives the following nine points on the graph of f: $(-1, -1, 2)$, $(-1, 0, 1)$, $(-1, 1, 2)$, $(0, -1, 1)$, $(0, 0, 0)$, $(0, 1, 1)$, $(1, -1, 2)$, $(1, 0, 1)$, and $(1, 1, 2)$. These points are shown in Figure 8.

The points on the xy-plane we chose for our table are the grid points in the xy-plane, and the corresponding points on the graph are marked with solid dots. The problem is that this small number of points hardly tells us what the surface looks like, and even if we plotted more points, it is not clear that we would get anything more than a mass of dots on the page.

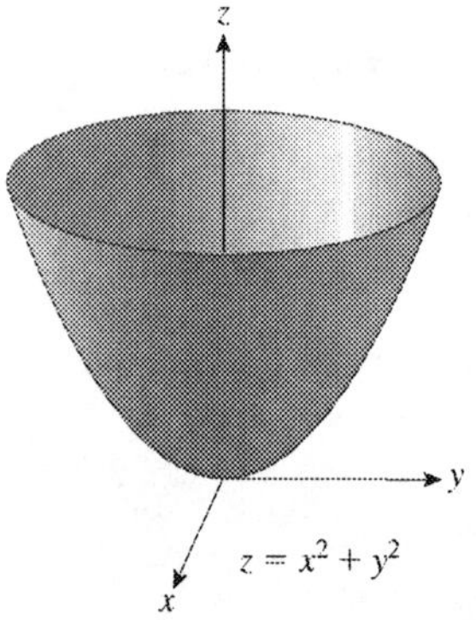

Figure 9

What can we do? There are several alternatives. One place to start is to use technology to draw the graph. (See the technology note on the next page.) We then obtain something like Figure 9. This particular surface is called a **paraboloid**.

If we slice vertically through this surface along the yz-plane, we get the picture in Figure 10. The shape of the front edge, where we cut, is a parabola. To see why, note that the yz-plane is the set of points where $x = 0$. To get the intersection of $x = 0$ and $z = x^2 + y^2$, we substitute $x = 0$ in the second equation, getting $z = y^2$. This is the equation of a parabola in the yz-plane.

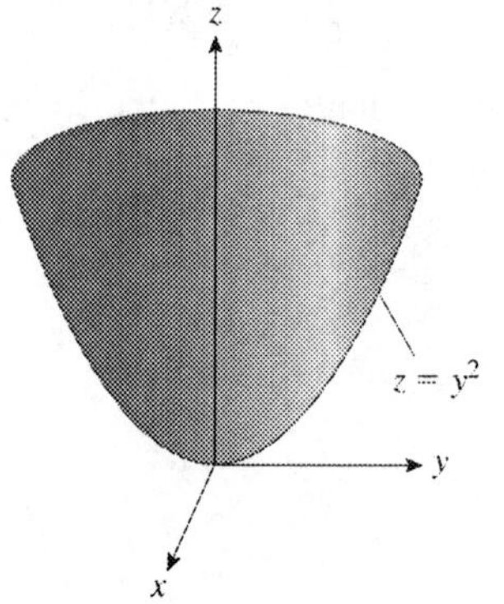

Figure 10

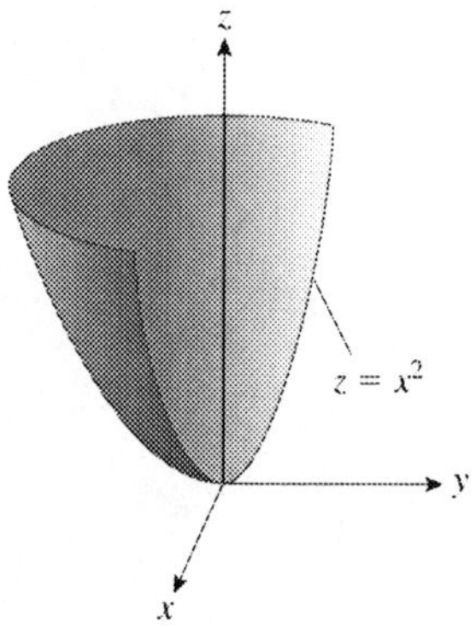

Figure 11

Similarly, we can slice through the surface with the xz-plane by setting $y = 0$. This gives the parabola $z = x^2$ in the xz-plane (Figure 11).

We can also look at horizontal slices through the surface, that is, slices by planes parallel to the xy-plane. These are given by setting $z = c$ for various numbers c. For example, if we set $z = 1$, we will see only the points with height 1. Substituting in the equation $z = x^2 + y^2$ gives the equation

$$1 = x^2 + y^2,$$

which is the equation of a circle of radius 1.* If we set $z = 4$, we get the equation of a circle of radius 2:

* See Section 0.7 for a discussion of equations of circles.

$$4 = x^2 + y^2.$$

In general, if we slice through the surface at height $z = c$, we get a circle (of radius $\sqrt{c}$). Figure 12 shows several of these circles.

using Technology

We can use technology to obtain the graph of the function in Example 5:

Spreadsheet

Table of values:
x-values −3 to 3 in B1–H1
y-values −3 to 3 in A2–A8
`=B$1^2+$A2^2`
in B2; copy down and across through H8.
Graph: Highlight A1 through H8 and insert a Surface chart. [More details on page 1148.]

Website

www.WanerMath.com
Online Utilities
→ Surface Graphing Utility
Enter `x^2+y^2` for $f(x, y)$
Set xMin = −3, xMax = 3, yMin = −3, yMax = 3
Press "Graph".

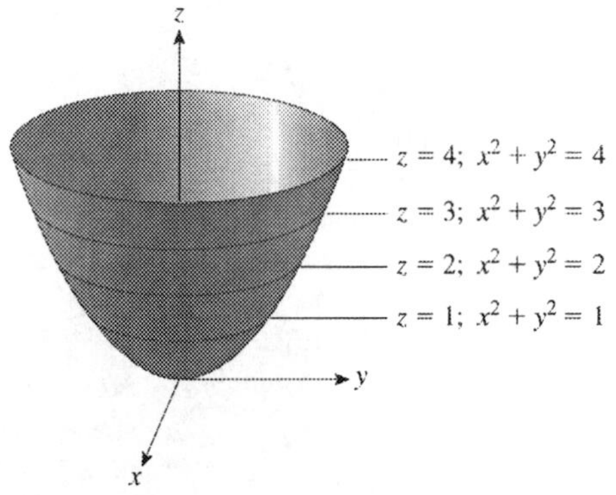

Figure 12

Looking at these circular slices, we see that this surface is the one we get by taking the parabola $z = x^2$ and spinning it around the z-axis. This is an example of what is known as a **surface of revolution**.

Before we go on... The graph of any function of the form $f(x, y) = Ax^2 + By^2 + Cxy + Dx + Ey + F$ ($A, B, \ldots, F$ constants), with $4AB - C^2$ positive, can be shown to be a paraboloid of the same general shape as that in Example 5 if A and B are positive, or upside-down if A and B are negative. If $A \neq B$, the horizontal slices will be ellipses rather than circles.

Notice that each horizontal slice through the surface in Example 5 was obtained by putting $z =$ *constant*. This gave us an equation in x and y that described a curve. These curves are called the **level curves** of the surface $z = f(x, y)$ (see the discussion on the next page). In Example 5, the equations are of the form $x^2 + y^2 = c$ (c constant), and so the level curves are circles. Figure 13 shows the level curves for $c = 0$, 1, 2, 3, and 4.

The level curves give a contour map or topographical map of the surface. Each curve shows all of the points on the surface at a particular height c. You can use this contour map to visualize the shape of the surface. Imagine moving the contour at $c = 1$ to a height of 1 unit above the xy-plane, the contour at $c = 2$ to a height of 2 units above the xy-plane, and so on. You will end up with something like Figure 12. ■

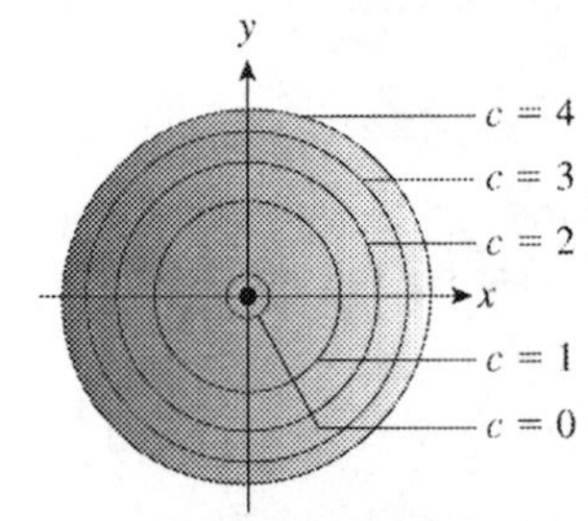

Level curves of the paraboloid $z = x^2 + y^2$

Figure 13

The following summary includes the techniques we have just used plus some additional ones:

Analyzing the Graph of a Function of Two Variables

If possible, use technology to render the graph $z = f(x, y)$ of a given function f of two variables. You can analyze its graph as follows:

Step 1 Obtain the ***x*-, *y*-, and *z*-intercepts** (the places where the surface crosses the coordinate axes).

***x*-Intercept(s):** Set $y = 0$ and $z = 0$ and solve for x.

***y*-Intercept(s):** Set $x = 0$ and $z = 0$ and solve for y.

***z*-Intercept:** Set $x = 0$ and $y = 0$ and compute z.

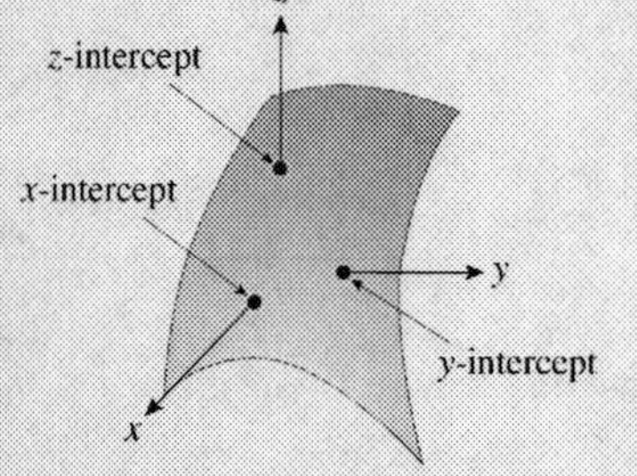

Step 2 Slice the surface along planes parallel to the *xy*-, *yz*-, and *xz*-planes.

z* = *constant Set $z = constant$ and analyze the resulting curves. These are the curves resulting from horizontal slices, and are called the **level curves** (see below).

x* = *constant Set $x = constant$ and analyze the resulting curves. These are the curves resulting from slices parallel to the *yz*-plane.

y* = *constant Set $y = constant$ and analyze the resulting curves. These are the curves resulting from slices parallel to the *xz*-plane.

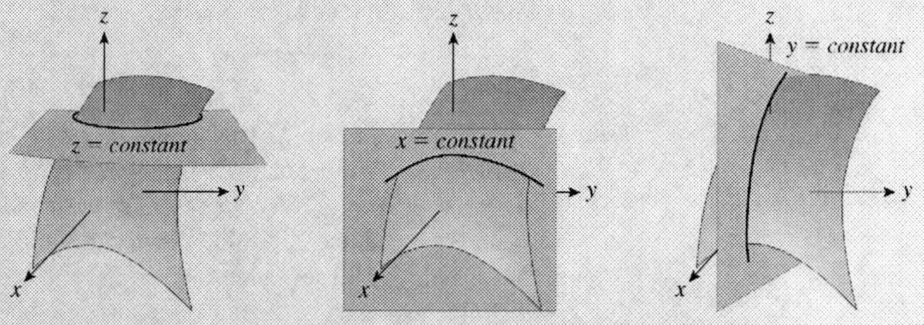

Level Curves

The **level curves** of a function f of two variables are the curves with equations of the form $f(x, y) = c$, where c is constant. These are the curves obtained from the graph of f by slicing it horizontally as above.

Quick Examples

1. Figure 13 above shows some level curves of $f(x, y) = x^2 + y^2$. The ones shown have equations $f(x, y) = 0, 1, 2, 3,$ and 4.

2. Let $f(x, y) = y - x^2 + 4$. Its level curves have the form $y - x^2 + 4 = c$ (c constant). If we solve this equation for y, we see that $y = x^2 + c - 4$, the equation of a parabola with its vertex on the y-axis at the point $c - 4$. The following figure shows a portion of the graph of f and some of its level curves.

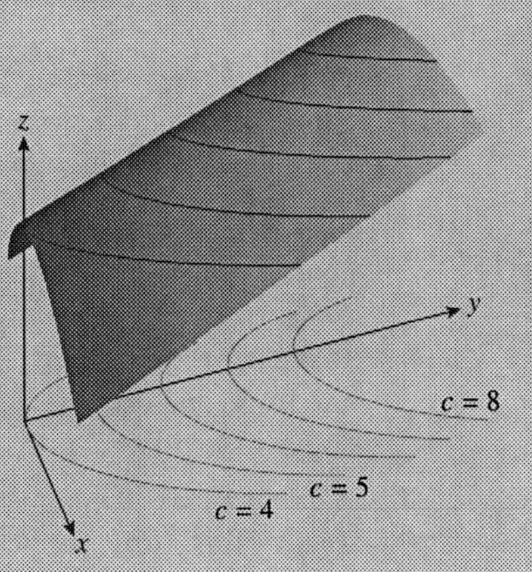

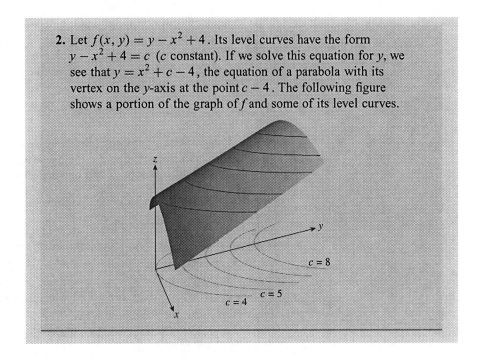

Spreadsheets often have built-in features to render surfaces such as the paraboloid in Example 5. In the following example, we use Excel to graph another surface and then analyze it as above.

EXAMPLE 6 Analyzing a Surface

Describe the graph of $f(x, y) = x^2 - y^2$.

Solution First we obtain a picture of the graph using technology. Figure 14 shows two graphs obtained using resources at the Website.

Chapter 15 → Math Tools for Chapter 15 → Surface Graphing Utility

Chapter 15 → Math Tools for Chapter 15 → Excel Surface Graphing Utility

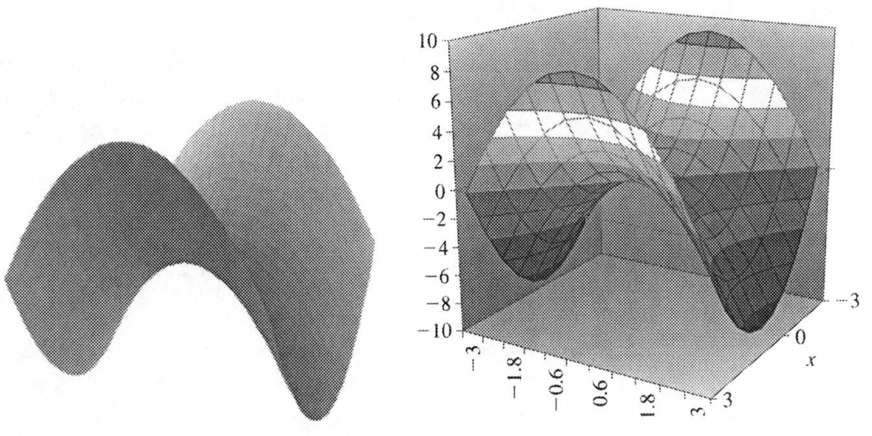

Figure 14

See the Technology Guides at the end of the chapter to find out how to obtain a similar graph from scratch using a spreadsheet.

The graph shows an example of a "saddle point" at the origin. (We return to this idea in Section 15.3.) To analyze the graph for the features shown in the box above, replace $f(x, y)$ by z to obtain

$$z = x^2 - y^2.$$

Step 1: *Intercepts* Setting any two of the variables x, y, and z equal to zero results in the third also being zero, so the x-, y-, and z-intercepts are all 0. In other words, the surface touches all three axes in exactly one point, the origin.

Step 2: *Slices* Slices in various directions show more interesting features.

Slice by $x = c$ This gives $z = c^2 - y^2$, which is the equation of a parabola that opens downward. You can see two of these slices ($c = -3, c = 3$) as the front and back edges of the surface in Figure 14. (More are shown in Figure 15(a).)

Slice by $y = c$ This gives $z = x^2 - c^2$, which is the equation of a parabola once again—this time, opening upward. You can see two of these slices ($c = -3, c = 3$) as the left and right edges of the surface in Figure 14. (More are shown in Figure 15(b).)

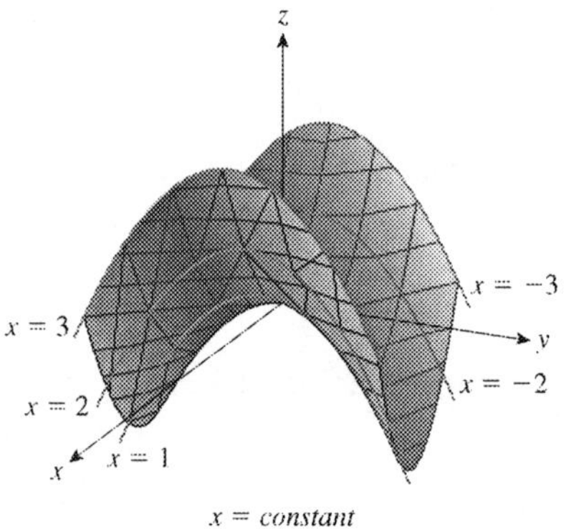

Figure 15(a)

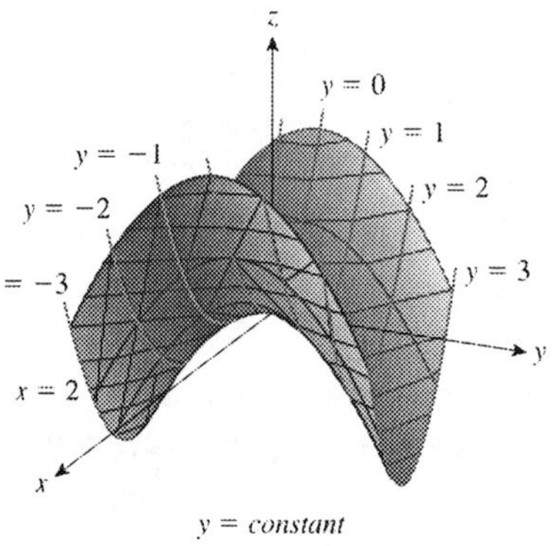

Figure 15(b)

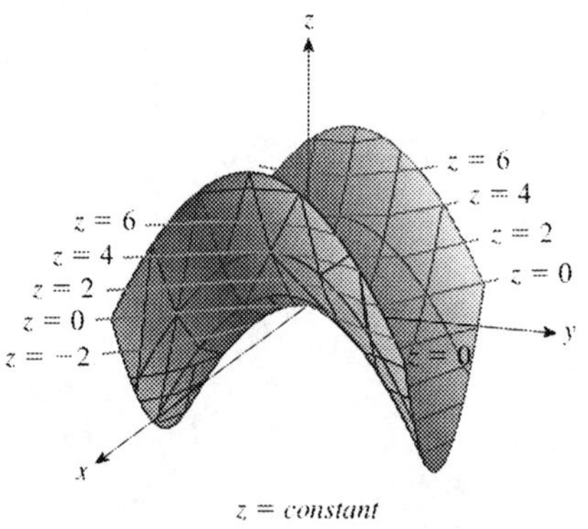

Figure 15(c)

Level Curves: Slice by $z = c$ This gives $x^2 - y^2 = c$, which is a hyperbola. The level curves for various values of c are visible in Figure 14 as the horizontal slices. (See Figure 15(c).) The case $c = 0$ is interesting: The equation $x^2 - y^2 = 0$ can be rewritten as $x = \pm y$ (why?), which represents two lines at right angles to each other.

To obtain really beautiful renderings of surfaces, you could use one of the commercial computer algebra software packages, such as Mathematica® or Maple®, or, if you use a Mac, the built-in grapher (grapher.app located in the Utilities folder).

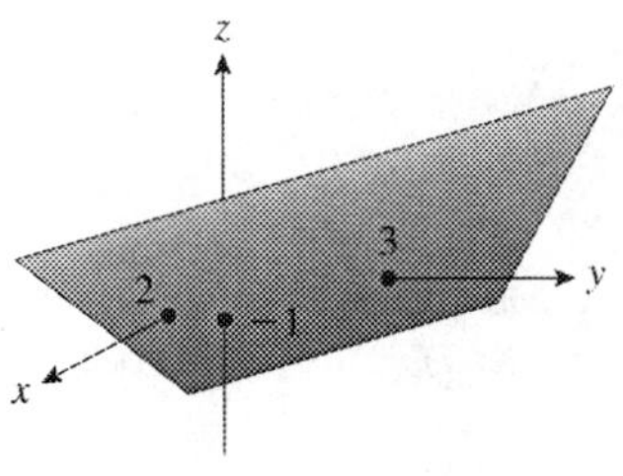

$z = \frac{1}{2}x + \frac{1}{3}y - 1$

Figure 16

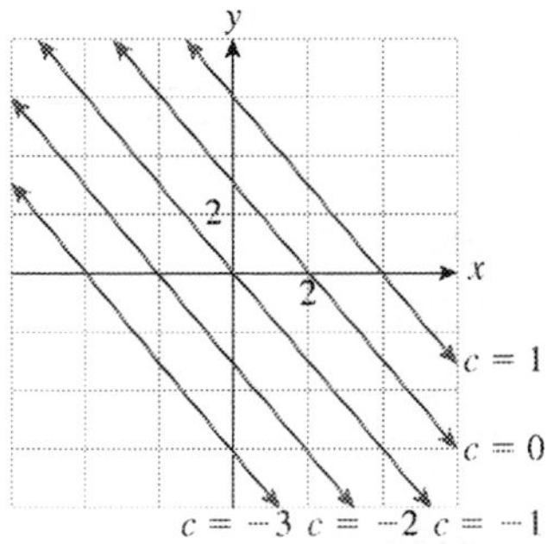

Level curves: $3x + 2y = 12$

Figure 17

* Think about what happens when the function is constant.

EXAMPLE 7 Graph and Level Curves of a Linear Function

Describe the graph of $g(x, y) = \dfrac{1}{2}x + \dfrac{1}{3}y - 1$.

Solution Notice first that g is a linear function of x and y. Figure 16 shows a portion of the graph, which is a plane.

We can get a good idea of what plane this is by looking at the x-, y-, and z-intercepts.

x-intercept Set $y = z = 0$, which gives $x = 2$.

y-intercept Set $x = z = 0$, which gives $y = 3$.

z-intercept Set $x = y = 0$, which gives $z = -1$.

Three points are enough to define a plane, so we can say that the plane is the one passing through the three points (2, 0, 0), (0, 3, 0), and (0, 0, −1). It can be shown that the graph of every linear function of two variables is a plane.

Level curves: Set $g(x, y) = c$ to obtain $\frac{1}{2}x + \frac{1}{3}y - 1 = c$, or $\frac{1}{2}x + \frac{1}{3}y = c + 1$. We can rewrite this equation as $3x + 2y = 6(c + 1)$, which is the equation of a straight line. Choosing different values of c gives us a family of parallel lines as shown in Figure 17. (For example, the line corresponding to $c = 1$ has equation $3x + 2y = 6(1 + 1) = 12$.) In general, the set of level curves of every non-constant linear function is a set of parallel straight lines.*

EXAMPLE 8 Using Level Curves

A certain function f of two variables has level curves $f(x, y) = c$ for $c = -2, -1, 0, 1$, and 2, as shown in Figure 18. (Each grid square is 1×1.)

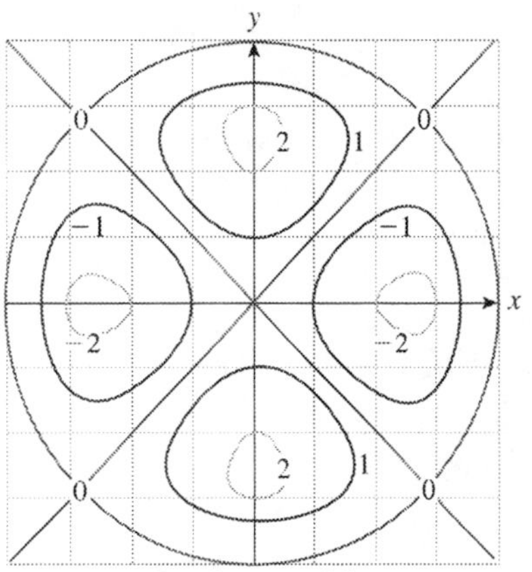

Level curves of f

Figure 18

Estimate the following: $f(1, 1)$, $f(1.5, -2)$, $f(1.5, 0)$, and $f(1, 2)$.

Solution The point (1, 1) appears to lie exactly on the red level curve $c = 0$, so $f(1, 1) \approx 0$. Similarly, the point $(1.5, -2)$ appears to lie exactly on the blue level curve $c = 1$, so $f(1.5, -2) \approx 1$. The point (1.5, 0) appears to lie midway between the level curves $c = -1$ and $c = -2$, so we estimate $f(1.5, 2) \approx -1.5$. Finally, the point (1, 2) lies between the level curves $c = 1$ and $c = 2$, but closer to $c = 1$, so we can estimate $f(1, 2)$ at around 1.3.

15.1 EXERCISES

▼ more advanced ◆ challenging

▮ indicates exercises that should be solved using technology

*For each function in Exercises 1–4, evaluate **(a)** $f(0, 0)$; **(b)** $f(1, 0)$; **(c)** $f(0, -1)$; **(d)** $f(a, 2)$; **(e)** $f(y, x)$; **(f)** $f(x+h, y+k)$* HINT [See Quick Examples page 1082.]

1. $f(x, y) = x^2 + y^2 - x + 1$

2. $f(x, y) = x^2 - y - xy + 1$

3. $f(x, y) = 0.2x + 0.1y - 0.01xy$

4. $f(x, y) = 0.4x - 0.5y - 0.05xy$

*For each function in Exercises 5–8, evaluate **(a)** $g(0, 0, 0)$; **(b)** $g(1, 0, 0)$; **(c)** $g(0, 1, 0)$; **(d)** $g(z, x, y)$; **(e)** $g(x+h, y+k, z+l)$, provided such a value exists.*

5. $g(x, y, z) = e^{x+y+z}$ **6.** $g(x, y, z) = \ln(x + y + z)$

7. $g(x, y, z) = \dfrac{xyz}{x^2 + y^2 + z^2}$ **8.** $g(x, y, z) = \dfrac{e^{xyz}}{x + y + z}$

9. Let $f(x, y, z) = 1.5 + 2.3x - 1.4y - 2.5z$. Complete the following sentences. HINT [See Example 1.]

a. f___ by ___ units for every 1 unit of increase in x.
b. f___ by ___ units for every 1 unit of increase in y.
c. ______ by 2.5 units for every ______.

10. Let $g(x, y, z) = 0.01x + 0.02y - 0.03z - 0.05$. Complete the following sentences.

a. g ___ by ___ units for every 1 unit of increase in z.
b. g ___ by ___ units for every 1 unit of increase in x.
c. ______ by 0.02 units for every ______.

In Exercises 11–18, classify each function as linear, interaction, or neither. HINT [See Quick Examples page 1085.]

11. $L(x, y) = 3x - 2y + 6xy - 4y^2$

12. $L(x, y, z) = 3x - 2y + 6xz$

13. $P(x_1, x_2, x_3) = 0.4 + 2x_1 - x_3$

14. $Q(x_1, x_2) = 4x_2 - 0.5x_1 - x_1^2$

15. $f(x, y, z) = \dfrac{x + y - z}{3}$

16. $g(x, y, z) = \dfrac{xz - 3yz + z^2}{4z} \quad (z \neq 0)$

17. $g(x, y, z) = \dfrac{xz - 3yz + z^2y}{4z} \quad (z \neq 0)$

18. $f(x, y) = x + y + xy + x^2y$

In Exercises 19 and 20, use the given tabular representation of the function f to compute the quantities asked for. HINT [See Example 3.]

19.

$y \downarrow$ \ $x \rightarrow$	10	20	30	40
10	−1	107	162	−3
20	−6	194	294	−14
30	−11	281	426	−25
40	−16	368	558	−36

a. $f(20, 10)$ **b.** $f(40, 20)$ **c.** $f(10, 20) - f(20, 10)$

20.

$y \downarrow$ \ $x \rightarrow$	10	20	30	40
10	162	107	−5	−7
20	294	194	−22	−30
30	426	281	−39	−53
40	558	368	−56	−76

a. $f(10, 30)$ **b.** $f(20, 10)$ **c.** $f(10, 40) + f(10, 20)$

▮ *In Exercises 21 and 22, use a spreadsheet or some other method to complete the given tables.*

21. $P(x, y) = x - 0.3y + 0.45xy$

$y \downarrow$ \ $x \rightarrow$	10	20	30	40
10				
20				
30				
40				

22. $Q(x, y) = 0.4x + 0.1y - 0.06xy$

$y \downarrow$ \ $x \rightarrow$	10	20	30	40
10				
20				
30				
40				

23. The following statistical table lists some values of the "Inverse F distribution" ($\alpha = 0.5$):

$d \downarrow$ \ $n \rightarrow$	1	2	3	4	5	6	7	8	9	10
1	161.4	199.5	215.7	224.6	230.2	234.0	236.8	238.9	240.5	241.9
2	18.51	19.00	19.16	19.25	19.30	19.33	19.35	19.37	19.39	19.40
3	10.13	9.552	9.277	9.117	9.013	8.941	8.887	8.812	8.812	8.785
4	7.709	6.944	6.591	6.388	6.256	6.163	6.094	5.999	5.999	5.964
5	6.608	5.786	5.409	5.192	5.050	4.950	4.876	4.772	4.772	4.735
6	5.987	5.143	4.757	4.534	4.387	4.284	4.207	4.099	4.099	4.060
7	5.591	4.737	4.347	4.120	3.972	3.866	3.787	3.677	3.677	3.637
8	5.318	4.459	4.066	3.838	3.688	3.581	3.500	3.388	3.388	3.347
9	5.117	4.256	3.863	3.633	3.482	3.374	3.293	3.179	3.179	3.137
10	4.965	4.103	3.708	3.478	3.326	3.217	3.135	3.020	3.020	2.978

In a spreadsheet, you can compute the value of this function at (n, d) by the formula

`=FINV(0.05, n, d)` The 0.05 is the value of alpha (α).

Use a spreadsheet to re-create this table.

24. The formula for body mass index $M(w, h)$, if w is given in kilograms and h is given in meters, is

$$M(w, h) = \frac{w}{h^2}.$$ See Example 3.

Use this formula to complete the following table in a spreadsheet:

$h \downarrow$ \ $w \rightarrow$	70	80	90	100	110	120	130
1.8							
1.85							
1.9							
1.95							
2							
2.05							
2.1							
2.15							
2.2							
2.25							
2.3							

In Exercises 25–28, use either a graphing calculator or a spreadsheet to complete each table. Express all your answers as decimals rounded to four decimal places.

25.

x	y	$f(x, y) = x^2\sqrt{1 + xy}$
3	1	
1	15	
0.3	0.5	
56	4	

26.

x	y	$f(x, y) = x^2e^y$
0	2	
−1	5	
1.4	2.5	
11	9	

27.

x	y	$f(x, y) = x\ln(x^2 + y^2)$
3	1	
1.4	−1	
e	0	
0	e	

28.

x	y	$f(x, y) = \dfrac{x}{x^2 - y^2}$
−1	2	
0	0.2	
0.4	2.5	
10	0	

29. Brand Z's annual sales are affected by the sales of related products X and Y as follows: Each \$1 million increase in sales of brand X causes a \$2.1 million decline in sales of brand Z, whereas each \$1 million increase in sales of brand Y results in an increase of \$0.4 million in sales of brand Z. Currently, brands X, Y, and Z are each selling \$6 million per year. Model the sales of brand Z using a linear function.

30. Brand Z's annual sales are affected by the sales of related products X and Y as follows: Each \$1 million increase in sales of brand X causes a \$2.5 million decline in sales of brand Z, whereas each \$2 million increase in sales of brand Y results in an increase of \$23 million in sales of brand Z. Currently, brands X and Y are each selling \$2 million per year and brand Z is selling \$62 million per year. Model the sales of brand Z using a linear function.

31. Sketch the cube with vertices (0, 0, 0), (1, 0, 0), (0, 1, 0), (0, 0, 1), (1, 1, 0), (1, 0, 1), (0, 1, 1), and (1, 1, 1). HINT [See Example 4.]

32. Sketch the cube with vertices $(-1, -1, -1)$, $(1, -1, -1)$, $(-1, 1, -1)$, $(-1, -1, 1)$, $(1, 1, -1)$, $(1, -1, 1)$, $(-1, 1, 1)$, and $(1, 1, 1)$. HINT [See Example 4.]

33. Sketch the pyramid with vertices $(1, 1, 0)$, $(1, -1, 0)$, $(-1, 1, 0)$, $(-1, -1, 0)$, and $(0, 0, 2)$.

34. Sketch the solid with vertices $(1, 1, 0)$, $(1, -1, 0)$, $(-1, 1, 0)$, $(-1, -1, 0)$, $(0, 0, -1)$, and $(0, 0, 1)$.

Sketch the planes in Exercises 35–40.

35. $z = -2$ **36.** $z = 4$

37. $y = 2$ **38.** $y = -3$

39. $x = -3$ **40.** $x = 2$

Match each equation in Exercises 41–48 with one of the graphs below. (If necessary, use technology to render the surfaces.) HINT [See Examples 5, 6, and 7.]

41. $f(x, y) = 1 - 3x + 2y$ **42.** $f(x, y) = 1 - \sqrt{x^2 + y^2}$

43. $f(x, y) = 1 - (x^2 + y^2)$ **44.** $f(x, y) = y^2 - x^2$

45. $f(x, y) = -\sqrt{1 - (x^2 + y^2)}$

46. $f(x, y) = 1 + (x^2 + y^2)$

47. $f(x, y) = \dfrac{1}{x^2 + y^2}$ **48.** $f(x, y) = 3x - 2y + 1$

(A)

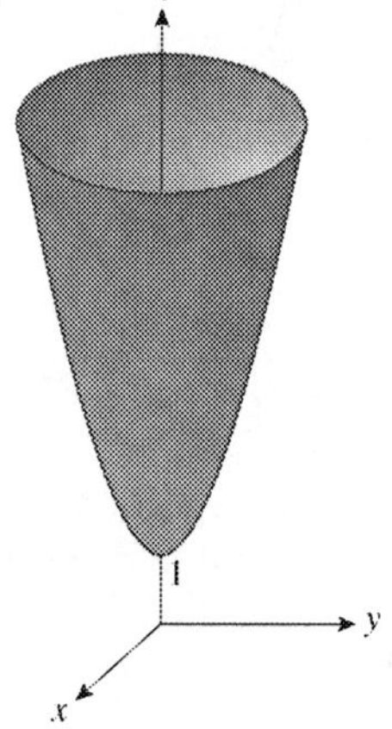

(B)

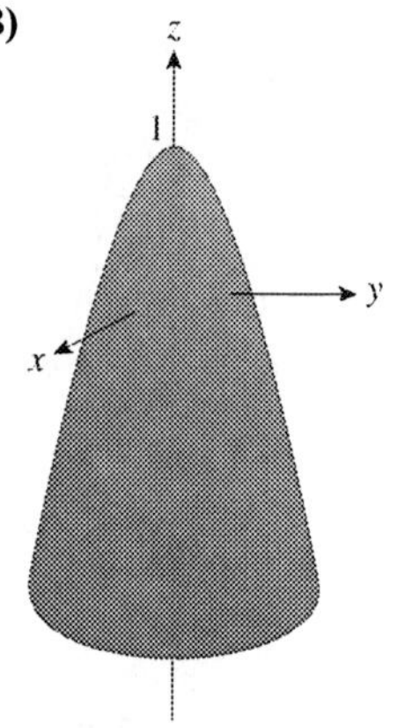

(C)

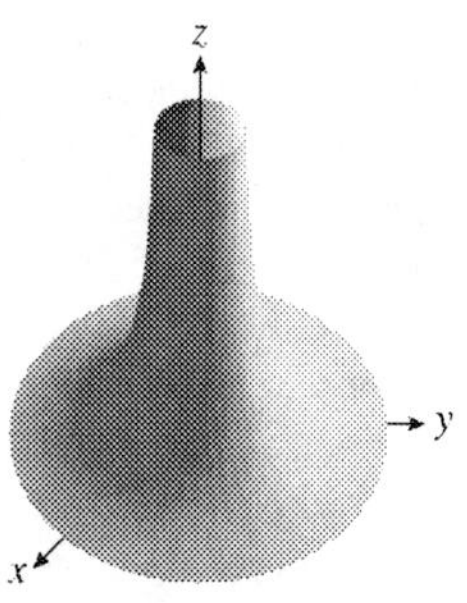

(D)

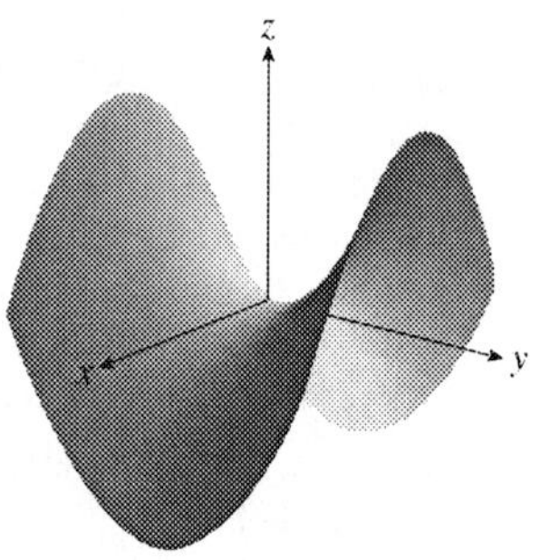

(E)

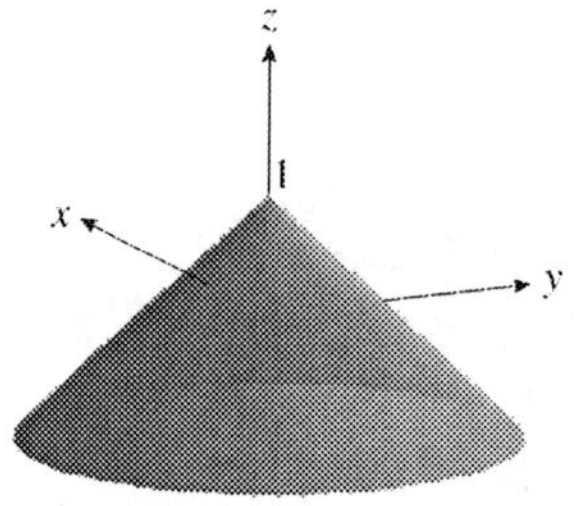

(F)

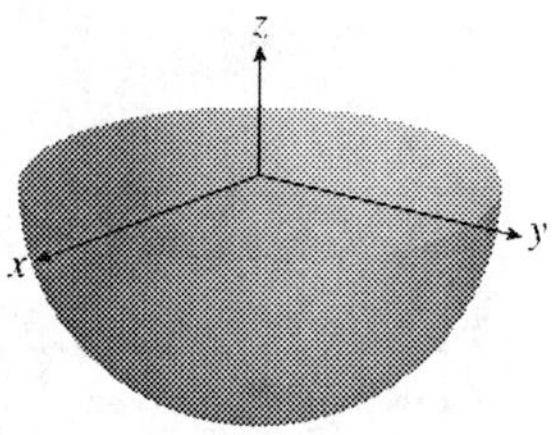

(G)

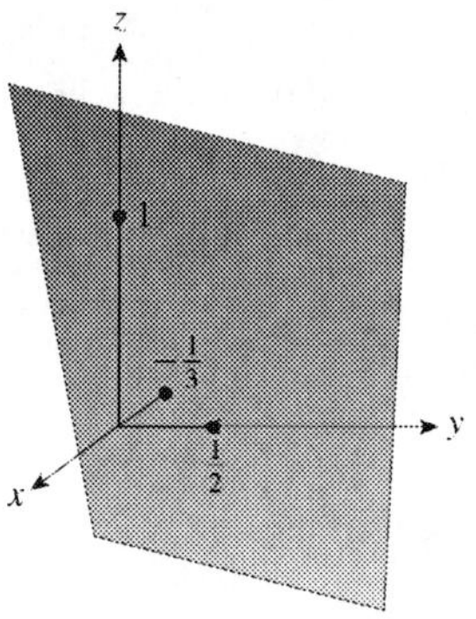

(H)

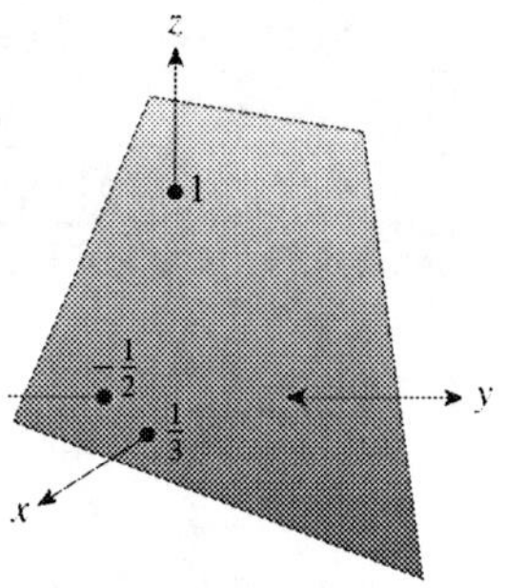

In Exercises 49–54, sketch the level curves $f(x, y) = c$ for the given function and values of c. HINT [See Example 5.]

49. $f(x, y) = 2x^2 + 2y^2$; $c = 0, 2, 18$

50. $f(x, y) = 3x^2 + 3y^2$; $c = 0, 3, 27$

51. $f(x, y) = y + 2x^2$; $c = -2, 0, 2$

52. $f(x, y) = 2y - x^2$; $c = -2, 0, 2$

53. $f(x, y) = 2xy - 1$; $c = -1, 0, 1$

54. $f(x, y) = 2 + xy$; $c = -2, 0, 2$

Exercises 55–58 refer to the following plot of some level curves of $f(x, y) = c$ for $c = -2, 0, 2, 4$, and 6. (Each grid square is 1 unit × 1 unit.) HINT [See Example 8.]

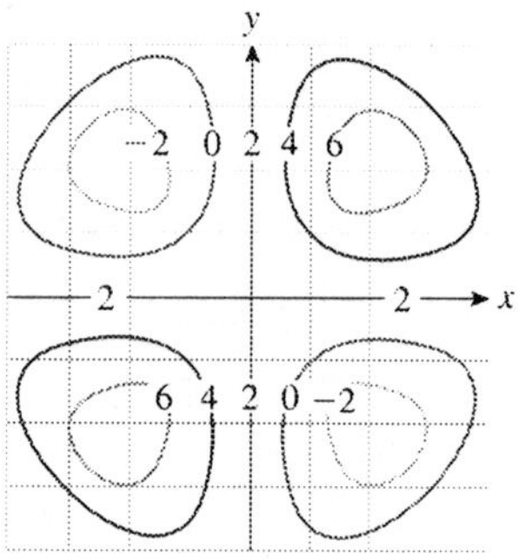

55. Estimate: **a.** $f(1, 1)$ **b.** $f(-2, -1)$ **c.** $f(3, -2.5)$

56. Estimate: **a.** $f(0, 1)$ **b.** $f(-1, -0.5)$ **c.** $f(-2, 1)$

57. At approximately which point or points does f appear to attain a maximum value?

58. At approximately which point or points does f appear to attain a minimum value?

Sketch the graphs of the functions in Exercises 59–74. HINT [See Example 7.]

59. $f(x, y) = 1 - x - y$

60. $f(x, y) = x + y - 2$

61. $g(x, y) = 2x + y - 2$

62. $g(x, y) = 3 - x + 2y$

63. $h(x, y) = x + 2$

64. $h(x, y) = 3 - y$

Use of technology is suggested in Exercises 65–74. HINT [See Example 6.]

65. $s(x, y) = 2x^2 + 2y^2$. Show cross sections at $z = 1$ and $z = 2$.

66. $s(x, y) = -(x^2 + y^2)$. Show cross sections at $z = -1$ and $z = -2$.

67. $f(x, y) = 2 + \sqrt{x^2 + y^2}$. Show cross sections at $z = 3$ and $y = 0$.

68. $f(x, y) = 2 - \sqrt{x^2 + y^2}$. Show cross sections at $z = 0$ and $y = 0$.

69. $f(x, y) = y^2$

70. $g(x, y) = x^2$

71. $h(x, y) = \frac{1}{y}$

72. $k(x, y) = e^y$

73. $f(x, y) = e^{-(x^2+y^2)}$

74. $g(x, y) = \frac{1}{\sqrt{x^2 + y^2}}$

APPLICATIONS

75. ***Cost*** Your weekly cost (in dollars) to manufacture x cars and y trucks is

$$C(x, y) = 240{,}000 + 6{,}000x + 4{,}000y.$$

a. What is the marginal cost of a car? Of a truck? HINT [See Example 1.]
b. Describe the graph of the cost function C. HINT [See Example 7.]
c. Describe the slice $x = 10$. What cost function does this slice describe?
d. Describe the level curve $z = 480{,}000$. What does this curve tell you about costs?

76. ***Cost*** Your weekly cost (in dollars) to manufacture x bicycles and y tricycles is

$$C(x, y) = 24{,}000 + 60x + 20y.$$

a. What is the marginal cost of a bicycle? Of a tricycle? HINT [See Example 1.]
b. Describe the graph of the cost function C. HINT [See Example 7.]
c. Describe the slice by $y = 100$. What cost function does this slice describe?
d. Describe the level curve $z = 72{,}000$. What does this curve tell you about costs?

77. ***Cost*** Your sales of online video and audio clips are booming. Your Internet provider, Moneydrain.com, wants to get in on the action and has offered you unlimited technical assistance and consulting if you agree to pay Moneydrain 3¢ for every video clip and 4¢ for every audio clip you sell on the site. Further, Moneydrain agrees to charge you only \$10 per month to host your site. Set up a (monthly) cost function for the scenario, and describe each variable.

78. ***Cost*** Your Cabaret nightspot "Jazz on Jupiter" has become an expensive proposition: You are paying monthly costs of \$50,000 just to keep the place running. On top of that, your regular cabaret artist is charging you \$3,000 per performance, and your jazz ensemble is charging \$1,000 per hour. Set up a (monthly) cost function for the scenario, and describe each variable.

79. ***Scientific Research*** In each year from 1983 to 2003, the percentage y of research articles in *Physical Review* written by researchers in the United States can be approximated by

$$y = 82 - 0.78t - 1.02x \text{ percentage points} \quad (0 \le t \le 20),$$

where t is the year since 1983 and x is the percentage of articles written by researchers in Europe.[2]

a. In 2003, researchers in Europe wrote 38% of the articles published by the journal that year. What percentage was written by researchers in the United States?
b. In 1983, researchers in the United States wrote 61% of the articles published that year. What percentage was written by researchers in Europe?
c. What are the units of measurement of the coefficient of t?

80. ***Scientific Research*** The number z of research articles in *Physical Review* that were written by researchers in the United States from 1993 through 2003 can be approximated by

$$z = 5{,}960 - 0.71x + 0.50y \quad (3{,}000 \le x, y \le 6{,}000)$$

articles each year, where x is the number of articles written by researchers in Europe and y is the number written by researchers in other countries (excluding Europe and the United States).[3]

a. In 2000, approximately 5,500 articles were written by researchers in Europe, and 4,500 by researchers in other countries. How many (to the nearest 100) were written by researchers in the United States?
b. According to the model, if 5,000 articles were written in Europe and an equal number by researchers in the United States and other countries, what would that number be?
c. What is the significance of the fact that the coefficient of x is negative?

---

[2]Based on a linear regression. Source for data: The American Physical Society/*New York Times*, May 3, 2003, p. A1.

[3]*Ibid.*

81. ***Market Share in the 1990s: Chrysler, Ford, General Motors*** In the late 1990s, the relationship between the domestic market shares of three major U.S. manufacturers of cars and light trucks could be modeled by

$$x_3 = 0.66 - 2.2x_1 - 0.02x_2,$$

where x_1, x_2, and x_3 are, respectively, the fractions of the market held by Chrysler, Ford, and General Motors.[4] Thinking of General Motors' market share as a function of the shares of the other two manufacturers, describe the graph of the resulting function. How are the different slices by $x_1 =$ *constant* related to one another? What does this say about market share?

82. ***Market Share in the 1990s: Kellogg, General Mills, General Foods*** In the late 1990s, the relationship among the domestic market shares of three major manufacturers of breakfast cereal was

$$x_1 = -0.4 + 1.2x_2 + 2x_3,$$

where x_1, x_2, and x_3 are, respectively, the fractions of the market held by Kellogg, General Mills, and General Foods.[5] Thinking of Kellogg's market share as a function of the shares of the other two manufacturers, describe the graph of the resulting function. How are the different slices by $x_2 =$ *constant* related to one another? What does this say about market share?

83. ***Prison Population*** The number of prisoners in federal prisons in the United States can be approximated by

$$N(x, y) = 27 - 0.08x + 0.08y + 0.0002xy \text{ thousand inmates,}$$

where x is the number, in thousands, in state prisons, and y is the number, in thousands, in local jails.[6]

a. In 2007 there were approximately 1.3 million in state prisons and 781 thousand in local jails. Estimate, to the nearest thousand, the number of prisoners in federal prisons that year.

b. Obtain N as a function of x for $y = 300$, and again for $y = 500$. Interpret the slopes of the resulting linear functions.

84. ***Prison Population*** The number of prisoners in state prisons in the United States can be approximated by

$$N(x, y) = -260 + 7x + 2y - 0.009xy \text{ thousand inmates,}$$

where x is the number, in thousands, in federal prisons, and y is the number, in thousands, in local jails.[7]

a. In 2007 there were approximately 189 thousand in federal prisons and 781 thousand in local jails. Estimate, to the nearest 0.1 million, the number of prisoners in state prisons that year.

b. Obtain N as a function of y for $x = 80$, and again for $x = 100$. Interpret the slopes of the resulting linear functions.

85. ***Marginal Cost (Interaction Model)*** Your weekly cost (in dollars) to manufacture x cars and y trucks is

$$C(x, y) = 240{,}000 + 6{,}000x + 4{,}000y - 20xy.$$

(Compare with Exercise 75.)

a. Describe the slices $x =$ constant and $y =$ constant.

b. Is the graph of the cost function a plane? How does your answer relate to part (a)?

c. What are the slopes of the slices $x = 10$ and $x = 20$? What does this say about cost?

86. ***Marginal Cost (Interaction Model)*** Repeat the preceding exercise using the weekly cost to manufacture x bicycles and y tricycles given by

$$C(x, y) = 24{,}000 + 60x + 20y + 0.3xy.$$

(Compare with Exercise 76.)

87. ***Online Revenue*** Your major online bookstore is in direct competition with Amazon.com, BN.com, and BooksAMillion.com. Your company's daily revenue in dollars is given by

$$R(x, y, z) = 10{,}000 - 0.01x - 0.02y - 0.01z + 0.00001yz,$$

where x, y, and z are the online daily revenues of Amazon .com, BN.com, and BooksAMillion.com, respectively.

a. If, on a certain day, Amazon.com shows revenue of \$12,000, while BN.com and BooksAMillion.com each show \$5,000, what does the model predict for your company's revenue that day?

b. If Amazon.com and BN.com each show daily revenue of \$5,000, give an equation showing how your daily revenue depends on that of BooksAMillion.com.

88. ***Online Revenue*** Repeat the preceding exercise, using the revised revenue function

$$R(x, y, z) = 20{,}000 - 0.02x - 0.04y - 0.01z + 0.00001yz.$$

89. ***Sales: Walmart, Target*** The following table shows the approximate net sales, in billions of dollars, of Walmart and Target in 2004, 2008, and 2010.[8]

	2004	2008	2010
Walmart	250	370	420
Target	42	62	68

Model Walmart's net earnings as a function of Target's net earnings and time, using a linear function of the form

$$f(x, t) = Ax + Bt + C \quad (A, B, C \text{ constants}),$$

where f is Walmart's net earnings (in billions of dollars), x is Target's net earnings (in billions of dollars), and t is time in years since 2004. In 2006 Target's net earnings were about \$52.5 billion. What, to the nearest billion dollars, does your model estimate as Walmart's net earnings that year?

[4]Based on a linear regression. Source of data: Ward's AutoInfoBank/*New York Times*, July 29, 1998, p. D6.

[5]Based on a linear regression. Source of data: Bloomberg Financial Markets/*New York Times*, November 28, 1998, p. C1.

[6]Source for data: Sourcebook of Criminal Justice Statistics Online (www.albany.edu/sourcebook/wk1/t6132007.wk1).

[7]*Ibid.*

[8]Sources: http://walmartstores.com/Investors, http://investors.target.com, www.wikinvest.com.

90. ▼ ***Sales: Nintendo, Nokia*** The following table shows the approximate net sales of Nintendo (in billions of yen) and Nokia (in billions of euro) in 2000, 2004, and 2008.[9]

	2004	2008	2010
Nintendo	510	1,700	1,010
Nokia	30	52	42

Model Nintendo's net earnings as a function of Nokia's net earnings and time, using a linear function of the form

$$f(x, t) = Ax + Bt + C \quad (A, B, C \text{ constants}),$$

where f is Nintendo's net earnings (in billions of yen), x is Nokia's net earnings (in billions of euro), and t is time in years since 2004. In 2007 Nokia's net earnings were about €50 billion. What, to the nearest billion yen, does your model estimate as Nintendo's net earnings that year?

91. ▼ ***Utility*** Suppose your newspaper is trying to decide between two competing desktop publishing software packages, Macro Publish and Turbo Publish. You estimate that if you purchase x copies of Macro Publish and y copies of Turbo Publish, your company's daily productivity will be

$$U(x, y) = 6x^{0.8}y^{0.2} + x,$$

where $U(x, y)$ is measured in pages per day (U is called a *utility function*). If $x = y = 10$, calculate the effect of increasing x by one unit, and interpret the result.

92. ▼ ***Housing Costs***[10] The cost C (in dollars) of building a house is related to the number k of carpenters used and the number e of electricians used by

$$C(k, e) = 15{,}000 + 50k^2 + 60e^2.$$

If $k = e = 10$, compare the effects of increasing k by one unit and of increasing e by one unit. Interpret the result.

93. ▼ ***Volume*** The volume of an ellipsoid with cross-sectional radii a, b, and c is $V(a, b, c) = \frac{4}{3}\pi abc$.

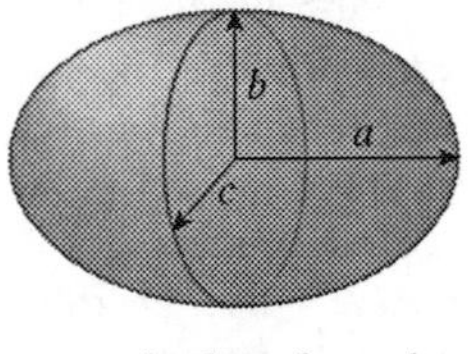

a. Find at least two sets of values for a, b, and c such that $V(a, b, c) = 1$.
b. Find the value of a such that $V(a, a, a) = 1$, and describe the resulting ellipsoid.

94. ▼ ***Volume*** The volume of a right elliptical cone with height h and radii a and b of its base is $V(a, b, h) = \frac{1}{3}\pi abh$.

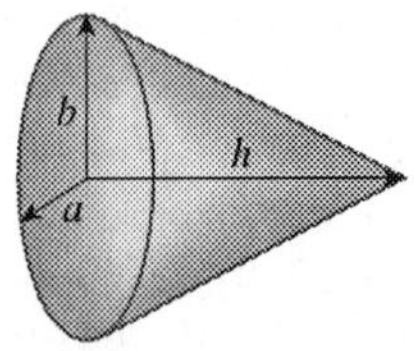

a. Find at least two sets of values for a, b, and h such that $V(a, b, h) = 1$.
b. Find the value of a such that $V(a, a, a) = 1$, and describe the resulting cone.

Exercises 95–98 involve "Cobb-Douglas" productivity functions. These functions have the form

$$P(x, y) = Kx^a y^{1-a},$$

where P stands for the number of items produced per year, x is the number of employees, and y is the annual operating budget. (The numbers K and a are constants that depend on the situation we are looking at, with $0 \le a \le 1$*.)*

95. ***Productivity*** How many items will be produced per year by a company with 100 employees and an annual operating budget of \$500,000 if $K = 1{,}000$ and $a = 0.5$? (Round your answer to one significant digit.)

96. ***Productivity*** How many items will be produced per year by a company with 50 employees and an annual operating budget of \$1,000,000 if $K = 1{,}000$ and $a = 0.5$? (Round your answer to one significant digit.)

97. ▼ ***Modeling Production with Cobb-Douglas*** Two years ago my piano manufacturing plant employed 1,000 workers, had an operating budget of \$1 million, and turned out 100 pianos. Last year, I slashed the operating budget to \$10,000, and production dropped to 10 pianos.

a. Use the data for each of the two years and the Cobb-Douglas formula to obtain two equations in K and a.
b. Take logs of both sides in each equation and obtain two linear equations in a and $\log K$.
c. Solve these equations to obtain values for a and K.
d. Use these values in the Cobb-Douglas formula to predict production if I increase the operating budget back to \$1 million but lay off half the work force.

98. ▼ ***Modeling Production with Cobb-Douglas*** Repeat the preceding exercise using the following data: Two years ago—1,000 employees, \$1 million operating budget, 100 pianos; last year—1,000 employees, \$100,000 operating budget, 10 pianos.

99. ▼ ***Pollution*** The burden of human-made aerosol sulfate in the Earth's atmosphere, in grams per square meter, is

$$B(x, n) = \frac{xn}{A},$$

where x is the total weight of aerosol sulfate emitted into the atmosphere per year and n is the number of years it remains in the atmosphere. A is the surface area of the Earth, approximately 5.1×10^{14} square meters.[11]

[9] Sources: www.nintendo.com/corp, http://investors.nokia.com, www.wikinvest.com.

[10] Based on an Exercise in *Introduction to Mathematical Economics* by A. L. Ostrosky Jr. and J. V. Koch (Waveland Press, Illinois, 1979).

[11] Source: Robert J. Charlson and Tom M. L. Wigley, "Sulfate Aerosol and Climatic Change," *Scientific American*, February, 1994, pp. 48–57.

a. Calculate the burden, given the 1995 estimated values of $x = 1.5 \times 10^{14}$ grams per year, and $n = 5$ days.

b. What does the function $W(x, n) = xn$ measure?

100. ▼ ***Pollution*** The amount of aerosol sulfate (in grams) was approximately 45×10^{12} grams in 1940 and has been increasing exponentially ever since, with a doubling time of approximately 20 years.[12] Use the model from the preceding exercise to give a formula for the atmospheric burden of aerosol sulfate as a function of the time t in years since 1940 and the number of years n it remains in the atmosphere.

101. ▼ ***Alien Intelligence*** Frank Drake, an astronomer at the University of California at Santa Cruz, devised the following equation to estimate the number of planet-based civilizations in our Milky Way galaxy willing and able to communicate with Earth:[13]

$$N(R, f_p, n_e, f_l, f_i, f_c, L) = Rf_pn_ef_lf_if_cL$$

R = the number of new stars formed in our galaxy each year
f_p = the fraction of those stars that have planetary systems
n_e = the average number of planets in each such system that can support life
f_l = the fraction of such planets on which life actually evolves
f_i = the fraction of life-sustaining planets on which intelligent life evolves
f_c = the fraction of intelligent-life-bearing planets on which the intelligent beings develop the means and the will to communicate over interstellar distances
L = the average lifetime of such technological civilizations (in years)

a. What would be the effect on N if any one of the variables were doubled?

b. How would you modify the formula if you were interested only in the number of intelligent-life-bearing planets in the galaxy?

c. How could one convert this function into a linear function?

d. (For discussion) Try to come up with an estimate of N.

102. ▼ ***More Alien Intelligence*** The formula given in the preceding exercise restricts attention to planet-based civilizations in our galaxy. Give a formula that includes intelligent planet-based aliens from the galaxy Andromeda. (Assume that all the variables used in the formula for the Milky Way have the same values for Andromeda.)

COMMUNICATION AND REASONING EXERCISES

103. Let $f(x, y) = \dfrac{x}{y}$. How are $f(x, y)$ and $f(y, x)$ related?

104. Let $f(x, y) = x^2y^3$. How are $f(x, y)$ and $f(-x, -y)$ related?

[12]Source: Robert J. Charlson and Tom M. L. Wigley, "Sulfate Aerosol and Climatic Change," *Scientific American*, February, 1994, pp. 48–57.

[13]Source: "First Contact" (Plume Books/Penguin Group)/*New York Times*, October 6, 1992, p. C1.

105. Give an example of a function of the two variables x and y with the property that interchanging x and y has no effect.

106. Give an example of a function f of the two variables x and y with the property that $f(x, y) = -f(y, x)$.

107. Give an example of a function f of the three variables x, y, and z with the property that $f(x, y, z) = f(y, x, z)$ and $f(-x, -y, -z) = -f(x, y, z)$.

108. Give an example of a function f of the three variables x, y, and z with the property that $f(x, y, z) = f(y, x, z)$ and $f(-x, -y, -z) = f(x, y, z)$.

109. Illustrate by means of an example how a real-valued function of the two variables x and y gives different real-valued functions of one variable when we restrict y to be different constants.

110. Illustrate by means of an example how a real-valued function of one variable x gives different real-valued functions of the two variables y and z when we substitute for x suitable functions of y and z.

111. ▼ If f is a linear function of x and y, show that if we restrict y to be a fixed constant, then the resulting function of x is linear. Does the slope of this linear function depend on the choice of y?

112. ▼ If f is an interaction function of x and y, show that if we restrict y to be a fixed constant, then the resulting function of x is linear. Does the slope of this linear function depend on the choice of y?

113. ▼ Suppose that $C(x, y)$ represents the cost of x CDs and y cassettes. If $C(x, y + 1) < C(x + 1, y)$ for every $x \geq 0$ and $y \geq 0$, what does this tell you about the cost of CDs and cassettes?

114. ▼ Suppose that $C(x, y)$ represents the cost of renting x DVDs and y video games. If $C(x + 2, y) < C(x, y + 1)$ for every $x \geq 0$ and $y \geq 0$, what does this tell you about the cost of renting DVDs and video games?

115. Complete the following: The graph of a linear function of two variables is a ____.

116. Complete the following: The level curves of a linear function of two variables are ____.

117. ▼ ***Heat-Seeking Missiles*** The following diagram shows some level curves of the temperature, in degrees Fahrenheit, of a region in space, as well as the location, on the 100-degree curve, of a heat-seeking missile moving through the region. (These level curves are called **isotherms**.) In which of the three directions shown should the missile be traveling so as to experience the fastest rate of increase in temperature at the given point? Explain your answer.

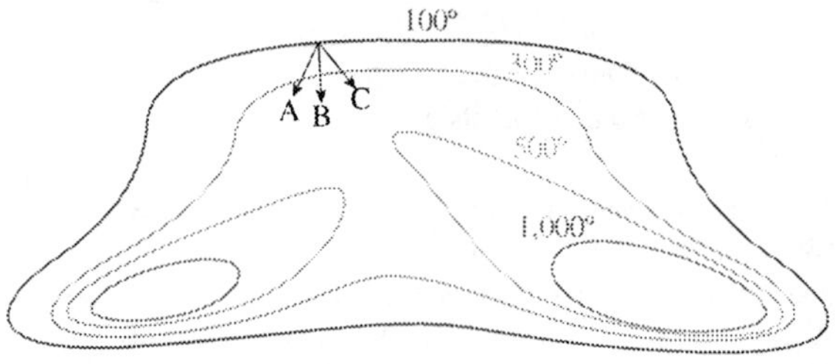

118. T ***Hiking*** The following diagram shows some level curves of the altitude of a mountain valley, as well as the location, on the 2,000-ft curve, of a hiker. The hiker is currently moving at the greatest possible rate of descent. In which of the three directions shown is he moving? Explain your answer.

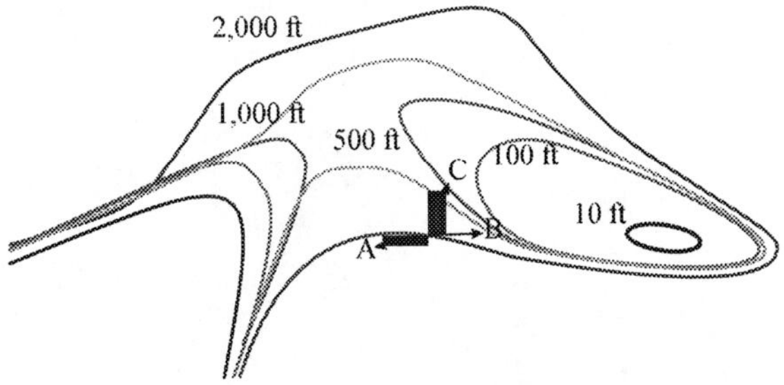

119. Your study partner Slim claims that because the surface $z = f(x, y)$ you have been studying is a plane, it follows that all the slices $x =$ *constant* and $y =$ *constant* are straight lines. Do you agree or disagree? Explain.

120. Your other study partner Shady just told you that the surface $z = xy$ you have been trying to graph must be a plane because you've already found that the slices $x =$ *constant* and $y =$ *constant* are all straight lines. Do you agree or disagree? Explain.

121. Why do we not sketch the graphs of functions of three or more variables?

122. The surface of a mountain can be thought of as the graph of what function?

123. Why is three-dimensional space used to represent the graph of a function of two variables?

124. Why is it that we can sketch the graphs of functions of two variables on the two-dimensional flat surfaces of these pages?

Practice Problems 15.1, Part 1

When a drug is injected into muscle tissue, it diffuses into the bloodstream. The concentration, C (in mg per liter), of the drug in the blood is a function of two variables: x, the amount (in mg) of the drug given in the injection, and t, the time (in hours) since the injection was administered. Suppose it is given that $C = f(x,t) = 1.5te^{-0.2t(5-x)}$ for $0 \le x \le 4$ and $t \ge 0$.

1. On the same set of axes, graph C as a function of t for injections of 1, 2, 3, and 4 mg. Put scale on your axes. Label each graph with the corresponding injection levels.

2. Describe how the graphs change for larger values of x and explain what this means in terms of drug concentration in the blood.

Practice Problems 15.1, Part 2

The number of units of a product that can be produced at a particular plant is a function of the number of workers and the operating budget. Let x denote the number of workers, let y denote the operating budget in tens of thousands of dollars, and let P denote the amount of product produced, in thousands of units. Suppose that $P = 0.2x^{0.5}y^{0.5}$, $0 \le x \le 36$, and $0 \le y \le 30$.

1. Sketch a contour diagram for these values of P: 1, 2, 3, 4. Label your axes and contours appropriately.

2. Suppose that the plant has 28 workers and an operating budget of $30,000. Which would have a greater impact on productivity: hiring one more worker, or adding $10,000 to the operating budget? Use your contour diagram to justify your conclusion.

3. Sketch graphs of $P = 0.2x^{0.5}y^{0.5}$ for these fixed values of x: 9, 16, 25, 36. Label your axes appropriately and provide scale on your axes.

15.2 Partial Derivatives

Recall that if f is a function of x, then the derivative df/dx measures how fast f changes as x increases. If f is a function of two or more variables, we can ask how fast f changes as each variable increases while the others remain fixed. These rates of change are called the "partial derivatives of f," and they measure how each variable contributes to the change in f. Here is a more precise definition.

Partial Derivatives

The **partial derivative of f with respect to x** is the derivative of f with respect to x, when all other variables are treated as constant. Similarly, the **partial derivative of f with respect to y** is the derivative of f with respect to y, with all other variables treated as constant, and so on for other variables. The partial derivatives are written as $\frac{\partial f}{\partial x}, \frac{\partial f}{\partial y}$, and so on. The symbol ∂ is used (instead of d) to remind us that there is more than one variable and that we are holding the other variables fixed.

1. Let $f(x, y) = x^2 + y^2$

$$\frac{\partial f}{\partial x} = 2x + 0 = 2x \qquad \text{Because } y^2 \text{ is treated as a constant}$$

$$\frac{\partial f}{\partial y} = 0 + 2y = 2y \qquad \text{Because } x^2 \text{ is treated as a constant}$$

2. Let $z = x^2 + xy$.

$$\frac{\partial z}{\partial x} = 2x + y \qquad \frac{\partial}{\partial x}(xy) = \frac{\partial}{\partial x}(x \cdot \text{constant}) = \text{constant} = y$$

$$\frac{\partial z}{\partial y} = 0 + x \qquad \frac{\partial}{\partial y}(xy) = \frac{\partial}{\partial y}(\text{constant} \cdot y) = \text{constant} = x$$

3. Let $f(x, y) = x^2y + y^2x - xy + y$.

$$\frac{\partial f}{\partial x} = 2xy + y^2 - y \qquad y \text{ is treated as a constant.}$$

$$\frac{\partial f}{\partial y} = x^2 + 2xy - x + 1 \qquad x \text{ is treated as a constant.}$$

Interpretation

$\frac{\partial f}{\partial x}$ is the rate at which f changes as x changes, for a fixed (constant) y.

$\frac{\partial f}{\partial y}$ is the rate at which f changes as y changes, for a fixed (constant) x.

EXAMPLE 1 Marginal Cost: Linear Model

We return to Example 1 from Section 15.1. Suppose that you own a company that makes two models of speakers, the Ultra Mini and the Big Stack. Your total monthly cost (in dollars) to make x Ultra Minis and y Big Stacks is given by

$$C(x, y) = 10{,}000 + 20x + 40y.$$

What is the significance of $\frac{\partial C}{\partial x}$ and of $\frac{\partial C}{\partial y}$?

Solution First we compute these partial derivatives:

$$\frac{\partial C}{\partial x} = 20$$

$$\frac{\partial C}{\partial y} = 40.$$

We interpret the results as follows: $\frac{\partial C}{\partial x} = 20$ means that the cost is increasing at a rate of \$20 per additional Ultra Mini (if production of Big Stacks is held constant); $\frac{\partial C}{\partial y} = 40$ means that the cost is increasing at a rate of \$40 per additional Big Stack (if production of Ultra Minis is held constant). In other words, these are the **marginal costs** of each model of speaker.

Before we go on... How much does the cost rise if you increase x by Δx and y by Δy? In Example 1, the change in cost is given by

$$\Delta C = 20\Delta x + 40\Delta y = \frac{\partial C}{\partial x}\Delta x + \frac{\partial C}{\partial y}\Delta y.$$

This suggests the **chain rule for several variables**. Part of this rule says that if x and y are both functions of t, then C is a function of t through them, and the rate of change of C with respect to t can be calculated as

$$\frac{dC}{dt} = \frac{\partial C}{\partial x} \cdot \frac{dx}{dt} + \frac{\partial C}{\partial y} \cdot \frac{dy}{dt}.$$

See the optional section on the chain rule for several variables for further discussion and applications of this interesting result. ■

EXAMPLE 2 Marginal Cost: Interaction Model

Another possibility for the cost function in the preceding example is an interaction model

$$C(x, y) = 10{,}000 + 20x + 40y + 0.1xy.$$

a. *Now* what are the marginal costs of the two models of speakers?

b. What is the marginal cost of manufacturing Big Stacks at a production level of 100 Ultra Minis and 50 Big Stacks per month?

Solution

a. We compute the partial derivatives:

$$\frac{\partial C}{\partial x} = 20 + 0.1y$$

$$\frac{\partial C}{\partial y} = 40 + 0.1x.$$

Thus, the marginal cost of manufacturing Ultra Minis increases by \$0.1 or 10¢ for each Big Stack that is manufactured. Similarly, the marginal cost of manufacturing Big Stacks increases by 10¢ for each Ultra Mini that is manufactured.

b. From part (a), the marginal cost of manufacturing Big Stacks is

$$\frac{\partial C}{\partial y} = 40 + 0.1x.$$

At a production level of 100 Ultra Minis and 50 Big Stacks per month, we have $x = 100$ and $y = 50$. Thus, the marginal cost of manufacturing Big Stacks at these production levels is

$$\left.\frac{\partial C}{\partial y}\right|_{(100,50)} = 40 + 0.1(100) = \$50 \text{ per Big Stack.}$$

Partial derivatives of functions of three variables are obtained in the same way as those for functions of two variables, as the following example shows.

EXAMPLE 3 Function of Three Variables

Calculate $\dfrac{\partial f}{\partial x}$, $\dfrac{\partial f}{\partial y}$, and $\dfrac{\partial f}{\partial z}$ if $f(x, y, z) = xy^2z^3 - xy$.

Solution Although we now have three variables, the calculation remains the same: $\partial f/\partial x$ is the derivative of f with respect to x, with *both* other variables, y and z, held constant:

$$\frac{\partial f}{\partial x} = y^2z^3 - y.$$

Similarly, $\partial f/\partial y$ is the derivative of f with respect to y, with both x and z held constant:

$$\frac{\partial f}{\partial y} = 2xyz^3 - x.$$

Finally, to find $\partial f/\partial z$, we hold both x and y constant and take the derivative with respect to z.

$$\frac{\partial f}{\partial z} = 3xy^2z^2.$$

Note The procedure for finding a partial derivative is the same for any number of variables: To get the partial derivative with respect to any one variable, we treat all the others as constants. ■

Geometric Interpretation of Partial Derivatives

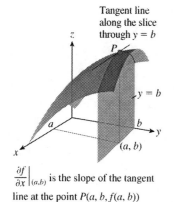

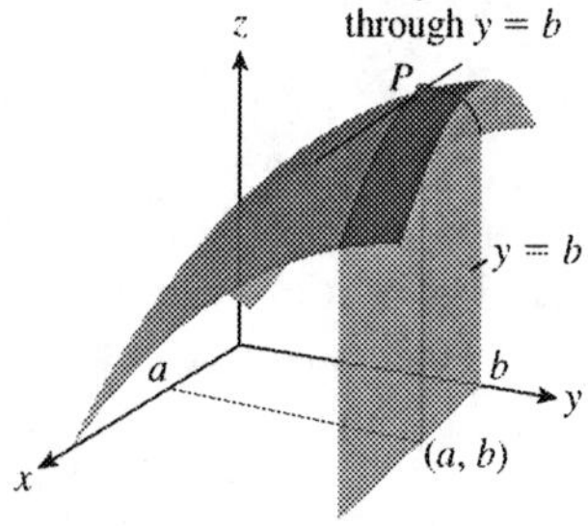

$\left.\dfrac{\partial f}{\partial x}\right|_{(a,b)}$ is the slope of the tangent line at the point $P(a, b, f(a, b))$ along the slice through $y = b$.

Figure 19

Recall that if f is a function of one variable x, then the derivative df/dx gives the slopes of the tangent lines to its graph. Now, suppose that f is a function of x and y. By definition, $\partial f/\partial x$ is the derivative of the function of x we get by holding y fixed. If we evaluate this derivative at the point (a, b), we are holding y fixed at the value b, taking the ordinary derivative of the resulting function of x, and evaluating this at $x = a$. Now, holding y fixed at b amounts to slicing through the graph of f along the plane $y = b$, resulting in a curve. Thus, the partial derivative is the slope of the tangent line to this curve at the point where $x = a$ and $y = b$, along the plane $y = b$ (Figure 19). This fits with our interpretation of $\partial f/\partial x$ as the rate of increase of f with increasing x when y is held fixed at b.

The other partial derivative, $\partial f/\partial y|_{(a,b)}$, is, similarly, the slope of the tangent line at the same point $P(a, b, f(a, b))$ but along the slice by the plane $x = a$. You should draw the corresponding picture for this on your own.

EXAMPLE 4 Marginal Cost

Referring to the interactive cost function $C(x, y) = 10{,}000 + 20x + 40y + 0.1xy$ in Example 2, we can identify the marginal costs $\partial C/\partial x$ and $\partial C/\partial y$ of manufacturing Ultra Minis and Big Stacks at a production level of 100 Ultra Minis and 50 Big Stacks per month as the slopes of the tangent lines to the two slices by $y = 50$ and $x = 100$ at the point on the graph where $(x, y) = (100, 50)$ as seen in Figure 20.

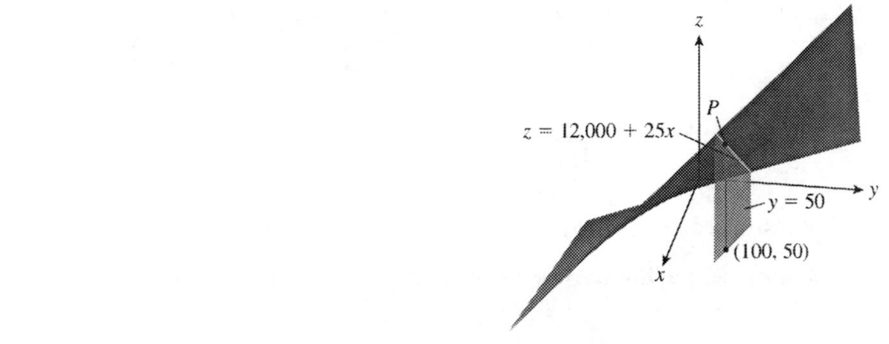

Figure 20(a)

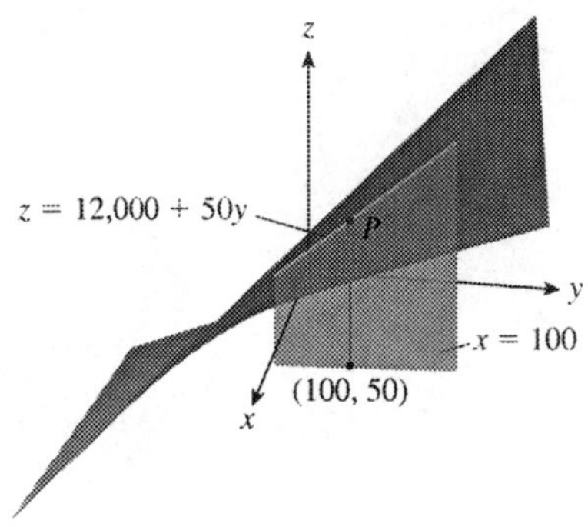

Figure 20(b)

Figure 20(a) shows the slice at $y = 50$ through the point $P = (100, 50, C(100, 50)) = (100, 50, 14{,}500)$. The equation of that slice is given by substituting $y = 50$ in the cost equation:

$$C(x, 50) = 10{,}000 + 20x + 40(50) + 0.1x(50) = 12{,}000 + 25x. \quad \text{A line of slope 25}$$

Because the slice is already a line, it coincides with the tangent line through P as depicted in Figure 19. This slope is equal to $\partial C/\partial x|_{(100,50)}$:

$$\frac{\partial C}{\partial x} = 20 + 0.1y \qquad \text{See Example 2.}$$

so $$\left.\frac{\partial C}{\partial x}\right|_{(100,50)} = 20 + 0.1(50) = 25.$$

Similarly, Figure 20(b) shows the slice at $x = 100$ through the same point P. The equation of that slice is given by substituting $x = 100$ in the cost equation:

$$C(100, y) = 10{,}000 + 20(100) + 40y + 0.1(100)y = 12{,}000 + 50y. \quad \text{A line of slope 50}$$

This slope is equal to $\partial C/\partial y|_{(100,50)} = 50$ as we calculated in Example 2.

Second-Order Partial Derivatives

Just as for functions of a single variable, we can calculate second derivatives. Suppose, for example, that we have a function of x and y, say, $f(x, y) = x^2 - x^2y^2$. We know that

$$\frac{\partial f}{\partial x} = 2x - 2xy^2.$$

If we take the partial derivative with respect to x once again, we obtain

$$\frac{\partial}{\partial x}\left(\frac{\partial f}{\partial x}\right) = 2 - 2y^2. \qquad \text{Take } \frac{\partial}{\partial x} \text{ of } \frac{\partial f}{\partial x}.$$

(The symbol $\partial/\partial x$ means "the partial derivative with respect to x," just as d/dx stands for "the derivative with respect to x.") This is called the **second-order partial derivative** and is written $\frac{\partial^2 f}{\partial x^2}$. We get the following derivatives similarly:

$$\frac{\partial f}{\partial y} = -2x^2y$$

$$\frac{\partial^2 f}{\partial y^2} = -2x^2. \qquad \text{Take } \frac{\partial}{\partial y} \text{ of } \frac{\partial f}{\partial y}.$$

Now what if we instead take the partial derivative with respect to y of $\partial f/\partial x$?

$$\frac{\partial^2 f}{\partial y \partial x} = \frac{\partial}{\partial y}\left(\frac{\partial f}{\partial x}\right) \qquad \text{Take } \frac{\partial}{\partial y} \text{ of } \frac{\partial f}{\partial x}.$$

$$= \frac{\partial}{\partial y}[2x - 2xy^2] = -4xy$$

Here, $\frac{\partial^2 f}{\partial y \partial x}$ means "first take the partial derivative with respect to x and then with respect to y" and is called a **mixed partial derivative**. If we differentiate in the opposite order, we get

$$\frac{\partial^2 f}{\partial x \partial y} = \frac{\partial}{\partial x}\left(\frac{\partial f}{\partial y}\right) = \frac{\partial}{\partial x}[-2x^2 y] = -4xy,$$

the same expression as $\frac{\partial^2 f}{\partial y \partial x}$. This is no coincidence: The mixed partial derivatives $\frac{\partial^2 f}{\partial x \partial y}$ and $\frac{\partial^2 f}{\partial y \partial x}$ are always the same as long as the first partial derivatives are both differentiable functions of x and y and the mixed partial derivatives are continuous. Because all the functions we shall use are of this type, we can take the derivatives in any order we like when calculating mixed derivatives.

Here is another notation for partial derivatives that is especially convenient for second-order partial derivatives:

f_x means $\frac{\partial f}{\partial x}$

f_y means $\frac{\partial f}{\partial y}$

f_{xy} means $(f_x)_y = \frac{\partial^2 f}{\partial y \partial x}$ (Note the order in which the derivatives are taken.)

f_{yx} means $(f_y)_x = \frac{\partial^2 f}{\partial x \partial y}$.

15.2 EXERCISES

▼ more advanced ◆ challenging

[T] indicates exercises that should be solved using technology

In Exercises 1–18, calculate $\frac{\partial f}{\partial x}, \frac{\partial f}{\partial y}, \left.\frac{\partial f}{\partial x}\right|_{(1,-1)}$, *and* $\left.\frac{\partial f}{\partial y}\right|_{(1,-1)}$ *when defined.* HINT [See Quick Examples pages 1101–1102.]

1. $f(x, y) = 10{,}000 - 40x + 20y$
2. $f(x, y) = 1{,}000 + 5x - 4y$
3. $f(x, y) = 3x^2 - y^3 + x - 1$
4. $f(x, y) = x^{1/2} - 2y^4 + y + 6$
5. $f(x, y) = 10{,}000 - 40x + 20y + 10xy$
6. $f(x, y) = 1{,}000 + 5x - 4y - 3xy$
7. $f(x, y) = 3x^2 y$
8. $f(x, y) = x^4 y^2 - x$
9. $f(x, y) = x^2 y^3 - x^3 y^2 - xy$
10. $f(x, y) = x^{-1} y^2 + xy^2 + xy$
11. $f(x, y) = (2xy + 1)^3$
12. $f(x, y) = \frac{1}{(xy + 1)^2}$
13. ▼ $f(x, y) = e^{x+y}$
14. ▼ $f(x, y) = e^{2x+y}$
15. ▼ $f(x, y) = 5x^{0.6} y^{0.4}$
16. ▼ $f(x, y) = -2x^{0.1} y^{0.9}$
17. ▼ $f(x, y) = e^{0.2xy}$
18. ▼ $f(x, y) = xe^{xy}$

In Exercises 19–28, find $\frac{\partial^2 f}{\partial x^2}, \frac{\partial^2 f}{\partial y^2}, \frac{\partial^2 f}{\partial x \partial y}$, *and* $\frac{\partial^2 f}{\partial y \partial x}$, *and evaluate them all at* $(1, -1)$ *if possible.* HINT [See discussion on pages 1105–1106.]

19. $f(x, y) = 10{,}000 - 40x + 20y$
20. $f(x, y) = 1{,}000 + 5x - 4y$
21. $f(x, y) = 10{,}000 - 40x + 20y + 10xy$

22. $f(x, y) = 1{,}000 + 5x - 4y - 3xy$

23. $f(x, y) = 3x^2y$

24. $f(x, y) = x^4y^2 - x$

25. ▼ $f(x, y) = e^{x+y}$

26. ▼ $f(x, y) = e^{2x+y}$

27. ▼ $f(x, y) = 5x^{0.6}y^{0.4}$

28. ▼ $f(x, y) = -2x^{0.1}y^{0.9}$

In Exercises 29–40, find $\frac{\partial f}{\partial x}, \frac{\partial f}{\partial y}, \frac{\partial f}{\partial z}$*, and their values at* $(0, -1, 1)$ *if possible.* HINT [See Example 3.]

29. $f(x, y, z) = xyz$

30. $f(x, y, z) = xy + xz - yz$

31. ▼ $f(x, y, z) = -\dfrac{4}{x + y + z^2}$

32. ▼ $f(x, y, z) = \dfrac{6}{x^2 + y^2 + z^2}$

33. ▼ $f(x, y, z) = xe^{yz} + ye^{xz}$

34. ▼ $f(x, y, z) = xye^z + xe^{yz} + e^{xyz}$

35. ▼ $f(x, y, z) = x^{0.1}y^{0.4}z^{0.5}$

36. ▼ $f(x, y, z) = 2x^{0.2}y^{0.8} + z^2$

37. ▼ $f(x, y, z) = e^{xyz}$

38. ▼ $f(x, y, z) = \ln(x + y + z)$

39. ▼ $f(x, y, z) = \dfrac{2{,}000z}{1 + y^{0.3}}$

40. ▼ $f(x, y, z) = \dfrac{e^{0.2x}}{1 + e^{-0.1y}}$

APPLICATIONS

41. ***Marginal Cost (Linear Model)*** Your weekly cost (in dollars) to manufacture x cars and y trucks is

$$C(x, y) = 240{,}000 + 6{,}000x + 4{,}000y.$$

Calculate and interpret $\frac{\partial C}{\partial x}$ and $\frac{\partial C}{\partial y}$. HINT [See Example 1.]

42. ***Marginal Cost (Linear Model)*** Your weekly cost (in dollars) to manufacture x bicycles and y tricycles is

$$C(x, y) = 24{,}000 + 60x + 20y.$$

Calculate and interpret $\frac{\partial C}{\partial x}$ and $\frac{\partial C}{\partial y}$.

43. ***Scientific Research*** In each year from 1983 to 2003, the percentage y of research articles in *Physical Review* written by researchers in the United States can be approximated by

$$y = 82 - 0.78t - 1.02x \text{ percentage points} \quad (0 \le t \le 20),$$

where t is the year since 1983 and x is the percentage of articles written by researchers in Europe.[14] Calculate and interpret $\frac{\partial y}{\partial t}$ and $\frac{\partial y}{\partial x}$.

[14] Based on a linear regression. Source for data: The American Physical Society/*New York Times*, May 3, 2003, p. A1.

44. ***Scientific Research*** The number z of research articles in *Physical Review* that were written by researchers in the United States from 1993 through 2003 can be approximated by

$$z = 5{,}960 - 0.71x + 0.50y \quad (3{,}000 \le x, y \le 6{,}000)$$

articles each year, where x is the number of articles written by researchers in Europe and y is the number written by researchers in other countries (excluding Europe and the United States).[15] Calculate and interpret $\frac{\partial z}{\partial x}$ and $\frac{\partial z}{\partial y}$.

45. ***Marginal Cost (Interaction Model)*** Your weekly cost (in dollars) to manufacture x cars and y trucks is

$$C(x, y) = 240{,}000 + 6{,}000x + 4{,}000y - 20xy.$$

(Compare with Exercise 41.) Compute the marginal cost of manufacturing cars at a production level of 10 cars and 20 trucks. HINT [See Example 2.]

46. ***Marginal Cost (Interaction Model)*** Your weekly cost (in dollars) to manufacture x bicycles and y tricycles is

$$C(x, y) = 24{,}000 + 60x + 20y + 0.3xy.$$

(Compare with Exercise 42.) Compute the marginal cost of manufacturing tricycles at a production level of 10 bicycles and 20 tricycles. HINT [See Example 2.]

47. ***Brand Loyalty*** The fraction of Mazda car owners who chose another new Mazda can be modeled by the following function:[16]

$$M(c, f, g, h, t) = 1.1 - 3.8c + 2.2f + 1.9g - 1.7h - 1.3t.$$

Here, c is the fraction of Chrysler car owners who remained loyal to Chrysler, f is the fraction of Ford car owners remaining loyal to Ford, g the corresponding figure for General Motors, h the corresponding figure for Honda, and t for Toyota.

a. Calculate $\frac{\partial M}{\partial c}$ and $\frac{\partial M}{\partial f}$ and interpret the answers.

b. One year it was observed that $c = 0.56$, $f = 0.56$, $g = 0.72$, $h = 0.50$, and $t = 0.43$. According to the model, what percentage of Mazda owners remained loyal to Mazda? (Round your answer to the nearest percentage point.)

48. ***Brand Loyalty*** The fraction of Mazda car owners who chose another new Mazda can be modeled by the following function:[17]

$$M(c, f) = 9.4 + 7.8c + 3.6c^2 - 38f - 22cf + 43f^2,$$

[15] *Ibid.*

[16] The model is an approximation of a linear regression based on data from the period 1988–1995. Source for data: Chrysler, Maritz Market Research, Consumer Attitude Research, and Strategic Vision/*New York Times*, November 3, 1995, p. D2.

[17] The model is an approximation of a second-order regression based on data from the period 1988–1995. Source for data: Chrysler, Maritz Market Research, Consumer Attitude Research, and Strategic Vision/*New York Times*, November 3, 1995, p. D2.

where c is the fraction of Chrysler car owners who remained loyal to Chrysler and f is the fraction of Ford car owners remaining loyal to Ford.

a. Calculate $\frac{\partial M}{\partial c}$ and $\frac{\partial M}{\partial f}$ evaluated at the point (0.7, 0.7), and interpret the answers.

b. One year it was observed that $c = 0.56$, and $f = 0.56$. According to the model, what percentage of Mazda owners remained loyal to Mazda? (Round your answer to the nearest percentage point.)

49. ***Marginal Cost*** Your weekly cost (in dollars) to manufacture x cars and y trucks is

$$C(x, y) = 200{,}000 + 6{,}000x + 4{,}000y - 100{,}000e^{-0.01(x+y)}.$$

What is the marginal cost of a car? Of a truck? How do these marginal costs behave as total production increases?

50. ***Marginal Cost*** Your weekly cost (in dollars) to manufacture x bicycles and y tricycles is

$$C(x, y) = 20{,}000 + 60x + 20y + 50\sqrt{xy}.$$

What is the marginal cost of a bicycle? Of a tricycle? How do these marginal costs behave as x and y increase?

51. ▼ ***Income Gap*** The following model is based on data on the median family incomes of Hispanic and white families in the United States for the period 1980–2008:[18]

$$z(t, x) = 31{,}200 + 270t + 13{,}500x + 140xt,$$

where

$$z(t, x) = \text{median family income}$$
$$t = \text{year } (t = 0 \text{ represents } 1980)$$
$$x = \begin{cases} 0 & \text{if the income was for a Hispanic family} \\ 1 & \text{if the income was for a white family} \end{cases}.$$

a. Use the model to estimate the median income of a Hispanic family and of a white family in 2000.

b. According to the model, how fast was the median income for a Hispanic family increasing in 2000? How fast was the median income for a white family increasing in 2000?

c. Do the answers in part (b) suggest that the income gap between white and Hispanic families was widening or narrowing during the given period?

d. What does the coefficient of xt in the formula for $z(t, x)$ represent in terms of the income gap?

52. ▼ ***Income Gap*** The following model is based on data on the median family incomes of black and white families in the United States for the period 1980–2008:[19]

$$z(t, x) = 24{,}500 + 390t + 20{,}200x + 20xt,$$

where

$$z(t, x) = \text{median family income}$$
$$t = \text{year } (t = 0 \text{ represents } 1980)$$
$$x = \begin{cases} 0 & \text{if the income was for a black family} \\ 1 & \text{if the income was for a white family} \end{cases}.$$

a. Use the model to estimate the median income of a black family and of a white family in 2000.

b. According to the model, how fast was the median income for a black family increasing in 2000? How fast was the median income for a white family increasing in 2000?

c. Do the answers in part (b) suggest that the income gap between white and black families was widening or narrowing during the given period?

d. What does the coefficient of xt in the formula for $z(t, x)$ represent in terms of the income gap?

53. ▼ ***Average Cost*** If you average your costs over your total production, you get the **average cost**, written $\bar{C}$:

$$\bar{C}(x, y) = \frac{C(x, y)}{x + y}.$$

Find the average cost for the cost function in Exercise 49. Then find the marginal average cost of a car and the marginal average cost of a truck at a production level of 50 cars and 50 trucks. Interpret your answers.

54. ▼ ***Average Cost*** Find the average cost for the cost function in Exercise 50. (See the preceding exercise.) Then find the marginal average cost of a bicycle and the marginal average cost of a tricycle at a production level of five bicycles and five tricycles. Interpret your answers.

55. ▼ ***Marginal Revenue*** As manager of an auto dealership, you offer a car rental company the following deal: You will charge \$15,000 per car and \$10,000 per truck, but you will then give the company a discount of \$5,000 times the square root of the total number of vehicles it buys from you. Looking at your marginal revenue, is this a good deal for the rental company?

56. ▼ ***Marginal Revenue*** As marketing director for a bicycle manufacturer, you come up with the following scheme: You will offer to sell a dealer x bicycles and y tricycles for

$$R(x, y) = 3{,}500 - 3{,}500e^{-0.02x-0.01y} \text{ dollars.}$$

Find your marginal revenue for bicycles and for tricycles. Are you likely to be fired for your suggestion?

57. ▼ ***Research Productivity*** Here we apply a variant of the Cobb-Douglas function to the modeling of research productivity. A mathematical model of research productivity at a particular physics laboratory is

$$P = 0.04x^{0.4}y^{0.2}z^{0.4},$$

where P is the annual number of groundbreaking research papers produced by the staff, x is the number of physicists on the research team, y is the laboratory's annual research budget, and z is the annual National Science Foundation subsidy to the laboratory. Find the rate of increase of research papers per government-subsidy dollar at a subsidy level of \$1,000,000 per year and a staff level of 10 physicists if the annual budget is \$100,000.

[18] Incomes are in 2007 dollars. Source for data: U.S. Census Bureau (www.census.gov).
[19] *Ibid.*

58. ▼ *Research Productivity* A major drug company estimates that the annual number P of patents for new drugs developed by its research team is best modeled by the formula

$$P = 0.3x^{0.3}y^{0.4}z^{0.3},$$

where x is the number of research biochemists on the payroll, y is the annual research budget, and z is the size of the bonus awarded to discoverers of new drugs. Assuming that the company has 12 biochemists on the staff, has an annual research budget of \$500,000, and pays \$40,000 bonuses to developers of new drugs, calculate the rate of growth in the annual number of patents per new research staff member.

59. ▼ *Utility* Your newspaper is trying to decide between two competing desktop publishing software packages, Macro Publish and Turbo Publish. You estimate that if you purchase x copies of Macro Publish and y copies of Turbo Publish, your company's daily productivity will be

$$U(x, y) = 6x^{0.8}y^{0.2} + x \text{ pages per day.}$$

a. Calculate $U_x(10, 5)$ and $U_y(10, 5)$ to two decimal places, and interpret the results.

b. What does the ratio $\dfrac{U_x(10, 5)}{U_y(10, 5)}$ tell about the usefulness of these products?

60. ▼ *Grades*[20] A production formula for a student's performance on a difficult English examination is given by

$$g(t, x) = 4tx - 0.2t^2 - x^2,$$

where g is the grade the student can expect to get, t is the number of hours of study for the examination, and x is the student's grade-point average.

a. Calculate $g_t(10, 3)$ and $g_x(10, 3)$ and interpret the results.

b. What does the ratio $\dfrac{g_t(10, 3)}{g_x(10, 3)}$ tell about the relative merits of study and grade-point average?

61. ▼ *Electrostatic Repulsion* If positive electric charges of Q and q coulombs are situated at positions (a, b, c) and (x, y, z), respectively, then the force of repulsion they experience is given by

$$F = K\frac{Qq}{(x - a)^2 + (y - b)^2 + (z - c)^2},$$

where $K \approx 9 \times 10^9$, F is given in newtons, and all positions are measured in meters. Assume that a charge of 10 coulombs is situated at the origin, and that a second charge of 5 coulombs is situated at $(2, 3, 3)$ and moving in the y-direction at one meter per second. How fast is the electrostatic force it experiences decreasing? (Round the answer to one significant digit.)

62. ▼ *Electrostatic Repulsion* Repeat the preceding exercise, assuming that a charge of 10 coulombs is situated at the origin and that a second charge of 5 coulombs is situated at $(2, 3, 3)$ and moving in the negative z direction at one meter per second. (Round the answer to one significant digit.)

63. ▼ *Investments* Recall that the compound interest formula for annual compounding is

$$A(P, r, t) = P(1 + r)^t,$$

where A is the future value of an investment of P dollars after t years at an interest rate of r.

a. Calculate $\dfrac{\partial A}{\partial P}, \dfrac{\partial A}{\partial r},$ and $\dfrac{\partial A}{\partial t}$, all evaluated at $(100, 0.10, 10)$. (Round your answers to two decimal places.) Interpret your answers.

b. What does the function $\left.\dfrac{\partial A}{\partial P}\right|_{(100, 0.10, t)}$ of t tell about your investment?

64. ▼ *Investments* Repeat the preceding exercise, using the formula for continuous compounding:

$$A(P, r, t) = Pe^{rt}.$$

65. ▼ *Modeling with the Cobb-Douglas Production Formula* Assume you are given a production formula of the form

$$P(x, y) = Kx^a y^b \quad (a + b = 1).$$

a. Obtain formulas for $\dfrac{\partial P}{\partial x}$ and $\dfrac{\partial P}{\partial y}$, and show that

$$\frac{\partial P}{\partial x} = \frac{\partial P}{\partial y} \text{ precisely when } x/y = a/b.$$

b. Let x be the number of workers a firm employs and let y be its monthly operating budget in thousands of dollars. Assume that the firm currently employs 100 workers and has a monthly operating budget of \$200,000. If each additional worker contributes as much to productivity as each additional \$1,000 per month, find values of a and b that model the firm's productivity.

66. ▼ *Housing Costs*[21] The cost C of building a house is related to the number k of carpenters used and the number e of electricians used by

$$C(k, e) = 15{,}000 + 50k^2 + 60e^2.$$

If three electricians are currently employed in building your new house and the marginal cost per additional electrician is the same as the marginal cost per additional carpenter, how many carpenters are being used? (Round your answer to the nearest carpenter.)

67. ▼ *Nutrient Diffusion* Suppose that one cubic centimeter of nutrient is placed at the center of a circular petri dish filled with water. We might wonder how the nutrient is distributed after a time of t seconds. According to the classical theory of diffusion, the concentration of nutrient (in parts of nutrient per part of water) after a time t is given by

$$u(r, t) = \frac{1}{4\pi Dt}e^{-\frac{r^2}{4Dt}}.$$

Here D is the *diffusivity*, which we will take to be 1, and r is the distance from the center in centimeters. How fast is the concentration increasing at a distance of 1 cm from the center 3 seconds after the nutrient is introduced?

---

[20]Based on an Exercise in *Introduction to Mathematical Economics* by A. L. Ostrosky Jr. and J. V. Koch (Waveland Press, Illinois, 1979).

[21]*Ibid.*

68. T ***Nutrient Diffusion*** Refer back to the preceding exercise. How fast is the concentration increasing at a distance of 4 cm from the center 4 seconds after the nutrient is introduced?

COMMUNICATION AND REASONING EXERCISES

69. Given that $f(a, b) = r$, $f_x(a, b) = s$, and $f_y(a, b) = t$, complete the following: _______ is increasing at a rate of

_____ units per unit of x, _____ is increasing at a rate of _____ units per unit of y, and the value of _____ is _____ when $x =$ _____ and $y =$ _____.

70. A firm's productivity depends on two variables, x and y. Currently, $x = a$ and $y = b$, and the firm's productivity is 4,000 units. Productivity is increasing at a rate of 400 units per unit *decrease* in x, and is decreasing at a rate of 300 units per unit increase in y. What does all of this information tell you about the firm's productivity function $g(x, y)$?

71. Complete the following: Let $f(x, y, z)$ be the cost to build a development of x cypods (one-bedroom units) in the city-state of Utarek, Mars, y argaats (two-bedroom units), and z orbici (singular: orbicus; three-bedroom units) in $\mathbb{Z}$ (zonars, the designated currency in Utarek). Then $\frac{\partial f}{\partial z}$ measures _____ and has units _____.

72. Complete the following: Let $f(t, x, y)$ be the projected number of citizens of the Principality State of Voodice, Luna in year t since its founding, assuming the presence of x lunar vehicle factories and y domed settlements. Then $\frac{\partial f}{\partial x}$ measures _____ and has units _____.

73. Give an example of a function $f(x, y)$ with $f_x(1, 1) = -2$ and $f_y(1, 1) = 3$.

74. Give an example of a function $f(x, y, z)$ that has all of its partial derivatives equal to nonzero constants.

75. T The graph of $z = b + mx + ny$ (b, m, and n constants) is a plane.

a. Explain the geometric significance of the numbers b, m, and n.

b. Show that the equation of the plane passing through (h, k, l) with slope m in the x direction (in the sense of $\partial/\partial x$) and slope n in the y direction is

$$z = l + m(x - h) + n(y - k).$$

76. T The **tangent plane** to the graph of $f(x, y)$ at $P(a, b, f(a, b))$ is the plane containing the lines tangent to the slice through the graph by $y = b$ (as in Figure 19) and the slice through the graph by $x = a$. Use the result of the preceding exercise to show that the equation of the tangent plane is

$$z = f(a, b) + f_x(a, b)(x - a) + f_y(a, b)(y - b).$$

Practice Problems 15.2, Part 1

Under the terms of a typical home loan, at a fixed interest rate your monthly loan payment depends on the amount of money you borrow and the number of payments to be made during the life of the loan. Given an annual interest rate of 6%, your monthly payment P (in hundreds of dollars) can be calculated according to $P(B,n)=\dfrac{0.005B}{1-1.005^{-n}}$, where B is the amount borrowed (in hundreds of dollars) and n is the number of payments to be made.

1. Calculate the monthly payment on a loan of \$120,000 if the loan is to be repaid over the course of 30 years (360 months). Give your result to the nearest penny.

2. Calculate $P_B(800,300)$. Label your result appropriately and interpret the result in terms of monthly loan payments, amount borrowed, and number of payments.

3. Calculate $P_n(800,300)$. Label your result appropriately and interpret the result in terms of monthly loan payments, amount borrowed, and number of payments.

Practice Problems 15.2, Part 2

1. Suppose $z = f(x, y) = \frac{8}{xy}$. Find a value of y so that $f_x(x, y) > 0$ for all values of x, or explain why this is not possible.

2. Give an example of a function $f(x, y)$ such that $f_x(x, y) > 0$ for all values of x and y while $f_y(x, y) < 0$ for all values of x and y.

3. The *temperature adjusted for wind chill* is a measure of the perceived air temperature and is dependent on the actual air temperature and the wind speed. Let $g(t, v)$ denote the temperature adjusted for wind chill, in degrees Fahrenheit, where t is the actual air temperature (also in degrees Fahrenheit) and v is the wind speed, in miles per hour. Give a meaningful interpretation of the statement $g_v(-10,14) \approx -0.7$. Include an appropriate label in your response.

Practice Problems 15.2, Part 3

1.) According to the *ideal gas law*, the volume V (in liters) of an ideal gas is related to its pressure P (in pascals) and temperature T (in degrees Kelvin) by the formula $V = \dfrac{kT}{P}$ where k is some appropriate constant. Given this, show that $\dfrac{\partial V}{\partial T} \cdot \dfrac{\partial T}{\partial P} \cdot \dfrac{\partial P}{\partial V} = -1$.

2.) The concentration C of bacteria in the blood (in millions of bacteria/ml) following the injection of an antibiotic is a function of the dose d (in gm) injected and the time t (in hours) since the injection. Suppose that $C = f(d,t) = te^{-dt}$ for $0 \leq d \leq 3$ and $0 \leq t \leq 4$. Calculate $f_d(1,2)$ and $f_t(1,2)$ and interpret your results. Label each quantity with appropriate units.

15.3 Maxima and Minima

In Chapter 12, on applications of the derivative, we saw how to locate relative extrema of a function of a single variable. In this section we extend our methods to functions of two variables. Similar techniques work for functions of three or more variables.

Figure 21 shows a portion of the graph of the function

$$f(x, y) = 2(x^2 + y^2) - (x^4 + y^4) + 1.$$

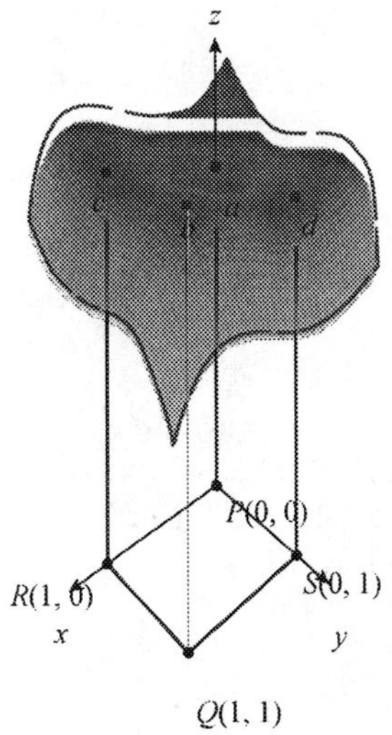

Figure 21

The graph in Figure 21 resembles a "flying carpet," and several interesting points, marked *a*, *b*, *c*, and *d*, are shown.

1. The point *a* has coordinates $(0, 0, f(0, 0))$, is directly above the origin (0, 0), and is the lowest point in its vicinity; water would puddle there. We say that *f* has a **relative minimum** at (0, 0) because $f(0, 0)$ is smaller than $f(x, y)$ for any (x, y) near (0, 0).
2. Similarly, the point *b* is higher than any point in its vicinity. Thus, we say that *f* has a **relative maximum** at (1, 1).
3. The points *c* and *d* represent a new phenomenon and are called **saddle points**. They are neither relative maxima nor relative minima but seem to be a little of both.

To see more clearly what features a saddle point has, look at Figure 22, which shows a portion of the graph near the point *d*.

If we slice through the graph along $y = 1$, we get a curve on which *d* is the *lowest* point. Thus, *d* looks like a relative minimum along this slice. On the other hand, if we slice through the graph along $x = 0$, we get another curve, on which *d* is the *highest*

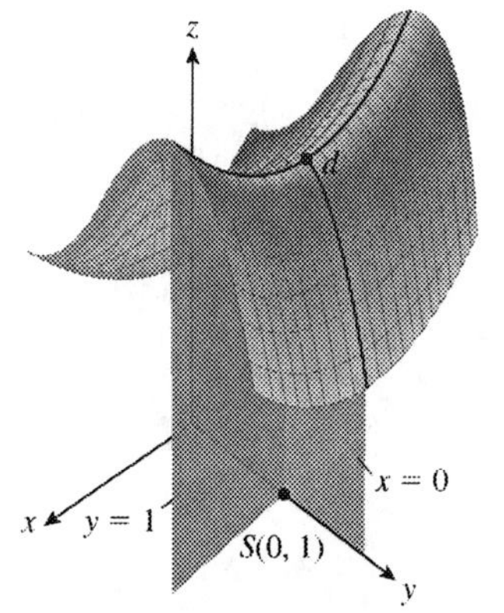

Figure 22

point, so d looks like a relative maximum along this slice. This kind of behavior characterizes a saddle point: f has a **saddle point** at (r, s) if f has a relative minimum at (r, s) along some slice through that point and a relative maximum along another slice through that point. If you look at the other saddle point, c, in Figure 21, you see the same characteristics.

While numerical information can help us locate the approximate positions of relative extrema and saddle points, calculus permits us to locate these points accurately, as we did for functions of a single variable. Look once again at Figure 21, and notice the following:

- The points P, Q, R, and S are all in the **interior** of the domain of f; that is, none lie on the boundary of the domain. Said another way, we can move some distance in any direction from any of these points without leaving the domain of f.
- The tangent lines along the slices through these points parallel to the x- and y-axes are *horizontal*. Thus, the partial derivatives $\partial f/\partial x$ and $\partial f/\partial y$ are zero when evaluated at any of the points P, Q, R, and S. This gives us a way of locating candidates for relative extrema and saddle points.

The following summary generalizes and also expands on some of what we have just said:

Relative and Absolute Maxima and Minima

The function f of n variables has a **relative maximum** at $(x_1, x_2, \ldots, x_n) = (r_1, r_2, \ldots, r_n)$ if $f(r_1, r_2, \ldots, r_n) \geq f(x_1, x_2, \ldots, x_n)$ for every point $(x_1, x_2, \ldots, x_n)$ near* $(r_1, r_2, \ldots, r_n)$ in the domain of f. We say that f has an **absolute maximum** at $(r_1, r_2, \ldots, r_n)$ if $f(r_1, r_2, \ldots, r_n) \geq f(x_1, x_2, \ldots, x_n)$ for every point $(x_1, x_2, \ldots, x_n)$ in the domain of f. The terms **relative minimum** and **absolute minimum** are defined in a similar way. Note that, as with functions of a single variable, absolute extrema are special kinds of relative extrema.

Locating Candidates for Extrema and Saddle Points in the Interior of the Domain of *f*

- Set $\dfrac{\partial f}{\partial x_1} = 0, \dfrac{\partial f}{\partial x_2} = 0, \ldots, \dfrac{\partial f}{\partial x_n} = 0$, simultaneously, and solve for $x_1, x_2, \ldots, x_n$.
- Check that the resulting points $(x_1, x_2, \ldots, x_n)$ are in the interior of the domain of f.

Points at which all the partial derivatives of f are zero are called **critical points.** The critical points are the only candidates for extrema and saddle points in the interior of the domain of f, assuming that its partial derivatives are defined at every point.†

Quick Examples

In each of the following Quick Examples, the domain is the whole Cartesian plane, and the partial derivatives are defined at every point, so the critical points give us the only candidates for extrema and saddle points:

1. Let $f(x, y) = x^3 + (y-1)^2$. Then $\dfrac{\partial f}{\partial x} = 3x^2$ and $\dfrac{\partial f}{\partial y} = 2(y-1)$.

   Thus, we solve the system

   $$3x^2 = 0 \quad \text{and} \quad 2(y-1) = 0.$$

* For $(x_1, x_2, \ldots, x_n)$ to be near $(r_1, r_2, \ldots, r_n)$ we mean that x_1 is in some open interval centered at r_1, x_2 is in some open interval centered at r_2, and so on.

† One can use the techniques of the next section to find extrema on the *boundary* of the domain of a function; for a complete discussion, see the optional extra section: *Maxima and Minima: Boundaries and the Extreme Value Theorem.* (We shall not consider the analogs of the singular points.)

The first equation gives $x = 0$, and the second gives $y = 1$. Thus, the only critical point is (0, 1).

2. Let $f(x, y) = x^2 - 4xy + 8y$. Then $\frac{\partial f}{\partial x} = 2x - 4y$ and $\frac{\partial f}{\partial y} = -4x + 8$. Thus, we solve

$$2x - 4y = 0 \quad \text{and} \quad -4x + 8 = 0.$$

The second equation gives $x = 2$, and the first then gives $y = 1$. Thus, the only critical point is (2, 1).

3. Let $f(x, y) = e^{-(x^2+y^2)}$. Taking partial derivatives and setting them equal to zero gives

$$-2xe^{-(x^2+y^2)} = 0 \qquad \text{We set } \frac{\partial f}{\partial x} = 0.$$

$$-2ye^{-(x^2+y^2)} = 0. \qquad \text{We set } \frac{\partial f}{\partial y} = 0.$$

The first equation implies that $x = 0$,* and the second implies that $y = 0$. Thus, the only critical point is (0, 0).

* Recall that if a product of two numbers is zero, then one or the other must be zero. In this case the number $e^{-(x^2+y^2)}$ can't be zero (because e^u is never zero), which gives the result claimed.

In the remainder of this section we will be interested in locating all critical points of a given function and then classifying each one as a relative maximum, minimum, saddle point, or none of these. Whether or not any relative extrema we find are in fact absolute is a subject we discuss in the next section.†

† In some of the applications in the exercises you will, however, need to consider whether the extrema you find are absolute.

EXAMPLE 1 Locating and Classifying Critical Points

Locate all critical points of $f(x, y) = x^2y - x^2 - 2y^2$. Graph the function to classify the critical points as relative maxima, minima, saddle points, or none of these.

Solution The partial derivatives are

$$f_x = 2xy - 2x = 2x(y - 1)$$
$$f_y = x^2 - 4y.$$

Setting these equal to zero gives

$$x = 0 \text{ or } y = 1$$
$$x^2 = 4y.$$

We get a solution by choosing either $x = 0$ or $y = 1$ and substituting into $x^2 = 4y$.

***Case 1:* $x = 0$** Substituting into $x^2 = 4y$ gives $0 = 4y$ and hence $y = 0$. Thus, the critical point for this case is $(x, y) = (0, 0)$.

***Case 2:* $y = 1$** Substituting into $x^2 = 4y$ gives $x^2 = 4$ and hence $x = \pm 2$. Thus, we get two critical points for this case: (2, 1) and (−2, 1).

We now have three critical points altogether: (0, 0), (2, 1), and (−2, 1). Because the domain of f is the whole Cartesian plane and the partial derivatives are defined at every point, these critical points are the only candidates for relative extrema and saddle points. We get the corresponding points on the graph by substituting for x and y in the equation for f to get the z-coordinates. The points are (0, 0, 0), (2, 1, −2), and (−2, 1, −2).

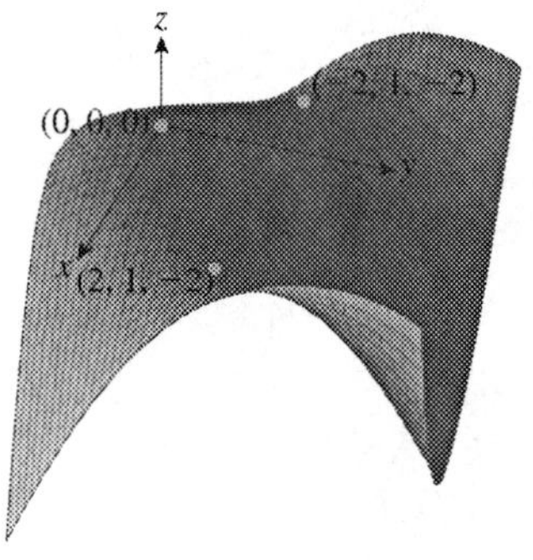

Figure 23

Classifying the Critical Points Graphically To classify the critical points graphically, we look at the graph of f shown in Figure 23.

Examining the graph carefully, we see that the point (0, 0, 0) is a relative maximum. As for the other two critical points, are they saddle points or are they relative maxima? They are relative maxima along the y-direction, but they are relative minima along the lines $y = \pm x$ (see the top edge of the picture, which shows a dip at (−2, 1, 2)) and so they are saddle points. If you don't believe this, we will get more evidence following and in a later example.

Classifying the Critical Points Numerically We can use a tabular representation of the function to classify the critical points numerically. The following tabular representation of the function can be obtained using a spreadsheet. (See the Spreadsheet Technology Guide discussion of Section 15.1 Example 3 at the end of the chapter for information on using a spreadsheet to generate such a table.)

$y \downarrow$ \ $x \rightarrow$	−3	−2	−1	0	1	2	3
−3	−54	−34	−22	−18	−22	−34	−54
−2	−35	−20	−11	−8	−11	−20	−35
−1	−20	−10	−4	−2	−4	−10	−20
0	−9	−4	−1	0	−1	−4	−9
1	−2	−2	−2	−2	−2	−2	−2
2	1	−4	−7	−8	−7	−4	1
3	0	−10	−16	−18	−16	−10	0

The shaded and colored cells show rectangular neighborhoods of the three critical points (0, 0), (2, 1), and (−2, 1). (Notice that they overlap.) The values of f at the critical points are at the centers of these rectangles. Looking at the gray neighborhood of $(x, y) = (0, 0)$, we see that $f(0, 0) = 0$ is the largest value of f in the shaded cells, suggesting that f has a maximum at (0, 0). The shaded neighborhood of (2, 1) on the right shows $f(2, 1) = -2$ as the maximum along some slices (e.g., the vertical slice), and a minimum along the diagonal slice from top left to bottom right. This is what results in a saddle point on the graph. The point (−2, 1) is similar, and thus f also has a saddle point at (−2, 1).

Q: *Is there an algebraic way of deciding whether a given point is a relative maximum, relative minimum, or saddle point?*

A: There is a "second derivative test" for functions of two variables, stated as follows.

Second Derivative Test for Functions of Two Variables

Suppose (a, b) is a critical point in the interior of the domain of the function f of two variables. Let H be the quantity

$$H = f_{xx}(a, b) f_{yy}(a, b) - [f_{xy}(a, b)]^2.$$

H is called the Hessian.

Then, if *H* is *positive*,

- f has a relative minimum at (a, b) if $f_{xx}(a, b) > 0$.
- f has a relative maximum at (a, b) if $f_{xx}(a, b) < 0$.

If *H* is *negative*,

- f has a saddle point at (a, b).

If $H = 0$, the test tells us nothing, so we need to look at the graph or a numerical table to see what is going on.

Quick Examples

1. Let $f(x, y) = x^2 - y^2$. Then
$$f_x = 2x \quad \text{and} \quad f_y = -2y,$$
which gives (0, 0) as the only critical point. Also,
$$f_{xx} = 2, f_{xy} = 0, \quad \text{and} \quad f_{yy} = -2,$$
Note that these are constant.
which gives $H = (2)(-2) - 0^2 = -4$. Because *H* is negative, we have a saddle point at (0, 0).
2. Let $f(x, y) = x^2 + 2y^2 + 2xy + 4x$. Then
$$f_x = 2x + 2y + 4 \quad \text{and} \quad f_y = 2x + 4y.$$
Setting these equal to zero gives a system of two linear equations in two unknowns:
$$x + y = -2$$
$$x + 2y = 0.$$
This system has solution (−4, 2), so this is our only critical point. The second partial derivatives are $f_{xx} = 2$, $f_{xy} = 2$, and $f_{yy} = 4$, so $H = (2)(4) - 2^2 = 4$. Because $H > 0$ and $f_{xx} > 0$, we have a relative minimum at (−4, 2).

Note There is a second derivative test for functions of three or more variables, but it is considerably more complicated. We stick with functions of two variables for the most part in this book. The justification of the second derivative test is beyond the scope of this book. ■

EXAMPLE 2 Using the Second Derivative Test

Use the second derivative test to analyze the function $f(x, y) = x^2y - x^2 - 2y^2$ discussed in Example 1, and confirm the results we got there.

Solution We saw in Example 1 that the first-order derivatives are
$$f_x = 2xy - 2x = 2x(y - 1)$$
$$f_y = x^2 - 4y$$
and the critical points are (0, 0), (2, 1), and (−2, 1). We also need the second derivatives:
$$f_{xx} = 2y - 2$$
$$f_{xy} = 2x$$
$$f_{yy} = -4.$$

The point (0, 0): $f_{xx}(0,0) = -2$, $f_{xy}(0,0) = 0$, $f_{yy}(0,0) = -4$, so $H = 8$. Because $H > 0$ and $f_{xx}(0,0) < 0$, the second derivative test tells us that f has a relative maximum at (0, 0).

The point (2, 1): $f_{xx}(2,1) = 0$, $f_{xy}(2,1) = 4$ and $f_{yy}(2,1) = -4$, so $H = -16$. Because $H < 0$, we know that f has a saddle point at (2, 1).

The point (−2, 1): $f_{xx}(-2,1) = 0$, $f_{xy}(-2,1) = -4$ and $f_{yy}(-2,1) = -4$, so once again $H = -16$, and f has a saddle point at $(-2, 1)$.

Deriving the Formulas for Linear Regression

Back in Section 1.4, we presented the following set of formulas for the **regression** or **best-fit** line associated with a given set of data points $(x_1, y_1), (x_2, y_2), \ldots, (x_n, y_n)$.

Regression Line

The line that best fits the n data points $(x_1, y_1), (x_2, y_2), \ldots, (x_n, y_n)$ has the form

$$y = mx + b,$$

where

$$m = \frac{n(\sum xy) - (\sum x)(\sum y)}{n(\sum x^2) - (\sum x)^2}$$

$$b = \frac{\sum y - m(\sum x)}{n}$$

n = number of data points.

Derivation of the Regression Line Formulas

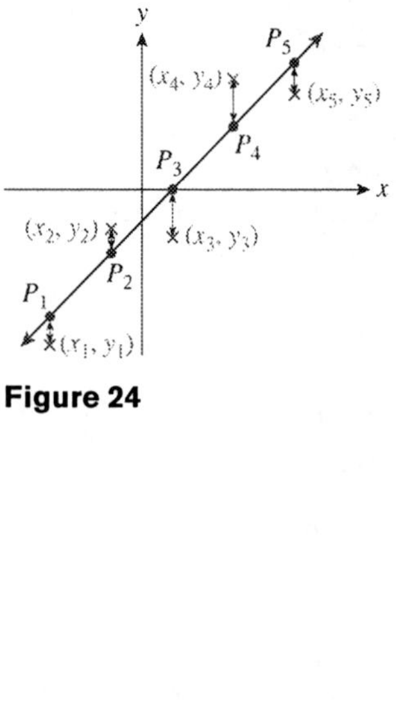

Figure 24

Recall that the regression line is defined to be the line that minimizes the sum of the squares of the **residuals**, measured by the vertical distances shown in Figure 24, which shows a regression line associated with $n = 5$ data points. In the figure, the points $P_1, \ldots, P_n$ on the regression line have coordinates $(x_1, mx_1 + b), (x_2, mx_2 + b), \ldots, (x_n, mx_n + b)$. The residuals are the quantities $y_{\text{Observed}} - y_{\text{Predicted}}$:

$$y_1 - (mx_1 + b), y_2 - (mx_2 + b), \ldots, y_n - (mx_n + b).$$

The sum of the squares of the residuals is therefore

$$S(m, b) = [y_1 - (mx_1 + b)]^2 + [y_2 - (mx_2 + b)]^2 + \cdots + [y_n - (mx_n + b)]^2$$

and this is the quantity we must minimize by choosing m and b. Because we reason that there is a line that minimizes this quantity, there must be a relative minimum at that point. We shall see in a moment that the function S has at most one critical point, which must therefore be the desired absolute minimum. To obtain the critical points of S, we set the partial derivatives equal to zero and solve:

$$S_m = 0: \quad -2x_1[y_1 - (mx_1 + b)] - \cdots - 2x_n[y_n - (mx_n + b)] = 0$$
$$S_b = 0: \quad -2[y_1 - (mx_1 + b)] - \cdots - 2[y_n - (mx_n + b)] = 0.$$

Dividing by -2 and gathering terms allows us to rewrite the equations as

$$m(x_1^2 + \cdots + x_n^2) + b(x_1 + \cdots + x_n) = x_1y_1 + \cdots + x_ny_n$$
$$m(x_1 + \cdots + x_n) + nb = y_1 + \cdots + y_n.$$

We can rewrite these equations more neatly using $\sum$-notation:

$$m\left(\sum x^2\right) + b\left(\sum x\right) = \sum xy$$
$$m\left(\sum x\right) + nb \qquad = \sum y.$$

This is a system of two linear equations in the two unknowns m and b. It may or may not have a unique solution. When there is a unique solution, we can conclude that the best-fit line is given by solving these two equations for m and b. Alternatively, there is a general formula for the solution of any system of two equations in two unknowns, and if we apply this formula to our two equations, we get the regression formulas above.

15.3 EXERCISES

▼ more advanced ◆ challenging

T indicates exercises that should be solved using technology

In Exercises 1–4, classify each labeled point on the graph as one of the following:

Relative maximum
Relative minimum
Saddle point
Critical point but neither a relative extremum nor a saddle point
None of the above HINT [See Example 1.]

1.

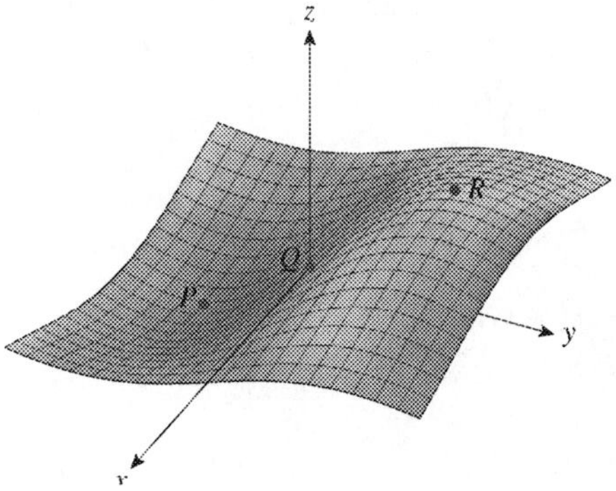

2.

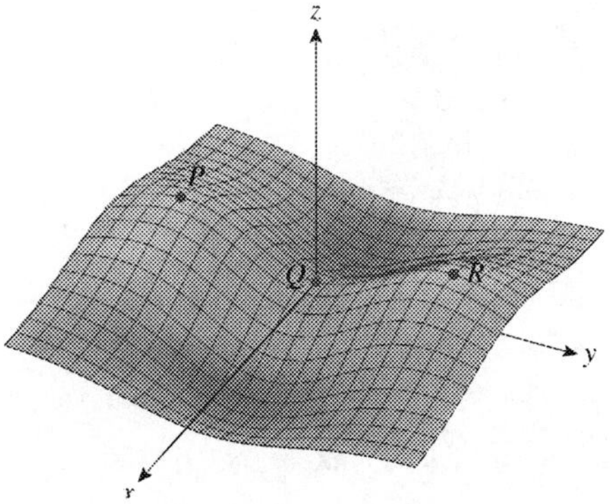

3.

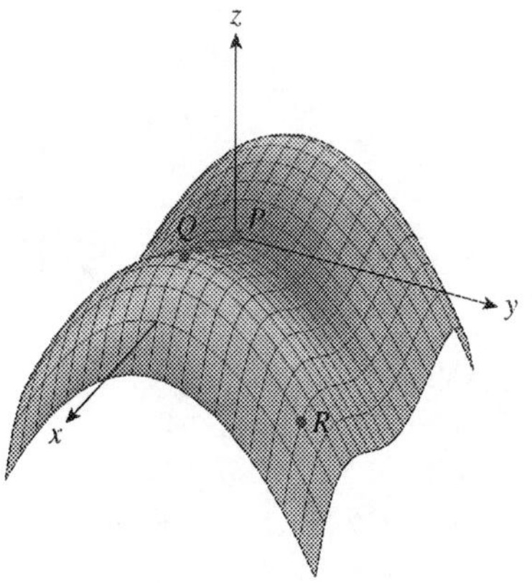

4.

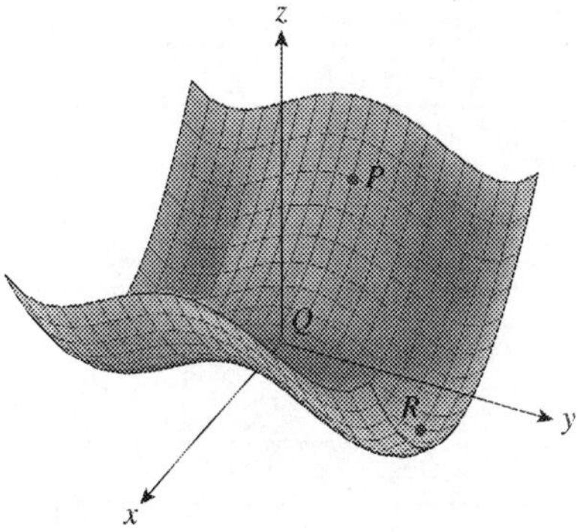

In Exercises 5–10, classify the shaded value in each table as one of the following:

Relative maximum
Relative minimum
Saddle point
Neither a relative extremum nor a saddle point

Assume that the shaded value represents a critical point.

5. $x \rightarrow$

$y \downarrow$	−3	−2	−1	0	1	2
−3	10	5	2	1	2	5
−2	9	4	1	0	1	4
−1	10	5	2	1	2	5
0	13	8	5	4	5	8
1	18	13	10	9	10	13
2	25	20	17	16	17	20
3	34	29	26	25	26	29

6. $x \rightarrow$

$y \downarrow$	−3	−2	−1	0	1	2
−3	5	0	−3	−4	−3	0
−2	8	3	0	−1	0	3
−1	9	4	1	0	1	4
0	8	3	0	−1	0	3
1	5	0	−3	−4	−3	0
2	0	−5	−8	−9	−8	−5
3	−7	−12	−15	−16	−15	−12

7. $x \rightarrow$

$y \downarrow$	−3	−2	−1	0	1	2
−3	5	0	−3	−4	−3	0
−2	8	3	0	−1	0	3
−1	9	4	1	0	1	4
0	8	3	0	−1	0	3
1	5	0	−3	−4	−3	0
2	0	−5	−8	−9	−8	−5
3	−7	−12	−15	−16	−15	−12

8. $x \rightarrow$

$y \downarrow$	−3	−2	−1	0	1	2
−3	2	3	2	−1	−6	−13
−2	3	4	3	0	−5	−12
−1	2	3	2	−1	−6	−13
0	−1	0	−1	−4	−9	−16
1	−6	−5	−6	−9	−14	−21
2	−13	−12	−13	−16	−21	−28
3	−22	−21	−22	−25	−30	−37

9. $x \rightarrow$

$y \downarrow$	−3	−2	−1	0	1	2
−3	4	5	4	1	−4	−11
−2	3	4	3	0	−5	−12
−1	4	5	4	1	−4	−11
0	7	8	7	4	−1	−8
1	12	13	12	9	4	−3
2	19	20	19	16	11	4
3	28	29	28	25	20	13

10. $x \rightarrow$

$y \downarrow$	−3	−2	−1	0	1	2
−3	100	101	100	97	92	85
−2	99	100	99	96	91	84
−1	98	99	98	95	90	83
0	91	92	91	88	83	76
1	72	73	72	69	64	57
2	35	36	35	32	27	20
3	−26	−25	−26	−29	−34	−41

Locate and classify all the critical points of the functions in Exercises 11–36. HINT [See Example 2.]

11. $f(x, y) = x^2 + y^2 + 1$

12. $f(x, y) = 4 - (x^2 + y^2)$

13. $g(x, y) = 1 - x^2 - x - y^2 + y$

14. $g(x, y) = x^2 + x + y^2 - y - 1$

15. $k(x, y) = x^2 - 3xy + y^2$

16. $k(x, y) = x^2 - xy + 2y^2$

17. $f(x, y) = x^2 + 2xy + 2y^2 - 2x + 4y$

18. $f(x, y) = x^2 + xy - y^2 + 3x - y$

19. $g(x, y) = -x^2 - 2xy - 3y^2 - 3x - 2y$

20. $g(x, y) = -x^2 - 2xy + y^2 + x - 4y$

21. $h(x, y) = x^2y - 2x^2 - 4y^2$

22. $h(x, y) = x^2 + y^2 - y^2x - 4$

23. $f(x, y) = x^2 + 2xy^2 + 2y^2$

24. $f(x, y) = x^2 + x^2y + y^2$

25. $s(x, y) = e^{x^2+y^2}$

26. $s(x, y) = e^{-(x^2+y^2)}$

27. $t(x, y) = x^4 + 8xy^2 + 2y^4$

28. $t(x, y) = x^3 - 3xy + y^3$

29. $f(x, y) = x^2 + y - e^y$

30. $f(x, y) = xe^y$

31. $f(x, y) = e^{-(x^2+y^2+2x)}$

32. $f(x, y) = e^{-(x^2+y^2-2x)}$

33. ▼ $f(x, y) = xy + \frac{2}{x} + \frac{2}{y}$

34. ▼ $f(x, y) = xy + \frac{4}{x} + \frac{2}{y}$

35. ▼ $g(x, y) = x^2 + y^2 + \dfrac{2}{xy}$

36. ▼ $g(x, y) = x^3 + y^3 + \dfrac{3}{xy}$

37. ▼ Refer back to Exercise 11. Which (if any) of the critical points of $f(x, y) = x^2 + y^2 + 1$ are absolute extrema?

38. ▼ Refer back to Exercise 12. Which (if any) of the critical points of $f(x, y) = 4 - (x^2 + y^2)$ are absolute extrema?

39. ▢ ▼ Refer back to Exercise 21. Which (if any) of the critical points of $h(x, y) = x^2 y - 2x^2 - 4y^2$ are absolute extrema?

40. ▢ ▼ Refer back to Exercise 22. Which (if any) of the critical points of $h(x, y) = x^2 + y^2 - y^2 x - 4$ are absolute extrema?

APPLICATIONS

41. *Brand Loyalty* Suppose the fraction of Mazda car owners who chose another new Mazda can be modeled by the following function:[22]

$$M(c, f) = 11 + 8c + 4c^2 - 40f - 20cf + 40f^2,$$

where c is the fraction of Chrysler car owners who remained loyal to Chrysler and f is the fraction of Ford car owners remaining loyal to Ford. Locate and classify all the critical points and interpret your answer. HINT [See Example 2.]

42. *Brand Loyalty* Repeat the preceding exercise using the function:

$$M(c, f) = -10 - 8f - 4f^2 + 40c + 20fc - 40c^2.$$

HINT [See Example 2.]

43. ▼ *Pollution Control* The cost of controlling emissions at a firm goes up rapidly as the amount of emissions reduced goes up. Here is a possible model:

$$C(x, y) = 4,000 + 100x^2 + 50y^2,$$

where x is the reduction in sulfur emissions, y is the reduction in lead emissions (in pounds of pollutant per day), and C is the daily cost to the firm (in dollars) of this reduction. Government clean-air subsidies amount to $500 per pound of sulfur and $100 per pound of lead removed. How many pounds of pollutant should the firm remove each day in order to minimize *net* cost (cost minus subsidy)?

44. ▼ *Pollution Control* Repeat the preceding exercise using the following information:

$$C(x, y) = 2,000 + 200x^2 + 100y^2$$

with government subsidies amounting to $100 per pound of sulfur and $500 per pound of lead removed per day.

45. ▼ *Revenue* Your company manufactures two models of speakers, the Ultra Mini and the Big Stack. Demand for each depends partly on the price of the other. If one is expensive, then more people will buy the other. If p_1 is the price of the Ultra Mini, and p_2 is the price of the Big Stack, demand for the Ultra Mini is given by

$$q_1(p_1, p_2) = 100,000 - 100p_1 + 10p_2,$$

where q_1 represents the number of Ultra Minis that will be sold in a year. The demand for the Big Stack is given by

$$q_2(p_1, p_2) = 150,000 + 10p_1 - 100p_2.$$

Find the prices for the Ultra Mini and the Big Stack that will maximize your total revenue.

46. ▼ *Revenue* Repeat the preceding exercise, using the following demand functions:

$$q_1(p_1, p_2) = 100,000 - 100p_1 + p_2$$
$$q_2(p_1, p_2) = 150,000 + p_1 - 100p_2.$$

47. ▼ *Luggage Dimensions: American Airlines* American Airlines requires that the total outside dimensions (length + width + height) of a checked bag not exceed 62 inches.[23] What are the dimensions of the largest volume bag that you can check on an American flight?

48. ▼ *Carry-on Bag Dimensions: American Airlines* American Airlines requires that the total outside dimensions (length + width + height) of a carry-on bag not exceed 45 inches.[24] What are the dimensions of the largest volume bag that you can carry on an American flight?

49. ▼ *Package Dimensions: USPS* The U.S. Postal Service (USPS) will accept only packages with a length plus girth no more than 108 inches.[25] (See the figure.)

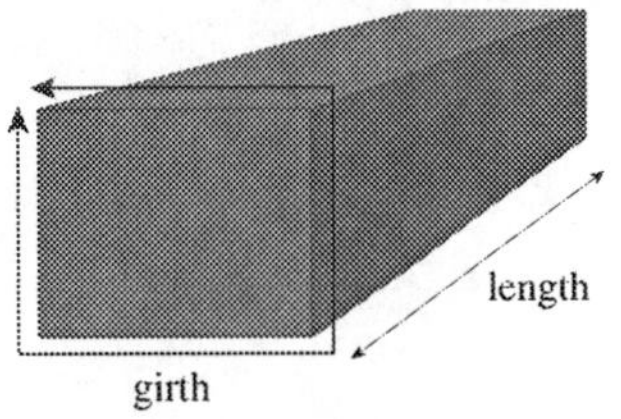

What are the dimensions of the largest volume package that the USPS will accept? What is its volume?

50. ▼ *Package Dimensions: UPS* United Parcel Service (UPS) will accept only packages with length no more than 108 inches and length plus girth no more than 165 inches.[26] (See figure for the preceding exercise.) What are the dimensions of the largest volume package that UPS will accept? What is its volume?

---

[22]This model is not accurate, although it was inspired by an approximation of a second-order regression based on data from the period 1988–1995. Source for original data: Chrysler, Maritz Market Research, Consumer Attitude Research, and Strategic Vision/ *New York Times*, November 3, 1995, p. D2.

[23]According to information on its Web site (www.aa.com).

[24]*Ibid.*

[25]The requirement for packages sent other than Parcel Post, as of August 2011 (www.usps.com).

[26]The requirement as of August 2011 (www.ups.com).

COMMUNICATION AND REASONING EXERCISES

51. Sketch the graph of a function that has one extremum and no saddle points.

52. Sketch the graph of a function that has one saddle point and one extremum.

53. ▼ Sketch the graph of a function that has one relative extremum, no absolute extrema, and no saddle points.

54. ▼ Sketch the graph of a function that has infinitely many absolute maxima.

55. Let $H = f_{xx}(a, b)f_{yy}(a, b) - f_{xy}(a, b)^2$. What condition on H guarantees that f has a relative extremum at the point (a, b)?

56. Let H be as in the preceding exercise. Give an example to show that it is possible to have $H = 0$ and a relative minimum at (a, b).

57. ▼ Suppose that when the graph of $f(x, y)$ is sliced by a vertical plane through (a, b) parallel to either the xz-plane or the yz-plane, the resulting curve has a relative maximum at (a, b). Does this mean that f has a relative maximum at (a, b)? Explain your answer.

58. ▼ Suppose that f has a relative maximum at (a, b). Does it follow that, if the graph of f is sliced by a vertical plane parallel to either the xz-plane or the yz-plane, the resulting curve has a relative maximum at (a, b)? Explain your answer.

59. ▼ ***Average Cost*** Let $C(x, y)$ be any cost function. Show that when the average cost is minimized, the marginal costs C_x and C_y both equal the average cost. Explain why this is reasonable.

60. ▼ ***Average Profit*** Let $P(x, y)$ be any profit function. Show that when the average profit is maximized, the marginal profits P_x and P_y both equal the average profit. Explain why this is reasonable.

61. ◆ The tangent plane to a graph was introduced in Exercise 76 in the preceding section. Use the equation of the tangent plane given there to explain why the tangent plane is parallel to the xy-plane at a relative maximum or minimum of $f(x, y)$.

62. ◆ Use the equation of the tangent plane given in Exercise 76 in the preceding section to explain why the tangent plane is parallel to the xy-plane at a saddle point of $f(x, y)$.

Practice Problems 15.3, Part 1

It is not surprising that the quantity of one product demanded may depend not only on the price of the product, but also on the price of another product (for instance, the demand for cars is affected not only by car prices, but by the price of gas). Suppose the quantities demanded, q_1 and q_2, of two products depend on their respective prices, p_1 and p_2, as follows:

$$q_1 = 150 - 2p_1 - p_2$$
$$q_2 = 200 - p_1 - 3p_2$$

Suppose one manufacturer sells both of these products. How should the manufacturer set prices to earn the maximum possible revenue? What is the maximum possible revenue?

Practice Problems 15.3, Part 2

Suppose the labor cost (in dollars) for manufacturing a precision camera can be approximated by

$$L(x, y) = \frac{3}{2}x^2 + y^2 - 2x - 2y - 2xy + 68,$$

where x is the number of hours required by a skilled craftsperson and y is the number of hours required by a semiskilled person. Find values of x and y that minimize the labor cost, and find the minimum labor cost.

15.4 Constrained Maxima and Minima and Applications

So far we have looked only at the relative extrema of functions with no constraints. However, in Section 12.2 we saw examples in which we needed to find the maximum or minimum of an objective function subject to one or more constraints on the independent variables. For instance, consider the following problem:

$$\text{Minimize } S = xy + 2xz + 2yz \quad \text{subject to } xyz = 4 \text{ with } x > 0,\ y > 0,\ z > 0.$$

One strategy for solving such problems is essentially the same as the strategy we used earlier: Solve the constraint equation for one of the variables, substitute into the objective function, and then optimize the resulting function using the methods of the preceding section. We will call this the *substitution method.** An alternative method, called the *method of Lagrange multipliers*, is useful when it is difficult or impossible to solve the constraint equation for one of the variables, and even when it is possible to do so.

* Although often the method of choice, the substitution method is not infallible (see Exercises 19 and 20).

Substitution Method

EXAMPLE 1 Using Substitution

Minimize $S = xy + 2xz + 2yz$ subject to $xyz = 4$ with $x > 0$, $y > 0$, $z > 0$.

Solution As suggested in the above discussion, we proceed as follows:

Solve the constraint equation for one of the variables and then substitute in the objective function. The constraint equation is $xyz = 4$. Solving for z gives

$$z = \frac{4}{xy}.$$

The objective function is $S = xy + 2xz + 2yz$, so substituting $z = 4/xy$ gives

$$S = xy + 2x\frac{4}{xy} + 2y\frac{4}{xy}$$
$$= xy + \frac{8}{y} + \frac{8}{x}.$$

Minimize the resulting function of two variables. We use the method in Section 15.4 to find the minimum of $S = xy + \frac{8}{y} + \frac{8}{x}$ for $x > 0$ and $y > 0$. We look for critical points:

$$S_x = y - \frac{8}{x^2} \qquad S_y = x - \frac{8}{y^2}$$
$$S_{xx} = \frac{16}{x^3} \qquad S_{xy} = 1 \qquad S_{yy} = \frac{16}{y^3}.$$

We now equate the first partial derivatives to zero:

$$y = \frac{8}{x^2} \quad \text{and} \quad x = \frac{8}{y^2}.$$

To solve for x and y, we substitute the first of these equations in the second, getting

$$x = \frac{x^4}{8}$$
$$x^4 - 8x = 0$$
$$x(x^3 - 8) = 0.$$

The two solutions are $x = 0$, which we reject because x cannot be zero, and $x = 2$. Substituting $x = 2$ in $y = 8/x^2$ gives $y = 2$ also. Thus, the only critical point is (2, 2). To apply the second derivative test, we compute

$$S_{xx}(2, 2) = 2 \qquad S_{xy}(2, 2) = 1 \qquad S_{yy}(2, 2) = 2$$

and find that $H = 3 > 0$ and $S_{xx}(2, 2) > 0$, so we have a relative minimum at (2, 2).

The corresponding value of z is given by the constraint equation:

$$z = \frac{4}{xy} = \frac{4}{4} = 1.$$

The corresponding value of the objective function is

$$S = xy + \frac{8}{y} + \frac{8}{x} = 4 + \frac{8}{2} + \frac{8}{2} = 12.$$

Figure 25 shows a portion of the graph of $S = xy + \frac{8}{y} + \frac{8}{x}$ for positive x and y (drawn using the Excel Surface Grapher in the Chapter 15 utilities at the Website) and suggests that there is a single absolute minimum, which must be at our only candidate point (2, 2).

We conclude that the minimum of S is 12 and occurs at (2, 2, 1).

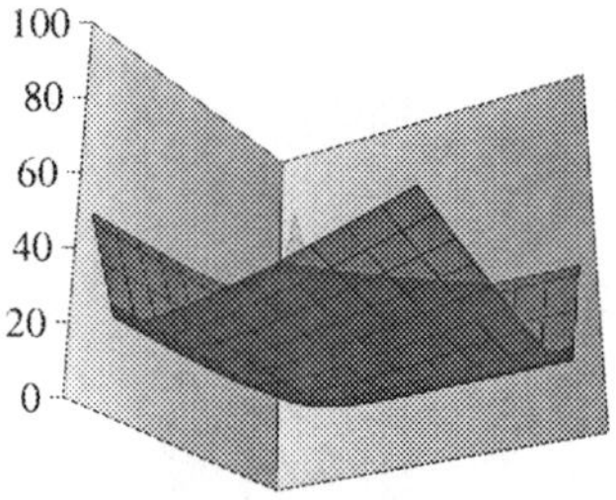

Graph of $S = xy + \frac{8}{y} + \frac{8}{x}$
$(0.2 \le x \le 5, 0.2 \le y \le 5)$
Figure 25

The Method of Lagrange Multipliers

As we mentioned above, the method of Lagrange multipliers has the advantage that it can be used in constrained optimization problems when it is difficult or impossible to solve a constraint equation for one of the variables. We restrict attention to the case of a single constraint equation, although the method also generalizes to any number of constraint equations.

Locating Relative Extrema Using the Method of Lagrange Multipliers

To locate the candidates for relative extrema of a function $f(x, y, \ldots)$ subject to the constraint $g(x, y, \ldots) = 0$:

1. Construct the **Lagrangian function**

$$L(x, y, \ldots) = f(x, y, \ldots) - \lambda g(x, y, \ldots)$$

where λ is a new unknown called a **Lagrange multiplier.**

2. The candidates for the relative extrema occur at the critical points of $L(x, y, \ldots)$. To find them, set all the partial derivatives of $L(x, y, \ldots)$ equal to zero and solve the resulting system, together with the constraint equation $g(x, y, \ldots) = 0$, for the unknowns $x, y, \ldots$ and λ.

The points $(x, y, \ldots)$ that occur in solutions are then the candidates for the relative extrema of f subject to $g = 0$.

Although the justification for the method of Lagrange multipliers is beyond the scope of this text (a derivation can be found in many vector calculus textbooks), we will demonstrate by example how it is used.

EXAMPLE 2 Using Lagrange Multipliers

Use the method of Lagrange multipliers to find the maximum value of $f(x, y) = 2xy$ subject to $x^2 + 4y^2 = 32$.

Solution We start by rewriting the problem with the constraint in the form $g(x, y) = 0$:

$$\text{Maximize } f(x, y) = 2xy \text{ subject to } x^2 + 4y^2 - 32 = 0.$$

Here, $g(x, y) = x^2 + 4y^2 - 32$, and the Lagrangian function is

$$\begin{aligned} L(x, y) &= f(x, y) - \lambda g(x, y) \\ &= 2xy - \lambda(x^2 + 4y^2 - 32). \end{aligned}$$

The system of equations we need to solve is thus

$$\begin{aligned} L_x = 0: &\quad 2y - 2\lambda x = 0 \\ L_y = 0: &\quad 2x - 8\lambda y = 0 \\ g = 0: &\quad x^2 + 4y^2 - 32 = 0. \end{aligned}$$

It is often convenient to solve such a system by first solving one of the equations for λ and then substituting in the remaining equations. Thus, we start by solving the first equation to obtain

$$\lambda = \frac{y}{x}.$$

(A word of caution: Because we divided by x, we made the implicit assumption that $x \neq 0$, so before continuing we should check what happens if $x = 0$. But if $x = 0$, then the first equation, $2y = 2\lambda x$, tells us that $y = 0$ as well, and this contradicts the third equation: $x^2 + 4y^2 - 32 = 0$. Thus, we can rule out the possibility that $x = 0$.) Substituting the value of λ in the second equation gives

$$2x - 8\left(\frac{y}{x}\right)y = 0 \quad \text{or} \quad x^2 = 4y^2.$$

We can now substitute $x^2 = 4y^2$ in the constraint equation, obtaining

$$\begin{aligned} 4y^2 + 4y^2 - 32 &= 0 \\ 8y^2 &= 32 \\ y &= \pm 2. \end{aligned}$$

We now substitute back to obtain

$$x^2 = 4y^2 = 16,$$

or $\quad x = \pm 4.$

We don't need the value of λ, so we won't solve for it. Thus, the candidates for relative extrema are given by $x = \pm 4$ and $y = \pm 2$; that is, the four points $(-4, -2)$, $(-4, 2)$, $(4, -2)$, and $(4, 2)$. Recall that we are seeking the values of x and y that give the maximum value for $f(x, y) = 2xy$. Because we now have only four points to choose from, we compare the values of f at these four points and conclude that the maximum value of f occurs when $(x, y) = (-4, -2)$ or $(4, 2)$.

Something is suspicious in Example 2. We didn't check to see whether these candidates were relative extrema to begin with, let alone absolute extrema! How do we justify this omission? One of the difficulties with using the method of Lagrange multipliers is that it does not provide us with a test analogous to the second derivative test for functions of several variables. However, if you grant that the function in question does have an absolute maximum, then we require no test, because one of the candidates must give this maximum.

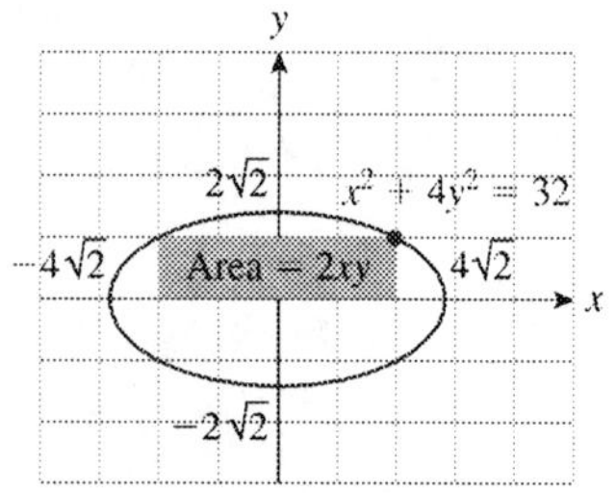

Figure 26

Q: *But how do we know that the given function has an absolute maximum?*

A: The best way to see this is by giving a geometric interpretation. The constraint $x^2 + 4y^2 = 32$ tells us that the point (x, y) must lie on the ellipse shown in Figure 26. The function $f(x, y) = 2xy$ gives the area of the rectangle shaded in the figure. There must be a *largest* such rectangle, because the area varies continuously from 0 when (x, y) is on the x-axis, to positive when (x, y) is in the first quadrant, to 0 again when (x, y) is on the y-axis, so f must have an absolute maximum for at least one pair of coordinates (x, y).

We now show how to use Lagrange multipliers to solve the minimization problem in Example 1:

EXAMPLE 3 Using Lagrange Multipliers: Function of Three Variables

Use the method of Lagrange multipliers to find the minimum value of $S = xy + 2xz + 2yz$ subject to $xyz = 4$ with $x > 0, y > 0, z > 0$.

Solution We start by rewriting the problem in standard form:

$$\text{Maximize } f(x, y, z) = xy + 2xz + 2yz$$
$$\text{subject to } xyz - 4 = 0 \text{ (with } x > 0, y > 0, z > 0).$$

Here, $g(x, y, z) = xyz - 4$, and the Lagrangian function is

$$\begin{aligned} L(x, y, z) &= f(x, y, z) - \lambda g(x, y, z) \\ &= xy + 2xz + 2yz - \lambda(xyz - 4). \end{aligned}$$

The system of equations we need to solve is thus

$$\begin{aligned} L_x = 0&: \quad y + 2z - \lambda yz = 0 \\ L_y = 0&: \quad x + 2z - \lambda xz = 0 \\ L_z = 0&: \quad 2x + 2y - \lambda xy = 0 \\ g = 0&: \quad xyz - 4 = 0. \end{aligned}$$

As in the last example, we solve one of the equations for λ and substitute in the others. The first equation gives

$$\lambda = \frac{1}{z} + \frac{2}{y}.$$

Substituting this into the second equation gives

$$x + 2z = x + \frac{2xz}{y}$$

or $\quad 2 = \frac{2x}{y},$ $\qquad$ Subtract x from both sides and then divide by z.

giving $\quad y = x.$

Substituting the expression for λ into the third equation gives

$$2x + 2y = \frac{xy}{z} + 2x$$

or $\quad 2 = \frac{x}{z},$ $\qquad$ Subtract $2x$ from both sides and then divide by y.

giving $\quad z = \frac{x}{2}.$

Now we have both y and z in terms of x. We substitute these values in the last (constraint) equation:

$$\begin{aligned} x(x)\left(\frac{x}{2}\right) - 4 &= 0 \\ x^3 &= 8 \\ x &= 2. \end{aligned}$$

Thus, $y = x = 2$, and $z = \frac{x}{2} = 1$. Therefore, the only critical point occurs at (2, 2, 1), as we found in Example 1, and the corresponding value of S is

$$S = xy + 2xz + 2yz = (2)(2) + 2(2)(1) + 2(2)(1) = 12.$$

Before we go on... Again, the method of Lagrange multipliers does not tell us whether the critical point in Example 3 is a maximum, minimum, or neither. However, if you grant that the function in question does have an absolute minimum, then the values we found must give this minimum value. ■

APPLICATIONS

EXAMPLE 4 Minimizing Area

Find the dimensions of an open-top rectangular box that has a volume of 4 cubic feet and the smallest possible surface area.

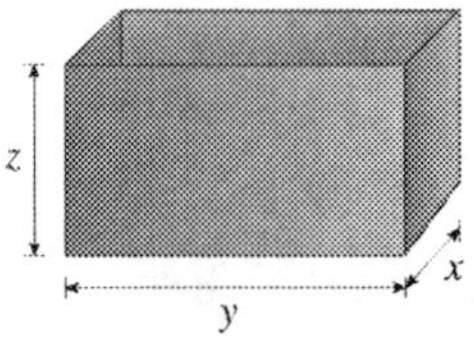

Figure 27

Solution Our first task is to rephrase this request as a mathematical optimization problem. Figure 27 shows a picture of the box with dimensions x, y, and z. We want to minimize the total surface area, which is given by

$$S = xy + 2xz + 2yz. \qquad \text{Base + Sides + Front and Back}$$

This is our objective function. We can't simply choose x, y, and z to all be zero, however, because the enclosed volume must be 4 cubic feet. So,

$$xyz = 4. \qquad \text{Constraint}$$

This is our constraint equation. Other unstated constraints are $x > 0$, $y > 0$, and $z > 0$, because the dimensions of the box must be positive. We now restate the problem as follows:

$$\text{Minimize } S = xy + 2xz + 2yz \quad \text{subject to } xyz = 4, x > 0, y > 0, z > 0.$$

But this is exactly the problem in Examples 1 and 3, and has a solution $x = 2$, $y = 2$, $z = 1$, $S = 12$. Thus, the required dimensions of the box are

$$x = 2 \text{ ft}, y = 2 \text{ ft}, z = 1 \text{ ft},$$

requiring a total surface area of 12 ft^2.

Q: *In Example 1 we checked that we had a relative minimum at $(x, y) = (2, 2)$ and we were persuaded graphically that this was probably an absolute minimum. Can we be sure that this relative minimum is an absolute minimum?*

A: Yes. There must be a least surface area among all boxes that hold 4 cubic feet. (Why?) Because this would give a relative minimum of S and because the only possible relative minimum of S occurs at (2, 2), this is the absolute minimum.

EXAMPLE 5 Maximizing productivity

An electric motor manufacturer uses workers and robots on its assembly line and has a Cobb-Douglas productivity function* of the form

$$P(x, y) = 10x^{0.2}y^{0.8} \text{ motors manufactured per day,}$$

where x is the number of assembly-line workers and y is the number of robots. Daily operating costs amount to \$100 per worker and \$16 per robot. How many workers and robots should be used to maximize productivity if the manufacturer has a daily budget of \$4,000?

* Cobb-Douglas production formulas were discussed in Section 11.6.

Solution Our objective function is the productivity $P(x, y)$, and the constraint is

$$100x + 16y = 4{,}000.$$

So, the optimization problem is:

$$\text{Maximize } P(x, y) = 10x^{0.2}y^{0.8} \text{ subject to } 100x + 16y = 4{,}000 \ (x \geq 0, y \geq 0).$$

Here, $g(x, y) = 100x + 16y - 4{,}000$, and the Lagrangian function is

$$\begin{aligned} L(x, y) &= P(x, y) - \lambda g(x, y) \\ &= 10x^{0.2}y^{0.8} - \lambda(100x + 16y - 4{,}000). \end{aligned}$$

The system of equations we need to solve is thus

$$\begin{aligned} L_x = 0: &\quad 2x^{-0.8}y^{0.8} - 100\lambda = 0 \\ L_y = 0: &\quad 8x^{0.2}y^{-0.2} - 16\lambda = 0 \\ g = 0: &\quad 100x + 16y = 4{,}000. \end{aligned}$$

We can rewrite the first two equations as:

$$2\left(\frac{y}{x}\right)^{0.8} = 100\lambda \qquad 8\left(\frac{x}{y}\right)^{0.2} = 16\lambda.$$

Dividing the first by the second to eliminate λ gives

$$\frac{1}{4}\left(\frac{y}{x}\right)^{0.8}\left(\frac{y}{x}\right)^{0.2} = \frac{100}{16}$$

that is,
$$\frac{1}{4}\frac{y}{x} = \frac{25}{4},$$

giving
$$y = 25x.$$

Substituting this result into the constraint equation gives

$$\begin{aligned} 100x + 16(25x) &= 4{,}000 \\ 500x &= 4{,}000 \end{aligned}$$

so
$$x = 8 \text{ workers}, \quad y = 25x = 200 \text{ robots}$$

for a productivity of

$$P(8{,}200) = 10(8)^{0.2}(200)^{0.8} \approx 1{,}051 \text{ motors manufactured per day.}$$

FAQ

When to Use Lagrange Multipliers

Q: *When can I use the method of Lagrange multipliers? When should I use it?*

A: We have discussed the method only when there is a single equality constraint. There is a generalization, which we have not discussed, that works when there are more equality constraints (we need to introduce one multiplier for each constraint). So, if you have a problem with more than one equality constraint, or with any inequality constraints, you must use the substitution method. On the other hand, if you have one equality constraint, and it would be difficult to solve it for one of the variables, then you should use Lagrange multipliers.

15.4 EXERCISES

▼ more advanced ◆ challenging

T indicates exercises that should be solved using technology

In Exercises 1–6, solve the given optimization problem by using substitution. HINT [See Example 1.]

1. Find the maximum value of $f(x, y, z) = 1 - x^2 - y^2 - z^2$ subject to $z = 2y$. Also find the corresponding point(s) (x, y, z).

2. Find the minimum value of $f(x, y, z) = x^2 + y^2 + z^2 - 2$ subject to $x = y$. Also find the corresponding point(s) (x, y, z).

3. Find the maximum value of $f(x, y, z) = 1 - x^2 - x - y^2 + y - z^2 + z$ subject to $3x = y$. Also find the corresponding point(s) (x, y, z).

4. Find the maximum value of $f(x, y, z) = 2x^2 + 2x + y^2 - y + z^2 - z - 1$ subject to $z = 2y$. Also find the corresponding point(s) (x, y, z).

5. Minimize $S = xy + 4xz + 2yz$ subject to $xyz = 1$ with $x > 0, y > 0, z > 0$.

6. Minimize $S = xy + xz + yz$ subject to $xyz = 2$ with $x > 0, y > 0, z > 0$.

In Exercises 7–18, use Lagrange multipliers to solve the given optimization problem. HINT [See Example 2.]

7. Find the maximum value of $f(x, y) = xy$ subject to $x + 2y = 40$. Also find the corresponding point(s) (x, y).

8. Find the maximum value of $f(x, y) = xy$ subject to $3x + y = 60$. Also find the corresponding point(s) (x, y).

9. Find the maximum value of $f(x, y) = 4xy$ subject to $x^2 + y^2 = 8$. Also find the corresponding point(s) (x, y).

10. Find the maximum value of $f(x, y) = xy$ subject to $y = 3 - x^2$. Also find the corresponding point(s) (x, y).

11. Find the minimum value of $f(x, y) = x^2 + y^2$ subject to $x + 2y = 10$. Also find the corresponding point(s) (x, y).

12. Find the minimum value of $f(x, y) = x^2 + y^2$ subject to $xy^2 = 16$. Also find the corresponding point(s) (x, y).

13. The problem in Exercise 1. HINT [See Example 3.]

14. The problem in Exercise 2. HINT [See Example 3.]

15. The problem in Exercise 3.

16. The problem in Exercise 4.

17. The problem in Exercise 5.

18. The problem in Exercise 6.

19. ◆ Consider the following constrained optimization problem:

$$\text{Minimize } f(x, y, z) = (x - 3)^2 + y^2 + z^2$$
$$\text{subject to } x^2 + y^2 - z = 0.$$

a. Explain why this minimization problem must have a solution, and solve it using the method of Lagrange multipliers.

b. Solve it again using the substitution method by solving the constraint equation for z.

c. Now try to solve it using the substitution method by solving the constraint equation for y.

d. Explain what goes wrong in part (c).

20. ◆ Consider the following constrained optimization problem:

$$\text{Minimize } f(x, y, z) = x^2 + (y + 3)^2 + (z - 4)^2$$
$$\text{subject to } 4 - x^2 - y^2 - z = 0.$$

a. Explain why this minimization problem must have a solution, and solve it using the method of Lagrange multipliers.

b. Solve it again using the substitution method by solving the constraint equation for z.

c. Now try to solve it using the substitution method by solving the constraint equation for x.

d. Explain what goes wrong in part (c).

APPLICATIONS

Exercises 21–24 were solved in Section 12.2. This time, use the method of Lagrange multipliers to solve them.

21. ***Fences*** I want to fence in a rectangular vegetable patch. The fencing for the east and west sides costs \$4 per foot, and the fencing for the north and south sides costs only \$2 per foot. I have a budget of \$80 for the project. What is the largest area I can enclose?

22. ***Fences*** My orchid garden abuts my house so that the house itself forms the northern boundary. The fencing for the southern boundary costs \$4 per foot, and the fencing for the east and west sides costs \$2 per foot. If I have a budget of \$80 for the project, what is the largest area I can enclose?

23. ***Revenue*** *Hercules Films* is deciding on the price of the video release of its film *Son of Frankenstein*. Its marketing people estimate that at a price of p dollars, it can sell a total of $q = 200{,}000 - 10{,}000p$ copies. What price will bring in the greatest revenue?

24. ***Profit*** *Hercules Films* is also deciding on the price of the video release of its film *Bride of the Son of Frankenstein*. Again, marketing estimates that at a price of p dollars it can sell $q = 200{,}000 - 10{,}000p$ copies, but each copy costs \$4 to make. What price will give the greatest *profit*?

25. ***Geometry*** At what points on the sphere $x^2 + y^2 + z^2 = 1$ is the product xyz a maximum? (The method of Lagrange multipliers can be used.)

26. ***Geometry*** At what point on the surface $z = (x^2 + x + y^2 + 4)^{1/2}$ is the quantity $x^2 + y^2 + z^2$ a minimum? (The method of Lagrange multipliers can be used.)

27. ▼ ***Geometry*** What point on the surface $z = x^2 + y - 1$ is closest to the origin? HINT [Minimize the square of the distance from (x, y, z) to the origin.]

28. ▼ ***Geometry*** What point on the surface $z = x + y^2 - 3$ is closest to the origin? HINT [Minimize the square of the distance from (x, y, z) to the origin.]

29. ▼ ***Geometry*** Find the point on the plane $-2x + 2y + z - 5 = 0$ closest to $(-1, 1, 3)$. HINT [Minimize the square of the distance from the given point to a general point on the plane.]

30. ▼ ***Geometry*** Find the point on the plane $2x - 2y - z + 1 = 0$ closest to $(1, 1, 0)$. HINT [Minimize the square of the distance from the given point to a general point on the plane.]

31. ***Construction Cost*** A closed rectangular box is made with two kinds of materials. The top and bottom are made with heavy-duty cardboard costing 20¢ per square foot, and the sides are made with lightweight cardboard costing 10¢ per square foot. Given that the box is to have a capacity of 2 cubic feet, what should its dimensions be if the cost is to be minimized? HINT [See Example 4.]

32. ***Construction Cost*** Repeat the preceding exercise assuming that the heavy-duty cardboard costs 30¢ per square foot, the lightweight cardboard costs 5¢ per square foot, and the box is to have a capacity of 6 cubic feet. HINT [See Example 4.]

33. ***Package Dimensions: USPS*** The U.S. Postal Service (USPS) will accept only packages with a length plus girth no more than 108 inches.[27] (See the figure.)

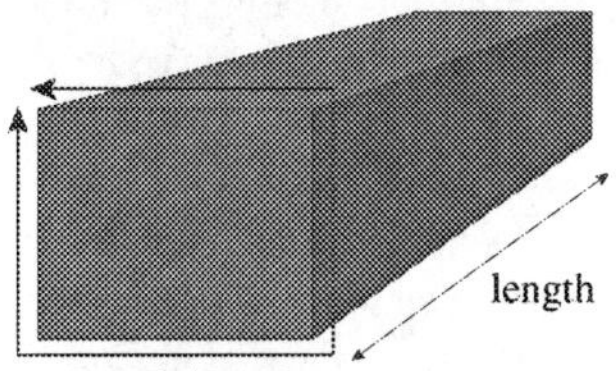

What are the dimensions of the largest volume package that the USPS will accept? What is its volume? (This exercise is the same as Exercise 49 in the preceding section. This time, solve it using Lagrange multipliers.)

34. ***Package Dimensions: UPS*** United Parcel Service (UPS) will accept only packages with length no more than 108 inches and length plus girth no more than 165 inches.[28] (See figure for the preceding exercise.) What are the dimensions of the largest volume package that UPS will accept? What is its volume? (This exercise is the same as Exercise 50 in the preceding section. This time, solve it using Lagrange multipliers.)

35. ▼ ***Construction Cost*** My company wishes to manufacture boxes similar to those described in Exercise 31 as cheaply as possible, but unfortunately the company that manufactures the cardboard is unable to give me price quotes for the heavy-duty and lightweight cardboard. Find formulas for the dimensions of the box in terms of the price per square foot of heavy-duty and lightweight cardboard.

36. ▼ ***Construction Cost*** Repeat the preceding exercise, assuming that only the bottoms of the boxes are to be made using heavy-duty cardboard.

37. ▼ ***Geometry*** Find the dimensions of the rectangular box with largest volume that can be inscribed above the xy-plane and under the paraboloid $z = 1 - (x^2 + y^2)$.

38. ▼ ***Geometry*** Find the dimensions of the rectangular box with largest volume that can be inscribed above the xy-plane and under the paraboloid $z = 2 - (2x^2 + y^2)$.

39. ***Productivity*** The Gym Shirt Company manufactures cotton socks. Production is partially automated through the use of robots. Daily operating costs amount to \$150 per laborer and \$60 per robot. The number of pairs of socks the company can manufacture in a day is given by a Cobb-Douglas production formula

$$q = 50n^{0.6}r^{0.4},$$

where q is the number of pairs of socks that can be manufactured by n laborers and r robots. Assuming that the company has a daily operating budget of \$1,500 and

---

[27]The requirement for packages sent other than Parcel Post, as of August 2011 (www.usps.com).

[28]The requirement as of August 2011 (www.ups.com).

wishes to maximize productivity, how many laborers and how many robots should it use? What is the productivity at these levels? HINT [See Example 5.]

40. ***Productivity*** Your automobile assembly plant has a Cobb-Douglas production function given by

$$q = 100x^{0.3}y^{0.7},$$

where q is the number of automobiles it produces per year, x is the number of employees, and y is the monthly assembly-line budget (in thousands of dollars). Annual operating costs amount to an average of \$60 thousand per employee plus the operating budget of \$$12y$ thousand. Your annual budget is \$1,200,000. How many employees should you hire and what should your assembly-line budget be to maximize productivity? What is the productivity at these levels? HINT [See Example 5.]

COMMUNICATION AND REASONING EXERCISES

41. Outline two methods of solution of the problem "*Maximize* $f(x, y, z)$ *subject to* $g(x, y, z) = 0$" and give an advantage and disadvantage of each.

42. Suppose we know that $f(x, y)$ has both partial derivatives in its domain D: $x > 0, y > 0$, and that (a, b) is the only point in D such that $f_x(a, b) = f_y(a, b) = 0$. Must it be the case that, if f has an absolute maximum, it occurs at (a, b)? Explain.

43. Under what circumstances would it be necessary to use the method of Lagrange multipliers?

44. Under what circumstances would the method of Lagrange multipliers not apply?

45. Restate the following problem as a maximization problem of the form "*Maximize* $f(x, y)$ *subject to* $g(x, y) = 0$":

Find the maximum value of $h(x) = 1 - 2x^2$.

46. Restate the following problem as a maximization problem of the form "*Maximize* $f(x, y, z)$ *subject to* $g(x, y, z) = 0$":

Find the maximum value of $h(x, y) = 1 - 2(x^2 + y^2)$.

47. ▼ If the partial derivatives of a function of several variables are always defined and never 0, is it possible for the function to have relative extrema when restricted to some domain? Explain your answer.

48. ▼ Give an example of a function f of three variables with an absolute maximum at (0, 0, 0) but where the partial derivatives of f are never zero wherever they are defined.

49. ◆ A **linear programming problem in two variables** is a problem of the form: *Maximize (or minimize)* $f(x, y)$ *subject to constraints of the form* $C(x, y) \geq 0$ *or* $C(x, y) \leq 0$. Here, the objective function f and the constraints C are linear functions. There may be several linear constraints in one problem. Explain why the solution cannot occur in the interior of the domain of f.

50. ◆ Refer back to Exercise 49. Explain why the solution will actually be at a corner of the domain of f (where two or more of the line segments that make up the boundary meet). This result—or rather a slight generalization of it—is known as the Fundamental Theorem of Linear Programming.

15.5 Double Integrals and Applications

When discussing functions of one variable, we computed the area under a graph by integration. The analog for the graph of a function of two variables is the *volume* V under the graph, as in Figure 28. Think of the region R in the xy-plane as the "shadow" under the portion of the surface $z = f(x, y)$ shown.

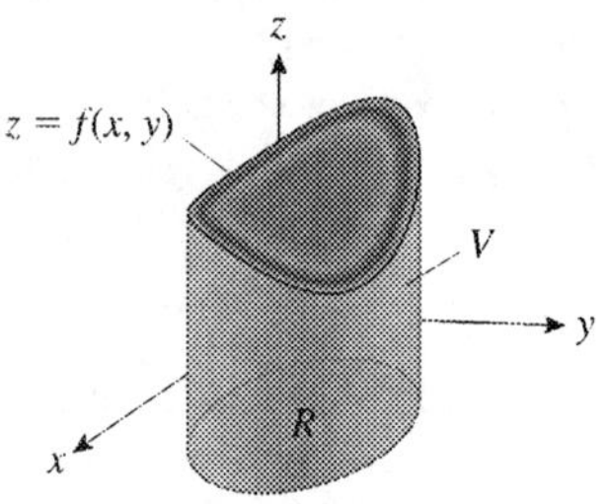

Figure 28

By analogy with the definite integral of a function of one variable, we make the following definition:

Geometric Definition of the Double Integral

The **double integral of $f(x, y)$ over the region R in the xy-plane** is defined as

(Volume *above* the region R and under the graph of f)
− (Volume *below* the region R and above the graph of f).

We denote the double integral of $f(x, y)$ over the region R by $\iint_R f(x, y)\,dx\,dy$.

Quick Example

Take $f(x, y) = 2$ and take R to be the rectangle $0 \le x \le 1, 0 \le y \le 1$. Then the graph of f is a flat horizontal surface $z = 2$, and

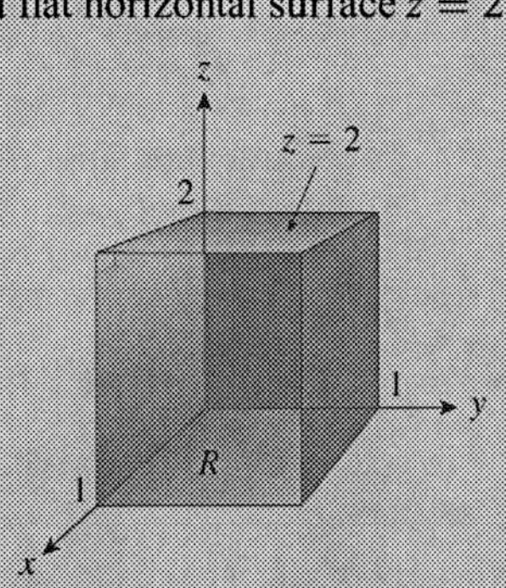

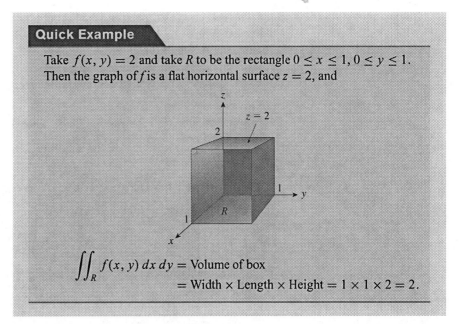

$$\iint_R f(x, y)\,dx\,dy = \text{Volume of box}$$
$$= \text{Width} \times \text{Length} \times \text{Height} = 1 \times 1 \times 2 = 2.$$

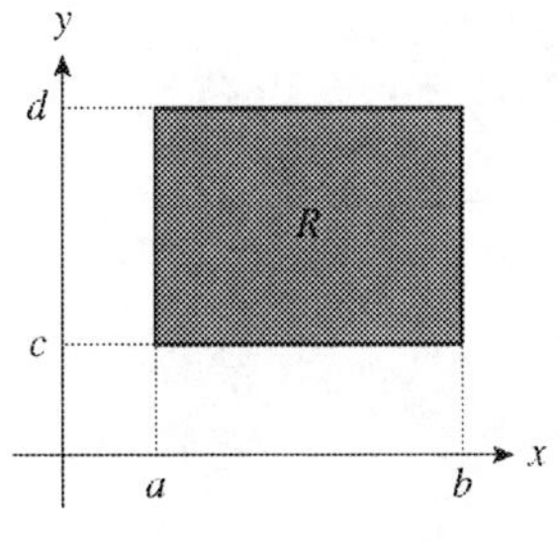

Figure 29

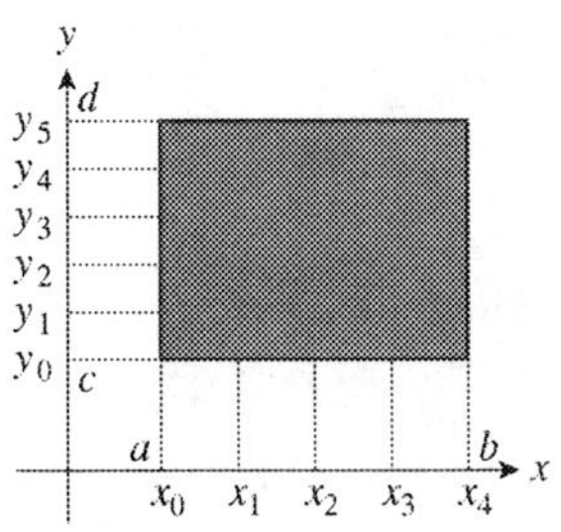

Figure 30

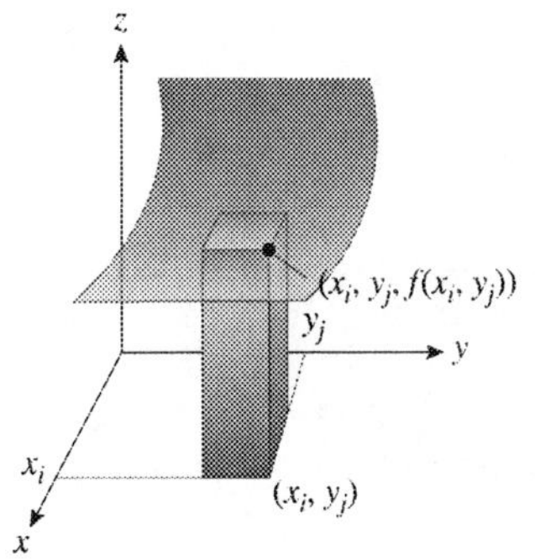

Figure 31

As we saw in the case of the definite integral of a function of one variable, we also desire *numerical* and *algebraic* definitions for two reasons: (1) to make the mathematical definition more precise, so as not to rely on the notion of "volume," and (2) for direct computation of the integral using technology or analytical tools.

We start with the simplest case, when the region R is a rectangle $a \le x \le b$ and $c \le y \le d$. (See Figure 29.) To compute the volume over R, we mimic what we did to find the area under the graph of a function of one variable. We break up the interval $[a, b]$ into m intervals all of width $\Delta x = (b - a)/m$, and we break up $[c, d]$ into n intervals all of width $\Delta y = (d - c)/n$. Figure 30 shows an example with $m = 4$ and $n = 5$.

This gives us mn rectangles defined by $x_{i-1} \le x \le x_i$ and $y_{j-1} \le y \le y_j$. Over one of these rectangles, f is approximately equal to its value at one corner—say $f(x_i, y_j)$. The volume under f over this small rectangle is then approximately the volume of the rectangular brick (size exaggerated) shown in Figure 31. This brick has height $f(x_i, y_j)$, and its base is Δx by Δy. Its volume is therefore $f(x_i, y_j)\Delta x\,\Delta y$. Adding together the volumes of all of the bricks over the small rectangles in R, we get

$$\iint_R f(x, y)\,dx\,dy \approx \sum_{j=1}^{n}\sum_{i=1}^{m} f(x_i, y_j)\Delta x\,\Delta y.$$

This double sum is called a **double Riemann sum**. We define the double integral to be the limit of the Riemann sums as m and n go to infinity.

Algebraic Definition of the Double Integral

$$\iint_R f(x, y)\,dx\,dy = \lim_{n\to\infty}\lim_{m\to\infty}\sum_{j=1}^{n}\sum_{i=1}^{m} f(x_i, y_j)\Delta x\,\Delta y$$

Note This definition is adequate (the limit exists) when f is continuous. More elaborate definitions are needed for general functions. ■

This definition also gives us a clue about how to compute a double integral. The innermost sum is $\sum_{i=1}^{m} f(x_i, y_j)\Delta x$, which is a Riemann sum for $\int_a^b f(x, y_j)\, dx$. The innermost limit is therefore

$$\lim_{m\to\infty} \sum_{i=1}^{m} f(x_i, y_j)\Delta x = \int_a^b f(x, y_j)\, dx.$$

The outermost limit is then also a Riemann sum, and we get the following way of calculating double integrals:

Computing the Double Integral over a Rectangle

If R is the rectangle $a \le x \le b$ and $c \le y \le d$, then

$$\iint_R f(x, y)\, dx\, dy = \int_c^d \left(\int_a^b f(x, y)\, dx\right) dy = \int_a^b \left(\int_c^d f(x, y)\, dy\right) dx.$$

The second formula comes from switching the order of summation in the double sum.

Quick Example

If R is the rectangle $1 \le x \le 2$ and $1 \le y \le 3$, then

$$\iint_R 1\, dx\, dy = \int_1^3 \left(\int_1^2 1\, dx\right) dy$$

$$= \int_1^3 [x]_{x=1}^2\, dy \qquad \text{Evaluate the inner integral.}$$

$$= \int_1^3 1\, dy \qquad [x]_{x=1}^2 = 2 - 1 = 1.$$

$$= [y]_{y=1}^3 = 3 - 1 = 2.$$

The Quick Example used a constant function for the integrand. Here is an example in which the integrand is not constant.

EXAMPLE 1 Double Integral over a Rectangle

Let R be the rectangle $0 \le x \le 1$ and $0 \le y \le 2$. Compute $\iint_R xy\, dx\, dy$. This integral gives the volume of the part of the boxed region under the surface $z = xy$ shown in Figure 32.

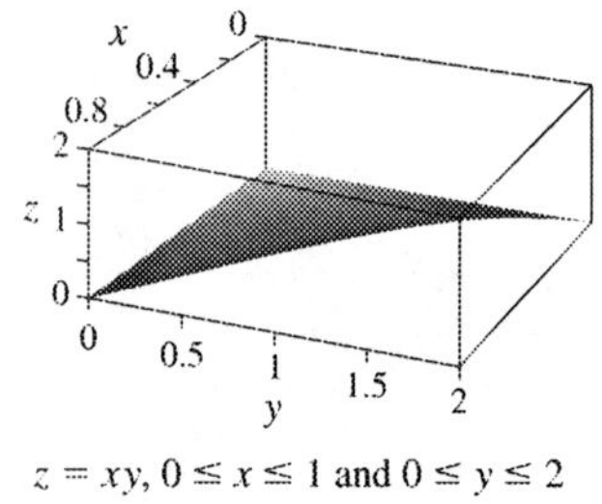

$z = xy$, $0 \le x \le 1$ and $0 \le y \le 2$

Figure 32

Solution

$$\iint_R xy\, dx\, dy = \int_0^2 \int_0^1 xy\, dx\, dy$$

(We usually drop the parentheses around the inner integral like this.) As in the Quick Example, we compute this **iterated integral** from the inside out. First we compute

$$\int_0^1 xy\, dx.$$

To do this computation, we do as we did when finding partial derivatives: We treat y as a constant. This gives

$$\int_0^1 xy\,dx = \left[\frac{x^2}{2}\cdot y\right]_{x=0}^1 = \frac{1}{2}y - 0 = \frac{y}{2}.$$

We can now calculate the outer integral.

$$\int_0^2\int_0^1 xy\,dx\,dy = \int_0^2 \frac{y}{2}\,dy = \left[\frac{y^2}{4}\right]_0^2 = 1$$

Before we go on... We could also reverse the order of integration in Example 1:

$$\int_0^1\int_0^2 xy\,dy\,dx = \int_0^1\left[x\cdot\frac{y^2}{2}\right]_{y=0}^2 = \int_0^1 2x\,dx = \left[x^2\right]_0^1 = 1.$$ ■

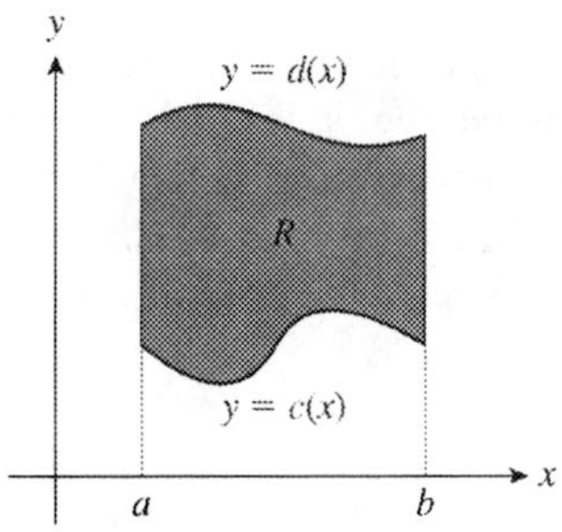

Figure 33

Often we need to integrate over regions R that are not rectangular. There are two cases that come up. The first is a region like the one shown in Figure 33. In this region, the bottom and top sides are defined by functions $y = c(x)$ and $y = d(x)$, respectively, so that the whole region can be described by the inequalities $a \le x \le b$ and $c(x) \le y \le d(x)$. To evaluate a double integral over such a region, we have the following formula:

Computing the Double Integral over a Nonrectangular Region

If R is the region $a \le x \le b$ and $c(x) \le y \le d(x)$ (Figure 33), then we integrate over R according to the following equation:

$$\iint_R f(x, y)\,dx\,dy = \int_a^b\int_{c(x)}^{d(x)} f(x, y)\,dy\,dx.$$

EXAMPLE 2 Double Integral over a Nonrectangular Region

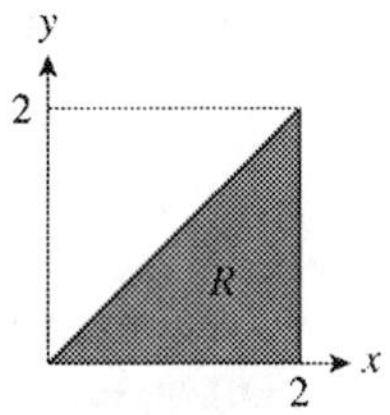

Figure 34

R is the triangle shown in Figure 34. Compute $\iint_R x\,dx\,dy$.

Solution R is the region described by $0 \le x \le 2$, $0 \le y \le x$. We have

$$\begin{aligned}\iint_R x\,dx\,dy &= \int_0^2\int_0^x x\,dy\,dx \\ &= \int_0^2 \left[xy\right]_{y=0}^x dx \\ &= \int_0^2 x^2\,dx \\ &= \left[\frac{x^3}{3}\right]_0^2 = \frac{8}{3}.\end{aligned}$$

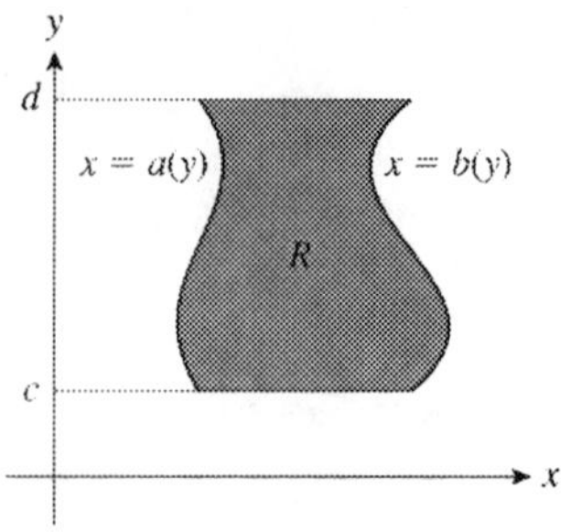

Figure 35

The second type of region is shown in Figure 35. This is the region described by $c \le y \le d$ and $a(y) \le x \le b(y)$. To evaluate a double integral over such a region, we have the following formula:

> **Double Integral over a Nonrectangular Region (continued)**
>
> If R is the region $c \le y \le d$ and $a(y) \le x \le b(y)$ (Figure 35), then we integrate over R according to the following equation:
>
> $$\iint_R f(x, y)\,dx\,dy = \int_c^d \int_{a(y)}^{b(y)} f(x, y)\,dx\,dy.$$

EXAMPLE 3 Double Integral over a Nonrectangular Region

Redo Example 2, integrating in the opposite order.

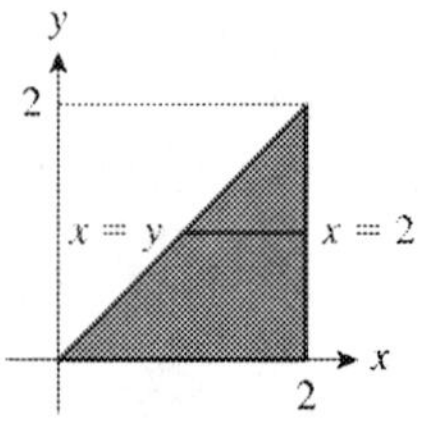

Figure 36

Solution We can integrate in the opposite order if we can describe the region in Figure 34 in the way shown in Figure 35. In fact, it is the region $0 \le y \le 2$ and $y \le x \le 2$. To see this, we draw a horizontal line through the region, as in Figure 36. The line extends from $x = y$ on the left to $x = 2$ on the right, so $y \le x \le 2$. The possible heights for such a line are $0 \le y \le 2$. We can now compute the integral:

$$\begin{aligned}\iint_R x\,dx\,dy &= \int_0^2 \int_y^2 x\,dx\,dy \\ &= \int_0^2 \left[\frac{x^2}{2}\right]_{x=y}^{2} dy \\ &= \int_0^2 \left(2 - \frac{y^2}{2}\right) dy \\ &= \left[2y - \frac{y^3}{6}\right]_0^2 = \frac{8}{3}.\end{aligned}$$

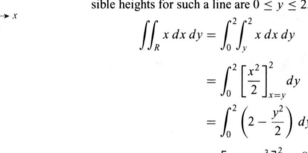

Note Many regions can be described in two different ways, as we saw in Examples 2 and 3. Sometimes one description will be much easier to work with than the other, so it pays to consider both. ■

APPLICATIONS

There are many applications of double integrals besides finding volumes. For example, we can use them to find *averages*. Remember that the average of $f(x)$ on $[a, b]$ is given by $\int_a^b f(x)\,dx$ divided by $(b - a)$, the length of the interval.

> **Average of a Function of Two Variables**
>
> The average of $f(x, y)$ on the region R is
>
> $$\bar{f} = \frac{1}{A}\iint_R f(x, y)\,dx\,dy.$$

Here, A is the area of R. We can compute the area A geometrically, or by using the techniques from the chapter on applications of the integral, or by computing

$$A = \iint_R 1\, dx\, dy.$$

Quick Example

The average value of $f(x, y) = xy$ on the rectangle given by $0 \le x \le 1$ and $0 \le y \le 2$ is

$$\bar{f} = \frac{1}{2}\iint_R xy\, dx\, dy \quad \text{The area of the rectangle is 2.}$$

$$= \frac{1}{2}\int_0^2\int_0^1 xy\, dx\, dy$$

$$= \frac{1}{2}\cdot 1 = \frac{1}{2}. \quad \text{We calculated the integral in Example 1.}$$

EXAMPLE 4 Average Revenue

Your company is planning to price its new line of subcompact cars at between \$10,000 and \$15,000. The marketing department reports that if the company prices the cars at p dollars per car, the demand will be between $q = 20{,}000 - p$ and $q = 25{,}000 - p$ cars sold in the first year. What is the average of all the possible revenues your company could expect in the first year?

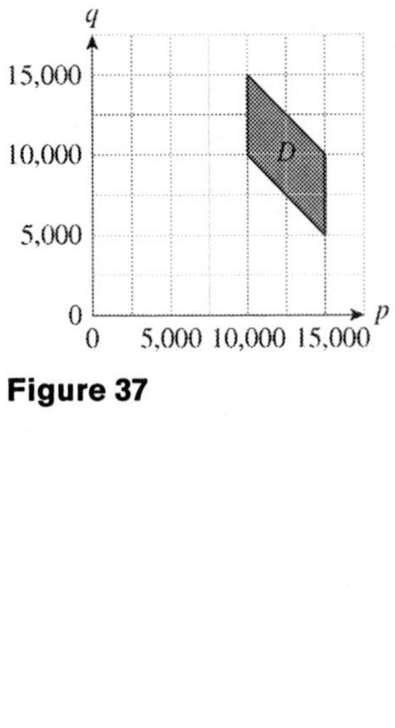

Figure 37

Solution Revenue is given by $R = pq$ as usual, and we are told that

$$10{,}000 \le p \le 15{,}000$$

and $\quad 20{,}000 - p \le q \le 25{,}000 - p.$

This domain D of prices and demands is shown in Figure 37.

To average the revenue R over the domain D, we need to compute the area A of D. Using either calculus or geometry, we get $A = 25{,}000{,}000$. We then need to integrate R over D:

$$\iint_D pq\, dp\, dq = \int_{10{,}000}^{15{,}000}\int_{20{,}000-p}^{25{,}000-p} pq\, dq\, dp$$

$$= \int_{10{,}000}^{15{,}000}\left[\frac{pq^2}{2}\right]_{q=20{,}000-p}^{25{,}000-p} dp$$

$$= \frac{1}{2}\int_{10{,}000}^{15{,}000}[p(25{,}000-p)^2 - p(20{,}000-p)^2]\, dp$$

$$= \frac{1}{2}\int_{10{,}000}^{15{,}000}[225{,}000{,}000p - 10{,}000p^2]\, dp$$

$$\approx 3{,}072{,}900{,}000{,}000{,}000.$$

The average of all the possible revenues your company could expect in the first year is therefore

$$\bar{R} = \frac{3{,}072{,}900{,}000{,}000{,}000}{25{,}000{,}000} \approx \$122{,}900{,}000.$$

Before we go on... To check that the answer obtained in Example 4 is reasonable, notice that the revenues at the corners of the domain are \$100,000,000 per year, \$150,000,000 per year (at two corners), and \$75,000,000 per year. Some of these are smaller than the average and some larger, as we would expect. ■

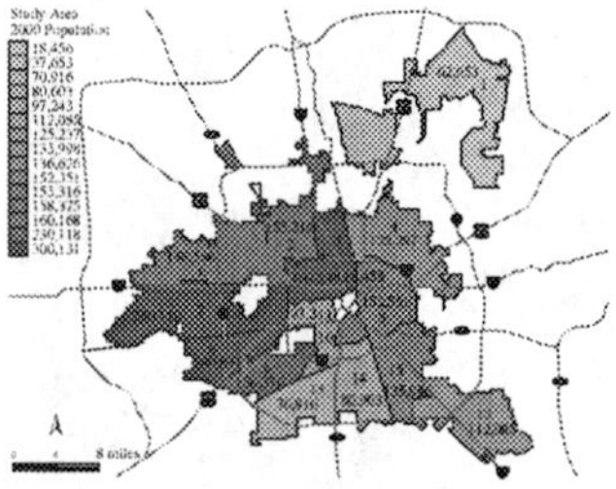

Darker regions have higher population density

Figure 38

Another useful application of the double integral comes about when we consider density. For example, suppose that $P(x, y)$ represents the population density (in people per square mile, say) in the city of Houston, shown in Figure 38.

If we break the city up into small rectangles (for example, city blocks), then the population in the small rectangle $x_{i-1} \le x \le x_i$ and $y_{j-1} \le y \le y_j$ is approximately $P(x_i, y_j)\Delta x \Delta y$. Adding up all of these population estimates, we get

$$\text{Total population} \approx \sum_{j=1}^{n} \sum_{i=1}^{m} P(x_i, y_j)\, \Delta x\, \Delta y.$$

Because this is a double Riemann sum, when we take the limit as m and n go to infinity, we get the following calculation of the population of the city:

$$\text{Total population} = \iint_{\text{City}} P(x, y)\, dx\, dy.$$

EXAMPLE 5 Population

Squaresville is a city in the shape of a square 5 miles on a side. The population density at a distance of x miles east and y miles north of the southwest corner is $P(x, y) = x^2 + y^2$ thousand people per square mile. Find the total population of Squaresville.

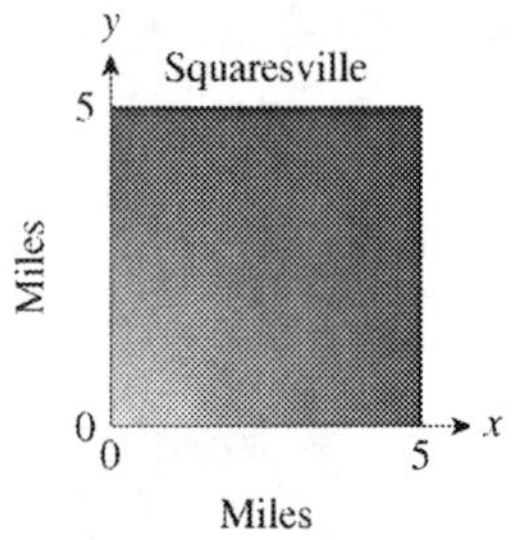

Figure 39

Solution Squaresville is pictured in Figure 39, in which we put the origin in the southwest corner of the city.

To compute the total population, we integrate the population density over the city S.

$$\begin{aligned}\text{Total population} &= \iint_{\text{Squaresville}} P(x, y)\, dx\, dy \\ &= \int_0^5 \int_0^5 (x^2 + y^2)\, dx\, dy \\ &= \int_0^5 \left[\frac{x^3}{3} + xy^2\right]_{x=0}^{5} dy \\ &= \int_0^5 \left[\frac{125}{3} + 5y^2\right] dy \\ &= \frac{1{,}250}{3} \approx 417 \text{ thousand people}\end{aligned}$$

Before we go on... Note that the average population density is the total population divided by the area of the city, which is about 17,000 people per square mile. Compare this calculation with the calculations of averages in the previous two examples. ■

15.5 EXERCISES

▼ more advanced ◆ challenging

T indicates exercises that should be solved using technology

Compute the integrals in Exercises 1–16. HINT [See Example 1.]

1. $\int_0^1 \int_0^1 (x - 2y)\,dx\,dy$

2. $\int_{-1}^1 \int_0^2 (2x + 3y)\,dx\,dy$

3. $\int_0^1 \int_0^2 (ye^x - x - y)\,dx\,dy$

4. $\int_1^2 \int_2^3 \left(\frac{1}{x} + \frac{1}{y}\right) dx\,dy$

5. $\int_0^2 \int_0^3 e^{x+y}\,dx\,dy$

6. $\int_0^1 \int_0^1 e^{x-y}\,dx\,dy$

7. $\int_0^1 \int_0^{2-y} x\,dx\,dy$

8. $\int_0^1 \int_0^{2-y} y\,dx\,dy$

9. $\int_{-1}^1 \int_{y-1}^{y+1} e^{x+y}\,dx\,dy$ HINT [See Example 2.]

10. $\int_0^1 \int_y^{y+2} \frac{1}{\sqrt{x+y}}\,dx\,dy$ HINT [See Example 2.]

11. $\int_0^1 \int_{-x^2}^{x^2} x\,dy\,dx$

12. $\int_1^4 \int_{-\sqrt{x}}^{\sqrt{x}} \frac{1}{x}\,dy\,dx$

13. $\int_0^1 \int_0^x e^{x^2}\,dy\,dx$

14. $\int_0^1 \int_0^{x^2} e^{x^3+1}\,dy\,dx$

15. $\int_0^2 \int_{1-x}^{8-x} (x+y)^{1/3}\,dy\,dx$

16. $\int_1^2 \int_{1-2x}^{x^2} \frac{x+1}{(2x+y)^3}\,dy\,dx$

In Exercises 17–24, find $\iint_R f(x, y)\,dx\,dy$, where R is the indicated domain. (Remember that you often have a choice as to the order of integration.) HINT [See Example 2.]

17. $f(x, y) = 2$

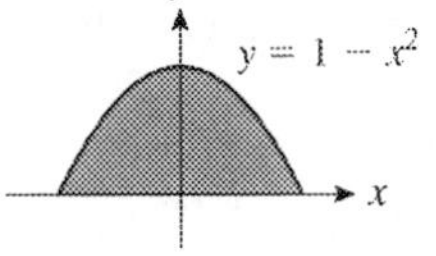

18. $f(x, y) = x$

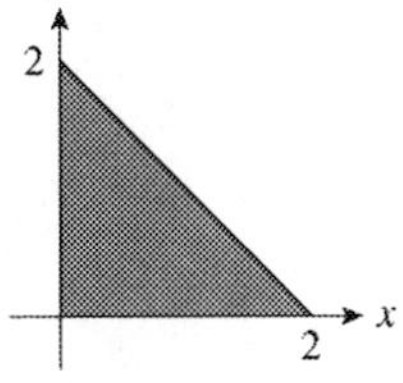

19. $f(x, y) = 1 + y$ HINT [See Example 3.]

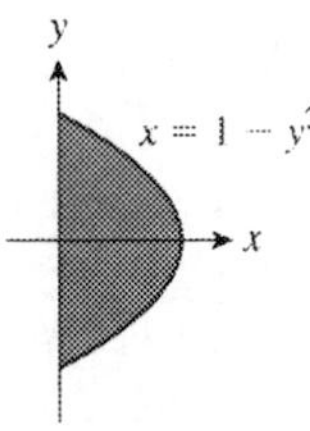

20. $f(x, y) = e^{x+y}$ HINT [See Example 3.]

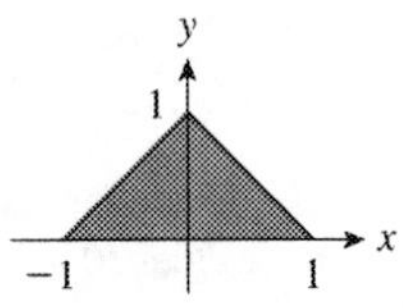

21. $f(x, y) = xy^2$

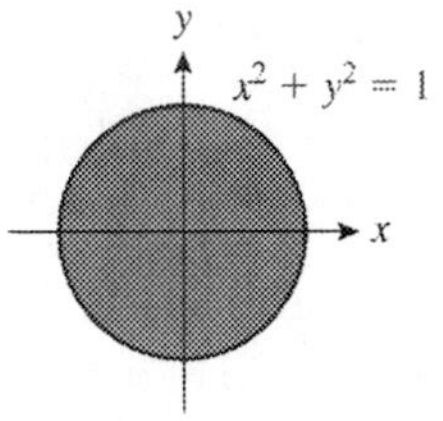

22. $f(x, y) = xy^2$

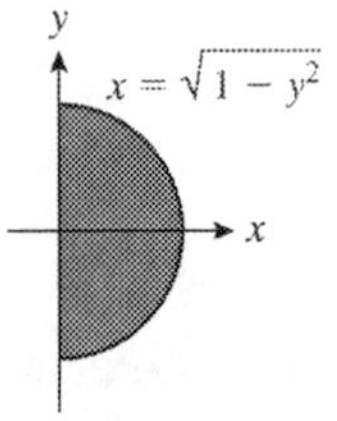

23. $f(x, y) = x^2 + y^2$

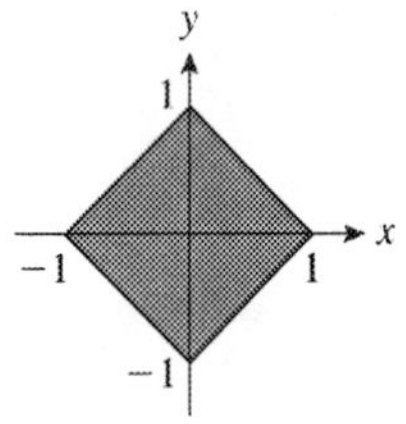

24. $f(x, y) = x^2$

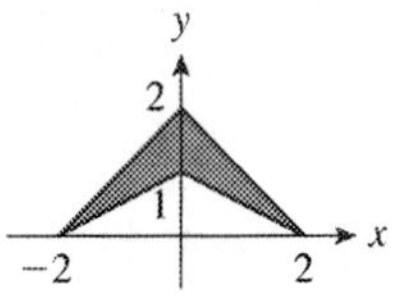

In Exercises 25–30, find the average value of the given function over the indicated domain. HINT [See Quick Example page 1133.]

25. $f(x, y) = y$

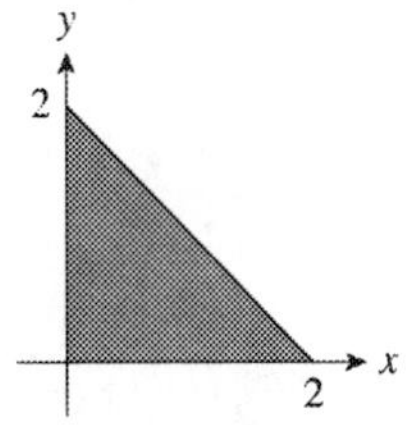

26. $f(x, y) = 2 + x$

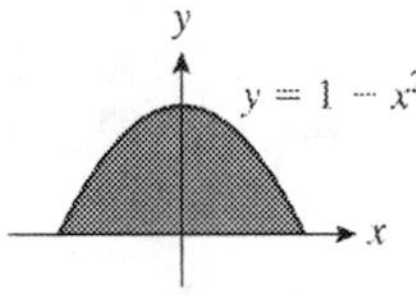

27. $f(x, y) = e^y$

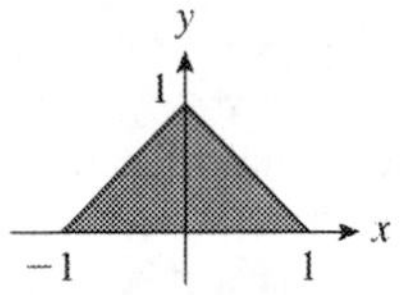

28. $f(x, y) = y$

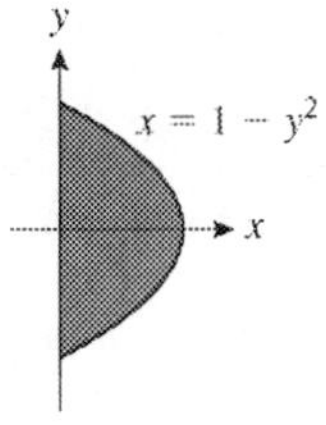

29. $f(x, y) = x^2 + y^2$

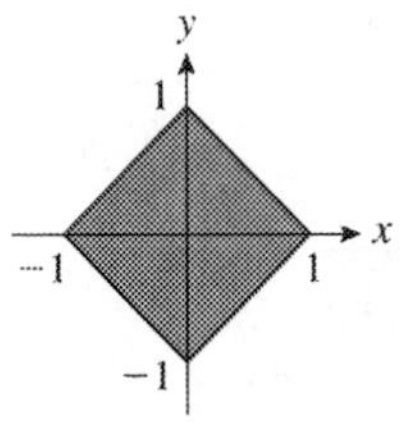

30. $f(x, y) = x^2$

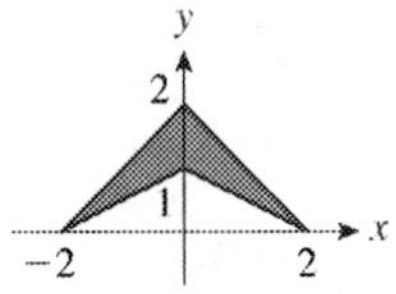

In Exercises 31–36, sketch the region over which you are integrating, and then write down the integral with the order of integration reversed (changing the limits of integration as necessary).

31. $\int_0^1 \int_0^{1-y} f(x, y)\,dx\,dy$ **32.** $\int_{-1}^1 \int_0^{1+y} f(x, y)\,dx\,dy$

33. $\int_{-1}^1 \int_0^{\sqrt{1+y}} f(x, y)\,dx\,dy$ **34.** $\int_{-1}^1 \int_0^{\sqrt{1-y}} f(x, y)\,dx\,dy$

35. $\int_1^2 \int_1^{4/x^2} f(x, y)\,dy\,dx$ **36.** $\int_1^{e^2} \int_0^{\ln x} f(x, y)\,dy\,dx$

37. Find the volume under the graph of $z = 1 - x^2$ over the region $0 \le x \le 1$ and $0 \le y \le 2$.

38. Find the volume under the graph of $z = 1 - x^2$ over the triangle $0 \le x \le 1$ and $0 \le y \le 1 - x$.

39. Find the volume of the tetrahedron shown in the figure. Its corners are (0, 0, 0), (1, 0, 0), (0, 1, 0), and (0, 0, 1).

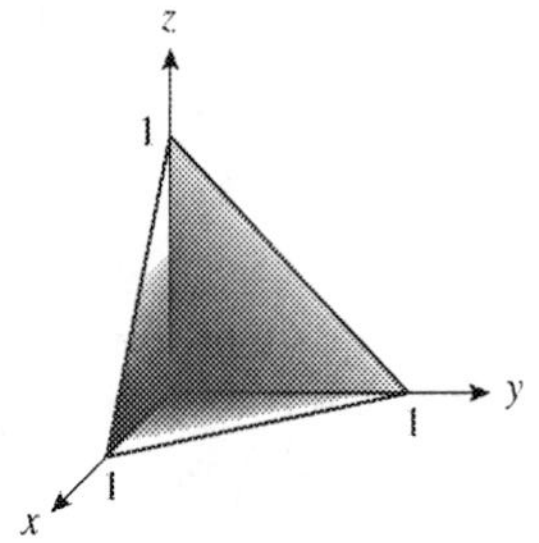

40. Find the volume of the tetrahedron with corners at (0, 0, 0), (*a*, 0, 0), (0, *b*, 0), and (0, 0, *c*).

APPLICATIONS

41. *Productivity* A productivity model at the *Handy Gadget Company* is

$$P = 10{,}000x^{0.3}y^{0.7},$$

where P is the number of gadgets the company turns out per month, x is the number of employees at the company, and y is the monthly operating budget in thousands of dollars. Because the company hires part-time workers, it uses anywhere between 45 and 55 workers each month, and its operating budget varies from \$8,000 to \$12,000 per month. What is the average of the possible numbers of gadgets it can turn out per month? (Round the answer to the nearest 1,000 gadgets.) HINT [See Quick Example page 1133.]

42. *Productivity* Repeat the preceding exercise using the productivity model

$$P = 10{,}000x^{0.7}y^{0.3}.$$

43. *Revenue* Your latest CD-ROM of clip art is expected to sell between $q = 8{,}000 - p^2$ and $q = 10{,}000 - p^2$ copies if priced at p dollars. You plan to set the price between \$40 and \$50. What is the average of all the possible revenues you can make? HINT [See Example 4.]

44. *Revenue* Your latest DVD drive is expected to sell between $q = 180{,}000 - p^2$ and $q = 200{,}000 - p^2$ units if priced at p dollars. You plan to set the price between \$300 and \$400. What is the average of all the possible revenues you can make? HINT [See Example 4.]

45. *Revenue* Your self-published novel has demand curves between $p = 15{,}000/q$ and $p = 20{,}000/q$. You expect to sell between 500 and 1,000 copies. What is the average of all the possible revenues you can make?

46. *Revenue* Your self-published book of poetry has demand curves between $p = 80{,}000/q^2$ and $p = 100{,}000/q^2$. You expect to sell between 50 and 100 copies. What is the average of all the possible revenues you can make?

47. *Population Density* The town of West Podunk is shaped like a rectangle 20 miles from west to east and 30 miles from north to south. (See the figure.) It has a population density of $P(x, y) = e^{-0.1(x+y)}$ hundred people per square mile x miles east and y miles north of the southwest corner of town. What is the total population of the town? HINT [See Example 5.]

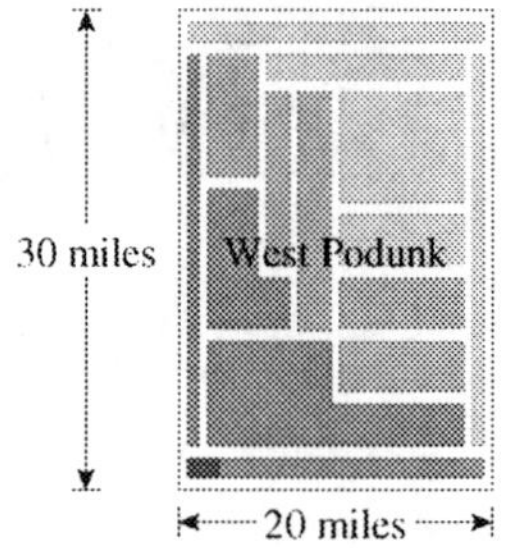

48. *Population Density* The town of East Podunk is shaped like a triangle with an east-west base of 20 miles and a north-south height of 30 miles. (See the figure.) It has a population density of $P(x, y) = e^{-0.1(x+y)}$ hundred people per square mile x miles east and y miles north of the southwest corner of town. What is the total population of the town? HINT [See Example 5.]

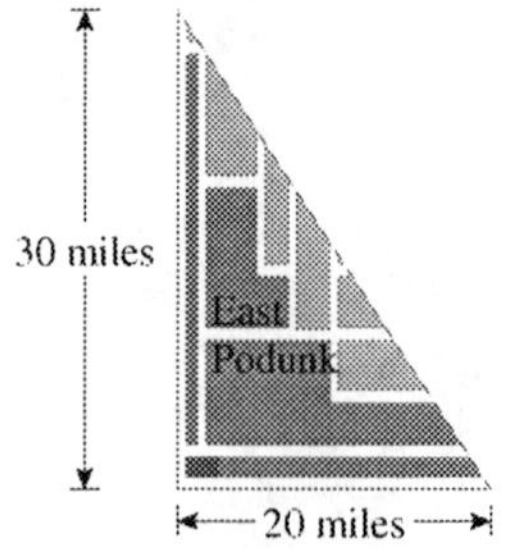

49. *Temperature* The temperature at the point (x, y) on the square with vertices (0, 0), (0, 1), (1, 0), and (1, 1) is given by $T(x, y) = x^2 + 2y^2$. Find the average temperature on the square.

50. ***Temperature*** The temperature at the point (x, y) on the square with vertices (0, 0), (0, 1), (1, 0), and (1, 1) is given by $T(x, y) = x^2 + 2y^2 - x$. Find the average temperature on the square.

COMMUNICATION AND REASONING EXERCISES

51. Explain how double integrals can be used to compute the area between two curves in the *xy* plane.

52. Explain how double integrals can be used to compute the volume of solids in 3-space.

53. Complete the following: The first step in calculating an integral of the form $\int_a^b \int_{r(x)}^{s(x)} f(x, y)\,dy\,dx$ is to evaluate the integral _____, obtained by holding ___ constant and integrating with respect to ___ .

54. If the units of $f(x, y)$ are zonars per square meter, and x and y are given in meters, what are the units of $\int_a^b \int_{r(x)}^{s(x)} f(x, y)\,dy\,dx$?

55. If the units of $\int_a^b \int_{r(x)}^{s(x)} f(x, y)\,dy\,dx$ are paintings, the units of x are picassos, and the units of y are dalis, what are the units of $f(x, y)$?

56. Complete the following: If the region R is bounded on the left and right by vertical lines and on the top and bottom by the graphs of functions of x, then we integrate over R by first integrating with respect to ____ and then with respect to ___.

57. ▼ Show that if a, b, c, and d are constant, then $\int_a^b \int_c^d f(x) g(y)\,dx\,dy = \int_c^d f(x)\,dx \int_a^b g(y)\,dy$. Test this result on the integral $\int_0^1 \int_1^2 ye^x\,dx\,dy$.

58. ▼ Refer to Exercise 57. If a, b, c, and d are constants, can $\displaystyle\int_a^b \int_c^d \frac{f(x)}{g(y)}\,dx\,dy$ be expressed as a product of two integrals? Explain.

CHAPTER 15 REVIEW

KEY CONCEPTS

WW Website www.WanerMath.com

Go to the Website at www.WanerMath.com to find a comprehensive and interactive Web-based summary of Chapter 15.

15.1 Functions of Several Variables from the Numerical, Algebraic, and Graphical Viewpoints

A real-valued function, f, of $x, y, z, \ldots$ *p. 1082*

Cost functions *p. 1083*

A linear function of the variables $x_1, x_2, \ldots, x_n$ is a function of the form $f(x_1, x_2, \ldots, x_n) = a_0 + a_1x_1 + \cdots + a_nx_n$ ($a_0, a_1, \ldots, a_n$ constants) *p. 1084*

Representing functions of two variables numerically *p. 1085*

Using a spreadsheet to represent a function of two variables *p. 1086*

Plotting points in three dimensions *p. 1086*

Graph of a function of two variables *p. 1087*

Analyzing the graph of a function of two variables *p. 1090*

Graph of a linear function *p. 1093*

15.2 Partial Derivatives

Definition of partial derivatives *p. 1101*

Application to marginal cost: linear cost function *p. 1102*

Application to marginal cost: interaction cost function *p. 1103*

Geometric interpretation of partial derivatives *p. 1104*

Second-order partial derivatives *p. 1105*

15.3 Maxima and Minima

Definition of relative maximum and minimum *p. 1111*

Locating candidates for relative maxima and minima *p. 1112*

Classifying critical points graphically *p. 1113*

Classifying critical points numerically *p. 1113*

Second derivative test for a function of two variables *p. 1113*

Using the second derivative test *p. 1114*

Formulas for Linear Regression

$$m = \frac{n\left(\sum xy\right) - \left(\sum x\right)\left(\sum y\right)}{n\left(\sum x^2\right) - \left(\sum x\right)^2}$$

$$b = \frac{\sum y - m\left(\sum x\right)}{n}$$

n = number of data points *p. 1115*

15.4 Constrained Maxima and Minima and Applications

Constrained maximum and minimum problem *p. 1119*

Solving constrained maxima and minima problems using substitution *p. 1120*

The method of Lagrange multipliers *p. 1121*

Using Lagrange multipliers *p. 1121*

15.5 Double Integrals and Applications

Geometric definition of the double integral *p. 1128*

Algebraic definition of the double integral

$$\iint_R f(x, y)\,dx\,dy = \lim_{n\to\infty} \lim_{m\to\infty} \sum_{j=1}^{n} \sum_{i=1}^{m} f(x_i, y_j)\Delta x\,\Delta y$$

p. 1129

Computing the double integral over a rectangle *p. 1130*

Computing the double integral over nonrectangular regions *p. 1131*

Average of $f(x, y)$ on the region R:

$$\bar{f} = \frac{1}{A}\iint_R f(x, y)\,dx\,dy \quad p.\ 1132$$

REVIEW EXERCISES

1. Let $f(x, y, z) = \dfrac{x}{y + xz} + x^2y$. Evaluate $f(0, 1, 1), f(2, 1, 1), f(-1, 1, -1), f(z, z, z)$, and $f(x + h, y + k, z + l)$.

2. Let $g(x, y, z) = xy(x + y - z) + x^2$. Evaluate $g(0, 0, 0), g(1, 0, 0), g(0, 1, 0), g(x, x, x)$, and $g(x, y + k, z)$.

3. Let $f(x, y, z) = 2.72 - 0.32x - 3.21y + 12.5z$. Complete the following: f___ by ___ units for every 1 unit of increase in x, and ___ by ___ units for every unit of increase in z.

4. Let $g(x, y, z) = 2.16x + 11y - 1.53z + 31.4$. Complete the following: g___ by ___ units for every 1 unit of increase in y, and ___ by ___ units for every unit of increase in z.

In Exercises 5–6 complete the given table for values for $h(x, y) = 2x^2 + xy - x$.

5.

$y \downarrow$ \ $x \rightarrow$	−1	0	1
−1			
0			
1			

6.

$y \downarrow$ \ $x \rightarrow$	−2	2	3
−2			
2			
3			

7. Give a formula for a (single) function f with the property that $f(x, y) = -f(y, x)$ and $f(1, -1) = 3$.

8. Let $f(x, y) = x^2 + (y + 1)^2$. Show that $f(y, x) = f(x + 1, y - 1)$.

Sketch the graphs of the functions in Exercises 9–14.

9. $r(x, y) = x + y$

10. $r(x, y) = x - y$

11. $t(x, y) = x^2 + 2y^2$. Show cross sections at $x = 0$ and $z = 1$.

12. $t(x, y) = \dfrac{1}{2}x^2 + y^2$. Show cross sections at $x = 0$ and $z = 1$.

13. $f(x, y) = -2\sqrt{x^2 + y^2}$. Show cross sections at $z = -4$ and $y = 1$.

14. $f(x, y) = 2 + 2\sqrt{x^2 + y^2}$. Show cross sections at $z = 4$ and $y = 1$.

In Exercises 15–20, compute the partial derivatives shown for the given function.

15. $f(x, y) = x^2 + xy$; find f_x, f_y, and f_{yy}

16. $f(x, y) = \dfrac{6}{xy} + \dfrac{xy}{6}$; find f_x, f_y, and f_{yy}

17. $f(x, y) = 4x + 5y - 6xy$; find $f_{xx}(1, 0) - f_{xx}(3, 2)$

18. $f(x, y) = e^{xy} + e^{3x^2-y^2}$; find $\dfrac{\partial f}{\partial x}$ and $\dfrac{\partial^2 f}{\partial x \partial y}$

19. $f(x, y, z) = \dfrac{x}{x^2 + y^2 + z^2}$; find $\dfrac{\partial f}{\partial x}, \dfrac{\partial f}{\partial y}, \dfrac{\partial f}{\partial z}$, and $\left.\dfrac{\partial f}{\partial x}\right|_{(0,1,0)}$.

20. $f(x, y, z) = x^2 + y^2 + z^2 + xyz$; find $f_{xx} + f_{yy} + f_{zz}$

In Exercises 21–26, locate and classify all critical points.

21. $f(x, y) = (x - 1)^2 + (2y - 3)^2$

22. $g(x, y) = (x - 1)^2 - 3y^2 + 9$

23. $k(x, y) = x^2y - x^2 - y^2$

24. $j(x, y) = xy + x^2$

25. $h(x, y) = e^{xy}$

26. $f(x, y) = \ln(x^2 + y^2) - (x^2 + y^2)$

In Exercises 27–30, solve the given constrained optimization problem by using substitution to eliminate a variable. (Do not use Lagrange multipliers.)

27. Find the largest value of xyz subject to $x + y + z = 1$ with $x > 0, y > 0, z > 0$. Also find the corresponding point(s) (x, y, z).

28. Find the minimum value of $f(x, y, z) = x^2 + y^2 + z^2 - 1$ subject to $x = y + z$. Also find the corresponding point(s) (x, y, z).

29. Find the point on the surface $z = \sqrt{x^2 + 2(y - 3)^2}$ closest to the origin.

30. Minimize $S = xy + x^2z^2 + 4yz$ subject to $xyz = 1$ with $x > 0, y > 0, z > 0$.

In Exercises 31–34, use Lagrange multipliers to solve the given optimization problem.

31. Find the minimum value of $f(x, y) = x^2 + y^2$ subject to $xy = 2$. Also find the corresponding point(s) (x, y).

32. The problem in Exercise 28.

33. The problem in Exercise 29.

34. The problem in Exercise 30.

In Exercises 35–40, compute the given quantities.

35. $\displaystyle\int_0^1 \int_0^2 (2xy)\,dx\,dy$

36. $\displaystyle\int_1^2 \int_0^1 xye^{x+y}\,dx\,dy$

37. $\displaystyle\int_0^2 \int_0^{2x} \frac{1}{x^2 + 1}\,dy\,dx$

38. The average value of xye^{x+y} over the rectangle $0 \le x \le 1$, $1 \le y \le 2$

39. $\iint_R (x^2 - y^2)\,dx\,dy$, where R is the region shown in the figure

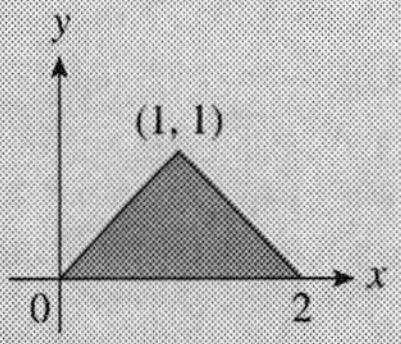

40. The volume under the graph of $z = 1 - y$ over the region in the xy plane between the parabola $y = 1 - x^2$ and the x-axis

APPLICATIONS: OHaganBooks.com

41. ***Web Site Traffic*** OHaganBooks.com has two principal competitors: JungleBooks.com and FarmerBooks.com. Current Web site traffic at OHaganBooks.com is estimated at 5,000 hits per day. This number is predicted to decrease by 0.8 for every new customer of JungleBooks.com and by 0.6 for every new customer of FarmerBooks.com.

    a. Use this information to model the daily Website traffic at OHaganBooks.com as a linear function of the new customers of its two competitors.

    b. According to the model, if Junglebooks.com gets 100 new customers and OHaganBooks.com traffic drops to 4,770 hits per day, how many new customers has FarmerBooks.com obtained?

    c. The model in part (a) did not take into account the growth of the total online consumer base. OHaganBooks .com expects to get approximately one additional hit per day for every 10,000 new Internet shoppers. Modify your model in part (a) so as to include this information using a new independent variable.

    d. How many new Internet shoppers would it take to offset the effects on traffic at OHaganBooks.com of 100 new customers at each of its competitor sites?

42. ***Productivity*** Billy-Sean O'Hagan is writing up his Ph.D. thesis in biophysics but finds that his productivity is affected by the temperature and the number of text messages he receives per hour. On a brisk winter's day when the temperature is 0°C and there are no text messages, Billy-Sean can produce 15 pages of his thesis. His productivity goes down by 0.3 pages per degree Celsius increase in the temperature and by 1.2 pages for each additional text message per hour.

    a. Use this information to model Billy-Sean's productivity p as a function of the temperature and the hourly rate of text messages.

    b. The other day the temperature was 20°C and Billy-Sean managed to produce only three pages of his thesis. What was the hourly rate of incoming text messages?

c. Billy-Sean reasons that each cup of coffee he drinks per hour can counter the effect on his productivity of two text messages per hour. Modify the model in part (a) to take consumption of coffee into account.

d. What would the domain of your function look like to ensure that p is never negative?

43. ***Internet Advertising*** To increase business at OHaganBooks.com, you have purchased banner ads at well-known Internet portals and have advertised on television. The following interaction model shows the average number h of hits per day as a function of monthly expenditures x on banner ads and y on television advertising (x and y are in dollars).

$$h(x, y) = 1{,}800 + 0.05x + 0.08y + 0.00003xy$$

a. Based on your model, how much traffic can you anticipate if you spend \$2,000 per month for banner ads and \$3,000 per month on television advertising?

b. Evaluate $\frac{\partial h}{\partial y}$, specify its units of measurement, and indicate whether it increases or decreases with increasing x.

c. How much should the company spend on banner ads to obtain 1 hit per day for each \$5 spent per month on television advertising?

44. ***Company Retreats*** Their companies having recently been bailed out by the government at taxpayer expense, Marjory Duffin and John O'Hagan are planning a joint winter business retreat in Cancun, but they are not sure how many sales reps to take along. The following interaction model shows the estimated cost C to their companies (in dollars) as a function of the number of sales reps x and the length of time t in days.

$$C(x, t) = 20{,}000 - 100x + 600t + 300xt$$

a. Based on the model, how much would it cost to take five sales reps along for a 10-day retreat?

b. Evaluate $\frac{\partial C}{\partial t}$, specify its units of measurement, and indicate whether it increases or decreases with increasing x.

c. How many reps should they take along if they wish to limit the marginal daily cost to \$1,200?

45. ***Internet Advertising*** Refer to the model in Exercise 43. One or more of the following statements is correct. Identify which one(s).

(A) If nothing is spent on television advertising, one more dollar spent per month in banner ads will buy approximately 0.05 hits per day at OHaganBooks.com.

(B) If nothing is spent on television advertising, one more hit per day at OHaganBooks.com will cost the company about 5¢ per month in banner ads.

(C) If nothing is spent on banner ads, one more hit per day at OHaganBooks.com will cost the company about 5¢ per month in banner ads.

(D) If nothing is spent on banner ads, one more dollar spent per month in banner ads will buy approximately 0.05 hits per day at OHaganBooks.com.

(E) Hits at OHaganBooks.com cost approximately 5¢ per month spent on banner ads, and this cost increases at a rate of 0.003¢ per month, per hit.

46. ***Company Retreats*** Refer to the model in Exercise 44. One or more of the following statements is correct. Identify which one(s).

(A) If the retreat lasts for 10 days, the daily cost per sales rep is \$400.

(B) If the retreat lasts for 10 days, each additional day will cost the company \$2,900.

(C) If the retreat lasts for 10 days, each additional sales rep will cost the company \$800.

(D) If the retreat lasts for 10 days, the daily cost per sales rep is \$2,900.

(E) If the retreat lasts for 10 days, each additional sales rep will cost the company \$2,900.

47. ***Productivity*** The holiday season is now at its peak and OHaganBooks.com has been understaffed and swamped with orders. The current backlog (orders unshipped for two or more days) has grown to a staggering 50,000, and new orders are coming in at a rate of 5,000 per day. Research based on productivity data at OHaganBooks.com results in the following model:

$$P(x, y) = 1{,}000x^{0.9}y^{0.1} \text{ additional orders filled per day,}$$

where x is the number of additional personnel hired and y is the daily budget (excluding salaries) allocated to eliminating the backlog.

a. How many additional orders will be filled per day if the company hires 10 additional employees and budgets an additional \$1,000 per day? (Round the answer to the nearest 100.)

b. In addition to the daily budget, extra staffing costs the company \$150 per day for every new staff member hired. In order to fill at least 15,000 additional orders per day at a minimum total daily cost, how many new staff members should the company hire? (Use the method of Lagrange multipliers.)

48. ***Productivity*** The holiday season has now ended, and orders at OHaganBooks.com have plummeted, leaving staff members in the shipping department with little to do besides spend their time on their Facebook pages, so the company is considering laying off a number of personnel and slashing the shipping budget. Research based on productivity data at OHaganBooks.com results in the following model:

$$C(x, y) = 1{,}000x^{0.8}y^{0.2} \text{ fewer orders filled per day,}$$

where x is the number of personnel laid off and y is the cut in the shipping budget (excluding salaries).

a. How many fewer orders will be filled per day if the company lays off 15 additional employees and cuts the budget by an additional \$2,000 per day? (Round the answer to the nearest 100.)

b. In addition to the cut in the shipping budget, the layoffs will save the company \$200 per day for every new staff member laid off. The company needs to meet a target of 20,000 fewer orders per day but, for tax reasons, it must minimize the total resulting savings. How many new staff members should the company lay off? (Use the method of Lagrange multipliers.)

49. ***Profit*** If OHaganBooks.com sells x paperback books and y hardcover books per week, it will make an average weekly profit of

$$P(x, y) = 3x + 10y \text{ dollars.}$$

If it sells between 1,200 and 1,500 paperback books and between 1,800 and 2,000 hardcover books per week, what is the average of all its possible weekly profits?

50. ***Cost*** It costs Duffin House

$$C(x, y) = x^2 + 2y \text{ dollars}$$

to produce x coffee table art books and y paperback books per week. If it produces between 100 and 120 art books and between 800 and 1,000 paperbacks per week, what is the average of all its possible weekly costs?

david pearson/Alamy

Modeling College Population

College Malls, Inc. is planning to build a national chain of shopping malls in college neighborhoods. However, malls in general have been experiencing large numbers of store closings due to, among other things, misjudgments of the shopper demographics. As a result, the company is planning to lease only to stores that target the specific age demographics of the national college student population.

As a marketing consultant to College Malls, you will be providing the company with a report that addresses the following specific issues:

- A quick way of estimating the number of students of any specified age and in any particular year, and the effect of increasing age on the college population
- The ages that correspond to relatively high and low college populations
- How fast the 20-year old and 25-year old student populations are increasing
- Some near-term projections of the student population trend

You decide that a good place to start would be with a visit to the Census Bureau's Web site at www.census.gov. After some time battling with search engines, all you can find is some data on college enrollment for three age brackets for the period 1980–2009, as shown in the following table:[29]

College Enrollment (Thousands)

Year	1980	1985	1990	1995	2000	2001	2002	2003	2004	2005	2006	2007	2008	2009
18–24	7,229	7,537	7,964	8,541	9,451	9,629	10,033	10,365	10,611	10,834	10,587	11,161	11,466	12,072
25–34	2,703	3,063	3,161	3,349	3,207	3,422	3,401	3,494	3,690	3,600	3,658	3,838	4,013	6,141
35–44	700	963	1,344	1,548	1,454	1,557	1,678	1,526	1,615	1,657	1,548	1,520	1,672	1,848

The data are inadequate for several reasons: The data are given only for certain years, and in age brackets rather than year-by-year; nor is it obvious as to how you would project the figures. However, you notice that the table is actually a numerical representation of a function of two variables: year and age. Since the age brackets are of different sizes, you "normalize" the data by dividing each figure by the number of years represented in the corresponding age bracket; for instance, you divide the 1980 figure for the first age group by 7 in order to obtain the average enrollment for each year of age in that group. You then rewrite the resulting table representing the years by values of t and each age bracket by the (rounded) age x at its center (enrollment values are rounded):

[29]Source: Census Bureau (www.census.gov/population/www/socdemo/school.html).

$t \rightarrow$

$x \downarrow$	0	5	10	15	20	21	22	23	24	25	26	27	28	29
21	1,033	1,077	1,138	1,220	1,350	1,376	1,433	1,481	1,516	1,548	1,512	1,594	1,638	1,725
30	270	306	316	335	321	342	340	349	369	360	366	384	401	614
40	70	96	134	155	145	156	168	153	162	166	155	152	167	185

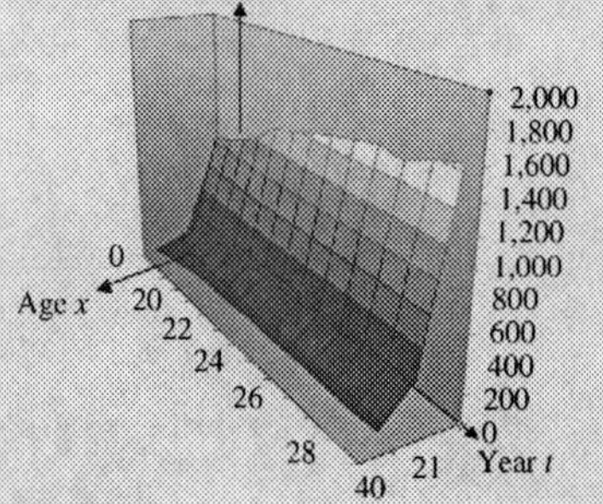

Figure 40

In order to see a visual representation of what the data are saying, you use Excel to graph the data as a surface (Figure 40). It is important to notice that Excel does not scale the t-axis as you would expect: It uses one subdivision for each year shown in the chart, and the result is an uneven scaling of the t-axis. Despite this drawback, you do see two trends after looking at views of the graph from various angles. First, enrollment of 21-year olds (the back edge of the graph) seems to be increasing faster than enrollment of other age groups. Second, the enrollment for all ages seem to be increasing approximately linearly with time, although at different rates for different age groups; for instance, the front and rear edges rise more-or-less linearly, but do not seem to be parallel.

At this point you realize that a mathematical model of these data would be useful; not only would it "smooth out the bumps" but it would give you a way to estimate enrollment N at each specific age, project the enrollments, and thereby complete the project for College Malls. Although technology can give you a regression model for data such as this, it is up to you to decide on the form of the model. It is in choosing an appropriate model that your analysis of the graph comes in handy. Because N should vary linearly with time t for each value of x, you would like

$$N = mt + k$$

for each value of x. Also, because there are three values of x for every value of time, you try a quadratic model for N as a function of x:

$$N = a + bx + cx^2.$$

Putting these together, you get the following candidate model:

$$N(t, x) = a_1 + a_2t + a_3x + a_4x^2,$$

where a_1, a_2, a_3, and a_4 are constants. However, for each specific age $x = k$, you get

$$N(t, k) = a_1 + a_2t + a_3k + a_4k^2 = \text{Constant} + a_2t$$

with the same slope a_2 for every choice of the age k, contrary to your observation that enrollment for different age groups is rising at different rates, so you will need a more elaborate model. You recall from your applied calculus course that interaction functions give a way to model the effect of one variable on the rate of change of another, so, as an experiment, you try adding interaction terms to your model:

Model 1: $N(t, x) = a_1 + a_2t + a_3x + a_4x^2 + a_5xt$ Second-order model

Model 2: $N(t, x) = a_1 + a_2t + a_3x + a_4x^2 + a_5xt + a_6x^2t.$ Third-order model

(Model 1 is referred to as a second-order model because it contains no products of more than two independent variables, whereas Model 2 contains the third-order term $x^2t = x \cdot x \cdot t$.) If you study these two models for specific values k of x you get:

Model 1: $N = \text{Constant} + (a_2 + a_5k)t$ Slope depends linearly on age.

Model 2: $N = \text{Constant} + (a_2 + a_5k + a_6k^2)t.$ Slope depends quadratically on age.

This is encouraging: Both models show different slopes for different ages. Model 1 would predict that the slope either increases with increasing age (a_5 positive) or decreases with increasing age (a_5 negative). However, the graph suggests that the slope is larger for both younger and older students, but smaller for students of intermediate age, contrary to what Model 1 predicts, so you decide to go with the more flexible Model 2, which permits the slope to decrease and then increase with increasing age, which is exactly what you observe on the graph, and so you decide to go ahead with Model 2.

You decide to use Excel to generate your model. However, the data as shown in the table are not in a form Excel can use for regression; the data need to be organized into columns; Column A for the dependent variable N and Columns B–C for the independent variables, as shown in Figure 41.

	A	B	C
1	*N*	*t*	*x*
2	1033	0	21
3	1077	5	21
4	1138	10	21
5	1220	15	21
6	1350	20	21
7	1376	21	21
8	1433	22	21
9	1481	23	21
10	1516	24	21
11	1548	25	21
12	1512	26	21
13	1594	27	21
14	1638	28	21
15	1725	29	21
16	270	0	30
17	306	5	30
18	316	10	30
19	335	15	30
20	321	20	30
21	342	21	30
22	340	22	30
23	349	23	30
24	369	24	30
25	360	25	30
26	366	26	30
27	384	27	30
28	401	28	30
29	614	29	30
30	70	0	40
31	96	5	40
32	134	10	40
33	155	15	40
34	145	20	40
35	156	21	40
36	168	22	40
37	153	23	40
38	162	24	40
39	166	25	40
40	155	26	40
41	152	27	40
42	167	28	40
43	185	29	40

Figure 41

You then add columns for the higher order terms x^2, xt, and x^2t as shown below:

	A	B	C	D	E	F
1	*N*	*t*	*x*	*x*^2	*x***t*	*x*^2**t*
2	1033	0	21	=C2^2	=C2*B2	=C2^2*B2
3	1077	5	21			
4	1138	10	21			
5	1220	15	21			
6	1350	20	21			
7	1376	21	21			
8	1433	22	21			
9	1481	23	21			

Figure 42

	A	B	C	D	E	F
1	*N*	*t*	*x*	*x*^2	*x***t*	*x*^2**t*
2	1033	0	21	441	0	0
3	1077	5	21	441	105	2205
4	1138	10	21	441	210	4410
5	1220	15	21	441	315	6615
6	1350	20	21	441	420	8820
7	1376	21	21	441	441	9261
8	1433	22	21	441	462	9702
9	1481	23	21	441	483	10143

Figure 43

Next, highlight a vacant 5 × 6 block (the block A46:F50 say), type the formula `=LINEST(A2:A43,B2:F43,,TRUE)`, and press Ctrl+Shift+Enter (not just Enter!). You will see a table of statistics like the following:

43	185	29	40	1600	1160	46400
44						
45						
46	=LINEST(A2:A43,B2:F43,,TRUE)					
47						
48						
49						
50						

Figure 44

43	185	29	40	1600	1160	46400
44						
45						
46	0.088570354	-6.46546922	3.21423521	-241.273271	120.009278	4594.62978
47	0.02096866	1.28767845	0.44955302	27.6069027	18.6958148	400.824866
48	0.99337478	49.506512	#N/A	#N/A	#N/A	#N/A
49	1079.5571	36	#N/A	#N/A	#N/A	#N/A
50	13229404.1	88232.2104	#N/A	#N/A	#N/A	#N/A

Figure 45

The desired constants $a_1, a_2, a_3, a_4, a_5, a_6$ appear in the first row of the data, but in *reverse order*. Thus, if we round to 5 significant digits, we have

$$a_1 = 4{,}594.6 \quad a_2 = 120.01 \quad a_3 = -241.27$$
$$a_4 = 3.2142 \quad a_5 = -6.4655 \quad a_6 = 0.088570,$$

which gives our regression model:

$$N(t, x) = 4{,}594.6 + 120.01t - 241.27x + 3.2142x^2 - 6.4655xt + 0.088570x^2t.$$

Fine, you say to yourself, now you have the model, but how good a fit is it to the data? That is where rest of the data shown in the output comes in: In the second row are the "standard errors" corresponding to the corresponding coefficients. Notice that each of the standard errors is small compared with the magnitude of the coefficient above it; for instance, 0.021 is only around 1/4 of the magnitude of $a_6 \approx 0.088$ and indicates that the dependence of N on x^2t is statistically significant. (What we do not want to see are standard errors of magnitudes comparable to the coefficients, as those could indicate the wrong choice of independent variables.) The third figure in the left column, 0.99337478, is R^2, where R generalizes the coefficient of correlation discussed in the section on regression in Chapter 1: The closer R is to 1, the better the fit. We can interpret R^2 as indicating that approximately 99.3% of the variation in college enrollment is explained by the regression model, indicating an excellent fit. The figure 1,079.5571 beneath R^2 is called the "F-statistic." The higher the F-statistic (typically, anything above 4 or so would be considered "high"), the more confident we can be that N does depend on the independent variables we are using.*

* We are being deliberately vague about the exact meaning of these statistics, which are discussed fully in many applied statistics texts.

As comforting as these statistics are, nothing can be quite as persuasive as a graph. You turn to the graphing software of your choice and notice that the graph of the model appears to be a faithful representation of the data. (See Figure 46.)

Now you get to work, using the model to address the questions posed by College Malls.

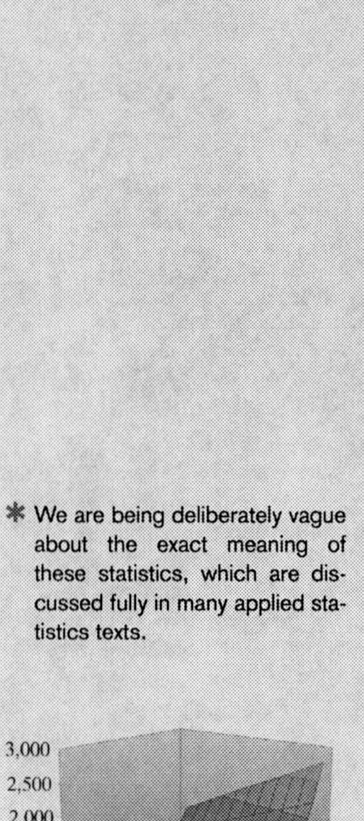

Figure 46

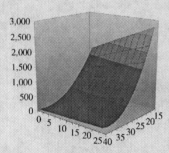

1. *A quick way of estimating the number of students of any specified age and in any particular year, and the effect of increasing age on the college population.* You already have a quantitative relationship in the form of the regression model. As for the second part of the question, the rate of change of college enrollment with respect to age is given by the partial derivative:

$$\frac{\partial N}{\partial x} = -241.27 + 6.4284x - 6.4655t + 0.17714xt \text{ thousand students per additional year of age.}$$

Thus, for example, with $x = 20$ in 2004 ($t = 24$), we have

$$\frac{\partial N}{\partial x} = -241.27 + 6.4284(20) - 6.4655(24) + 0.17714(20)(24)$$
$$\approx -183 \text{ thousand students per additional year of age,}$$

so there were about 183,000 fewer students of age 21 than age 20 in 2004.

On the other hand, when $x = 38$ in the same year, we have

$$\frac{\partial N}{\partial x} = -241.27 + 6.4284(38) - 6.4655(24) + 0.17714(38)(24)$$
$$\approx 9.4 \text{ thousand students per additional year of age,}$$

so there were about 9,400 more students of age 39 than age 38 that year.

2. *The ages that correspond to relatively high and low college populations.* Although a glance at the graph shows you that there are no relative maxima, holding t constant (that is, on any given year) gives a parabola along the corresponding slice and hence a minimum somewhere along the slice.

$$\frac{\partial N}{\partial x} = 0$$

when $$-241.27 + 6.4284x - 6.4655t + 0.17714xt = 0,$$

which gives $x = \dfrac{241.27 + 6.4655t}{6.4284 + 0.17714t}$ years of age

For instance, in 2010 ($t = 30$; we are extrapolating the model slightly), the age at which there were fewest students (in the given range) is 37 years of age. The relative maxima for each slice occur at the front and back edges of the surface, meaning that there are relatively more students of the lowest and highest ages represented. The absolute maximum for each slice occurs, as expected, at the lowest age. In short, a mall catering to college students in 2010 should have focused mostly on freshman age students, least on 37-year-olds, and somewhat more on people around age 40.

3. *How fast the 20-year-old and 25-year-old student populations are increasing.* The rate of change of student population with respect to time is

$$\frac{\partial N}{\partial t} = 120.01 - 6.4655x + 0.088570x^2 \text{ thousand students per year.}$$

For the two age groups in question, we obtain

$$x = 20\text{: } 120.01 - 6.4655(20) + 0.088570(20)^2 \approx 26.1 \text{ thousand students/year}$$

$$x = 25\text{: } 120.01 - 6.4655(25) + 0.088570(25)^2 \approx 13.7 \text{ thousand students/year.}$$

(Note that these rates of change are independent of time as we chose a model that is linear in time.)

4. *Some near-term projections of the student population trend.* As we have seen throughout the book, extrapolation can be a risky venture; however, near-term extrapolation from a good model can be reasonable. You enter the model in an Excel spreadsheet to obtain the following predicted college enrollments (in thousands) for the years 2010–2015:

$t \rightarrow$

$x \downarrow$	30	31	32	33	34	35
21	1,644	1,668	1,691	1,714	1,737	1,761
30	422	428	434	439	445	451
40	180	183	186	189	192	195

EXERCISES

1. Use a spreadsheet to obtain Model 1:

$$N(t, x) = a_1 + a_2t + a_3x + a_4x^2 + a_5xt.$$

Compare the fit of this model with that of the quadratic model above. Comment on the result.

2. Obtain Model 2 using only the data through 2005, and also obtain the projections for 2010–2015 using the resulting model. Compare the projections with those based on the more complete set of data in the text.

3. Compute and interpret $\left.\frac{\partial N}{\partial t}\right|_{(10,18)}$ and $\left.\frac{\partial^2 N}{\partial t \partial x}\right|_{(10,18)}$ for the model in the text. What are their units of measurement?

4. Notice that the derivatives in the preceding exercise do not depend on time. What additional polynomial term(s) would make both $\partial N/\partial t$ and $\partial^2 N/\partial t \partial x$ depend on time? (Write down the entire model.) Of what order is your model?

5. Test the model you constructed in the preceding question by inspecting the standard errors associated with the additional coefficients.

TI-83/84 Plus Technology Guide

Section 15.1

Example 1 (page 1083) You own a company that makes two models of speakers: the Ultra Mini and the Big Stack. Your total monthly cost (in dollars) to make x Ultra Minis and y Big Stacks is given by

$$C(x, y) = 10{,}000 + 20x + 40y.$$

Compute several values of this function.

Solution with Technology

You can have a TI-83/84 Plus compute $C(x, y)$ numerically as follows:

1. In the "Y=" screen, enter

Y_1=10000+20X+40Y

2. To evaluate, say, $C(10, 30)$ (the cost to make 10 Ultra Minis and 30 Big Stacks), enter

10→X
30→Y
Y_1

```
10→X
                10
30→Y
                30
Y1
             11400
```

and the calculator will evaluate the function and give the answer $C(10, 30) = 11{,}400$.

This procedure is too laborious if you want to calculate $f(x, y)$ for a large number of different values of x and y.

SPREADSHEET Technology Guide

Section 15.1

Example 1 (page 1083) You own a company that makes two models of speakers: the Ultra Mini and the Big Stack. Your total monthly cost (in dollars) to make x Ultra Minis and y Big Stacks is given by

$$C(x, y) = 10{,}000 + 20x + 40y.$$

Compute several values of this function.

Solution with Technology

Spreadsheets handle functions of several variables easily. The following setup shows how a table of values of C can be created, using values of x and y you enter:

	A	B	C
1	x	y	C(x, y)
2	10	30	=10000+20*A2+40*B2
3	20	30	
4	15	0	
5	0	30	
6	30	30	

↓

	A	B	C
1	x	y	C(x, y)
2	10	30	11400
3	20	30	11600
4	15	0	10300
5	0	30	11200
6	30	30	11800

A disadvantage of this layout is that it's not easy to enter values of x and y systematically in two columns. Can you find a way to remedy this? (See Example 3 for one method.)

Example 3 (page 1085) Use technology to create a table of values of the body mass index

$$M(w, h) = \frac{0.45w}{(0.0254h)^2}.$$

Solution with Technology

We can use this formula to recreate a table in a spreadsheet, as follows:

	A	B	C	D
1		130	140	150
2	60	=0.45*B$1/(0.0254*$A2)^2		
3	61			
4	62			
5	63			
6	64			
7	65			
8	66			
9	67			

In the formula in cell B2 we have used B$1 instead of B1 for the w-coordinate because we want all references to w to use the same row (1). Similarly, we want all references to h to refer to the same column (A), so we used $A2 instead of A2.

We copy the formula in cell B2 to all of the red shaded area to obtain the desired table:

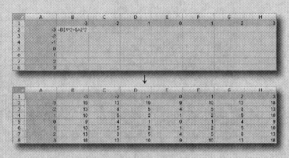

	A	B	C	D	
1		130	140	150	
2	60	25.18755038	27.12505425	29.06255813	3
3	61	24.36849808	26.24299793	28.11749778	29.9
4	62	23.58875685	25.40327661	27.21779637	29.0
5	63	22.84585068	24.60322381	26.36059694	28.1
6	64	22.13749545	23.84037971	25.54326398	27.2
7	65	21.46158138	23.11247226	24.76336314	26.4
8	66	20.81615733	22.41740021	24.01864308	25.6
9	67	20.19941665	21.75321793	23.30701921	24.8

Example 5 (page 1088) Obtain the graph of $f(x, y) = x^2 + y^2$.

Solution with Technology

1. Set up a table showing a range of values of x and y and the corresponding values of the function (see Example 3):

	A	B	C	D	E	F	G	H
1		-3	-2	-1	0	1	2	3
2	-3	=B1^2+A2^2						
3	-2							
4	-1							
5	0							
6	1							
7	2							
8	3							

↓

	A	B	C	D	E	F	G	H
1		-3	-2	-1	0	1	2	3
2	-3	18	13	10	9	10	13	18
3	-2	13	8	5	4	5	8	13
4	-1	10	5	2	1	2	5	10
5	0	9	4	1	0	1	4	9
6	1	10	5	2	1	2	5	10
7	2	13	8	5	4	5	8	13
8	3	18	13	10	9	10	13	18

2. Select the cells with the values (B2: H8) and insert a chart, with the "Surface" option selected and "Series in Columns" selected as the data option, to obtain a graph like the following:

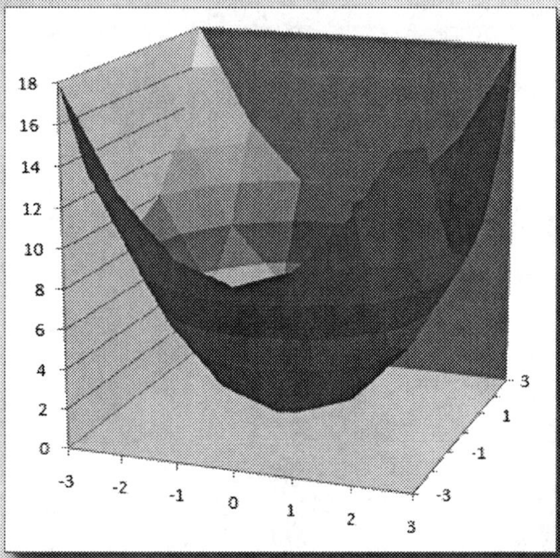

Answers to Selected Exercises

Chapter 2

Section 2.1

1. $INT = \$120$, $FV = \$2{,}120$
3. $INT = \$505$, $FV = \$20{,}705$
5. $INT = \$250$, $FV = \$10{,}250$ **7.** $PV = \$9{,}090.91$
9. $PV = \$966.18$ **11.** $PV = \$14{,}457.83$ **13.** \$5,200
15. \$787.40 **17.** 5% **19.** About 0.2503%
21. In 2 years **23.** 3.775% **25.** 65% **27.** 10%
29. 86.957% **31.** 48.04% **33.** 58.96% if you had sold in November 2010 **35.** No. Simple interest increase is linear. The graph is visibly not linear in that time period. Further, the slopes of the lines through the successive pairs of marked points are quite different. **37.** 9.2%
39. 3,260,000 **41.** $P = 500 + 46t$ thousand (t = time in years since 1950)

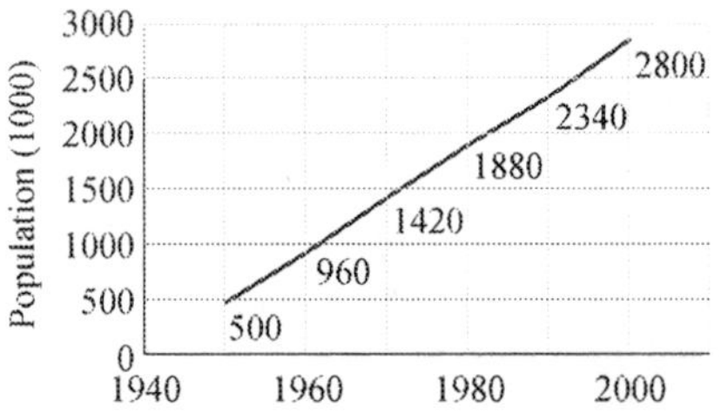

43. Graph (A) is the only possible choice, because the equation $FV = PV(1 + rt) = PV + PVrt$ gives the future value as a linear function of time. **45.** Wrong. In simple interest growth, the change each year is a fixed percentage of the *starting* value, and not the preceding year's value. (Also see Exercise 46.)
47. Simple interest is always calculated on a constant amount, PV. If interest is paid into your account, then the amount on which interest is calculated does not remain constant.

Section 2.2

1. \$13,439.16 **3.** \$11,327.08 **5.** \$19,154.30
7. \$12,709.44 **9.** \$613.91 **11.** \$810.65
13. \$1,227.74 **15.** 5.09% **17.** 10.47% **19.** 10.52%
21. \$268.99 **23.** \$728.91 **25.** \$2,927.15
27. \$21,161.79 **29.** \$163,414.56
31. \$55,526.45 per year **33.** \$174,110 **35.** \$750.00
37. \$27,171.92 **39.** \$111,678.96 **41.** \$1,039.21
43. The one earning 11.9% compounded monthly
45. Yes. The investment will have grown to about \$394,020 million. **47.** 136 reals **49.** 245 bolivianos
51. 223 bolivars **53.** The Nicaragua investment is better: It is worth about 1.006 units of currency (in constant units) per unit invested as opposed to about 1.003 units for Mexico. **55.** 53.81%
57. 65.99% if you had sold in November 2010
59. No. Compound interest increase is exponential, and exponential curves either increase continually (in the case of appreciation) or decrease continually (in the case of depreciation). The graph of the stock price has both increases and decreases during the given period, so the curve cannot model compound interest change. **61.** 31 years; about \$26,100 **63.** 2.3 years
65. a. \$1,510.31 **b.** \$54,701.29 **c.** 23.51%
67. The function $y = P(1 + r/m)^{mx}$ is not a linear function of x, but an exponential function. Thus, its graph is not a straight line. **69.** Wrong. Its growth is exponential and can be modeled by $0.01(1.10)^t$.
71. The graphs are the same because the formulas give the same function of x; a compound interest investment behaves as though it was being compounded once a year at the effective rate.
73. The effective rate exceeds the nominal rate when the interest is compounded more than once a year because then interest is being paid on interest accumulated during each year, resulting in a larger effective rate. Conversely, if the interest is compounded less often than once a year, the effective rate is less than the nominal rate. **75.** Compare their future values in constant dollars. The investment with the larger future value is the better investment. **77.** The graphs are approaching a particular curve as m gets larger, approximately the curve given by the largest two values of m.

Section 2.3

1. \$15,528.23 **3.** \$171,793.82 **5.** \$23,763.28
7. \$147.05 **9.** \$491.12 **11.** \$105.38 **13.** \$90,155.46
15. \$69,610.99 **17.** \$95,647.68 **19.** \$554.60
21. \$1,366.41 **23.** \$524.14 **25.** \$248.85
27. \$1,984.65 **29.** \$999.61 **31.** \$998.47
33. \$917.45 **35.** 3.617% **37.** 3.059% **39.** 6.038%
41. You should take the loan from Solid Savings & Loan: It will have payments of \$248.85 per month. The payments on the other loan would be more than \$300 per month. **43.** \$973.54 **45.** \$7,451.49

47. Answers using correctly rounded intermediate results:

Year	Interest	Payment on Principal
1	$3,934.98	$1,798.98
2	$3,785.69	$1,948.27
3	$3,623.97	$2,109.99
4	$3,448.84	$2,285.12
5	$3,259.19	$2,474.77
6	$3,053.77	$2,680.19
7	$2,831.32	$2,902.64
8	$2,590.39	$3,143.57
9	$2,329.48	$3,404.48
10	$2,046.91	$3,687.05
11	$1,740.88	$3,993.08
12	$1,409.47	$4,324.49
13	$1,050.54	$4,683.42
14	$661.81	$5,072.15
15	$240.84	$5,491.80

49. 1st 5 years: $402.62/month; last 25 years: $601.73 **51.** Original monthly payments were $824.79. The new monthly payments will be $613.46. You will save $36,481.77 in interest. **53.** 10.81% **55.** 13 years **57.** 4.5 years **59.** 24 years **61.** He is wrong because his estimate ignores the interest that will be earned by your annuity—both while it is increasing and while it is decreasing. Your payments will be considerably smaller (depending on the interest earned). **63.** He is not correct. For instance, the payments on a $100,000 10-year mortgage at 12% are $1,434.71, while for a 20-year mortgage at the same rate, they are $1,101.09, which is a lot more than half the 10-year mortgage payment. **65.** $PV = FV(1 + i)^{-n} =$

$$PMT\frac{(1 + i)^n - 1}{i}(1 + i)^{-n} = PMT\frac{1 - (1 + i)^{-n}}{i}$$

Chapter 2 Review

1. $7,425.00 **3.** $7,604.88 **5.** $6,757.41 **7.** $4,848.48 **9.** $4,733.80 **11.** $5,331.37 **13.** $177.58 **15.** $112.54 **17.** $187.57 **19.** $9,584.17 **21.** 5.346% **23.** 14.0 years **25.** 10.8 years **27.** 7.0 years **29.** 168.85% **31.** 85.28% if she sold in February 2010. **33.** No. Simple interest increase is linear. We can compare slopes between successive points to see if the slope remained roughly constant: From December 2002 to August 2004 the slope was $(16.31 - 3.28)/(20/12) = 7.818$ while from August 2004 to March 2005 the slope was $(33.95 - 16.31)/(7/12) = 30.24$. These slopes are quite different. **35.** 2003

Year	2000	2001	2002	2003	2004
Revenue	$180,000	$216,000	$259,200	$311,040	$373,248

37. At least 52,515 shares **39.** $3,234.94 **41.** $231,844 **43.** 7.75% **45.** $420,275 **47.** $140,778 **49.** $1,453.06 **51.** $2,239.90 per month **53.** $53,055.66 **55.** 5.99%

Chapter 5

Section 5.1

1.

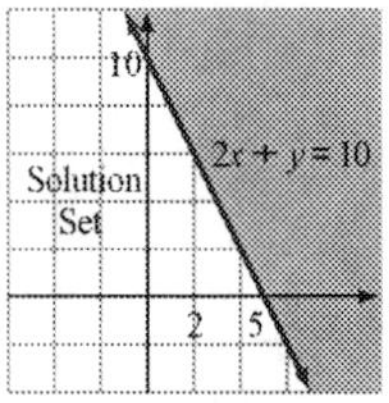

Unbounded

3.

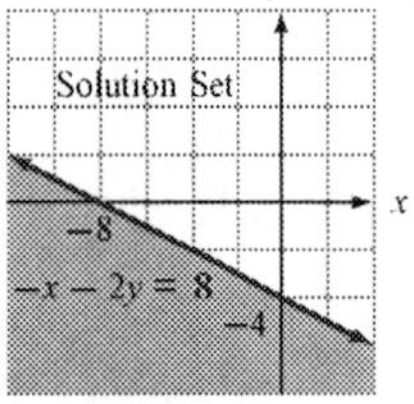

Unbounded

5.

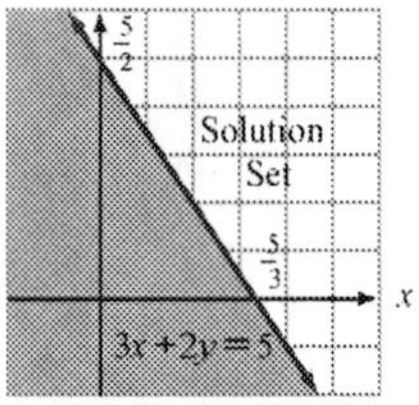

Unbounded

7.

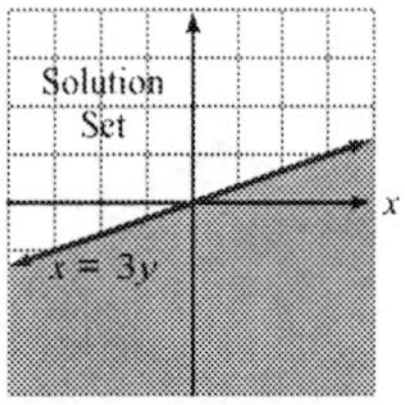

Unbounded

9.

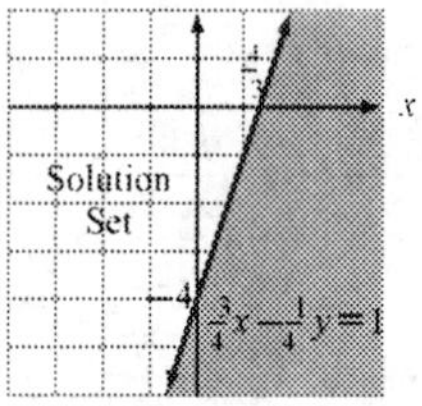

Unbounded

11.

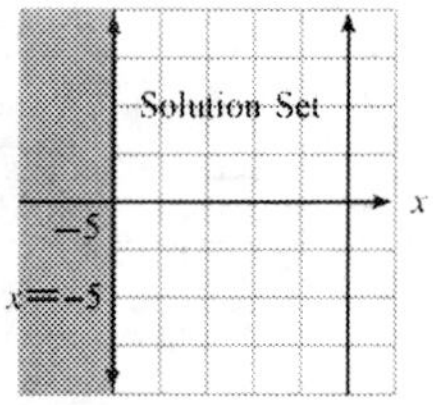

Unbounded

13.

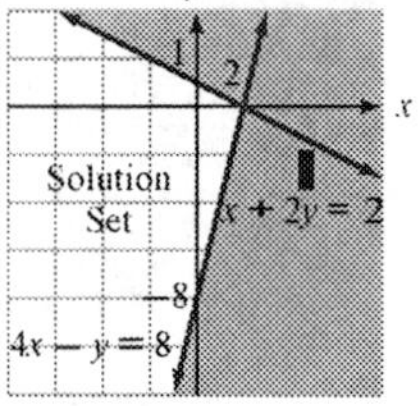

Unbounded; corner point: (2, 0)

15.

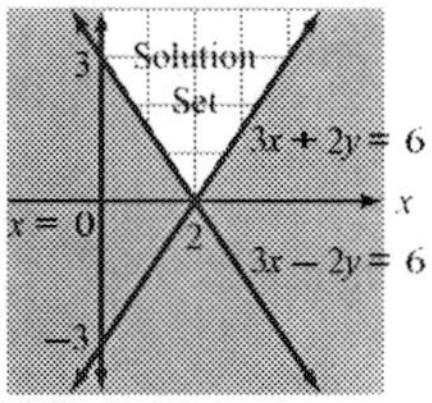

Unbounded; corner points: (2, 0), (0, 3)

17.

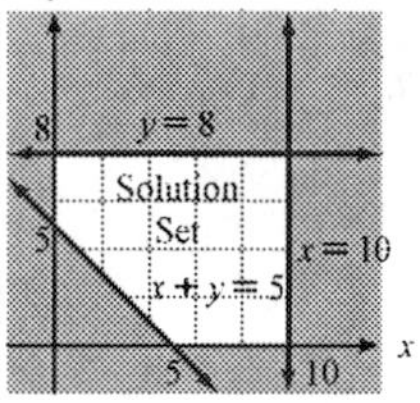

Bounded; corner points: (5, 0), (10, 0), (10, 8), (0, 8), (0, 5)

19.

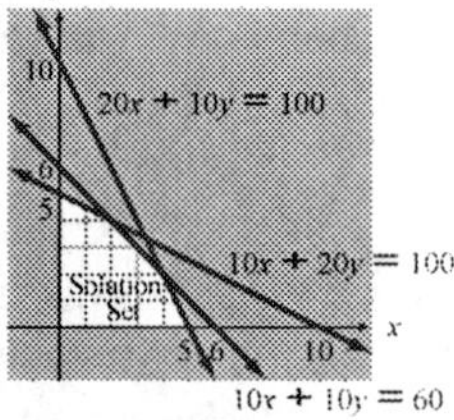

Bounded; corner points: (0, 0), (5, 0), (0, 5), (2, 4), (4, 2)

21.

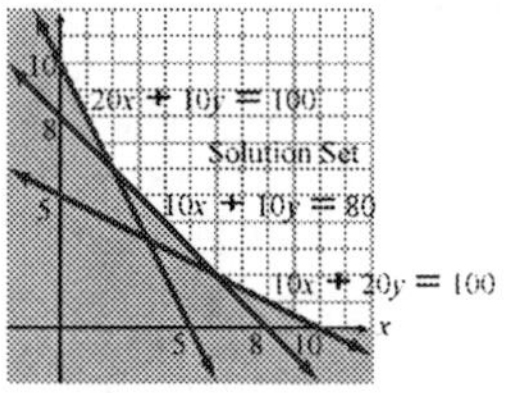

Unbounded; corner points: (0, 10), (10, 0), (2, 6), (6, 2)

23.

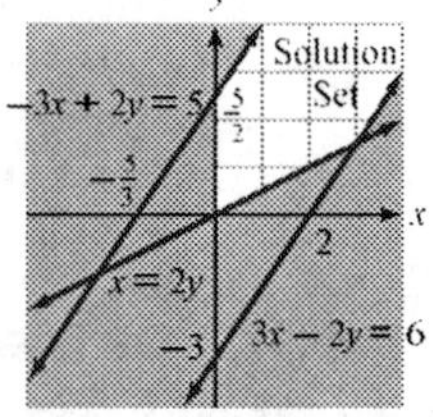

Unbounded; corner points:(0, 0), (0, 5/2), (3, 3/2)

25.

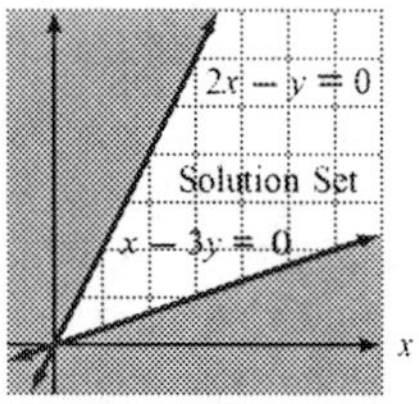

Unbounded; corner point: (0, 0)

27.

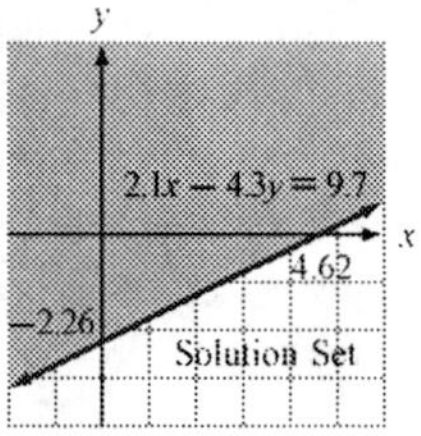

29.

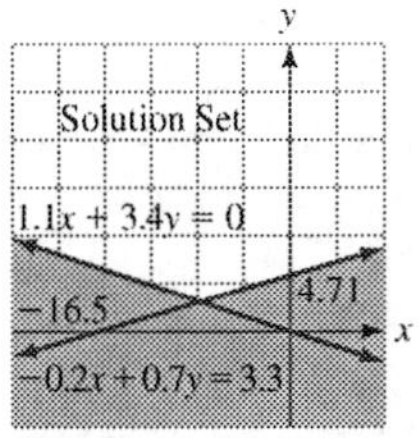

Corner point:
(−7.74, 2.50)

31.

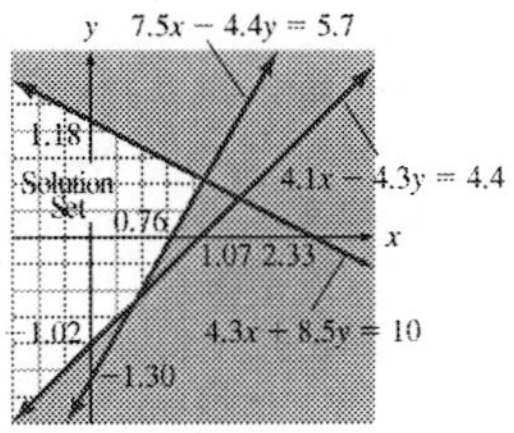

Corner points:
(0.36, −0.68), (1.12, 0.61)

33. x = # quarts of Creamy Vanilla,
y = # quarts of Continental Mocha

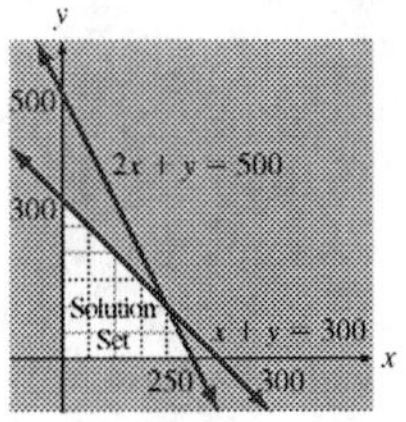

Corner points: (0, 0), (250, 0), (0, 300), (200, 100)

35. x = # ounces of chicken, y = # ounces of grain

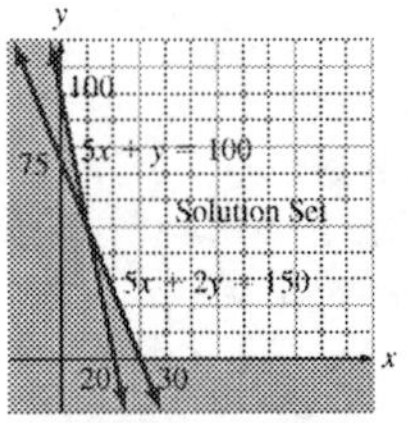

Corner points: (30, 0), (10, 50), (0, 100)

37. x = # servings of Mixed Cereal for Baby,
y = # servings of Mango Tropical Fruit Dessert

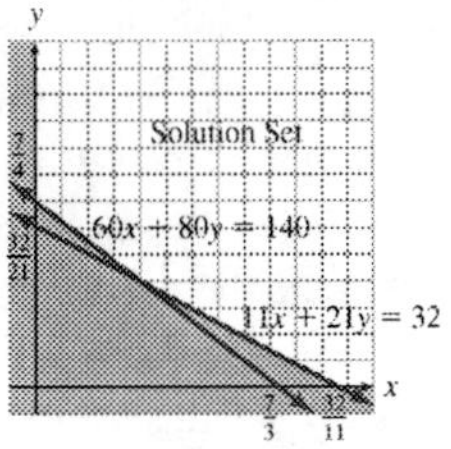

Corner points: (0, 7/4), (1, 1), (32/11, 0)

39. x = # dollars in PNF, y = # dollars in FDMMX.

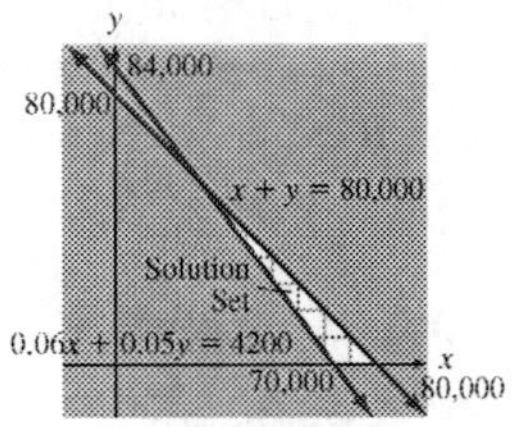

Corner points: (70,000, 0), (80,000, 0), (20,000, 60,000)

41. Let x = number of shares of BOH; y = number of shares of JPM.

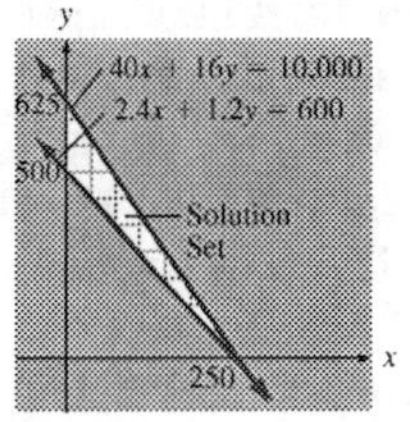

Corner points: (200, 400), (556, 0), (422, 0)

43. x = # full-page ads in Sports Illustrated,
y = # full-page ads in GQ

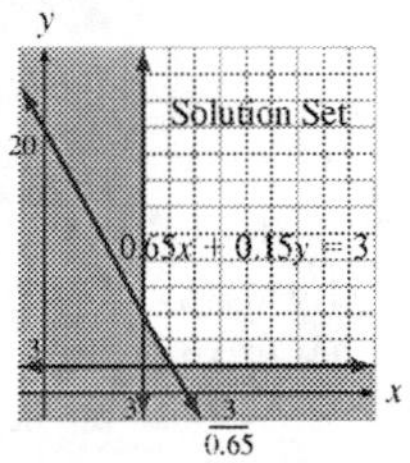

Corner points: (3, 7), (4, 3) (Rounded)

45. An example is $x \geq 0$, $y \geq 0$, $x + y \geq 1$.
47. The given triangle can be described as the solution set of the system $x \geq 0$, $y \geq 0$, $x + 2y \leq 2$.
49. Answers may vary. One limitation is that the method is only suitable for situations with two unknown quantities. Accuracy is also limited when graphing. **51. (C)** **53. (B)** **55.** There are no feasible solutions; that is, it is impossible to satisfy all the constraints. **57.** Answers will vary.

Section 5.2

1. $p = 6, x = 3, y = 3$ **3.** $c = 4, x = 2, y = 2$
5. $p = 24, x = 7, y = 3$ **7.** $p = 16, x = 4, y = 2$
9. $c = 1.8, x = 6, y = 2$ **11.** Max: $p = 16, x = 4, y = 6$. Min: $p = 2, x = 2, y = 0$ **13.** No optimal solution; objective function unbounded **15.** $c = 28$; $(x, y) = (14, 0)$ and $(6, 4)$ and the line connecting them **17.** $c = 3, x = 3, y = 2$ **19.** No solution; feasible region empty **21.** You should make 200 quarts of vanilla and 100 quarts of mocha. **23.** Ruff, Inc., should use 100 oz of grain and no chicken.
25. Feed your child 1 serving of cereal and 1 serving of dessert. **27.** Purchase 60 compact fluorescent light bulbs and 960 square feet of insulation for a saving of \$312 per year in energy costs. **29.** Mix 5 servings of Cell-Tech and 6 servings of RiboForce HP for a cost of \$20.60. **31.** Make 200 Dracula Salamis and 400 Frankenstein Sausages, for a profit of \$1,400.
33. 30 spots on *WWE Raw* and 30 spots on *Family Guy* **35.** 88.89 shares of FDX and 100 shares of WU

37. 422.2 shares of BOH and no shares of JPM **39.** He should instruct in diplomacy for 10 hours per week and in battle for 40 hours per week, giving a weekly profit of 2,400 ducats. **41.** Gillian could expend a minimum of 360,000 pico-shirleys of energy by using 480 sleep spells and 160 shock spells. (There is actually a whole line of solutions joining the one above with $x = 2{,}880/7$, $y = 1{,}440/7$.) **43.** 100 hours per week for new customers and 60 hours per week for old customers. **45. (A)** **47.** Every point along the line connecting them is also an optimal solution. **49.** Answers may vary. Maximize $p = x + y$ subject to $x + y \le 10$; $x + y \ge 11$, $x \ge 0$, $y \ge 0$. **51.** Answers may vary. **53.** A simple example is the following: Maximize profit $p = 2x + y$ subject to $x \ge 0$, $y \ge 0$. Then p can be made as large as we like by choosing large values of x and/or y. Thus there is no optimal solution to the problem. **55.** Mathematically, this means that there are infinitely many possible solutions: one for each point along the line joining the two corner points in question. In practice, select those points with integer solutions (since x and y must be whole numbers in this problem) that are in the feasible region and close to this line, and choose the one that gives the largest profit. **57.** Proof

Section 5.3

1. $p = 8$; $x = 4$, $y = 0$ **3.** $p = 4$; $x = 4$, $y = 0$ **5.** $p = 80$; $x = 10$, $y = 0$, $z = 10$ **7.** $p = 53$; $x = 5$, $y = 0$, $z = 3$ **9.** $z = 14{,}500$; $x_1 = 0$, $x_2 = 500/3$, $x_3 = 5{,}000/3$ **11.** $p = 6$; $x = 2$, $y = 1$, $z = 0$, $w = 3$ **13.** $p = 7$; $x = 1$, $y = 0$, $z = 2$, $w = 0$, $v = 4$ (or: $x = 1$, $y = 0$, $z = 2$, $w = 1$, $v = 3$.) **15.** $p = 21$; $x = 0$, $y = 2.27$, $z = 5.73$ **17.** $p = 4.52$; $x = 1$, $y = 0$, $z = 0.67$, $w = 1.52$; or: $x = 1.67$, $y = 0.67$, $z = 0$, $w = 1.52$ **19.** $p = 7.7$; $x = 1.1$, $y = 0$, $z = 2.2$, $w = 0$, $v = 4$ **21.** You should purchase 500 calculus texts, no history texts, and no marketing texts. The maximum profit is $5,000 per semester. **23.** The company can make a maximum profit of $650 by making 100 gallons of PineOrange, 200 gallons of PineKiwi, and 150 gallons of OrangeKiwi. **25.** The department should offer no Ancient History, 30 sections of Medieval History, and 15 sections of Modern History, for a profit of $1,050,000. There will be 500 students without classes, but all sections and professors are used. **27.** Plant 80 acres of tomatoes and leave the other 20 acres unplanted. This will give you a profit of $160,000. **29.** It can make a profit of $10,000 by selling 1,000 servings of granola, 500 servings of nutty granola, and no nuttiest granola. It is left with 2,000 oz almonds. **31.** Allocate 5 million gals to process A and 45 million gals to process C. Another solution: Allocate 10 million gals to process B and 40 million gals to process C. **33.** Use 15 servings of RiboForce HP and none of the others for a maximum of 75 g creatine. **35.** She is right; you should buy 142.9 shares of DO and no others. **37.** Allocate $2,250,000 to automobile loans, $500,000 to signature loans, and $2,250,000 to any combination of furniture loans and other secured loans. **39.** Invest $75,000 in Universal, none in the rest. Another optimal solution is: Invest $18,750 in Universal, and $75,000 in EMI. **41.** Tucson to Honolulu: 290 boards; Tucson to Venice Beach: 330 boards; Toronto to Honolulu: 0 boards; Toronto to Venice Beach: 200 boards, giving 820 boards shipped. **43.** Fly 10 people from Chicago to Los Angeles, 5 people from Chicago to New York, and 10 people from Denver to New York. **45.** Yes; the given problem can be stated as: Maximize $p = 3x - 2y$ subject to $-x + y - z \le 0$, $x - y - z \le 6$, $x \ge 0$, $y \ge 0$, $z \ge 0$. **47.** The graphical method applies only to LP problems in two unknowns, whereas the simplex method can be used to solve LP problems with any number of unknowns. **49.** She is correct. There are only two constraints, so there can be only two active variables, giving two or fewer nonzero values for the unknowns at each stage. **51.** A basic solution to a system of linear equations is a solution in which all the nonpivotal variables are taken to be zero; that is, all variables whose values are arbitrary are assigned the value zero. To obtain a basic solution for a given system of linear equations, one can row reduce the associated augmented matrix, write down the general solution, and then set all the parameters (variables with "arbitrary" values) equal to zero. **53.** No. Let us assume for the sake of simplicity that all the pivots are 1s. (They may certainly be changed to 1s without affecting the value of any of the variables.) Because the entry at the bottom of the pivot column is negative, the bottom row gets replaced by itself plus a positive multiple of the pivot row. The value of the objective function (bottom-right entry) is thus replaced by itself plus a positive multiple of the nonnegative rightmost entry of the pivot row. Therefore, it cannot decrease.

Section 5.4

1. $p = 20/3$; $x = 4/3$, $y = 16/3$ **3.** $p = 850/3$; $x = 50/3$, $y = 25/3$ **5.** $p = 750$; $x = 0$, $y = 150$, $z = 0$ **7.** $p = 450$; $x = 10$, $y = 10$, $z = 10$

9. $p = 260/3$; $x = 50/3$, $y = 0$, $z = 70/3$, $w = 0$
11. $c = 80$; $x = 20/3$, $y = 20/3$
13. $c = 100$; $x = 0$, $y = 100$, $z = 0$
15. $c = 111$; $x = 1$, $y = 1$, $z = 1$
17. $c = 200$; $x = 200$, $y = 0$, $z = 0$, $w = 0$
19. $p = 136.75$; $x = 0$, $y = 25.25$, $z = 0$, $w = 15.25$
21. $c = 66.67$; $x = 0$, $y = 66.67$, $z = 0$
23. $c = -250$; $x = 0$, $y = 500$, $z = 500$, $w = 1{,}500$ **25.** Plant 100 acres of tomatoes and no other crops. This will give you a profit of \$200,000. (You will be using all 100 acres of your farm.)
27. 10 mailings to the East Coast, none to the Midwest, 10 to the West Coast. Cost: \$900. Another solution resulting in the same cost is no mailings to the East Coast, 15 to the Midwest, none to the West Coast. **29.** 10,000 quarts of orange juice and 2,000 quarts of orange concentrate **31.** Sell 25,000 regional music albums, 10,000 pop/rock music albums, and 5,000 tropical music albums per day for a maximum revenue of \$195,000. **33.** One serving of cereal, one serving of juice, and no dessert! **35.** 15 bundles from Nadir, 5 from Sonny, and none from Blunt. Cost: \$70,000. Another solution resulting in the same cost is 10 bundles from Nadir, none from Sonny, and 10 from Blunt. **37.** Mix 6 servings of Riboforce HP and 10 servings of Creatine Transport for a cost of \$15.60. **39. a.** Build 1 convention-style hotel, 4 vacation-style hotels, and 2 small motels. The total cost will amount to \$188 million. **b.** Because 20% of this is \$37.6 million, you will still be covered by the subsidy. **41.** Tucson to Honolulu: 500 boards/week; Tucson to Venice Beach: 120 boards/week; Toronto to Honolulu: 0 boards/week; Toronto to Venice Beach: 410 boards/week. Minimum weekly cost is \$9,700.
43. \$2,500 from Congressional Integrity Bank, \$0 from Citizens' Trust, \$7,500 from Checks R Us.
45. Fly 5 people from Chicago to LA, 15 from Chicago to New York, 5 from Denver to LA, none from Denver to New York at a total cost of \$4,000.
47. Hire no more cardiologists, 12 rehabilitation specialists, and 5 infectious disease specialists.
49. The solution $x = 0, y = 0, \ldots$, represented by the initial tableau may not be feasible. In Phase I we use pivoting to arrive at a basic solution that is feasible. **51.** The basic solution corresponding to the initial tableau has all the unknowns equal to zero, and this is not a feasible solution because it does not satisfy the given inequality. **53.** (C) **55.** Answers may vary. Examples are Exercises 1 and 2.
57. Answers may vary. A simple example is: Maximize $p = x + y$ subject to $x + y \le 10$, $x + y \ge 20$, $x \ge 0$, $y \ge 0$.

Section 5.5

1. Minimize $c = 6s + 2t$ subject to $s - t \ge 2$, $2s + t \ge 1$, $s \ge 0$, $t \ge 0$
3. Maximize $p = 100x + 50y$ subject to $x + 2y \le 2$, $x + y \le 1$, $x \le 3$, $x \ge 0$, $y \ge 0$. **5.** Minimize $c = 3s + 4t + 5u + 6v$ subject to $s + u + v \ge 1$, $s + t + v \ge 1$, $s + t + u \ge 1$, $t + u + v \ge 1$, $s \ge 0$, $t \ge 0$, $u \ge 0$, $v \ge 0$. **7.** Maximize $p = 1{,}000x + 2{,}000y + 500z$ subject to $5x + z \le 1$, $-x + z \le 3$, $y \le 1$, $x - y \le 0$, $x \ge 0$, $y \ge 0$, $z \ge 0$.
9. $c = 4$; $s = 2$, $t = 2$ **11.** $c = 80$; $s = 20/3$, $t = 20/3$ **13.** $c = 1.8$; $s = 6$, $t = 2$
15. $c = 25$; $s = 5$, $t = 15$ **17.** $c = 30$; $s = 30$, $t = 0$, $u = 0$ **19.** $c = 100$; $s = 0$, $t = 100$, $u = 0$
21. $c = 30$; $s = 10$, $t = 10$, $u = 10$
23. $R = [3/5 \quad 2/5]$, $C = [2/5 \quad 3/5 \quad 0]^T$, $e = 1/5$
25. $R = [1/4 \quad 0 \quad 3/4]$, $C = [1/2 \quad 0 \quad 1/2]^T$, $e = 1/2$ **27.** $R = [0 \quad 3/11 \quad 3/11 \quad 5/11]$, $C = [8/11 \quad 0 \quad 2/11 \quad 1/11]^T$, $e = 9/11$
29. 4 ounces each of fish and cornmeal, for a total cost of 40¢ per can; 5/12¢ per gram of protein, 5/12¢ per gram of fat. **31.** 100 oz of grain and no chicken, for a total cost of \$1; 1/2¢ per gram of protein, 0¢ per gram of fat. **33.** One serving of cereal, one serving of juice, and no dessert! for a total cost of 37¢; 1/6¢ per calorie and 17/120¢ per % U.S. RDA of vitamin C.
35. 10 mailings to the East coast, none to the Midwest, 10 to the West Coast. Cost: \$900; 20¢ per Democrat and 40¢ per Republican. OR 15 mailings to the Midwest and no mailing to the coasts. Cost: \$900; 20¢ per Democrat and 40¢ per Republican.
37. Gillian should use 480 sleep spells and 160 shock spells, costing 360,000 pico-shirleys of energy OR 2,880/7 sleep spells and 1,440/7 shock spells.
39. T. N. Spend should spend about 73% of the days in Littleville, 27% in Metropolis, and skip Urbantown. T. L. Down should spend about 91% of the days in Littleville, 9% in Metropolis, and skip Urbantown. The expected outcome is that T. L. Down will lose about 227 votes per day of campaigning. **41.** Each player should show one finger with probability 1/2, two fingers with probability 1/3, and three fingers with probability 1/6. The expected outcome is that player A will win 2/3 point per round, on average. **43.** Write moves as (*x*, *y*), where *x* represents the number of regiments sent to the first location and *y* represents the number sent to the second location. Colonel Blotto should play (0, 4) with probability 4/9, (2, 2) with probability 1/9, and (4, 0) with probability 4/9. Captain Kije has several optimal strategies, one of which is to play (0, 3) with probability 1/30, (1, 2) with probability 8/15, (2, 1) with probability 16/45,

and (3, 0) with probability 7/90. The expected outcome is that Colonel Blotto will win 14/9 points on average. **45.** The dual of a standard minimization problem satisfying the nonnegative objective condition is a standard maximization problem, which can be solved using the standard simplex algorithm, thus avoiding the need to do Phase I. **47.** Answers will vary. An example is: Minimize $c = x - y$ subject to $x - y \geq 100$, $x + y \geq 200$, $x \geq 0$, $y \geq 0$. This problem can be solved using the techniques in Section 5.4. **49.** If the given problem is a standard minimization problem satisfying the nonnegative objective condition, its dual is a standard maximization problem, and so can be solved using a single-phase simplex method. Otherwise, dualizing may not save any labor, since the dual will not be a standard maximization problem.

Chapter 5 Review

1.

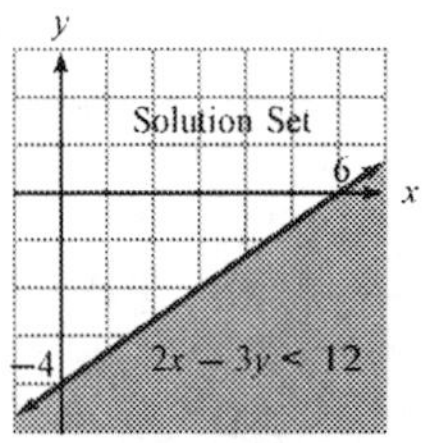

Unbounded

3.

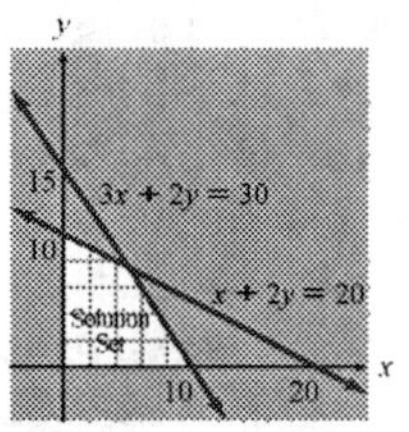

Bounded; corner points: (0, 0), (0, 10), (5, 15/2), (10, 0)

5. $p = 21; x = 9, y = 3$ **7.** $c = 22; x = 8, y = 6$
9. $p = 45;\ x = 0, y = 15, z = 15$
11. $p = 220; x = 20, y = 20, z = 60$
13. $c = 30; x = 30, y = 0, z = 0$
15. No solution; feasible region unbounded
17. $c = 50; x = 20, y = 10, z = 0, w = 20$, OR $x = 30, y = 0, z = 0, w = 20$
19. $c = 60; x = 24, y = 12$ OR $x = 0, y = 60$
21. $c = 20; x = 0,\ y = 20$
23. $R = [1/2 \quad 1/2 \quad 0]$, $C = [0 \quad 1/3 \quad 2/3]^T$, $e = 0$
25. $R = [1/27 \quad 7/9 \quad 5/27]$, $C = [8/27 \quad 5/27 \quad 14/27]^T$, $e = 8/27$
27. (A) **29.** 35 **31.** 400 packages from each for a minimum cost of $52,000 **33. a.** (B), (D) **b.** 450 packages from Duffin House, 375 from Higgins Press for a minimum cost of $52,500 **35.** 220 shares of EEE and 20 shares of RRR. The minimum total risk index is 500. **37.** 240 Sprinkles, 120 Storms, and no Hurricanes **39.** Order 600 packages from Higgins and none from the others, for a total cost of $90,000. **41. a.** Let x = # science credits, y = # fine arts credits, z = # liberal arts credits, and w = # math credits. Minimize $C = 300x + 300y + 200z + 200w$ subject to: $x + y + z + w \geq 120$; $x - y \geq 0$; $-2x + w \leq 0$; $-y + 3z - 3w \leq 0$; $x \geq 0$, $y \geq 0$, $z \geq 0$, $w \geq 0$. **b.** Billy-Sean should take the following combination: Sciences—24 credits, Fine Arts—no credits, Liberal Arts—48 credits, Mathematics—48 credits, for a total cost of $26,400. **43.** Smallest cost is $20,000; New York to OHaganBooks.com: 600 packages, New York to FantasyBooks.com: 0 packages, Illinois to OHaganbooks.com: 0 packages, Illinois to FantasyBooks.com: 200 packages.
45. FantasyBooks.com should choose between "2 for 1" and "3 for 2" with probabilities 20% and 80%, respectively. OHaganBooks.com should choose between "3 for 1" and "Finite Math" with probabilities 60% and 40%, respectively. OHaganBooks.com expects to gain 12,000 customers from FantasyBooks.com.

Chapter 9

Section 9.1

1. Vertex: $(-3/2, -1/4)$, y-intercept: 2, x-intercepts: $-2, -1$

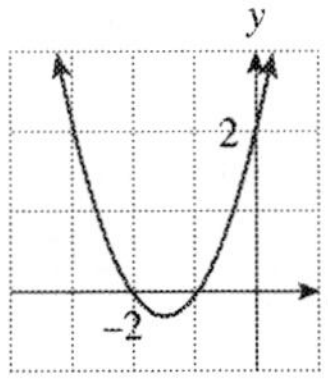

3. Vertex: $(2,0)$, y-intercept: -4, x-intercept: 2

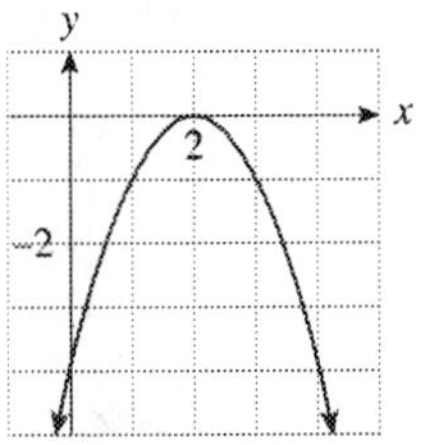

5. Vertex: $(-20, 900)$, y-intercept: 500, x-intercepts: -50, 10

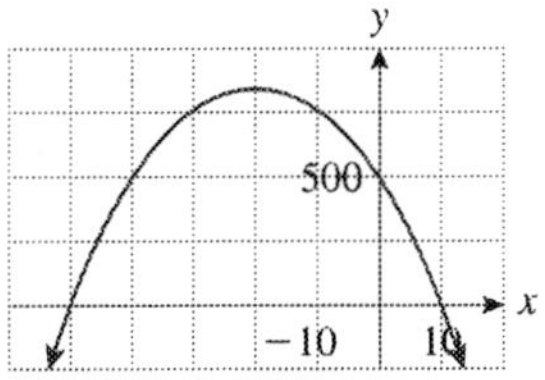

7. Vertex: $(-1/2, -5/4)$, y-intercept: -1, x-intercepts: $-1/2 \pm \sqrt{5}/2$

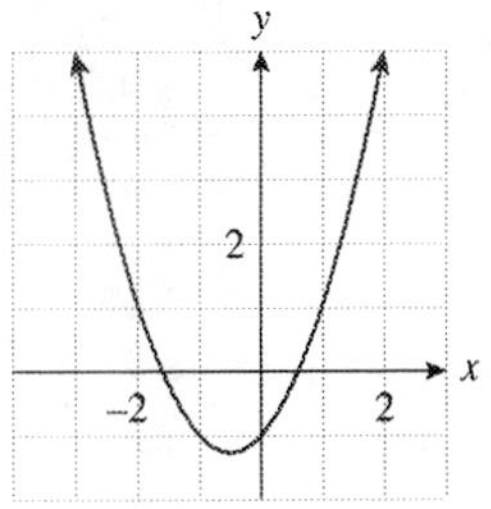

9. Vertex: $(0, 1)$, y-intercept: 1, no x-intercepts

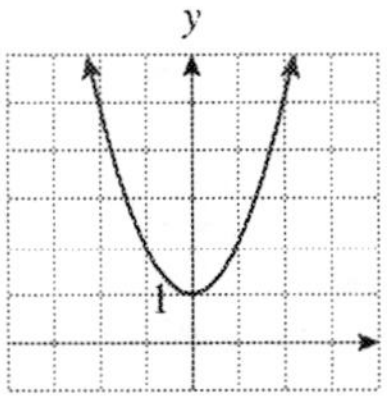

11. $R = -4p^2 + 100p$; Maximum revenue when $p = \$12.50$

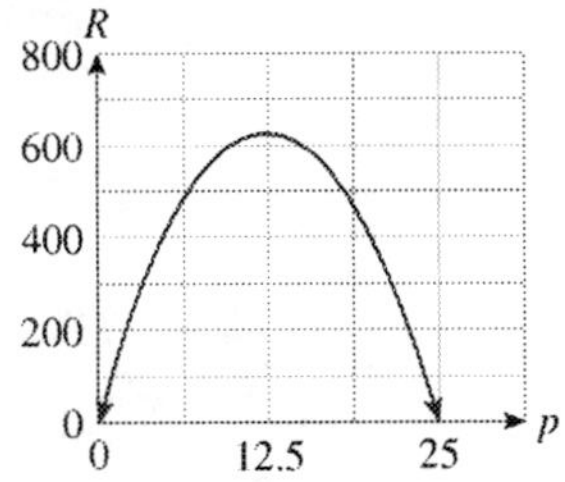

13. $R = -2p^2 + 400p$; Maximum revenue when $p = \$100$

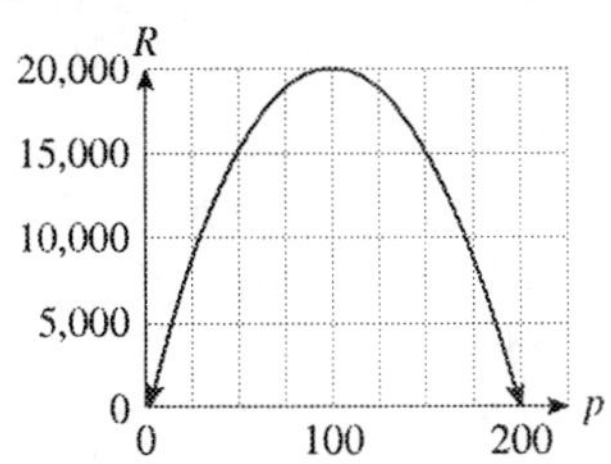

15. $y = -0.7955x^2 + 4.4591x - 1.6000$
17. $y = -1.1667x^2 - 6.1667x - 3.0000$
19. a. Positive because the data suggest a curve that is concave up. **b.** (C) **c.** 1998. Extrapolating in the positive direction leads one to predict more and more steeply rising military expenditure, which may or may not occur; extrapolating in the negative direction predicts continually more an more steeply rising military expenditure as we go back in time, contradicting history. **21.** 2003; about 1.6 million barrels/day **23.** 2006; About \$21 billion; No, as the model predicts net income dropping without bound. **25.** Maximum revenue when $p = \$140$, $R = \$9{,}800$ **27.** Maximum revenue with 70 houses, $R = \$9{,}800{,}000$ **29. a.** $q = -4{,}500p + 41{,}500$ **b.** \$4.61 for a daily revenue of \$95,680.55 **c.** No **31. a.** $q = -560x + 1{,}400$; $R = -560x^2 + 1{,}400x$ **b.** $P = -560x^2 + 1{,}400x - 30$; $x = \$1.25$; $P = \$845$ per month **33.** $C = -200x + 620$; $P = -400x^2 + 1{,}400x - 620$; $x = \$1.75$ per log-on; $P = \$605$ per month **35. a.** $q = -10p + 400$ **b.** $R = -10p^2 + 400p$ **c.** $C = -30p + 4{,}200$ **d.** $P = -10p^2 + 430p - 4{,}200$; $p = \$21.50$ **37.** $f(t) = 6.25t^2 - 100t + 1{,}200$; \$1,425 billion, which is \$25 billion lower than the actual value. **39. a.** $S(t) = 3.0t^2 - 37t + 120$;
Graph:

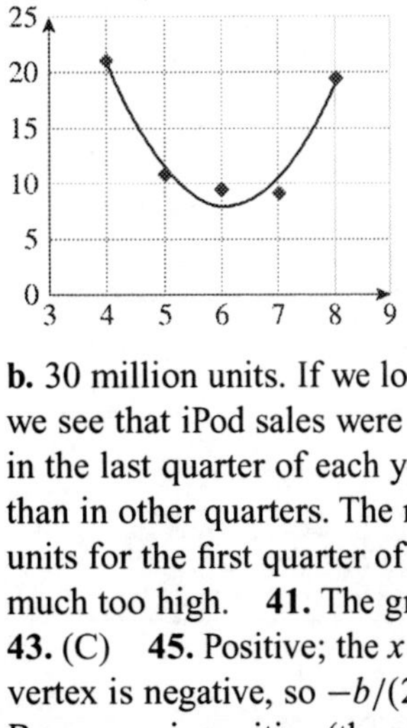

b. 30 million units. If we look at more historical data, we see that iPod sales were highly seasonal, with sales in the last quarter of each year being significantly higher than in other quarters. The model's figure of 30 million units for the first quarter of 2011 is therefore probably much too high. **41.** The graph is a straight line. **43.** (C) **45.** Positive; the x coordinate of the vertex is negative, so $-b/(2a)$ must be negative. Because a is positive (the parabola is concave up), this means that b must also be positive to make $-b/(2a)$ negative. **47.** The x-coordinate of the vertex represents the unit price that leads to the maximum revenue, the y-coordinate of the vertex gives the maximum possible revenue, the x-intercepts give the unit prices that result in zero revenue, and the y-intercept gives the revenue resulting from zero unit price (which is obviously zero). **49.** Graph the data to see whether the points suggest a curve rather than a straight line. It the curve suggested by the graph is concave up or concave down, then a quadratic model would be a likely candidate. **51.** No; the graph of a quadratic function is a parabola. In the case of a concave-up parabola, the curve would unrealistically predict sales increasing without bound in

the future. In the case of a concave-down parabola, the curve would predict "negative" sales from some point on. **53.** If $q = mp + b$ (with $m < 0$), then the revenue is given by $R = pq = mp^2 + bp$. This is the equation of a parabola with $a = m < 0$, and so is concave down. Thus, the vertex is the highest point on the parabola, showing that there is a single highest value for R, namely, the y-coordinate of the vertex.
55. Since $R = pq$, the demand must be given by

$$q = \frac{R}{p} = \frac{-50p^2 + 60p}{p} = -50p + 60.$$

Section 9.2

1. `4^x`

x	−3	−2	−1	0	1	2	3
$f(x)$	$\frac{1}{64}$	$\frac{1}{16}$	$\frac{1}{4}$	1	4	16	64

3. `3^(-x)`

x	−3	−2	−1	0	1	2	3
$f(x)$	27	9	3	1	$\frac{1}{3}$	$\frac{1}{9}$	$\frac{1}{27}$

5. `2*2^x or 2*(2^x)`

x	−3	−2	−1	0	1	2	3
$f(x)$	$\frac{1}{4}$	$\frac{1}{2}$	1	2	4	8	16

7. `-3*2^(-x)`

x	−3	−2	−1	0	1	2	3
$f(x)$	−24	−12	−6	−3	$-\frac{3}{2}$	$-\frac{3}{4}$	$-\frac{3}{8}$

9. `2^x-1`

x	−3	−2	−1	0	1	2	3
$f(x)$	$-\frac{7}{8}$	$-\frac{3}{4}$	$-\frac{1}{2}$	0	1	3	7

11. `2^(x-1)`

x	−3	−2	−1	0	1	2	3
$f(x)$	$\frac{1}{16}$	$\frac{1}{8}$	$\frac{1}{4}$	$\frac{1}{2}$	1	2	4

13.

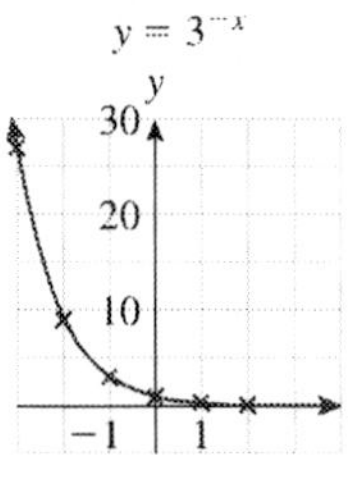

15.

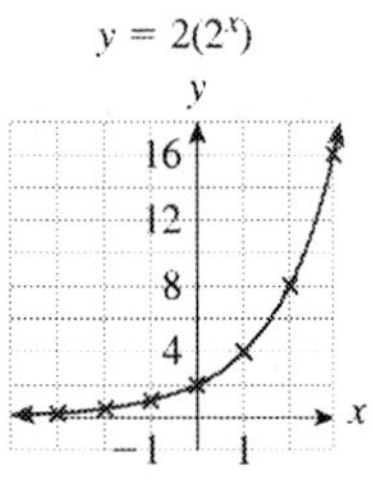

17.

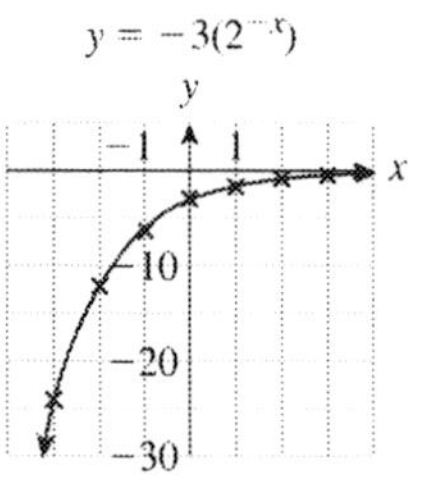

19. Both; $f(x) = 4.5(3^x)$. $g(x) = 2(1/2)^x$, or $2(2^{-x})$
21. Neither **23.** g; $g(x) = 4(0.2)^x$

25. `e^(-2*x)` or `EXP(-2*x)`

x	-3	-2	-1	0	1	2	3
$f(x)$	403.4	54.60	7.389	1	0.1353	0.01832	0.002479

27. `1.01*2.02^(-4*x)`

x	-3	-2	-1	0	1	2	3
$f(x)$	4662	280.0	16.82	1.01	0.06066	0.003643	0.0002188

29. `50*(1+1/3.2)^(2*x)`

x	-3	-2	-1	0	1	2	3
$f(x)$	9.781	16.85	29.02	50	86.13	148.4	255.6

31. `2^(x-1)` *not* `2^x-1` **33.** `2/(1-2^(-4*x))` *not* `2/1-2^-4*x` *and not* `2/1-2^(-4*x)`
35. `(3+x)^(3*x)/(x+1)` or `((3+x)^(3*x))/(x+1)` *not* `(3+x)^(3*x)/x+1` *and not* `(3+x^(3*x))/(x+1)`
37. `2*e^((1+x)/x)` or `2*EXP((1+x)/x)` *not* `2*e^1+x/x` *and not* `2*e^(1+x)/x` *and not* `2*EXP(1+x)/x`

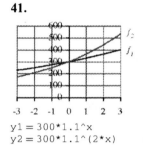

39.

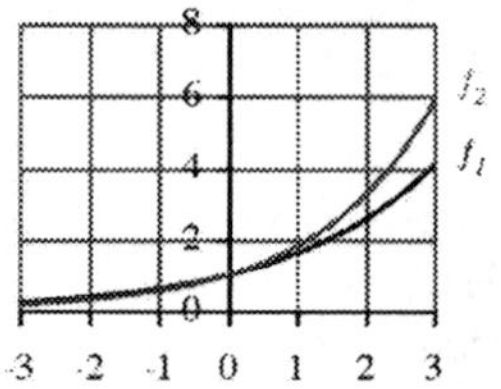

`y1 = 1.6^x y2 = 1.8^x`

41.

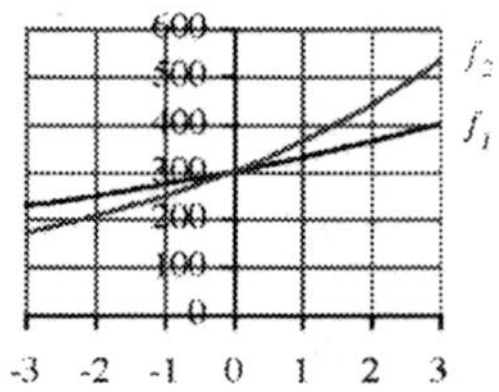

`y1 = 300*1.1^x`
`y2 = 300*1.1^(2*x)`

43.

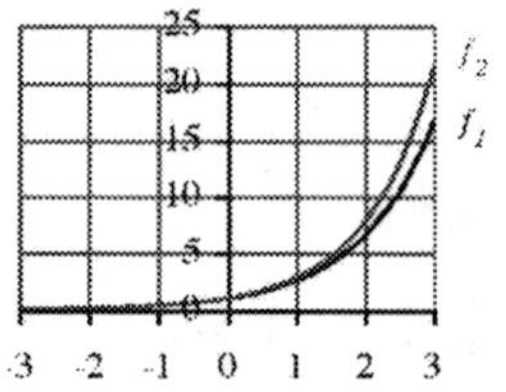

`y1 = 2.5^(1.02*x)`
`y2 = e^(1.02*x)`
`or exp(1.02*x)`

45.

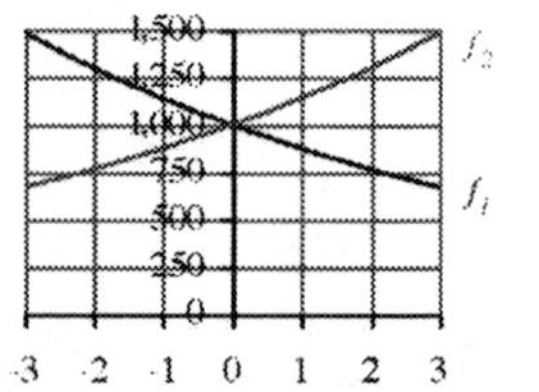

`y1 = 1000*1.045^(-3*x)`
`y2 = 1000*1.045^(3*x)`

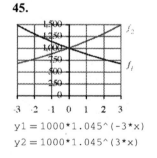

47. $f(x) = 500(0.5)^x$ **49.** $f(x) = 10(3)^x$
51. $f(x) = 500(0.45)^x$ **53.** $f(x) = -100(1.1)^x$
55. $y = 4(3^x)$ **57.** $y = -1(0.2^x)$
59. $y = 2.1213(1.4142^x)$ **61.** $y = 3.6742(0.9036^x)$
63. $f(t) = 5{,}000e^{0.10t}$ **65.** $f(t) = 1{,}000e^{-0.063t}$
67. $y = 1.0442(1.7564)^x$ **69.** $y = 15.1735(1.4822)^x$
71. $f(t) = 300(0.5)^t$; 9.375 mg **73. a.** Linear model: $F = 65t - 60$. Exponential model: $F = 97.2(1.20)^t$. The exponential model is more appropriate. **b.** 418 tons, not too far off the projected figure

75. a. $P = 180(1.01087)^t$ million **b.** 6 significant digits **c.** 344 million **77. a.** $y = 50{,}000(1.5^{t/2})$, t = time in years since two years ago **b.** 91,856 tags **79.** $y = 1{,}000(2^{t/3})$; 65,536,000 bacteria after 2 days **81.** $A(t) = 167(1.18)^t$; 1,695 cases **83.** $A(t) = 5{,}000(1 + 0.003/12)^{12t}$; \$5,106 **85.** 2024 **87.** 491.82 **89.** $A(t) = 4.9e^{0.032t}$ million homes; 2010: 5.2 million homes; 2012: 5.6 million homes
91. a.

Year	1950	2000	2050	2100
$C(t)$ parts per million	355	377	400	425

b. 2030
93. a. $P(t) = 0.339(1.169)^t$.
Graph:

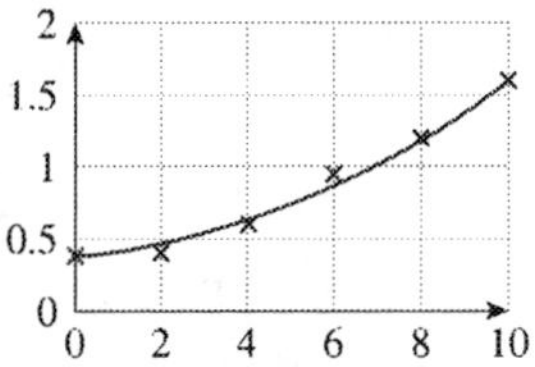

b. \$1.9 million
95. a. $n = 1.127(3.544)^t$
Graph:

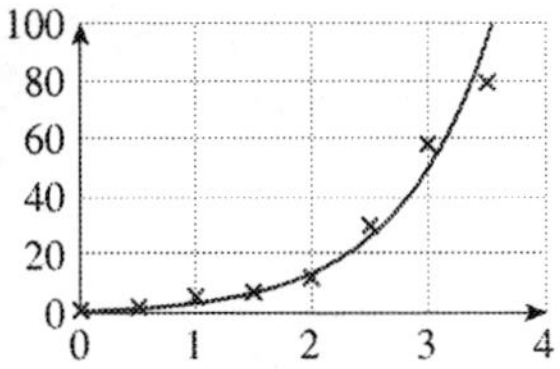

b. 3.544 **c.** 178 million **97.** (B) **99.** Exponential functions of the form $f(x) = Ab^x$ $(b > 1)$ increase rapidly for large values of x. In real-life situations, such as population growth, this model is reliable only for relatively short periods of growth. Eventually, population growth tapers off because of pressures such as limited resources and overcrowding. **101.** The article was published about a year before the "housing bubble" burst in 2006, whereupon house prices started to fall, contrary to the prediction of the graph—they continued to drop for several years, as documented in Exercise 90. This shows the danger of using any mathematical model to extrapolate. The blogger was, however, cautious in the choice of words, claiming only to be estimating what the future U.S. median house price "might be." **103.** Linear functions better: cost models where there is a fixed cost and a variable cost; simple interest, where interest is paid on the original amount invested. Exponential models better: compound interest, population growth. (In both of these, the rate of growth depends on the present number of items, rather than on some fixed quantity.) **105.** Take the ratios y_2/y_1 and y_3/y_2. If they are the same, the points fit on an exponential curve. **107.** This reasoning is suspect—the bank need not use its computer resources to update all the accounts every minute, but can instead use the continuous compounding formula to calculate the balance in any account at any time.

Section 9.3

1.

Logarithmic Form	$\log_{10} 10{,}000 = 4$	$\log_4 16 = 2$	$\log_3 27 = 3$	$\log_5 5 = 1$	$\log_7 1 = 0$	$\log_4 \frac{1}{16} = -2$

3.

Exponential Form	$(0.5)^2 = 0.25$	$5^0 = 1$	$10^{-1} = 0.1$	$4^3 = 64$	$2^8 = 256$	$2^{-2} = \frac{1}{4}$

5. 1.4650 **7.** −1.1460 **9.** −0.7324 **11.** 6.2657
13.

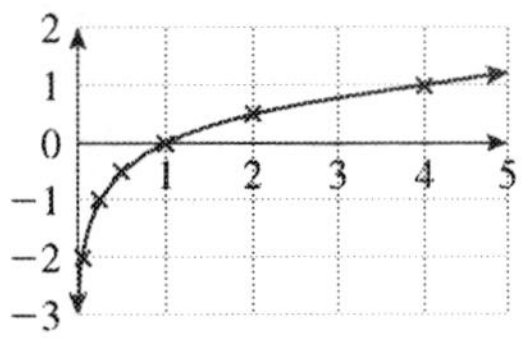

15.

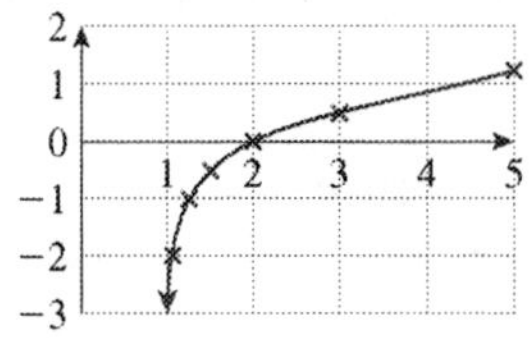

17.

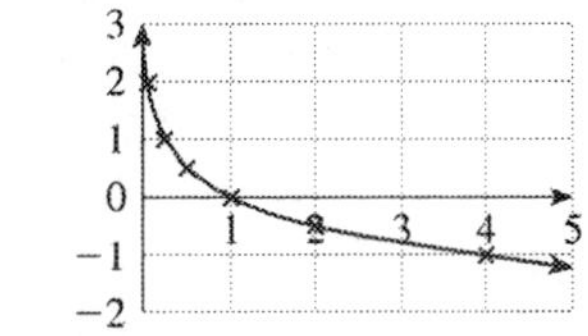

19. $Q = 1{,}000e^{-t \ln 2}$ **21.** $Q = 1{,}000e^{t(\ln 2)/2}$ **23.** Doubling time = 2 ln 2 **25.** Half-life = (ln 2)/4 **27.** $f(x) = 4(7.389)^x$ **29.** $f(t) = 2.1e^{0.000\,9995t}$ **31.** $f(t) = 10e^{-0.01309t}$. **33.** 3.36 years **35.** 11 years **37.** 23.1% **39.** 63,000 years old **41.** 12 years **43.** 238 months **45.** 13 years **47.** 20.39 years **49.** 1,600 years **51. a.** $b = 3^{1/6} \approx 1.20$ **b.** 3.8 months **53. a.** $Q(t) = Q_0e^{-0.139t}$ **b.** 3 years **55.** 2,360 million years **57.** 3.2 hours **59.** 3.89 days **61. a.** $P(t) = 6.591 \ln(t) - 17.69$ **b.** 1 digit **c.** (A) **63.** $S(t) = 55.49 \ln t + 39.67$
Graph:

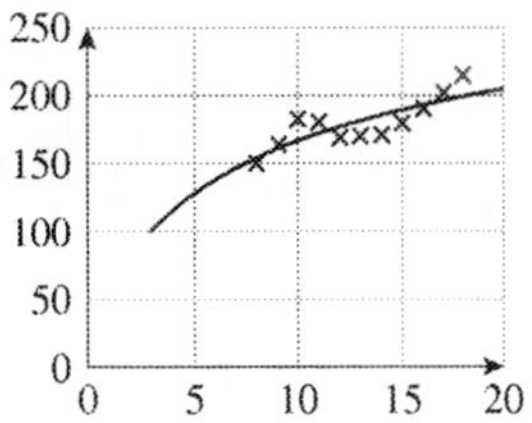

Positive direction; extrapolating in the negative direction eventually leads to negative values, which do not model reality.
65. a. About 4.467×10^{23} ergs **b.** About 2.24% **c.** $E = 10^{1.5R+11.8}$ **d.** Proof **e.** 1,000 **67. a.** 75 dB, 69 dB, 61 dB **b.** $D = 95 - 20 \log r$ **c.** 57,000 feet
69. Graph:

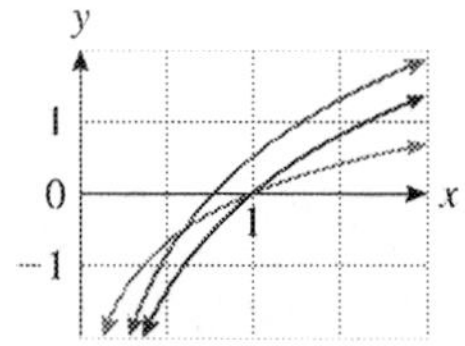

The green curve is $y = \ln x$. The blue curve is $y = 2\ln x$, and the red curve is $y = 2\ln x + 0.5$. Multiplying by A stretches the graph in the y-direction by a factor of A. Adding C moves the graph C units vertically up. **71.** The logarithm of a negative number, were it defined, would be the power to which a base must be raised to give that negative number. But raising a base to a power never results in a negative number, so there can be no such number as the logarithm of a negative number. **73.** Any logarithmic curve $y = \log_b t + C$ will eventually surpass 100%, and hence not be suitable as a long-term predictor of market share. **75.** $\log_4 y$ **77.** 8 **79.** x **81.** Time is increasing logarithmically with population; solving $P = Ab^t$ for t gives $t = \log_b(P/A) = \log_b P - \log_b A$, which is of the form $t = \log_b P + C$. **83.** (Proof)

Section 9.4

1. $N = 7, A = 6, b = 2$;

```
7/(1+6*2^-x)
```

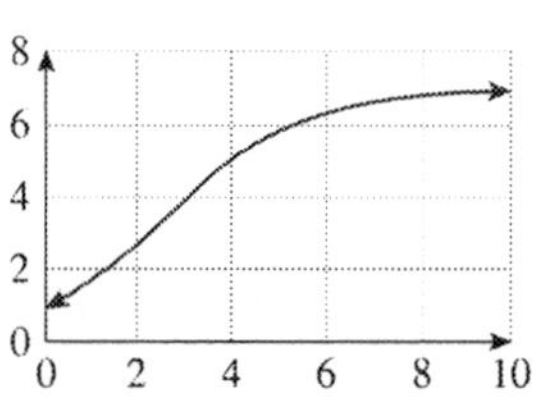

3. $N = 10, A = 4, b = 0.3$;

```
10/(1+4*0.3^-x)
```

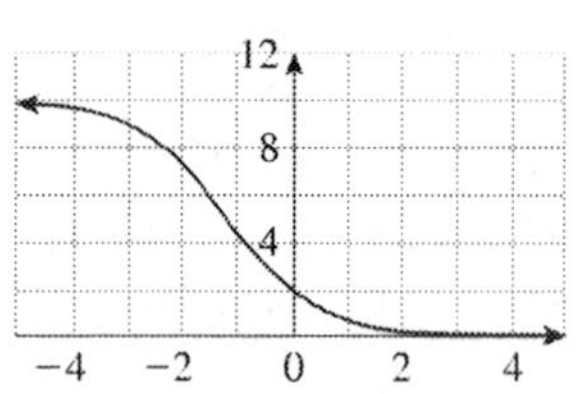

5. $N = 4, A = 7, b = 1.5$;

```
4/(1+7*1.5^-x)
```

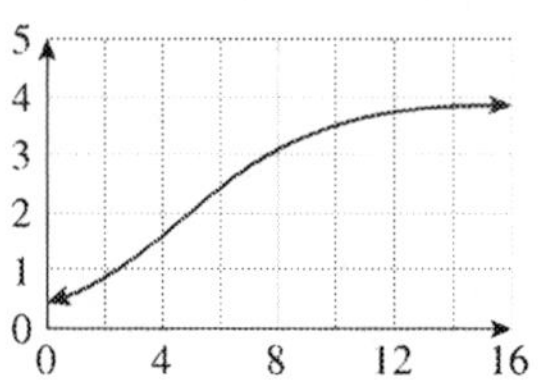

7. $f(x) = \dfrac{200}{1 + 19(2^{-x})}$ **9.** $f(x) = \dfrac{6}{1 + 2^{-x}}$

11. (B) **13.** (B) **15.** (C)

17. $y = \dfrac{7.2}{1 + 2.4(1.04)^{-x}}$

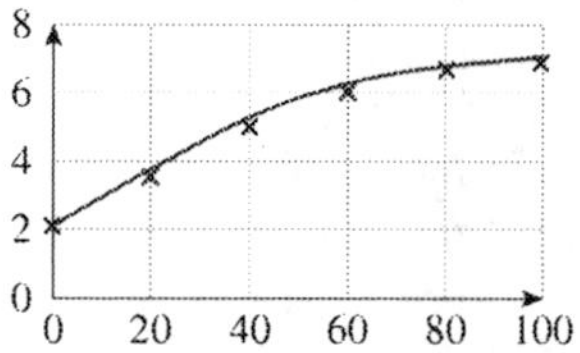

19. $y = \dfrac{97}{1 + 2.2(0.942)^{-x}}$

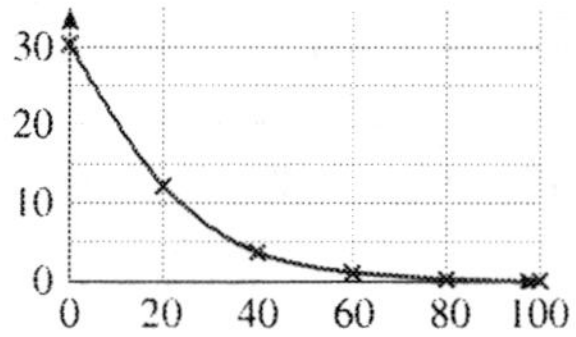

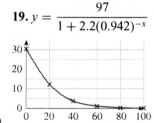

21. a. (A) **b.** 2003 **23. a.** (A) **b.** 20% per year
25. a. 95.0% **b.** $P(x) \approx 25.13(1.064)^x$ **c.** \$18,000
27. $N(t) = \dfrac{10{,}000}{1 + 9(1.25)^{-t}}$; $N(7) \approx 3{,}463$ cases
29. $N(t) = \dfrac{3{,}000}{1 + 29(2^{1/5})^{-t}}$; $t = 16$ days
31. a. $A(t) = \dfrac{6.3}{1 + 4.8(1.2)^{-t}}$; 6,300 articles
b. 5,200 articles **33. a.** $B(t) = \dfrac{1{,}090}{1 + 0.410(1.09)^{-t}}$; 1,090 teams **b.** $t \approx -10.3$. According to the model, the number of teams was rising fastest about 10.3 years *prior* to 1990; that is, sometime during 1979. **c.** The number of men's basketball teams was growing by about 9% per year in the past, well before 1979.
35. $y = \dfrac{4{,}500}{1 + 1.1466(1.0357)^{-t}}$; 2013 **37.** Just as diseases are communicated via the spread of a pathogen (such as a virus), new technology is communicated via the spread of information (such as advertising and publicity). Further, just as the spread of a disease is ultimately limited by the number of susceptible individuals, so the spread of a new technology is ultimately limited by the size of the potential market. **39.** It can be used to predict where the sales of a new commodity might level off. **41.** The curve is still a logistic curve, but decreases when $b > 1$ and increases when $b < 1$. **43.** (Proof)

Chapter 9 Review

1.

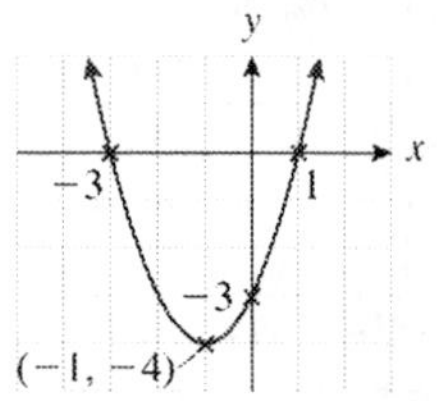

3. f: $f(x) = 5(1/2)^x$, or $5(2^{-x})$

5.

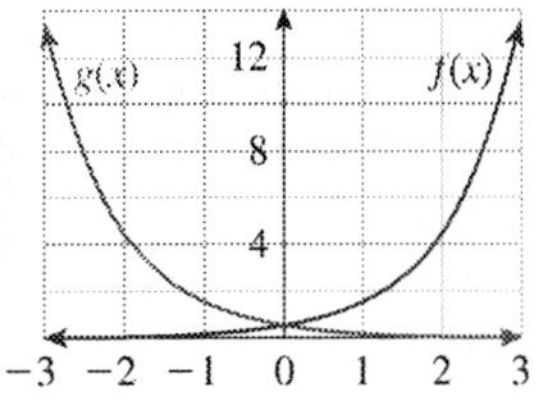

7.

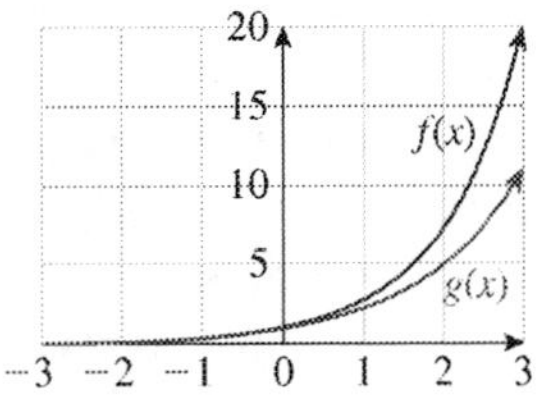

9. \$3,484.85 **11.** \$3,705.48 **13.** \$3,485.50
15. $f(x) = 4.5(9^x)$ **17.** $f(x) = \frac{2}{3}3^x$ **19.** $-\frac{1}{2}\log_3 4$
21. $\frac{1}{3}\log 1.05$

23.

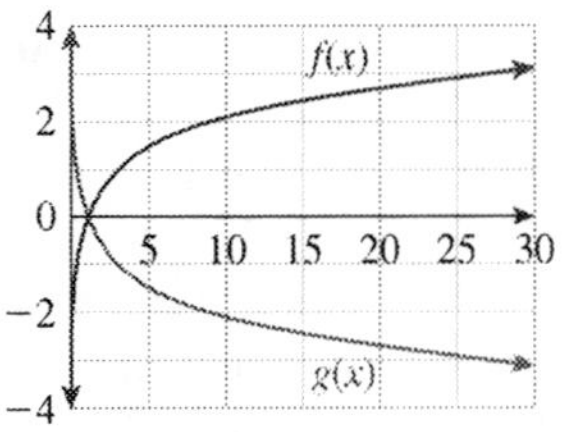

25. $Q = 5e^{-0.00693t}$ **27.** $Q = 2.5e^{0.347t}$
29. 10.2 years **31.** 10.8 years
33. $f(x) = \dfrac{900}{1 + 8(1.5)^{-x}}$
35. $f(x) = \dfrac{20}{1 + 3(0.8)^{-x}}$ **37. a.** \$8,500 per month; an average of approximately 2,100 hits per day **b.** \$29,049 per month **c.** The fact that −0.000005, the coefficient of c^2, is negative.
39. a. $R = -60p^2 + 950p$; $p = \$7.92$ per novel, Monthly revenue = \$3,760.42
b. $P = -60p^2 + 1{,}190p - 4{,}700$; $p = \$9.92$ per novel, Monthly profit = \$1,200.42 **41. a.** 9.1, 19
b. About 310,000 pounds **43.** 2016
45. 1.12 million pounds **47.** $n(t) = 9.6(0.80^t)$ million pounds of lobster **49.** (C)

Chapter 10

Section 10.1

1. 0 **3.** 4 **5.** Does not exist **7.** 1.5 **9.** 0.5
11. Diverges to $+\infty$ **13.** 0 **15.** 1 **17.** 0 **19.** 0
21. a. −2 **b.** −1 **23. a.** 2 **b.** 1 **c.** 0 **d.** $+\infty$
25. a. 0 **b.** 2 **c.** −1 **d.** Does not exist **e.** 2 **f.** $+\infty$
27. a. 1 **b.** 1 **c.** 2 **d.** Does not exist **e.** 1 **f.** 2
29. a. 1 **b.** Does not exist **c.** Does not exist **d.** 1
31. a. 1 **b.** $+\infty$ **c.** $+\infty$ **d.** $+\infty$ **e.** not defined **f.** −1
33. a. −1 **b.** $+\infty$ **c.** $-\infty$ **d.** Does not exist **e.** 2 **f.** 1
35. 210 trillion pesos per month. In the long term, the model predicts that the value of sold goods in Mexico will approach 210 trillion pesos per month. **37.** $+\infty$; In the long term, Amazon's revenue will grow without bound. **39.** 7.0; In the long term, the number of research articles in *Physical Review* written by researchers in Europe approaches 7,000 per year.
41. 573. This suggests that students with an exceptionally large household income earn an average of 573 on the math SAT test. **43. a.** $\lim_{t\to 14.75^-} r(t) = 21$, $\lim_{t\to 14.75^+} r(t) = 21$, $\lim_{t\to 14.75} r(t) = 21$, $r(14.75) = 0.01$ **b.** Just prior to 2:45 pm, the stock was approaching \$21, but then fell suddenly to a penny (\$0.01) at 2:45 exactly, after which time it jumped back to values close to \$21. **45.** 100; In the long term, the home price index will level off at 100 points.
47. $\lim_{t\to 1^-} C(t) = 0.06$, $\lim_{t\to 1^+} C(t) = 0.08$, so $\lim_{t\to 1} C(t)$ does not exist. **49.** $\lim_{t\to +\infty} I(t) = +\infty$, $\lim_{t\to +\infty}(I(t)/E(t)) \approx 2.5$. In the long term, U.S. imports from China will rise without bound and be 2.5 times U.S. exports to China. In the real world, imports and exports cannot rise without bound. Thus, the given models should not be extrapolated far into the future.
51. To approximate $\lim_{x\to a} f(x)$ numerically, choose values of x closer and closer to, and on either side of $x = a$, and evaluate $f(x)$ for each of them. The limit (if it exists) is then the number that these values of $f(x)$ approach. A disadvantage of this method is that it may never give the exact value of the limit, but only an approximation. (However, we can make this as accurate as we like.) **53.** Any situation in which there is a sudden change can be modeled by a function in which $\lim_{t\to a^+} f(t)$ is not the same as $\lim_{t\to a^-} f(t)$. One example is the value of a stock market index before and after a crash: $\lim_{t\to a^-} f(t)$ is the value immediately before the crash at time $t = a$, while $\lim_{t\to a^+} f(t)$ is the value immediately after the crash. Another example might be the price of a commodity that is suddenly increased from one level to another. **55.** It is possible for $\lim_{x\to a} f(x)$ to exist even though $f(a)$ is not defined. An example is $\lim_{x\to 1} \dfrac{x^2 - 3x + 2}{x - 1}$.
57. An example is $f(x) = (x - 1)(x - 2)$.
59. These limits are all 0.

Section 10.2

1. Continuous on its domain **3.** Continuous on its domain **5.** Discontinuous at $x = 0$
7. Discontinuous at $x = -1$ **9.** Continuous on its domain **11.** Continuous on its domain
13. Discontinuous at $x = -1$ and 0 **15.** (A), (B), (D), (E) **17.** 0 **19.** −1 **21.** No value possible
23. −1 **25.** Continuous on its domain

27. Continuous on its domain **29.** Discontinuity at $x = 0$ **31.** Discontinuity at $x = 0$ **33.** Continuous on its domain **35.** Not unless the domain of the function consists of all real numbers. (It is impossible for a function to be continuous at points not in its domain.) For example, $f(x) = 1/x$ is continuous on its domain—the set of nonzero real numbers—but not at $x = 0$. **37.** True. If the graph of a function has a break in its graph at any point a, then it cannot be continuous at the point a. **39.** Answers may vary. $f(x) = 1/[(x-1)(x-2)(x-3)]$ is such a function; it is undefined at $x = 1, 2, 3$ and so its graph consists of three distinct curves. **41.** Answers may vary.

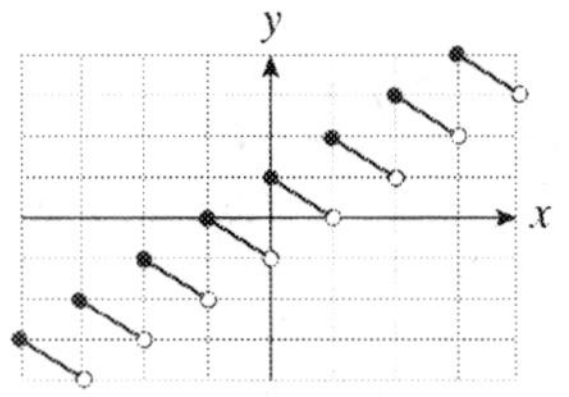

43. Answers may vary. The price of OHaganBooks.com stocks suddenly drops by \$10 as news spreads of a government investigation. Let $f(x)$ = Price of OHaganBooks.com stocks.

Section 10.3

1. $x = 1$ **3.** 2 **5.** Determinate; diverges to $+\infty$ **7.** Determinate; does not exist **9.** Determinate; diverges to $-\infty$ **11.** Determinate; 0 **13.** Indeterminate; $-1/3$ **15.** Indeterminate; 0 **17.** Determinate; 0 **19.** Determinate; -60 **21.** 1 **23.** 2 **25.** 0 **27.** 6 **29.** 4 **31.** 2 **33.** 0 **35.** 0 **37.** 12 **39.** $+\infty$ **41.** Does not exist; left and right (infinite) limits differ. **43.** $-\infty$ **45.** Does not exist **47.** $+\infty$ **49.** 0 **51.** $1/6$ **53.** $3/2$ **55.** $1/2$ **57.** $+\infty$ **59.** $3/2$ **61.** $1/2$ **63.** $-\infty$ **65.** 0 **67.** 12 **69.** 0 **71.** $+\infty$ **73.** 0 **75.** Discontinuity at $x = 0$ **77.** Continuous everywhere **79.** Discontinuity at $x = 0$ **81.** Discontinuity at $x = 0$ **83. a.** $\lim_{t\to 15^-} v(t) = 3{,}800$, $\lim_{t\to 15^+} v(t) = 3{,}800$; Shortly before 2005 the speed of Intel processors was approaching 3,800 MHz. Shortly after 2005 the speed of Intel processors was close to 3,800 MHz **b.** Continuous at $t = 15$; No abrupt changes. **85. a.** 0.49, 1.16. Shortly before 1999 annual advertising expenditures were close to \$0.49 billion. Shortly after 1999 annual advertising expenditures were close to \$1.16 billion. **b.** Not continuous; movie advertising expenditures jumped suddenly in 1999. **87.** 1.59; if the trend continued indefinitely, the annual spending on police would be 1.59 times the annual spending on courts in the long run. **89.** 573. This suggests that students with an exceptionally large household income earn an average of 573 on the math SAT test. **91.** $\lim_{t\to+\infty} I(t) = +\infty$, $\lim_{t\to+\infty}(I(t)/E(t)) = 2.5$. In the long term, U.S. imports from China will rise without bound and be 2.5 times U.S. exports to China. In the real world, imports and exports cannot rise without bound. Thus, the given models should not be extrapolated far into the future. **93.** $\lim_{t\to+\infty} p(t) = 100$. The percentage of children who learn to speak approaches 100% as their age increases. **95.** To evaluate $\lim_{x\to a} f(x)$ algebraically, first check whether $f(x)$ is a closed-form function. Then check whether $x = a$ is in its domain. If so, the limit is just $f(a)$; that is, it is obtained by substituting $x = a$. If not, then try to first simplify $f(x)$ in such a way as to transform it into a new function such that $x = a$ is in its domain, and then substitute. A disadvantage of this method is that it is sometimes extremely difficult to evaluate limits algebraically, and rather sophisticated methods are often needed. **97.** $x = 3$ is not in the domain of the given function f, so, yes, the *function* is undefined at $x = 3$. However, the *limit* may well be defined. In this case, it leads to the indeterminate form 0/0, telling us that we need to try to simplify, and that leads us to the correct limit of 27. **99.** She is wrong. Closed-form functions are continuous only at points in their domains, and $x = 2$ is not in the domain of the closed-form function $f(x) = 1/(x-2)^2$.

101. Answers may vary. (1) See Example 1(b): $\lim_{x\to 2}\frac{x^3-8}{x-2}$, which leads to the indeterminate form 0/0 but the limit is 12. (2) $\lim_{x\to+\infty}\frac{60x}{2x}$, which leads to the indeterminate form ∞/∞, but where the limit exists and equals 30. **103.** $\pm\infty/\infty$; The limits are zero. This suggests that limits resulting in $\frac{p(\infty)}{e^{\infty}}$ are zero.

105. The statement may not be true, for instance, if $f(x) = \begin{cases} x+2 & \text{if } x < 0 \\ 2x-1 & \text{if } x \ge 0 \end{cases}$, then $f(0)$ is defined and equals -1, and yet $\lim_{x\to 0} f(x)$ does not exist. The statement can be corrected by requiring that f be a closed-form function: "If f is a closed-form function, and $f(a)$ is defined, then $\lim_{x\to a} f(x)$ exists and equals $f(a)$." **107.** Answers may vary, for example

$$f(x) = \begin{cases} 0 & \text{if } x \text{ is any number other than 1 or 2} \\ 1 & \text{if } x = 1 \text{ or } 2 \end{cases}$$

109. Answers may vary.

(1) $\lim_{x\to+\infty}[(x+5)-x] = \lim_{x\to+\infty} 5 = 5$

(2) $\lim_{x\to+\infty}[x^2-x] = \lim_{x\to+\infty} x(x-1) = +\infty$

(3) $\lim_{x\to+\infty}[(x-5)-x] = \lim_{x\to+\infty} -5 = -5$

Section 10.4

1. −3 **3.** 0.3 **5.** −$25,000 per month **7.** −200 items per dollar **9.** $1.33 per month **11.** 0.75 percentage point increase in unemployment per 1 percentage point increase in the deficit **13.** 4 **15.** 2 **17.** 7/3

19.

h	Ave. Rate of Change
1	2
0.1	0.2
0.01	0.02
0.001	0.002
0.0001	0.0002

21.

h	Ave. Rate of Change
1	−0.1667
0.1	−0.2381
0.01	−0.2488
0.001	−0.2499
0.0001	−0.24999

23.

h	Ave. Rate of Change
1	9
0.1	8.1
0.01	8.01
0.001	8.001
0.0001	8.0001

25. a. $60 billion per year; World military expenditure increased at an average rate of $60 billion per year during 2005–2010. **b.** $50 billion per year; World military expenditure increased at an average rate of $50 billion per year during 2000–2010. **27. a.** −20,000 barrels/year; during 2002–2007, daily oil production by Pemex was decreasing at an average rate of 20,000 barrels of oil per year. **b.** (C) **29. a.** 1.7; the percentage of mortgages classified as subprime was increasing at an average rate of around 1.7 percentage points per year between 2000 and 2006. **b.** 2004–2006 **31. a.** 2007–2009; During 2007–2009 immigration to Ireland was decreasing at an average rate of 22,500 people per year. **b.** 2008–2010; During 2008–2010 immigration to Ireland was decreasing at an average rate of 7,500 people per year. **33. a.** [3, 5]; −0.25 thousand articles per year. During the period 1993–1995, the number of articles authored by U.S. researchers decreased at an average rate of 250 articles per year. **b.** Percentage rate ≈ −0.1765; Average rate = −0.09 thousand articles/year. Over the period 1993–2003, the number of articles authored by U.S. researchers decreased at an average rate of 90 per year, representing a 17.65% decrease over that period. **35. a.** 12 teams per year **b.** Decreased **37. a.** (A) **b.** (C) **c.** (B) **d.** Approximately −$0.088 per year (if we round to two significant digits). This is less than the slope of the regression line, about −$0.063 per year.

39. Answers may vary. Graph:

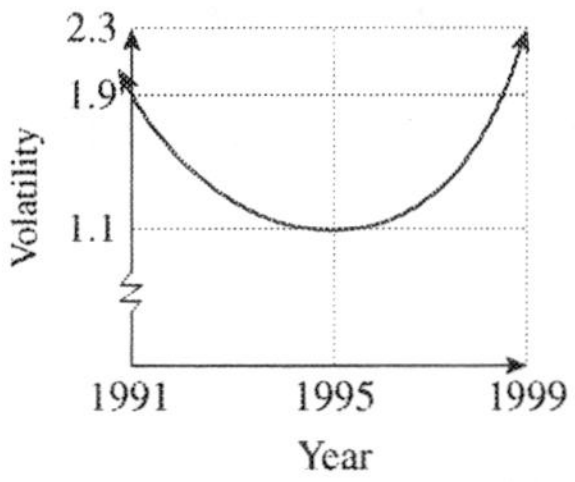

41. The index was increasing at an average rate of 300 points per day. **43. a.** $0.15 per year **b.** No; according to the model, during that 25-year period the price of oil went down from around $93 to a low of around $25 in 1993 before climbing back up. **45. a.** 47.3 new cases per day; the number of SARS cases was growing at an average rate of 47.3 new cases per day over the period March 17 to March 23. **b.** (A) **47. a.** 8.85 manatee deaths per 100,000 boats; 23.05 manatee deaths per 100,000 boats **b.** More boats result in more manatee deaths per additional boat. **49. a.** The average rates of change are shown in the following table

Interval	[0, 40]	[40, 80]	[80, 120]	[120, 160]	[160, 200]
Average Rate of Change of S	1.35	0.80	0.48	0.28	0.17

b. For household incomes between $40,000 and $80,000, a student's math SAT increases at an average rate of 0.80 points per $1,000 of additional income. **c.** (A) **d.** (B) **51.** The average rate of change of f over an interval $[a, b]$ can be determined numerically, using a table of values, graphically, by measuring the slope of the corresponding line segment through two points on the graph, or algebraically, using an algebraic formula for the function. Of these, the least precise is the graphical method, because it relies on reading coordinates of points on a graph. **53.** No, the formula for the average rate of a function f over $[a, b]$ depends only on $f(a)$ and $f(b)$, and not on any values of f between a and b. **55.** Answers will vary. Graph:

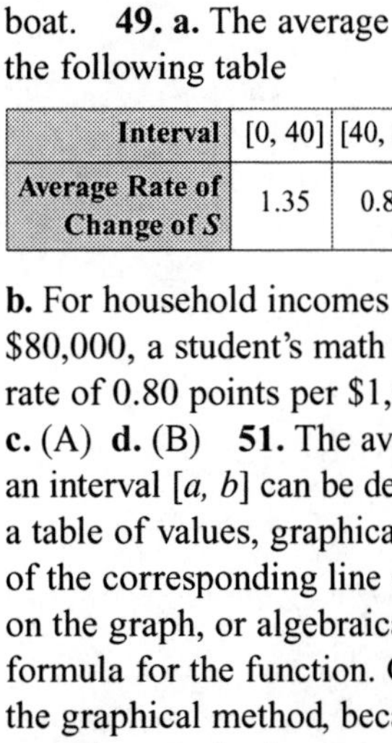

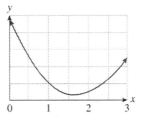

57. 6 units of quantity A per unit of quantity C
59. (A)

61. Yes. Here is an example:

Year	2000	2001	2002	2003
Revenue ($ billion)	$10	$20	$30	$5

63. (A)

Section 10.5

1. 6 **3.** −5.5

5.

h	1	0.1	0.01
Ave. rate	39	39.9	39.99

Instantaneous rate = $40 per day

7.

h	1	0.1	0.01
Ave. Rate	140	66.2	60.602

Instantaneous rate = $60 per day

9.

h	10	1
C_{ave}	4.799	4.7999

11.

h	10	1
C_{ave}	99.91	99.90

$C'(1{,}000) = \$4.80$ per item $C'(100) = \$99.90$ per item

13. $1/2$ **15.** 0 **17. a.** R **b.** P **19. a.** P **b.** R **21. a.** Q **b.** P **23. a.** Q **b.** R **c.** P **25. a.** R **b.** Q **c.** P **27. a.** $(1, 0)$ **b.** None **c.** $(-2, 1)$ **29. a.** $(-2, 0.3)$, $(0, 0)$, $(2, -0.3)$ **b.** None **c.** None **31.** $(a, f(a))$; $f'(a)$ **33.** (B) **35. a.** (A) **b.** (C) **c.** (B) **d.** (B) **e.** (C) **37.** −2 **39.** −1.5 **41.** −5 **43.** 16 **45.** 0 **47.** −0.0025

49. a. 3 **b.** $y = 3x + 2$

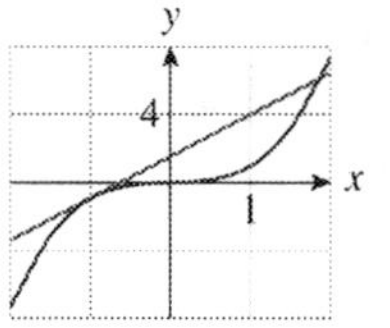

51. a. $\frac{3}{4}$ **b.** $y = \frac{3}{4}x + 1$

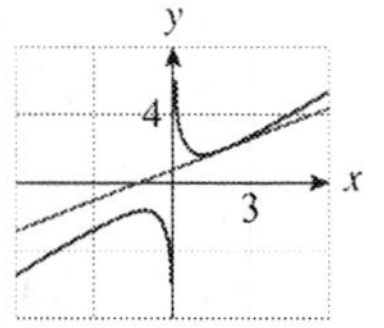

53. a. $\frac{1}{4}$ **b.** $y = \frac{1}{4}x + 1$

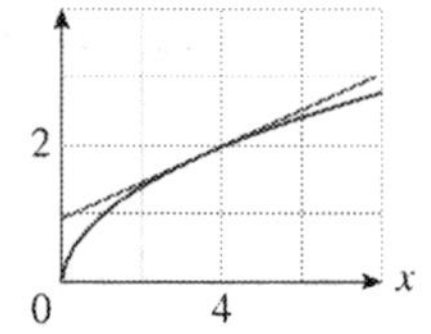

55. 1.000 **57.** 1.000 **59.** (C) **61.** (A) **63.** (F) **65.** Increasing for $x < 0$; decreasing for $x > 0$. **67.** Increasing for $x < -1$ and $x > 1$; decreasing for $-1 < x < 1$ **69.** Increasing for $x > 1$; decreasing for $x < 1$. **71.** Increasing for $x < 0$; decreasing for $x > 0$.

73. $x = -1.5$, $x = 0$
Graph:

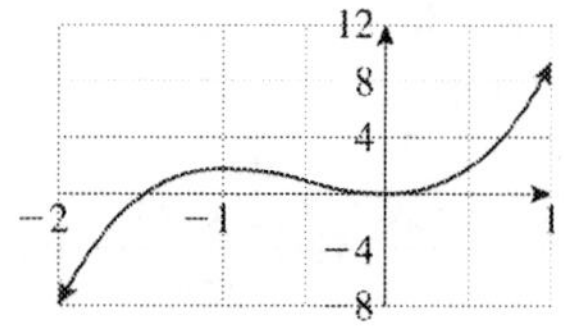

75. Note: Answers depend on the form of technology used. Excel ($h = 0.1$):

	A	B	C	D	E	F
1	x	f(x)	f'(x)	xmin	4	
2	4	6	-4.545454545	h	0.1	
3	4.1	5.545454545	-3.787878788			
4	4.2	5.166666667	-3.205128205			
5	4.3	4.846153846	-2.747252747			
6	4.4	4.571428571	-2.380952381			
7	4.5	4.333333333	-2.083333333			
8	4.6	4.125	-1.838235294			
9	4.7	3.941176471	-1.633986928			
10	4.8	3.777777778	-1.461988304			
11	4.9	3.631578947	-1.315789474			
12	5	3.5				
13						
14						

Graphs:

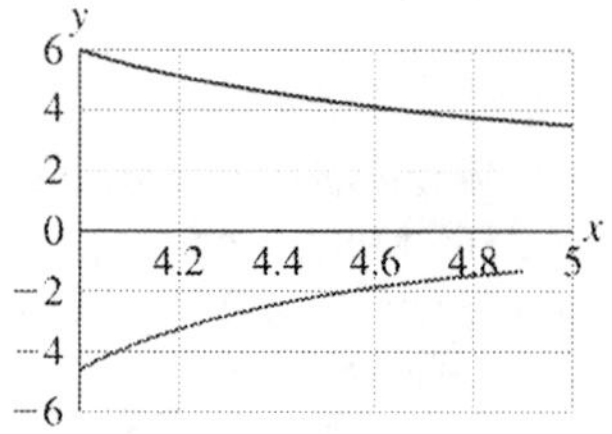

77. $q(100) = 50{,}000$, $q'(100) = -500$. A total of 50,000 pairs of sneakers can be sold at a price of $100, but the demand is decreasing at a rate of 500 pairs per $1 increase in the price. **79. a.** −0.05; daily oil imports from Mexico in 2005 were 1.6 million barrels and declining at a rate of 0.05 million barrels (or 50,000 barrels) per year. **b.** Decreasing **81. a.** (B) **b.** (B) **c.** (A) **d.** 2004 **e.** 0.033; in 2004 the U.S. prison population was increasing at a rate of 0.033 million prisoners (33,000 prisoners) per year. **83. a.** −96 ft/sec **b.** −128 ft/sec **85. a.** $0.60 per year; the price per barrel of crude oil in constant 2008 dollars was growing at an average rate of about 60¢ per year over the 28-year period beginning at the start of 1980.
b. −$12 per year; the price per barrel of crude oil in constant 2008 dollars was dropping at an instantaneous rate of about $12 per year at the start of 1980.
c. The price of oil was decreasing in January 1980, but eventually began to increase (making the average rate of change in part (a) positive). **87. a.** 144.7 new cases per day; the number of SARS cases was growing at a rate of about 144.7 new cases per day on March 27. **b.** (A)

89. $S(5) \approx 109$, $\left.\dfrac{dS}{dt}\right|_{t=5} \approx 9.1$. After 5 weeks, sales are 109 pairs of sneakers per week, and sales are increasing at a rate of 9.1 pairs per week each week. **91.** $A(0) = 4.5$ million; $A'(0) = 60{,}000$ subscribers/week **93. a.** 60% of children can speak at the age of 10 months. At the age of 10 months, this percentage is increasing by 18.2 percentage points per month. **b.** As t increases, p approaches 100 percentage points (all children eventually learn to speak), and dp/dt approaches zero because the percentage stops increasing. **95. a.** $A(6) \approx 12.0$; $A'(6) \approx 1.4$; at the start of 2006, about 12% of U.S. mortgages were subprime, and this percentage was increasing at a rate of about 1.4 percentage points per year
b. Graphs:

Graph of A:

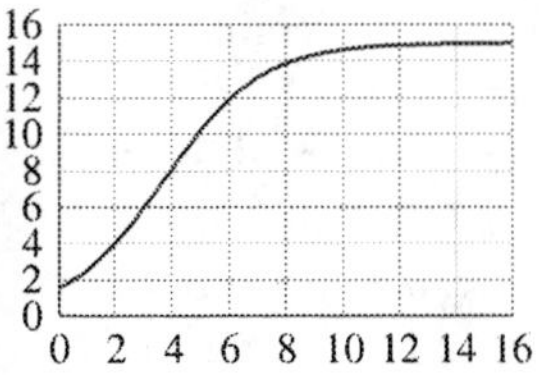

Graph of A':

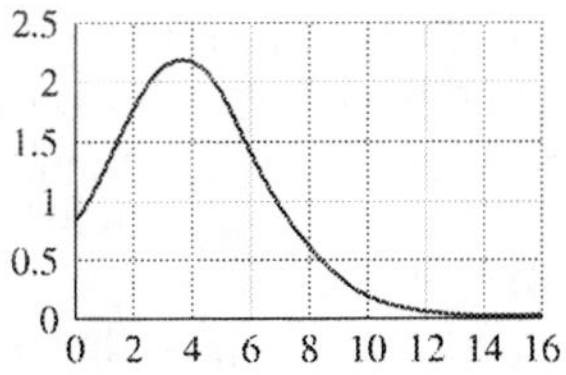

From the graphs, $A(t)$ approaches 15 as t becomes large (in terms of limits, $\lim_{x\to+\infty} A(t) = 15$) and $A'(t)$ approaches 0 as t becomes large (in terms of limits, $\lim_{x\to+\infty} A'(t) = 0$). Interpretation: If the trend modeled by the function A had continued indefinitely, in the long term 15% of U.S. mortgages would have been subprime, and this percentage would not be changing. **97. a.** (D) **b.** 33 days after the egg was laid **c.** 50 days after the egg was laid. Graph:

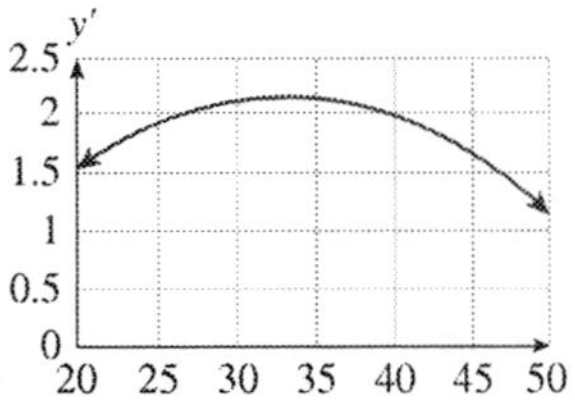

99. $L(.95) \approx 31.2$ meters and $L'(.95) \approx -304.2$ meters/warp. Thus, at a speed of warp 0.95, the spaceship has an observed length of 31.2 meters and its length is decreasing at a rate of 304.2 meters per unit warp, or 3.042 meters per increase in speed of 0.01 warp. **101.** The difference quotient is not defined when $h = 0$ because there is no such number as $0/0$. **103.** (D) **105.** The derivative is positive and decreasing toward zero. **107.** Company B. Although the company is currently losing money, the derivative is positive, showing that the profit is increasing. Company A, on the other hand, has profits that are declining. **109.** (C) is the only graph in which the instantaneous rate of change on January 1 is greater than the one-month average rate of change. **111.** The tangent to the graph is horizontal at that point, and so the graph is almost horizontal near that point.
113. Answers may vary.

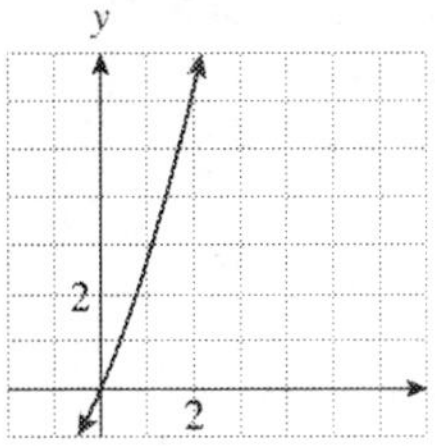

115. If $f(x) = mx + b$, then its average rate of change over any interval $[x, x + h]$ is $\dfrac{m(x + h) + b - (mx + b)}{h} = m$. Because this does not depend on h, the instantaneous rate is also equal to m. **117.** Increasing because the average rate of change appears to be rising as we get closer to 5 from the left. (See the bottom row.)

119. Answers may vary.

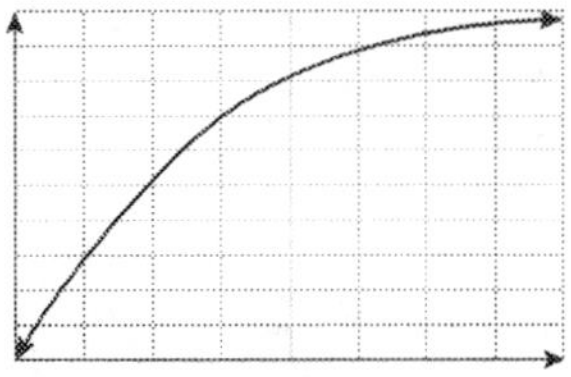

121. Answers may vary.

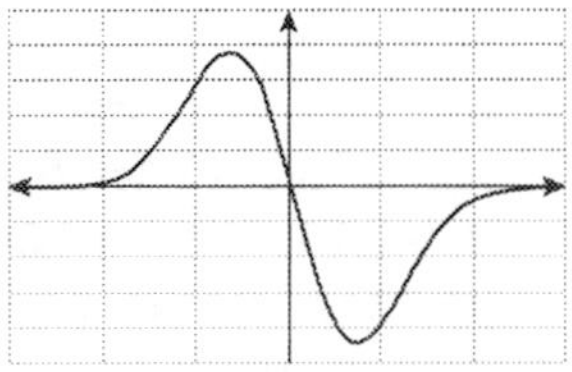

123. (B) **125.** Answers will vary.

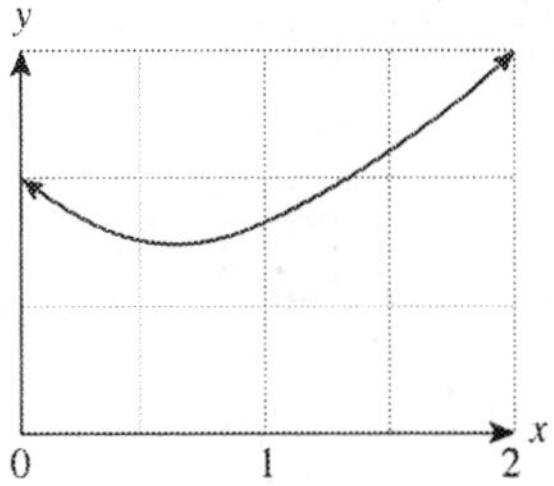

Section 10.6

1. 4 **3.** 3 **5.** 7 **7.** 4 **9.** 14 **11.** 1 **13.** m **15.** $2x$ **17.** 3 **19.** $6x+1$ **21.** $2-2x$ **23.** $3x^2+2$ **25.** $1/x^2$ **27.** m **29.** -1.2 **31.** 30.6 **33.** -7.1 **35.** 4.25 **37.** -0.6 **39.** $y=4x-7$ **41.** $y=-2x-4$ **43.** $y=-3x-1$ **45.** $s'(t)=-32t$; $s'(4)=-128$ ft/sec **47.** $dI/dt=-0.030t+0.1$; daily oil imports were decreasing at a rate of 0.11 million barrels per year. **49.** $R'(t)=-90t+900$; Increasing at a rate of 450 million gallons per year **51.** $f'(8)=26.6$ manatee deaths per 100,000 boats. At a level of 800,000 boats, the number of manatee deaths is increasing at a rate of 26.6 manatees per 100,000 additional boats. **53.** Yes; $\lim_{t\to 20^-} C(t) = \lim_{t\to 20^+} C(t) = 700 = C(20)$. **b.** No; $\lim_{t\to 20^-} C'(t) = 31.1$ while $\lim_{t\to 20^+} C'(t) = 90$. Until 1990, the cost of a Super Bowl ad was increasing at a rate of \$31,100 per year. Immediately thereafter, it was increasing at a rate of \$90,000 per year. **55.** The algebraic method because it gives the exact value of the derivative. The other two approaches give only approximate values (except in some special cases). **57.** The error is in the second line: $f(x+h)$ is *not* equal to $f(x)+h$. For instance, if $f(x)=x^2$, then $f(x+h)=(x+h)^2$, whereas $f(x)+h=x^2+h$. **59.** The error is in the second line: One could only cancel the h if it were a *factor* of both the numerator and denominator; it is not a factor of the numerator. **61.** Because the algebraic computation of $f'(a)$ is exact and not an approximation, it makes no difference whether one uses the balanced difference quotient or the ordinary difference quotient in the algebraic computation. **63.** The computation results in a limit that cannot be evaluated.

Chapter 10 Review

1. 5 **3.** Does not exist **5. a.** -1 **b.** 3 **c.** Does not exist **7.** $-4/5$ **9.** -1 **11.** -1 **13.** Does not exist **15.** 10/7 **17.** Does not exist **19.** $+\infty$ **21.** 0 **23.** Diverges to $-\infty$ **25.** 0 **27.** 2/5 **29.** 1

31.

h	1	0.01	0.001
Ave. Rate of Change	-0.5	-0.9901	-0.9990

Slope ≈ -1

33.

h	1	0.01	0.001
Avg. Rate of Change	6.3891	2.0201	2.0020

Slope ≈ 2

35. a. P **b.** Q **c.** R **d.** S **37. a.** Q **b.** None **c.** None **d.** None **39. a.** (B) **b.** (B) **c.** (B) **d.** (A) **e.** (C) **41.** $2x+1$ **43.** $2/x^2$

45.

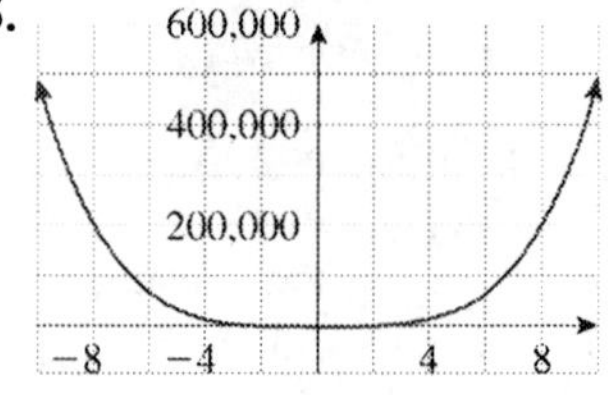

47.

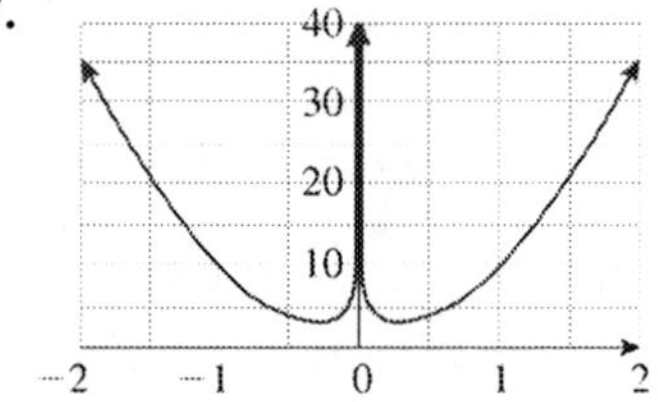

49. a. $P(3)=25$: O'Hagan purchased the stock at \$25. $\lim_{t\to 3^-} P(t)=25$: The value of the stock had been approaching \$25 up to the time he bought it. $\lim_{t\to 3^+} P(t)=10$: The value of the stock dropped to \$10 immediately after he bought it. **b.** Continuous but not differentiable. Interpretation: the stock price changed continuously but suddenly reversed direction (and started to go up) the instant O'Hagan sold it. **51. a.** $\lim_{t\to 3} p(t)\approx 40$; $\lim_{t\to +\infty} p(t)=+\infty$. Close to 2007 ($t=3$), the home price index was about 40. In the long term, the home price index will rise without bound. **b.** 10 (The slope of the linear portion of the curve is 10.) In the long term, the home price index will rise about 10 points per year. **53. a.** 500 books per week **b.** [3, 4], [4, 5] **c.** [3, 5]; 650 books per week **55. a.** 3 percentage points per year **b.** 0 percentage points per year **c.** (D) **57. a.** $72t+250$ **b.** 322 books per week **c.** 754 books per week.

Chapter 11

Section 11.1

1. $5x^4$ **3.** $-4x^{-3}$ **5.** $-0.25x^{-0.75}$ **7.** $8x^3+9x^2$ **9.** $-1-1/x^2$ **11.** $\frac{dy}{dx}=10(0)=0$ (constant multiple and power rule) **13.** $\frac{dy}{dx}=\frac{d}{dx}(x^2)+\frac{d}{dx}(x)$ (sum rule) $=2x+1$ (power rule) **15.** $\frac{dy}{dx}=\frac{d}{dx}(4x^3)+\frac{d}{dx}(2x)-\frac{d}{dx}(1)$ (sum and difference) $=4\frac{d}{dx}(x^3)+2\frac{d}{dx}(x)-\frac{d}{dx}(1)$ (constant multiples) $=12x^2+2$ (power rule) **17.** $f'(x)=2x-3$ **19.** $f'(x)=1+0.5x^{-0.5}$ **21.** $g'(x)=-2x^{-3}+3x^{-2}$ **23.** $g'(x)=-\frac{1}{x^2}+\frac{2}{x^3}$ **25.** $h'(x)=-\frac{0.8}{x^{1.4}}$ **27.** $h'(x)=-\frac{2}{x^3}-\frac{6}{x^4}$

29. $r'(x) = -\dfrac{2}{3x^2} + \dfrac{0.1}{2x^{1.1}}$

31. $r'(x) = \dfrac{2}{3} - \dfrac{0.1}{2x^{0.9}} - \dfrac{4.4}{3x^{2.1}}$

33. $t'(x) = |x|/x - 1/x^2$ **35.** $s'(x) = \dfrac{1}{2\sqrt{x}} - \dfrac{1}{2x\sqrt{x}}$

37. $s'(x) = 3x^2$ **39.** $t'(x) = 1 - 4x$

41. $2.6x^{0.3} + 1.2x^{-2.2}$ **43.** $1.2(1 - |x|/x)$

45. $3at^2 - 4a$ **47.** $5.15x^{9.3} - 99x^{-2}$

49. $-\dfrac{2.31}{t^{2.1}} - \dfrac{0.3}{t^{0.4}}$ **51.** $4\pi r^2$ **53.** 3 **55.** -2 **57.** -5

59. $y = 3x + 2$

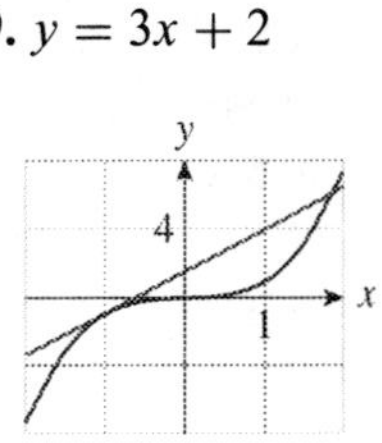

61. $y = \dfrac{3}{4}x + 1$

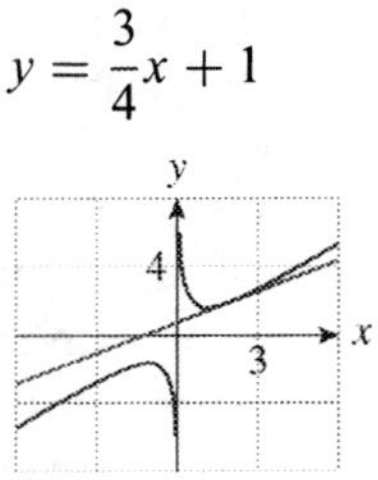

63. $y = \dfrac{1}{4}x + 1$

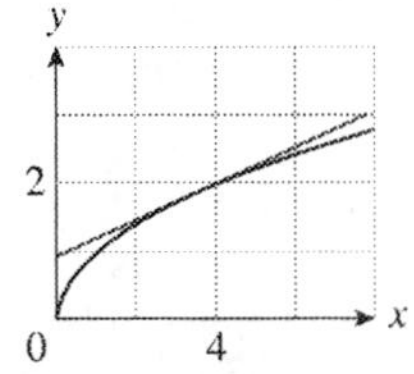

65. $x = -3/4$
67. No such values
69. $x = 1, -1$
71. See Solutions Manual.
73. a. 2/3 **b.** Not differentiable at 0
75. a. 5/2 **b.** Not differentiable at 0
77. Yes; 0 **79.** Yes; 12 **81.** No; 3 **83.** Yes; 3/2
85. Yes; diverges to $-\infty$ **87.** Yes; diverges to $-\infty$
89. $P'(t) = 0.9t - 12$; $P'(20) = 6$; the price of a barrel of crude oil was increasing at a rate of \$6 per year in 2000. **91.** 0.55 **93. a.** $s'(t) = -32t$; 0, -32, -64, -96, -128 ft/s **b.** 5 seconds; downward at 160 ft/s **95. a.** $P'(t) = -4.0t + 6.6$; Decreasing at a rate of \$5.4 billion per year **b.** (B)
97. a. $f'(x) = 7.1x - 30.2$; $f'(8) = 26.6$ manatees per 100,000 boats; At a level of 800,000 boats, manatee deaths are increasing at a rate of 26.6 deaths each year per 100,000 additional boats. **b.** Increasing; the number of manatees killed per additional 100,000 boats increases as the number of boats increases.
99. a. $I - A$ measures the amount by which the iPhone market share exceeds the Android market share. $(I - A)'$ measures the rate at which this difference is changing. **b.** (B) **c.** $-0.2t + 0.5$ percentage points per month; (C); The vertical distance between the graphs at first increases, and then decreases; the iPhone increases its advantage over the Android share at first, but then the Android begins to catch up.
d. -0.3 percentage points per month; In May 2009, the iPhone's advantage over Android was decreasing at a rate of 0.3 percentage points per month.
101. After graphing the curve $y = 3x^2$, draw the line passing through $(-1, 3)$ with slope -6. **103.** The slope of the tangent line of g is twice the slope of the tangent line of f. **105.** $g'(x) = -f'(x)$ **107.** The left-hand side is not equal to the right-hand side. The *derivative* of the left-hand side is equal to the right-hand side, so your friend should have written $\dfrac{d}{dx}(3x^4 + 11x^5) = 12x^3 + 55x^4$. **109.** $\dfrac{1}{2x}$ is not equal to $2x^{-1}$. Your friend should have written $y = \dfrac{1}{2x} = \dfrac{1}{2}x^{-1}$, so $\dfrac{dy}{dx} = -\dfrac{1}{2}x^{-2}$. **111.** The derivative of a constant times a function is the constant times the derivative of the function, so that $f'(x) = (2)(2x) = 4x$. Your enemy mistakenly computed the *derivative* of the constant times the derivative of the function. (The derivative of a product of two functions is not the product of the derivative of the two functions. The rule for taking the derivative of a product is discussed later in the chapter.).
113. For a general function f, the derivative of f is defined to be $f'(x) = \lim_{h\to 0} \dfrac{f(x+h) - f(x)}{h}$. One then finds by calculation that the derivative of the specific function x^n is nx^{n-1}. In short, nx^{n-1} is the derivative of a specific function: $f(x) = x^n$, it is not the *definition* of the derivative of a general function or even the definition of the derivative of the function $f(x) = x^n$. **115.** Answers may vary.

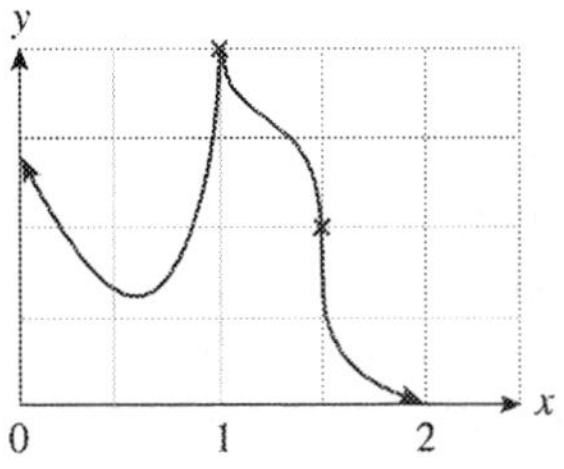

Section 11.2

1. $C'(1{,}000) = \$4.80$ per item **3.** $C'(100) = \$99.90$ per item **5.** $C'(x) = 4$; $R'(x) = 8 - 0.002$; $P'(x) = 4 - 0.002x$; $P'(x) = 0$ when $x = 2{,}000$. Thus, at a production level of 2,000, the profit is stationary (neither increasing nor decreasing) with respect to the production level. This may indicate a maximum profit at a production level of 2,000.
7. a. (B) **b.** (C) **c.** (C) **9. a.** $C'(x) = 2{,}500 - 0.04x$; The cost is going up at a rate of \$2,499,840 per television commercial. The exact cost of airing the fifth

television commercial is \$2,499,820. **b.** $\overline{C}(x) = 150/x + 2{,}500 - 0.02x$; $\overline{C}(4) = 2{,}537.42$ thousand dollars. The average cost of airing the first four television commercials is \$2,537,420. **11. a.** $R'(x) = 0.90$, $P'(x) = 0.80 - 0.002x$ **b.** Revenue: \$450, Profit: \$80, Marginal revenue: \$0.90, Marginal profit: $-\$0.20$. The total revenue from the sale of 500 copies is \$450. The profit from the production and sale of 500 copies is \$80. Approximate revenue from the sale of the 501st copy is 90¢. Approximate loss from the sale of the 501st copy is 20¢. **c.** $x = 400$. The profit is a maximum when you produce and sell 400 copies. **13.** The profit on the sale of 1,000 DVDs is \$3,000, and is decreasing at a rate of \$3 per additional DVD sold. **15.** Profit ≈ \$257.07; Marginal profit ≈ 5.07. Your current profit is \$257.07 per month, and this would increase at a rate of \$5.07 per additional magazine sold. **17. a.** \$2.50 per pound **b.** $R(q) = 20{,}000/q^{0.5}$ **c.** $R(400) = \$1{,}000$. This is the monthly revenue that will result from setting the price at \$2.50 per pound. $R'(400) = -\$1.25$ per pound of tuna. Thus, at a demand level of 400 pounds per month, the revenue is decreasing at a rate of \$1.25 per pound. **d.** The fishery should raise the price (to reduce the demand). **19.** $P'(50) = \$350$. This means that, at an employment level of 50 workers, the firm's daily profit will increase at a rate of \$350 per additional worker it hires. **21. a.** (B) **b.** (B) **c.** (C)

23. a. $C(x) = 500{,}000 + 1{,}600{,}000x - 100{,}000\sqrt{x}$;

$$C'(x) = 1{,}600{,}000 - \frac{50{,}000}{\sqrt{x}};$$

$$\overline{C}(x) = \frac{500{,}000}{x} + 1{,}600{,}000 - \frac{100{,}000}{\sqrt{x}}$$

b. $C'(3) \approx \$1{,}570{,}000$ per spot, $\bar{C}(3) \approx \$1{,}710{,}000$ per spot. The average cost will decrease as x increases. **25. a.** \$2,000 per one-pound reduction in emissions. **b.** 2.5 pounds per day reduction. **c.** $N(q) = 100q^2 - 500q + 4{,}000$; 2.5 pounds per day reduction. The value of q is the same as that for part (b). The net cost to the firm is minimized at the reduction level for which the cost of controlling emissions begins to increase faster than the subsidy. This is why we get the answer by setting these two rates of increase equal to each other. **27.** $M'(10) \approx 0.0002557$ mpg/mph. This means that, at a speed of 10 mph, the fuel economy is increasing at a rate of 0.0002557 miles per gallon per 1-mph increase in speed. $M'(60) = 0$ mpg/mph. This means that, at a speed of 60 mph, the fuel economy is neither increasing nor decreasing with increasing speed. $M'(70) \approx -0.00001799$. This means that, at 70 mph, the fuel economy is decreasing at a rate of 0.00001799 miles per gallon per 1-mph increase in speed. Thus 60 mph is the most fuel-efficient speed for the car. **29.** (C) **31.** (D) **33.** (B) **35.** Cost is often measured as a function of the number of items x. Thus, $C(x)$ is the cost of producing (or purchasing, as the case may be) x items. **a.** The average cost function $\overline{C}(x)$ is given by $\overline{C}(x) = C(x)/x$. The marginal cost function is the derivative, $C'(x)$, of the cost function. **b.** The average cost $\overline{C}(r)$ is the slope of the line through the origin and the point on the graph where $x = r$. The marginal cost of the rth unit is the slope of the tangent to the graph of the cost function at the point where $x = r$. **c.** The average cost function $\overline{C}(x)$ gives the average cost of producing the first x items. The marginal cost function $C'(x)$ is the rate at which cost is changing with respect to the number of items x, or the incremental cost per item, and approximates the cost of producing the $(x + 1)$st item. **37.** Answers may vary. An example is $C(x) = 300x$. **39.** The marginal cost **41.** Not necessarily. For example, it may be the case that the marginal cost of the 101st item is larger than the average cost of the first 100 items (even though the marginal cost is decreasing). Thus, adding this additional item will *raise* the average cost. **43.** The circumstances described suggest that the average cost function is at a relatively low point at the current production level, and so it would be appropriate to advise the company to maintain current production levels; raising or lowering the production level will result in increasing average costs.

Section 11.3

1. 3 **3.** $3x^2$ **5.** $2x + 3$ **7.** $210x^{1.1}$ **9.** $-2/x^2$ **11.** $2x/3$ **13.** $36x^2 - 3$ **15.** $3x^2 - 5x^4$ **17.** $8x + 12$ **19.** $-8/(5x - 2)^2$ **21.** $-14/(3x - 1)^2$ **23.** 0 **25.** $-|x|/x^3$ **27.** $3\sqrt{x}/2$ **29.** $(x^2 - 1) + 2x(x + 1) = (x + 1)(3x - 1)$ **31.** $(x^{-0.5} + 4)(x - x^{-1}) + (2x^{0.5} + 4x - 5)(1 + x^{-2})$ **33.** $8(2x^2 - 4x + 1)(x - 1)$ **35.** $(1/3.2 - 3.2/x^2)(x^2 + 1) + 2x(x/3.2 + 3.2/x)$ **37.** $2x(2x + 3)(7x + 2) + 2x^2(7x + 2) + 7x^2(2x + 3)$ **39.** $5.3(1 - x^{2.1})(x^{-2.3} - 3.4) - 2.1x^{1.1}(5.3x - 1)(x^{-2.3} - 3.4) - 2.3x - 3.3(5.3x - 1)(1 - x^{2.1})$

41. $\frac{1}{2\sqrt{x}}\left(\sqrt{x} + \frac{1}{x^2}\right) + \left(\sqrt{x} + 1\right)\left(\frac{1}{2\sqrt{x}} - \frac{2}{x^3}\right)$

Answers to Selected Exercises

43. $\dfrac{(4x+4)(3x-1)-3(2x^2+4x+1)}{(3x-1)^2} = (6x^2-4x-7)/(3x-1)^2$

45. $\dfrac{(2x-4)(x^2+x+1)-(x^2-4x+1)(2x+1)}{(x^2+x+1)^2} = (5x^2-5)/(x^2+x+1)^2$

47. $\dfrac{(0.23x^{-0.77}-5.7)(1-x^{-2.9})-2.9x^{-3.9}(x^{0.23}-5.7x)}{(1-x^{-2.9})^2}$

49. $\dfrac{\frac{1}{2}x^{-1/2}(x^{1/2}-1)-\frac{1}{2}x^{-1/2}(x^{1/2}+1)}{(x^{1/2}-1)^2} = \dfrac{-1}{\sqrt{x}\left(\sqrt{x}-1\right)^2}$ **51.** $-3/x^4$

53. $\dfrac{[(x+1)+(x+3)](3x-1)-3(x+3)(x+1)}{(3x-1)^2} = (3x^2-2x-13)/(3x-1)^2$

55. $\dfrac{[(x+1)(x+2)+(x+3)(x+2)+(x+3)(x+1)](3x-1)-3(x+3)(x+1)(x+2)}{(3x-1)^2}$

57. $4x^3-2x$ **59.** 64 **61.** 3 **63.** Difference; $4x^3-12x^2+2x-480$ **65.** Sum; $1+2/(x+1)^2$ **67.** Product; $\left[\dfrac{x}{x+1}\right]+(x+2)\dfrac{1}{(x+1)^2}$ **69.** Difference; $2x-1-2/(x+1)^2$ **71.** $y=12x-8$ **73.** $y=x/4+1/2$ **75.** $y=-2$ **77.** $q'(5)=1{,}000$ units/month (sales are increasing at a rate of 1,000 units per month); $p'(5)=-\$10$/month (the price of a sound system is dropping at a rate of \$10 per month); $R'(5)=900{,}000$ (revenue is increasing at a rate of \$900,000 per month). **79.** \$703 million; increasing at a rate of \$67 million per year **81.** Decreasing at a rate of \$1 per day **83.** Decreasing at a rate of approximately \$0.10 per month **85.** $M'(x)=\dfrac{3{,}000(3{,}600x^{-2}-1)}{\left(x+3{,}600x^{-1}\right)^2}$; $M'(10)\approx 0.7670$ mpg/mph. This means that, at a speed of 10 mph, the fuel economy is increasing at a rate of 0.7670 miles per gallon per one mph increase in speed. $M'(60)=0$ mpg/mph. This means that, at a speed of 60 mph, the fuel economy is neither increasing nor decreasing with increasing speed. $M'(70)\approx -0.0540$. This means that, at 70 mph, the fuel economy is decreasing at a rate of 0.0540 miles per gallon per one mph increase in speed. 60 mph is the most fuel-efficient speed for the car. (In the next chapter we shall discuss how to locate largest values in general.) **87. a.** $P(t)-I(t)$ represents the daily production of oil in Mexico that was not exported to the United States. $I(t)/P(t)$ represents U.S. imports of oil from Mexico as a fraction of the total produced there. **b.** -0.023 per year; at the start of 2008, the fraction of oil produced in Mexico that was imported by the United States was decreasing at a rate of 0.023 (or 2.3 percentage points) per year. **89.** Increasing at a rate of about \$3,420 million per year. **91.** $R'(p)=-\dfrac{5.625}{(1+0.125p)^2}$; $R'(4)=-2.5$ thousand organisms per hour, per 1,000 organisms. This means that the reproduction rate of organisms in a culture containing 4,000 organisms is declining at a rate of 2,500 organisms per hour, per 1,000 additional organisms. **93.** Oxygen consumption is decreasing at a rate of 1,600 milliliters per day. This is due to the fact that the number of eggs is decreasing, because $C'(25)$ is positive. **95.** 20; 33 **97.** $5/4$; $-17/16$ **99.** The analysis is suspect, as it seems to be asserting that the annual increase in revenue, which we can think of as dR/dt, is the product of the annual increases, dp/dt in price, and dq/dt in sales. However, because $R=pq$, the product rule implies that dR/dt is not the product of dp/dt and dq/dt, but is instead $\dfrac{dR}{dt}=\dfrac{dp}{dt}\cdot q+p\cdot\dfrac{dq}{dt}$. **101.** Answers will vary $q=-p+1{,}000$ is one example. **103.** Mine; it is increasing twice as fast as yours. The rate of change of revenue is given by $R'(t)=p'(t)q(t)$ because $q'(t)=0$. Thus, $R'(t)$ does not depend on the selling price $p(t)$. **105.** (A)

Section 11.4

1. $4(2x+1)$ **3.** $-(x-1)^{-2}$ **5.** $2(2-x)^{-3}$ **7.** $(2x+1)^{-0.5}$ **9.** $-3/(3x-1)^2$

11. $4(x^2+2x)^3(2x+2)$ **13.** $-4x(2x^2-2)^{-2}$
15. $-5(2x-3)(x^2-3x-1)^{-6}$ **17.** $-6x/(x^2+1)^4$
19. $1.5(0.2x-4.2)(0.1x^2-4.2x+9.5)^{0.5}$
21. $4(2s-0.5s^{-0.5})(s^2-s^{0.5})^3$ **23.** $-x/\sqrt{1-x^2}$
25. $\dfrac{3|3x-6|}{3x-6}$ **27.** $\dfrac{(-3x^2+5)|-x^3+5x|}{-x^3+5x}$
29. $-[(x+1)(x^2-1)]^{-3/2}(3x-1)(x+1)$
31. $6.2(3.1x-2)+6.2/(3.1x-2)^3$
33. $2[(6.4x-1)^2+(5.4x-2)^3]\times$ $[12.8(6.4x-1)+16.2(5.4x-2)^2]$
35. $-2(x^2-3x)^{-3}(2x-3)(1-x^2)^{0.5}$ $-x(x^2-3x)^{-2}(1-x^2)^{-0.5}$
37. $-56(x+2)/(3x-1)^3$ **39.** $3z^2(1-z^2)/(1+z^2)^4$
41. $3[(1+2x)^4-(1-x)^2]^2[8(1+2x)^3+2(1-x)]$
43. $6|3x-1|$ **45.** $\dfrac{|x-(2x-3)^{1/2}|}{x-(2x-3)^{1/2}}[1-(2x-3)^{-1/2}]$
47. $-\dfrac{\left(\dfrac{1}{\sqrt{2x+1}}-2x\right)}{\left(\sqrt{2x+1}-x^2\right)^2}$
49. $54(1+2x)^2(1+(1+2x)^3)^2(1+(1+(1+2x)^3)^3)^2$
51. $(100x^{99}-99x^{-2})\,dx/dt$
53. $(-3r^{-4}+0.5r^{-0.5})\,dr/dt$ **55.** $4\pi r^2 dr/dt$
57. $-47/4$ **59.** $1/3$ **61.** $-5/3$ **63.** $1/4$
65. $\left.\dfrac{dP}{dn}\right|_{n=10}=146{,}454.9$. At an employment level of 10 engineers, Paramount will increase its profit at a rate of \$146,454.90 per additional engineer hired. **67.** $y=35(7+0.2t)^{-0.25}$; -0.11 percentage points per month. **69.** $-\$30$ per additional ruby sold. The revenue is decreasing at a rate of \$30 per additional ruby sold.
71. $\dfrac{dy}{dt}=\dfrac{dy}{dx}\dfrac{dx}{dt}=(1.5)(-2)=-3$ murders per 100,000 residents/yr each year. **73.** $5/6\approx 0.833$; relative to the 2003 levels, home sales were changing at a rate of about 0.833 percentage points per percentage point change in price. (Equivalently, home sales in 2008 were dropping at a rate of about 0.833 percentage points per percentage point drop in price.) **75.** 12π mi^2/h **77.** $\$200{,}000\pi$/week $\approx$ \$628,000/week **79. a.** $q'(4)\approx 333$ units per month **b.** dR/dq = \$800/unit **c.** $dR/dt\approx$ \$267,000 per month **81.** 3% per year **83.** 8% per year **85.** The glob squared, times the derivative of the glob. **87.** The derivative of a quantity cubed is three times the *original quantity* squared, times the derivative of the quantity, not three times the derivative of the quantity squared. Thus, the correct answer is $3(3x^3-x)^2(9x^2-1)$.
89. First, the derivative of a quantity cubed is three times the *original quantity* squared times the derivative of the quantity, not three times the derivative of the quantity squared. Second, the derivative of a quotient is not the quotient of the derivatives; the quotient rule needs to be used in calculating the derivative of $\dfrac{3x^2-1}{2x-2}$. Thus, the correct result (before simplifying) is

$$3\left(\frac{3x^2-1}{2x-2}\right)^2\left(\frac{6x(2x-2)-(3x^2-1)(2)}{(2x-2)^2}\right).$$

91. Following the calculation thought experiment, pretend that you were evaluating the function at a specific value of x. If the last operation you would perform is addition or subtraction, look at each summand separately. If the last operation is multiplication, use the product rule first; if it is division, use the quotient rule first; if it is any other operation (such as raising a quantity to a power or taking a radical of a quantity) then use the chain rule first. **93.** An example is $f(x)=\sqrt{x+\sqrt{x+\sqrt{x+\sqrt{x+\sqrt{x+1}}}}}$.

Section 11.5

1. $1/(x-1)$ **3.** $1/(x\ln 2)$ **5.** $2x/(x^2+3)$
7. e^{x+3} **9.** $-e^{-x}$ **11.** $4^x\ln 4$ **13.** $2^{x^2-1}2x\ln 2$
15. $1+\ln x$ **17.** $2x\ln x+(x^2+1)/x$
19. $10x(x^2+1)^4\ln x+(x^2+1)^5/x$
21. $3/(3x-1)$ **23.** $4x/(2x^2+1)$
25. $(2x-0.63x^{-0.7})/(x^2-2.1x^{0.3})$
27. $-2/(-2x+1)+1/(x+1)$
29. $3/(3x+1)-4/(4x-2)$
31. $1/(x+1)+1/(x-3)-2/(2x+9)$
33. $5.2/(4x-2)$
35. $2/(x+1)-9/(3x-4)-1/(x-9)$
37. $\dfrac{1}{(x+1)\ln 2}$ **39.** $\dfrac{1-1/t^2}{(t+1/t)\ln 3}$ **41.** $\dfrac{2\ln|x|}{x}$
43. $\dfrac{2}{x}-\dfrac{2\ln(x-1)}{x-1}$ **45.** $e^x(1+x)$
47. $1/(x+1)+3e^x(x^3+3x^2)$ **49.** $e^x(\ln|x|+1/x)$
51. $2e^{2x+1}$ **53.** $(2x-1)e^{x^2-x+1}$ **55.** $2xe^{2x-1}(1+x)$
57. $4(e^{2x-1})^2$ **59.** $2\cdot 3^{2x-4}\ln 3$
61. $2\cdot 3^{2x+1}\ln 3+3e^{3x+1}$
63. $\dfrac{2x3^{x^2}[(x^2+1)\ln 3-1]}{(x^2+1)^2}$
65. $-4/(e^x-e^{-x})^2$

67. $5e^{5x-3}$ **69.** $-\frac{\ln x+1}{(x\ln x)^2}$ **71.** $2(x-1)$ **73.** $\frac{1}{x\ln x}$
75. $\frac{1}{2x\ln x}$ **77.** $y=(e/\ln 2)(x-1)\approx 3.92(x-1)$
79. $y=x$ **81.** $y=-[1/(2e)](x-1)+e$ **83.** $163 billion and increasing at a rate of $5.75 billion per year **85.** $163 billion and increasing at a rate of $5.75 billion per year. **87.** −1,653 years per gram; the age of the specimen is decreasing at a rate of about 1,653 years per additional one gram of carbon 14 present in the sample. (Equivalently, the age of the specimen is increasing at a rate of about 1,653 years per additional one gram less of carbon 14 in the sample.) **89.** Average price: $1.4 million; increasing at a rate of about $220,000 per year.
91. a. $N(15)\approx 1{,}762\approx 1{,}800$ (rounded to 2 significant digits) wiretap orders; $N'(15)\approx 89.87\approx 90$ wiretap orders per year (rounded to 2 significant digits). The constants in the model are specified to 2 significant digits, so we cannot expect the answer to be accurate to more than 2 digits. **b.** In 2005, the number of people whose communications were intercepted was about 180,000 and increasing at a rate of about 9,000 people per year. **c.** (C) **93.** $451.00 per year
95. $446.02 per year **97.** $A(t)=167(1.18)^t$; 280 new cases per day **99. a.** (A) **b.** The math SAT increases by approximately 0.97 points. **c.** $S'(x)$ decreases with increasing x, so that as parental income increases, the effect on math SAT scores decreases.
101. a. −6.25 years/child; when the fertility rate is 2 children per woman, the average age of a population is dropping at a rate of 6.25 years per one-child increase in the fertility rate. **b.** 0.160
103. 3,300,000 cases/week; 11,000,000 cases/week; 640,000 cases/week **105.** 2.1 percentage points per year; the rate of change is the slope of the tangent at $t=3$. This is also approximately the average rate of change over [2, 4], which is about $4/2=2$, in approximate agreement with the answer.
107. a. 2.1 percentage points per year
b. $\lim_{t\to+\infty} A(t)=15$; Had the trend continued indefinitely, the percentage of mortgages that were subprime would have approached 15% in the long term. $\lim_{t\to+\infty} A'(t)=0$; Had the trend continued indefinitely, the rate of change of the percentage of mortgages that were subprime would have approached 0 percentage points per year in the long term.
109. 277,000 people per year **111.** 0.000283 g/yr
113. $R(t)=350e^{-0.1t}(39t+68)$ million dollars; $R(2)\approx$ $42 billion; $R'(2)\approx$ $7 billion per year

115. e raised to the glob, times the derivative of the glob. **117.** 2 raised to the glob, times the derivative of the glob, times the natural logarithm of 2.
119. The derivative of ln $|u|$ is not $\frac{1}{|u|}\frac{du}{dx}$; it is $\frac{1}{u}\frac{du}{dx}$. Thus, the correct derivative is $\frac{3}{3x+1}$.
121. The power rule does not apply when the exponent is not constant. The derivative of 3 raised to a quantity is 3 raised to the quantity, times the derivative of the quantity, times ln 3. Thus, the correct answer is $3^{2x}\,2\ln 3$. **123.** No. If $N(t)$ is exponential, so is its derivative. **125.** If $f(x)=e^{kx}$, then the fractional rate of change is $\frac{f'(x)}{f(x)}=\frac{ke^{kx}}{e^{kx}}=k$, the fractional growth rate. **127.** If $A(t)$ is growing exponentially, then $A(t)=A_0e^{kt}$ for constants A_0 and k. Its percentage rate of change is then
$\frac{A'(t)}{A(t)}=\frac{kA_0e^{kt}}{A_0e^{kt}}=k$, a constant.

Section 11.6

1. −2/3 **3.** x **5.** $(y-2)/(3-x)$ **7.** $-y$
9. $-\frac{y}{x(1+\ln x)}$ **11.** $-x/y$ **13.** $-2xy/(x^2-2y)$
15. $-(6+9x^2y)/(9x^3-x^2)$ **17.** $3y/x$
19. $(p+10p^2q)/(2p-q-10pq^2)$
21. $(ye^x-e^y)/(xe^y-e^x)$ **23.** $se^{st}/(2s-te^{st})$
25. $ye^x/(2e^x+y^3e^y)$ **27.** $(y-y^2)/(-1+3y-y^2)$
29. $-y/(x+2y-xye^y-y^2e^y)$ **31. a.** 1
b. $y=x-3$ **33. a.** −2 **b.** $y=-2x$
35. a. −1 **b.** $y=-x+1$ **37. a.** −2,000
b. $y=-2{,}000x+6{,}000$ **39. a.** 0 **b.** $y=1$
41. a. −0.1898 **b.** $y=-0.1898x+1.4721$
43. $\frac{2x+1}{4x-2}\left[\frac{2}{2x+1}-\frac{4}{4x-2}\right]$
45. $\frac{(3x+1)^2}{4x(2x-1)^3}\left[\frac{6}{3x+1}-\frac{1}{x}-\frac{6}{2x-1}\right]$
47. $(8x-1)^{1/3}(x-1)\left[\frac{8}{3(8x-1)}+\frac{1}{x-1}\right]$
49. $(x^3+x)\sqrt{x^3+2}\left[\frac{3x^2+1}{x^3+x}+\frac{1}{2}\frac{3x^2}{x^3+2}\right]$
51. $x^x(1+\ln x)$ **53.** −$3,000 per worker. The monthly budget to maintain production at the fixed level P is decreasing by approximately $3,000 per additional worker at an employment level of 100 workers and a monthly operating budget of $200,000.

55. −125 T-shirts per dollar; when the price is set at \$5, the demand is dropping by 125 T-shirts per \$1 increase in price. **57.** $\left.\frac{dk}{de}\right|_{e=15} = -0.307$ carpenters per electrician. This means that, for a \$200,000 house whose construction employs 15 electricians, adding one more electrician would cost as much as approximately 0.307 additional carpenters. In other words, one electrician is worth approximately 0.307 carpenters. **59. a.** 22.93 hours. (The other root is rejected because it is larger than 30.) **b.** $\frac{dt}{dx} = \frac{4t - 20x}{0.4t - 4x}$; $\left.\frac{dt}{dx}\right|_{x=3.0} \approx$ −11.2 hours per grade point. This means that, for a 3.0 student who scores 80 on the examination, 1 grade point is worth approximately 11.2 hours.
61. $\frac{dr}{dy} = 2\frac{r}{y}$, so $\frac{dr}{dt} = 2\frac{r}{y}\frac{dy}{dt}$ by the chain rule.
63. x, y, y, x **65.** Let $y = f(x)g(x)$. Then $\ln y = \ln f(x) + \ln g(x)$, and

$$\frac{1}{y}\frac{dy}{dx} = \frac{f'(x)}{f(x)} + \frac{g'(x)}{g(x)},$$

so

$$\frac{dy}{dx} = y\left(\frac{f'(x)}{f(x)} + \frac{g'(x)}{g(x)}\right) = f(x)g(x)\left(\frac{f'(x)}{f(x)} + \frac{g'(x)}{g(x)}\right) = f'(x)g(x) + f(x)g'(x).$$

67. Writing $y = f(x)$ specifies y as an explicit function of x. This can be regarded as an equation giving y as an *implicit* function of x. The procedure of finding dy/dx by implicit differentiation is then the same as finding the derivative of y as an explicit function of x: We take d/dx of both sides. **69.** Differentiate both sides of the equation $y = f(x)$ with respect to y to get $1 = f'(x) \cdot \frac{dx}{dy}$, giving $\frac{dx}{dy} = \frac{1}{f'(x)} = \frac{1}{dy/dx}$.

Chapter 11 Review

1. $50x^4 + 2x^3 - 1$ **3.** $9x^2 + x^{-2/3}$ **5.** $1 - 2/x^3$
7. $-\frac{4}{3x^2} + \frac{0.2}{x^{1.1}} + \frac{1.1x^{0.1}}{3.2}$ **9.** $e^x(x^2 + 2x - 1)$
11. $(-3x|x| + |x|/x - 6x)/(3x^2 + 1)^2$
13. $-4(4x - 1)^{-2}$ **15.** $20x(x^2 - 1)^9$
17. $-0.43(x + 1)^{-1.1}[2 + (x + 1)^{-0.1}]^{3.3}$
19. $e^x(x^2 + 1)^9(x^2 + 20x + 1)$
21. $3^x[(x - 1)\ln 3 - 1]/(x - 1)^2$ **23.** $2xe^{x^2-1}$
25. $2x/(x^2 - 1)$ **27.** $x = 7/6$ **29.** $x = \pm 2$
31. $x = (1 - \ln 2)/2$ **33.** None **35.** $\frac{2x - 1}{2y}$
37. $-y/x$ **39.** $\frac{(2x - 1)^4(3x + 4)}{(x + 1)(3x - 1)^3} \times \left[\frac{8}{2x - 1} + \frac{3}{3x + 4} - \frac{1}{x + 1} - \frac{9}{3x - 1}\right]$
41. $y = -x/4 + 1/2$ **43.** $y = -3ex - 2e$
45. $y = x + 2$ **47. a.** 274 books per week **b.** 636 books per week **c.** The function w begins to decrease more and more rapidly after $t = 14$ Graph:

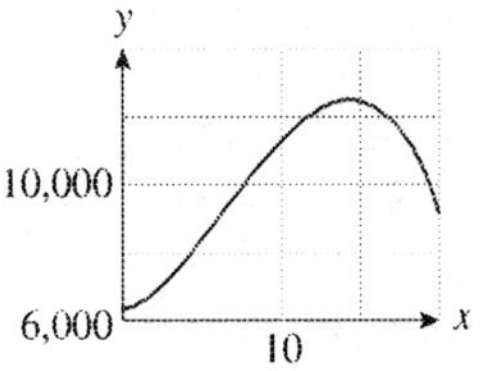

d. Because the data suggest an upward curving parabola, the long-term prediction of sales for a quadratic model would be that sales will increase without bound, in sharp contrast to (c) **49. a.** \$2.88 per book **b.** \$3.715 per book **c.** Approximately −\$0.000104 per book, per additional book sold. **d.** At a sales level of 8,000 books per week, the cost is increasing at a rate of \$2.88 per book (so that the 8,001st book costs approximately \$2.88 to sell), and it costs an average of \$3.715 per book to sell the first 8,000 books. Moreover, the average cost is decreasing at a rate of \$0.000104 per book, per additional book sold.
51. a. \$3,000 per week (rising) **b.** 300 books per week
53. $R = pq$ gives $R' = p'q + pq'$. Thus, $R'/R = R'/(pq) = (p'q + pq')/pq = p'/p + q'/q$
55. \$110 per year **57. a.** $s'(t) = \frac{2{,}475e^{-0.55(t-4.8)}}{(1 + e^{-0.55(t-4.8)})^2}$; 556 books per week **b.** 0; In the long term, the rate of increase of weekly sales slows to zero. **59.** 616.8 hits per day per week. **61. a.** −17.24 copies per \$1. The demand for the gift edition of *The Complete Larry Potter* is dropping at a rate of about 17.24 copies per \$1 increase in the price. **b.** \$138 per dollar is positive, so the price should be raised.

Chapter 12

Section 12.1

1. Absolute min: (−3, −1), relative max: (−1, 1), relative min: (1, 0), absolute max: (3, 2) **3.** Absolute min: (3, −1) and (−3, −1), absolute max: (1, 2)
5. Absolute min: (−3, 0) and (1, 0), absolute max: (−1, 2) and (3, 2) **7.** Relative min: (−1, 1)
9. Absolute min: (−3, −1), relative max: (−2, 2), relative min: (1, 0), absolute max: (3, 3)

11. Relative max: $(-3, 0)$, absolute min: $(-2, -1)$, stationary nonextreme point: $(1, 1)$ **13.** Absolute max: $(0, 1)$, absolute min: $(2, -3)$, relative max: $(3, -2)$ **15.** Absolute min: $(-4, -16)$, absolute max: $(-2, 16)$, absolute min: $(2, -16)$, absolute max: $(4, 16)$ **17.** Absolute min: $(-2, -10)$, absolute max: $(2, 10)$ **19.** Absolute min: $(-2, -4)$, relative max: $(-1, 1)$, relative min: $(0, 0)$ **21.** Relative max: $(-1, 5)$, absolute min: $(3, -27)$ **23.** Absolute min: $(0, 0)$ **25.** Absolute maxima at $(0, 1)$ and $(2, 1)$, absolute min at $(1, 0)$ **27.** Relative maximum at $(-2, -1/3)$, relative minimum at $(-1, -2/3)$, absolute maximum at $(0, 1)$ **29.** Relative min: $(-2, 5/3)$, relative max: $(0, -1)$, relative min: $(2, 5/3)$ **31.** Relative max: $(0, 0)$; absolute min: $(1/3, -2\sqrt{3}/9)$ **33.** Relative max: $(0, 0)$, absolute min: $(1, -3)$ **35.** No relative extrema **37.** Absolute min: $(1, 1)$ **39.** Relative max: $(-1, 1 + 1/e)$, absolute min: $(0, 1)$, absolute max: $(1, e - 1)$ **41.** Relative max: $(-6, -24)$, relative min: $(-2, -8)$ **43.** Absolute max $(1/\sqrt{2}, \sqrt{e/2})$, absolute min: $(-1/\sqrt{2}, -\sqrt{e/2})$ **45.** Relative min at $(0.15, -0.52)$ and $(2.45, 8.22)$, relative max at $(1.40, 0.29)$ **47.** Absolute max at $(-5, 700)$, relative max at $(3.10, 28.19)$ and $(6, 40)$, absolute min at $(-2.10, -392.69)$ and relative min at $(5, 0)$. **49.** Stationary minimum at $x = -1$ **51.** Stationary minima at $x = -2$ and $x = 2$, stationary maximum at $x = 0$ **53.** Singular minimum at $x = 0$, stationary nonextreme point at $x = 1$ **55.** Stationary minimum at $x = -2$, singular nonextreme points at $x = -1$ and $x = 1$, stationary maximum at $x = 2$

57. Answers will vary.

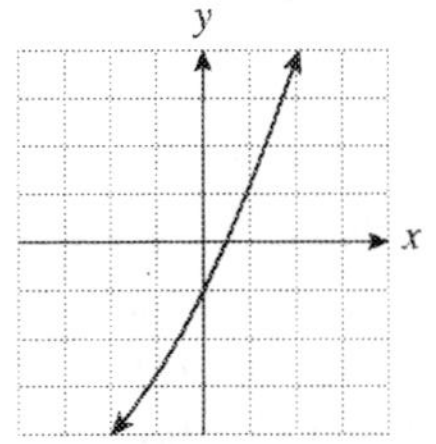

59. Answers will vary.

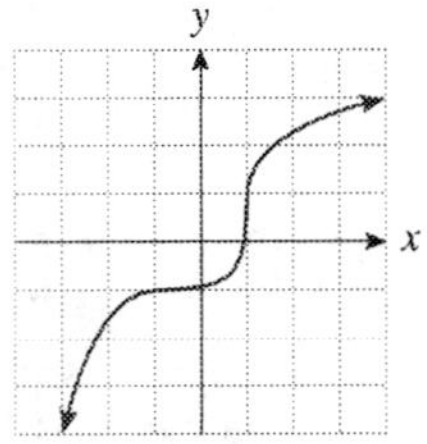

61. Not necessarily; it could be neither a relative maximum nor a relative minimum, as in the graph of $y = x^3$ at the origin.

63. Answers will vary.

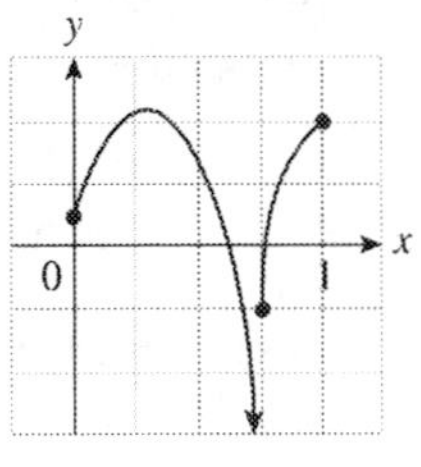

65. The graph oscillates faster and faster above and below zero as it approaches the end-point at 0, so 0 cannot be either a relative minimum or maximum.

Section 12.2

1. $x = y = 5$; $P = 25$ **3.** $x = y = 3$; $S = 6$ **5.** $x = 2$, $y = 4$; $F = 20$ **7.** $x = 20$, $y = 10$, $z = 20$; $P = 4{,}000$ **9.** 5×5 **11.** 1,500 per day for an average cost of \$130 per iPod **13.** $\sqrt{40} \approx 6.32$ pounds of pollutant per day, for an average cost of about \$1,265 per pound **15.** 2.5 lb **17.** 5×10 **19.** 50×10 for an area of 250 sq. ft. **21.** 11×22 **23.** \$10 **25.** \$78 for a quarterly revenue of \$6,084 million, or \$6.084 billion **27.** \$4.61 for a daily revenue of \$95,680.55 **29. a.** \$1.41 per pound **b.** 5,000 pounds **c.** \$7,071.07 per month **31.** 34.5¢ per pound, for an annual (per capita) revenue of \$5.95 **33.** \$98 for an annual profit of \$3,364 million, or \$3.364 billion **35. a.** 656 headsets, for a profit of \$28,120 **b.** \$143 per headset **37.** Height = Radius of base $\approx$ 20.48 cm. **39.** Height $\approx$ 10.84 cm; Radius $\approx$ 2.71 cm; Height/Radius = 4 **41.** $13\frac{1}{3}$ in $\times$ $3\frac{1}{3}$ in $\times$ $1\frac{1}{3}$ in for a volume of $1{,}600/27 \approx 59$ cubic inches **43.** $5 \times 5 \times 5$ cm **45.** $l = w = h \approx 20.67$ in, volume $\approx 8{,}827$ in^3 **47.** $l = 30$ in, $w = 15$ in, $h = 30$ in **49.** $l = 36$ in, $w = h = 18$ in, $V = 11{,}664$ in^3 **51. a.** 1.6 years, or year 2001.6; **b.** $R_{max} = \$28{,}241$ million **53.** $t = 2.5$ or midway through 1972; $D(2.5)/S(2.5) \approx 4.09$. The number of new (approved) drugs per \$1 billion of spending on research and development reached a high of around four approved drugs per \$1 billion midway through 1972. **55.** 30 years from now **57.** 55 days **59.** 1,600 copies. At this value of x, average profit equals marginal profit; beyond this the marginal profit is smaller than the average. **61.** 40 laborers and 250 robots **63.** 71 employees **65.** Increasing most rapidly in 1990; increasing least rapidly in 2007 **67.** Maximum when $t = 17$ days. This means that the embryo's oxygen consumption is increasing most rapidly 17 days after the egg is laid. **69.** Graph of derivative:

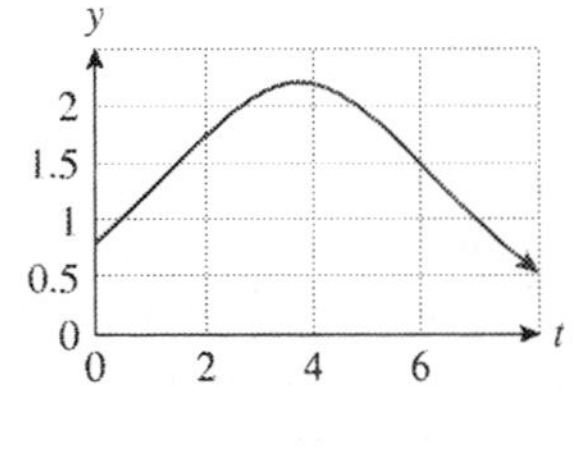

The absolute maximum occurs at approximately (3.7, 2.2) during the year 2003. The percentage of mortgages that were subprime was increasing most rapidly during 2003, when it increased at a rate of around 2.2 percentage points per year. **71.** You should sell them in 17 years' time, when they will be worth approximately \$3,960. **73.** 25 additional trees **75.** (D) **77.** (A); (B) **79.** The problem is uninteresting because the company can accomplish the objective by cutting away the entire sheet of cardboard, resulting in a box with surface area zero. **81.** Not all absolute extrema occur at stationary points; some may occur at an endpoint or singular point of the domain, as in Exercises 29, 30, 65, and 66. **83.** The minimum of dq/dp is the fastest that the demand is dropping in response to increasing price.

Section 12.3

1. 6 **3.** $4/x^3$ **5.** $-0.96x^{-1.6}$ **7.** $e^{-(x-1)}$ **9.** $2/x^3 + 1/x^2$ **11. a.** $a = -32$ ft/sec^2 **b.** $a = -32$ ft/sec^2 **13. a.** $a = 2/t^3 + 6/t^4$ ft/sec^2 **b.** $a = 8$ ft/sec^2 **15. a.** $a = -1/(4t^{3/2}) + 2$ ft/sec^2 **b.** $a = 63/32$ ft/sec^2 **17.** (1, 0) **19.** (1, 0) **21.** None **23.** (−1, 0), (1, 1) **25.** Points of inflection at $x = -1$ and $x = 1$ **27.** One point of inflection, at $x = -2$ **29.** Points of inflection at $x = -2, x = 0, x = 2$ **31.** Points of inflection at $x = -2$ and $x = 2$ **33.** $x = 2$; minimum **35.** Maximum at $x = -2$, minimum at $x = 2$ **37.** Maximum at $t = -1/\sqrt{3}$, minimum at $t = 1/\sqrt{3}$ **39.** Nonextreme stationary point at $x = 0$ minimum at $x = 3$ **41.** Maximum at $x = 0$ **43.** Minimum at $x = -1/\sqrt{2}$; maximum at $x = 1/\sqrt{2}$ **45.** $f'(x) = 8x - 1$; $f''(x) = 8$; $f'''(x) = f^{(4)}(x) = \ldots = f^{(n)}(x) = 0$ **47.** $f'(x) = -4x^3 + 6x$; $f''(x) = -12x^2 + 6$; $f'''(x) = -24x$; $f^{(4)}(x) = -24$; $f^{(5)}(x) = f^{(6)}(x) = \ldots = f^{(n)}(x) = 0$ **49.** $f'(x) = 8(2x+1)^3$; $f''(x) = 48(2x+1)^2$; $f'''(x) = 192(2x+1)$; $f^{(4)}(x) = 384$; $f^{(5)}(x) = f^{(6)}(x) = \ldots = f^{(n)}(x) = 0$ **51.** $f'(x) = -e^{-x}$; $f''(x) = e^{-x}$; $f'''(x) = -e^{-x}$; $f^{(4)}(x) = e^{-x}$; $f^{(n)}(x) = (-1)^n e^{-x}$ **53.** $f'(x) = 3e^{3x-1}$; $f''(x) = 9e^{3x-1}$; $f'''(x) = 27e^{3x-1}$; $f^{(4)}(x) = 81e^{3x-1}$; $f^{(n)}(x) = 3^n e^{3x-1}$ **55.** −3.8 m/s^2 **57.** $6t - 2$ ft/s^2; increasing **59.** Decelerating by 90 million gals/yr^2 **61. a.** 400 ml **b.** 36 ml/day **c.** −1 ml/day^2 **63. a.** 0.6% **b.** Speeding up **c.** Speeding up for $t < 3.33$ (prior to 1/3 of the way through March) and slowing for $t > 3.33$ (after that time) **65. a.** December 2005: −0.202% (deflation rate of 0.202%) February 2006: 0.363% **b.** Speeding up **c.** Speeding up for $t > 4.44$ (after mid-November) and decreasing for $t < 4.44$ (prior to that time). **67.** Concave up for $8 < t < 20$, concave down for $0 < t < 8$, point of inflection around $t = 8$. The percentage of articles written by researchers in the United States was decreasing most rapidly at around $t = 8$ (1991). **69. a.** (B) **b.** (B) **c.** (A) **71.** Graphs:

$A(t)$:

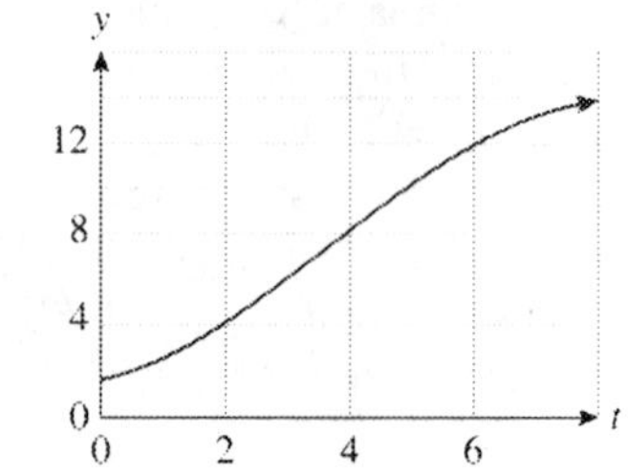

$A'(t)$:

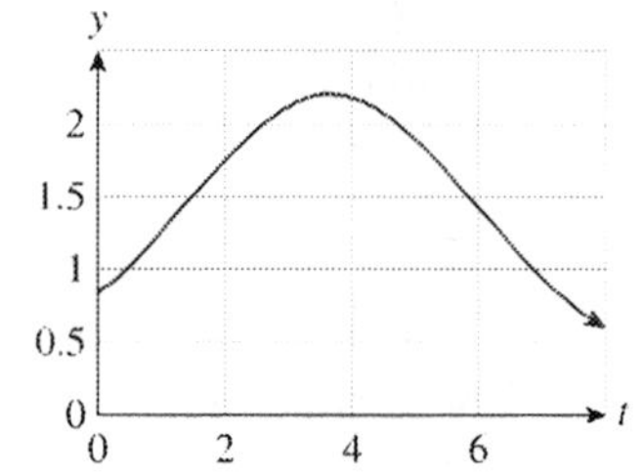

$A''(t)$:

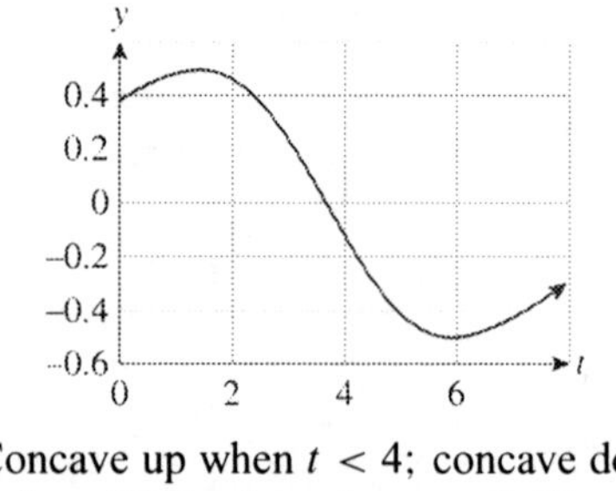

Concave up when $t < 4$; concave down when $t > 4$; point of inflection when $t \approx 4$. The percentage of U.S. mortgages that were subprime was increasing fastest at the beginning of 2004. **73. a.** 2 years into the epidemic **b.** 2 years into the epidemic **75. a.** 2024 **b.** 2026 **c.** 2022; (A) **77. a.** There are no points of inflection in the graph of S. **b.** Because the graph is concave up, the derivative of S is increasing, and so the rate of *decrease* of SAT scores with increasing numbers of prisoners was diminishing. In other words, the apparent effect of more prisoners on SAT scores was diminishing. **79. a.** $\left.\frac{d^2n}{ds^2}\right|_{s=3} = -21.494$. Thus, for a firm with annual sales of \$3 million, the rate at which new patents are produced decreases with increasing firm size. This means that the returns (as measured in the number of new patents per increase of \$1 million in sales) are diminishing as the firm size increases. **b.** $\left.\frac{d^2n}{ds^2}\right|_{s=7} = 13.474$. Thus, for a firm with annual sales of \$7 million, the rate at which new patents are produced increases with increasing firm size by 13.474 new patents per \$1 million increase in annual sales. **c.** There is a point of inflection when $s \approx 5.4587$, so that in a firm with sales of \$5,458,700 per year, the number of new patents produced per additional \$1 million in sales is a minimum.

81. Graphs:

$I(t)/P(t)$:

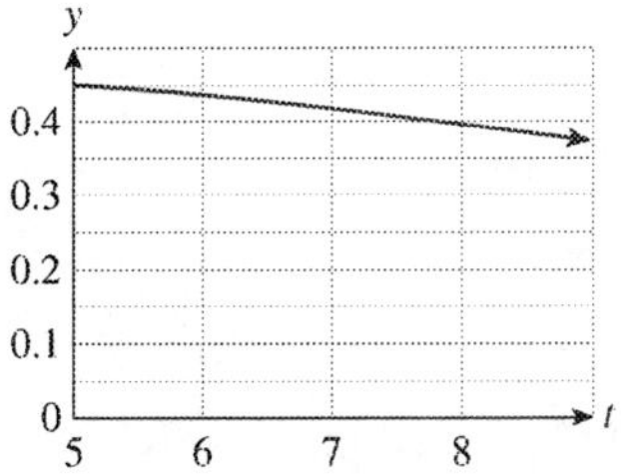

$[I(t)/P(t)]'$:

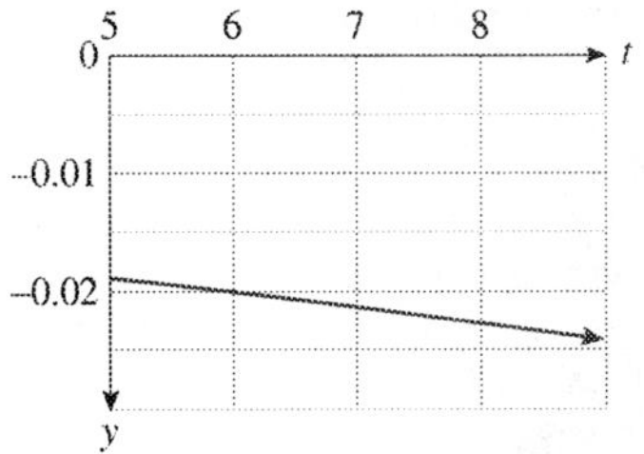

Concave down; (D) **83.** (Proof) **85.** $t \approx 4$; the population of Puerto Rico was increasing fastest in 1954. **87.** About \$570 per year, after about 12 years **89.** Increasing most rapidly in 17.64 years, decreasing most rapidly now (at $t = 0$) **91.** Non-negative **93.** Daily sales were decreasing most rapidly in June 2002.

95.

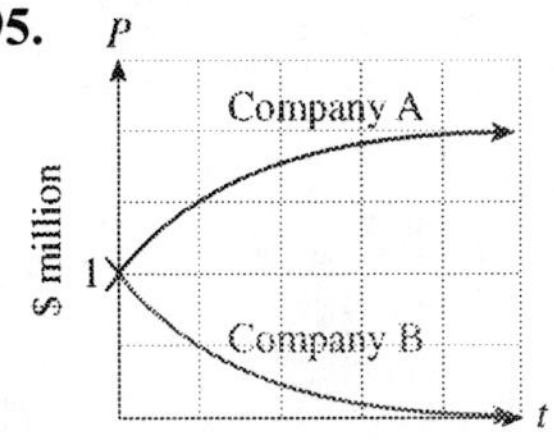

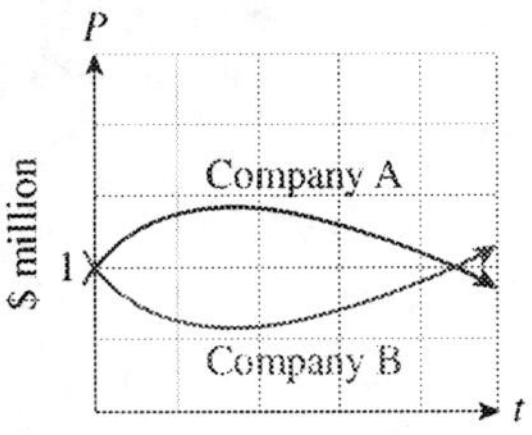

97. At a point of inflection, the graph of a function changes either from concave up to concave down, or vice versa. If it changes from concave up to concave down, then the derivative changes from increasing to decreasing, and hence has a relative maximum. Similarly, if it changes from concave down to concave up, the derivative has a relative minimum.

Section 12.4

1. a. x-intercept: -1; y-intercept: 1 **b.** Absolute min at $(-1, 0)$ **c.** None **d.** None **e.** $y \to +\infty$ as $x \to \pm\infty$
Graph:

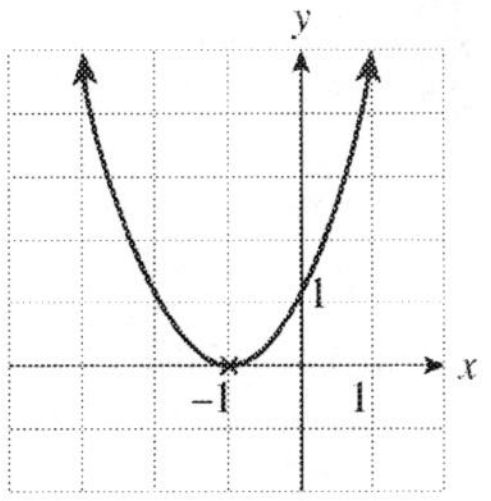

3. a. x-intercepts: $-\sqrt{12}$, 0, $\sqrt{12}$; y-intercept: 0
b. Absolute min at $(-4, -16)$ and $(2, -16)$, absolute max at $(-2, 16)$ and $(4, 16)$ **c.** $(0, 0)$ **d.** None
e. None
Graph:

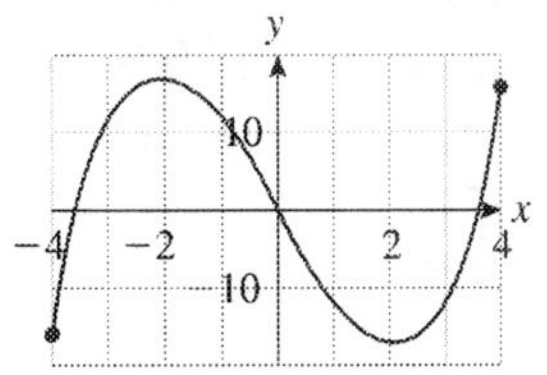

5. a. x-intercepts: -3.6, 0, 5.1; y-intercept: 0
b. Relative max at $(-2, 44)$, relative min at $(3, -81)$
c. $(0.5, -18.5)$ **d.** None **e.** $y \to -\infty$ as $x \to -\infty$; $y \to +\infty$ as $x \to +\infty$
Graph:

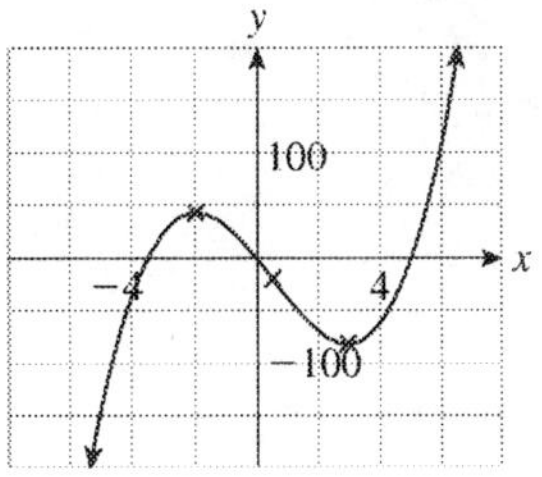

7. a. x-intercepts: -3.3, 0.1, 1.8; y-intercept: 1
b. Relative max at $(-2, 21)$, relative min at $(1, -6)$
c. $(-1/2, 15/2)$ **d.** None **e.** $y \to -\infty$ as $x \to -\infty$; $y \to +\infty$ as $x \to +\infty$

Answers to Selected Exercises

Graph:

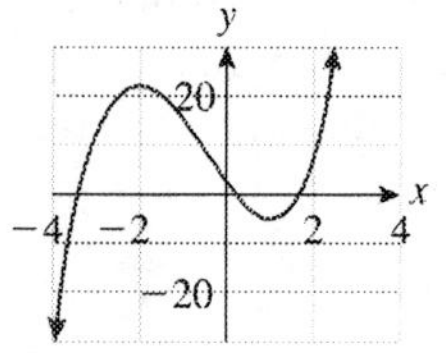

9. a. x-intercepts: $-2.9, 4.2$; y-intercept: 10 **b.** Relative max at $(-2, 74)$, relative min at $(0, 10)$, absolute max at $(3, 199)$ **c.** $(-1.12, 44.8)$, $(1.79, 117.3)$ **d.** None **e.** $y \to -\infty$ as $x \to -\infty$; $y \to -\infty$ as $x \to +\infty$

Graph:

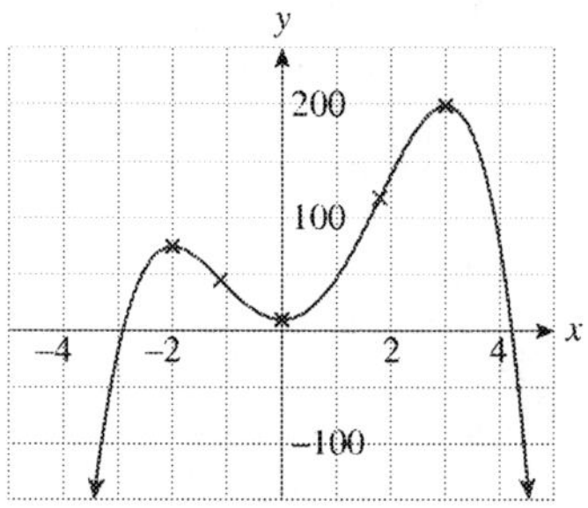

11. a. t-intercepts: $t = 0$; y-intercept: 0 **b.** Absolute min at $(0, 0)$ **c.** $(1/3, 11/324)$ and $(1, 1/12)$ **d.** None **e.** $y \to +\infty$ as $t \to -\infty$; $y \to +\infty$ as $t \to +\infty$

Graph:

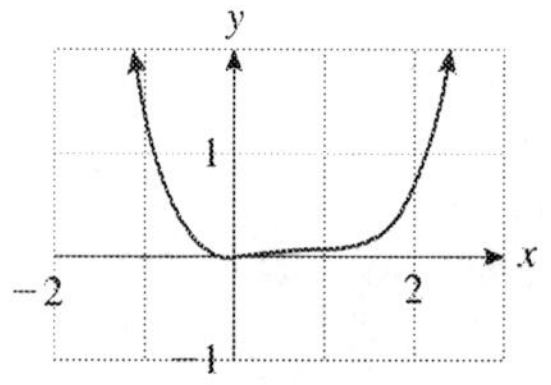

13. a. x-intercepts: None; y-intercept: None **b.** Relative min at $(1, 2)$, relative max at $(-1, -2)$ **c.** None **d.** $y \to -\infty$ as $x \to 0^-$; $y \to +\infty$ as $x \to 0^+$, so there is a vertical asymptote at $x = 0$. **e.** $y \to -\infty$ as $x \to -\infty$; $y \to +\infty$ as $x \to +\infty$

Graph:

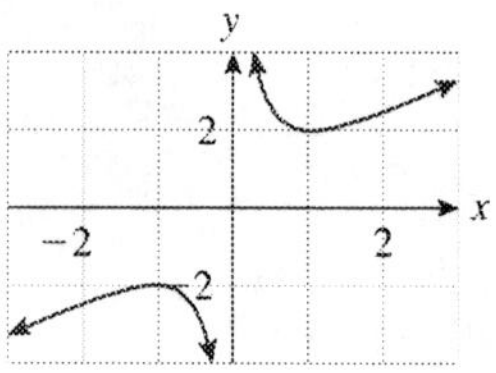

15. a. x-intercept: 0; y-intercept: 0 **b.** None **c.** $(0, 0)$, $(-3, -9/4)$, and $(3, 9/4)$ **d.** None **e.** $y \to -\infty$ as $x \to -\infty$; $y \to +\infty$ as $x \to +\infty$

Graph:

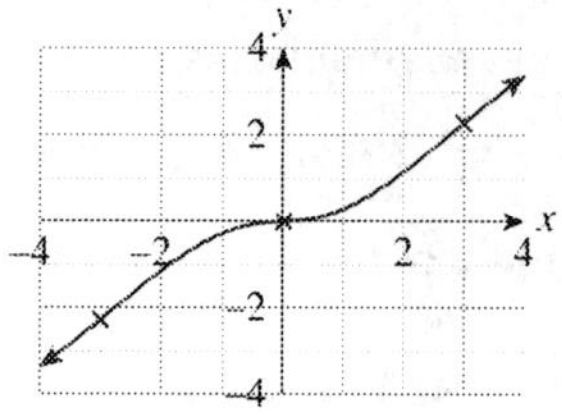

17. a. t-intercepts: None; y-intercept: -1 **b.** Relative min at $(-2, 5/3)$ and $(2, 5/3)$, relative max at $(0, -1)$ **c.** None **d.** $y \to +\infty$ as $t \to -1^-$; $y \to -\infty$ as $t \to -1^+$; $y \to -\infty$ as $t \to 1^-$; $y \to +\infty$ as $t \to 1^+$; so there are vertical asymptotes at $t = \pm 1$. **e.** None

Graph:

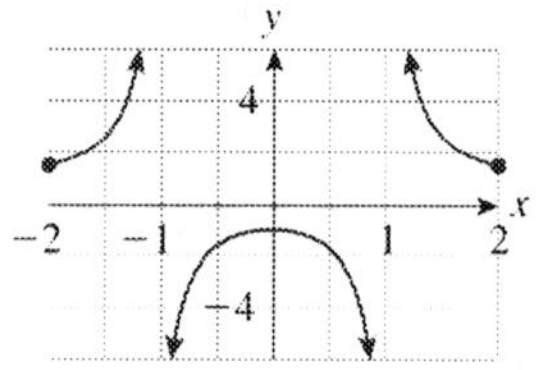

19. a. x-intercepts: -0.6; y-intercept: 1 **b.** Relative maximum at $(-2, -1/3)$, relative minimum at $(-1, -2/3)$ **c.** None **d.** None. **e.** $y \to -\infty$ as $x \to -\infty$; $y \to +\infty$ as $x \to +\infty$

Graph:

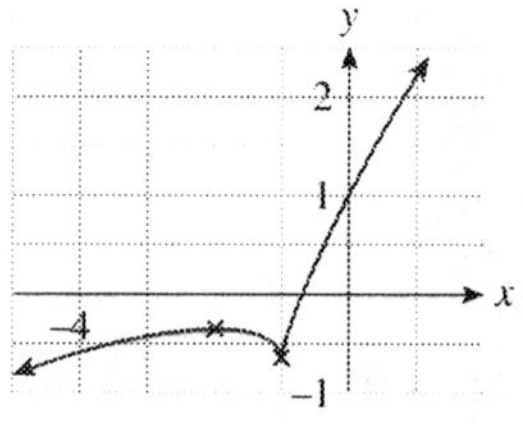

21. a. x-intercepts: None; y-intercept: None **b.** Absolute min at $(1, 1)$ **c.** None **d.** Vertical asymptote at $x = 0$ **e.** $y \to +\infty$ as $x \to +\infty$

Graph:

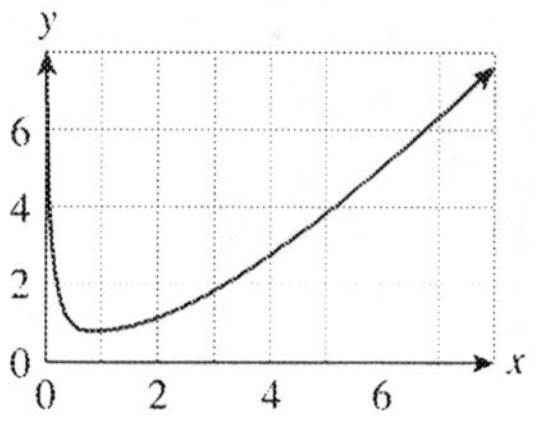

23. a. x-intercepts: ± 0.8; x-intercept: None **b.** None **c.** $(1,1)$ and $(-1, 1)$ **d.** $y \to -\infty$ as $x \to 0$; vertical asymptote at $x = 0$ **e.** $y \to +\infty$ as $x \to \pm\infty$

Graph:

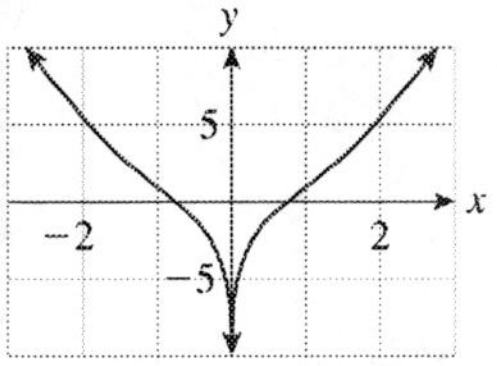

25. a. t-intercepts: None; y-intercept: 1 **b.** Absolute min at (0, 1). Absolute max at $(1, e - 1)$, relative max at $(-1, e^{-1} + 1)$. **c.** None **d.** None **e.** None
Graph:

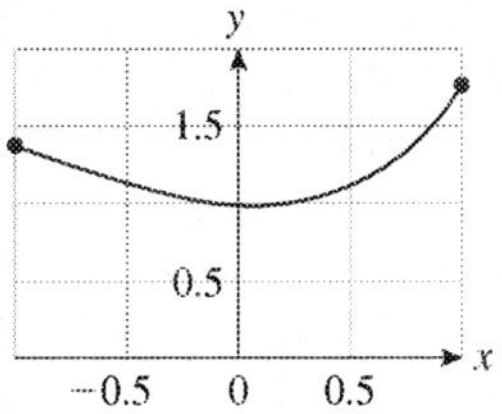

27. Absolute min at (1.40, −1.49); points of inflection: (0.21, 0.61), (0.79, −0.55)
Graph:

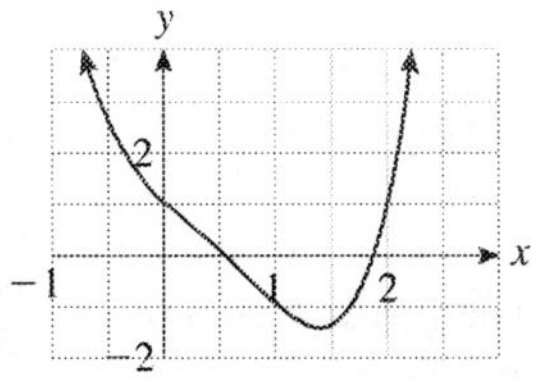

29. $f(x) = e^x - x^3$. Relative min at (−0.46, 0.73), relative max at (0.91, 1.73), absolute min at (3.73, −10.22); points of inflection at (0.20, 1.22) and (2.83, −5.74)
Graph:

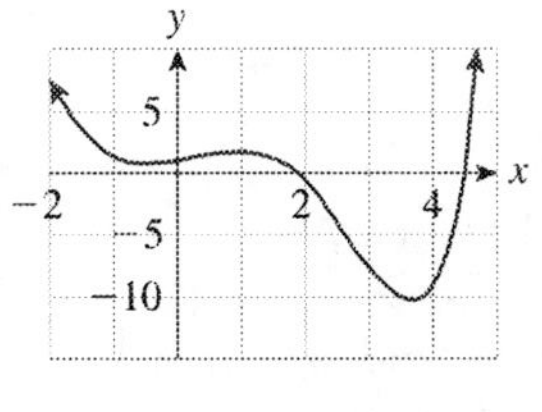

31. y-intercept: 125; t-intercepts: None. The median home price was about $125,000 at the start of 2000 ($t = 0$). Extrema: Absolute minimum at (0, 125); absolute maximum at (6, 225). The median home price was lowest in 2000 ($t = 0$) when it stood at $125,000; the median home price was at its highest at the start of 2006 ($t = 6$) at $225,000. Points of inflection at (3, 175) and (10, 200). The median home price was increasing most rapidly at the start of 2003 ($t = 3$) when it was $175,000, and decreasing most rapidly at the start of 2010 when it was $200,000. Points where the function is not defined: None. Behavior at infinity: As $t \to +\infty$, $y \to 175$. Assuming the trend shown in the graph continues indefinitely, the median home price will approach a value of $175,000 in the long term. **33. a.** Intercepts: No t-intercept; y-intercept at $I(0) = 195$. The CPI was never zero during the given period; in July 2005 the CPI was 195. Absolute min at (0, 195), absolute max at (8, 199.3), relative max at (2.9, 198.7), relative min at (6.0, 197.8). The CPI was at a low of 195 in July 2005, rose to 198.7 around October 2005, dipped to 197.8 around January 2006, and then rose to a high of 199.3 in March 2006. There is a point of inflection at (4.4, 198.2). The rate of change of the CPI (inflation) reached a minimum around mid-November 2005 when the CPI was 198.2. **b.** The inflation rate was zero at around October 2005 and January 2006. **35.** Extrema: Relative max at (0, 100), absolute min at (1, 99); point of inflection (0.5, 99.5); $s \to +\infty$ as $t \to +\infty$. At time $t = 0$ seconds, the UFO is 100 ft away from the observer, and begins to move closer. At time $t = 0.5$ seconds, when the UFO is 99.5 feet away, its distance is decreasing most rapidly (it is moving toward the observer most rapidly). It then slows down to a stop at $t = 1$ sec when it is at its closest point (99 ft away) and then begins to move further and further away.
Graph:

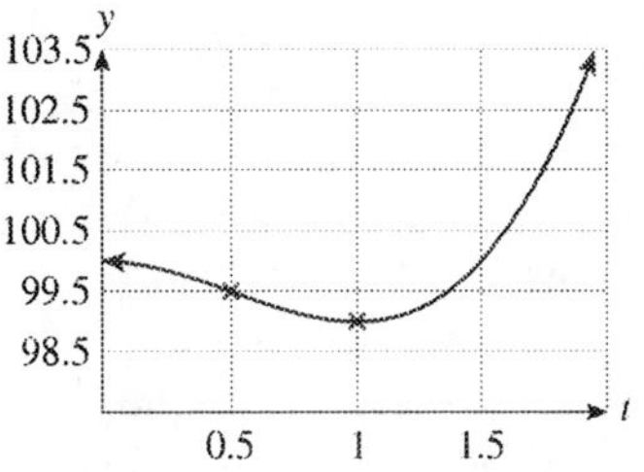

37. Intercepts: None; Absolute minimum at (1,500, 130); No points of inflection; vertical asymptote at $x = 0$. As $x \to +\infty$, $y \to +\infty$. The average cost is never zero, nor is it defined for zero iPods. The average cost is a minimum ($130) when 1,500 iPods are manufactured per day. The average cost becomes extremely large for very small or very large numbers of iPods.

Graph:

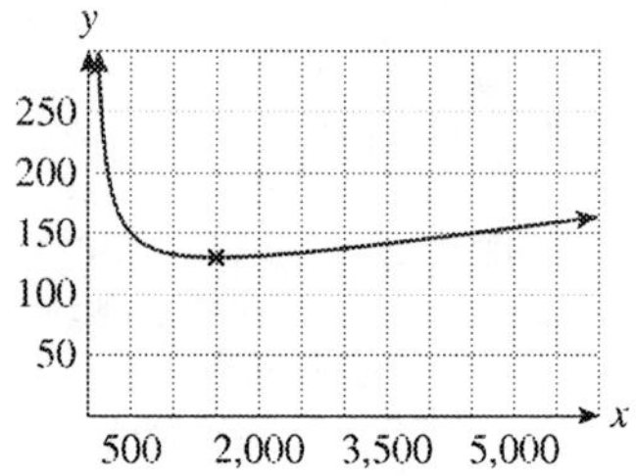

39. Graph of derivative:

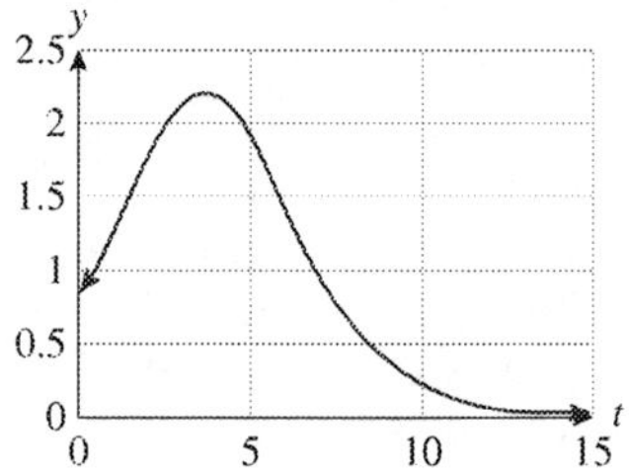

The absolute maximum occurs at approximately (3.7, 2.2); during the year 2003. The percentage of mortgages that were subprime was increasing most rapidly during 2003, when it increased at a rate of around 2.2 percentage points per year. As $t \to +\infty$, $A'(t) \to 0$; In the long term, assuming the trend shown in the model continues, the rate of change of the percentage of mortgages that were subprime approaches zero; that is, the percentage of mortgages that were subprime approaches a constant value. **41.** No; yes. Near a vertical asymptote the value of y increases without bound, and so the graph could not be included between two horizontal lines; hence, no vertical asymptotes are possible. Horizontal asymptotes are possible, as for instance in the graph in Exercise 31. **43.** It too has a vertical asymptote at $x = a$; the magnitude of the derivative increases without bound as $x \to a$. **45.** No. If the leftmost critical point is a relative maximum, the function will decrease from there until it reaches the rightmost critical point, so can't have a relative maximum there. **47.** Between every pair of zeros of $f(x)$ there must be a local extremum, which must be a stationary point of $f(x)$, hence a zero of $f'(x)$.

Section 12.5

1. $P = 10{,}000$; $\dfrac{dP}{dt} = 1{,}000$ **3.** Let R be the annual revenue of my company, and let q be annual sales. $R = 7{,}000$ and $\dfrac{dR}{dt} = -700$. Find $\dfrac{dq}{dt}$. **5.** Let p be the price of a pair of shoes, and let q be the demand for shoes. $\dfrac{dp}{dt} = 5$. Find $\dfrac{dq}{dt}$. **7.** Let T be the average global temperature, and let q be the number of Bermuda shorts sold per year. $T = 60$ and $\dfrac{dT}{dt} = 0.1$. Find $\dfrac{dq}{dt}$. **9. a.** $6/(100\pi) \approx 0.019$ km/sec **b.** $6/(8\sqrt{\pi}\,) \approx 0.4231$ km/sec **11.** $3/(4\pi) \approx 0.24$ ft/min **13.** 7.5 ft/sec **15.** Decreasing at a rate of \$1.66 per player per week **17.** Monthly sales will drop at a rate of 26 T-shirts per month. **19.** Raise the price by 3¢ per week. **21.** Increasing at a rate of \$233.68 million per year **23.** 1 laborer per month **25.** Dropping at a rate of \$2.40 per year. **27.** The price is decreasing at a rate of approximately 31¢ per pound per month. **29.** $2{,}300/\sqrt{4{,}100} \approx 36$ miles/hour. **31.** About 10.7 ft/sec **33.** The y coordinate is decreasing at a rate of 16 units per second. **35.** \$534 per year **37.** Their prior experience must increase at a rate of approximately 0.97 years every year. **39.** $\dfrac{2{,}500}{9\pi}\left(\dfrac{3}{5{,}000}\right)^{2/3} \approx 0.63$ m/sec **41.** $\dfrac{\sqrt{1+128\pi}}{4\pi} \approx 1.6$ cm/sec **43.** 0.5137 computers per household, and increasing at a rate of 0.0230 computers per household per year. **45.** The average SAT score was 904.71 and decreasing at a rate of 0.11 per year. **47.** Decreasing by 2 percentage points per year **49.** The section is called "related rates" because the goal is to compute the rate of change of a quantity based on a knowledge of the rate of change of a related quantity. **51.** Answers may vary: A rectangular solid has dimensions 2 cm × 5 cm × 10 cm, and each side is expanding at a rate of 3 cm/second. How fast is the volume increasing? **53.** (Proof) **55.** Linear **57.** Let x = my grades and y = your grades. If $dx/dt = 2\,dy/dt$, then $dy/dt = (1/2)\,dx/dt$.

Section 12.6

1. $E = 1.5$; the demand is going down 1.5% per 1% increase in price at that price level; revenue is maximized when $p = \$25$; weekly revenue at that price is \$12,500. **3. a.** $E = 6/7$; the demand is going down 6% per 7% increase in price at that price level; thus, a price increase is in order. **b.** Revenue is maximized when $p = 100/3 \approx \$33.33$ **c.** 4,444 cases per week **5. a.** $E = (4p - 33)/(-2p + 33)$ **b.** 0.54; the demand for $E = mc^2$ T-shirts is going down by about 0.54% per 1% increase in the price. **c.** \$11 per shirt for a daily revenue of \$1,331 **7. a.** $E = 1.81$. Thus, the demand is elastic at the given tuition level, showing that a decrease in tuition will result in an increase in revenue. **b.** They should charge an average of \$2,250 per student, and this will result in an enrollment of about 4,950 students, giving a revenue of about \$11,137,500. **9. a.** $E = 51$; the demand is going down 51% per 1% increase in price at that price level; thus, a large price decrease is advised. **b.** ¥50 **c.** About 78 paint-by-number sets per month **11. a.** $E = -\dfrac{mp}{mp+b}$ **b.** $p = -\dfrac{b}{2m}$ **13. a.** $E = r$ **b.** E is independent of p. **c.** If $r = 1$, then the revenue is not affected by the price. If $r > 1$, then the revenue is always elastic, while if $r < 1$, the revenue is always inelastic. This is an unrealistic model because there should always be a price at which the revenue is a maximum. **15. a.** $q = -1{,}500p + 6{,}000$. **b.** \$2 per hamburger, giving a total weekly revenue of \$6,000 **17.** $E \approx 0.77$. At a family income level of \$20,000, the fraction of children attending a live theatrical performance is increasing by 0.77% per 1% increase in household income. **19. a.** $E = \dfrac{1.554xe^{-0.021x}}{-74e^{-0.021x} + 92}$; $E(100) \approx 0.23$: At a household income level of \$100,000, the percentage of people using broadband in 2010 was increasing by 0.23% per 1% increase in household income. **b.** The model predicts elasticity approaching zero for households with large incomes. **21. a.** $E \approx 0.46$. The demand for computers is increasing by 0.46% per 1% increase in household income. **b.** E decreases as income increases. **c.** Unreliable; it predicts a likelihood greater than 1 at incomes of \$123,000 and above. In a more appropriate model, we would expect the curve to level off at or below 1. **d.** $E \approx 0$

23. The income elasticity of demand is

$$\frac{dQ}{dY} \cdot \frac{Y}{Q} = a\beta P^{\alpha} Y^{\beta - 1} \frac{Y}{aP^{\alpha}Y^{\beta}} = \beta.$$

25. a. $q = 1{,}000e^{-0.30p}$ **b.** At $p = \$3$, $E = 0.9$; at $p = \$4$, $E = 1.2$; at $p = \$5$, $E = 1.5$ **c.** $p = \$3.33$ **d.** $p = \$5.36$. Selling at a lower price would increase demand, but you cannot sell more than 200 pounds anyway. You should charge as much as you can and still be able to sell all 200 pounds. **27.** The price is lowered. **29.** Start with $R = pq$, and differentiate with respect to p to obtain $\dfrac{dR}{dp} = q + p\dfrac{dq}{dp}$. For a stationary point, $dR/dp = 0$, and so $q + p\dfrac{dq}{dp} = 0$. Rearranging this result gives $p\dfrac{dq}{dp} = -q$, and hence $-\dfrac{dq}{dp} \cdot \dfrac{p}{q} = 1$, or $E = 1$, showing that stationary points of R correspond to points of unit elasticity. **31.** The distinction is best illustrated by an example. Suppose that q is measured in weekly sales and p is the unit price in dollars. Then the quantity $-dq/dp$ measures the drop in weekly sales per \$1 increase in price. The elasticity of demand E, on the other hand, measures the *percentage* drop in sales per 1% increase in price. Thus, $-dq/dp$ measures absolute change, while E measures fractional, or percentage, change.

Chapter 12 Review

1. Relative max: $(-1, 5)$, absolute min: $(-2, -3)$ and $(1, -3)$ **3.** Absolute max: $(-1, 5)$, absolute min: $(1, -3)$ **5.** Absolute min: $(1, 0)$ **7.** Absolute min: $(-2, -1/4)$ **9.** Relative max at $x = 1$, point of inflection at $x = -1$ **11.** Relative max at $x = -2$, relative min at $x = 1$, point of inflection at $x = -1$ **13.** One point of inflection, at $x = 0$ **15. a.** $a = 4/t^4 - 2/t^3$ m/sec² **b.** 2 m/sec² **17.** Relative max: $(-2, 16)$; absolute min: $(2, -16)$; point of inflection: $(0, 0)$; no horizontal or vertical asymptotes

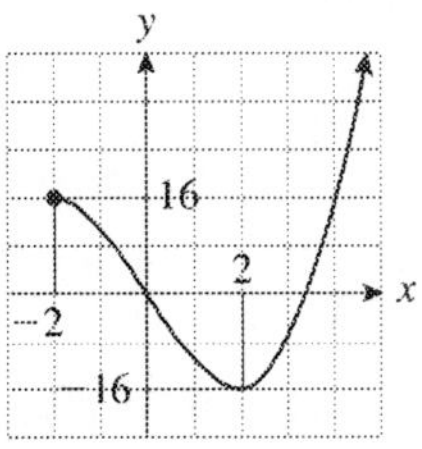

19. Relative min: $(-3, -2/9)$; relative max: $(3, 2/9)$; inflection: $(-3\sqrt{2}, -5\sqrt{2}/36)$, $(3\sqrt{2}, 5\sqrt{2}/36)$; vertical asymptote: $x = 0$; horizontal asymptote: $y = 0$

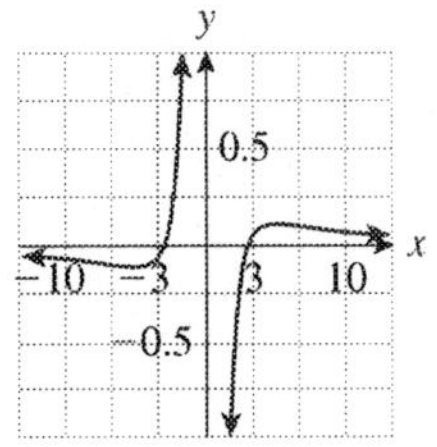

21. Relative max at $(0, 0)$, absolute min at $(1, -2)$, no asymptotes

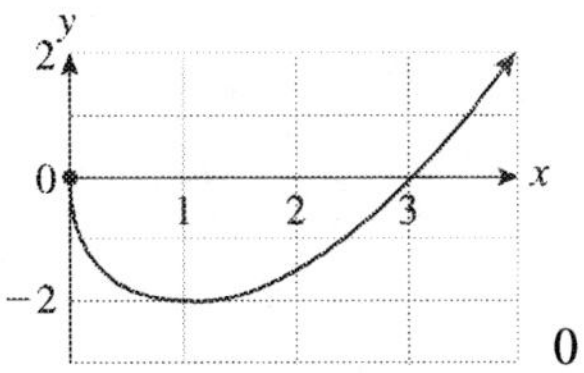

23. \$22.14 per book **25. a.** Profit $= -p^3 + 42p^2 - 288p - 181$ **b.** \$24 per copy; \$3,275 **c.** For

maximum revenue, the company should charge \$22.14 per copy. At this price, the cost per book is decreasing with increasing price, while the revenue is not decreasing (its derivative is zero). Thus, the profit is increasing with increasing price, suggesting that the maximum profit will occur at a higher price.
27. 12 in × 12 in × 6 in, for a volume of 864 in^3
29. a. $E = \dfrac{2p^2 - 33p}{-p^2 + 33p + 9}$ **b.** 0.52, 2.03; when the price is \$20, demand is dropping at a rate of 0.52% per 1% increase in the price; when the price is \$25, demand is dropping at a rate of 2.03% per 1% increase in the price. **c.** \$22.14 per book **31. a.** $E = 2p^2 - p$ **b.** 6; the demand is dropping at a rate of 6% per 1% increase in the price. **c.** \$1.00, for a monthly revenue of \$1,000 **33. a.** Week 5 **b.** Point of inflection on the graph of s; maximum on the graph of s', t-intercept in the graph of s''. **c.** 10,500; if weekly sales continue as predicted by the model, they will level off at around 10,500 books per week in the long term. **d.** 0; if weekly sales continue as predicted by the model, the rate of change of sales approaches zero in the long term. **35. a.–d.** $10/\sqrt{2}$ ft/sec

Chapter 15

Section 15.1

1. a. 1 **b.** 1 **c.** 2 **d.** $a^2 - a + 5$ **e.** $y^2 + x^2 - y + 1$ **f.** $(x + h)^2 + (y + k)^2 - (x + h) + 1$ **3. a.** 0 **b.** 0.2 **c.** −0.1 **d.** $0.18a + 0.2$ **e.** $0.1x + 0.2y - 0.01xy$ **f.** $0.2(x + h) + 0.1(y + k) - 0.01(x + h)(y + k)$ **5. a.** 1 **b.** e **c.** e **d.** e^{x+y+z} **e.** $e^{x+h+y+k+z+l}$ **7. a.** Does not exist **b.** 0 **c.** 0 **d.** $xyz/(x^2 + y^2 + z^2)$ **e.** $(x + h)(y + k)(z + l)/[(x + h)^2 + (y + k)^2 + (z + l)^2]$ **9. a.** Increases; 2.3 **b.** Decreases; 1.4 **c.** Decreases; 1 unit increase in z **11.** Neither **13.** Linear **15.** Linear **17.** Interaction **19. a.** 107 **b.** −14 **c.** −113

21.

$y \downarrow$ \ $x \rightarrow$	10	20	30	40
10	52	107	162	217
20	94	194	294	394
30	136	281	426	571
40	178	368	558	748

25. 18, 4, 0.0965, 47,040 **27.** 6.9078, 1.5193, 5.4366, 0 **29.** Let z = annual sales of Z (in millions of dollars), x = annual sales of X, and y = annual sales of Y. The model is $z = -2.1x + 0.4y + 16.2$.

31.

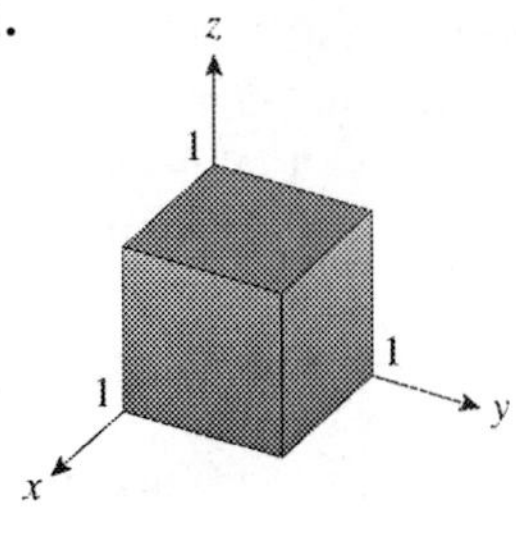

33.

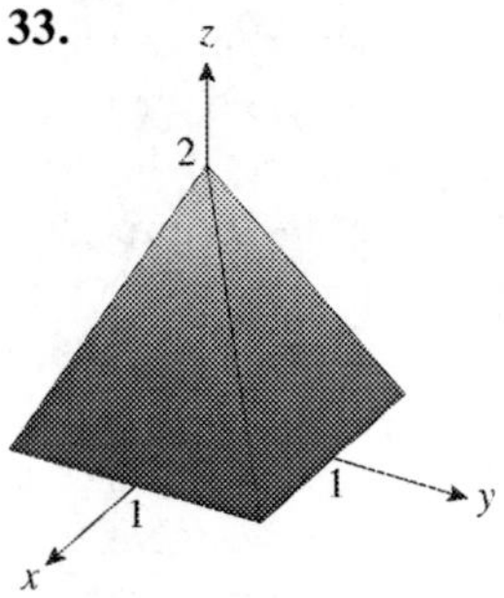

35.

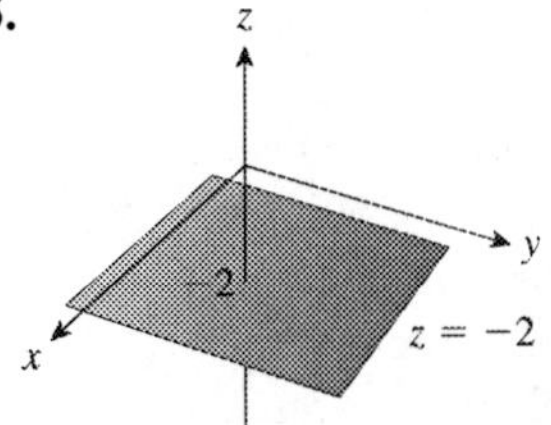

37.

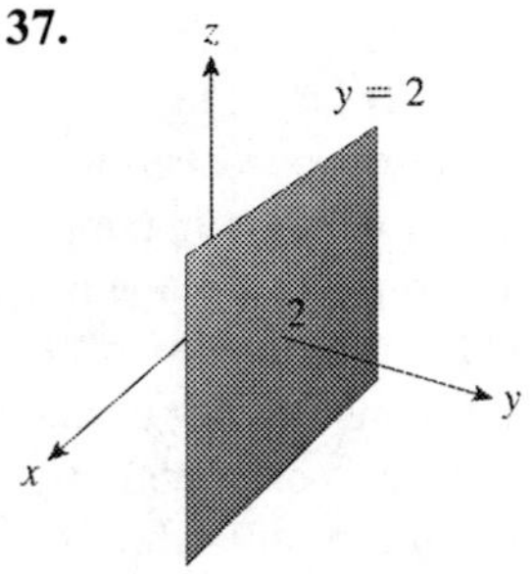

39.

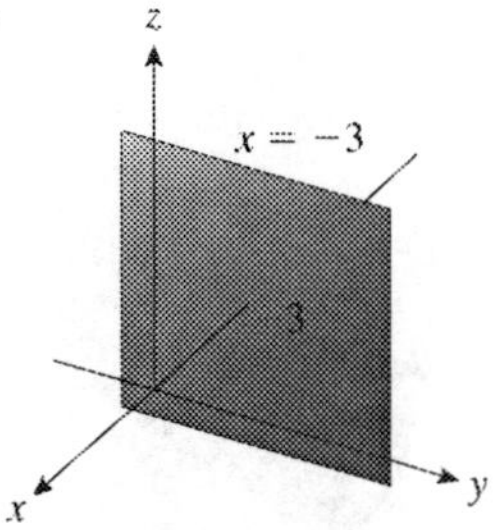

41. (H) **43.** (B) **45.** (F) **47.** (C)

49.

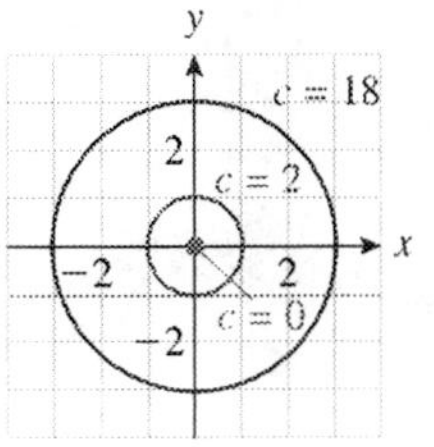

51.

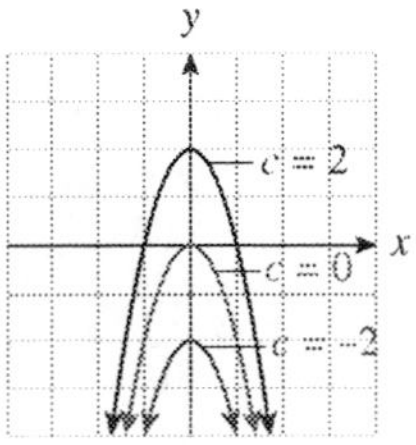

53.

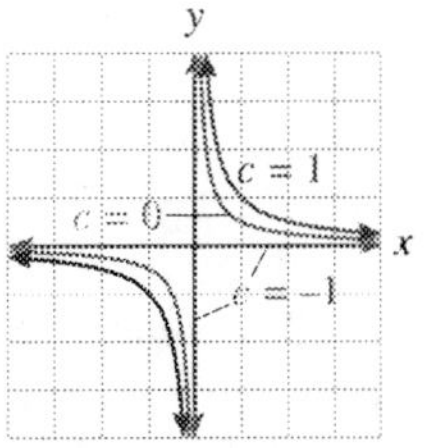

55. a. 4 **b.** 5 **c.** −1

57. (2, 2) and (−2, −2)

59.

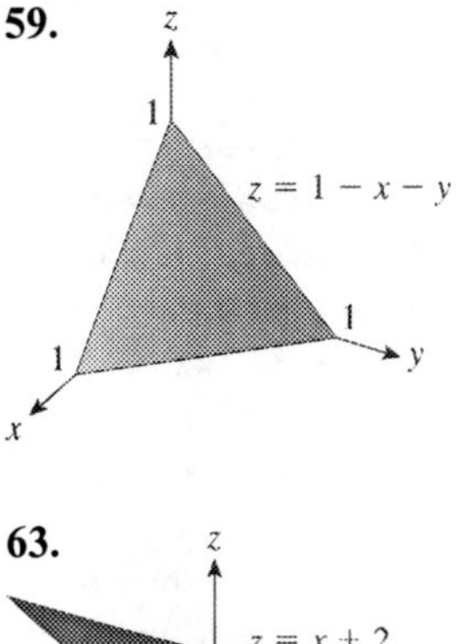

61.

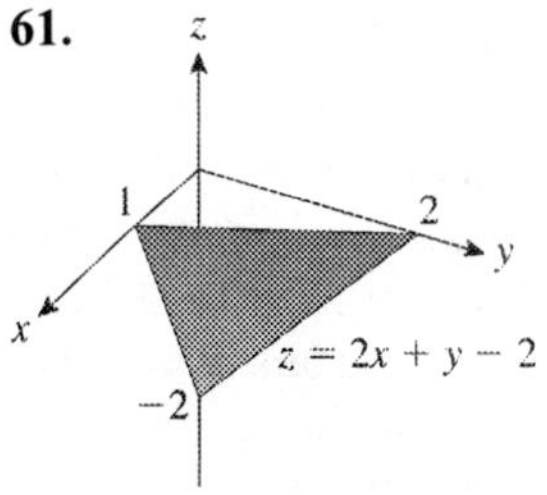

63.

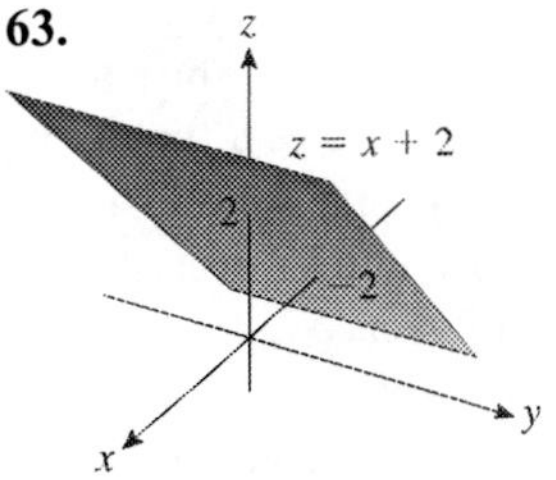

65.

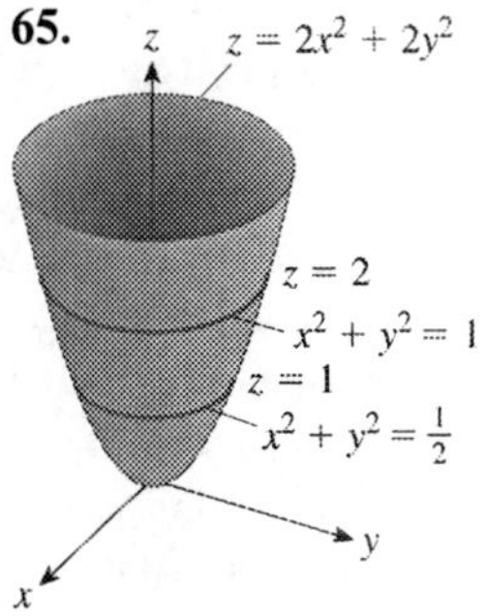

67.

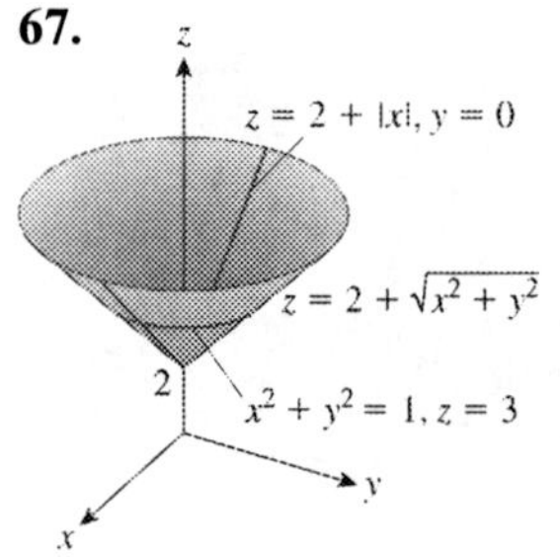

69.

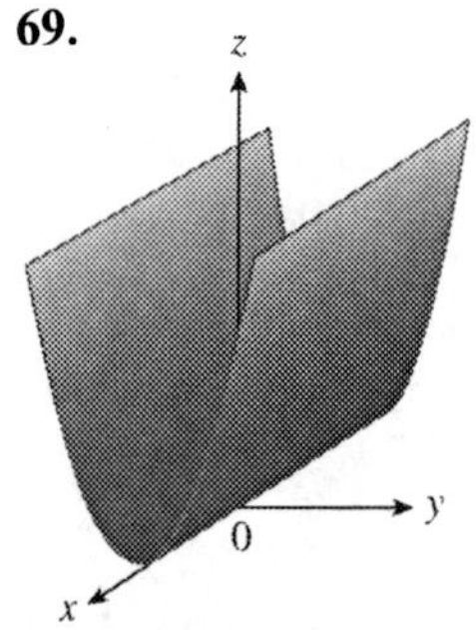

71.

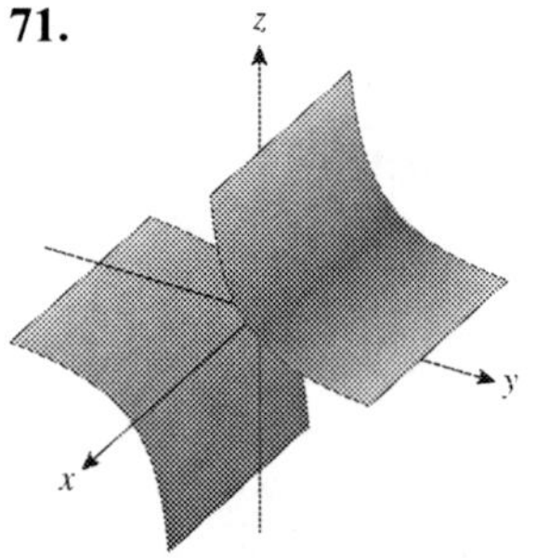

73.

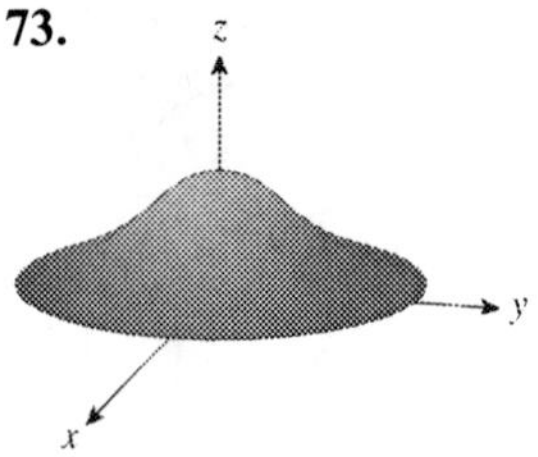

75. a. The marginal cost of cars is \$6,000 per car. The marginal cost of trucks is \$4,000 per truck. **b.** The graph is a plane with x-intercept -40, y-intercept -60, and z-intercept 240,000. **c.** The slice $x = 10$ is the straight line with equation $z = 300{,}000 + 4{,}000y$. It describes the cost function for the manufacture of trucks if car production is held fixed at 10 cars per week. **d.** The level curve $z = 480{,}000$ is the straight line $6{,}000x + 4{,}000y = 240{,}000$. It describes the number of cars and trucks you can manufacture to maintain weekly costs at \$480,000. **77.** $C(x, y) = 10 + 0.03x + 0.04y$, where C is the cost in dollars, x = # video clips sold per month, y = # audio clips sold per month **79. a.** 28% **b.** 21% **c.** Percentage points per year **81.** The graph is a plane with x_1-intercept 0.3, x_2-intercept 33, and x_3-intercept 0.66. The slices by x_1 = constant are straight lines that are parallel to each other. Thus, the rate of change of General Motors' share as a function of Ford's share does not depend on Chrysler's share. Specifically, GM's share decreases by 0.02 percentage points per one percentage-point increase in Ford's market share, regardless of Chrysler's share. **83. a.** 189 thousand prisoners **b.** $y = 300$: $N = -0.02x + 51$; $y = 500$: $N = 0.02x + 67$; when there are 300,000 prisoners in local jails, the number in federal prisons decreases by 20 per 1,000 additional prisoners in state prisons. When there are 500,000 prisoners in local jails, the number in federal prisons increases by 20 per 1,000 additional prisoners in state prisons. **85. a.** The slices x = constant and y = constant are straight lines. **b.** No. Even though the slices x = constant and y = constant are straight lines, the level curves are not, and so the surface is not a plane. **c.** The slice $x = 10$ has a slope of 3,800. The slice $x = 20$ has a slope of 3,600. Manufacturing more cars lowers the marginal cost of manufacturing trucks. **87. a.** \$9,980 **b.** $R(z) = 9{,}850 + 0.04z$ **89.** $f(x, t) = 2.5x + 17.5t + 145$; \$311 billion **91.** $U(11, 10) - U(10, 10) \approx 5.75$. This means that, if your company now has 10 copies of Macro Publish and 10 copies of Turbo Publish, then the purchase of one additional copy of Macro Publish will result in a productivity increase of approximately 5.75 pages per day. **93. a.** Answers will vary. $(a, b, c) = (3, 1/4, 1/\pi)$; $(a, b, c) = (1/\pi, 3, 1/4)$. **b.** $a = \left(\frac{3}{4\pi}\right)^{1/3}$. The resulting ellipsoid is a sphere with radius a. **95.** 7,000,000 **97. a.** $100 = K(1{,}000)^a(1{,}000{,}000)^{1-a}$; $10 = K(1{,}000)^a(10{,}000)^{1-a}$ **b.** $\log K - 3a = -4$; $\log K - a = -3$ **c.** $a = 0.5$, $K \approx 0.003162$ **d.** $P = 71$ pianos (to the nearest piano) **99. a.** 4×10^{-3} gram per square meter **b.** The total weight of sulfates in the Earth's atmosphere **101. a.** The value of N would be doubled. **b.** $N(R, f_p, n_e, f_l, f_i, L) = R\, f_p\, n_e\, f_l\, f_i\, L$, where L is the average lifetime of an intelligent civilization **c.** Take the logarithm of both sides, since this would yield the linear function $\ln(N) = \ln(R) + \ln(f_p) + \ln(n_e) + \ln(f_l) + \ln(f_i) + \ln(f_c) + \ln(L)$. **103.** They are reciprocals of each other. **105.** For example, $f(x, y) = x^2 + y^2$. **107.** For example, $f(x, y, z) = xyz$. **109.** For example, take $f(x, y) = x + y$. Then setting $y = 3$ gives $f(x, 3) = x + 3$. This can be viewed as a function of the single variable x. Choosing other values for y gives other functions of x. **111.** The slope is independent of the choice of $y = k$. **113.** That CDs cost more than cassettes **115.** plane **117. (B)** Traveling in the direction B results in the shortest trip to nearby isotherms, and hence the fastest rate of increase in temperature. **119.** Agree: Any slice through a plane is a straight line. **121.** The graph of a function of three or more variables lives in four-dimensional (or higher) space, which makes it difficult to draw and visualize. **123.** We need one dimension for each of the variables plus one dimension for the value of the function.

Section 15.2

1. $f_x(x, y) = -40$; $f_y(x, y) = 20$; $f_x(1, -1) = -40$; $f_y(1, -1) = 20$ **3.** $f_x(x, y) = 6x + 1$; $f_y(x, y) = -3y^2$; $f_x(1, -1) = 7$; $f_y(1, -1) = -3$ **5.** $f_x(x, y) = -40 + 10y$; $f_y(x, y) = 20 + 10x$; $f_x(1, -1) = -50$; $f_y(1, -1) = 30$ **7.** $f_x(x, y) = 6xy$; $f_y(x, y) = 3x^2$; $f_x(1, -1) = -6$; $f_y(1, -1) = 3$ **9.** $f_x(x, y) = 2xy^3 - 3x^2y^2 - y$; $f_y(x, y) = 3x^2y^2 - 2x^3y - x$; $f_x(1, -1) = -4$; $f_y(1, -1) = 4$ **11.** $f_x(x, y) = 6y(2xy + 1)^2$; $f_y(x, y) = 6x(2xy + 1)^2$; $f_x(1, -1) = -6$; $f_y(1, -1) = 6$ **13.** $f_x(x, y) = e^{x+y}$; $f_y(x, y) = e^{x+y}$; $f_x(1, -1) = 1$; $f_y(1, -1) = 1$ **15.** $f_x(x, y) = 3x^{-0.4}y^{0.4}$; $f_y(x, y) = 2x^{0.6}y^{-0.6}$; $f_x(1, -1)$ undefined; $f_y(1, -1)$ undefined **17.** $f_x(x, y) = 0.2ye^{0.2xy}$; $f_y(x, y) = 0.2xe^{0.2xy}$; $f_x(1, -1) = -0.2e^{-0.2}$; $f_y(1, -1) = 0.2e^{-0.2}$ **19.** $f_{xx}(x, y) = 0$; $f_{yy}(x, y) = 0$; $f_{xy}(x, y) = f_{yx}(x, y) = 0$; $f_{xx}(1, -1) = 0$; $f_{yy}(1, -1) = 0$; $f_{xy}(1, -1) = f_{yx}(1, -1) = 0$ **21.** $f_{xx}(x, y) = 0$; $f_{yy}(x, y) = 0$; $f_{xy}(x, y) = f_{yx}(x, y) = 10$; $f_{xx}(1, -1) = 0$; $f_{yy}(1, -1) = 0$; $f_{xy}(1, -1) = f_{yx}(1, -1) = 10$ **23.** $f_{xx}(x, y) = 6y$; $f_{yy}(x, y) = 0$; $f_{xy}(x, y) = f_{yx}(x, y) = 6x$; $f_{xx}(1, -1) = -6$; $f_{yy}(1, -1) = 0$; $f_{xy}(1, -1) = f_{yx}(1, -1) = 6$ **25.** $f_{xx}(x, y) = e^{x+y}$; $f_{yy}(x, y) = e^{x+y}$; $f_{xy}(x, y) = f_{yx}(x, y) = e^{x+y}$; $f_{xx}(1, -1) = 1$; $f_{yy}(1, -1) = 1$; $f_{xy}(1, -1) = f_{yx}(1, -1) = 1$ **27.** $f_{xx}(x, y) = -1.2x^{-1.4}y^{0.4}$; $f_{yy}(x, y) = -1.2x^{0.6}y^{-1.6}$; $f_{xy}(x, y) = f_{yx}(x, y) = 1.2x^{-0.4}y^{-0.6}$; $f_{xx}(1, -1)$ undefined; $f_{yy}(1, -1)$ undefined; $f_{xy}(1, -1)$ & $f_{yx}(1, -1)$ undefined **29.** $f_x(x, y, z) = yz$; $f_y(x, y, z) = xz$; $f_z(x, y, z) = xy$; $f_x(0, -1, 1) = -1$; $f_y(0, -1, 1) = 0$; $f_z(0, -1, 1) = 0$ **31.** $f_x(x, y, z) = 4/(x + y + z^2)^2$; $f_y(x, y, z) = 4/(x + y + z^2)^2$; $f_z(x, y, z) = 8z/(x + y + z^2)^2$; $f_x(0, -1, 1)$ undefined; $f_y(0, -1, 1)$ undefined; $f_z(0, -1, 1)$ undefined **33.** $f_x(x, y, z) = e^{yz} + yze^{xz}$; $f_y(x, y, z) = xze^{yz} + e^{xz}$; $f_z(x, y, z) = xy(e^{yz} + e^{xz})$; $f_x(0, -1, 1) = e^{-1} - 1$; $f_y(0, -1, 1) = 1$; $f_z(0, -1, 1) = 0$ **35.** $f_x(x, y, z) = 0.1x^{-0.9}y^{0.4}z^{0.5}$; $f_y(x, y, z) = 0.4x^{0.1}y^{-0.6}z^{0.5}$; $f_z(x, y, z) = 0.5x^{0.1}y^{0.4}z^{-0.5}$; $f_x(0, -1, 1)$ undefined; $f_y(0, -1, 1)$ undefined, $f_z(0, -1, 1)$ undefined **37.** $f_x(x, y, z) = yze^{xyz}$, $f_y(x, y, z) = xze^{xyz}$, $f_z(x, y, z) = xye^{xyz}$; $f_x(0, -1, 1) = -1$; $f_y(0, -1, 1) = f_z(0, -1, 1) = 0$ **39.** $f_x(x, y, z) = 0$; $f_y(x, y, z) = -\dfrac{600z}{y^{0.7}(1 + y^{0.3})^2}$; $f_z(x, y, z) = \dfrac{2{,}000}{1 + y^{0.3}}$; $f_x(0, -1, 1)$ undefined; $f_y(0, -1, 1)$ undefined; $f_z(0, -1, 1)$ undefined **41.** $\partial C/\partial x = 6{,}000$, the marginal cost to manufacture each car is \$6,000. $\partial C/\partial y = 4{,}000$, the marginal cost to manufacture each truck is \$4,000. **43.** $\partial y/\partial t = -0.78$. The number of articles written by researchers in the United States was decreasing at a rate of 0.78 percentage points per year. $\partial y/\partial x = -1.02$. The number of articles written by researchers in the United States was decreasing at a rate of 1.02 percentage points per one percentage-point increase in articles written in Europe. **45.** \$5,600 per car **47. a.** $\partial M/\partial c = -3.8$, $\partial M/\partial f = 2.2$. For every 1 point increase in the percentage of Chrysler owners who remain loyal, the percentage of Mazda owners who remain loyal decreases by 3.8 points. For every 1 point increase in the percentage of Ford owners who remain loyal, the percentage of Mazda owners who remain loyal increases by 2.2 points. **b.** 16% **49.** The marginal cost of cars is $\$6{,}000 + 1{,}000e^{-0.01(x+y)}$ per car. The marginal cost of trucks is $\$4{,}000 + 1{,}000e^{-0.01(x+y)}$ per truck. Both marginal costs decrease as production rises. **51. a.** \$36,600; \$52,900 **b.** \$270 per year; \$410 per year **c.** Widening **d.** The rate at which the income gap is widening **53.** $\bar{C}(x, y) = \dfrac{200{,}000 + 6{,}000x + 4{,}000y - 100{,}000e^{-0.01(x+y)}}{x + y}$; $\bar{C}_x(50, 50) = -\$2.64$ per car. This means that at a production level of 50 cars and 50 trucks per week, the average cost per vehicle is decreasing by \$2.64 for each additional car manufactured. $\bar{C}_y(50, 50) = -\$22.64$ per truck. This means that at a production level of 50 cars and 50 trucks per week, the average cost per vehicle is decreasing by \$22.64 for each additional truck manufactured. **55.** No; your marginal revenue from the sale of cars is $\$15{,}000 - \dfrac{2{,}500}{\sqrt{x + y}}$ per car and $\$10{,}000 - \dfrac{2{,}500}{\sqrt{x + y}}$ per truck from the sale of trucks. These increase with increasing x and y. In other words, you will earn more revenue per vehicle with increasing sales, and so the rental company will pay more for each additional vehicle it buys. **57.** $P_z(10, 100{,}000, 1{,}000{,}000) \approx 0.0001010$ papers/\$ **59. a.** $U_x(10, 5) = 5.18$, $U_y(10, 5) = 2.09$. This means that if 10 copies of Macro Publish and 5 copies of Turbo Publish are purchased, the company's daily productivity is increasing at a rate of 5.18 pages per day for each additional copy of Macro purchased and by 2.09 pages per day for each additional copy of Turbo purchased. **b.** $\dfrac{U_x(10, 5)}{U_y(10, 5)} \approx 2.48$ is the ratio

of the usefulness of one additional copy of Macro to one of Turbo. Thus, with 10 copies of Macro and 5 copies of Turbo, the company can expect approximately 2.48 times the productivity per additional copy of Macro compared to Turbo. **61.** 6×10^9 N/sec **63. a.** $A_P(100, 0.1, 10) = 2.59$; $A_r(100, 0.1, 10) = 2{,}357.95$; $A_t(100, 0.1, 10) = 24.72$. Thus, for a \$100 investment at 10% interest, after 10 years the accumulated amount is increasing at a rate of \$2.59 per \$1 of principal, at a rate of \$2,357.95 per increase of 1 in r (note that this would correspond to an increase in the interest rate of 100%), and at a rate of \$24.72 per year. **b.** $A_P(100, 0.1, t)$ tells you the rate at which the accumulated amount in an account bearing 10% interest with a principal of \$100 is growing per \$1 increase in the principal, t years after the investment.
65. a. $P_x = Ka\left(\frac{y}{x}\right)^b$ and $P_y = Kb\left(\frac{x}{y}\right)^a$. They are equal precisely when $\frac{a}{b} = \left(\frac{x}{y}\right)^b \left(\frac{x}{y}\right)^a$. Substituting $b = 1 - a$ now gives $\frac{a}{b} = \frac{x}{y}$. **b.** The given information implies that $P_x(100, 200) = P_y(100, 200)$. By part (a), this occurs precisely when $a/b = x/y = 100/200 = 1/2$. But $b = 1 - a$, so $a/(1 - a) = 1/2$, giving $a = 1/3$ and $b = 2/3$. **67.** Decreasing at 0.0075 parts of nutrient per part of water/sec **69.** $\underline{f}$ is increasing at a rate of $\underline{s}$ units per unit of x, $\underline{f}$ is increasing at a rate of $\underline{t}$ units per unit of y, and the value of $\underline{f}$ is $\underline{r}$ when $x = \underline{a}$ and $y = \underline{b}$ **71.** the marginal cost of building an additional orbicus; zonars per unit.
73. Answers will vary. One example is $f(x, y) = -2x + 3y$. Others are $f(x, y) = -2x + 3y + 9$ and $f(x, y) = xy - 3x + 2y + 10$. **75. a.** b is the z-intercept of the plane. m is the slope of the intersection of the plane with the xz-plane. n is the slope of the intersection of the plane with the yz-plane.
b. Write $z = b + rx + sy$. We are told that $\partial z/\partial x = m$, so $r = m$. Similarly, $s = n$. Thus, $z = b + mx + ny$. We are also told that the plane passes through (h, k, l). Substituting gives $l = b + mh + nk$. This gives b as $l - mh - nk$. Substituting in the equation for z therefore gives $z = l - mh - nk + mx + ny = l + m(x - h) + n(y - k)$, as required.

Section 15.3

1. P: relative minimum; Q: none of the above; R: relative maximum **3.** P: saddle point; Q: relative maximum; R: none of the above
5. Relative minimum **7.** Neither
9. Saddle point **11.** Relative minimum at $(0, 0, 1)$
13. Relative maximum at $(-1/2, 1/2, 3/2)$
15. Saddle point at $(0, 0, 0)$ **17.** Minimum at $(4, -3, -10)$ **19.** Maximum at $(-7/4, 1/4, 19/8)$
21. Relative maximum at $(0, 0, 0)$, saddle points at $(\pm 4, 2, -16)$ **23.** Relative minimum at $(0, 0, 0)$, saddle points at $(-1, \pm 1, 1)$ **25.** Relative minimum at $(0, 0, 1)$ **27.** Relative minimum at $(-2, \pm 2, -16)$, $(0, 0)$ a critical point that is not a relative extremum
29. Saddle point at $(0, 0, -1)$ **31.** Relative maximum at $(-1, 0, e)$ **33.** Relative minimum at $(2^{1/3}, 2^{1/3}, 3(2^{2/3}))$ **35.** Relative minimum at $(1, 1, 4)$ and $(-1, -1, 4)$ **37.** Absolute minimum at $(0, 0, 1)$
39. None; the relative maximum at $(0, 0, 0)$ is not absolute. **41.** Minimum of 1/3 at $(c, f) = (2/3, 2/3)$. Thus, at least 1/3 of all Mazda owners would choose another new Mazda, and this lowest loyalty occurs when 2/3 of Chrysler and Ford owners remain loyal to their brands. **43.** It should remove 2.5 pounds of sulfur and 1 pound of lead per day.
45. You should charge \$580.81 for the Ultra Mini and \$808.08 for the Big Stack. **47.** $l = w = h \approx 20.67$ in, volume $\approx$ 8,827 cubic inches **49.** 18 in $\times$ 18 in $\times$ 36 in, volume = 11,664 cubic inches

51.

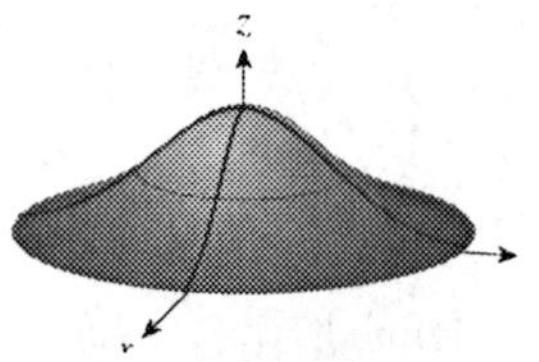

53.

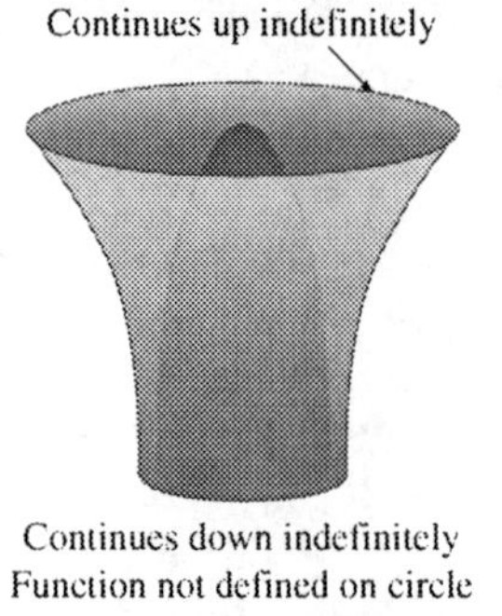

55. H must be positive. **57.** No. In order for there to be a relative maximum at (a, b), *all* vertical planes through (a, b) should yield a curve with a relative maximum at (a, b). It could happen that a slice by another vertical plane through (a, b) (such as $x - a = y - b$) does not yield a curve with a relative maximum at (a, b). [An example is $f(x, y) = x^2 + y^2 - \sqrt{xy}$, at the point $(0, 0)$. Look at the slices through $x = 0$, $y = 0$ and $y = x$.]

59. $\bar{C}_x = \dfrac{\partial}{\partial x}\left(\dfrac{C}{x+y}\right) = \dfrac{(x+y)C_x - C}{(x+y)^2}$. If this is zero, then $(x+y)C_x = C$, or $C_x = \dfrac{C}{x+y} = \bar{C}$. Similarly, if $\bar{C}_y = 0$, then $C_y = \bar{C}$. This is reasonable because if the average cost is decreasing with increasing x, then the average cost is greater than the marginal cost C_x. Similarly, if the average cost is increasing with increasing x, then the average cost is less than the marginal cost C_x. Thus, if the average cost is stationary with increasing x, then the average cost equals the marginal cost C_x. (The situation is similar for the case of increasing y.) **61.** The equation of the tangent plane at the point (a, b) is $z = f(a, b) + f_x(a, b)(x - a) + f_y(a, b)(y - b)$. If f has a relative extremum at (a, b), then $f_x(a, b) = 0 = f_y(a, b)$. Substituting these into the equation of the tangent plane gives $z = f(a, b)$, a constant. But the graph of $z =$ *constant* is a plane parallel to the xy-plane.

Section 15.4

1. 1; (0, 0, 0) **3.** 1.35; (1/10, 3/10, 1/2) **5.** Minimum value = 6 at (1, 2, 1/2) **7.** 200; (20, 10) **9.** 16; (2, 2) and (−2, −2) **11.** 20; (2, 4) **13.** 1; (0, 0, 0) **15.** 1.35; (1/10, 3/10, 1/2) **17.** Minimum value = 6 at (1, 2, 1/2) **19. a.** $f(x, y, z)$ is the square of the distance from the point (x, y, z) to (3, 0, 0), and the constraint tells us that (x, y, z) must lie on the paraboloid $z = x^2 + y^2$. Because there must be such a point (or points) on the paraboloid closest to (3, 0, 0), the given problem must have at least one solution. Solution: $(x, y, z) = (1, 0, 1)$ for a minimum value of 5. **b.** Same solution as part (a) **c.** There are no critical points using this method. **d.** The constraint equation $y^2 = z - x^2$ tells us that $z - x^2$ cannot be negative, and thus restricts the domain of f to the set of points (x, y, z) with $z - x^2 \geq 0$. However, this information is lost when $z - x^2$ is substituted in the expression for f, and so the substitution in part (c) results in a different optimization problem; one in which there is no requirement that $z - x^2$ be ≥ 0. If we pay attention to this constraint we can see that the minimum will occur when $z = x^2$, which will then lead us to the correct solution. **21.** 5 × 10 = 50 sq. ft. **23.** \$10 **25.** $(1/\sqrt{3}, 1/\sqrt{3}, 1/\sqrt{3})$, $(-1/\sqrt{3}, -1/\sqrt{3}, 1/\sqrt{3})$, $(1/\sqrt{3}, -1/\sqrt{3}, -1/\sqrt{3})$, $(-1/\sqrt{3}, 1/\sqrt{3}, -1/\sqrt{3})$ **27.** (0, 1/2, −1/2) **29.** (−5/9, 5/9, 25/9) **31.** $l \times w \times h = 1 \times 1 \times 2$ **33.** 18 in × 18 in × 36 in, volume = 11,664 cubic inches **35.** $(2l/h)^{1/3} \times (2l/h)^{1/3} \times 2^{1/3}(h/l)^{2/3}$, where l = cost of lightweight cardboard and h = cost of heavy-duty cardboard per square foot **37.** 1 × 1 × 1/2 **39.** 6 laborers, 10 robots for a productivity of 368 pairs of socks per day **41.** Method 1: Solve $g(x, y, z) = 0$ for one of the variables and substitute in $f(x, y, z)$. Then find the maximum value of the resulting function of two variables. Advantage (answers may vary): We can use the second derivative test to check whether the resulting critical points are maxima, minima, saddle points, or none of these. Disadvantage (answers may vary): We may not be able to solve $g(x, y, z) = 0$ for one of the variables. Method 2: Use the method of Lagrange multipliers. Advantage (answers may vary): We do not need to solve the constraint equation for one of the variables. Disadvantage (answers may vary): The method does not tell us whether the critical points obtained are maxima, minima, points of inflection, or none of these. **43.** If the only constraint is an equality constraint, and if it is impossible to eliminate one of the variables in the objective function by substitution (solving the constraint equation for a variable or some other method). **45.** Answers may vary: Maximize $f(x, y) = 1 - x^2 - y^2$ subject to $x = y$. **47.** Yes. There may be relative extrema at points on the boundary of the domain. The partial derivatives of the function need not be 0 at such points. **49.** In a linear programming problem, the objective function is linear, and so the partial derivatives can never all be zero. (We are ignoring the simple case in which the objective function is constant.) It follows that the extrema cannot occur in the interior of the domain (since the partial derivatives must be zero at such points).

Section 15.5

1. −1/2 **3.** $e^2/2 - 7/2$ **5.** $(e^3 - 1)(e^2 - 1)$ **7.** 7/6 **9.** $[e^3 - e - e^{-1} + e^{-3}]/2$ **11.** 1/2 **13.** $(e - 1)/2$ **15.** 45/2 **17.** 8/3 **19.** 4/3 **21.** 0 **23.** 2/3 **25.** 2/3 **27.** $2(e - 2)$ **29.** 1/3

31. $\displaystyle\int_0^1 \int_0^{1-x} f(x, y)\,dy\,dx$

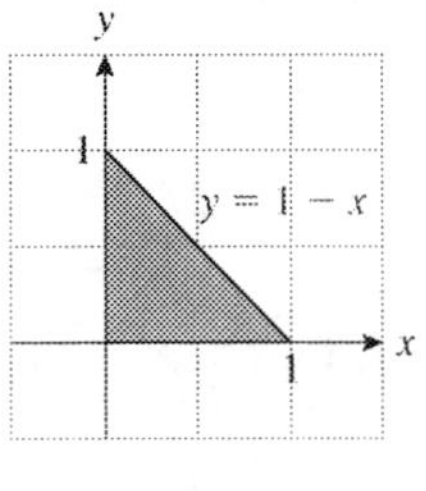

33. $\int_0^1 \int_0^{1-x} f(x, y)\,dy\,dx$

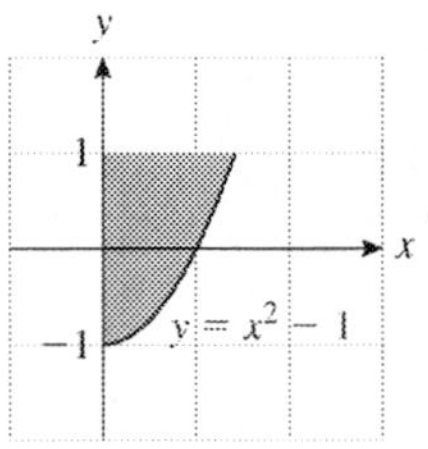

35. $\int_1^4 \int_1^{2/\sqrt{y}} f(x, y)\,dx\,dy$

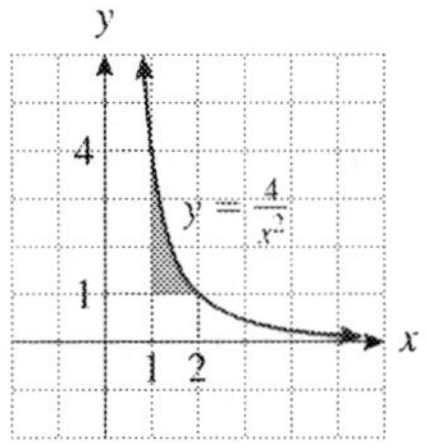

37. 4/3 **39.** 1/6 **41.** 162,000 gadgets **43.** \$312,750 **45.** \$17,500 **47.** 8,216 **49.** 1 degree **51.** The area between the curves $y = r(x)$ and $y = s(x)$ and the vertical lines $x = a$ and $x = b$ is given by $\int_a^b \int_{r(x)}^{s(x)} dy\,dx$ assuming that $r(x) \le s(x)$ for $a \le x \le b$. **53.** The first step in calculating an integral of the form $\int_a^b \int_{r(x)}^{s(x)} f(x, y)\,dy\,dx$ is to evaluate the integral $\int_{r(x)}^{s(x)} f(x, y)\,dy$, obtained by holding x constant and integrating with respect to y. **55.** Paintings per picasso per dali **57.** Left-hand side is $\int_a^b \int_c^d f(x)\,g(y)\,dx\,dy = \int_a^b \left(g(y) \int_c^d f(x)\,dx\right) dy$ (because $g(y)$ is treated as a constant in the inner integral) $= \left(\int_c^d f(x)\,dx\right) \int_a^b g(y)\,dy$ (because $\int_c^d f(x)\,dx$ is a constant and can therefore be taken outside the integral). $\int_0^1 \int_1^2 ye^x\,dx\,dy = \frac{1}{2}(e^2 - e)$ no matter how we compute it.

Chapter 15 Review

1. 0; 14/3; 1/2; $\frac{1}{1+z} + z^3$; $\frac{x+h}{y+k+(x+h)(z+l)} + (x+h)^2(y+k)$ **3.** Decreases by 0.32 units; increases by 12.5 units **5.** Reading left to right, starting at the top: 4, 0, 0, 3, 0, 1, 2, 0, 2 **7.** Answers may vary; two examples are $f(x, y) = 3(x - y)/2$ and $f(x, y) = 3(x - y)^3/8$.

9.

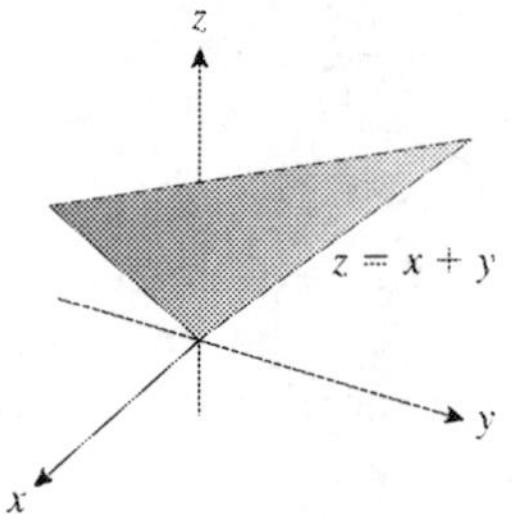

11.

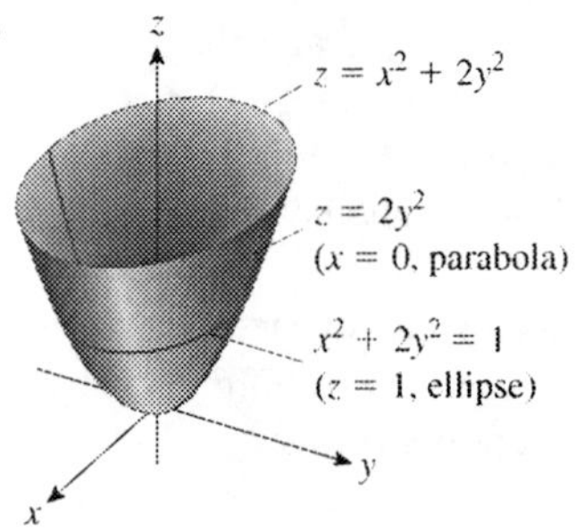

13.

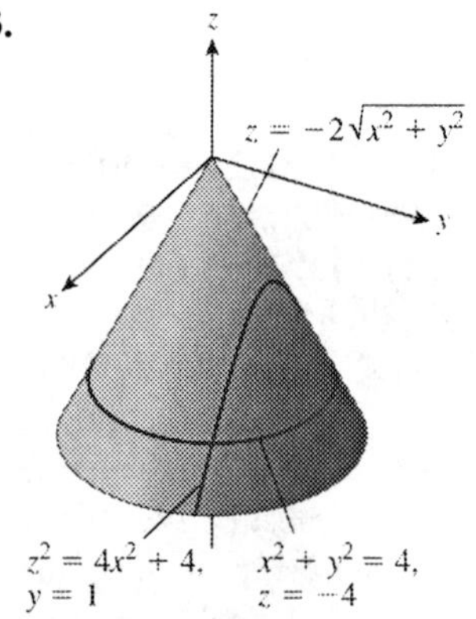

15. $f_x = 2x + y$, $f_y = x$, $f_{yy} = 0$ **17.** 0

19. $\frac{\partial f}{\partial x} = \frac{-x^2 + y^2 + z^2}{(x^2 + y^2 + z^2)^2}$, $\frac{\partial f}{\partial y} = \frac{2xy}{(x^2 + y^2 + z^2)^2}$, $\frac{\partial f}{\partial z} = -\frac{2xz}{(x^2 + y^2 + z^2)^2}$, $\left.\frac{\partial f}{\partial x}\right|_{(0,1,0)} = 1$

21. Absolute minimum at (1, 3/2) **23.** Maximum at (0, 0), saddle points at $(\pm\sqrt{2}, 1)$ **25.** Saddle point at (0, 0) **27.** 1/27 at (1/3, 1/3, 1/3) **29.** $(0, 2, \sqrt{2})$ **31.** 4; $(\sqrt{2}, \sqrt{2})$ and $(-\sqrt{2}, -\sqrt{2})$ **33.** $(0, 2, \sqrt{2})$ **35.** 2 **37.** ln 5 **39.** 1 **41. a.** $h(x, y) = 5{,}000 - 0.8x - 0.6y$ hits per day (x = number of new customers at JungleBooks.com, y = number of new customers at FarmerBooks.com) **b.** 250 **c.** $h(x, y, z) = 5{,}000 - 0.8x - 0.6y + 0.0001z$ (z = number of new Internet shoppers) **d.** 1.4 million **43. a.** 2,320 hits per day **b.** $0.08 + 0.00003x$ hits (daily) per dollar spent on television advertising per month; increases with increasing x **c.** \$4,000 per month **45.** (A) **47. a.** About 15,800 additional orders per day **b.** 11 **49.** \$23,050

Index